**he second generation of Hydrofoil Boats built with
he KNOW-HOW of L. RODRIQUEZ SHIPYARD
and stabilized with HAMILTON S.A.S.**
MILITARY TYPES ALSO AVAILABLE

(THE RHS 140 FOR PASSENGER SERVICE)

Length overall	28·70 m	Passenger seats	125-140
Breadth overall (foil)	10·72 m	Range	300 miles
Draft, afloat	3·50 m	Cruising speed	32 knots
Draft, foilborne	1·50 m	Max. power	2 x 1350 hp
Displacement	65·6 tons		

(THE RHS 160 FOR PASSENGER SERVICE)

Length overall	30.95 m	Displacement at full load	82 tons
Moulded breadth	6.20 m	Maximum power	2 x 1950 Hp
Width across foils	12.60 m	Cruising speed	36 knots
Draught, afloat	3.70 m	Cruising range	200 miles
Draught, cruising	1.35 m	Passenger seats	160/180

NAVALTECNICA S.p.A. Shipyard, MESSINA - ITALY

Telex: 98030   Telephone: 44801 (6 lines)

The new air-stabilised Hydrofoil Vessel SUPRAMAR PTS 75 MK III built by Messrs. VOSPER THORNYCROFT LTD. Paulsgrove, Hants., England. Photograph by courtesy of VOSPER THORNYCROFT LTD.

HYDROFOILS=SUPRAMAR

Supramar=Hydrofoil: Simple as it sounds but basically factual ● Hydrofoils came to this world, first by Supramar, both militarily and commercially ● Nearly 40 years of painstaking research, testing, development and accumulated experience in Hydrofoil technology ● Over 20 years of production and licensing major shipyards around the world ● Over 18 years of solid and continuous operations with some 160 Hydrofoils operating the world's rivers, lakes, coastal waters and rough seas ● Over two billion passenger kilometers without a single fatality ● Supramar Hydrofoils could have an important and profitable place in your plan of operation ● They are used by over 100 scheduled ferry services using different types of Supramar Hydrofoils ● Shell Oil have used Supramar hydrofoils for over 10 years to service offshore drilling rigs ● Several Navies use Supramar Hydrofoils for coastal patrol duties ● Supramar Hydrofoils are now fully developed with a simple system of air stabilization, another revolutionary technique exclusively developed and patented internationally by Supramar ● If your business is water transportation, we have an experienced team to handle your purchase, long-term financing, leasing, operational or equity participation requirements ● You should get the facts from Supramar before making any decision ● Write on your letterhead to:

SUPRAMAR AG, DENKMALSTR 2, 6006 Lucerne, Switzerland
Telephone: 041-369636   Telex: 78228

[2]

JANE'S
SURFACE SKIMMERS
Hovercraft and Hydrofoils

Compiled and Edited by **Roy McLeavy**

Order of Contents

World Sales Distribution

Jane's Yearbooks,
St. Giles House, 49/50 Poland Street,
London W1A 2LG, England

All the World
except

United States of America and Canada:
Franklin Watts Inc.,
730 Fifth Avenue,
New York, NY 10019.

Editorial communication to:

The Editor, Jane's Surface Skimmers
Jane's Yearbooks, St. Giles House, 49/50 Poland Street
London W1A 2LG, England
Telephone 01-437 9844

Advertisement communication to:

Jane's Advertising Department
Jane's Yearbooks, St. Giles House, 49/50 Poland Street
London W1A 2LG, England
Telephone 01-437 9844

ALPHABETICAL LIST OF ADVERTISERS

1974/75 EDITION

Floating wings.

Modern ship designs call for light, high-speed diesel engines and gearboxes to match.

Despite its exacting role, the gearbox must not be heavy. Its range of efficiency should be wide. It should be capable of long service life – dependable to a degree. And for good measure, quiet-running and simple to maintain.

ZF – Europe's No. 1 gearbox specialist – has developed a series of modern marine reversing gearboxes which meet the requirement pre-

cisely. They are compact, surprisingly light – give outstanding performance in ratings from 30 to 5000 hp.

Gearboxes of this quality demand first-class materials – backed by uncompromising manufacturing and inspection standards. For instance, gears are of forged, case-hardened alloy steel with ground tooth flanks. They are inspected with meticulous care.

ZF gearboxes utilise every ounce of engine power in the hydrofoil. If you'd like the facts, ZF will be happy to fill you in.

ZF – the sign of progress

ZAHNRADFABRIK FRIEDRICHSHAFEN AG
D-7990 Friedrichshafen 1
P. O. Box 307. W.-Germany

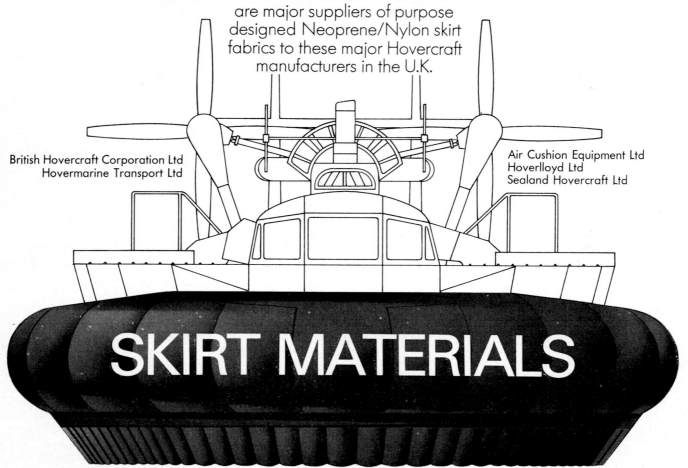

A STABLE PLATFORM BY GRUMMAN

Grumman's 67-ton Flagstaff (PG(H)-1) was the first of a new class of U.S. Navy gunboats designed to offer an excellent high speed stable gun platform in rough water.

With capability for a wide variety of mission applications

- Missile carrier
- Coastal patrol
- Search & rescue
- Crew boat
- Gun platform
- Anti-submarine warfare
- Fast transport
- Cargo carrier

Offering these design features:

- Open ocean habitability
- Operational economy
- Rugged construction
- Proven technology
- Highspeed performance
- 65,000 lbs. of useful load

For further information:

Mr. Joseph Barbetta, Marine Systems Requirement
Grumman Aerospace Corporation, Bethpage, New York 11714
Telephone: (516) 575-2735, Telex: 961430

 **GRUMMAN** AEROSPACE CORPORATION
BETHPAGE, NEW YORK 11714

CLASSIFIED LIST OF ADVERTISERS
1974-75 EDITION

The companies advertising in this publication have informed us that they are involved in the fields of manufacture indicated below:

A1. ACV MANUFACTURERS
Air Bearings Limited
Avco Lycoming Div. of Avco Corp.
Bell Aerospace Division of Textron
British Hovercraft Corporation
Mackley Ace Limited
SEDAM (Div. of Bertin & Co.)
Vosper Thornycroft Ltd.

A2. ACV OPERATORS
Mackley Ace Limited

A3. ACV RESEARCH & DESIGN
Bell Aerospace Division of Textron
Bertin et Cie
British Hovercraft Corporation
Mackley Ace Ltd.
SEDAM (Division of Bertin & Cie.)
Vosper Thornycroft Ltd.

A4. AUTOMATIC VOLTAGE AND CURRENT REGULATORS

B1. BATTERY CHARGERS

D1. DIESEL ENGINES
C.R.M. Fabrica Motori Marina
Motoren- und Turbinen-Union
 Friedrichshafen GmbH
Zahnradfabrik Friedrichshafen AG.

E1. ELECTRONIC EQUIPMENT
British Hovercraft Corporation
Motoren- und Turbinen-Union
 Friedrichshafen GmbH
Vosper Thornycroft Ltd.

F1. FINISHED MACHINE PARTS

G1. GLASS FIBRE-RESINS

G2. GUIDED MISSILE GROUND HANDLING EQUIPMENT

H1. HOVERCRAFT COMMAND STAFF TRAINING
British Rail Hovercraft Seaspeed
SEDAM (Div. of Bertin & Co.)

H2. HOVERCRAFT CONSULTANTS
British Rail Hovercraft Limited
British Rail Hovercraft Seaspeed
SEDAM (Div. of Bertin & Co.)

H3. HOVERCRAFT FERRY SERVICE
British Rail Hovercraft Seaspeed
SEDAM (Div. of Bertin & Co.)

H4. HOVERCRAFT GAS TURBINES
Avco Lycoming Div. of Avco Corp.
Motoren- und Turbinen-Union
 Friedrichshafen GmbH

H5. HOVERCRAFT INTERIOR DESIGN
Marine Line Seating Limited
SEDAM (Div. of Bertin & Co.)
Vosper Thornycroft Ltd.

H6. HOVERCRAFT INTERIOR FURNISHINGS
Marine Line Seating Limited
Vosper Thornycroft Ltd.

H7. HOVERCRAFT MANUFACTURERS
Air Bearings Limited
British Hovercraft Corporation
Mitsui Shipbuilding & Engineering Co.
 Ltd.
Sealand Hovercraft Ltd.
SEDAM (Div. of Bertin & Co.)
Vosper Thornycroft Ltd.

H8. HOVERCRAFT OPERATORS
SEDAM (Div. of Bertin & Co.)

H9. HOVERCRAFT SEATING
Marine Line Seating Limited

H10. HOVERPALLET MANUFACTURERS
Bertin et Cie
British Hovercraft Corporation

H11. HOVER SURVEYORS

H12. HOVER VICTUALLERS

H13. HYDROFOIL BOATS AND SHIPS
Cantiere Navale Leopoldo Rodriquez
Supramar AG.
Vosper Thornycroft Ltd.

H14. HYDROFOIL INTERIOR DESIGN
Cantiere Navale Leopoldo Rodriquez
Marine Line Seating Limited
Vosper Thornycroft Ltd.

H15. HYDROFOIL INTERIOR FURNISHING
Cantiere Navale Leopoldo Rodriquez
Marine Line Seating Limited
Vosper Thornycroft Ltd.

H16. HYDROFOIL MISSILE/GUN BOATS
Cantiere Navale Leopoldo Rodriquez
Supramar AG
Vosper Thornycroft Ltd.

H17. HYDROFOIL RESEARCH AND DESIGN
Cantiere Navale Leopoldo Rodriquez
Supramar AG
Vosper Thornycroft Ltd.

H18. HYDROFOIL SEATING
Cantiere Navale Leopoldo Rodriquez
Marine Line Seating Limited

I 1. INSTRUMENTS, ELECTRONIC

I 2. INSTRUMENTS, NAVIGATION

I 3. INSTRUMENTS, PRECISION

I 4. INSTRUMENTS, TEST EQUIPMENT

M1. MARINE FUELS & LUBRICANTS

P1. PATROL BOATS
Bell Aerospace Division of Textron
Cantiere Navale Leopoldo Rodriquez
Supramar AG
Vosper Thornycroft Ltd.

P2. PUBLICATIONS
Vosper Thornycroft Ltd.

R1. RADAR FOR NAVIGATION, WARNING INTERCEPTION, FIRE CONTROL

R2. RADIO NAVIGATION EQUIPMENT

R3. REVERSE-REDUCTION GEARS
C.R.M. Fabrica Motori Marina
Vosper Thornycroft Ltd.
Zahnradfabrik Friedrichshafen AG

S1. SIMULATORS

S2. SKIRT MATERIALS
Northern Rubber Co. Ltd.

S3. SPEED CONTROL DEVICES
Vosper Thornycroft Ltd.

S4. SURVEILLANCE SYSTEMS

T1. TRANSMISSION EQUIPMENT

V1. VOLTAGE AND CURRENT REGULATORS

ELETTRONICA SAN GIORGIO
ELSAG   S.p.A.

COMBAT SYSTEM ENGINEERING   AND   SHIPBORNE WEAPON CONTROL SYSTEMS

SINCE 1928 ONE OF THE MOST PROMINENT AND NOW THE LEADING ITALIAN FIRM IN THE FIELD OF DESIGN AND PRODUCTION OF NAVAL FIRE CONTROL SYSTEMS.

MAIN SUPPLIERS OF FIRE CONTROL SYSTEMS TO THE ITALIAN NAVY AND TO A NUMBER OF FOREIGN NAVIES, POSSESSING A SOUND EXPERIENCE IN COMBAT SYSTEM INSTALLATION AND REFITTING.

THE MOST SIGNIFICANT MILITARY PRODUCTION:

« NA 10 » WEAPON CONTROL SYSTEMS.
GUNNERY DATA SYSTEMS.
SHIPBORNE MULTI-ROLE ROCKETS
LAUNCHING CONTROL SYSTEM.
SERVOSYSTEMS.
SPECIAL EQUIPMENT.

Pictures show the NA10 mod. 1 lightweight system fitted into the Italian Navy hydrofoil P.420 built by ALINAVI S.p.A.
Tracking radar is the Orion 10X
made by SELENIA S.p.A.
LLL TV camera is made by DALMO VICTOR Co.

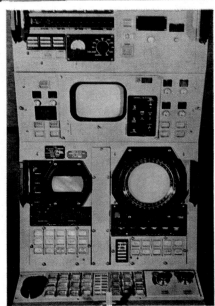

ELETTRONICA SAN GIORGIO
ELSAG   S.p.A.

Weapon Control Systems Department

16155 GENOVA SESTRI   ITALY
Telephone   426.841 - 426.851
                   via Hermada 6
Telex   27660   ELSAG

The Aerotrain System tested in France and in the U.S.A. is under economic study in 21 countries.

Société de l'Aérotrain
Tour Anjou—33, quai National
92806 PUTEAUX (France)
Tél. 776.43.34   Télex 61385
is depositor of
the Bertin TACV Technique.

SEDAM

F 75017 PARIS — 80 avenue de la Grande Armée
Tél.: 380.17.69

Depositor of the
BERTIN ACV technique
SEDAM having built
the N 300 and the
N 102 has now started
the construction of
the N 500 of 230 tons
carrying 400 passengers
and 41 cars or 200
passengers and 60 cars
at a maximum speed of
75 knots.

N 500 will be in
operation during the
Summer 1976.

The N 500 T

[12]

Some things ...like Edo excellence ...never change

In 1935 Edo floats crossed Antarctica with Bernt Balchen on Lincoln Ellsworth's Polar Star. Today, Edo sonar routinely dives under the Polar ice cap aboard the nuclear submarines of the U.S. Navy. In 46 years our standard of excellence has never been lowered...in Edo systems developed for antisubmarine warfare, oceanography, mine countermeasures, strike warfare, airborne navigation, hydrodynamics and airframes, command and control. And speaking of sonar, sonar designed and built by Edo is standard equipment aboard all the nuclear-powered submarines of the U.S. Navy and many of our modern destroyers.

EDO Corporation
College Point, N.Y. 11356

JANE'S
SURFACE SKIMMERS

Hovercraft and Hydrofoils

EIGHTH EDITION

COMPILED AND EDITED BY
ROY McLEAVY

1974-75

I.S.B.N. 0 354 00508 1

JANE'S YEARBOOKS

LONDON

Sealand SH2.
The exciting low cost, six seater amphibian

Most six-seater hovercraft will travel over sand, sea, snow and ice, marsh, mud, rocks and root crops at speeds up to 50 mph. Many of them can turn in their own length and cope with up to force 5 winds on scheduled runs. But using a standard car engine? And with complete transportability between job locations?

The Sealand Hovercraft SH2 can and does. Powered by a Chrysler 440 CD V8 engine, it will carry the pilot and five passengers, or two passengers and a 500 lb payload, or even just a 1,000 lb payload over a range of 200 miles. The engine is designed to run for 1,000 hours between overhauls and when the time comes, can be serviced by any competent car mechanic; the entire engine, transmission and fans assembly is unit mounted and can be withdrawn completely after the removal of eight bolts. That's obviously going to make quite a difference to your operating costs.

It also makes quite a difference to your initial capital outlay, no matter which model you choose. The SH2 is available for Civil Service duties, military applications, as a commercial craft or, fitted with dual controls, as a training craft for larger hovercraft.

Its versatility is further enhanced by supreme transportability. The sidebodies fold flat to make shipping or air freight in standard containers possible. Bolt on wheels and towing bar – supplied standard – also do away with the need for clumsy trailers and special clearance when transporting on the open road.

If you feel this adds up to a really versatile and cost efficient proposition, contact us direct for a test drive.

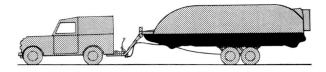

Sealand SH2

Sealand Hovercraft Ltd
2-5 Old Bond Street,
London W1X 3TB.
Tel: 01-493 7681 Telex: 24620

FOREWORD

FOR the skimmer industry it was "all systems go" in 1974. Profits have leapt ahead for manufacturers and operators alike, and for the first time world demand was threatening to outstrip production.

At the root of the new flurry of activity is the growing awareness of the cost benefits that can stem from replacing conventional ships with fast, compact craft, that overcome the water speed barrier and complete a given task in less than one-third of the time required previously. Additional attractions are smaller crews, the ability of the more advanced hydrofoils to maintain high speeds in almost any sea states, and the versatility of the skirted, multi-terrain ACV.

As it matures the industry is beginning to show a closer understanding of customer problems and it reacts faster to the challenge of building or adapting craft to undertake special requirements. The diversity of the roles which its products can fulfil in world transportation is indicated by six of its latest design concepts:

* *500-ton capacity, freight-carrying aerodynamic ACVs, capable of cruising at 200 knots. 50-70 ft above the surface.*
* *Fast river buses employing the same wing-in-ground-effect principle and flying at 70-150 knots.*
* *Air-cushion icebreaking units for attachment to the bows of conventional ships entering arctic waters.*
* *A skirted hoversled with buoyant pontoons that maintain surface contact to give positive directional control. Also air-cushion-supported crawler tractors for towing hoverplatforms across soft terrain.*
* *1,300-1,600 ton hydrofoil warships with transocean range for escort and ASW duties.*
* *Massive amphibious platforms for carrying drilling rigs and plant across deserts and tundra. One 6,000-ton hoverbarge is designed to break-up sea ice then lay oil pipelines in the sea beneath.*

In recent months the combined effects of the energy crisis, the high cost of fossil fuel and rising inflation, have focussed attention on what is almost certainly the most efficient ACV transport concept of all—the Aerofoil boat, or wing-in-ground-effect machine, known in the Soviet Union as the ekranoplan.

NEW FLYING-BOAT AGE

Looking like flying-boats equipped with stubby, short-span wings, these vehicles are designed to operate low down, at a height equal to approximately half their wing span, where they ride on a cushion of air set up between the machine and the surface below.

At this height, or lower, there is a sharp drop in their induced drag, which has the effect of lowering their fuel consumption and increasing their range by half as much again. Tests have shown that 50 per cent less power is required in ground effect and that 50-ton-miles per gallon of fuel is easily attained at speeds up to 190 knots. The ride within ground effect is remarkably smooth, and since the machines themselves become inherently stable within the cushion, pilots are able to release their controls and allow their machines to fly themselves.

Knowledge of the phenomenon is by no means new. It was first employed in the early 1930s by pilots of commercial planes to help them extend the range of their machines while crossing the South Atlantic. Several generations of naval pilots, including today's, have been instructed that this is the way to make base if their fuel is running low.

What is completely new is the development of machines designed specifically to exploit to the full the substantial economies that can be realised. The concept offers, for the first time, a form of transportation that combines the speed of a freight plane with the cargo space and low operating costs of a coventional ship.

Research in this new area of ACV technology is being undertaken in the USA, Japan, West Germany, France and the Soviet Union. Projects range from two-seat runabouts to giant 1,000-ton freighters, capable of providing low-cost transportation in the 50-250-knot speed range, thus narrowing the wide performance gap that exists between 15-knot cargo vessels and high-speed jet planes. Military applications range from fast patrol and assault boats to ASW duties and long-range logistics.

The biggest vehicle to be completed so far is the 500-ton research machine built in the Soviet Union by the Sormovo shipyard at Gorki, and currently undergoing trials on the Caspian Sea. Thrust from eight gas turbines mounted above a forward stub wing is deflected downwards on take-off to augment lift, after which it is re-directed over the upper surface of the main wing to create additional aerodynamic lift during full flight.

The span of the main wing is about 125 ft, suggesting an operating height of between 40-75 ft, which is sufficient for transocean crossings or for operation across the Arctic wastelands where the tallest ice ridges are no higher than 25 ft.

The Soviet navy is displaying great interest in these vehicles which can be employed as fast re-supply vessels for both surface ships and submarines and as long range patrol and ASW craft.

The extent of the activity in the WIG field within the Soviet Union can be judged from an announcement made by the Ministry of the River Fleet that a number of designs are being developed to operate high-speed services along the country's waterways. An impression of a catamaran-hulled ekranoplan water-bus will be found in this issue, together with photographs of the two-seat Ezka, an amphibious, high-speed rescue craft and general utility vehicle, with a wide range of applications in underdeveloped areas.

The foremost protagonist of this class of air-cushion vehicle in the West is Dr. Alexander Lippisch, "father" of the delta wing and the designer of the Me 163 rocket fighter. Dr. Lippisch has conducted research in the ACV field for well over a decade, a great deal of it performed under contract or in co-operation with Rhein-Flugzeugbau and Dornier. An important feature of his Aerofoil boat, or "winged hull" concept, is that by employing a low aspect-ratio wing of special design, he has overcome the pitch instability of conventional wings when flown at various distances from the surface. Normally the centre of pressure travels rearwards as the surface is approached, causing the nose of the craft to pitch downwards. The wing shape designed by Dr. Lippisch creates a stable ground effect, enabling the craft to maintain a selected height from the supporting surface automatically. It also solves the stability problem as the centre of pressure remains constant whether the craft is in or out of ground effect.

Because of its inherent stability, the "winged hull" can fly out of ground effect to fly above obstacles such as bridges, or to operate above a fogbank. It manoeuvres at altitude in much the same way as a slow-flying aircraft but is least efficient in terms of fuel consumption during the short time it may be required to do so.

In a paper specially prepared for this edition, Dr. Lippisch presents a technical evaluation of the progress made with the X-112 and X-113 Am Aerofoil boats, and illustrates some of his larger projects, including one of 500 tons.

Further support for the fast, low-flying transocean freighter concept comes from France, where a team of ACV experts headed by Jean Bertin is working on a craft capable of operating at any height from zero level up to 10,000 ft at a speed of 200 knots. The project involves two machines, Cygne 10 and Cygne 14, of 1,000 and 1,400 tonnes all-up weight, and gross payloads of 550 tonnes and 867 tonnes respectively. Due to the limited output of the turbojets available at the present time, each craft will have either eight or twelve propeller-turbines, some mounted forward above the main wing and the remainder above an aerofoil-shaped hull aft.

Bertin compares the use of multiple engines with the formula employed by many larger seaplanes and flying boats in the early thirties, particularly the Dornier Do X, which once set a remarkable performance record while flying in its ground cushion.

One major difference between the Bertin project and its present day contemporaries is that it will have an air-cushion landing system (ACLS) allowing it to take-off and land on unprepared surfaces in open fields, open water, sand, snow, ice or dirt. It also permits the craft to take-off and land with far heavier loads than can be borne by conventional multi-wheel undercarriages.

One conspicuous non-starter in the new flying boat era is the United Kingdom. The lack of interest of British aerospace companies is all the more surprising since, in the past, most acquired wide experience in the design and construction of high-performance seaplanes and flying-boats for both the armed services and civil airlines.

Soviet engineers have not been slow to point out that British aerodynamicists were among the first to make a complete study of the ground effect phenomenon.

HIGH-SPEED SEAPOWER

Even larger than the proposed giant wing-in-ground-effect machines are the US Navy's projected 2,000-ton combat-capable SES prototypes. In July 1974, cost plus fixed fee contracts for further development work were awarded by the Surface Effect Ship Project Office to Bell Aerospace ($36 million) and Rohr Industries Inc ($35 million). Both companies will undertake the design, development and testing of full-scale subsystems and components including transmission, waterjet systems, lift fans and skirts as well as a method of controlling the vessels' ride characteristics at high speed in a variety of sea states.

This new interim programme will put the US Navy in a better position to judge the wisdom of jumping straight from the Aerojet-General and Bell 100-ton testcraft to a substantially larger vessel of 2,000 tons, or whether the next step should be a craft of more modest size. The projected vessel will be ten times the size of the biggest hovercraft operating today—the 200-ton SR.N4.

Should it be felt necessary at the end of the next eighteen months to build a smaller vessel first, there is little doubt that the US Navy's goal of having a 10,000-ton SES in operation by the early 1980s will be set back by several years. The reason for this is that US Navy officials believe that a 2,000-ton SES is the smallest size craft suitable for testing on the open ocean, and until a vessel of this size is available, it will be difficult to determine the feasibility of even bigger ships in the 6,000-10,000-ton class. The tests would be similar to those undertaken by the 100-ton SES-100A and B, which were used to provide data for the SES-2,000.

Both the projected 2,000-ton designs will be powered by General Electric LM-2500 gas-turbines driving waterjets and their top speed is expected to be 70-75 knots. If the new programme proves the systems under development to be satisfactory, an order for either one or two prototypes is expected to be placed in late 1975. The 2,000-ton craft, of about the same size as a small World War II destroyer, will be employed on ASW duties and as convoy escorts. If the prototypes prove effective, one of the US Navy's initial aims is the establishment of a class in the 2-3,000-ton range for use as escorts, small helicopter and V/STOL platforms and as missile-armed surface combatants.

Projects for very much larger SESs of 6,000-10,000 tons are being examined with a view to their use as sea control ships, small carriers and high-value cargo lift vessels.

British Hovercraft Corporation, with whom Bell has had a licensing agreement for the past eleven years, will design the seals and undertake various engineering tasks. The bow and stern skirts of the SR.N4 are similar in shape and approximately half the size of those of the proposed 2,000-ton SES.

Interest in ACVs for military and paramilitary applications continues to grow the world over. In the United States, work continues on large all-weather vehicles for arctic patrol, and proposals for military variants of both the Bell Voyageur and Viking are under examination.

British Hovercraft Corporation, which has supplied SR.N6s to eight military and paramilitary forces, is handling an increasing number of enquiries, particularly from countries in the Middle East. The company is at present consolidating the design of three twin-propeller derivatives of the SR.N6 Winchester—the Mk. 6A gunship, the Mk 6B logistic support vehicle and the Mk. 6C coastal security and command vehicle.

Evaluation of the BH.7 Wellington as a mine-countermeasures craft continues and once the present studies are complete a decision is expected to be taken on the size and configuration of the MCM variant. In all probability the design will be similar to that of the projected BH.7 Mk 6, a 100-ton, twin-engined version which could be used in conjunction with the Edo Mk 105 hydrofoil MCM system.

By mid-1975, the Vosper Thornycroft VT 2, also in the 100-ton range, will be undergoing trials. This is the first fully amphibious ACV to be built by the company and employs air propulsion instead of water propellers. Development of this craft is being watched closely by a number of the world's navies. Derivatives will include models for mine countermeasures, logistic support, and a 65-knot missile-armed fast patrol boat.

Defence departments around the world are currently examining the whole range of ACVs, present and projected, from ocean-going giants to lightweights. Two lightweight vehicles arousing a great deal of interest are the Air Vehicle AV 2 six-seater, which has been employed in exercises with units of the British Special Air Service (SAS) and the Pindair Skima 4, a 350 lb inflatable four-seater, which can be assembled in 30 minutes. It has been recommended by the British Interservice Hovercraft Unit as an alternative to the Gemini inflatable boat, particularly where its amphibious capability would be an advantage.

FAST COMMERCIAL CRAFT

Although the emphasis has continued to be on military applications, the demand for commercial craft continues to rise. The world's fastest selling passenger hovercraft is Hovermarine's well-proven HM.2. Sales climb year by year and by August 1974 some thirty-six were in service or on order. Plans are now underway for the operation of these craft in Taiwan and Hong Kong. Production for North and Central America is being undertaken by Hovermarine's new factory at Titusville, Florida, and the company's UK subsidiary in Southampton will build craft for the rest of the world. Larger derivatives of the HM.2 are being developed and production in the USA will open up the substantial market that exists for this type of craft in North and Central America.

Given a choice, water transport operators in underdeveloped countries would almost certainly select a diesel-powered craft in preference to one fitted with a gas-turbine. The advantages of the diesel-engined machine are that the first cost, operating costs, and maintenance overheads are lower and skilled diesel engineers are more readily available.

In a move that will be welcomed almost everywhere, BHC, after a penetrating look at its world markets, is planning to launch an entirely new range of craft powered by either a single or by twin lightweight marine diesels. Research is being concentrated on a vehicle larger than the SR.N6 seating about 100 passengers. Favourable repercussions in the company's sales of small hovercraft are expected.

In Japan, further orders are being negotiated for the Mitsui MV-PP5, nine of which are in service with five operators. Tests of the larger PP15 are progressing well and the development of a 500-seat hoverferry is underway. In Canada, Bell has started the series production of the Voyageur, and the first Voyageurs and the Viking prototype are in service. In France, Sedam has begun the construction of the N500T, 215-ton mixed-traffic ferry and in the Soviet Union the design of a new waterjet-propelled sidewall vessel —the Rassvet (Dawn)—is now complete. The vessel, which has a displacement of 50 tons, is designed to carry up to 80 passengers on short sea routes. Development of the Zarnitsa, Zarya and Skate continues and plans for much larger amphibious craft are being prepared. A totally new area of activity is the construction of large, air-lubricated hull vessels which ride on a thin layer of air ejected by nozzles built into the base of the hull. The first of these craft, for 400 passengers, will be built at Gorky. The use of air lubrication will not only increase the vessel's speed, but also soften wave impact.

ACV research and development activity in the Soviet Union is now widespread. There are almost forty national enterprises supporting teams involved in the design and construction of ACVs for transport and industrial applications. In an appeal for the co-ordination of the efforts of these teams, the director of the USSR's Gosplan Institute of Integrated Transport, L. P. Chertkov, stated recently, "We are ahead of everyone else in the theory, design and construction of air-cushion transport. We have, as it were, a winning hand. A new branch of industry is being born."

While many would readily dispute the idea that Soviet designers have established any significant technological lead at present— except possibly in the construction of large ekranoplans—there is every indication that a major, government-backed ACV development programme will begin in 1975. This could very easily put Russian ACVs on a par with those of the rest of the world within two to three years.

HYDROFOILS

Twenty-one years have elapsed since a 32-seat Supramar PT 10 began the world's first scheduled passenger service on Lake Maggiore, between Switzerland and Italy, in May 1953.

Since then the hydrofoil has graduated from a minor tourist attraction to a mode of travel used annually by well over 25 million commuters and tourists in nearly forty countries. The industry is now rated as being viable, successful and survivable and could easily become one of the most profitable sections of the shipbuilding industry within a decade.

In 1974 orders grew at a rate which manufacturers described as "unprecedented". More new craft were being designed, built or tested than ever before, and for the first time substantial military orders were being placed.

Among the major events of the past twelve months were the launchings, by Boeing, of both the 106-ton Jetfoil prototype and the 230-ton NATO/PHM, and the completion by Vosper Thornycroft of the first Supramar PTS 75 Mk 111.

De Havilland Canada, builder of the highly successful FHE-400 ocean-going all-weather warship, announced plans to build and market a 'scaled-down', 100-ton multi-purpose derivative, the DHC-MP-100; Grumman released its plans for an 83-ton Super Flagstaff and International Hydrolines introduced a series of new fast ferries designed by Helmut Kock.

Restricted funds and manpower shortage are causing an increasing number of navies to adopt the "more and smaller" philosophy. From this standpoint the multi-duty 50-knot-plus seagoing hydrofoil with a fully submerged foil system is an outstanding candidate to replace many classes of ageing combat ships. It operates at more than double the speed of comparable displacement vessels, it has greater manoeuvrability, costs less, and requires a crew only one-tenth the size of that of a frigate. Armed with anti-ship missiles the small hydrofoil can face very much larger displacement craft on equal terms, and its retractable foils mean that, unlike the larger vessels, it can operate from shallow waters.

Among the purchasers of the Boeing/NATO/PHM are the US Navy, the German Federal Republic and the Italian Navy. The first two craft will be delivered to the US Navy in the summer of 1975, and the contract calls tentatively for 28 craft to follow. The German Federal Republic plans to buy ten PHMs from Boeing and the Italian Navy one, with another four to six craft being built in Italy. Interested observers in the programme include Canada, Denmark, The Netherlands, France and the United Kingdom. It is almost certain that one or more of these nations will be placing an order for the PHM within the next twelve months.

In Italy, trials of the Advanced Marine Systems-Alinavi Swordfish are reported to be going well and the first missile-firing trials were completed during the summer. The Italian Navy has now ordered its first production batch of four craft.

In the Soviet Union, the hydrofoil equipped ASW version of the Osa missilecraft has been put into series production and it has been suggested that its success may well result in a new version equipped with anti-ship missiles in the manner of its predecessors, the Osa 1 and II. It is understood that a smaller naval patrol hydrofoil, of approximately the same size as the Swordfish, and capable of "sprint" speeds approaching 100 knots, has been undergoing trials.

One unexpected development in the military field was the transfer to the Pakistan navy of four 45-ton Hu Chwan (White Swan) hydrofoil fast attack torpedo boats by the navy of the Chinese People's Republic. Pakistan is the only country, apart from Albania, to receive this Chinese-built craft. Although basically an adaptation of an existing FPB hull, the Hu Chwan has proved quite a formidable vessel which, in calm conditions, is capable of foiling at 55 knots.

De Havilland Canada's latest design is the DHC-MP (Maritime Patrol)—100, a multi-duty vessel of 104 tons displacement and a top speed of 50 knots. Twin 3,100 shp gas-turbines provide foil-borne power instead of the single turbine employed in the FHE-400 and the foil system has been simplified. Although much smaller than its predecessor, it is designed to maintain the same seakeeping performance.

Grumman's new Super Flagstaff was conceived as a high-speed patrol gunboat or missilecraft, but it can be equipped for a number of alternative roles, including anti-submarine warfare, search and rescue and fast military transport. The chief differences between the Super Flagstaff and the PGH-1 lie in the installation of a gas-turbine of greater output, the introduction of an improved Z-drive and the provision of larger foils. Displacement, fully loaded, is increased from 67·5 to 83·5 tons and the maximum payload, including fuel is 65,475 lbs.

The US Naval Sea Systems Command is currently undertaking the design of larger and faster hydrofoils, one reported requirement being for a destroyer escort hydrofoil with ocean-crossing capability in the 1,100-1,300-ton range. Representative of the current state-of-the-art applied to large naval hydrofoils is the projected Boeing DEH which would be available in several configurations including an ASW ship and a multi-purpose weapon platform. A paper, prepared earlier in the year by members of the Boeing's DEH preliminary design team, is reproduced in this edition. The authors conclude that the technological development of the 50-knot hydro-foil has now reached maturity, and without the inauguration of any significant new research or development programme, an effective hydrofoil escort ship in the 1,200-1,600-ton size range is feasible, viable and available.

Most established hydrofoil companies are now working to capacity to meet growing world demand. Commercial hydrofoils have long been an accepted mode of rapid transit on short and medium distance routes in the Soviet Union, Scandinavia, the Mediterranean,

around Japan and in many parts of the Pacific. They are now in demand in Western Europe, the Middle East, West Africa, Canada, United States, South America and Australia.

To cope with the increasing orders, Supramar has established a wholly-owned shipbuilding subsidiary in Hong Kong, and will also build vessels of its own design in Singapore in conjunction with Vosper Thornycroft Private Ltd. Initially both yards will concentrate on building PTS 75 Mk IIIs, but the construction of very much larger vessels is planned, including the PT 150 and a new 500-seat ferry.

In Italy, Leopoldo Rodriquez is currently building RHS 70s, RHS 140s and RHS 160s, and has a substantial backlog of orders for these models. Construction of its first 116-ton RHS 200 is due to begin in 1975, but instead of gas-turbines, power will be supplied by two 2,415 hp MTU diesels.

Seaflight's first 60-ton L.90 is operating successfully between the Italian mainland and Sardinia and it is expected that more craft of this design will follow the "Squalo Bianco" (White Shark) into service.

Boeing's first 106-ton Jetfoil was launched on March 29th 1974. During initial foilborne trials on Puget Sound it was tested at speeds up to 37 knots. Later in the year, it was due to be tested under operational conditions in the Pacific before being delivered to Far East Hydrofoil Co. Hong Kong, where it will start operating on the company's Hong Kong-Macao service in the spring of 1975. Four other Jetfoils are on order, three for Pacific Sea Transportation of Honolulu and another one for Far East Hydrofoil Co.

Boeing is also evaluating various utility models of the Jetfoil with open load decks suitable for search and rescue duties, offshore oil-rig support and firefighting. A number of oil companies are interested in the 50- and 100-seat rig crew/supply boat versions which have considerable cargo capacity for supporting rigs within 50-250 nautical miles from the shore.

International Hydrolines, another manufacturer in the United States, is planning to build three new designs, a 72-passenger, waterjet-propelled ferry for sheltered waters, a 67-ton passenger ferry with seats for 127, and a 306-seat ferry with a displacement of 138-tons. It plans to install a closed cycle lightweight steam engine on an Albatross hydrofoil for test and evaluation. The burner accepts a number of fuels including gas oil, kerosene, gasoline and powdered coal. The weight to output ratio is 1 lb/hp or 350 lb/350 hp. Preliminary figures suggest that by adopting the engine for the Albatross and other designs it will be possible to either halve the present power or double the payload.

One of the most successful hydrofoils on the export market is the Soviet Union's Kometa, which is currently in service in Cuba, Italy, Iran, France, Morocco, Poland, Rumania, Bulgaria and Yugoslavia. The two variants currently available are the standard Kometa M, seating 113-116 passengers and the MT, a "tropicalised" model. Because of its air-conditioning and other refinements, the seating capacity is reduced to 102.

Demand for Kometas from other countries is rising rapidly, and new models with improved seakeeping characteristics, increased accommodation, and revised powerplant and drive arrangements are likely to be available within the next eighteen months. Output of the Kometa in particular is being increased, and consideration is being given to the setting up of a yard on the Black Sea to handle exclusively the building of hydrofoils for export. The range of designs to be assembled by the yard will almost certainly include the Kometa, Voskhod—a Raketa-replacement—and in another few years, the 250-seat Cyclone.

In the meantime an enterprising company in the United Kingdom, Airavia Ltd, is specialising in adapting Sormovo hydrofoils to meet various international operating and safety requirements. Early in 1974 it undertook the modification, to British Department of Trade standards of two Raketa Ts, both of which have been issued with British Civil Passenger Operating Certificates. One was exported to the Philippines and the other is operating a commuter service on the Thames. Plans are now being made to modify further craft, including Kometas, Meteors, Voskhods and Cyclones, in a similar way.

Throughout the world the skimmer industry's role in transportation is strengthening annually. Its products are in constant demand and there is ample evidence that orders will continue to grow in future. The present looks promising and the years ahead look even better.

Roy McLeavy
September, 1974

Der Antrieb kommt von

mtu

power to the power of experience

Motoren- und Turbinen-Union Friedrichshafen GmbH

ACKNOWLEDGEMENTS

The editor would like to thank the following for their assistance and encouragement.

Baron Hanns von Schertel, Volker Jost, Ernst Jaksch, Supramar; Charles H. Slater. Advanced Marine Systems-Alinavi SpA; E. K. Liberatore and Gerald O. Rennerts, Aeromar Corporation; J. M. George, British Hovercraft Corporation; Leopoldo Rodriquez Jr, The Leopoldo Rodriquez Shipyard; Albert W. Spindler and Donald J. Norton, Bell Aerospace; Alan Bingham, Arnaud de Cosson and John Brooks, Hovercraft Division, Vosper Thornycroft; Dr. William R. Bertelsen, Bertelsen Manufacturing Company; M. Muto, Mitsubishi Heavy Industries; T. Adachi, Mitsui Shipbuilding and Engineering Co; L. Flammand, Bertin & Cie; J. F. Lstiburek, Water Spyder Marine Ltd; M. W. Beardsley, Skimmers Inc; Franklin A. Dobson, Dobson Products Co; A. Latham, Air Cushion Equipment Ltd; Dr. Alexander M. Lippisch and Dr. Hershel Shosteck, Lippisch Research Corporation; Prof. L. Kobylinski, Gdansk Ship Research Institute; John Vass, Daily Express; Nigel Seale, Coelacanth Gemco; P. Watson, URBA; Jacques Beaudequin; Einer Bergström, Aeronautical Research Institute of Sweden; Peter Gooch; Sadao Aoyama, Hitachi Shipbuilding and Engineering; Neil MacDonald, Hovercraft Development Ltd; R. V. Taylor, Taylorcraft Transport Pty; Andre Autrusson, Societe Nationale Industrielle Aerospatiale, Joe Dell, Gustav Elm; Admiral J. R. Evenou, SEDAM; P. Lightfoot, Hovermarine Transport Ltd; C. D. J. Bland and P. H. Winter, Air Vehicles Ltd; Mrs I. Smith, Novosti Press Agency; Herbert Snowball, Airavia; John Gould; Gerald Grisman, Gemco; Christopher Hook; D. Williamson, Hovertrailers International; Warsaw Aviation Institute; Masahiro Mino, Nihon University; Mrs. J. C. A. Freeman, Sealand Hovercraft; R. P. Honan, Aerojet-General Corporation; James L. Schuler and Dr. D. A. Jewell, Department of the Navy; C. P. Kirwan, Hover-Jak Ltd; R. Schneider, Hoverjet Inc; Mike Pinder, Pindair Ltd; Carl-Magnus Fogelholm, Keksintösäätiö; Gordon J. Komar, Komar Engineering; Georges Hennebutte, Ets Georges Hennebutte; Gregory Grunbelich, Grumman; Jim McCurdy, Hovertec Inc; John Jukes, Hoverking; Toshiro Nagata, Hitachi; Walter G. Wohleking, Grumman Aerospace, Marine Division; Rigoberto Gisbert, FEI; Richard L. Routh, Ford Motor Company; J. F. Baker, Fairey Australasia Pty Ltd; John M. Savage, Volkswagen; C. F. de Jersey, De Havilland Aircraft of Canada; R. Danner Graves, Boeing; Jan Dilbeck, Arctic Engineers & Constructors; David Snoeyenbos, Airfloat Corporation; Ralph Wortmann, Airesearch Mfg; W. W. Buckley, Aircushion Boat Co.

He would also like to express his appreciation to Brenda Perfect for her assistance with this years correspondence and to the production team headed by Tricia MacPhee and Roger Abraham for their dedication and hard work.

Finally, he would like to thank Lippisch Research Corporation, and the Boeing Company, Naval Systems Division, for permission to reproduce the following Papers:

The Aerofoil Boat, A Free Flying Ram Wing Surface Effect Vehicle, by Dr. Alexander M. Lippisch and

DEH, A High Endurance Escort Hydrofoil for the Fleet, by Richard Aroner and Robert M. Hubbard.

You're getting something special with a Soviet-designed Hydrofoil

There's a wealth of experience built into Soviet Hydrofoils. For instance the RAKETA, the very first multi-seat passenger craft, was launched 17 years ago. It was also the first of its type to employ the Alexeyev shallow-draught submerged foil system. Hundreds of RAKETA Hydrofoils are now in regular operation, and a BRITISH PASSENGER CERTIFICATE has now been granted to this craft.

Scientific design, skilled engineering and robust construction all combine to ensure trouble-free operation for all types of Soviet Hydrofoils . . . that's surely something special !

THE RAKETA

The shallow draught RAKETA has been in operation in the U.S.S.R. since 1957 and has actually crossed the Black Sea (a run of 250 sea miles in unfavourable weather with a moderate sea) to demonstrate the absolute reliability of her hull and engineering design. Designed specifically for fast passenger services on all types of inland waterways with the special advantage of being able to operate in shallow waters.
Accommodation for 64 passengers.
Cruising speed: 33 knots (60 k.p.h.).

THE METEOR
116 seater Hydrofoil.

This larger type craft, needing a crew of four, is some 7½ metres longer than the RAKETA and is fitted with two 1,100 h.p. diesel engines. Its high performance and very comfortable accommodation for 116 passengers has made it a successful operator under the most diverse conditions. The foil-borne draught is only 1·2 metres. Cruising speed: 35 knots (65 k.p.h.).

The Kometa
the first hydrofoil passenger
motorship to have cruised
all round Europe

THE KOMETA has literally winged its way round Europe covering a total distance of 11,545 miles from the Black Sea through the Bay of Biscay to Leningrad.

Just over 35 metres long with a full-load displacement of 56 tons, a KOMETA class hydrofoil can carry 116 passengers in real comfort. As an example of performance it takes a KOMETA only 90 seconds to develop a speed of 30 knots. Its stability is amazing due to three stern air stabilisers positioned at the sides and amidships. Even in comparatively high seas, a KOMETA can maintain a cruising speed of 33/34 knots (60/63 k.p.h.) and has well earned its title of 'a greyhound of the seas'.

THE VOLGA 70

Here's a real fun craft designed for inland waterways or off-shore cruising. It has real performance as its Volvo Penta 90 engine gives it a maximum of 33 knots (60 k.p.h.). When foil-borne, the VOLGA needs a draught of about half a metre. Although only 8½ metres in length, there is comfortable accommodation for six persons.

Sole Concessionaires for U.S.S.R. Hydrofoils

AIRAVIA LTD

20 North Road, Shanklin, Isle-of-Wight.
Telephone: 098-386 3643

SUDOIMPORT
Moscow K-6, U.S.S.R.

[26]

CONTENTS

"JANE'S" is a registered trade mark

Hoverborne Strikepower
BH.7 Mk.6

Instant Reaction – Quick Target Contact
All-weather Availability – Formidable Firepower

Equipped with surface/surface missiles and a large calibre radar-controlled gun, the 60-knot BH.7 Mk.6 provides an instant response to emergencies.

Outpacing displacement craft, it ensures quick target contact taking a direct line towards its objective regardless of reefs, shoals, sandbanks and tidal variations.

The BH.7 Mk.6 is a twin-engine development of the well-proven BH.7 already in use with the Royal Navy and Imperial Iranian Navy and it enjoys the same all-weather performance.

It also combines the high speed amphibious qualities inherent in all BHC craft with the low speed patrol performance and firepower of conventional patrol boats.

The BH.7 Mk.6 represents an invaluable asset to coastal defence forces and is now available to the Navies of the World.

Can you afford to ignore it?

For further information please contact:

british hovercraft corporation

EAST COWES · ISLE OF WIGHT · ENGLAND
Telephone: Cowes 4121

A member of the Westland Group of Companies –
6 times winner of the Queen's Award to Industry

ACV MANUFACTURERS AND DESIGN GROUPS

ARGENTINA

BRUZZONE

ADDRESS:

Peru 327, Buenos Aires, Republic of Argentina

Jorge Oscar Bruzzone, an Argentinian aeronautical engineer, has designed an amphibious craft, the Guaipo BMX-1, which has been built and tested by the Argentine Navy. (Described in JSS 1971-72 edition).

Mr. Bruzzone has experimented with ACVs for nearly ten years. At the present time he is building privately a light single-seater and a three-seater. Preliminary details of his Yacare JOB-3 single-seat recreational craft are given below.

YACARE JOB-3

The prototype of this new amphibious runabout is under construction.

LIFT AND PROPULSION: Lift air is provided by a Citroen 3 hp automotive engine driving a centrifugal fan. Propulsive thrust is supplied by a 60 hp engine driving a ducted, two-bladed propeller.

CONTROLS: Twin aerodynamic rudders control craft heading.

HULL: Moulded glass reinforced plastics structure.

DIMENSIONS:

Length	14 ft 5¼ in (4·40 m)
Beam	7 ft 10½ in (2·40 m)

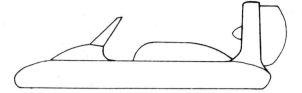

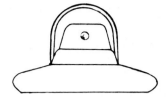

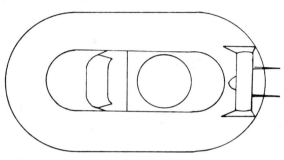

Bruzzone JOB-3 single-seat recreational craft

Height	3 ft 11¼ in (1·20 m)	Normal payload	397 lb (180 kg)
WEIGHT:		PERFORMANCE:	
Normal all-up weight	992 lb (450 kg)	Max speed	40·40 mph (65 km/h)
Normal empty weight	595 lb (270 kg)	Vertical obstacle clearance	9¾ in (0·25 m)

AUSTRALIA

FAIREY AUSTRALASIA PTY LTD

HEAD OFFICE:

Box 221, Elizabeth, South Australia 5112

TELEPHONE:

(08) 255192

CABLES:

Fairey, Adelaide

DIRECTORS:

F. R. Green, BE, CEng, FRAeS, FAIM, Chairman and Managing Director

R. B. Wiltshire, FCA

Fairey Australasia, incorporated in New South Wales, was founded in August 1949. Its Operations Division is located within the Weapons Research Establishment area in Salisbury, South Australia.

The primary activities of the Company are the design, development and manufacture of mechanical, optical, electro-mechanical, and electronic equipment for the aircraft and missile industry and the armed services.

Under a licencing agreement concluded in the autumn of 1972 between the company and Taylorcraft Transport Pty Ltd, it will build, develop and market the Skimaire range, which currently includes the Skimaire I 3-seater, the Skimaire II, a 6-seat, twin-engined craft, and the Skimaire III, a utility version of the Mk II with a 1,000 lb (453·59 kg) load capacity.

SKIMAIRE I

A small amphibious ACV of glass fibre and ply construction, the Skimaire seats three in an enclosed, pressurized and ventilated cabin. Power is supplied by an adapted Volkswagen industrial engine and the maximum speed over calm water is 50 mph (80·46 km/h).

The Skimaire, a 2-3 seat amphibious ACV, powered by a single 68 bhp Volkswagen engine

The production prototype Skimaire was completed in September 1969, and trials were completed in February 1970. The craft is now in full production. Skimaires have been supplied to purchasers in Australia, Canada, Taiwan, Indonesia and Japan.

LIFT AND PROPULSION: Immediately aft of the cockpit is a single, internally mounted 68 bhp Volkswagen 127V air-cooled four-cylinder, four-stroke petrol engine which drives via a gear box a 2 ft (609 mm) diameter aluminium alloy centrifugal lift fan, and a 4 ft 2 in (1·27 m) diameter, 4-bladed, fixed-pitch propeller. The propeller is surrounded by a metal guard.

Fuel is carried in two external 5 gallon tanks with amidships refuelling points. Recommended fuel is super grade automotive gasoline.

CONTROLS: Twin rudders mounted on the

propeller guard are operated via Bowden cables by the steering wheel. A set of louvre doors mounted below the lift fan controls the supply of air to the plenum and these can be employed as a braking control. Engine speed is controlled by a hand throttle linked to a foot pedal set so that the hand throttle sets the lower limit of engine speed.

HULL: Built in three grp sections—cabin top and deck, hull bottom and cabin interior —bonded together to form a rigid cell. The lower part of the hull is filled with closed cell structure foam and is reinforced below the cabin by a corrugated section. All mechanical components are mounted on a tubular steel frame which can be removed for major servicing.

SKIRT: Closed bag type, attached around the hull periphery where the outer flange joins top and bottom components. Drainage holes provided at rear.

ACCOMMODATION: Access to the cabin is through either of two gullwing doors, located amidships, one each side. The normal seating arrangement places the driver forward, centrally, and there are removable seats for two passengers at the rear. 300 lb (136 kg) of cargo can be carried with the passenger seats removed. The cabin is heated and ventilated.

SAFETY EQUIPMENT: 2 lb fire extinguisher amidships and Spot-a-Fire system.

SYSTEMS: Electrical: 12 volt, 77Ah battery, with 240 w generator for starting and lights.

COMMUNICATIONS: Provision is made for the installation of a marine type transmitter/receiver.

DIMENSIONS, EXTERNAL:
Length   17 ft 0 in (5·18 m)
Beam   8 ft 0 in (2·43 m)
Height overall, power off
                       5 ft 10 in (1·77 m)
Height overall, skirt inflated
                       6 ft 0 in (1·82 m)
Draft afloat   2½ in (63 mm)
Skirt depth   1 ft (304 mm)

WEIGHTS:
Normal empty weight   1,200 lb (544·28 kg)
Normal all-up weight   1,850 lb (839·10 kg)
Normal payload   650 lb (294·82 kg)

PERFORMANCE:
Max speed over calm water
                       50 mph (80·46 km/h)
Cruising speed over calm water
                       35 mph (56·32 km/h)
Turning circle diameter at 30 knots
                       130 ft (39·62 m)
Max wave capability
                       2-3 ft waves (·609-·914 m)
Still air range and endurance at cruising
  speed   170 miles (273·58 km)
Max gradient, static conditions   6 in 1
Vertical obstacle clearance
                       1 ft 0 in (304 mm)

PRICE AND TERMS:

Approximate cost of craft, ex works, Aust $11,500.

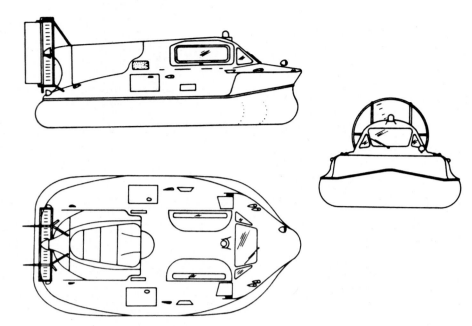

The Skimaire I light amphibious ACV

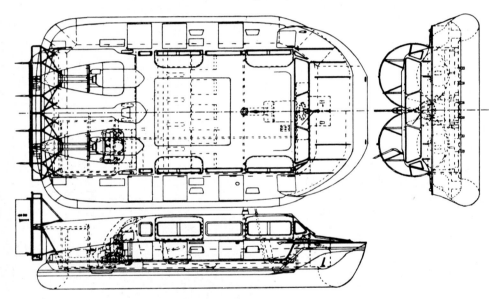

Skimaire II amphibious six-seater

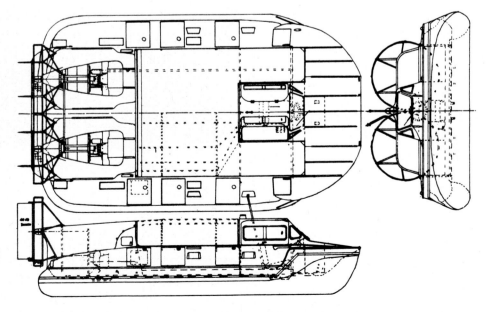

A utility model of the twin-engined Skimaire, the Mk III carries up to a 1,200 lb (544.8) kg payload on its amidship load deck

SKIMAIRE II

This is a 60 mph (96·60 km/h) twin-engined six-seat derivative of the Skimaire Mk I. Trials were in progress as this edition went to press.

LIFT AND PROPULSION: Motive power for the integrated lift/propulsion system is supplied by two internally-mounted 68 hp Volkswagen 127V air-cooled four-cylinder, four-stroke piston engines, each of which drives a 2 ft 0 in (·61 m) diameter centrifugal lift fan and a 4-bladed fixed pitch propeller. Two 4-bladed reversible-pitch propellers can be supplied as optional extras. Each propeller is surrounded by a metal guard. Cushion area is 190 sq ft (17·65 m²), and cushion pressure is 21 lbs/sq ft. Fuel capacity is 27 Imp gallons (122·85 l). Recommended fuel is super grade automotive gasoline.

CONTROLS: Twin rudders hinged to the rear of the two propeller guards and differential thrust control craft heading. A set of louvre doors mounted below the lift fans controls the supply of air to the plenum and these can be employed as a braking control.

HULL: Basically glass reinforced plastic with aluminium and stainless steel reinforcement.

DIMENSIONS:
Length overall	23 ft 3 in (7·086 m)
Beam, power on	13 ft 9 in (4·19 m)
power off	12 ft 9 in (3·89 m)
Height overall, power on	6 ft 6 in (1·98 m)
power off	5 ft 6 in (1·68 m)

WEIGHTS:
Empty weight, with fuel	2,800 lb (1,271·2 kg)
Payload	1,200 lb (544·8 kg)
Gross weight	4,000 lb (1,816 kg)

PERFORMANCE:
Max speed over land	60 mph (96·60 km/h)
over calm water	50 mph (80·50 km/h)

Fairey Skimaire II amphibious six-seater, powered by two 68 bhp Volkswagen air-cooled engines and capable of 60 mph (96·60 km/h) over land and 50 mph (80·50 km/h) over water

Max gradient		1 in 8
Vertical clearance	1 ft 6 in (457 mm)	

Range and endurance
app 220 miles (355 km), 4 hours
PRICE: Ex works, standard fittings, Aust. $25,000.

SKIMAIRE III

This light utility ACV has a cargo deck aft of the driver and is designed to transport general freight loads weighing up to 1,200 lb (544·8 kg).

The amidship load deck has a large removable hatch to facilitate loading.

The specification is similar in most respects to that of Skimaire II.

PRICE: Ex works, standard fittings, Aust. $25,000.

STOLKRAFT PTY LTD

HEAD OFFICE:
52 Hilltop Road, Clareville Beach, NSW 2107, Australia
EXECUTIVES:
L. D. Stolk, Chief Designer
CONSULTANTS:
James H. Eken, FRTNA, MIE AUST, MIME,
Commercial Marine Design Pty Ltd, 24 Thomas Street, Chatswood, NSW 2067, Australia
OVERSEAS REPRESENTATIVE, EUROPE:
Richard M. Jones,
22 Elmore Street, Islington, London, N1
TELEPHONE:
226 8570

Mr. L. D. Stolk's Stolcraft concept is a new approach to the air-lubricated planing hull. His main objectives have been to overcome the basic pitch instability apparent in some earlier designs and to eliminate bow wash.

The basic Stolkraft hull is of trimaran configuration and is designed to roll the waves beneath the hull to provide hydrodynamic lift at speeds below 30 mph (40·28 km/h).

Inceptor prototype at 50 mph (80·46 km/h) during trials. A combination of ram-air cushion at the bow and air fed through a ventilated step beneath the hull aft reduces the maximum load draft by as much as 80%.

At speed an appreciable amount of aerodynamic lift is built up by a ram-air cushion at the bow, and this, combined with air fed through twin bow intakes and vented from a transverse step beneath the hull aft, lifts the craft in order to reduce frictional resistance.

A feature of the concept is the absence of trim variation. During trials undertaken on the torpedo range of the Royal Australian Navy at Pittwater, near Sydney, it was demonstrated that the craft rises bodily, parallel to the surface and has no tendency to porpoise. At speed it creates neither bow-wash nor hull spray.

The aerodynamic lift on the prototype is about 65% and the maximum load draft is reduced by 80%.

The hull design is applicable to a wide range of vessels from passenger ferries for inland waterways to seagoing craft.

INCEPTOR

The prototype Inceptor is of grp construction and features a trimaran hull, the bow of which is designed to contain a ram-air cushion. An air-vented step, halfway along the hull, produces a second air cushion aft.

At speed, the aerodynamic lift generated by the inclined surface at the bow and the air-vented tunnel surfaces aft reduce the hull draft by 85%.

The craft, which seats three, is powered by a 125 hp Mercury outboard driving a 3in (330 mm) diameter propeller.

DIMENSIONS:

Length	14 ft 3 in (4·34 m)
Beam	6 ft 3 in (1·90 m)

WEIGHTS:

Gross weight (3 passengers plus ballast)
2,660 lbs (1,206·54 kg)

PERFORMANCE:

Max speed	50 mph (80·46 km/h)

Preliminary specifications for three Stolkraft design project are given below:

HARBOUR FERRY OR RIVER FREIGHTER

Length overall	65 ft 0 in (19·81 m)
Width	26 ft 0 in (7·92 m)
Displacement	65 tons
Passengers	135
Powerplant (diesel)	2,650 shp
Speed	45 mph plus (72·42 km/h)

Draught at 45 mph, waves not exceeding 5 ft (1·52 m) 1 ft 3 in (381 mm)

CRUISER OR WATER TAXI

Length overall	33 ft 0 in (10·05 m)
Beam	13 ft 6 in (4·11 m)
Displacement (payload 30 pass)	9 tons
Speed (full load)	50 mph (80·46 km/h)
Powerplant 2 × 300 shp petrol or diesel	600 shp

Draught at rest (full load) 2 ft 6 in (0·76 m)
Draught at approximately 50 mph,
6 in (152 mm)

Top. Inceptor's trimaran hull, designed for maximum ram-wing effect. The twin intakes feed pressurised air to a ventilated transverse step and thence to a second air cushion created beneath the hull aft. *Bottom:* Impression of a passenger ferry employing a Stolkraft hull

RUNABOUT

Length	15 ft 6 in (4·72 m)
Beam	6 ft 6 in (1·98 m)
Displacement (payload 1,200 lbs)	
	2,600 lbs (1,179·32 kg)
Speed (full load)	50 mph plus (80·46 km/h)
Powerplant, outboard	125 shp
Draught at rest (full load)	1 ft 0 in (304 mm)
Draught at 50 mph (full load)	2 in (50 mm)
(waves not exceeding 1 ft 3 in (381 mm))	

TAYLORCRAFT TRANSPORT (DEVELOPMENT) PTY LTD

HEAD OFFICE:
Parafield Airport, South Australia 5106
TELEPHONE:
258 4944
DIRECTORS:
R. V. Taylor, Managing Director
J. Taylor

Taylorcraft has been active in ACV research and development since 1966. It is currently developing and marketing machines ranging from the Kartaire, a light single-seater for home builders, to a mixed-traffic sidewall craft designed to carry ten cars and up to 100 passengers.

Other additions to the company's range are the Islander 1A for coastal medical work and the Islander IV freighter.

KARTAIRE Mk I and II

This is a single-seat vehicle for home builders and initial training. It is supplied in partial kit form in the interests of safety. The engines, engine mounting and wooden

components are found by the constructor.
The craft will carry its driver—either adult or child—over flat terrain, sand or water, and if required to traverse deep water, the hull can be fitted with a expanded polystyrene buoyancy block. The latest production model, the Kartaire Mk II has a grp hull and a top speed of 35 mph (56·32 km/h) over water.

LIFT AND PROPULSION: Lift power is furnished by a Victa 160cc two-stroke driving a 1 ft 6 in (457 mm) diameter centrifugal, alloy lift fan. Propulsive thrust on both versions is supplied by a second Victa 160cc two-stroke driving a 3-bladed fixed-pitch, 2 ft 10 in (863 mm) diameter Taylorcraft propeller.

Mk III will be propelled by a 15 bhp two-stroke engine driving a 2-bladed plastic propeller when a suitable engine is available in Australia.

CONTROL: An aircraft-type control column operates twin aerodynamic rudders set in the airscrew slipstream for directional control.

HULL: Kit parts are in ¼ in (6·35 mm) marine plywood; in assembled form the components are in marine ply and glassfibre reinforced plastics.

SKIRT: Bag type skirt in Linatex rubber or Neolon.

The following details apply to the Kartaire Mk II.

DIMENSIONS:
Length overall	9 ft 0 in (2·74 m)
Beam overall	4 ft 0 in (1·21 m)
Height overall	4 ft 0 in (1·21 m)

WEIGHTS:
Normal empty weight	120 lb (54·42 kg)

PERFORMANCE:
Max speed over calm water	35 mph
Max gradient	1 in 8
Vertical obstacle clearance	6 in

PRICES:
Kartaire I, single-seat ultra-light recreational craft in kit form, $180·00.
Kartaire II, with grp hull, assembled, $950·00.

KARTAIRE IV

The Kartaire IV is an ultra-light air cushion vehicle designed for use over water, mud flats and sand. It may be used as emergency transport in flooded areas or as a dinghy in sheltered waters. Its useful hard-structure clearance allows it to operate over fairly rough surfaces.

LIFT AND PROPULSION: Lift power is supplied by a single Victa 160cc two-stroke driving a 1 ft 6 in (457 mm) diameter 10-bladed centrifugal fan. Propulsive thrust is furnished by an 8 hp Robin driving a 3-bladed, fixed-pitch 2 ft 10 in (863 mm) diameter Taylorcraft propeller. The lift fan and propeller ducts are of grp and alloy construction.

CONTROLS: Stick-operated rudder and throttle levers for lift and thrust engines. Both engines are fitted with pull starters.

HULL: The hull is a simple inflatable raft, from which is suspended a finger type skirt. All fabric parts are made from neoprene and hypalon-coated nylon. The hull side and end members are inflated by hand bellows. A light alloy frame with plug-in side stringers supports the two engines.

The Taylorcraft Kartaire II   a light single-seater for home builders

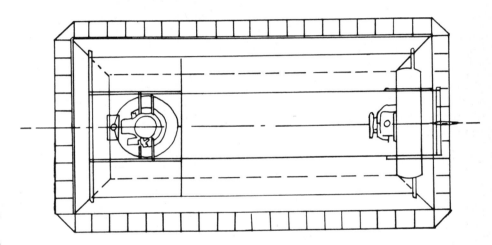

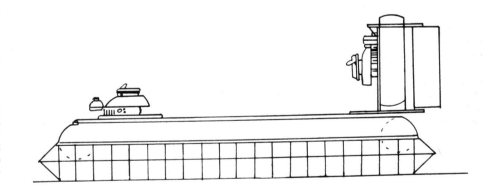

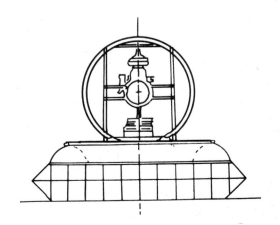

Taylorcraft Kartaire IV

ACCOMMODATION: The open cockpit is 5 ft (1·52 m) long and 1 ft 10 in (0·55 m) wide and is provided with a single inflated seat which is adjustable to ensure correct trim. Although designed as a single-seater, a passenger may be carried under overload conditions.

DIMENSIONS:

Length, hardstructure	10 ft 0 in (3·04 m)
Beam	5 ft 0 in (1·52 m)
Height	4 ft 6 in (1·37 m)

WEIGHTS:

Empty	100 lb (45·35 kg)
Gross	280 lb (127·00 kg)

PERFORMANCE (Still Air):

Max speed over land 45 mph (72·42 km/h)
over water 40 mph (64·37 km/h)

INTERCEPTAIRE

This new 17 ft (5·18 m) long, airjet propelled two-seater was due to enter production during 1974.

The hull is of glassfibre construction and power is supplied by an adapted Volkswagen engine. A single control column operates two hinged thrust vanes for directional control. Speed over land is expected to be about 60 mph (96·56 km/h) and over water about 35 mph (65·32 km/h).

Retail price will be $A3,500.

PUFFAIRE II

This small, sturdily built utility vehicle is intended for operation over land, rivers and sheltered waters. It has an open cockpit with two seats and an open deck which can accommodate bulky loads of up to 1,000 lb (453 kg). Various alternative accommodation arrangements can be made, including the installation of a folding awning to protect both the crew and cargo, or a 5-seat modular passenger cabin, which fits into the well deck immediately aft of the control cabin. A Trailaire ACV trailer unit (see company's entry in section covering ACV Trailers, Tractors and Heavy Lift Systems) can be towed by the craft, increasing the payload capacity to two tons.

LIFT AND PROPULSION: Integrated system powered by a 145 hp Holden 309 V8 watercooled automotive engine. Mounted

The Kartaire IV inflatable-hulled single-seat runabout

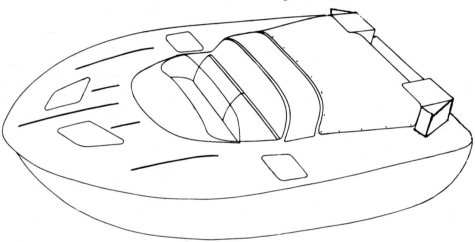

Taylorcraft Interceptaire air-jet propelled two-seater. Two hinged thrust vanes operated by a control column provide directional control

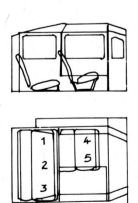

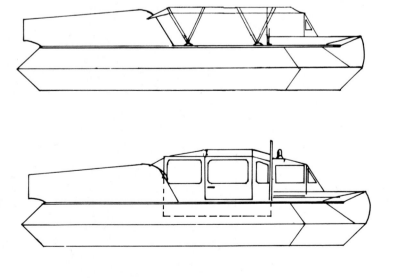

General arrangement of the Taylorcraft Transport Puffaire II open deck utility vehicle, showing optional configurations including the addition of a 5-seat cabin module. A 200 hp Holden V8 petrol engine powers the integrated lift/propulsion system. Payload is 1,000 lb (453 kg)

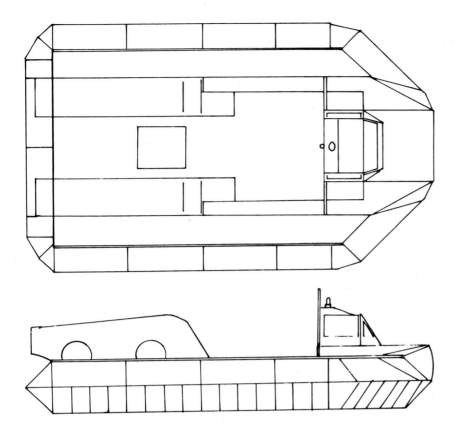

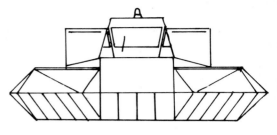

Taylorcraft Transport Puffaire II

inboard, the engine drives two centrifugal fans through a torque convertor. Both fans are totally enclosed in ducts to eliminate any danger from rotating parts. A high thrust unit can be supplied for special applications.
SKIRT: 1 ft 6 in (457 mm) high skirt with 100% segments. Fingers and groups of fingers are easily replaced when necessary.
CONTROLS: Directional control is effected by a skirt shift system and supplemented by differential use of airjet thrust. A single control column, on which is mounted the throttle lever, is located on the right hand side of the cockpit. Pedals control reverse thrust.

DIMENSIONS:

Length overall:	
on cushion	22 ft 0 in (6·7 m)
hard structure	19 ft 0 in (5·8 m)
Beam overall:	
on cushion	14 ft 0 in (4·27 m)
hard structure	8 ft 2 in (2·09 m)
Height overall:	
on cushion	7 ft 0 in (2·13 m)
hard structure	5 ft 7 in (1·69 m)
Draft afloat	9in (229mm)
Cargo deck size	
7 ft 0 in × 6 ft 3 in (2·13 m × 1·83 m)	

WEIGHTS:

Empty	2,630 lb (1,193 kg)
Payload	1,000 lb (453 kg)
Fuel and driver	370 lb (168 kg)
Gross weight	4,000 lb (1,814 kg)

PERFORMANCE:

Max speed over land	45 mph (70 km/h)
over water	35 mph (55 km/h)
Max gradient	1 : 6
Hump speed	12 mph (20 km/h)
Hard structure clearance	1 ft 6 in (457 mm)
Max wave height	3 ft 0 in (·914 m)

ISLANDAIR IV

This is a new multi-purpose amphibious ACV, powered by three 145 hp General

Model of the Taylorcraft Puffaire II, showing the location of the centrifugal fans and load deck. The removable passenger module has five seats

Motors-Holden automotive engines. Four variants are projected, the Islandaire 1A ambulance and search and rescue craft; Islandaire II, a twelve-seater; Islandaire III, a 20-seat passenger ferry, and the Islandaire IV, a freighter with a payload/fuel capacity of 5,800 lb (2,630 kg).

Half the load deck is enclosed and the remaining area can be protected by a canopy. Bulky items up to 20 ft (6·09 m) long may be carried subject to weight distribution requirements.

LIFT AND PROPULSION: Cushion air is supplied by a single GM-H 308 V8 water-cooled automotive engine driving two 40 in (1·01 m) diameter centrifugal, double intake fans, via a torque converter and bevel gears. Propulsive thrust is furnished by two pylon-mounted engines of identical type, each driving a 6 ft (1·82 m) diameter, reversible-pitch propeller.
CONTROLS: Directional control is effected by twin aerodynamic rudders and supplemented by differential propeller thrust.

HULL: Access to the well deck is via a rear loading door, 7 ft 0 in (2·13 m) wide.
ACCOMMODATION: Elevated control cabin forward with seats for driver, engineer and third crew member.

DIMENSIONS:

Length overall on cushion
　　　　　　　　48 ft 6 in (14·78 m)
Length overall, off cushion
　　　　　　　　44 ft 3 in (14·17 m)
Beam overall, on cushion
　　　　　　　　24 ft 0 in (7·31 m)
Beam overall, off cushion
　　　　　　　　20 ft 0 in (6·09 m)
Height (excl mast):
　on cushion　　12 ft 0 in (3·65 m)
　off cushion　　8 ft 6 in (2·59 m)
Freight deck, width　7 ft 0 in (2·13 m)
　　　　　length　14 ft 0 in (4·26 m)

DIMENSIONS, INTERNAL:

Cabin, 3 seats:
　length　　7 ft 9 in (2·36 m)
　width　　8 ft 0 in (2·43 m)
Cabin, single-seat:
　length　　6 ft 0 in (1·82 m)
　width　　4 ft 0 in (1·21 m)

WEIGHTS:

Gross weight　12,700 lb (5,760 kg)
Fuel and payload　5,800 lb (2,630·8 kg)

PERFORMANCE:

Cruising speed　45 mph (72·42 km/h)
Max speed　　65 mph (104·37 km/h)
Max wave length　6 ft-8 ft (1·82-2·43 m),
　　　　　　　　　　　　long sea
Gradient, standing start　1 : 7·5
Isolated obstacle　　3 ft (0·91 m)
Fuel consumption
　　19 gph (81·8 b/ph) at cruising speed
Endurance　　　5 hours

PRICE (approx only):

Islandaire I (8 seat)　　$A75,000
Islandaire II (12 seat)　$A100,000
Islandaire III (20 seat)　$A125,000
Islandaire IV (2 ton payload)　$A100,000

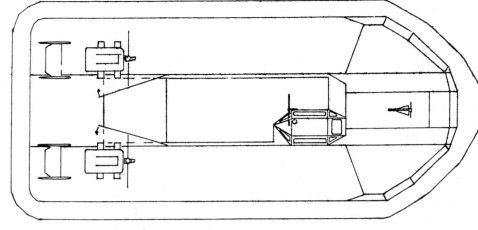

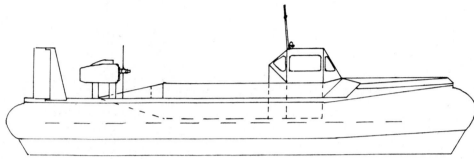

Taylorcraft Islandaire IV multi-duty ACV freighter

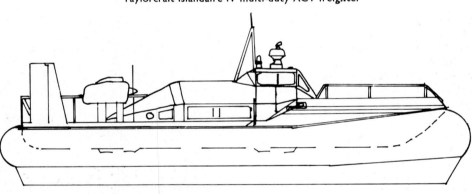

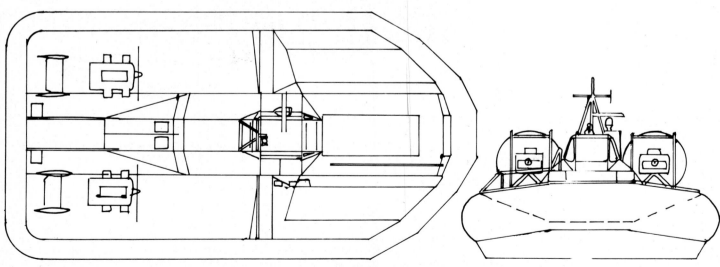

Taylorcraft Islandaire IA, ACV ambulance and Search and Rescue craft

BRAZIL

BRAZIL
FEI
FACULTY OF INDUSTRIAL ENGINEER-ING

ADDRESS:
Research Vehicle Department (DEPV),
Faculty of Industrial Engineering, São
Bernado do Campo, Avenido Oreste
Romano 112, São Paulo

TELEPHONE:
443 1155
SENIOR EXECUTIVE:
Eng. Rigoberto Soler Gisbert, Director of
Vehicle Research

The Vehicle Research Department of the FEI was founded in 1968. Its first major task was to conduct a full-scale investigation into Brazil's transport problems and its likely future requirements. An outcome of this was the design and construction by students and faculty of a 51 ft (15·54 m) long prototype of a tracked ACV, the TALAV, which was exhibited during the 150th anniversary of Brazilian Independence in August 1972 (see Tracked Skimmers).

Since then the Department, under the direction of Eng. Rigoberto Soler Gisbert, has designed, built and tested a number of light amphibious ACVs, including the VA and the VA-1, which, according to recent newspaper reports is to be put into production.

Preliminary details of these vehicles were received as this edition went to press in July 1974.

VA

A glassfibre-hulled amphibious two-seater, the VA is powered by a single Volkswagen VW 1300 automotive engine and has a top speed of about 50 mph (80 km/h).

LIFT AND PROPULSION: Integrated system powered by a single 50 hp VW 1300 automotive engine driving a ducted fan. Air from the fan feeds into the plenum below for lift and aft for propulsion. Total fuel capacity is 6·6 gals (30 litres).

CONTROLS: Single aerodynamic rudder, hinged to rear of fan duct, provides heading control.

HULL: Moulded grp structure.

SKIRT: Bag-type, 6 in (15 cm) deep.

ACCOMMODATION: Open cockpit with seating for two, side-by-side.

DIMENSIONS:

Length overall	13 ft 5⅜ in (4·10 m)
Beam	6 ft 10⅝ in (2·10 m)
Height	4 ft 11 in (1·5 m)

WEIGHTS:

Empty weight	882 lb (400 kg)
Loaded weight	1,654 lb (750 kg)

PERFORMANCE:

Maximum speed:	
over land	50 mph (80 km/h)
over water	31 mph (50 km/h)
Maximum gradient, static conditions 1 : 10	
Vertical obstacle clearance	6 in (15 cm)

VA-1

It has been reported that this novel 4-seat utility vehicle is now in production at Jacarei, one of Brazil's industrial centres. The VA-1 and its derivatives will be employed in a variety of projects aimed at opening up and developing areas of the Amazon and traversing the swamps of the Matto Grosso.

LIFT AND PROPULSION: Cushion lift is provided by a single 40 hp Volkswagen 1300 automotive engine driving twin fans located on the centre line, one each end of the open load deck. Thrust is supplied by two 90 hp Volkswagen 2000 engines, each driving a ducted 2-bladed propeller aft. Cushion area is 13·5 m², and cushion pressure 11 gr/cm². Total fuel capacity is 22 gal (100 l).

CONTROLS: A single aerodynamic rudder provides directional control.

HULL: Moulded fibreglass.

SKIRT: Bag type flexible skirt, 10 in (25 cm) deep.

ACCOMMODATION: Enclosed cabin, forward, seats a driver and three passengers.

Top: FEI VA two-seat light sports ACV during trials.

Centre: Power for the VA is supplied by a single 50 hp VW 1300 automotive engine which gives it a top speed over water of 43.5 mph (70 kmh)

Bottom: A model of VEI's VAI four-seat utility vehicle for operation over land, rivers and sheltered water.

Access is via two hinged doors, one port, one starboard.

DIMENSIONS:

Length overall	21 ft 7⅞ in (6·60 m)
Beam	10 ft 1⅛ in (3·05 m)
Height	7 ft 8½ in (2·35 m)

WEIGHTS:

Empty weight	1,764 lb (800 kg)
Loaded weight	3,308 lb (1,500 kg)

PERFORMANCE:

Maximum speed:	
overwater	43·5 mph (70 km/h)
over land	74·5 mph (120 km/h)
Max gradient, static conditions	20%
Vertical obstacle clearance	10 in (25 cm)

CANADA

BELL AEROSPACE CANADA
(A division of Textron Canada Ltd.)
DIRECTORS:
  William G. Gisel, President
  Norton C. Willcox, Vice President
  James L. Decker, Vice President and General Manager, Grand Bend Operation
HEAD OFFICE:
  P.O. Box 160, Grand Bend, Ontario, Canada
TELEPHONE:
  Area Code 519 238-2333
OTTAWA OFFICE:
  Suite 1400, 130 Albert Street, Ottawa KIP 5G4, Ontario, Canada
TELEPHONE:
  Area Code 613 236-0705

In January 1971, Bell Aerospace Canada acquired facilities at Grand Bend, Ontario, for the development and production of its Voyageur heavy haul ACV.

The facilities at Grand Bend Airport include two buildings with a total of 30,000 sq ft (3,350 m²) of floor space on a 52-acre (21 Ha) site.

The company has worked closely with the Canadian Department of Industry, Trade and Commerce in planning a programme which has led to the establishment in Canada of a commercially viable air cushion industry to meet the growing requirements for Coast Guard, remote area cargo hauling, high speed passenger ferry services and other specialised applications.

Two 40 gross ton Voyageurs have been built under a joint agreement between the company and the Canadian Department of Industry, Trade and Commerce. Costs were shared by Bell and the Canadian government up to a limit of $5·2 million, which covered the cost of development, manufacture and testing of the first two craft.

The first of an initial production batch of four Voyageurs was completed in January 1974 and an option was taken on the craft. The remaining three were scheduled for completion in 1974 and options have been taken on two of these.

A one-prototype cost-sharing programme similar to that under which the Voyageur was developed is now underway for the smaller Viking. Bell's agreement with the Canadian government (under its programme for the advancement of industrial technology —PAIT) will continue until 1980.

Both Voyageur and Viking feature a basic flatbed hull of all-welded extruded marine aluminium that can be adapted to a variety of operational needs by adding the required equipment and superstructure.

Construction of the first two Voyageurs started in March 1971. The first craft began operational trials and certification testing in November 1971. This particular craft was employed in military lighterage operations for the joint US Army/Navy/Marine Corps OSDOC II, in October 1972. The operation involved ship-to-shore cargo hauling, including transition of surf and travel across lines of sand dunes.

The first Voyageurs differ in the power plants installed. The first has two GE LM-100 PD-101 Marine gas turbines, and the second has two Pratt & Whitney UAC ST6T-75 Twin Pac engines.

Early in 1973, the first craft was chartered to KAPS Transport Ltd, and completed a run

Top: Voyageur prototype carrying two standard Milvan containers ashore during Exercise OSDOC II (Off-Shore Discharge of Containerships), conducted jointly by the US Army and Navy in October 1972. The craft averaged 30 knots during the discharge of containers from a ship one mile off shore. It proved to be five times faster than existing conventional lighters and transported the containers one mile inland to a logistic area

Centre: A Voyageur, operated in Canada by Northern Transportation Co, equipped to lay 1 in cable from a 17-ton reel mounted on the deck, forward of the bridge

Bottom: Impression of a mixed-ferry version of the Voyageur with passenger cabins flanking the load deck. Up to six cars can be carried

on the Mackenzie River carrying two Arctic housing modules. Since then it has been operated by KAPS in an oil industry logistics support role. Typical loads are a Nodwell seismic driller weighing 46,000 lb, a 3,300 Imperial gallon fuel tank (filled), and miscellaneous items of earth moving equipment. The craft was also used to lay 12 miles of 1 in cable from a 17-ton reel mounted on the deck.

The second craft, completed in March 1972, was acquired by the Transport Development Agency of the Canadian Ministry of Transport for operation by Northern Transportation Co. Ltd.

Arctic trials began in early 1973, after the craft had been flown by C-130 Hercules to Tuktoyaktuk. Operations were conducted successfully in temperatures as low as —40°C.

At the end of the winter, the craft was driven south on the frozen Mackenzie river,

negotiating ice ridges as high as 4·6 ft (1·21-1·82 m). After the installation of buoy-handling gear, it was used for Canadian Coast Guard aids-to-navigation trials, then for tundra environmental impact trials.

In January 1974, after refurbishing, the craft was acquired by the Canadian Coast Guard, and is at present being operated from the CCG base at Parry Sound, Lake Huron, in aids-to-navigation and air/sea rescue roles. Ice breaking trials have also been conducted from Parry Sound. Ice up to 15 in (381 mm) thick had been broken successfully at the time of going to press.

A second batch of four Voyageurs is now in production, with deliveries beginning in the first half of 1974. The first Viking, designed to meet Canadian Coast Guard requirements for an inshore search-and-rescue craft, was completed in April 1974.

MODEL 7380 VOYAGEUR

The Bell Model 7380 is a twin-engined fully amphibious hovercraft designed to haul payloads of up to 25 tons over Arctic and other terrain at speeds up to 87 km/h (54 mph).

The 25 ton payload is equal to that of most transport aircraft engaged in regular supply operations in the North and other remote regions, including the C-130 Hercules. The Model 7380 therefore provides a direct transport link from the airstrips to settlements and support bases for the movement of men, equipment and supplies.

The craft has been tested extensively by the Canadian Coast Guard and the US Army for a variety of high speed amphibious missions.

Modular construction is employed and the craft can be dismantled into easily handled units, plus skirts, for ease of transportation by road, rail or air.

Estimates indicate that ton-mile operating costs will be less than 25% of those experienced with heavy lift helicopters and 50% that of existing small ACVs.

By adding superstructure to the basic flatbed hull, the craft can be used for various alternative roles from a 140 seat passenger ferry to military weapons platform.

LIFT AND PROPULSION: Two 1,300 hp Pratt & Whitney ST6T-75 Twin-Pac gas-turbines mounted aft, one each side of the roll-on/roll-off cargo deck, power the integrated lift/propulsion systems, which employ fans, propellers and transmissions similar to those of the Bell SK-5 and BHC SR-N6. Each engine has two separate gas-turbine sections which drive into a combining gearbox, providing twin-engine reliability for each integrated lift fan and propeller. The second gearbox employed in the Twin-Pac installation is a strengthened version of the integrated drive used in the SR.N5, developed by the SPECO Division of Kelsey-Hayes. The output of each engine is absorbed by a three-bladed Hamilton Standard 43D50 reversible-pitch propeller of 9 ft (2·74 m) diameter and

The basic Voyageur hard structure breaks down into ten major modules, plus a cab module and pedestal, to permit transport by road, rail or sea. A partly assembled Voyageur is seen above en route to Lake Huron by road. Final assembly took 24 hours and the craft is now operated by the Canadian Coast Guard base at Parry Sound in aids-to-navigation and air/sea rescue roles

by a 12-bladed 7 ft (2·13 m) diameter light alloy centrifugal lift fan. The fans deliver air to the cushion via a 4 ft (1·21 m) deep peripheral skirt which incorporates stability trunks. Air drawn by the engines first enters a Donaldson filter that traps and removes dust particles. It then passes through a fine knitmesh filter and into a Peerless Vane filter that gathers water droplets. Lift fans and propellers are linked mechanically and the power output of each engine can be apportioned between the propellers and lift fans allowing speed and hoverheight to be varied to suit prevailing operating conditions. The engines have multifuel capability and can be started in extremely low temperatures (—65°F). Two

fuel tanks, each consisting of three interconnected bays containing flexible rubber cells, are built into the aft end of the port and starboard forward flotation boxes. Total fuel capacity is 15,000 litres (3,300 Imp gal), sufficient for a range of approximately 550 nautical miles with a 15-ton payload. Types of fuel which may be used are kerosene, AVTUR, JETA, JP4, JP5 and Arctic diesel. CONTROLS: Steering is by means of two aerodynamically-balanced rudders hinged to the rear of propeller, supplemented by the use of differential propeller pitch control. Side-located bow thrusters aid low-speed manoeuvring. All controls are located in the raised cab, which seats a crew of two plus four passengers. Propeller pitch controls are

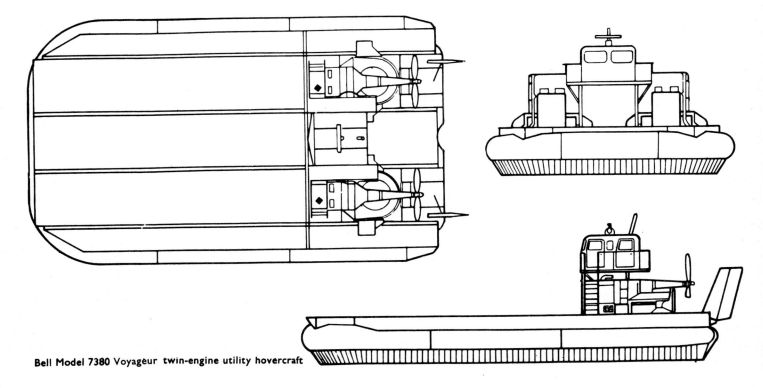

Bell Model 7380 Voyageur **twin-engine utility hovercraft**

located on the starboard side of the operator's seat, so that they can be operated by the right hand, while power can be controlled with the left hand. A conventional foot-operated control bar is provided for rudder actuation.

HULL: Exceptionally rugged all-metal structure, fabricated in corrosion-resistant 6,000 series extruded aluminium alloys, with double wall skinning and multiple watertight compartments. The design of the modular structure incorporates hollow-core, thin-walled aluminium extrusions similar to those employed in the superstructures of commercial and naval ships. Use of this material, with extruded corners for constructing joints, produces a structural box of great strength and stiffness. The hull design is based on flat surfaces, thus eliminating the need for formed parts and simplifying repairs. The structural modules are welded using gas-shielded metal arc and gas shielded tungsten arc processes.

The basic craft hard structure is broken down for transportation into twelve sections. These consist of three forward flotation boxes, two forward and two aft side decks, two power modules, an aft centre flotation box, a cabin support pedestal and the control cabin.

The three forward flotation boxes are almost identical in appearance and measure 40 ft long, 8 ft wide and 3 ft 1½ in deep (12.19 × 2.43 × 0.952 m). The port and starboard boxes each contain a fuel tank and a landing pad support structure.

The aft centre flotation box is of similar construction, but shorter in length. Scallops are formed in each side to prevent airflow blockage around the perimeter of the lift fans, which are contained in the power modules

located on either side of the centre box. This module, together with the three forward boxes, forms the structural backbone of the craft. Loads from the side decks and power modules are transmitted into this primary structure.

The main deck is designed to accept loadings of up to 4,882 kg/m² (1,000 lb/sq ft.) Cargo tiedown-rings and craft handling gear are provided. Off-cushion, the cargo deck is sufficiently low to permit rapid loading and unloading from trucks and fork lifts.

The craft is completely amphibious and has a reserve buoyancy in excess of 100%.

SKIRT: 1.22 m (4 ft) deep neoprene nylon skirt developed from that of BHC SR.N6. 50% peripheral fingers. High attachment line at bow, similar to that employed on the BH.7. Airflow to the side and bow skirts is supplied through the duct formed by the side hulls. The transverse stability trunks are also supplied from the side hull airflow, via a duct built into the outboard forward flotation boxes immediately forward of the fuel tanks. The port and starboard rear trunks are supplied by rearward airflow from the respective fans. The longitudinal keel is fed by ducts leading from each fan forward to the centre of the aft centre flotation box, then downwards into the keel bag.

ACCOMMODATION: The control cabin is supported on a raised platform aft of the deck between the power modules. It is raised sufficiently to provide 1.93 m (6 ft 4 in) of headroom for personnel or cargo and provides the operator with a 360 deg view. The unit is basically a modified four door truck cab, measuring 2.64 × 2.38 m (8 ft 8 in long by 7 ft 10 in wide). The operating crew of two are seated forward. The operator's position

is on the starboard side, and the relief driver or radar operator is at the port position. The control console is located between the two seats and contains the control levers for the engines.

A full-width bench seat is located across the back of the cab, with access provided by the two rear doors. Seat belts are provided for four passengers. Cabin heating and window defrosting is provided by a dual heater, operating on vehicle fuel, and located at the forward end, beneath the port walkway to the control cabin. Electronically heated windows are also installed. Thermal insulation and double glazing are provided throughout the cab and this also attenuates engine noise.

Additional features provided in the cab design are structural provisions for roof mounted radar, air-conditioning and the provision of space in the control console for radio communications and navigation equipment.

SYSTEMS: Electrical: Four gearbox-driven brushless generators, each supplying 28 volts dc, and two 28 volt Nickel-Cadmium batteries. External power: 28 volts dc.

DIMENSIONS:

Length overall	19.8 m (64.8 ft)
Beam overall	11.2 m (36.7 ft)
Height overall, power on	6.7 m (22.0 ft)
Height overall, power off	5.74 m (18 ft 10 in)
Height of cargo deck, power off	1.17 m (3 ft 10 in)
Skirt height	1.22 m (4 ft 0 in)
Cushion area	166 m² (1,789 sq ft)
Cushion loading at 38,917 kg (88,000 lb)	240 kg/m² (49.2 lb/sq ft)
Buoyancy reserve at 38,917 kg (88,000 lb)	169%

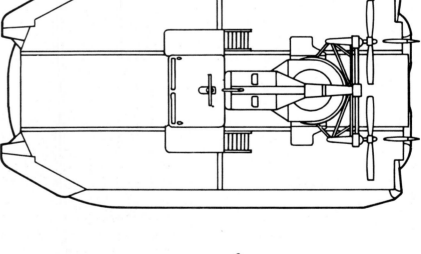

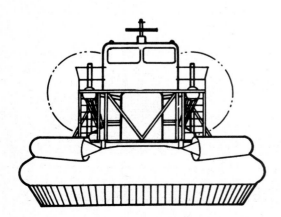

Power for the Viking multi-purpose ACV is provided by a single 1,300 hp Twin-Pac T75, coupled to two variable-pitch propellers via a V-drive transmission. Maximum speed, calm water, is 92 km/h (57 mph)

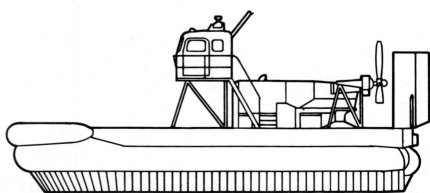

Cargo deck size   40 × 32 ft (1,280 sq ft)
                     (12·19 m × 9·75 m) (119 m²)
WEIGHTS:
Basic weight, empty 16,202 kg (35,720 lb)
Design gross weight   40,823 kg (90,000 lb)
Max permissible gross weight
                     40,823 kg (90,000 lb)
PERFORMANCE:
Max speed over calm water, still air conditions, at a sea level standard day
temperature of 59 deg F (15 deg C) with a
20 ton payload.
At 78,000 lb (35,381 kg) gross, 2,600 shp
                     54 mph (87 km/h)
Endurance at cruise power with 600 US
gallons (2,280 l) and 30-ton payload
                     3 hours
Endurance can be extended to 10-13·5 hours
by trading off payload for fuel, with maximum fuel of 15,000 litres (3,300 Imp gal)
the payload will be in the region of 18
tons at the maximum permissible gross
weight of 40,823 kg (90,000 lb).

MODEL 7501 VIKING

Evolved from the 40-ton Voyageur, the 17-ton
Viking has been designed to meet the need
for a smaller but similar multi-purpose craft
capable of hauling a 6-7-ton payload at a
speed of 92 km/h (57 mph).

The cost of the project is estimated at $2
million, approximately half of which is
being funded under the Programme for
Advancement of Industrial Technology
(PAIT) agreement with the Canadian Department of Industry, Trade and Commerce
(DOITC).

The Viking prototype, equipped to meet
Canadian Coast Guard requirements for an
inshore search-and-rescue craft, was completed in early 1974. A study has been made of
a lighterage variant for the US Marine Corps
and the craft also has applications as a
seismic survey/hydrographic vehicle.

Features of the Viking include a tapered
skirt, a more effective bow thrust-port system
and a vee-drive transmission operable collectively and differentially to provide a high
degree of manoeuvrability. A number of
mechanical components are interchangeable
with those of the Voyageur, simplifying
maintenance and spares holdings. Modular
construction features of the Voyageur have
been retained to facilitate transport by road,
rail and air, and speedy reassembly and
maintenance on site.

LIFT AND PROPULSION: A single UACL
ST6T-75 Twin-Pac gas-turbine, delivering
1,300 shp continuous and 1,700 shp intermittent, powers the integrated lift/propulsion
system, which employs a number of components identical to those used on the
Voyageur. Engine output is transferred to
a single 2·13 m (7 ft 0 in) diameter light alloy
centrifugal lift fan and, via a V-drive transmission, to two 2·74 m (9 ft 0 in) diameter
Hamilton Standard 3-blade variable-pitch
propellers for thrust. Maximum cushion
pressure is 193·2 kg/sq m (39·6 lb/sq ft).
Total fuel capacity is 6,954 l (1,530 Imp gals.
1,837 US gals). Types of fuel allowed are
kerosene, JP4, JP5, JETA, AVTUR or
Arctic diesel.
CONTROLS: Craft heading is controlled by
twin aerodynamically balanced rudders,
supplemented by differential propeller thrust.
Bow thrust-ports, port and starboard, assist
directional control at low speeds.

Above: Impression of a possible US Marine Corps' lighterage variant of the Bell Aerospace Canada
Model 7501 Viking
Centre: The Viking equipped to meet Canadian Coast Guard requirements for an inshore search-
and-rescue craft
Bottom: Viking prototype at the start of a series of overland tests

Bell Viking prototype undergoing trials at a test site at Goderich, Ontario

HULL: All-metal structure fabricated in 6,000 series corrosion-resistant extruded marine aluminium. Basic craft hard structure comprises six modules which are unbolted for transportation. Cargo deck has a total area of 76·2 sq m (820 sq ft).

SKIRT: 1·22 m (4 ft 0 in) deep neoprene-nylon tapered skirt developed from that of BHC SR.N6. with 50% peripheral fingers and a high attachment line at the bow.

ACCOMMODATION: Operating crew of two (commander/operator; navigator/relief operator), seated in a cabin supported on a raised platform amidships. Basic flat-deck configuration will accommodate a wide range of payloads, or superstructure and/or special equipment.

SYSTEMS:
ELECTRICAL: Two gearbox-driven brushless generators, each supplying 28 volts dc, and two 28 volt Nickel-Cadmium batteries. External power 28 volts dc.

DIMENSIONS:
Length overall	13·6 m (44·5 ft)
Beam overall	7·9 m (26·0 ft)
Height overall	6·1 m (20·0 ft)
Cargo deck area	76·2 sq m (820 sq ft)
Deck height, off cushion	1·2 m (3·9 ft)

WEIGHTS:
Empty weight	9,383 kg (20,685 lb)
Max permissible gross weight	14,742 kg (32,500 lb)

PERFORMANCE:
Max speed, calm water	92 km/h (57 mph)
Continuous gradient capability, standing start	10%
Vertical obstacle clearance	1·2 m (4 ft)
Ditch crossing width	2·1 m (7 ft)
Endurance with maximum fuel	13 hours
Max wave height	in excess of 1·8 m (6 ft)
Max range	680 nautical miles

FLYLO CORPORATION LTD
HEAD OFFICE:
King Street, W. Ingersoll, Ontario
TELEPHONE:
(519) 485-3003
DIRECTORS:
J. D. Loveridge, President
J. D. Duncan, Secretary Treasurer
Michael Herling
Paul Ivanier

Flylo Corporation, a subsidiary of Ingersoll Machine and Tool Co Ltd, was formed in July 1969 to design, construct and market ACVs in North America. The company is now building the Caliban for which it has exclusive world-wide manufacturing rights, and the Flylo 240A, described in JSS 1971-2 and earlier editions.

CALIBAN
This is a direct descendant of the lightweight sporting craft designed and built by Geoffrey Kent for the first International Hovercraft Rally held at Appethorpe in 1967. One of the most successful craft in the competition field in the United Kingdom, it was the first amateur-built machine to cross the Solent.

Extended marketing of the Caliban revealed a demand for fibreglass rather than a plywood hull, and also a preference for a two-seater with an enclosed cabin.

A new model incorporating these features is now in production.

LIFT AND PROPULSION: Lift engine is a 12·5 hp Canadian Curtiss Wright two-stroke. Thrust is provided by a 23 hp twin Canadian

Two-seat, fibreglass-hulled variant of the Caliban, built in Canada by Flylo Corporation

Curtiss Wright driving a 2-bladed, fixed-pitch metal propeller at half engine speed through a timing belt. A centrifugal clutch is fitted.

HULL: Fibreglass construction.

ACCOMMODATION: Side-by-side seating for driver and one passenger in enclosed cabin with sliding canopy. At the rear of the cabin is a protective roll bar, which is also used as a handhold when stepping into the craft.

DIMENSIONS:
Length overall	13 ft 6 in (4·11 m)
Beam overall	6 ft 9 in (2·05 m)
Vertical obstacle clearance	9 in (228 mm)

WEIGHTS:
Unladen weight, complete with canopy, battery, and electric starter for both
engines	490 lb (222 kg)
Carrying capacity	450 lb (204 kg)
PRICE: C$2,895·00.

HOVER-JAK LIMITED
HEAD OFFICE:
169 Centre Street East, Richmond Hill, Ontario, Canada L4C IA5
TELEPHONE:
Area Code 416-884-7735 and 884-6650
OFFICERS:
G. Grass, President
J. Flett, Vice-President
C. Flinders, General Manager
C. P. Kirwan, Marketing Manager

This company was registered by the Ontario Provincial Government to manufacture, sell and service air cushion vehicles, including those designed by Jones Kirwan and Associates.

The Company, which is the Canadian licence holder for the manufacture of craft employing the Bertin system of independently fed multiple plenum chambers, is currently concentrating on the production of the HJ-105.

The company's HJ-15 air cushion trailer is illustrated in the section devoted to Heavy Load Carrying Systems.

Hover-Jak HJ-105 utility vehicle, powered by a single V8 industrial engine. A prototype has been delivered to the National Research Council of Canada for trials

HJ-105
This circular platform utility vehicle is a direct descendent of the Canive BV-104 described in JSS 1972-73 and earlier editions. A prototype has been delivered to the National Research Council of Canada for trials, and further vehicles are under construction.

LIFT AND PROPULSION: Integrated system powered by a V8 industrial engine driving a Joy axial fan. Airflow is ducted to individually-fed jupes for lift and via outlets aft for thrust.

CONTROLS: Thrust deflection system operated by single lever. Rudders provide directional trimming.

HULL: Corrosion resistant aluminium and fibreglass. Two retractable wheels are provided for surface contact when hovering. These also permit the craft, with sidebodies folded, to be towed by a car.

DIMENSIONS:

Diameter	20 ft 0 in (6·09 m)
Beam, with outer sections folded for trans-port	8 ft 6 in (2·59 m)
Height on cushion	6 ft 10½ in (2·10 m)

WEIGHTS:

Empty weight	4,300 lb (1,950·44 kg)
Payload	1,000 lb (453·59 kg)
Gross weight	5,500 lb (2,496·75 kg)

PERFORMANCE:

Max speed	40 mph (64·37 km/h)
Endurance, 1,000 lb (453·59 kg) load, standard tanks	2½ hours

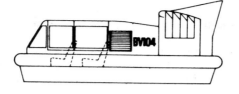
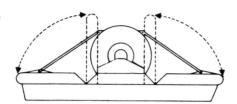
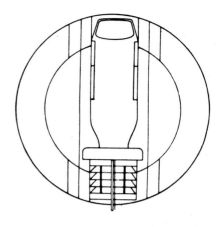

BV 104 multipurpose four-seater powered by a Ford V-8 engine. Outer sections of the circular planform hull fold upwards, and the centre section has two retractable wheels to permit towing by an automobile

HOVERJET INC

HEAD OFFICE:
58 Glen Cameron Road No. 21, Thornhill, Ontario, Canada

TELEPHONE:
(416) 881-0737

DIRECTORS AND SENIOR EXECUTIVES:
Ralph Schneider, President
Bruce Halliwell, Vice-President
E. De Asis, Chief Engineer
D. Epp, Plant Superintendent

SUBSIDIARIES AND AFFILIATED COMPANIES:
Alpha Aerospace Corporation Ltd, Continental Hoverjet Ltd, Kamloops BC, Canada (manufacturer of HJ-100).

Hoverjet Inc is currently producing the HJ-1000, 5-seat passenger and utility craft, the prototype of which completed its trials in April 1974. The company is engaged primarily in ACV research and development and undertakes contract design, consultancy and prototype construction for other companies. Ralph Schneider, formerly director of research and development at Hoverair Corporation and Airfloat Ltd, is responsible for Hoverjet's development and engineering programmes.

HOVERJET HJ-1000

An amphibious "workhorse" designed to meet the needs of exploration parties, the HJ-1000 is of frp construction and carries a payload of up to 1,000 lb (453·59 kg). Power is provided by three 42 hp Kohler engines.

The craft has been designed to permit transport by air, sea and road. It will fit into a transport aircraft with an 8 ft (2·43 m) door opening; it can be accommodated in a standard 8 ft × 8 ft × 20 ft (2·43 m × 2·43 m × 6·09 m) container for delivery by sea, or it can be loaded onto an 8 ft × 20 ft (2·43 m × 6·09 m) boat trailer.

LIFT AND PROPULSION: Lift is supplied by a single 42 hp Kohler K440-2AS two-cycle aircooled engine driving two 1 ft 8 in (0·50 m) diameter 10-bladed aluminium fans mounted vertically at the opposite ends of a transverse shaft. Cushion pressure is 15·9 lb sq ft. Propulsive thrust is supplied by two duct-mounted, 42 hp Kohler K440-2AS two-cycle aircooled engines, each driving a single 2 ft 6 in (0·762 m) diameter 10-bladed axial fan. For manoeuvring and hullborne operation over water a 7 hp outboard motor on a

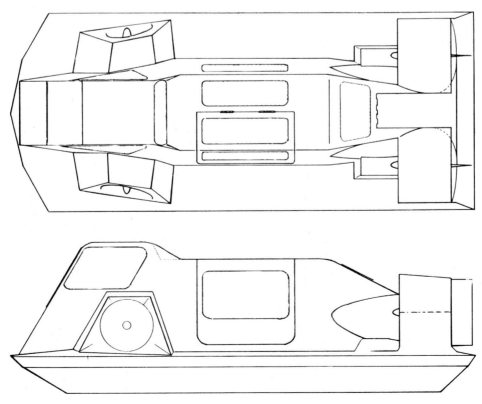

HJ-1000, 5-seat utility craft, powered by three 42 h.p. Kohler engines

remotely-operated swing mount can be fitted as an optional extra. Fuel is carried in two 10-gallon (45·46 litre) tanks, one port, one starboard, each with a refuelling neck located on deck. Recommended fuel is 2-cycle mix, 40 : 1.

CONTROLS: Craft heading is controlled by a column which activates twin rudders at the rear of the thrust ducts via push-pull cables.

HULL: Two-piece construction, comprising upper and lower bodies in colour impregnated fibreglass on welded steel inner frame. Engine and fan mounts are of tubular, welded steel construction.

SKIRT: Segmented loop in laminated 16 oz nylon/neoprene.

ACCOMMODATION: Driver sits forward and up to four passengers are accommodated in a wide cabin aft. Access is via a large door and roof opening on the port side. The passenger seats fold against the sides of the cabin to provide a cargo hold measuring 4 ft wide × 8 ft 0 in long by 4 ft 4 in high (1·21 m × 2·43 m × 1·32 m). Safety equipment includes "pop-out" emergency exit windows, built-in buoyancy, a fire extinguisher and an electric bilge pump.

SYSTEMS, Electrical: 12 volts for starting and generating. 75 W engine generators, 80 amp/hr battery.

OPTIONAL EQUIPMENT: Navigation lights, flashing beacon, spotlight, radio, lifejacket.

DIMENSIONS:

Length overall, power off	18 ft 0 in (5·48 m)
Length overall, skirt inflated	19 ft 2 in (5·84 m)
Beam overall, power off	7 ft 10 in (2·38 m)
skirt inflated	8 ft 11 in (2·71 m)
Draft afloat	4 in (101 mm)
Cushion area	142 sq ft (13·19 sq m)

Height overall, power off	5 ft 4 in (1·62 m)
skirt inflated	6 ft 5 in (1·95 m)

DIMENSIONS, INTERNAL:

Main cabin:

Length	8 ft 0 in (2·43 m)
Max width	4 ft 0 in (1·21 m)
Max height	4 ft 4 in (1·32 m)
Floor area	32·5 sq ft (3·01 sq m)

WEIGHTS:

Normal empty weight	970 lb (439·96 kg)
Normal all-up weight	2,000 lb (907·185 kg)
Normal gross weight	2,000 lb (907·185 kg)
Normal payload	1,000 lb (453·59 kg)
Maximum payload	1,200 lb (544·28 kg)

PERFORMANCE:

Details of speed and range not available at time of going to press.

Vertical obstacle clearance	1 ft 1 in (330 mm)

PRICE: C$7,500, FOB, Toronto, Canada.

HOVERTEC INC

HEAD OFFICE:
355, Rayette Road, Unit 6, Concord, Ontario. L4K 1BI

TELEPHONE:
1-416-669-9801

DIRECTORS:
Jim McCurdy, President

The first craft to be marketed by Hovertec Inc is the Chinook miniature ACV runabout. The vehicle is in production and is being sold through a national dealer network. Sales will begin in the USA in late 1974.

CHINOOK

This is a lightweight amphibious single seater with a maximum payload capacity of about 250 lb (113·39 kg). Built in fibreglass reinforced plastics it is 11 ft 3 in long and sufficiently small and light to be transported on the roof of a family car.

Maximum speed over water is 30 mph (48·28 km/h).

LIFT AND PROPULSION: Cushion air is supplied by a 5 hp Tecumseh 2-cycle engine driving a 2ft 0 in (0·60 m) diameter five bladed polypropylene fan. A 20 hp Kohler 295-1, 2 cycle engine drives a 2 ft 0 in (0·60 m) diameter, 10-bladed ducted fan for thrust. Fuel capacity is 4·5 Imp gallons (20 litres). Fuel recommended is regular low lead petrol and oil mixed 35:1.

HULL: Moulded in fibreglass reinforced plastic.

Hovertec's light amphibious single-seater, the 30 mph (48 km/h) Chinook, The craft measures 11 ft 3 in (3·42 m) by 5 ft (1·52 m) and can be carried on the roof of a family car

SKIRT: Bag type in neoprene impregnated nylon.

ACCOMMODATION: Open cockpit with single seat for driver.

DIMENSIONS:

Length overall	11 ft 3 in (3·42 m)
Beam overall	5 ft 0 in (1·52 m)
Height overall	3 ft 7 in (1·09 m)
Hoverheight, hard structure to ground	8 in (203 mm)

WEIGHTS:

Normal empty weight	285 lb (129·26 kg)
Normal payload	250 lb (113·39 kg)

PERFORMANCE (at normal operating weight):

Max speed over calm water	30 mph (48·28 km/h)
Max speed overland	up to 40 mph (64·37 km)
over ice and snow	up to 45 mph (72·42 km)
Still air range and endurance at cruising speed	2-2½ hours
Max gradient, static conditions	20°
Vertical obstacle clearance	8 in (203 mm)

KOMAR ENGINEERING LTD

HEAD OFFICE:
42 Dundas Street, W Trenton, Ontario

TELEPHONE:
613-392-4477

DIRECTORS:
Gordon J. Komar, MSc, PEng, MEIC, AMCASI, President
J. W. Tuck, BSc, PEng, Secretary
Erla Komar, Treasurer
H. A. Komarechka

SENIOR EXECUTIVE:
G. Komar, General Manager

Komar Engineering was formed in June 1969 as a mechanical engineering consultancy and also to design and develop air cushion vehicles. The company's first production design is the Aquaterra 65T, a 14 ft (3·26 m) long 3-seater with a moulded fibreglass hull. Development of the craft is continuing and arrangements for production are underway.

Aquaterra 65T, an amphibious 3-seater built by Komar Engineering Ltd. Maximum speed over water is 50 mph (80·46 km/h)

AQUATERRA

Recent modification to this fully amphibious 3-seater includes the provision of an enclosed cockpit for all-weather operation and a more powerful thrust engine, raising the top speed to 60 mph (96·56 km/h) over ice. The craft is designed primarily for recreational use and is stated to be an ideal vehicle for sportsmen in hunting and fishing areas.

LIFT AND PROPULSION: The craft is of plenum type, with a single 36 hp Canadian Curtiss Wright 2-cycle air-cooled engine mounted ahead of the cabin and driving a 3 ft (914 mm) 12-bladed axial-flow fan in cast aluminium for cushion lift. Aft of the cockpit is a 65 hp air cooled Volkswagen engine driving a 2-bladed Banks-Maxwell propeller for thrust. Fuel capacity is 12·5 gallons (56·82 1).

CONTROLS: Craft heading is controlled by twin aerodynamic rudders operated by a steering wheel. Other operating controls include a hand-operated locking lift throttle, foot operated thrust accelerator, push button starters and a dual manual choke.

HULL: Moulded fibreglass structure mounted on a tubular aluminium frame. Peripheral bag skirt, 1 ft 0 in (304 mm) deep, fabricated in nylon reinforced neoprene.

ACCOMMODATION: Operator and up to two passengers sit side by side in an enclosed cabin in the centre of the craft. The enclosed cabin is standard. A heater-defroster is supplied as an optional extra.

SYSTEMS: Electrical: 12 volts for engine starting, internal and external lights, windshield wiper.

DIMENSIONS, EXTERNAL:

Length overall:	
power off	14 ft 0 in (4·26 m)
skirt inflated	15 ft 0 in (4·57 m)

Beam overall:	
power off	6 ft 6 in (1·98 m)
skirt inflated	7 ft 6 in (2·28 m)
Height overall:	
power off	6 ft 6 in (1·98 m)
skirt inflated	7 ft 4 in (2·23 m)

WEIGHTS:

Normal empty weight	750 lb (340·17 kg)
Normal all up weight	1,250 lb (566·96 kg)
Normal gross weight	1,450 lb (657·67 kg)
Max payload	600 lb (272·14 kg)
Normal payload	400 lb (181·42 kg)

PERFORMANCE:

Max speed:	
calm water	50 mph (80·46 km/h)
ice	60 mph (96·56 km/h)
Cruising speed	45 mph (72·42 km/h)
Max gradient	20%
Vertical obstacle clearance	1 ft 0 in (304 mm)

Price   App C$8,100, fob Trenton, Ontario

CHANNEL ISLANDS

T. S. GOOCH

ADDRESS:
 La Genètière, Route Orange, St. Brelade,
  Jersey, C.I.
TELEPHONE:
 Central (0534) 42980

Mr T. S. Gooch has designed and built a number of lightweight air cushion vehicles, the latest of which is the J-5. In May 1969, his J-4 became the first home-built ACV to make a Channel crossing to France under its own power. The craft completed the 18-mile (28·96 km) outward crossing from Gorey, C.I., to Carteret in Brittany in 65 minutes and the return journey in 40 minutes.

The J-4 won first place in the Thames Hover Race in 1970 in the under 500 cc class, and has since been acquired by Hovercraft Development Ltd for research and development applications.

Mr Gooch is now concentrating on the development of the J-5 four-seater with almost double the cushion area of the J-4.

Plans of the J-4 are available for amateur construction and are selling well.

GOOCH J-4

This distinctive 13 ft (3·96 m) long amphibious two-seater has been designed with quiet operation and safety in mind. Instead of the more usual propeller, therefore, two axial fans mounted in a transverse duct across the stern are employed for propulsive thrust. The craft is of ply and aluminium construction and cruises at 40 mph (64·37 km/h). To facilitate storage or towing, the two ply sidewings carrying the skirt periphery and running the full length of the main hull structure hinge upwards to reduce the overall beam (power off) from 7 ft (2·13 m) to 4 ft (1·21 m).

The prototype J-4 was finished in June 1968 and the craft completed its trials in July of that year. No variants of the basic design are being contemplated at present, but alternative engines may be fitted.

The Gooch J-4 air-jet propelled, two-seat recreational hovercraft

LIFT AND PROPULSION: Lift is supplied by a Villiers 8E 197cc two-stroke motor-cycle engine mounted in the bow and driving a 24 in (0·609 mm) diameter 10-blade axial multiwing fan attached directly to its crankshaft. The propulsion engine is a 250cc Ariel Arrow, twin two-stroke which drives, via a timing belt or vee belt, two 24 in (0·609 mm) diameter 5-bladed Multiwing axial fans mounted vertically on a common shaft inside a transverse duct. Propulsive air is drawn in by the fans from each side of the duct and expelled through a rectangular outlet at the stern. An aluminium reverse thrust/braking bucket is fitted above the air-jet aperture. Total fuel capacity is 4 gallons, carried in two 2-gallon tanks, one each side of the craft on the CG. A filler cap is fitted to each tank. Recommended fuel is two-stroke mixture or regular grade petrol with 20 : 1 fuel/oil ratio.

CONTROLS: Craft direction is controlled by deflection of the thrust from the air-jet propulsion system by four rudders which are operated by a tiller in the cockpit. A foot pedal controls the raising and lowering of the braking/reverse thrust bucket. No trim controls are required as all variable vehicle has been designed primarily as a bumper car for amusement centres.

HULL: Construction is primarily of 4 mm exterior grade ply skinning with spruce frame members. Buoyancy compartments are provided fore and aft. Fan intakes are in glass fibre and the reverse/braking bucket is constructed in aluminium. A 9 in (228·6 mm) deep segmented skirt in 4 oz (124 gr) neoprene-coated nylon is attached to the hull periphery.

ACCOMMODATION: Side-by-side seating is provided for two on a bench type seat with foam rubber cushions. A small fire extinguisher is carried in the cockpit.

SYSTEMS: ELECTRICAL: 6v battery, charged by an alternator on the propulsion engine via a rectifier for starting.

DIMENSIONS, EXTERNAL:
Length overall, power off
13 ft 0 in (3·96 m)
Length overall, skirt inflated
13 ft 0 in (3·96 m)
Beam overall, power off   7 ft 0 in (2·13 m)
Beam overall, skirt inflated
7 ft 10 in (2·38 m)
Height overall, power off 3 ft 4 in (1·01 m)
Height overall, skirt inflated
4 ft 0 in (1·21 m)
DIMENSIONS, INTERNAL:
Cabin
4 ft × 4 ft × 1 ft 9 in
(1·21 m × 1·21 × 0·533 m)
WEIGHTS:

Normal empty weight	310 lb (140·60 kg)
Normal all up weight	470 lb (213·17 kg)
Normal gross weight	630 lb (285·75 kg)
Normal payload	320 lb (145·14 kg)
Max payload	680 lb (308·42 kg)

PERFORMANCE:
Max cruising speed over land and water
40 mph (63·74 km/h)
Endurance   2 hours
Max survival sea state
1 ft waves (304 mm)
Max gradient, static conditions   1 in 8
Vertical obstacle clearance   8 in (203 mm)

PLANS:
Plans available, price £5.00   cash with
order

J-5

The prototype of this new four-seat recreational craft, a derivative of the J-4, is
undergoing trials. The new design may be
made available either in plan or kit form.
LIFT AND PROPULSION: Motive power
for the integrated lift/propulsion system is
provided by a single 900 cc Hillman Imp
engine which develops about 30 hp. Power is
transmitted via a chain drive to two pairs of
1 ft 11 in (0·58 m) diameter, double-entry
centrifugal fans, mounted on a common
shaft, with each pair located in a transverse
duct aft of the cockpit. Air is drawn from
both sides of each fan housing and expelled
forward through the side bodies to pressurise
the cushion, and aft through rectangular
ducts for propulsion. Cushion pressure is
about 10 lb/sq ft. Air can also be ejected
through thrust ports forward for braking and
manoeuvring at low speeds. Two pedal-
operated, aluminium braking/reverse buckets
are fitted above each air-jet duct. Total
fuel capacity is 10 gallons (45·56 l) carried

Top: Bow on view of the new Gooch J-5 showing the bow thrust ports and the 3 ft (0·91 m)
wide sidewings which hinge upwards to reduce the overall beam for transport
Bottom: One application forseen for the J-5 is that of beach rescue craft. The cockpit, which
can be enclosed by a plexiglas canopy, is large enough to accommodate a standard stretcher

in tanks under the rear passenger seats on
C/P.
CONTROLS: Heading is controlled by
differential thrust and by twin sets of rudders
operating in the air-jets.

ACCOMMODATION: Seats are provided for
an operator and three passengers. The
cockpit, which can be open or closed, is
sufficiently large to accommodate a standard
hospital stretcher, should craft of this type
be employed for beach rescue.
HULL: Wooden construction, similar to that
employed for J-4. Structure consists primarily of 1 in square spruce frame members
glued and screwed to 4 mm marine ply sheet.
Hull base is in 6 mm ply sheet. Buoyancy
compartments are provided fore and aft.
Fan intakes are in glassfibre and the braking
buckets are in aluminium.

SKIRT: Loop-and-segment type in 4 oz
Briflon. The skirt is attached to the outer

edges of the two 3 ft (0·91 m) wide ply
sidewings which run the full length of the
hull structure and hinge upwards to reduce
the overall beam for transport.
UNDERCARRIAGE: Two retractable, independently sprung trailing wheels can be
fitted. In the retracted position they can be
employed as landing skids.

DIMENSIONS:
Length overall, skirt inflated
15 ft 0 in (4·57 m)
Beam overall:
skirt inflated   12 ft 4 in (3·75 m)
sideways folded   6 ft 2 in (1·87 m)
Height overall, skirt inflated
4 ft 6 in (1·37 m)
WEIGHTS:
Empty weight   410 lb (185·96 kg)
PERFORMANCE:
Maximum speed:
over water   about 35 knots
over land   40 mph (64·37 km/h)

WINFIELD HOVERCRAFT LTD
HEAD OFFICE:
La Colline, Mont Cambrai, Millbrook,
Jersey C.I.
TELEPHONE:
Central 21089
DIRECTORS:
W. D. W. Knight
J. Knight
E. Bisson
Winfield Hovercraft Ltd builds and operates
single-seat hovercraft "bumper cars" at the

The Winfield circular hovercraft for amusement
centres

Hoverdrome, Belle Vue Pleasure Park, Jersey. The original Hoverdrome at Belle Vue has now been reconstructed to form a 63 ft 0 in (19·20 m) diameter arena contoured like a saucer and with a 7 ft (2·13 m) × 2 ft (0·60 m) outer lip. This allows customers to fly round the outer edge, but come back to rest on the level section in the centre.

The company has devised a system by which a signal, automatically controlled by a time switch, is received by each craft at the end of the specified running time, reducing the 4,000 rpm necessary for hovering to about 700 rpm for tickover. This stops the craft but leaves all the engines running for the next customers.

WINFIELD AMUSEMENT HOVERCRAFT

This small, sturdily constructed single-seat vehicle has been designed primarily as a bumper car for amusement centres. The chassis, built on racing car principles, is of light tubular steel, and the circular body, 6 ft 0 in (1·82 m) in diameter, is in fibreglass. Around the periphery is a 4 in (101 mm) wide pneumatic bumper.

Power for the integrated lift/propulsion system is provided by a single 150 cc engine. The control system permits the craft to travel forwards, backwards, sideways or spin around its own axis.

On a smooth level ground, such as a beach it will exceed 40 mph (64·37 km/h), but at the Hoverdrome the maximum speed is limited to around 7 mph (11·26 km/h).

CHINA

An ACV research programme is being undertaken by a shipyard in the Shanghai area. Two small amphibious ACVs are currently employed as test craft, it is reported, one imported from Australia, the other built at the yard.

EIRE

CROSS, SELLWOOD & SYMONDS LTD

HEAD OFFICE:
Rostellan, Co. Cork
TELEPHONE:
Cork (021) 61255
DIRECTORS:
F. G. Cross
D. M. Sellwood
M. R. Symonds
R. D. Gordon
Mrs J. E. Sellwood

This company is producing an amphibious 5-6 seater, the AFV 12, which has been ordered for export to many parts including Scandinavia. Other designs available include a "stretched" version—the ACV 13—with 10-12 seats; the ACV 14, a light commercial craft for 30 passengers, and the ACV 7, a heavy duty load carrier with a payload of 20 tons. Preliminary details of these craft were received as this edition went to press.

ACV 12

This is an amphibious 5-6 seater, powered by twin 30 hp 2-stroke petrol engines and designed to operate on one engine only in the event of one failing. Cruising speed over land and water is 40 mph (64·37 km/h). The second prototype was in the final stages of completion at the time of going to press in June 1974.

LIFT AND PROPULSION: Motive power is supplied by two 30 hp 2-stroke petrol engines mounted aft. Each engine drives two 1 ft 6 in (0·45 m) diameter lift fans and a 3 ft (0·91 m) diameter Cross & Jackson 4-bladed variable-pitch propeller. The lift and propulsion systems are integrated enabling either engine to drive the craft should one engine become inoperable.
CONTROLS: Directional control is provided by twin aerodynamic rudders and differential thrust.
SKIRT: 2 ft (0·60 m) deep loop skirt in nylon fabric, supported by freely swinging, hinged tubular alloy arms.
HULL: Primary structure is built in mahogany and marine plywood. Buoyancy is provided by three expanded polystyrene foam blocks. Two, located outboard beneath the two side structures, are vented to permit pressurised air from the lift fans to flow down into the cushion, while the central

An ACV 12 amphibious 5/6 seater built by Cross, Sellwood & Symonds Ltd at Rostellan, Co. Cork. Wooden construction is employed and the top speed is 50 mph (80·46 km/h)

 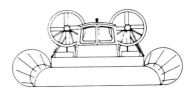

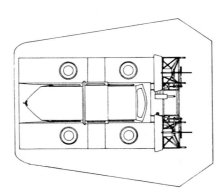

General arrangement of the ACV 12. Two 30 hp 2-strokes power the integrated lift and propulsion system

block is located beneath the cabin structure.

DIMENSIONS:
Length	15 ft 0 in (4·57 m)
Beam	8 ft 9 in (2·66 m)
Height	6 ft 3 in (1·90 m)
Skirt depth	2 ft 0 in (0·60 m)

WEIGHTS:
Empty weight	1,100 lb (498·92 kg)
Payload	1,000 lb (453·57 kg)
All-up weight	2,100 lb (952·50 kg)

PERFORMANCE:
Cruising speed, land and water	40 mph (64·37 km/h)
Max speed	50 mph (80·46 km/h)
Vertical clearance	1 ft 4 in (0·40 m)

Gradient capability:
driver only	1 in 6
at 2,000 lb (907·18 kg) auw	1 in 10

Range at cruising speed
350 miles (563·26 km)
PRICE: £5,500, ex-works

ACV 13

This is a "stretched" version of the ACV 12 with the seating capacity increased to 10-12 seats. Like the earlier model, it can operate on one engine only.

LIFT AND PROPULSION: Integrated system powered by two 40 hp petrol engines. Each drives three 1 ft 6 in (0·45 m) diameter lift fans and two 3 ft 6 in (1·06 m) diameter Cross & Jackson, 5-bladed manually variable-pitch propellers. Either engine can drive the complete lift/propulsion system should the other become inoperable.

CONTROLS: Craft heading is controlled by twin aerodynamic rudders and differential thrust.

SKIRT: 2 ft (0·60 m) deep loop skirt in nylon fabric supported by freely swinging, hinged tubular alloy arms.

HULL: Built in mahogany and marine plywood to BS 1088. Buoyancy is provided by expanded polystyrene foam blocks.

DIMENSIONS:

Length	20 ft 0 in (6·09 m)
Beam	8 ft 9 in (2·66 m)
Height	6 ft 3 in (1·90 m)
Skirt depth	1 ft 4 in (0·40 m)

WEIGHTS:

Empty	1,500 lb (680·35 kg)
Payload	1,800 lb (816·42 kg)
All-up weight	3,300 lb (1,496·84 kg)

PERFORMANCE:

Max speed	50 mph (80·46 km/h)
Cruising speed	40 mph (64·37 km/h)
Gradient capability:	
driver only	1 : 5
at 3,300 lb auw	1 : 10
Vertical clearance	1 ft 6 in (0·457 m)
Range at cruising speed	
	350 miles (563·26 km)

PRICE: £8,000, ex-works.

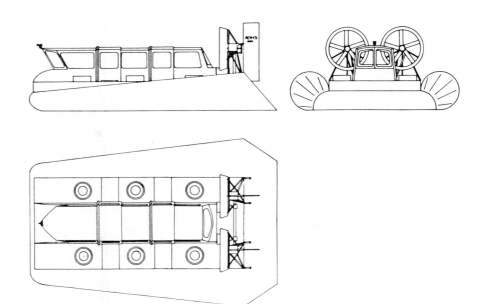

Seating capacity on the ACV 13—a "stretched" version of the ACV 12—is increased to 10-12. A feature of the craft is the ability to operate with one of the two engines stopped

ACV 14

Powered by two air-cooled diesels, this light commercial craft is available as either a passenger ferry or fast freighter. In the former role it seats a crew of two and 30 passengers; in the latter it has a payload capacity of 5,500 lb (2,495 kg). Wooden construction is employed and the craft dismantles into three sections for ease of transport.

LIFT AND PROPULSION: Integrated system powered by two air-cooled diesel engines. Each drives two 3 ft 0 in (0·91 m) diameter centrifugal lift fans and one 7 ft 6 in (2·28 m) diameter, 4-bladed Cross & Jackson variable-pitch propeller mounted in a thrust augmenting ring. Either engine can drive the complete lift/propulsion system should the other fail.

CONTROLS: Craft heading is controlled by twin aerodynamic rudders and differential thrust.

SKIRT: 3 ft 9 in (1·14 m) deep loop skirt in nylon fabric supported by freely-swinging, hinged tubular alloy arms.

HULL: Built in mahogany and marine plywood to BS 1088. Dismantles into three sections for ease of transport. Buoyancy is provided by expanded polystyrene foam blocks.

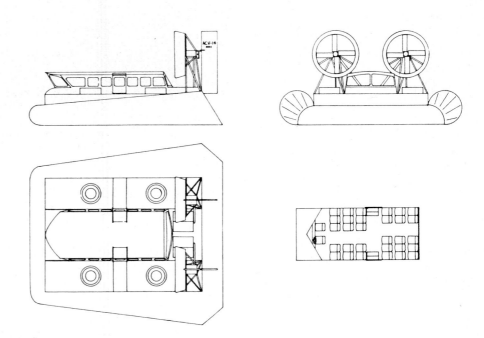

ACV14—a light commercial vehicle seating 30 passengers and a crew of two. Two air-cooled diesels supply motive power

DIMENSIONS:

Length	30 ft 0 in (9·14 m)
Beam	22 ft 0 in (6·70 m)
Height	15 ft 0 in (4·57 m)
Skirt depth	3 ft 9 in (1·14 m)

WEIGHTS:

Empty weight	7,500 lb (3,401·94 kg)
Payload	5,500 lb (2,495 kg)
All-up weight	13,000 lb (5,897 kg)

PERFORMANCE:

Max speed	65 mph (104·60 km/h)
Cruising speed, land and water	
	50 mph (80·46 km/h)
Gradient capability:	
driver only	1 : 6
at 13,000 lb auw	1 : 10
Vertical clearance	3 ft 0 in (0·914 m)
Range at cruising speed	
	800 miles (1,287 km)

PRICE: Ex-works, £25,000.

ACV 7

This heavy duty fast freighter has been designed for use in underdeveloped areas. Built in welded steel, it has an open freight deck 14 ft wide by 50 ft long and 3 ft deep (4·57 × 15·24 × 0·91 m) and will carry a normal payload of 20 tons over land and water. Overload capacity is 36 tons, but at this weight the over-water speed is reduced as the machine is optimised for use over land. The company states that should over-water operation be the main requirement, an additional 10 ft (3·04 m) can be added to the length to restore the speed with a 36-ton payload.

LIFT AND PROPULSION: Integrated system powered by two petrol engines. Each drives two 6 ft 0 in (1·82 m) diameter lift fans and one 10 ft 0 in (3·04 m) diameter, 4-bladed Cross & Jackson variable-pitch propeller mounted in thrust augmenting rings. Either engine can drive the complete lift/propulsion system should the other fail.

CONTROLS: Craft heading is controlled by twin aerodynamic rudders and differential thrust.

SKIRT: 5 ft 6 in (1·67 m) deep loop skirt in nylon fabric supported by freely swinging, hinged tubular alloy arms.

HULL: Welded steel construction, employing tubular sections for the load deck. Basic structure breaks down into three major sections to permit transport by road, rail or sea. The two outer sections measure 50 ft by 10 ft (15·24 × 3·04 m) and the load deck 50 ft by 15 ft (15·24 × 4·57 m). Buoyancy is provided by expanded foam, which gives

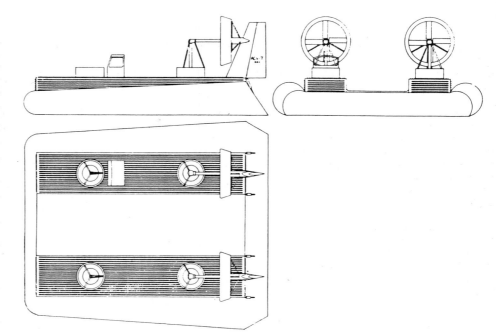

Built in welded steel, the ACV 7 is a heavy-duty load carrier for general freight duties in under-developed areas. Optimised for overland use it will carry a normal payload of 20 tons and an overload of 36 tons

a 50% reserve at the maximum all-up weight of 110,000 lb (49,896 kg).

DIMENSIONS:

Length	50 ft 0 in (15·24 m)
Beam	35 ft 0 in (10·66 m)
Height	18 ft 6 in (5·63 m)
Skirt depth	5 ft 6 in (1·67 m)

WEIGHTS:

Normal all-up weight	32 tons
Normal payload	20 tons
Max all-up weight	49 tons

PERFORMANCE:

Cruising speed at normal all-up weight	60 mph (96·56 km/h)
Gradient at normal auw	1 : 14
Vertical clearance	at least 3 ft (0·91 m)
Max wave height	4 ft 0 in (1·21 m)

PRICE: £120,000 ex-works.

FINLAND

ERKKI PERI

OFFICE ADDRESS:

c/o Keksintösäätiö, Uppfinningsstiftelsen (Foundation of Finnish Inventions), Haameentie 6A, 00530 Helsinki 53, Finland

TELEPHONE:
90 71 72 99

TELEX:
92204-9

HOME ADDRESS:
Hammina, Finland

Since 1959, Mr Erkki Peri has been developing multi terrain vehicles capable of operating in the severe snow, ice and flood conditions found in northern latitudes. His latest approach combines the advantages of the ACV with those of an aerosled. One of the major design objectives has been to decrease the weight carried by the pontoon-type skis without raising the vehicle from the ground. Because of the contact between the vehicle's skis and the supporting surface beneath, directional control is a great improvement on that of most conventional skirted ACVs. The forward skis and the air rudder aft move simultaneously to control craft heading.

Additional design features are the improved stability offered by the skirt/ski arrangement and the mounting of the skis on a spring suspension system to ensure a smooth ride.

The project, which covers two prototypes, is offered for licensing and exploitation by the Foundation of Finnish Inventions, an

Smaller and of lighter construction than the first Peri Hoversled, this new test craft was awaiting the installation of a lift engine and skirt when this photograph was taken. The four ski/pontoons are in foam-filled ABS plastic and provide sufficient buoyancy to support the vehicle and its load when off-cushion.

organisation supported by the Finnish Ministry of Trade and Industry, the Finnish Fund for Research & Development and the Finnish Cultural Foundation.

The first prototype is the larger of the two. The second has been designed and built in an endeavour to offer a lighter and less expensive vehicle and also to provide a test bed for technical innovations. Both vehicles are constructed in light aluminium.

FIVE-SEAT HOVERSLED

The designer's principal objective has been to provide an easily controlled vehicle capable of carrying relatively heavy loads at high speed across snow, ice, inland waterways, slush and sludge. This has been achieved by raising the hull with the aid of an air cushion while retaining a percentage of the load on pontoon-like skis which maintain full contact with the supporting surface beneath. The vehicle is steered by turning the front pontoons and the air rudder simultaneously. All four pontoons are buoyant and support the vehicle and its load on water, lift engine off.

The craft was tested extensively during the winter 1973-74 on water, ice and snow and the maximum speed attained was 28 mph (45 km/h) on ice.

LIFT AND PROPULSION: Cushion air is supplied by a single 55 hp Renault R8TS driving a centrifugal fan at the base of a cylindrical intake aft of the cabin. From the plenum the air is fed into a bag and finger skirt system fitted to the front and rear of the vehicle and above and between the pontoon/skis at the sides. The bag skirt areas above the pontoons act as pneumatic springs. Thrust is supplied by 92 hp Renault TS driving an 80 m (204 cm) diameter McCauley propeller. Max static thrust is 500 lb (230 kg). Fuel is carried in three tanks, each with a capacity of 6·6 gal (30 l).

CONTROLS: Craft direction is controlled by turning forward pontoons and the air rudder simultaneously.

HULL: Frame and cabin of conventional construction in light aluminium. Ski/pontoons are fabricated in aluminium filled with polyurethane foam.

ACCOMMODATION: Heated cabin seating driver and four passengers, plus room for casualty on a stretcher.

DIMENSIONS:

Length overall	23 ft 0 in (7 m)
Beam overall	9 ft 10 in (3 m)
Cushion area	150 sq ft (14 m²)

WEIGHTS:

Normal gross weight	3,300 lb (1,500 kg)

PERFORMANCE (Design):

Max speed, calm water	45 mph (75 km/h)
Cruising speed	25 mph (40 km/h)
Fuel consumption	3-4½ gal/hr (15-20 l/hr)

HOVERSLED UTILITY

Smaller than the Peri Hoversled prototype this model is of lighter construction than its

Above and below: Prototype of a new vehicle designed for service in northern latitudes—a combination ACV and aerosled. The forward ski/pontoons and the air rudder aft move simultaneously to control craft heading. The designer, Erkki Peri, has provided the pontoons with both sprung and pneumatic suspension for a smooth ride.

predecessor and is less expensive to build. At the time of going to press it was still incomplete. After the installation of the lift engine and skirt, the total basic weight was expected to be in the region of 1,170 lb (430 kg).

LIFT AND PROPULSION: Propulsive thrust is supplied by a 25 hp Sachs SA 340 2 cyl engine driving a 6 ft 11 in (2·10 m) diameter wooden two-bladed propeller. Details of the lift system had not been received by early July 1974.

CONTROLS: Craft heading controlled by turning forward pontoons and air rudder simultaneously.

HULL: Frame and cabin built in light aluminium. Ski/pontoons in ABS-plastic and filled with polyurethane foam plastic for buoyancy.

DIMENSIONS:

Length overall	19 ft 0½ in (5·8 m)
Beam	9 ft 10 in (3 m)
Beam with skirt and pontoons removed for transport	8 ft 2½ in (2·5 m)

WEIGHTS:

Gross weight	2,205 lb (1,000 kg)

FRANCE

CLUB FRANCAIS DES AEROGLISSEURS

HEAD OFFICE:
85 Rue Republique, 92150 Suresnes, France

WORKS:
45 Rue Aristide Briande, 95130 Meung sur Loire

OFFICERS:
Jacques Beaudequin, Director
Gabriel Vernier, Chief Designer

M. Jacques Beaudequin, President of the Club Francais des Aeroglisseurs has designed a number of successful lightweight amphibious ACVs, including the Moise III and the Skimmercraft, described in the 1971-72 edition.

His latest design is the Motoglisseur V Beach, preliminary details of which are given below.

Club Francais des Aeroglisseurs is to build this new amphibious two-seater in series. The production model will be powered by two Citroen engines and have a top speed of 62 mph (100 km/h)

MOTOGLISSEUR V BEACH

Derived from the earlier Skimmercraft, the V Beach is a lightweight amphibious two-seater with an inflatable catamaran hull. Trials of the production prototype were due to start in June 1974. Series production is scheduled to begin in 1975.

LIFT AND PROPULSION: Cushion lift is supplied by a 22 hp 425 cc Citroen air-cooled 4-stroke driving a 24·4 in (620 mm) Multiwing fan.

Propulsive thrust is provided by an adapted Citroen AMI 8 602 cc 4-stroke driving a 4 ft 7⅛ in (1·40 m) diameter four-bladed Merville propeller via a reduction and reverse gearbox.

CONTROLS: Craft direction is controlled by twin aerodynamic rudders aft and operated by a steering wheel. Elevators operating in the propeller slipstream provide trim.

HULL: Basic structural member is the central load carrying deck on which the lift and propulsion units are mounted. The inflatable hull is of catamaran configuration and features flexible bow and stern skirts.

The two inflatable hulls are in polyester coated with neoprene and hypalon.

ACCOMMODATION: Open cockpit for three side-by-side with individual seats.

DIMENSIONS:
Length overall	21 ft 0 in (6·40 m)
Beam overall	9 ft 4¼ in (2·85 m)
Height	5 ft 11 in (1·80 m)

WEIGHTS:
Loaded weight	926 lb (420 kg)
Payload	529 lb (240 kg)

PERFORMANCE:
Max speed	62 mph (100 km/h)
Range	124 miles (200 km)
Turning radius	
	82 ft at 37 mph (25 m at 60 km/h)

GEORGES HENNEBUTTE
Societe d'Exploitation et de Developpement des Brevets Georges Hennebutte

HEAD OFFICE:
43 Avenue Foch 64200, Biarritz
WORKS:
23 Impasse Labordotte, Biarritz
TELEPHONE:
24.22.40
SENIOR DIRECTOR:
M. Ellia
CHIEF EXECUTIVE.
G. Hennebutte

Ets G. Hennebutte was founded in 1955 to design and build inflatable dinghies. Its Espadon series of sports craft is used extensively by French lifeguard patrols and the French Navy.

Development of the Espadon to meet a range of special requirements led to the construction of a number of experimental craft, including one equipped with foils, one with hydroskis and a third with an inflatable parasol delta wing for aerodynamic lift.

The success of the latter has resulted in the adaptation of a standard Espadon 542 dinghy by adding a pair of wings, one of which is of half-venturi configuration, and air propulsion.

The wings have been designed by M. Clement, President of the Basque Flying Club, and the prototype, a single-seater, was due to begin tests during the summer of 1974. Construction of two and four-seat prototypes, were due to start as soon as the trials of the first machine were completed.

The company hopes to start production of the single-seater by the end of 1974, and the four-seater by mid-1975.

FLYING BOAT No. 1

This is the first of a new series of lightweight ram-wings based on the Espadon series of inflatable hulls built by Ets. Georges Hennebutte. The wings, comprising a variable-incidence lifting surface forward, and a fixed, half-venturi, U channel wing aft, have been designed by M. Clement, President of the Basque Flying Club and a specialist in aerodynamics.

The prototype, under construction at the time of going to press, was expected to be ready for trials by the summer of 1974. Features of the craft are shown in the accompanying three-view.

The company's principal objective is the development of a small, high-speed marine craft for offshore and inter-island travel, able to match the average family car in price and cruising speed.

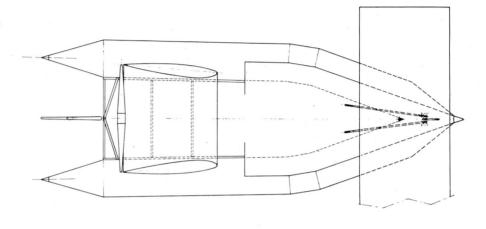

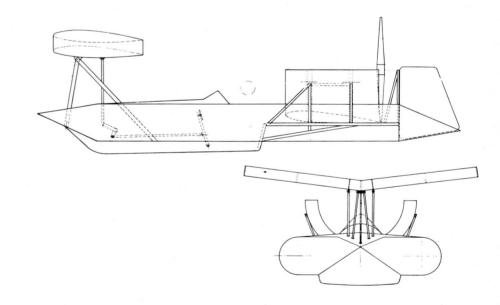

General arrangement of the Hennebutte Flying Boat No. I, ram-wing ACV research vehicle. Features include a variable-incidence wing forward and a channel-flow wing aft. Thrust is supplied by a 32 hp engine driving a two-bladed propeller aft. Two- and four-seat versions are planned

PROPULSION: Motive power is provided by a 32 hp automotive engine driving a two-bladed propeller. The two-seat model will have a 60 hp engine and the four-seater, will have an 82 hp car engine driving twin propellers.

CONTROLS: Craft heading is controlled by a combined aerodynamic and water rudder aft. Incidence of the forward wing is varied by fore and aft movement of the control column.

HULL: Rigid central hull frame in polyester with inflatable nylon-coated neoprene outer sections based on those of the Espadon 542. Struts are provided to support the forward parasol wing, and a special cradle is fitted aft for the propulsion engine.

ACCOMMODATION: Open cockpit for driver only.

DIMENSIONS:
Length overall	17 ft 9½ in (5·42 m)
Beam overall	6 ft 10½ in (2·10 m)

PERFORMANCE:
Estimated cruising altitude	
	9 ft 10 in - 16 ft 5 in (3-5 m)

SOCIÉTÉ BERTIN & CIE

OFFICE AND WORKS:
BP No. 3, 78370 Plaisir, France
TELEPHONE:
462.25.00
TELEX: 26.619
DIRECTORS:
Jean Bertin, President Director General
Benjamin Salmon, Director General
Michel Perineau, Director General

Société Bertin & Cie has been engaged in developing the Bertin principle of separately fed multiple plenum chambers surrounded by flexible skirts since 1956. A research and design organization the company employs a staff of more than 500, mainly scientists and design engineers who are involved in many areas of industrial research, including air cushion techniques and applications.

Société de l'Aérotrain is responsible for the construction and development of Bertin tracked air cushion vehicles (Aérotrain) and the SEDAM is responsible for developing the Naviplane and Terraplane vehicles. Designs based upon the Bertin technique are described under the entries for these two companies in this volume.

The Bertin principle for air cushions has also led to numerous applications in the area of industrial handling and aeronautics. These applications, developed by Bertin, are described in the sections devoted to Air Cushion Applicators, Conveyors and Pallets; and Air Cushion Landing Systems.

Z. O. ORLEY

ADDRESS:
21 Rue Mademoiselle, 75 Paris 15ème
TELEPHONE:
828-2949

Mr. Z. O. Orley and Mr. Ivan Labat have designed a range of lightweight recreational craft employing the glider-craft air cushion system invented by Mr. Orley. The object of the system is to reduce the loss of cushion air by fully skirted vehicles when crossing uneven surfaces.

Beneath the hard structure of the glider craft is an air cushion chamber in rubberised fabric, the base of which is divided into a number of small cell compartments.

Each cell is equipped at the lower end with a perforated shutter, pivoted around a shaft across the cell bay, and linked with a lid which fits tightly into the aperture of an air-supply duct.

A short surface sensor protruding beneath each shutter is designed to open up the delivery of cushion air fully whenever the cell encounters an obstacle rising above the general plane of the reaction surface, and reduce cushion air delivery when crossing a hollow.

A design study is being undertaken for a small commercial craft for operations in South America to carry 12 passengers and freight.

Mr Orley and his partner will build to order commercial and military prototypes employing his system for use over arctic and tropical terrain. Illustrations of a dynamic model incorporating the glider-craft air cushion system appears in JSS 1973-74 and earlier editions.

SEDAM
SOCIETE D'ETUDES ET DE DEVELOPPE-MENT DES AEROGLISSEURS MARINS, TERRESTRES ET AMPHIBIES

HEAD OFFICE:
80 Avenue de la Grande Armée, 75 Paris 17eme
TELEPHONE:
380-17-69
TELEX:
29-124 Paris
OFFICERS:
Bernard Guillain, President Director General
Benjamin Salmon, Director General
Paul Guienne, Director Technique
Admiral J. R. Evenou, Conseil de Direction

SEDAM was incorporated on July 9th 1965, to study, develop and test the Naviplane series of amphibious ACVs based on principles conceived by Bertin & Cie. In April 1968, the company was vested with similar responsibilities for the Terraplane wheeled ACVs based on identical principles. The company holds the exclusive world licence for Bertin patents involving both the Naviplane and Terraplane series.

In 1965, the 5-ton Naviplane BC 8 was completed, after which SEDAM built several small research craft, including the N 101, a quarter-scale manned research model of the 27-ton 90-passenger N 300. Two N 300s were completed in the winter of 1967/68 and operated along the Cote d'Azur during the summer of 1969. One has since been purchased by the Department of Gironde and operates a passenger/car ferry across the Gironde estuary.

Following reorganisation in late 1972, the company is concentrating on three main objectives: the final design, construction and marketing of the N 500 Naviplane series; incorporation of improvements in the N 300 and the development and construction of a new Terraplane.

Two firm orders have been received for the N 500. One, for the 40 m long model,

Naviplane N 102C 14 seat ferry or light utility craft, powered by a single 700 hp Astazou XIV gas-turbine. Pitch trim is provided by a variable incidence elevator mounted on the fin

N102L with revised planform

has been placed by the Department of Gironde, the other, for a 49 m long "stretched" model, has been placed by SNCF. The former will be employed as a mixed-traffic ferry in the Gironde estuary, where there is increasing need for such a craft due to the tremendous growth of the industrial areas of Bordeaux. SNCF will operate its craft across the English Channel. Options on two more "stretched" models are held by Compagnie Generale Transmediterranee, which plans to operate a service between Nice and Corsica.

At the time of going to press, a Sedam plant for the assembly of the N 500s, was being built on the banks of the Gironde, near

Bordeaux. Construction of the first craft was due to begin in 1974.

The aim of the new N 300 programme is to design a production model which will incorporate various improvements felt necessary in the light of the operations conducted by the two prototypes since 1969. Modification will be introduced in the interests of both economy and ease of production. Construction of the first of the new series is unlikely to take place until 1975.

A completely new Terraplane, based on the T3S, was completed in 1973. A combined ACV and wheeled vehicle, it is designed for use in under-developed territory, regardless of season or state of the soil. The primary market is French-speaking Black Africa.

One entirely new development is a Sedam air cushion platform of 25 metric tons load capacity for carrying prefabricated building sections and other bulky loads across uneven ground.

In September 1972, Sedam and Fiat SpA. Turin, signed an agreement under which Fiat received exclusive rights for the manufacture in Italy of Naviplane vehicles employing patents evolved by Bertin et Cie and Sedam. Within the agreement is the right to market these craft in Italy, the Soviet Union, Poland, Yugoslavia, Egypt and other countries in the Near East, Africa and South America.

The company is also undertaking feasibility studies for multi-thousand-ton surface effect warships for the French Navy. Current studies are focussed on vessels in the 1,200-2,000 metric ton bracket, but it is anticipated that they will be extended to cover vessels of up to 4,000 metric tons.

In July 1972, in response to an E.E.C. request, Sedam completed a study for a 2,000 metric ton mixed-traffic sidewall vessel propelled by waterjets. Designed for fast ferry services between the main European and Mediterranean ports, the vessel would carry 2,000 passengers and up to 500 cars at a cruising speed of 50 knots.

NAVIPLANE N 102C

A 13-14 seat, single engine ACV employing a plenum chamber enclosed by a labyrinth skirt developed from Bertin's patents, the Naviplane 102C is designed for a wide range of civil and military applications, including customs and police patrol, watertaxi, light cargo and ambulance work, military reconnaissance and dual-control training for the commanders of large Naviplanes.

Two prototypes were completed during 1959 and the first N 102C production craft was launched in 1970. In June 1970 the craft was flown to Kinshasa, in the Congo, for trials and demonstrations. Ten N 102s have since been built, including one 'stretched' variant, the Naviplane N 102L, with its length increased from 33 ft 6 in (10·20 m) to 35 ft 9 in (10·90 m). Two are being employed by the Departments of Montpellier and Perpignan, two have been supplied to the French Navy, one has been sold to Fiat, two are being used by Sedam for research, and the remaining craft are for sale.

LIFT AND PROPULSION: A single 700 hp Turboméca Astazou XIV or 565 hp Astazou II shaft turbine powers the integrated lift

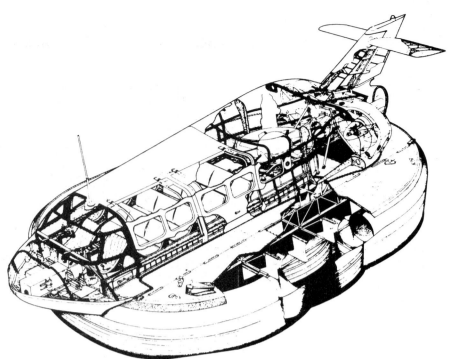

Cutaway of the N102L showing internal arrangements

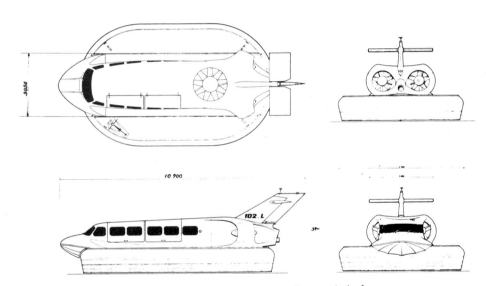

"Stretched" version of the N102—the model L—with revised planform

A Naviplane N 300, equipped with a lightweight cabin structure and seats for up to 90 passengers. A mixed traffic-model is in service with the Bordeaux Port Authority operating across the Gironde estuary. It operates thirty crossings per day, seven days a week, carrying four cars and up to 35 passengers per crossing

propulsion system. Mounted at the rear of the cabin, the engine drives a 5 ft 3 in (1·60 m) variable-pitch axial lift fan and two five-bladed variable and reversible pitch shrouded propellers for propulsion.

CONTROL: Directional control at cruising speed and above is maintained by an aerodynamic rudder hinged to the rear of the tail fin and differential pitch of the two propellers. At low speeds, steering is assisted by pneumatically-operated side thrust ports. Pitch trim at cruising speed is controlled by a manually operated variable-incidence elevator mounted on the fin.

HULL: The basic hull structure comprises a doughnut-shaped inflated buoyancy chamber in neoprene nylon fabric, surrounding a corrosion resistant light alloy sandwich platform. The buoyancy chamber is divided into twelve watertight compartments for safety. Reserve buoyancy is in excess of 200%. The main components of the superstructure—the shaped bow, cockpit, passenger/freight cabin, engine housing, fan and propeller ducts—are in moulded glass reinforced plastics. The side-wings can be removed to facilitate transport by road, rail or air.

The cabin seats a crew of either one or two and either thirteen or twelve passengers. There are two bucket seats forward and three bench-type seats behind accommodating three or four passengers each, according to traffic requirements. Access is through two wide gull-wing doors. The central section of the cabin superstructure can be quickly removed to provide a freight deck for pallets, containers or military equipment.

OVERLAND USE: Provision is made on the underside of the main hull structure for the attachment of a three-legged, retractable undercarriage. The front wheel is steered hydraulically to provide precise directional control. Lowering of the under-carriage facilitates repairs to the hull underside and skirt maintenance. The arrangement also allows an extra 1 ton payload to be carried over land. Speed over relatively smooth ground, with undercarriage lowered, is close to 40 mph (64·37 km/h).

DIMENSIONS, EXTERNAL (N 102C):

Length overall	33 ft 5⅞ in (10·20 m)
Beam	25 ft 3⅛ in (7·70 m)
Height overall on landing pads	13 ft 1½ in (4·00 m)
Skirt depth	2 ft 7½ in (0·80 m)

DIMENSIONS, INTERNAL:

Cabin length	11 ft 9¾ in (3·60 m)
Max width	7 ft 3 in (2·20 m)

Size of gull-wing doors, one each side:

Height	2 ft 9½ in (0·85 m)
Width	6 ft 2 in (1·90 m)

WEIGHTS:

Empty weight	6,600 lb (3,200 kg)
Normal gross weight	8,800 lb (4,200 kg)
Normal payload	2,200 lb (1,000 kg)
Fuel load	1,100 lb (600 l)
Normal load over water	2-2,400 lb (900-1,100 kg)
over land	4,200-4,600 lb (1,900-2,100 kg)

PERFORMANCE: (Normal all-up weight):

Max speed, max power, over calm water	54 knots
Max speed, max continuous power	55 knots
Cruising speed (IAS) in 2 ft 6 in (0·75 m) waves	40-45 knots
Endurance (max continuous power)	3-4 hours
Max gradient	12-18%
Acceptable wave height	3 ft (1 m)

A Naviplane N 300,

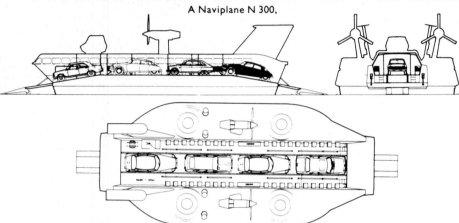

Above: Mixed ferry version of the N 300, accommodating thirty-eight passengers and four cars
Below. Internal arrangements of the N300. The drawings show the craft in open deck freighter configuration. The all-passenger version seats 90 in a lightweight cabin structure which is attached to the freight deck

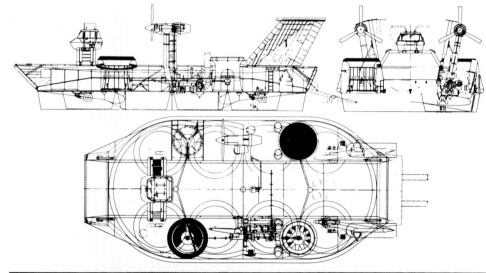

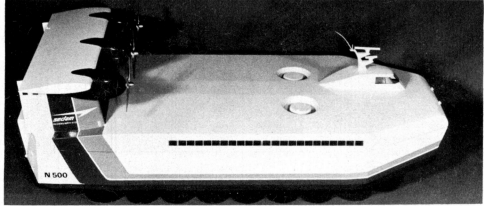

Model of the N500T, 225-ton mixed traffic ferry which will be built at a new SEDAM plant at Bordeaux, on the banks of the Gironde.

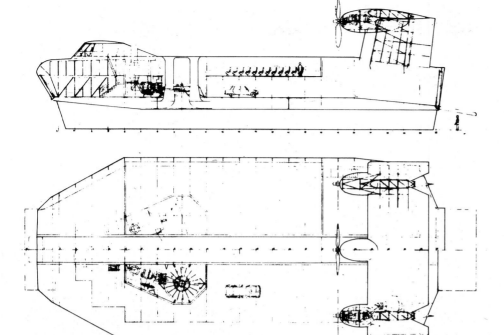
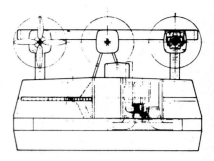

General arrangement of the SEDAM N500T, which will be powered by five 3,200 hp Avco Lycoming TF 40 marinised gas-turbines, two for the lift system and three for propulsion

DIMENSIONS, EXTERNAL (N 102L):

Length overall	35 ft 9 in (10·90 m)
Beam overall, on cushion	19ft 4¼ in (5·90m)
Beam overall, hardstructure	10 ft 0 in (3·05 m)
Height overall, on cushion	12 ft 9½ in (3·90 m)

NAVIPLANE N 300

A 27-ton multi-purpose transport for amphibious operation, the N 300 was the first full-scale vehicle in the Naviplane series designed for commercial use.

The first two N 300s were built at Biarritz at the Breguet factory and started tethered hovering and preliminary handling trials in December 1967. Afterwards they were transported by sea to the Sedam test centre at l'Etang de Berre. In September 1968 N 300-01 and -02 went to Nice for a series of experimental services and tests conducted by the French armed services.

During the summer of 1970 the two craft operated a scheduled passenger service along the Cote d'Azur. One N 300 has been acquired by the Gironde Department and operates a passenger/car ferry service across the Gironde estuary between Blaye and Lamarque. The craft, which is operated by the Bordeaux Port Authority carries up to four cars and thirty-five passengers per crossing. It operates thirty crossings per day, seven days a week.

The passenger version seats 90 in a lightweight cabin structure above the open deck. Possible military uses include coastal patrol, salvage, rescue, landing craft, assault craft and logistic supply vehicle.

A production model is under development and construction of the first of the new series is expected to begin in 1975.

LIFT AND PROPULSION: Motive power is provided by two Turboméca Turmo IIIN3 gas turbines located in separate engine rooms, port and starboard and drawing filtered air from plenum compartments behind the forward fan ducts. Each engine is coupled via a main gearbox located directly beneath each propeller pylon to a 3-bladed Ratier-

Figeac 11 ft 10 in (3·60 m) diameter, variable and reversible pitch propeller and via a secondary gearbox to a two 11-blade 6 ft 3 in (1·90 m) diameter axial lift fans. The main gearboxes are cross-connected by a shaft so that in the event of one engine failing or malfunctioning the four fans and two propellers can all be driven by the remaining engine. The fans deliver air to eight individual Bertin skirts, each 6 ft 7 in (2 m) deep and with a hemline diameter of 10 ft 2 in (3·09 m). These are in turn surrounded by a single wrap-round skirt.

CONTROLS: The wheelhouse, which seats a captain and navigator, is located above a bridge spanning the foredeck to provide a 360° view. The main driving controls and the instrumentation are positioned in front of the port seat.

The wheel of a control column varies the pitch of the two propellers differentially and fore and aft movement of the column alters pitch collectively.

HULL: The hull is a raft-like structure built in marine corrosion resistant aluminium alloys. Main buoyancy compartments are beneath the freight deck. Fans and machinery are installed in separate structures on either side of the freight/passenger deck, port and starboard.

ACCOMMODATION: Aircraft-type seats are provided for 100-120 passengers. Baggage areas are provided in the centre of the passenger saloon, port and starboard, and at the rear of the saloon where there is also a dinghy stowage area. Access to the passenger compartment is by steps built into the bow and stern ramp/doors.

DIMENSIONS:

Length overall	78 ft 9 in (24 m)
Beam	34 ft 5 in (10·5 m)
Height overall	24 ft 7 in (7·5 m)
Skirt depth	6 ft 7 in (2·0 m)
Cabin floor area	861 sq ft (80 m²)
Cushion area	1,722 sq ft (160 m²)

WEIGHTS:

Basic weight	14 tons
Passenger version	100-120 passengers
Freight version	13 ton
Normal all-up weight	27 tons

PERFORMANCE:

Max speed	57/62 knots
Cruising speed	44/50 knots
Endurance	3 hours

NAVIPLANE N500-25B
N 500T

Two firm orders have been placed for the N 500T, a 225-ton mixed-traffic ferry, with a maximum speed of 76 knots. The first will be built for the Department of Gironde, for the Bordeaux port authority, and the second is for SNCF (French National Railways), who will operate a service across the English Channel.

The French government is contributing half the development and production costs of the first two craft, a total of Fr.74 million.

An option on two further craft is held by Compagnie Generale Transmediterranee, which plans to operate a service between Nice and Corsica.

Sedam is planning to build the N 500s in a new factory on the banks of the Gironde. The site selected for the assembly plant is adjacent to the projected Bordeaux hoverport.

LIFT AND PROPULSION: Motive power will be supplied by five 3,200 hp Avco Lycoming TF 40 marinised gas-turbines. Two will drive the two 14 ft 1 in (4·3 m) diameter axial-flow lift fans, and the remaining three, mounted on the horizontal stabilizer aft, will each drive a 21 ft 4 in (6·5 m) diameter, variable-pitch propeller for thrust.

CONTROLS: Craft directional control will be provided by aerodynamic rudders and differential propeller pitch.

ACCOMODATION: Twin-deck layout, with passengers accommodated on the upper deck and vehicles on the lower deck. The basic model is designed to carry 200 passengers and

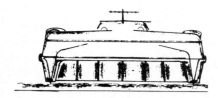

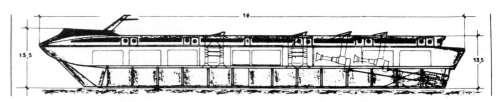

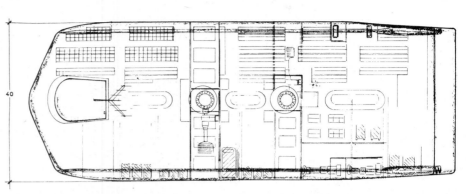

Three-view drawing of the 2,000 ton Navi plane sidewall vessel, designed by Sedam for an EEC transport project. Four gas-turbine driven waterjets, two in each sidewall, aft, would provide a cruising speed of 50 knots

sixty cars, sixteen of which can be replaced by three buses. An alternative version carries 400 passengers and forty-one cars.

DIMENSIONS:

Length overall	177 ft 2 in (54 m)
Beam overall	78 ft 9 in (24 m)
Height	55 ft 9 in (17 m)

WEIGHTS:

Empty weight	105 metric tons
Fuel and crew	20·85 metric tons
Payload	85 metric tons
Normal all-weight	225 metric tons

PERFORMANCE:

Maximum speed	76 knots
Endurance	5 hours
Maximum wave capability	13 ft 0 in (4 m)

2,000 TON NAVIPLANE

A study for a 2,000-ton sidewall-type Naviplane was completed for the European Economic Community in July 1972.

The project called for a cost assessment of a high speed vessel capable of providing mixed-traffic ferry services between the main European and Mediterranean ports.

Sedam's proposal covers a vessel capable of carrying 2,000 passengers and 500 cars. Four gas-turbine driven waterjets, two in each sidewall, aft, would give the craft a cruising speed of 50 knots. The lift system would comprise two 6,250 hp gas turbines, each driving two 13 ft 1 in (4 m) diameter, contrarotating axial fans.

DIMENSIONS:

Length overall	328 ft 1 in (100 m)
Beam overall	131 ft 3 in (40 m)
Height on cushion	50 ft 10 in (15·50 m)
Height, vehicle compartment	18 ft 0 in (5·50 m)
Height, passenger cabin	7 ft 3 in (2·20 m)

WEIGHTS:

Empty weight	1,010 metric tons
Payload	700 metric tons
Gross weight	2,000 metric tons

PERFORMANCE:

Maximum continuous cruising speed	50 knots
Endurance	10 hours, plus 10% reserve
Gross weight	382,000 lb (174 tonnes)

The Terraplane T3S, combined ground effect machine and wheeled vehicle for off-the-road transport in underdeveloped areas

TERRAPLANE T3S

The Terraplane T3S is a combined ground effect machine and wheeled vehicle, driven like a car or truck, but with the essential difference that it can be run at speeds up to 31 mph (50 km/h) over uneven ground, water or liquid mud.

It is designed for use over unprepared land in underdeveloped territories regardless of the season or the state of the soil. A hydraulic system allows selection of weight transference to the road wheels ranging from 20-50% of the total weight of the vehicle, according to the nature of the ground surface and gradient.

On roads the entire weight can be supported by the wheels and the vehicle is then operated in a similar way to the traditional lorry. The air cushion only can be employed when crossing rivers and when manoeuvring the craft in a confined space.

LIFT AND PROPULSION: The front wheels are fitted with heavy duty tyres and are steered by a normal steering wheel from the driver's cab.

Motive power for the lift/propulsion system is provided by an adapted 250 hp Chevrolet V8 petrol engine. This drives an axial fan for lift and a hydro-

static transmission circuit which provides either two or four-wheel drive. Cushion air is ducted into seven individual neoprene-coated tergal skirts, six of which are surrounded by a lightweight wrap-round skirt. Transmission to the four wheels is via an engine-mounted pump circulating fluid through lines to four hydraulic motors which drive the wheels.

Special paddle vanes which can be attached to the wheels allow travel over water at speeds up to 4·35 mph (7 km/h).

WEIGHTS:

Weight empty	2 tons
Weight loaded	3·6 tons

DIMENSIONS:

Length	20 ft 8 in (6·3 m)
Width	8 ft 2¼ in (2·5 m)

PERFORMANCE:

Speed over flat surfaces	43·5 mph (70 km/h)
Speed over uneven ground	31 mph (50 km/h)
Speed over water	4·35 mph (7 km/h)
Endurance	3 hours
Gradient capability	8-20%
Vertical obstacle clearance	1 ft 4 in (0·40 m)

GERMAN FEDERAL REPUBLIC

RHEIN-FLUGZEUGBAU GmbH

(Subsidiary of VFW-Fokker GmbH)

HEAD OFFICE AND MAIN WORKS:
405 Mönchengladbach, Flugplatz, Postfach 408

TELEPHONE:
02161/62031

TELEX:
08/52506

EXECUTIVE DIRECTORS:
Dipl-Volkswirt Wolfgang Kutsher
Dipl-Ing Alfred Schneider

TECHNICAL AND SCIENTIFIC MANAGER, X-113
AM AEROFOIL PROJECT:
Dr A. M. Lippisch FRAeS

HEAD OF TESTS:
Ing. D. Schönfelder

RFB is engaged in the development and construction of airframe structural components, an emphasis being placed on wings fabricated entirely in glass fibre reinforced plastics. Research and design activities include studies for the Federal German Government, which is also providing assistance for the development of the X-113 Am Aerofoil boat.

RFB (LIPPISCH) X-113 Am AEROFOIL BOAT

The Aerofoil Boat was conceived in the United States by Dr A. M. Lippisch. The first wing-in-ground-effect machine built to Lippisch designs was the Collins X-112, which was employed by Lippisch to examine the stability problems likely to be encountered in the design of larger machines of this type.

Since 1967 further development of the concept has been undertaken by RFB, with government backing. The single-seat X-113 has been built as a test craft to provide data for the design of larger craft of the same type.

The X-113 Am underwent its first airworthiness test from Lake Constance in October 1970.

During the first series of tests, the craft demonstrated its operating ability on water as well as flight capability at very low altitudes. These tests were followed in the autumn of 1971 by a second series of trials during which performance measurements were taken. A cine camera built into the cockpit recorded instrument readings and a camera built into the lateral stabilisers took pictures of small threads on the upper wing surface for current flow analysis.

The earlier trials on the Bodensee were followed in November/December 1972 by a third series of tests in the North Sea in the Weser estuary area.

Apart from various performance measurements, the aim of these trials was to investigate the machine's capabilities in roughish weather conditions, Although the machine was originally designed only for a brief general demonstration on calm water, the intention was now to perform take-offs and landings in a moderate sea.

Remarkably good sea behaviour was shown from the outset. Taking-offs and landings in wave heights of about 2 ft 6 in (0·75 m) presented no problem, During the course of these tests, flights were made in the

Top: Dr Alexander Lippisch's X-113 Am Aerofoil boat during demonstrations in the Waser estuary, North Sea. Built by VFW-Rhein-Flugzeugbau, GmbH, this is one of the world's first wing-in-ground effect machines capable of full flight. It takes off and begins to skim above its supporting surface at 31 mph (50 km/h) *Centre:* Seen in this photograph are the anhedral delta wing and the dihedral tips outboard of the two wing floats. Power is supplied by a single 40 hp Nelson H63-CP engine *Bottom:* Underside of the X-113 Am, showing the anhedral reversed delta wing which overcomes the problem of pitch instability during the transition from surface effect to free-flight and back again

coastal region, and sometimes on the Wattenmeer, in wind forces of up to 25 knots, without any uncontrollable flying tendencies being observed in low-level flight.

The flight performance measurements gave a gliding angle of 1:30, which cannot be greatly improved by enlarging the machine. It is also of interest to note that the relatively thin outer laminate of the GFR wing sandwich, with a thickness of 0.4 mm, stood up to the loads involved in taking off in a roughish sea and also remained watertight throughout the whole period of trials.

Towards the end of the trials, in order to reduce noise and give the airscrew better protection from spray, the machine was converted to pusher propulsion.

Flight performance could not be investigated because of the weather.

It is now planned to enlarge the machine into a 2-seater. Trials are due to be undertaken in 1974.

According to the speed selected, the Aerofoil boat can perform three functions. At very low speeds it corresponds to an ordinary boat; at 9 mph (15 km/h) it operates like a hydroplane and starting from about 31 mph (50 km/h) it begins skimming the surface. It will also climb out of ground effect. During its first series of tests it was reported to have made several flights of up to 328 ft (100 m).

Operating in ground effect, the craft is stated by its designers to exceed in effectiveness any other form of water transport, and have power requirements 30% less than that of similar water craft. The craft is operated at a height above the surface of up to one-half the hull beam (wing span) for optimum performance.

The company envisages a range of Aerofoil craft for a variety of civil and military purposes, from single-seat runabouts to cargo transporters with payloads of up to 10 tons. As transports they could be employed on coastal, inter-island and river services. Military variants could be used as assault craft, FPBs and ASW vessels.

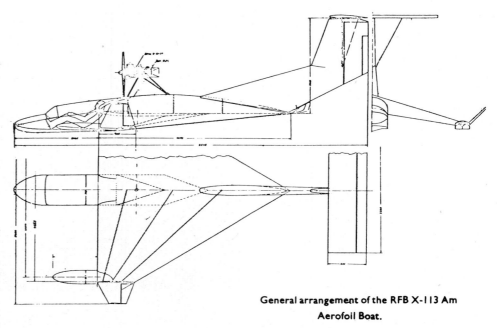

General arrangement of the RFB X-113 Am Aerofoil Boat.

Flight tests, including a series performed over rough water in the North Sea near Bremmerhaven, have established that 50% less power is required in ground effect, enabling operations in excess of 50-ton-miles per gallon of fuel at speeds in the 90-180 knot range.

POWER PLANT: Thrust is supplied by a 48 hp (derated to 40 hp) Nelson H63-CP horizontally-opposed four-cylinder, two stroke engine driving a 3 ft 10 in (1·17 m) diameter 2-bladed wooden propeller.

STRUCTURE: Glassfibre sandwich construction with a core of tubular or foam plastic. Tailplane and rudder are made in cloth-covered wood, and wing floats are in styrofoam. Side walls of the hull are of Conticell sandwich construction. Wing is of sandwich construction with a 0·4 mm covering laminate.

DIMENSIONS, EXTERNAL:

Wing span	19 ft 3¾ in (5·89 m)
Length overall	27 ft 8 in (8·43 m)
Height overall	6 ft 9½ in (2·07 m)

WEIGHTS:

Weight empty	562 lb (255 kg)
Max T-O weight	760 lb (345 kg)

ITALY

ITALY
FIAT SpA

HEAD OFFICE:
Direzione Centrale Ricerca e Sviluppo, Corso Giovanni Agnelli 200, Turin, Italy.

TELEPHONE:
33331

TELEX:
Fiat MRFR 21022

OFFICERS:
Dr. Ing. Oscar Montabone

Fiat has been licensed by Sedam, the French ACV company, for the manufacture of Sedam Naviplane vehicles, and has been granted exclusive rights for their sale in Italy, Argentina, Egypt, Yugoslavia, Poland, Turkey, the Soviet Union and other countries.

Fiat's "Direzione Centrale Ricerca e Sviluppo", is currently undertaking a research programme in this field.

HOVERCRAFT ITALIANA SRL

HEAD OFFICE:
Via A. Borelli, 5, 00161 Rome, Italy

TELEPHONE:
4956148—5127308

EXECUTIVES:
Captain Tito Bettocchi, Technical Manager
M. Ilo Roberto Bruschina, Production Manager

BT.4-74

This new fibreglass-hulled three-seater, based on the earlier BT-3-72, is about to go into series production. The prototype was completed with the assistance of the Italian Air Force and has been undergoing trials on Lake Bracciano. Captain Bettocchi reports that his latest machine is capable of carrying six people instead of three, as was intended, and that the overall performance is well in excess of expectations.

The craft is the first Italian design hover-

First hovercraft of Italian design to go into production, the BT.4-74 is a fibreglass-hulled 3-seater employing a patented double skirt. The prototype was completed with the assistance of the Italian Air Force and has been undergoing trials on Lake Bracciano. The two vanes outboard of the single rudder are employed as air brakes.

craft to be available commercially. The skirt and certain other features are covered in Italian patent 47918A/71. Possible uses include family runabout and patrol craft.

LIFT AND PROPULSION: A 21 hp JLO 295 two-stroke engine located behind the cockpit and mounted in an open plastic duct drives a 2 ft 1½ in (64·8 cm) fan at 3,200 rpm for cushion lift. Thrust is provided by a 3 ft 6 in (107 cm) diameter wooden 2-bladed propeller driven by a 50 hp JLO LR 760/Z engine mounted aft of the lift fan duct. Production models will be fitted with a 72 hp McCulloch Model 438.

CONTROLS: Twin aerodynamic rudders, hinged to the rear of the propeller duct, provide directional control. Twin vanes aft for braking,

HULL: Two piece moulded grp structure with upper and lower hulls bolted together at skirt line.

SKIRT: Double "Italian" style skirt of new design, fabricated in 17 oz nylon neoprene and 10 in (25 cm) deep.

ACCOMMODATION: Driver and up to two passengers seated side-by-side in a pressurised cabin.

SYSTEMS, ELECTRICAL: 12 volt battery for starting, navigation lights and headlamps.

DIMENSIONS:

Length overall	17 ft (5·20 m)
Beam	8 ft 6 in (2·60 m)
Height on landing pads	4 ft 9 in (1·45 m)

The BT.4-74 fibreglass-hulled 3-seater The prototype was completed with the assistance of the Italian Air Force and has been undergoing trials on Lake Bracciano. The two vanes outboard of the single rudder are employed as air brakes.

Height, skirt inflated	5 ft 6 in (1·68 m)	
WEIGHTS:		
Empty	860 lb (390 kg)	
Useful load	460 lb (210 kg)	
Gross weight	1,320 lb (600 kg)	
PERFORMANCE:		
Max speed	41 mph (66 km/h)	
Cruising speed	34 mph (55 km/h)	
Speed in 1 ft (30 cm) waves and 15 knot wind	20 mph (30 km/h)	
Vertical obstacle clearance	10 in (25 cm)	
Acceptable wave height	2 ft (0·60 m)	

Max gradient	12-18%
Endurance, max cont power	
	2 hr + 15 min reserve

PRICE AND DELIVERY:
Approx cost, basic craft $12,000, including 10% tax, FOB, Rome, Italy. Delivery time from acceptance of order, 4 months.

FAN-JET 6-SEATER

In June 1974, the company announced that plans were underway for the development of a fan-jet propelled six-seater.

JAPAN

ASHIKAGA INSTITUTE OF TECHNOLOGY

ADDRESS:
Mechanical Design Study Group, Institute of Technology, 268 Ohmae cho, Ashikag-ishi, 26326, Japan

DIRECTORS:
T. Imamura
E. Sakai
S. Suzuku

The Mechanical Design Study Group at the Ashikaga Institute of Technology is conducting an ACV research programme in conjunction with the Aerodynamics Section of the Physical Science Laboratory, Nihon University. It has recently taken over the Pastoral 1, constructed at Nihon University in 1970, and introduced various modifications. In its new form the craft is some 35% lighter, and has been redesignated Pastoral 2.

PASTORAL 2

This is a light amphibious single-seater employed to gather data for research and development projects. At the time of going to press the modified craft had completed nearly five hours of tests over sand, grass and mud and had attained a speed of 55 mph (98 km/h).

LIFT AND PROPULSION: A single 8 hp Fuji Heavy Industries 2-cycle single-cylinder

Pastoral single-seat research ACV

air-cooled engine installed immediately aft of the cockpit drives a 5-bladed 1 ft 9¼ in (540 mm) diameter axial-flow fan for lift. Propulsion is supplied by a 36 hp Toyota 2U-B 4-cycle, 2-cylinder engine driving a 3 ft 11¼ in (1,200 mm) diameter two-bladed propeller.

CONTROLS: Twin aerodynamic rudders operated by a wheel in the cockpit control craft heading.

HULL: Moulded glassfibre, with inflatable fabric-reinforced neoprene sidebody/skirt.

DIMENSIONS:

Length overall, skirt inflated	13 ft 9½ in (4·20 m)
Beam overall, skirt inflated	5 ft 11 in (1·80 m)
Height, skirt inflated	5 ft 1 in (1·55 m)

WEIGHTS:

Normal all-up weight	706 lb (320 kg)

PERFORMANCE:

Max speed over land	56 mph (90 km/h)
over water	37 mph (60 km/h)

MITSUBISHI HEAVY INDUSTRIES LTD

HEAD OFFICE:
5-1, Marunouchi 2-chome, Chiyoda-ku, Tokyo, Japan

TELEPHONE:
Tokyo (212)-3111

WORKS:
Kobe Shipyard & Engine Works, 1, 3-chome

Wadasaki-cho, Hyogo-ku, Kobe

TELEPHONE:
Kobe (671) 5061

CABLES:
Dock Kobe

PRESIDENT:
G. Moriya

MANAGING DIRECTOR & SENIOR MANAGER

OF SHIPBUILDING DIVISION:
I. Takezawa

SENIOR EXECUTIVES:
Y. Terada, Manager of Domestic Ship Department (Head Office)
K. Ichikawa, Manager of Warship Department (Head Office)
A. Tomi, General Manager of Kobe Shipyard

& Engine Works

M. Muto, Manager of Hovercraft Section

Kobe Shipyard and Engine Works

Mitsubishi completed a 3 ton experimental ACV in 1962 and is now engaged in technical studies for large commercial craft for Japanese inland sea services.

The company concluded a licence agreement with British Hovercraft Corporation and Hovercraft Development Ltd in 1964. In February 1965 the company imported for evaluation and demonstration an SR.N5 which was returned in August of that year.

The company imported an SR.N6 in November 1966. A trial passenger ferry service was undertaken by Kyushu Shosen, a Japanese Shipping Company, in Kyushu, between Kumamoto and Shimabara, and Kumamoto and Hondo during the nine month period from September 1, 1967 until May 31, 1968.

The craft was also operated as a pleasure craft on Lake Biwa, Shiga Prefecture, from September to November, 1968.

Since July 1969, the craft has been operated as a passenger ferry between Toba and Gamagohri in Ise Bay.

The craft has been granted a certificate for passenger carrying under legislation covering air cushion vehicles introduced by the Japanese Ministry of Transport.

Descriptions of the SR.N5-M and SR.N6-M appeared in JSS 1971-72 and earlier editions.

Mitsui Shipbuilding & Engineering Co. Ltd.

HEAD OFFICE:
6-4, Tsukiji 5-chome, Chuo-ku, Tokyo, Japan

TELEPHONE:
544-3450

TELEX:
J22821, J22924

CABLE:
Mituizosen Tokyo

BOARD OF DIRECTORS:
Teiji Asano, Chairman of the Board
Isamu Yamashita, President
Saburo Sakamoto, Senior Managing Director
Sobei Kudo, Senior Managing Director
Masami Fukuyama, Senior Managing Director
Jiro Komatsu, Managing Director
Kyoichi Kato, Managing Director
Shoji Massaki, Managing Director
Shoichi Takeuchi, Managing Director
Kazuo Hamano, Managing Director
Sasaburo Kobayashi, Director
Ryoji Kawazura, Director
Kazuo Nagai, Director
Takashi Teramura, Director
Kazuo Maeda, Director
Hiroshi Yamaguchi, Director
Yasuhisa Sawada, Director
Tatsuhiko Ueno, Director
Masahiko Irie, Director
Michio Sugimoto, Director
Kiyofumi Karashima, Auditor
Nobuo Yashima, Auditor
Yoshinori Takahashi, Auditor
Tetsujiro Tomita, Manager, Hovercraft Dept.

Mitsui's Hovercraft Department was formed on May 1st 1964, following the signing of a licencing agreement in 1963 with Hovercraft Development Ltd and Vickers Ltd, whose ACV interests were later merged with those of British Hovercraft Corporation. In addition the company was licenced by Westland S.A. in 1967, following the formation of BHC.

The company has built two eleven-seat MV-PP1s, one of which has been supplied to the Thai Customs Department, twelve MV-PP5s and two MV-PP15s.

The MV-PP5 is now in production at the initial rate of four craft a year. In the summer of 1969 the craft was put into service by Meitetsu Kaijo Kankosen Co Ltd between Gamagoori and Toba, Ise Bay.

Since October 1971 three MV-PP5s designated Hobby 1, 2 and 3 have been operated by Oita Hoverferry Co., Ltd on a coastal route linking Oita airport with the cities of Oita and Beppu. The three craft complete a total of sixteen round trips per day to link with flight schedules at the airport.

To cope with the anticipated increase in passenger traffic on this route, Oita is planning to introduce 150-seat MV-PP15s when they become available. The prototype

Mitsui's MV-PP15 50-ton passenger ferry, powered by twin 1,950 hp Avco Lycoming TF25 gas turbines. The craft seats 155 passengers and has a top speed of 65 knots. Seen in these photographs are the raised control cabin, the pylon mounted propellers, lift fan air intakes and the thrust ports beneath the passenger door entrances, port and starboard

began its trials in November 1972. The company is now building the prototype MV-PP05, a 5-seater, and has started the design of a 200-ton mixed-traffic ferry.

MV-PP15

Developed from the earlier PP5, the Mitsui MV-PP15 is designed for high speed passenger ferry services on coastal and inland waterways. Accommodation is provided for 155 passengers and a crew of 5.

The prototype was completed in the autumn of 1972. Potential operators include the Oita Hoverferry Co, which plans to put MV PP15s into service on the route Oita Airport-Oita-Beppu.

LIFT AND PROPULSION: Two Avco Lycoming TF25 gas-turbines, each with a maximum continuous output of 1,950 hp at 30°C, drive the integrated lift/propulsion system. Each turbine drives a 7 ft 6 in (2·3 m) diameter, 13-bladed centrifugal fan and a 10 ft 6 in (3·2 m) diameter, 4-bladed variable-pitch propeller. Power is transmitted via a main gearbox, propeller gearbox,

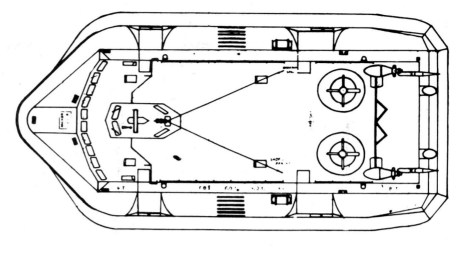

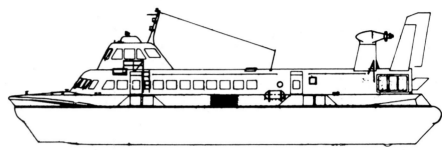

Mitsui MV-PP15 155-seat hoverferry. Twin AVCO Lycoming TF25 gas-turbines power the integrated lift propulsion system and give the craft a maximum speed of 60 knots

fan gearbox and an auxiliary gearbox, all connected by shafting and flexible couplings. Auxiliary systems, such as hydraulic pumps for propeller pitch and lubricating oil pumps, are driven directly by auxiliary gears. Fuel is carried in two flexible tanks located immediately ahead of the lift fan assemblies. Total volume of the fuel tanks is 21·2 ft³ (6 m³).

CONTROLS: Twin aerodynamic rudders in the propeller slipstream and differential propeller pitch provide directional control. The rudders are operated hydraulically by a wheel from the commander's position. In addition, two retractable wheels, located aft, one each side of the main buoyancy tank, can be extended downwards into the water to prevent drift when turning and assist braking at high speeds. On land, the wheels asssit manoeuvring and help to reduce skirt wear.

A thrust port air bleed system provides lateral control at slow speeds. Four ports are located beneath the passenger door entrances, port and starboard. A water ballast system is provided for longitudinal and transverse cg adjustment.

HULL: Construction is primarily in corrosion resistant aluminium alloy. The basic structure is the main buoyancy chamber which is divided into watertight sub-divisions for safety, and includes the fore and aft ballast tanks. Overall dimensions of the main buoyancy raft structure are 64 ft 10½ in (19·8 m) long by 23 ft 3½ in (7·1 m) wide by 2 ft 4 in (0·7 m) high. Sidebodies of riveted construction are attached to the sides of the main buoyancy structure. The outer shell of the main buoyancy chamber. machinery deck space, the forward deck and passageways around the cabin interior, are all constructed in honeycomb panels with aluminium cores. The lift fan air intake, inner window

frames and hood for the electric motor that rotates the radar scanner are in glassfibre reinforced plastics.

Six rubber-soled landing pads are fitted to the hull base, together with jacking pads. Four lifting eyes for hoisting the craft are provided in the buoyancy chamber.

SKIRT: 5 ft 3 in (1·60 m) deep fingered-bag skirt of Mitsui design, fabricated in nylon-based sheet and coated both sides with synthetic rubber. Two transverse stability bags are included in the skirt system to minimise pitch and roll.

ACCOMMODATION: The passenger cabin, containing 155 seats, is located above the forward part of the main buoyancy chamber. The seats are arranged in three groups and divided by two longitudinal aisles. Seats in the two outer sections are arranged in rows of three abreast, and in the centre section, six abreast.

The four cabin entrance doors, two port, two starboard, are divided horizontally, the top section opening upwards and the lower section opening sideways. A lavatory, toilet unit, pantry and luggage room are provided aft, and a second luggage room is located forward. Lockers are sited close to the forward entrance doors. The control cabin is located above the passenger cabin superstructure and provides a 360 deg. view. It is reached from the passenger saloon by a companion ladder. An emergency exit is provided on the starboard side.

The cabin has a total of four seats, one each for the commander and navigator, plus two spare ones of the flip-up type. The wheel for the air rudders, the two propeller pitch-control levers, instrument panel and switches are arranged on a console ahead of the commander; and the radio, fuel tank gauge, water ballast gauge and fire warning system

are arranged ahead of the navigator.

On the cabin roof are the radar-scanner, mast for navigation lights, a siren and a searchlight.

SYSTEMS:

ELECTRICAL: 28·5 volts dc. Two 9kw generators are driven by belts from auxiliary gearbox. One 24 volt 175 Ah battery is employed for starting, and another for control. Both are located in the engine room and are charged by the generators when the main engines are operating. A shore-based power source is used for battery charging when the main engines are not in use.

RADIO/NAVIGATION: Equipment includes one 10 in radar, compass, radio and one 20 cm, 250 W searchlight.

AIR CONDITIONING: Two Daikin RKA 1000R-PP15 air coolers, each with a capacity of 20,000 Kcal/hr. Compressors are driven by the main engine via the auxiliary gearbox, and cooled air is supplied via four ceiling ventilating ports, each equipped with a 40W fan.

SAFETY: Remotely-controlled BCF fire extinguishers provided in the engine room. Portable extinguishers provided in the passenger cabin. Inflatable life rafts, life jackets, automatic SPS signal transmitter and other equipment carried according to Japanese Ministry of Transport regulations.

DIMENSIONS, EXTERNAL:

Length overall on cushion	80 ft 1 in (24·70 m)
Length overall on landing pads	79 ft 1½ in (24·14 m)
Beam overall on cushion	41 ft 8 in (12·70 m)
Beam overall on landing pads	36 ft 5 in (11·10 m)
Height on cushion	25 ft 11 in (7·90 m)
Height on landing pads to tip of propeller blade	22 ft 8 in (6·90 m)

Skirt depth   5 ft 3 in (1·60 m)

DIMENSIONS, INTERNAL:

(Passenger cabin including toilet, pantry and locker rooms):

Length	46 ft 5 in (14·14 m)
Maximum breadth	23 ft 2 in (7·06 m)
Maximum height	6 ft 11 in (2·10 m)
Floor area	1,001 sq ft (93 m²)

WEIGHTS:

All-up weight   about 50 tons

PERFORMANCE:

Max speed	about 65 knots
Cruising speed	about 50 knots

Fuel consumption

       about 296 gr/SHP/hr at 30 deg C

Endurance   about 4 hours

MV-PP5

Mitsui's first large hovercraft is the 50-seat MV-PP5, a gas-turbine powered craft intended primarily for fast ferry services on Japanese coastal and inland waters. The craft is now in production at the rate of four a year.

LIFT AND PROPULSION: All machinery is located aft to reduce to a minimum the noise level in the passenger cabin. A single IHI IM-100 gas-turbine (license-built General Electric LM100) with a maximum continuous rating of 1,050 hp at 19,500 rpm drives the integrated lift/propulsion system. Its output shaft passes first to the main gearbox from which shafts extend sideways and upwards to two 3-bladed Hamilton/Sumitomo variable-pitch propulsion propellers of 8 ft 6 in (2·59 m) diameter. A further shaft runs forward to the fan gearbox from which a drive shaft runs vertically downwards to a 7 ft 7 in (2·27 m) 13-bladed lift fan mounted beneath the air intake immediately aft of the passenger saloon roof. The fan is constructed in aluminium alloy and the disc plate is a 1½ in (40 mm) thick honeycomb structure.

To prevent erosion from water spray the propeller blades are nickel plated.

Fuel is carried in two metal tanks, with a total capacity of 416 gallons (1,900 litres), located immediately ahead of the lift fan assembly.

CONTROLS: Twin aerodynamic rudders in the propeller slipstream and differential thrust from the propellers provide directional control. The rudders are controlled hydraulically from the commander's position. In addition two retractable water rods, located slightly aft of amidships on each side of the main buoyancy tank, can be extended downwards to prevent drift when turning and these also assist braking at high speeds. The water rods are operated hydraulically by foot-pedals. When used in conjunction with the rudders, the turning radius is reduced to about a third of that taken when only air rudders are used.

A thrust-port air bleed system provides lateral control at slow speeds. The thrust ports are actuated by air extracted from the engine compressor and are located beneath the passenger door entrances, port and starboard.

HULL: Construction is primarily of high strength AA502 aluminium alloy suitably protected against the corrosive effects of sea water. The basic structure is the main buoyancy chamber which is divided into eight watertight sub-divisions for safety, and includes fore and aft trimming tanks. Two further side body tanks, each divided into three watertight compartments, are attached to the sides of the main buoyancy chamber. To facilitate shipment the side body tanks can be removed, reducing the width to 12 ft 4 in (3·75 mm).

The outer shell of the main buoyancy chamber, the machinery deck space, the forward deck and the passage decks around the cabin exterior are all constructed in honeycomb panels with aluminium cores.

The lift fan air intake, radar cover, part of the air conditioning duct, and inside window frames are in glass-fibre reinforced plastic.

Design loads are as required by the Provisional British ACV Safety Regulations.

SKIRT: The flexible skirt was designed by Mitsui in the light of research conducted with aid of the RH-4 (MV-PP1 prototype) It is made of $\frac{3}{32}$ in (0·8 mm) thick chloroprene-coated nylon sheet. A fringe of finger type nozzles is attached to the skirt base at the bow and on both sides. At the stern a D-section bag skirt is used to avoid scooping up water.

Two transverse and one longitudinal stability bag are fitted.

ACCOMMODATION: The passenger cabin is sited above the forward end of the main buoyancy chamber. Seats for the two crew members are on a raised platform at the front of the cabin. All controls, navigation and radio equipment are concentrated around the seats. The windows ahead are of reinforced tempered glass and have electric wipers.

The two cabin entrance doors are divided horizontally, the lower part opening sideways, the top part upwards. The standard seating arrangement is for 42 passengers but ten additional seats can be placed in the centre aisle.

In accordance with Japanese Ministry of Transport regulations a full range of safety equipment is carried, including two inflatable life rafts, 54 life jackets, one automatic, manually activated fire extinguisher for the engine casing and two portable fire extinguishers in the cabin. Other standard equipment includes ship's navigation lights, marine horn, searchlight and mooring equipment, including an anchor. The twelve side windows can be used as emergency exits and are made of acrylic resin.

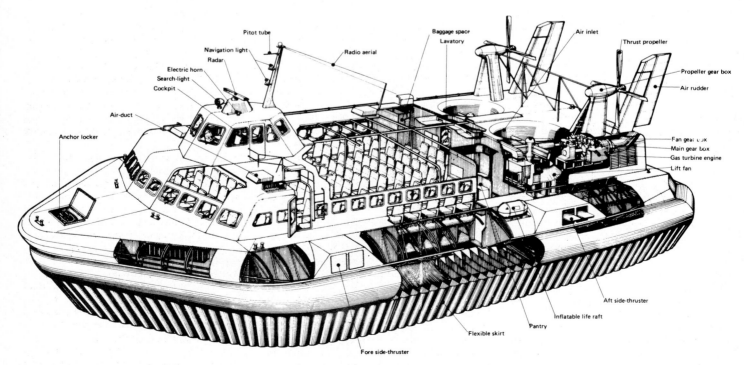

Cutaway of the Mitsui MU-PP15, showing the seating arrangements for the 155 passengers. Seats are arranged in three groups, divided by two longitudinal aisles. In the two outer sections they are arranged in rows of three abreast, and in the centre, six abreast

SYSTEMS:
ELECTRICAL SYSTEM: Two 2 kW, 28·5 volt ac/dc generators driven by belts from the main gearbox. 1 24 volt, 68 Ah battery for engine starting.
HYDRAULIC AND PNEUMATIC SYSTEM: A 99·56 lb/in² (7·0 kg/cm²) hydraulic system pressure for water rods and 56·8-99·5 lb/in² (4·7-7 kg/cm²) pneumatic system for thrust port operation.
COMMUNICATION AND NAVIGATION: Equipment includes a radio and radar.

DIMENSIONS, EXTERNAL:

Length overall	52 ft 6 in (16·0 m)
Beam overall	28 ft 2 in (8·6 m)
Height overall on landing pad	14 ft 5 in (4·4 m)
Skirt depth	3 ft 11 in (1·2 m)
Draft afloat	11 in (0·2 m)
Cushion area	741 sq ft (88· m²)

DIMENSIONS, INTERNAL:

Cabin:

Length	23 ft 4 in (7·1 m)
Max width	12 ft 6 in (3·8 m)
Max height	6 ft 3 in (1·9 m)
Floor area	280 sq ft (26 m²)

Doors:
Two (0·65 m) × (1·4 m), one each side of cabin

Baggage-hold volume	24 cu ft (0·6 m³)

WEIGHTS:

Normal all-up weight	14 tons
Normal payload	5·5 tons

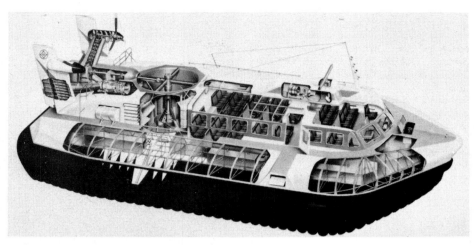

Internal arrangement of the MV-PP5 showing passenger accommodation and the gas-turbine powered lift/propulsion system aft of the cabin

PERFORMANCE:
Max speed, calm water 55 knots (102 km/h)
Cruising speed, calm water
45 knots (83 km/h)
Still air range and endurance at cruising speed of about 160 nautical miles, 4 hours approximately
Vertical obstacle clearance 2 ft (0·6 m) approximately.

MV-PP1
The MV-PP1 is a small peripheral jet ACV built for river and coastal services and fitted with a flexible skirt. It seats a pilot and ten passengers and cruises at 40 knots.

Two craft of this type have been built to date—the prototype, which was completed in July 1964 and has been designated RH-4, and the first production model, the PP1-01.

The latter was sold to the Thai Customs Department, for service in the estuary of the Menam Chao Phya and adjacent waters, and has been named Customs Hovercraft 1. It has been in service with the Thai Customs Department since September 1967.

Details of construction weights, performance, etc will be found in JSS 1970-71 edition.

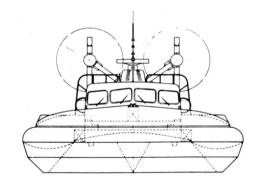

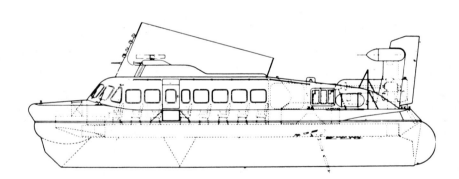

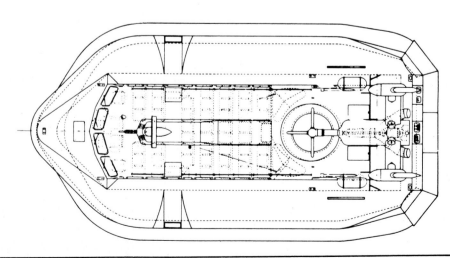

Mitsui MV-PP5 50-seat hovercraft, designed for fast ferry services on Japanese coastal and inland waters

NIHON UNIVERSITY, NARASHIÑO

ADDRESS:
Aerodynamics Section, Nihon University at Narashino, 7-1591 Narashinodai, Funabashi, Chiba-Ken, Japan
TELEPHONE:
0474-66-1111-4
EXECUTIVES:
Masahira Mino, Senior Director
Toyoaki Enda, Director

The Aerodynamics Section of the Physical Science Laboratory, Nihon University, is conducting an extensive ACV research programme, which includes the construction and test of three small experimental craft: the Pastoral light amphibious single-seater, the Mistral, propelled by either water-screw or waterjet, and the Floral, a two-seat sidewall craft.

An air boat, the Ripple, is employed as a "chase" craft to record on film the behaviour of these light ACVs over water.

Nihon University's ACV design group works in close co-operation with similar groups at the Institute of Technology, Ashikaga, and the University of Aoyama-Gakuin. Pastoral, in modified form, is now being employed in a research programme conducted by the Institute of Technology, Ashikaga.

A new design, the LJ-10 Jimny, a combined ground effect machine and wheeled vehicle, has been completed by Nihon in conjunction with Aoyama Gakuin University.

FLORAL 1

This experimental two-seater was completed in February 1971, and was the first sidewall craft to be built in Japan. In calm water the performance has proved to be superior to that of standard displacement runabouts of similar size and output. The craft was reconstructed in 1972 when the twin outboard propulsion units were replaced by a single unit, and a new stern skirt and trim flaps were introduced. Instrumentation includes trim, roll angle and speed indicators and gauges for measuring pressure in the plenum chamber.

LIFT AND PROPULSION: Lift is provided by a single 8 hp ZD-305 2 cycle single-cylinder air-cooled engine, located aft of the open cockpit and driving an F. S. Anderson 710-20-3L plastic fan. Propulsion is provided by a single Penta 550 outboard engine driving a waterscrew.

CONTROL: Engine/propeller unit turns for steering.

DIMENSIONS:

Length overall	17 ft 1 in (5·2 m)
Beam overall	5 ft 11 in (1·8 m)
Height overall	2 ft 7½ in (0·8 m)

WEIGHTS:

Normal gross weight	1,191 lb (540 kg)

PERFORMANCE:

Max speed over calm water	39 mph (62·7 km/h)
Max speed, 16 in (·40 m) waves	32 mph (52·1 km/h)

Above and below: Floral 1, two-seater sidewall ACV, built by students of the Aerodynamics Section of Nihon University, Narashino, Japan

MISTRAL 2

Developed jointly by Nihon University, Masahiro Mino and the Institute of Technology, Ashikaga, the Mistral 2 is an experimental water-screw propelled single-seater derived from the SEA-NAC.

LIFT AND PROPULSION: A single 8 hp Fuji ES-162DS- 2-cycle single-cylinder air-cooled engine mounted immediately aft of the cockpit drives a 22⅞ in (580 mm) S11-03-FS03 5-bladed aluminium alloy fan for lift. Propulsion is supplied by either a 22 hp Fuji KB-2 or 50 hp Mercury 500 driving a waterscrew.

HULL: Moulded glass fibre, with inflated fabric-reinforced neoprene side-body/skirt.

CONTROLS: Engine/propeller unit turns for steering.

DIMENSIONS:

Length overall	13 ft 5 in (4·10 m)
Beam overall	5 ft 11 in (1·80 m)
Height overall	3 ft 7 in (1·09 m)

WEIGHTS:

Normal gross weight	664 lb (310 kg)

Mistral 2 single seat research ACV

PERFORMANCE:
Max speed over calm water
42 mph (67·5 km/h)
Max speed, 2 ft (0·6 m) waves
28 mph (45·5 km/h)

LJ-10 JIMNY

Based on a reconditioned Suzuki Auto Co LN-360 Jimny—a jeep counterpart—this is a combined ground effect machine and wheeled vehicle, and can be driven like a car or truck. It was built by the Aerodynamics Section of Nihon University, headed by Masahiro Minot, in conjunction with the Traffic Engineering Dept, Aoyoma Gakuin University, headed by Eiji Tonokura. The vehicle is designed for use over uneven ground, and, marshes, and other terrain which cannot be traversed by wheeled or tracked cars and trucks. During 1973, the craft successfully completed running tests over normal road surfaces, unprepared tracks and stretches of water.

LIFT AND PROPULSION: Motive power for the lift system is provided by a single 55 hp Nissan A-10 988 cc engine which drives two 23½ in (595 mm) diameter 10-bladed centrifugal fans mounted on a common shaft to the rear of the driving position. Air is drawn through two inward facing metal ducts and expelled downwards into a fingered-bag skirt system. The vehicle has a four wheel drive system, powered by a Suzuki FB 395 cc petrol engine developing 27 hp at 6,000 rpm. Heading is controlled by a normal steering wheel located ahead of the driver.

DIMENSIONS
Length   17 ft 8 in (5,390 mm)
Width   10 ft 11 in (3,440 mm)
Height   5 ft 11 in (1,820 mm)
WEIGHTS:
All-up weight   2,200 lb (998 kg)
PERFORMANCE:
No details received

Above and below: LJ-10 Jimny a combined ground effect machine and wheeled vehicle. Designed for use over terrain normally unpassable to wheeled or crawler-equipped tractors the vehicle comprises a Suzuki Auto Co LN-360 Jimny—a counterpart to the US Army's jeep—equipped with a sidebody to support the skirt system and two lift fan assemblies. Cushion air is supplied by a 55 hp Nissan engine driving two 10-bladed centrifugal fans

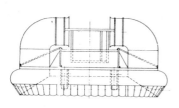
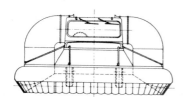
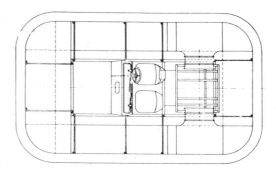
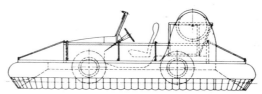

General arrangement of the AVC adaption of the Suzuki Jimny, undertaken jointly by ACV study groups at Nihon and Aoyama-Gakuin Universities

NETHERLANDS

MACHINEFABRIEK ENBE BV

Air Cushion Vehicle Design and Manufacturing Subsidiary:

B. V. LUCHTKUSSENVOERTUIGEN FABRIEK

HEAD OFFICE:
Industrieterrein, Asperen, Netherlands
TELEPHONE:
03451-2743/2744
TELEX:
ENBE NL 47864
WORKS:
LKV Fabr. Industrieterrein, Asperen

DIRECTORS:
W. A. G. v. Burgeler
N. C. Nap
SHAREHOLDERS, (BV ENBE)
N. C. Nap
A. H. Nap
W. A. G. v. Burgeler

ENBE has built three light amphibious ACV prototypes, the B-1, B-2 and B-3, all designed by Mr. W. A. G. v. Burgeler.

Since January 1st, 1974, the company has been the distributor in the Netherlands for the Air Vehicles AV.2 light utility ACV.

B2

A multi-purpose amphibious four-seater of mixed plastics and aluminium construction, the B-2 is powered by three 42 hp Volkswagen automotive engines, and has a maximum speed over calm water of 62 mph (100 km/h).
LIFT AND PROPULSION: A single, internally-mounted 42 hp, 4-cycle, 4-cylinder Volkswagen 1,600 cc air-cooled engine drives an aluminium centrifugal fan of $31\frac{1}{2}$ in (800 mm) diameter for lift. Propulsive power is supplied by two pylon-mounted engines of the same type driving two four-bladed propellers. Fuel is carried in four tanks with a total capacity of 63 gallons (240 litres).
CONTROLS: Craft direction is controlled by twin, hydraulically-operated aerodynamic rudders aft, and differential thrust from the propellers.
HULL: Mixed plastics and metal construction.
SKIRT: Segmented skirt, 1 ft 8in (50 cm) deep.
ACCOMMODATION: Seats are provided for a driver and four passengers in a heated and ventilated cabin. Access is through either of two sliding doors, one each side.
SYSTEMS: Electrical: An engine-operated generator supplies 12 volts to an aircraft-type battery for the operation of lights and engine starting.

DIMENSIONS:
Length	22 ft 11⅛ in (7·0 m)
Beam	12 ft 3⅜ in (3·75 m)
Height overall on landing pads	8 ft 2⅜ in (2·5 m)
Height overall skirt inflated	9 ft 10¼ in (3·0 m)
Draft afloat	7 ft 10½ in (2·4 m)
Skirt depth	1 ft 7⅝ in (50 cm)

WEIGHTS:
Normal empty weight	3,528 lb (1,600 kg)
Normal payload	1,102 lb (500 kg)

The NVLI B-2 four-seater, powered by three 42 hp Volkswagen automotive engines.

Above and below: Prototype of the B.3 tracked utility vehicle, designed for operation across marshes and rough country and capable of negotiating 30 deg gradients

PERFORMANCE (at normal operating weight):
Max speed over calm water	62 mph (100 km/h)
Max wave capability	1 ft 4 in (40 cm)

B3

The B3 is an unusual combination of ground effect machine and tracked vehicle, driven like a tractor or tank, but capable of negotiating high gradient slopes, rough country, ice, snow and marshes at speeds up to 20 km/h (12·42 mph). The prototype illustrated seats 16-18 passengers but a projected utility version, intended for operations ranging from dredging to oil survey support services, will mount a small hydraulic crane and/or excavating equipment.
LIFT AND PROPULSION: Motive power is supplied by a water-cooled NSU-Wankel rotary engine delivering 135 bhp at 6,000

rpm. Transmission is via an engine-mounted pump circulating fluid through lines to three hydraulic motors, one driving an axial lift fan, the other two driving crawler-type tracks, Fuel is carried in a single rear tank with a capacity of 120 l (26 Imp gals).

CONTROLS: Vehicle heading controlled by differential variance of track speeds.

HULL: Metal construction.

ACCOMMODATION: Cabin is heated and ventilated and provides seats for a driver and up to 18 passengers. Access is via a rear door. An emergency exit is provided at the front of the cabin. In the utility role the vehicle will carry up to two tons of freight.

SYSTEMS: Electrical: An engine-operated generator supplied 12 volts to an aircraft-type battery for the operation of lights and engine starting.

DIMENSIONS, EXTERNAL:

Length overall, skirt inflated
6·70 m (20 ft 4⅛ in)
Beam overall, skirt inflated
3·30 m (10 ft 9⅞ in)
Height overall, power off 1·95 m (5 ft 1¼ in)
Height overall, skirt inflated
1·87 m (6 ft 2 in)
Skirt depth 30 cm (11¾ in)

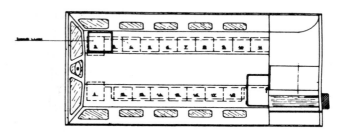

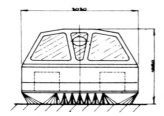
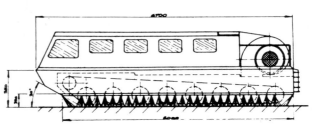

General arrangement of ENBE's 16-18 seat combined ACV and tracked vehicle. Power is supplied by a 135 hp NSU-Wankel rotary engine

DIMENSIONS, INTERNAL:
Cabin length 4 m (13 ft 1½ in)
Cabin width 3 m (9 ft 10¾ in)
Max height 1·5 m (4 ft 11 in)
PERFORMANCE:
Max speed, forward and reverse
20 km/h (14·42 mph)

Gradient up to 30 deg

TERMS:
Terms of payment, 50% with order, remainder on delivery. Export orders: 25% on order. 75% irrevocable L.O.C.

Since January 1974 LKV has been the distributor in the Netherlands for Air Vehicles' AV.2 twin engined amphibious 5-6 seater. A demonstration model is seen above during tests by the Netherlands Army

KUWAIT

AL-RODHAN TRADING AND CONTRACT-ING EST
HEAD OFFICE:
P.O. Box 5020, Kuwait, Arabian Gulf

Al-Rodhan is the representative for Eglen Hovercraft Inc in Kuwait, United Arab Emirates, Bahrain, Oman and Muscat, Yemen and Saudi Arabia.

NEW ZEALAND

HOVER VEHICLES (N.Z.) LTD
ADDRESS:
PO Box 25008, Wellington, New Zealand
TELEPHONE:
882-616
EXECUTIVES:
Roy Blake
David Clemow
Jim Pavitt
Ron Wadman
Brian Shaw
Mel Douglas

Hover Vehicles (N.Z.) Ltd has been formed by a group of New Zealand pilots, engineers and businessmen in association with Roy Blake, winner of the "Hovernaut of the Year" title in the United Kingdom in 1968, who afterwards emigrated to New Zealand.

The company plans to build vehicles which can be employed either on light utility applications or as recreational craft. The first craft under development is the H.V.4, a 6·4 m (21 ft) long amphibious four-seater,

the final design for which is expected to be completed in 1974.

Large scale production is not envisaged, although the local market will be satisfied by craft made at the company's own factory. It is hoped to sell the manufacturing rights to another concern while pursuing further models for development. Government financial assistance may be forthcoming for research and development work. Design of a larger craft has started, but the final configuration will depend upon the success of the H.V.4. Preliminary details of the company's first craft are given below.

H.V.4

The prototype of this attractive six-seat recreational ACV is almost complete and trials were expected to begin in 1974. It is intended as a quiet, easily controlled craft which can be driven by an "above average" car driver after two hours training.

LIFT AND PROPULSION: Power for the integrated lift/propulsion system is provided by a single 185 hp Rover V8 automobile engine which drives a 3 ft (914 mm) diameter centrifugal lift fan and two 3 ft (814 mm) diameter variable-pitch shrouded airscrews.

ACCOMMODATION: Seats are provided for a driver and five passengers in a fully enclosed cabin.

WEIGHTS:
Normal loaded weight
                1,043·25 kg (2,300 lb)

Model of the Hover Vehicles H.V.4.   A single 185 Rover V8 3,500 cc hp automobile engine drives a 3 ft (914 mm) diameter centrifugal lift fan and two 3 ft (914 mm) diameter variable pitch shrouded airscrews.   Maximum speed is expected to be about 45 mph (72·42 km/h)

DIMENSIONS:		PERFORMANCE:	
Length overall	6·4 m (21 ft 0 in)	Max speed	72·42 km/h (45 mph)
Ground clearance	609 mm (2 ft 0 in		

COMMERCIAL HOVERCRAFT INDUSTRIES LTD

HEAD OFFICE:
23 Selwyn Street, Onehunga, New Zealand

This company is currently engaged in the manufacture of the C.H.700, a 4-5 seater powered by three 18 hp Wankel rotary engines. Six craft of this type were built by the company in 1972.

C.H.700

This is a fully amphibious recreational craft with a payload capacity of 680 lb (308·42 kg). The enclosed cabin is pressurised to prevent the ingestion of dust and spray.

LIFT AND PROPULSION: Immediately aft of the cabin is an 18 hp Wankel K.M. 419 rotary engine which drives a centrifugal fan for lift. Propulsive thrust is supplied by twin Wankel engines of identical type driving two fixed-pitch propellers. Fuel capacity is 11 gallons (50 l); consumption, 3·5 gph (15·19 l/ph).

CONTROLS: Craft heading is controlled by twin aerodynamic rudders hinged to the rear of the propeller ducts and by differential thrust.

HULL: Mixed construction, employing a combination of marine ply, glass fibre and anodised aluminium. Buoyancy is provided by ten watertight compartments and poly-styrene foam blocks.

ACCOMMODATION: Enclosed, pressurised cabin with seats for driver and 3-4 passengers.

PERFORMANCE:
Max speed over land 35 mph (56·32 km/h)
Max speed over water 25 mph (40·23 km/h)

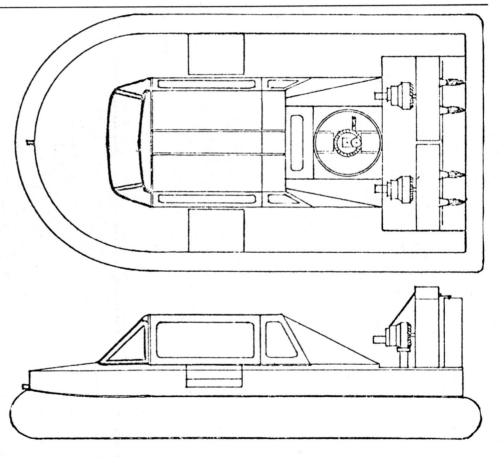

C.H.700, a 4-5 seater powered by three 18 hp Wankel engines

Endurance	3 hours	SYSTEMS: .Electrical: 12 volts for engine
Vertical clearance	8-12 in (203-304 mm)	starting, lights etc.

WEIGHTS:

		DIMENSIONS:	
Empty weight	1,100 lb (498·92 kg)	Length	15 ft 9 in (4·80 m)
Gross weight	1,780 lb (807·35 kg)	Beam	8 ft 0 in (2·43 m)
Useful load	680 lb (308·42 kg)	Height	4 ft 6 in (1·37 m)

POLAND

WARSAW AGRICULTURAL INSTITUTE

HEAD OFFICE:
Rakowieka 8, Warsaw 12, Poland
The Warsaw Agricultural Institute has developed a range of small air cushion vehicles intended primarily for agricultural applica-tions. The latest of these is the Ursinov M-6, designed for crop-spraying and spreading liquid fertilisers on small farms, the size and location of which prevents the employment of agricultural aircraft. The prototype is undergoing tests on Polish farms.

URSINOV M-6

This is a small, sturdily constructed amphibious ACV, designed for crop-spraying and capable of operating across farmland at speeds of up to 31 mph (50 km/h).

LIFT AND PROPULSION: Motive power is supplied by two 45 hp Wartburg petrol engines mounted aft. One drives via a transmission shaft and reduction gearbox a 4 ft 3 in (1·3 m) diameter lift fan, the other a 6 ft 7 in (2 m) diameter controllable-pitch ducted propeller for thrust. Air bled from the fan is fed through a chemical tank, where it mixes with spray or fertiliser and scatters the particles through ventral slots.

HULL: Riveted aluminium construction. Propeller shroud in grp.

SKIRT: Fingered-bag type.

ACCOMMODATION: Open cockpit with single bench-type seat. Production model will have enclosed cabin.

CONTROLS: Craft heading is controlled by a single aerodynamic rudder hinged to the aft of the propeller duct. An elevator provides pitch trim at cruising speed. Speed is selected by engine rpm and propeller pitch controls.

DIMENSIONS:

Length	18 ft 0 in (5·5 m)
Beam	10 ft 2 in (3·1 m)
Height	9 ft 2 in (2·8 m)

WEIGHTS:

Basic craft empty	1,534 lb (700 kg)
Gross weight	2,425 lb (1,100 kg)

PERFORMANCE:

Max speed	31 mph (50 km/h)

Ursinov M-6, an amphibious single-seater developed by the Warsaw Agricultural Institute for crop spraying

SWEDEN

FLYGTEKNISKA FORSOKSANSTALTEN THE AERONAUTICAL RESEARCH INSTITUTE OF SWEDEN

HEAD OFFICE:
PO Box 11021, S-161 11 Bromma 11

TELEPHONE:
08.26 28 40

TELEX:
107 25

TELEGRAMS:
Flygtekniska

EXECUTIVE RESPONSIBLE FOR ACV DEVELOPMENT:
Einar Bergström,

FAA has conducted an ACV research programme for several years and is now working on designs for a series of full-size craft.

The FAA concept, described as a "semi-hovercraft", has three flexible, inflated rubber keels, a bow cushion seal and one or more fans situated aft.

The fans produce both propulsive thrust and cushion pressure. Air from the fans is blown rearwards beneath two adjustable flaps. These control the pressure in the two halves of the cushion, which is divided into two by a central keel. The hover gap is normally zero, hovering being limited to that necessary to clear stretches of ice and shallow water, and for parking on concrete terminals. beaches and pontoons. Hovering, turns, side thrust and reverse thrust are controlled by the operation of two adjustable side keels aft and the bow seal.

The concept is aimed towards lower initial and operating costs, reduced noise, and improved manoeuvrability.

A small dynamic test vehicle with a 10 hp engine was followed in 1971 by a larger test craft which has successfully completed a major trials programme. Development of a 4-seat recreational ACV based on the test craft and a 41-seat hoverferry started in 1972.

FFA's test vehicle at 34 knots, while accelerating at 1·3 knots per second. Powered by a 57 hp Volkswagen engine, it has attained 56 knots on half-power

FFA's projected single-seat sports craft.

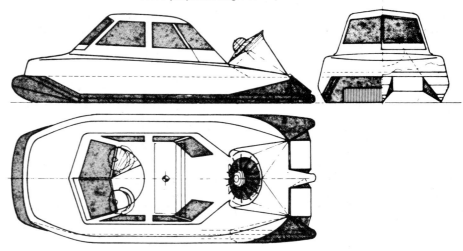

A 50-knot, four-seat runabout designed by FFA

Negotiations for the construction of prototypes are complete. Development of the
FFA ACV system is continuing and a production prototype of a two-seat sportscraft
was due to be completed in September 1974.

Preliminary details of FFA's initial range
of commercial designs are given below.

FFA SPORTSCRAFT

This glassfibre hulled lightweight ACV is
projected in single and two-seat versions, the
latter being available with either tandem or
side-by-side seating. It will operate across
water, snow and ice and can be parked on
beaches.

LIFT/PROPULSION: Integrated system
powered by a single 18-20 hp Wankel engine
or suitable two-stroke, mounted aft in an
inclined nacelle and driving a two-bladed fan
in a circular entry duct. Air from the fan
is fed into a divided plenum chamber for lift
and blown rearwards beneath a single aft
flap for propulsion.

CONTROLS: Fore and aft movement of
single control column operates aft propulsion
flap. Craft direction is controlled by asym-
metric discharge of cushion air.

HULL: Basic structure comprises two main
components: a glassfibre upper shell, to which
are attached the side keels and open cockpit,
and a lower shell comprising the cockpit base
and the engine nacelle/fan duct. Lower
sections of the central and outer keels and
forward seal are of thin, steel reinforced
rubber material.

ACCOMMODATION: Single-seat model has
an open cockpit. Two-seat versions are
available with either tandem or side-by-side
seating. Folding cabin hood will be fitted to
latter model.

DIMENSIONS (TWO-SEAT MODEL):

Length overall	11 ft 9¾ in (3·6 m)
Beam overall	5 ft 10⅞ in (1·8 m)

WEIGHTS:

Empty	220 lb (100 kg)
Loaded	573 lb (260 kg)

PERFORMANCE:

Cruising speed	30 knots plus

FFA TEST VEHICLE

FFA's second test vehicle is also the
prototype of the organisation's four-seat
runabout. During its initial trials programme
it attained an overwater speed of 50 mph
(80·46 km/hr).

The craft is fully amphibious and operates
over ice, snow and water. It can be parked
on any suitable flat beach.

LIFT AND PROPULSION: Motive power
for the integrated lift/propulsion system is
provided by a single VW 57 hp automotive
engine driving via rubber belts two 23⅝ in
(0·60 m) 6-bladed Bahco axial fans.

CONTROLS: Directional control was provided initially by the differential setting of
two flaps, operating in the port and starboard
propulsion airjet slots aft. This form of
control has now been replaced by an improved
system in which fan air is discharged asym-
metrically.

Clearance height, roll angle, pitch and trim
are controlled by adjusting the thrust port
flaps.

DIMENSIONS:

Length overall	17 ft 8½ in (5·4 m)
Cushion area	96 ft² (9·0 m²)

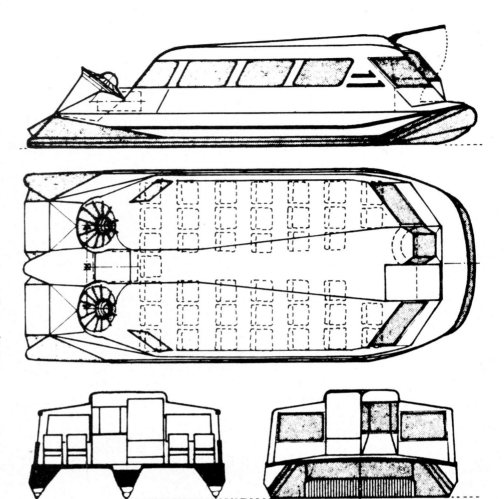

FFA's high-speed hover-bus, designed to link outlying areas with the heart of Stockholm by operating along the city's waterways. Seats are provided for 41 passengers and the top speed is
expected to be about 80 knots

WEIGHT:

Total test weight	1,609 lb (730 kg)

PERFORMANCE:

Max. speed at full power, estimated	76 knots
Max. speed with half power	56 knots
Normal test speed	23-35 knots
Acceleration at 34 knots, tested	1·3 knots/sec

FFA FOUR-SEAT RUNABOUT

LIFT AND PROPULSION: Integrated
system powered by a 35 hp two-stroke
driving a two-bladed duct-mounted fan.
Immediately below the fan, the duct is
divided to feed the two halves of the cushion
which are separated by a central keel. Aft
airjet flap ends are connected to the outer
and central keels by triangular webs, which
limit up and down flap movement and
eliminate side flow.

HULL: The basic hull structure, including
the rigid upper sections of the three keels,
fan ducting and canopy, are fabricated in
glass reinforced plastics. The upper grp keel
sections are filled with foam plastic for
buoyancy. The lower sections, in textile
reinforced neoprene, are inflated by fan air.
The contours of the keels when inflated are
maintained by an internal stay system
employing nylon ropes located in six positions along each keel.

The forward flexible seal is made in a single
piece in textile reinforced rubber.

HULL: Similar structure to that of the test
craft.

ACCOMMODATION: Entry to the fully
enclosed four-seat cabin is through a hinged
door at the front. The driver's position is on
the starboard side, and the cabin roof section
immediately above swings to one side permitting the craft to be steered from a standing
position. Both front seats can be turned to
face inwards. The two passengers at the
rear sit side-by-side on a single seat.

DIMENSIONS:
Similar to those of the FFA testcraft.

PERFORMANCE:

Max speed over water	50 knots

FFA HOVER BUS

FFA's 41-seat Hover Bus is designed to
provide high frequency links between towns
on the outskirts of Stockholm and an underground station located by the waterside in
the heart of the city, from which trains leave
every two minutes to all parts of the metropo-
lis. The proposed Hover Bus services are
intended to open new areas for population
growth, and will provide connections to the
city centre at intervals of 5-20 minutes
during the morning and evening rush hour
periods.

The craft is designed for year round operation across archipelagos, rivers and lakes.
It will traverse ice, snow, shallow water and
beaches.

LIFT AND PROPULSION: Integrated system with motive power supplied by a single 400 hp Avco Lycoming 10-720 piston engine located above the central keel aft and driving two ducted fans via shafts and bevel gears.

HULL: Mixed construction employing marine aluminium alloy and glass reinforced plastics. Lower (inflatable) sections of the three keels are in a synthetic rubber material; similar material is also used for the bow seal.

ACCOMMODATION: Seats are provided for 41 passengers, most of whom sit three abreast in twelve rows either side of a central aisle. An additional four seats are provided forward and there is a single seat at the end of the aisle aft. The driver sits forward on the port side, with the passenger entry door to his immediate right.

DIMENSIONS:
Length overall	36 ft 9 in (11·2 m)

WEIGHTS:
Empty	3·4 tons
Loaded	6·9 tons

PERFORMANCE:
Max speed, calm water	80 knots

TRINIDAD

COELACANTH GEMCO LTD

HEAD OFFICE:
1 Richardson Street, Point Fortin, Trinidad, W.I.

TELEPHONE:
Point Fortin 2439

CABLES:
Coelacanth, Trinidad

DIRECTORS:
Nigel Seale
Kelvin Corbie
Teddy Watson

SECRETARY:
R. Varma

Coelacanth Gemco Ltd, the first company to specialise in the design and construction of air cushion vehicles in the West Indies, has been granted Pioneer Status for the manufacture of hovercraft in Trinidad by the government-controlled Industrial Development Corporation. The company has obtained the approval of the Town and Country Planning Commission to construct an ACV factory and a hoverport at Guapo beach, Trinidad. Guapo Bay and the neighbouring Antilles Bay will be used by the company for sea tests and a disused runway adjacent to the site will be used for overland tests.

The company also plans to build a two-mile long, 100 ft wide ACV roadway between Guapo Beach and the Point Fortin Industrial Estate.

Meetings have been held with the Trinidad Government to negotiate a right-of-way over Government owned land.

A freight operation is planned with ACVs taking aboard finished goods from the factories, and delivering them to Port-of-Spain, 40 minutes away at a speed of 60 knots.

Craft at present under development by the company are the Pluto, Jupiter, Venus, Arctutus and Mars, a military ACV, A manned test model of the latter is expected to be ready for trials in 1975.

PLUTO Mk. I and II

The Pluto is a two-seat test vehicle, built in marine ply, and designed to provide data for a sport and recreational craft which will be marketed under the same name.

The production prototype, which is based on the existing hull and designated Pluto Mk II is undergoing trials. A four-seat version, Pluto Mk III, is due to go into production in 1975.

By the end of March 1974, Pluto II had exceeded 40 hours hover time while gathering data for the production model—Pluto Mk III.

Two and four-seat versions are planned. A standard feature of the production models will be a two-berth cabin and cooking facilities, which will allow the craft to be used for cruising to the northwest of Trinidad in the Gulf of Paria.

Pluto Mk. II, a manned test model of Coelacanth Gemco's Pluto series, puts to sea for a test run off Point Fortin, Trinidad.

Prototype of the Pluto Mk III under construction at Point Fortin. The craft is designed as a family runabout and is equipped for weekend cruises in the Gulf of Paria

LIFT AND PROPULSION: Lift power on Pluto Mk II is supplied by two 6 hp Briggs and Stratton motor-mower engines driving two Rotafoil fans. Thrust is supplied by two 250cc Velocettes driving two 2 ft 3 in (0·685 m) diameter ducted Hordern-Richmond propellers at 5,000 rpm.

DIMENSIONS, EXTERNAL:
Length	16 ft 0 in (4·87 m)
Width	7 ft 10 in (2·38 m)
Height	6 ft 0 in (1·82 m)

WEIGHTS:
Empty weight	1,100 lb (498·92 kg)
Loaded weight, 2 seat model	1,500 lb (680·35 kg)

PERFORMANCE:
Speed over water	22 mph (35·40 km/h)
Speed over land (with one person)	39 mph (62·76 km/h)
Vertical obstacle clearance	8 in (203 mm)

PLUTO Mk III

Developed from Pluto Mk. II, Mk. III is a

four-seater runabout and yacht.

The hull of the first production machine was 90% complete at the time of going to press, and it was anticipated that trials would be in progress by September 1974.

Production is expected to be underway in early 1975.

LIFT AND PROPULSION: Lift is provided by a single 20 hp Sachs Wankel rotary engine driving two Rotafoil fans, and propulsion by two 250cc Velocettes driving two 2 ft 3 in (0·685 m) diameter ducted Hordern Richmond propellers at 5,000 rpm.

All series production craft will be powered by three Sachs Wankel engines—one for lift and two for propulsion.

CONTROLS: Craft heading is controlled by twin rudders aft operating in the slipstreams of the two propellers. Thrust ports are fitted port and starboard, fore and aft, to provide additional control at slow speeds when approaching and leaving jetties.

HULL: First production craft will be in $\frac{3}{16}$ in mahogany marine ply, with the bottom and sides sheathed to 6 in (152 mm) above the waterline in glassfibre.

ACCOMMODATION: The cabin accommodates a family of four—two adults and two children—and stores for an overnight stay. The seats are removable and can be used on the beach. On board the craft, the position of the seats can be altered if necessary to adjust craft trim. Built-in steps are provided on each side of the hull to simplify access to the craft after bathing. A hatch is provided aft for baggage items and stores and another forward to facilitate the handling of mooring lines and the anchor. The cabin windows, in $\frac{3}{16}$ in plexiglass, slide rearwards in their frames for access to the cabin.

DIMENSIONS, EXTERNAL:

Length	18 ft 0 in (5·48 m)
Width	7 ft 10 in (2·38 m)
Height, inflated skirt	6 ft 0 in (1·82 m)
Cushion depth	1 ft 3 in (381 mm)
Freeboard in displacement mode	
	2 ft 6 in (0·76 m)

DIMENSIONS, INTERNAL:

Cabin floor area (total useable area)	
	40 sq ft (3·71 m²)

WEIGHTS:

Normal gross weight (4 passengers and 20 gallons of petrol)	1,950 lb (884·5 kg)
Empty weight	1,250 lb (566·90 kg)

PERFORMANCE:

Speed over water	25 mph (40·23 km/h)
Speed over land	40 mph (64·37 km/h)

COST: Estimated price, g.r.p. model £3,500 (West Indies $16,800).

VENUS

This craft has been designed principally for carrying oil company executives to and from wells in the Gulf of Paria, in Soldado and other areas in the West Indies. Ten and fifteen seat versions will be built, and like the Jupiter, the craft will be available in either amphibious form with a continuous skirt or as a rigid sidewall type with bow and stern skirts.

A manned scale model hull of the craft was completed in November 1968. This craft is also being used as a test bed for the two and four-seat Pluto series.

JUPITER

A projected four-seat ACV runabout, Jupiter is designed around the basic hull of

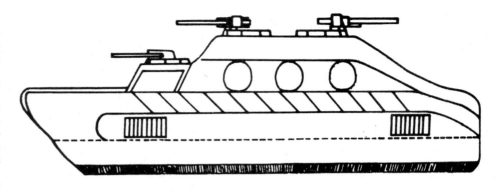
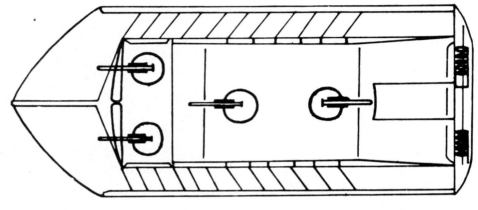
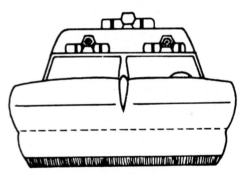

Provisional three-view drawing of the Mars light patrol craft

the company's Super Bee cabin cruiser, and will be available either as an amphibious craft, with a continuous peripheral skirt, or as a rigid sidewall type with bow and stern skirts.

Lift will be provided by a 75 hp modified outboard driving two Rotafoil fans, and propulsive thrust by a 90 hp modified outboard driving a reversible pitch-ducted propeller.

DIMENSIONS:

Length	18 ft 0 in
Beam	10 ft 0 in
Height	7 ft 0 in

WEIGHT:

Weight, incl fuel	2,810 lb

PERFORMANCE:

Max speed (est)	50 knots

ARCTURUS

The Arcturus is a 35-seat amphibious ACV designed by Nigel Seale. Motive power for the lift and propulsion system will be supplied by high speed diesel generators driving Lear Siegler Electric Motors.

Work has started on a manned scale model

but activity has been suspended temporarily while the company concentrates its resources on the development of the Pluto series.

MARS

Coelacanth Gemco's first military design is the 35 ft (10·66 m) long Mars, a 10-ton patrol craft designed to operate in sheltered waters. It will carry seven fully armed men.

A manned scale model capable of testing hovering performance is being built and is expected to be ready for trials in 1975.

Construction will be in g.r.p., with aluminium extrusions and panels. Six Rotafoil fans will be employed in the integrated lift/propulsion system.

A feature of the craft will be the employment of stabilisers to reduce drift.

DIMENSIONS:

Length	35 ft 0 in (10·66 m)
Beam	15 ft 0 in (4·57 m)
Height	15 ft 0 in (4·57 m)

WEIGHTS:

Normal all-up weight	10 tons

PERFORMANCE:

Cruising speed	35 knots

UNITED KINGDOM

AIRAVIA LTD.

HEAD OFFICE:

20 North Road, Shanklin, Isle of Wight

TELEPHONE:

098-386-3643

098-386-2850

LONDON OFFICE:

Ivory House

World Trade Centre,

St. Katharine's Way

London, E1 9LD

TELEPHONE:

790 7979

DIRECTORS:

H. S. Snowball

K. Wainwright

R. Snowball

Count A. de Lasta

General H. Alexander

Airavia is the sales representative for Sudoimport air cushion vehicles and hydrofoils in the United Kingdom, British Commonwealth countries, Scandinavia and Western Europe. The company is also planning to lease air cushion vehicles on wet or dry charters in these areas.

AIR BEARINGS LTD

HEAD OFFICE AND WORKS:

Quay Lane, Hardway, Gosport, Hampshire
PO12 4LJ

TELEPHONE:

(070) 17-87421

TELEX:

47674

TELEGRAMS:

AIR BEAR—GOSPORT

DIRECTORS:

P. Murray-Jones, Chairman

J. E. Cook, Managing

J. M. Grant, A.C.A., Finance

P. C. Nicholson

A. R. Hawker

ASSOCIATE DIRECTORS:

R. H. Arrow, Engineering

J. J. Eadie, TD MInstM, Marketing

Air Bearings Ltd was formed in March 1965 to manufacture light ACVs employing the company's own integrated lift/propulsion system and skirt design. Production of the AB 11 Crossbow three-seater began in 1974. Four craft were on order at the time of going to press.

AB 11 CROSSBOW

This general purpose amphibious ACV is based on the company's experience with the HC 9, HC 10, and earlier prototypes. Luxury, commercial and lightly armoured military variants are available.

LIFT AND PROPULSION: Motive power for the integrated lift/propulsion system is provided by a 135 hp Johnson (OMC) 135 ESL 74 V4 two-stroke, driving a single four-bladed axial fan. The fan, 32½ in (812 mm) in diameter, is built in laminated wood and mounted on top of the engine crankshaft. Thrust is provided by ejecting fan air horizontally from the rear of the hull. Fuel is carried in two 16 gallon bagged tanks located in the sides of the hull close to the c of g. Refuelling points are provided port and starboard, amidships. Fuel recommended is 94 octane, 45:1 petrol/oil mix.

CONTROLS: Triple rudders operating in the airjet exit provide directional control. An elevator beneath the airjet provides trim control at speed. Reverse thrust is by a shutter and vane system. Two 4 gallon ballast tanks are located fore and aft.

Driving controls consist of a steering wheel and three hand-operated levers, console mounted, which control engine throttle, reverse thrust mechanism and craft pitch.

INSTRUMENTATION: Instruments include tachometer, air speed indicator, trim indicat-

Above: Pre-production prototype of the Airbearings AB 11 Crossbow during trials on the Solent
Below: Interior of Crossbow's cabin showing the instrument layout and controls. The bench seat accommodates the driver and two passengers

or, static ballast gauge, fuel and water temperature and battery condition gauges, clock and hours-run indicator. Panel mounted switches operate flashing beacon, navigation and headlights and ballast pump controls.

HULL: The hull and superstructure constructed in grp throughout. Bulkheads and longitudinal members are in aluminium sandwich. A continuous 100% finger skirt of HDL design is fitted giving a 12 in (30 cm) hard structure clearance.

ACCOMMODATION: Single bench seat for driver and up to two passengers abreast. Entry is through two gullwing doors, one port, one starboard.

DIMENSIONS:

Length overall	18 ft 9 in (5·72 m)
Beam (skirt inflated)	11 ft 6 in (3·50 m)
Beam (power off)	7 ft 6 in (2·28 m)
Height on landing pads	4 ft 3 in (1·27 m)
Cushion area	147·6 sq ft (13·52 m²)

DIMENSIONS, INTERNAL:

Cabin:

Length	4 ft 8 in (1·42 m)
Max width	4 ft 8 in (1·42 m)
Max height	3 ft 2 in (804 cm)
Floor area	28 sq ft (2·0 sq m)

WEIGHTS:

Normal empty weight	1,340 lb (607 kg)
Normal all-up weight	2,100 lb (952 kg)
Normal gross weight	2,100 lb (952 kg)
Normal payload	600 lb (272 kg)

PERFORMANCE (normal operating weight, calm water):

Cruising speed	30-35 knots
Still air range at cruising speed	175 miles (280 km)
Max gradient, static conditions	1:9·5
Vertical obstacle clearance	1 ft (30 cm)

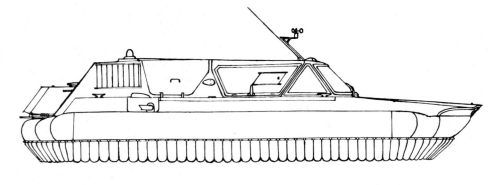

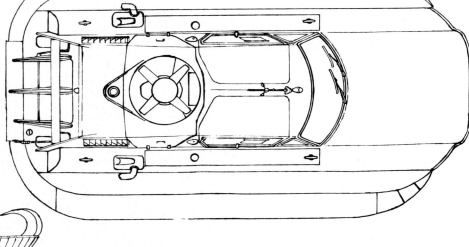

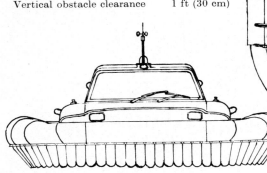

General arrangement of the AB II Crossbow

AIRHOVER LTD

HEAD OFFICE:
  Hoverplane Works,
  Main Road,
  Arlesford,
  Colchester,
  Essex
TELEPHONE:
  Boxted 356
DIRECTORS:
  R. P. Wingfield, Managing Director
  J. E. Wingfield

Airhover Ltd is licenced by Skimmers Inc, Severna Park, Maryland, USA, to build and market the Fan-Jet Skimmer single-seat sports ACV. The company has modified the design to enable it to be produced and sold in kit form. A number of kits are now being exported to North and South America, Western Germany, Finland, Switzerland, Tahiti, Australia, and East and West Africa. The craft is assembled from five basic pre-fabricated parts and is supplied complete with a two-cycle engine. Kits are available to order. Details of the Fan-Jet Skimmer are given under Skimmers Incorporated in the USA section.

In addition to the Fan-Jet Skimmer, the company is marketing the Aero Sabre Mk I and Mk II light hovercraft—both open single or two seaters—and the more sophisticated Aero Sabre III, high performance sports ACV.

AERO SABRE Mk I

The new Aero Sabre Mk I is derived from the company's experience with the earlier

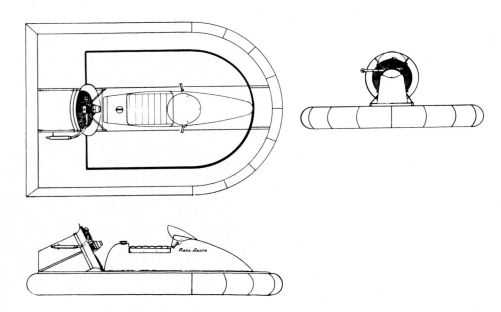

General arrangement of the new Aero Sabre Mk I

Fan-Jet Skimmer. A high performance amphibious light sports hovercraft it is now in production and is available either complete or in kit form. Two models are offered: Mk I, with a single engine and lift/propulsion duct assembly and Mk II with twin engines and ducts.

LIFT AND PROPULSION: Power for the integrated lift/propulsion system can be provided by a wide choice of engines ranging from a 9 bhp or 13 bhp Stihl to a 12 bhp Kyoritsu. The primary airflow from the eight-bladed axial-flow flan is ejected through a propulsive slot aft of the fan duct, and the secondary airflow, for the cushion, passes downwards into the plenum chamber.

HULL: Mixed aluminium, glassfibre and wooden construction. Laminated wooden outer frame amd similar inner frame. The engine, aluminium duct and outlet, moulded glassfibre seat and streamlined nose fairing are all carried on the two longitudinals and can be detached as one separate unit. Upper surface covered with lightweight nylon, impregnated on both sides with pvc. Fuel tank is integral with glassfibre superstructure with filler neck aft of driver's seat.

SKIRT: Made in extra strong nylon fabric and reinforced with double skin of pvc. Skirt is in eleven segments and is stitched with rot-proofed thread. Skirt attachment rails provided.

ACCOMMODATION: Open motor-cycle type upholstered seating for one or two in tandem.

CONTROLS: Throttle twist grip control, with dummy grip opposite and ignition cut-out switch. Steering is by kinesthetic control (body movement). The manufacturer points out that as the performance is "very lively," experience at low speeds is desirable before attempting high speed runs. With the Kyoritsu engine 50 mph is easily attained in calm conditions.

DIMENSIONS:
Length	9 ft (2·74 m)
Beam	6 ft (1·82 m)
Height	3 ft (91·44 m)

WEIGHTS:
Unladen, single engine	100 lb (45·35 kg)
twin engine	140 lb (63·60 kg)
Payload, single	210 lb (95·25 kg)
twin	350 lb (158·75 kg)

PERFORMANCE:
Designed speed,	
single engine, land	36 mph (57·93 km/h)
water	20 mph (32·18 km/h)
Twin engine, land	50 mph (80·46 kmh)
water	30 mph (48·28 km/h)
Fuel consumption	
single engine	1 gph (4·5 lph)
twin	2 gph (9·09 lph)
Obstacle clearance	6 in (15·24 cm)

PRICE: Full kit assembly, ex works, Colchester, £575·00 plus (UK) VAT.

AERO SABRE Mk III

The prototype of this exceptionally elegant two-seater is undergoing tests. One of the aims of the designers has been to produce a high-performance light ACV which combines the lines of a racing aircraft with the comfort of a modern sports car. Various alternative layouts are available to suit commercial applications. Performance depends upon the power installed: but the designed maximum speed is 60 mph (95·56 km/h)

LIFT AND PROPULSION: The lift engine, located forward of the cabin beneath a protective metal mesh panel, drives a 1 ft 9 in (0·53 m) diameter fan with blades set at 30 deg. Each blade is detachable to facilitate replacement. Located aft of the cabin, the propulsion engine, a horizontally-opposed-twin Volkswagen aero-engine, drives a 3 ft 0 in (0·914 m) diameter two-bladed variable-pitch propeller. The entire thrust unit will be surrounded by a plated protective mesh guard. Both engines have electric starters. No final decision had been made on the choice of lift engine at the time of going to

Above and below: Aero Sabre Mk I high-performance light sports ACV. In Mk II configuration with twin Go-Kart engines, it attains 50 mph (80.46 km/h) in calm conditions

Aero Sabre, a 60 mph (96·56 km/h) amphibious two-seater, combines elegance and high performance with the comfort of a modern sports car.

press.

CONTROLS: Heading is controlled by a single, swept back aerodynamic rudder operating in the propeller slipstream. Aircraft-type wheel, instrumentation, switches and throttles.

HULL: Built in high grade marine ply and incorporating three watertight buoyancy compartments. In the event of either one or two of these sustaining damage, the remaining compartments will keep the craft afloat. The superstructure, which includes the canopy, forward, decking and air intake is a one-piece moulding in grp. Windows and windshields are in perspex. Cabin access is via two light alloy gull-wing doors which are raised electrically.

SKIRT: Conventional bag-type, 1 ft 0 in (304 mm) deep.

CABIN: Access is via gull-wing doors. Semi-reclining, upholstered seats are provided side-by-side for driver and passenger. Panels and pillars are finished in matching colours.

DIMENSIONS:
Length overall	17 ft
Beam overall	8 ft
Height to top of rudder (on landing pads)	
	5 ft
Skirt depth	12 in (304 mm)
Cushion height	8 in (203 mm)

WEIGHTS:
Not available at time of going to press

PERFORMANCE:
Max speed	60 mph (96·56 km/h)

AIR RIDER RESEARCH LTD

SALES OFFICE:
  166 Harcourt Avenue, Sidcup, Kent
TELEPHONE:
  01-302-2133
REGISTERED OFFICE:
  Rosenhaugh Works, Newbarn Lane, Cudham, Kent
DIRECTORS:
  David Goodman
  Evelyn Vass

Air Rider Research is currently developing light hovercraft for agricultural and recreational uses. It is also the UK agent for the Hover Centre of Canada and representative for Devon Air Cushion Industries Ltd.

AIR RIDER 2-3 SEATER

The Air Rider, an amphibious 2-3 seater powered by three Wankel rotary engines, was introduced in January 1972 and three craft of this type have been sold. Top speed over calm water is 30 knots and over land 40 knots.

LIFT AND PROPULSION: Lift is provided by a single Fischel and Sachs 300 cc rotary two-stroke driving a 2 ft 2½ in (0·673 mm) diameter axial fan. Thrust is supplied by two engines of the same type, each driving a 2 ft 7½ in (0·800 m) duct-mounted propeller.

CONTROLS: Twin aerodynamic rudders hinged to the rear of the propeller ducts provide directional control.

HULL: Moulded glass fibre construction, with built-in engine mounts. Reserve buoyancy 150%.

ACCOMMODATION: Open cockpit with seats for driver and up to two passengers.

DIMENSIONS:

Length overall	12 ft 0 in (3·65 m)
Beam overall	6 ft 6 in (1·98 m)
Height overall on landing pads	3 ft 4 in (1·01 m)
Height overall, skirt inflated	4 ft 4 in (1·32 m)

WEIGHTS:

Normal empty weight	500 lb (226·78 kg)
Normal payload	400 lb (181·42 kg)
Max payload	800 lb (362·85 kg)

PERFORMANCE:

Max speed over land	40 knots
over water	30 knots
Vertical obstacle clearance	11 in (279 mm)
Max gradient, static conditions	1 : 8

PRICE:
  Hull shell £150. Complete craft with single propulsion engine £950, with two propulsion engines £1,200.

The 2-3 seat Air Rider prototype during trials. Maximum speed of this Wankel-engined recreational craft is 40 knots

Single-seat wing-in-ground-effect research craft designed and built by Air Rider Research Ltd.

WIG RESEARCH CRAFT

Development of this craft began in 1972. Initial static hovering tests were undertaken during the spring of 1974 but the controls for dynamic hovering have proved inefficient and further tests and modifications are in hand.

Technicians of the Biggin Hill Squadron, Air Training Corps, are spending 1974 experimenting with control systems for the craft.

LIFT AND PROPULSION: Lift air for initial hovering and low speed manoeuvring is supplied by a 1 ft 8 in (500 mm) diameter fan powered by a 700 cc Reliant engine. Thrust is supplied by a single 1,500 cc Volkswagen unit driving a 3 ft (900 mm) diameter twin-bladed propeller. Charging and accessory current is supplied by generators belt-driven by the engines.

CONTROLS: Lift, thrust and directional controls are operated by one lever and the anti-porpoising flap/spoiler aft by another lever.

HULL: Main body profile conforms to NACA 12 aerofoil section. Hull is built in 1·5 mm ply on spruce formers and ribs.

ACCOMMODATION: Single seat for driver in open cockpit.

DIMENSIONS:

Length overall	15 ft (4·57 m)
Beam overall	12 ft (3·65 m)
Height, max (max thickness aerofoil section, excluding fin and rudder)	3 ft (0·914 m)

WEIGHTS:

Empty weight	1,000 lb (453·59 kg)

PERFORMANCE:
  Static hovering tests only undertaken at time of going to press.

AIR VEHICLES LIMITED

HEAD OFFICE AND WORKS:
  1 Sun Hill, Cowes, Isle of Wight
TELEPHONES:
  Cowes 3194 and 4439
TELEX:
  86513 (Hoverwork, Ryde)
DIRECTORS:
  P. H. Winter, MSc
  C. D. J. Bland
  C. B. Eden

Since its inception in 1968, Air Vehicles Ltd has concentrated on the development of a small 5/6 seater amphibious hovercraft, the AV2. The prototype was completed in 1970 and development has continued during 1971 and 1972. The first pre-production AV2 was completed in 1973. This machine has performed well and the company has launched a marketing programme for this design.

The second and third machines have been purchased by LKV in the Netherlands who will also take delivery of the next four machines for various customers. AV2-002 has been tested extensively by the Rijkswaterstaat, Netherlands, by the British army and by the British Interservices Hovercraft Unit.

Air Vehicles also undertakes modifications to the British Hovercraft Corporation range of SR.N5 and SR.N6 hovercraft. These include flat deck conversions (see photo), power assisted rudder packs and various

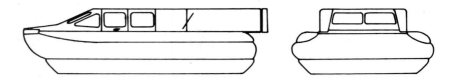

other units designed to assist commercial and military users, in particular, the new ducted propeller installation designed and built by the company.

AV.2

A feature of this twin-engined amphibious 5-6 seater is the use of fan-jet propulsion to minimise noise. The prototype, built in 1970, has completed several hundred hours of development testing to prove the basic reliability of the machine and its components. This was followed by various operations, charters and tests undertaken with AV2-002. As a result the production version embodies various improvements in terms of construction, payload and control. The craft is suitable for both civil and para-military roles. It can operate on either of its two engines enabling it to return to base in the event of one engine failing.

LIFT AND PROPULSION: Two converted outboard engine powerheads drive two centrifugal fans for lift and propulsion. Kits will be available to convert the engines from petrol to kerosene fuel.

CONTROLS: Rudder vane control and throttles for the two engines, auxiliary control systems for trim and reverse thrust.

HULL: Robust foam/fibreglass structure. Hull sidebodies are inflated for buoyancy but can be deflated for transport.

ACCOMMODATION: Enclosed cabin for driver and up to five passengers.

SKIRT: Pressurised bag with separate segments.

DIMENSIONS:
Length overall	19 ft 0 in (5·79 m)
Beam overall	11 ft 2 in (3·40 m)
Beam, sidebodies deflated for transport	
	7 ft 10½ in (2·39 m)

WEIGHTS:
Empty weight	2,000 lb (907·12 kg)
Loaded weight	3,000 lb (1,360·8 kg)

PERFORMANCE:
Cruising speed, calm water	35 knots
Fuel consumption (petrol) at full throttle	
	15 gal/hr (68 l/hr)
Fuel consumption, cruising	
	10 gal/hr (45 l/hr)

PRICE: Standard craft, ex factory £11,500·00.

N5 HOVERFREIGHTER

Converted by Air Vehicles Ltd from the original N5 craft, this provides a fast personnel and supply carrier for application anywhere in the world.

It has been employed on civil engineering and survey contracts in the Wash and on Maplin Sands.

Accommodation is provided for up to 19 passengers.

DIMENSIONS:
Length overall	38 ft 9 in (11·80 m)
Beam overall	23 ft 0 in (7·01 m)
Deck area	450 sq ft (41·81 sq m)

WEIGHTS:
Max deck load	6,700 lb

DUCTED PROPELLER N6

A ducted propeller installation has been built by Air Vehicles Ltd for the SR.N6 hovercraft. The propeller, 6 ft 10 in (2·08 m) in diameter, is designed to maintain the

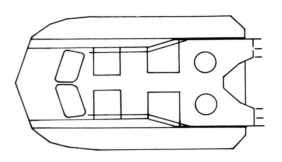

AV.2 002

Above: AV2-002 crossing the mud swamps of the Wadden See, Netherlands, at speed. The area floods to a depth of 10 ft (3.04 m) at high tide. *Below:* AV2-002 has undergone tests with the British Army and the Interservices Hovercraft Unit. Seen clearly in this photograph are the segmented bag skirt and the sidebodies which are deflated for transport. Cruising speed, calm water, is 35 knots

A military SR.N6 equipped with an Air Vehicles' ducted propeller, reducing the noise level by more than 10dBA

original thrust of the N6 but to reduce the noise level by more than 10 dBA. The unit can be fitted very simply to any standard N6 or N5 and the first installation has been made on a military N6.

N6 HOVERFREIGHTER

Converted from a standard SR.N6 by Air Vehicles Limited this craft was operated by Hoverwork in the Arctic in 1971. In one operation undertaken in heavy fog it carried up to ten tons per hour between ships and a shore base over floating ice.

ACCOMMODATION: Front cabin: 8 men or 3 plus stretcher; rear cabin: 2 men.

AUXILIARY EQUIPMENT: Heavy duty air conditioner, Kelvin Hughes Type 17 radar, long-range fuel tanks (7 hours duration), vhf radio, mf radio.

DIMENSIONS:

Length overall	48 ft 5 in (14·76 m)
Beam overall	23 ft 0 in (7·01 m)
Deck area	500 sq ft (46·4 m²)
Underfloor storage	650 cu ft (18·0 m³)

WEIGHTS:

Normal payload	7,000 lb (3,175 kg)
Maximum payload	10,000 lb (4,536 kg)
Gross overload	15,000 lb (6,804 kg)

Two craft modified by Air Vehicles Ltd for freighting operations. *Above:* an SR.N6 and *below*, SR.N5 GH-2009

BRITISH HOVERCRAFT CORPORATION

HEAD OFFICE:
East Cowes, Isle of Wight
TELEPHONE:
Cowes 4121
WORKS:
Cowes 4101
TELEX:
86190
TELEGRAMS:
BRITHOVER COWES TELEX

DIRECTORS:

D. C. Collins, CBE, CEng, FIMechE, FIProdE, FRAeS, Chairman
Sir Christopher Hartley, KCB, CBE, DFC, AFC, BA, Deputy Chairman
R. Stanton-Jones, MA, DCAe, CEng, AFRAeS, Managing Director
A. N. Street, Works Director
T. Bretherton, Finance Director and Secretary
R. L. Wheeler, MSc, DIC, CEng, AFRAeS, Technical Director
J. M. George, BSc(Eng), DCAe, Sales Director
W. A. Oppenheimer, FCA
G. S. Hislop, PhD, BSc, ARCST, CEng, FIMechE. FRAeS, FRSA
B. D. Blackwell, MA, BSc(Eng), CEng, FIMechE, FRAeS, FBIM

The British Hovercraft Corporation is the world's largest hovercraft manufacturer. It was formed in 1966 to concentrate the British hovercraft industry's major technical and other resources under a single management.

The corporation deals with a wide variety of applications of the air cushion principle, the emphasis being on the development and production of amphibious hovercraft. Other activities include the investigation of industrial applications of the air cushion principle.

The capital of the corporation is £5 million, which is wholly owned by Westland Aircraft Ltd.

BHC established the world's first full-scale hovercraft production line in 1964. Currently it is producing the 10-ton Winchester (SR.N6) Class craft, the 50-ton Wellington (BH.7) Class craft and the 190-ton Mountbatten (SR.N4) Class craft at East Cowes.

At present five Mountbatten Class craft are in service as passenger/car ferries on the Dover/Boulogne and Ramsgate/Calais routes; two with British Rail Hovercraft,and three with Hoverlloyd Ltd.

One BH.7 is in service with the British Interservice Hovercraft Unit and three have been delivered to the Imperial Iranian Navy. Three additional BH.7 Mk 5s have been ordered by the Imperial Iranian Navy and are under construction.

Military and general duty variants of the Warden and Winchester Class hovercraft are now in service with the British Interservice Hovercraft Unit, Imperial Iranian Navy, Italian Interservice Hovercraft Unit, Brunei Malay Regiment and the Canadian and Saudi Arabian Coast Guard.

Winchesters have been employed since 1967 in trials and sales demonstrations in Africa, Canada, Denmark, Finland, India, South America and the middle and far East, logging well over 150,000 operating hours.

During 1973 British Rail's two SRN4s carried between them 606,500 passengers and 106,000 cars on the Dover-Boulogne, Dover-Calais Seaspeed services

Swift, the first 200-ton SR.N4 Mk 2 mixed-traffic hovercraft. Converted from a standard craft for Hoverlloyd Limited, the Mk. 2 carries up to 280 passengers and 37 vehicles compared with 254 passengers and 30 vehicles on the standard craft

Control cabin of the SR.N4. Basic manning requirement is for a commander, a first officer and a radar operator/navigator. A seat is provided for a fourth crew member or a crew member in training. The moving map display of the Decca Flight Log is located above the commander's windscreen at the left

Commercial general purpose variants of the Warden and Winchester are in service with British Rail Hovercraft Ltd, Dept. of Civil Aviation, New Zealand, Department of Transport, Canada, Hovertravel Ltd, Hoverwork Ltd and Mitsubishi Heavy Industries Ltd. In recent years the Winchester has been used increasingly for general purposes roles including hydrographic and seismic survey, freighting and search and rescue duties.

MOUNTBATTEN (SR.N4) CLASS Mk. 1

The world's largest hovercraft, the Mountbatten is a 190-ton passenger car/ferry designed for stage lengths of up to 100 n miles (184 km) on coastal water routes. It has an average service speed of 40-50 knots in waves up to 10 ft (3·04 m) in height and is able to operate in 12 ft (3·7 m) seas at a speed of about 20 knots.

The first craft entered commercial service with British Rail Hovercraft Ltd. in August 1968 on the Dover/Boulogne route and British Rail took delivery of a second craft for service on the same route late in the summer of 1969.

Two further craft entered service with Hoverlloyd Limited in April 1969 on the Ramsgate/Calais route—and a third craft joined this operation in 1972.

LIFT AND PROPULSION: Power is supplied by four 3,400 shp Rolls-Royce Marine Proteus free-turbine, turboshaft engines located in pairs at the rear of the craft on either side of the vehicle deck. Each has a maximum rating of 4,250 shp, but usually operates at 3,400 shp when cruising. Each engine is connected to one of four identical propeller/fan units, two forward and two aft. The propulsion propellers, made by Hawker Siddeley Dynamics, are of the 4-bladed, variable and reversible pitch type 19 ft (5·79 m) in diameter. The lift fans, made by BHC, are of the 12-bladed centrifugal type, 11 ft 6 in (3·5 m) in diameter.

Since the gear ratios between the engine, fan and propeller are fixed, the power distribution can be altered by varying the propeller pitch and hence changing the speed of the system, which accordingly alters the power absorbed by the fixed pitch fan. The power absorbed by the fan can be varied from almost zero shp (i.e. boating with minimum power) to 2,100 shp, within the propeller and engine speed limitations. A typical division on maximum cruise power would be 2,000 shp to the propeller and 1,150 shp to the fan; the remaining 250 shp can be accounted for by engine power fall-off due to the turbine rpm drop, transmission losses and auxiliary drives.

The drive shafts from the engines consist of flanged light-alloy tubes approximately 7ft 6 in (2·28 m) long supported by steady bearings and connected by self-aligning couplings. Shafting to the rear propeller/fan units is comparatively short, but to the forward units is approximately 60 ft (18·27 m).

The main gearbox of each unit comprises a spiral bevel reduction gear, with outputs at the top and bottom of the box to the vertical propeller and fan drive shafts respectively. The design of the vertical shafts and couplings is similar to the main transmission shafts, except that the shafts above the main gearbox are of steel instead of light alloy to transmit the much greater torque loads to the propeller. This gearbox is equipped with a power take-off for an auxiliary gearbox with drives for pressure and scavenge lubricating oil pumps, and also a hydraulic pump for the pylon and fin steering control.

The upper gearbox, mounted on top of the pylon, turns the propeller drive through 90° and has a gear ratio of 1·16 : 1. This gearbox has its own self-contained lubricating system.

Engines and auxiliaries are readily accessible for maintenance from inside the craft, while engine, propellers, pylons and all gearboxes can be removed for overhaul without disturbing the main structure.

The fan rotates on a pintle which is attached to the main structure. The assembly may be detached and removed inboard onto the car deck without disturbing the major structure.

CONTROLS: The craft control system enables the thrust lines and pitch angles of the propellers to be varied either collectively or differentially. The fins and rudders move in step with the aft pylons. The pylons, fins and rudders move through ±35°, ±30° and ±40° respectively.

Demand signals for pylon and fin angles are transmitted from the commander's controls electrically. These are compared with the pylon or fin feed-back signals and the differences are then amplified to actuate the hydraulic jacks mounted at the base of the pylon or fin structure. Similar electro-hydraulic signalling and feed-back systems are used to control propeller pitches.

The commander's controls include a rudder bar which steers the craft by pivoting the propeller pylons differentially.

For example, if the right foot is moved forward, the forward pylons move clockwise, viewed from above, and the aft pylons and fins move anti-clockwise, thus producing a

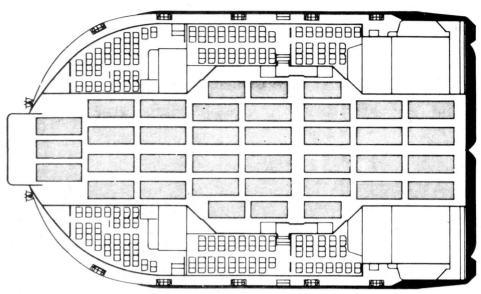

In most respects, the SR.N4 Mk. 2 is identical to the standard version. The increased capacity of 282 passengers and 37 cars was achieved by removing two inner passenger cabins to increase the car deck area and by widening the outer passenger cabins

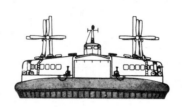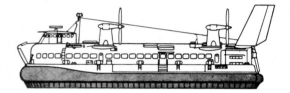

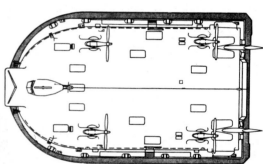

Typical internal arrangements of the SR.N4 include an all-passenger layout, seating 609, and mixed traffic ferries for either 174 passengers and 34 cars, or 254 passengers and 30 cars. Average service waterspeed is 40-60 knots

Cars being loaded aboard the SR.N4 via the 18 ft (5·49 m) wide articulated bow door/ramp

turning moment to starboard. The foregoing applies with positive thrust on the propellers, but if negative thrust is applied, as in the case of using the propellers for braking, the pylons and fins are automatically turned to opposing angles, thus maintaining the turn. A wheel mounted on a control column enables the

commander to move the pylons and fins in unison to produce a drift to either port or starboard as required. The control of the distribution of power between each propeller and fan is by propeller pitch lever. The pitch of all four propellers can be adjusted collectively over a limited range by a fore-

and-aft movement of the control wheel.

HULL: Construction is primarily of high strength, aluminium-clad, aluminium alloy, suitably protected against the corrosive effects of sea water.

The basic structure is the buoyancy chamber, built around a grid of longitudinal and transversal frames, which form twenty-four watertight sub-divisions for safety. The design ensures that even a rip from end-to-end would not cause the craft to sink or overturn. The reserve buoyancy is 250% the total available buoyancy amounting to more than 550 tons.

Top and bottom surfaces of the buoyancy chamber are formed by sandwich construction panels bolted onto the frames, the top surface being the vehicle deck. Panels covering the central 16 ft (4·9 m) section of the deck are reinforced to carry unladen coaches, or commercial vehicles up to 9 tons gross weight (max axle load 13,000 lb (5,900 kg)), while the remainder are designed solely to carry cars and light vehicles (max axle load 4,500 lb (2,040 kg)). An articulated loading ramp, 18 ft (5·5m) wide, which can be lowered to ground level, is built into the bows, whilst doors extending the full width of the centre deck are provided at the aft end.

Similar grid construction is used on the elevated passenger-carrying decks and the roof, where the panels are supported by deep transverse and longitudinal frames. The buoyancy chamber is joined to the roof by longitudinal walls to form a stiff fore-and-aft structure. Lateral bending is taken mainly by the buoyancy tanks. All horizontal surfaces are of pre-fabricated sandwich panels with the exception of the roof, which is of skin and stringer panels.

Double curvature has been avoided other than in the region of the air intakes and bow. Each fan air intake is bifurcated and has an athwartships bulkhead at both front and rear, supporting a beam carrying the transmission main gearbox and the propeller pylon. The all-moving fins and rudders behind the aft pylons pivot on pintles just ahead of the rear bulkhead.

The fans deliver air to the cushion via a peripheral fingered bag skirt.

The material used for both bags and fingers is nylon, coated with neoprene and/or natural rubber, the fingers and cones being made from a heavier weight material than the trunks.

ACCOMMODATION: The basic manning requirement is for a commander, an engineer/radio operator and a radar operator/navigator. A seat is provided for a fourth crew member or a crew member in training. The remainder of the crew, i.e. those concerned with passenger service or car handling, are located in the main cabins. The arrangement may be modified to suit individual operator's requirements.

The control cabin is entered by either of two ways. The normal method, when the cars are arranged in four lanes, is by a hatch in the cabin floor, reached by a ladder from the car deck. When heavy vehicles are carried on the centre section, or if for some other reason the ladder has to be retracted, a door in the side of the port forward passenger cabin gives access to a ladder leading onto the main cabin roof. From the roof an

Panels covering the central 16 ft (4·9 m) of the vehicle decks are reinforced to carry unladen coaches or commercial vehicles up to 9 tons gross weight while the remainder is designed solely to carry cars and light vehicles

Passenger seating in one of the side cabins flanking the car deck on a Hoverlloyd SR.N4

entrance door gives access into the control cabin.

The craft currently in service carry 254 passengers and 30 cars but the basic design permits variations from an all-passenger craft (609 seats) to one carrying 174 passengers and 34 cars.

The car deck occupies the large central area of the craft, with large stern doors and a bow ramp providing a drive-on/drive-off facility.

Separate side doors give access to the passenger cabins which flank the car deck. The outer cabins have large windows which extend over the full length of the craft. The control cabin is sited centrally and forward on top of the superstructure to give maximum view.

DIMENSIONS, EXTERNAL:

Overall length	130 ft 2 in (39·68 m)
Overall beam	78 ft 0 in (23·77 m)
Overall height on landing pads	
	37 ft 8 in (11·48 m)
Skirt depth	8 ft 0 in (2·44 m)

DIMENSIONS, INTERNAL:

Passenger/vehicle floor area
5,800 sq ft (539 m²)
Vehicle deck headroom-centre line
11 ft 3 in (3·43 m)
Bow ramp door aperture size (height × width) 11 ft 6 in × 18 ft (3·51 × 5·48 m)
Stern door aperture size (height × width)
11 ft × 31 ft (3·51 m × 9·45 m)

WEIGHTS:

Normal gross weight	190 tons
Fuel capacity	
4,500 Imp gallons (20·456 litres)	

PERFORMANCE (at normal gross weight at 15°C):

Max waterspeed over calm water, zero wind (cont power rating)	70 knots
Average service waterspeed	40-60 knots
Normal stopping distance from 50 knots	525 yards (480 m)
Endurance at max cont power on 2,800 Imp gallons	2-5 hours
Negotiable gradient from standing start	1 : 11

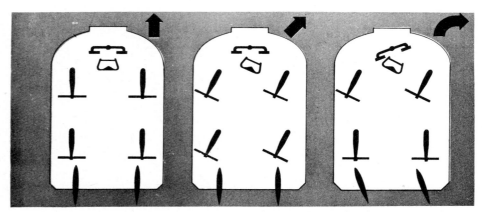

SR.N4 Mk.2

To cope with the increasing public demand for their cross-Channel service, Hoverlloyd has increased the capacity of its craft from 254 passengers and 30 vehicles to 280 passengers and 37 vehicles.

Modification of the first of these craft was completed in January 1973, and the remaining two craft underwent similar conversions during the winter 1973/74.

This increase in capacity has been achieved by the removal of the two inner passenger cabins on the car deck level to accommodate more vehicles. Passenger capacity has been increased by widening the outer cabins to the periphery of the craft structure.

At a maximum gross weight of 200 tons, the SR.N4 Nk.2 is heavier than the standard craft, but the effect of this increase in weight on performance is minimal ensuring that high frequency schedules continue to be met. The craft is also fitted with a 'tapered' skirt which is now standard for all SR.N4 craft.

SR.N4 Mk 3

This is a design study for a 'stretched' model undertaken for British Rail. It would be capable of carrying 396 passengers and up to 53 vehicles.

The four marine Proteus gas-turbines would be up-rated to 3,800 shp each, and each would drive a propeller/fan unit with a 21 ft (6·40 m) diameter propeller. The additional power would ensure that the performance of the current craft is maintained.

Craft motion would be less than that experienced on the standard SR.N4, and for similar comfort levels the larger craft should be capable of operating in waves up to 2 ft (0·61 m) higher than the present craft.

DIMENSIONS:

Length overall	177 ft 0 in (53·95 m)
Beam, hard structure	75 ft 0 in (22·86 m)
Skirt height, bow	12 ft 0 in (3·65 m)
stern	8 ft 0 in (2·43 m)

WEIGHTS:

Basic weight	157 tons
Maximum disposable load (incl fuel etc)	108 tons

WINCHESTER (SR.N6) CLASS

Designed primarily as a fast ferry for operation in sheltered waters, the Winchester can accommodate either 38 passengers or 3 tons of freight.

Fully amphibious, it can operate from relatively unsophisticated bases above the high water mark, irrespective of tidal state. Directional control is achieved by twin rudders and a thrust port system. Two

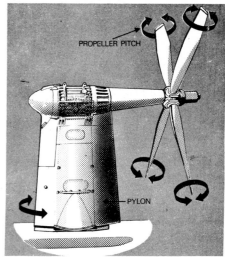

Propeller pitch on the SR.N4, i.e. the angle of the propeller blades in relation to the hub, is used to control the speed of the craft In a state of zero pitch, the craft simply stands still as in the case of lift-off when the air cushion is being built up. However, by pushing the control wheel forward, positive pitch is induced to move the craft forward. Forward speed can then be varied by pulling the wheel back for slower speeds, or by pushing it forward for higher speeds. Negative pitch is applied to reverse the craft, as is sometimes necessary for manoeuvring at terminals, or for braking whilst in operation

The pylons carrying the propellers, and the fins at the rear of the craft move through ±35° and ±30° respectively, to give directional control. Various combinations of pylon angle and fin may be achieved by use of the handwheel and rudder bar, to allow turns without drift or unnecessary manoeuvring in confined spaces. Operation of these controls is carried out in conjunction with the variation of propeller pitch. Examples of pylon/fin movement under normal cruise conditions are illustrated

Impression of the "stretched" SR.N4 Mk. 3, a design study undertaken for British Rail. The craft, which would have a normal gross weight of about 265 tons, would carry up to 396 passengers and 53 vehicles

manually actuated elevators provide pitch trim at cruising speed.

Winchesters have been in regular commercial service since 1965 and current operators include: British Rail Hovercraft Ltd., Hovertravel Ltd, Hoverwork Ltd, and Mitsubishi. A further Winchester is in service with the Civil Aviation Department, Ministry of Transport, New Zealand, as a

crash rescue craft at Auckland International Airport. Its smaller, 7-ton predecessor, the SR.N5 (see JSS 1971-72 and earlier editions) is in service with the Canadian Coast Guard.

Military variants are in service with the British Interservice Hovercraft Unit, the Imperial Iranian Navy, the Brunei Malay Regiment and the Saudi Arabian Frontier Force and Coast Guard.

LIFT AND PROPULSION: Power for the intergrated lift/propulsion system is provided by a Rolls-Royce Marine Gnome gas turbine with a maximum continuous rating at 15°C of 900 shp. This drives a BHC 12-blade centrifugal 7 ft (2·13 m) diameter lift fan, and a Dowty Rotol 4 blade variable pitch 9 ft (2·14 m) diameter propeller for propulsion.

DIMENSIONS, EXTERNAL:
Overall length   48 ft 5 in (14·76 m)
Overall beam (solid structure) 23 ft (7·01m)
Overall height on landing pads 15ft (4·57m)
Skirt depth   4 ft (1·22 m)

DIMENSIONS, INTERNAL:
Cabin size (length × width)
   21 ft 9 in × 7 ft 8 in (6·62 m × 2·34 m)
Cabin headroom-centre line   6 ft (1·83 m)
Door aperture size (height × width)
   5 ft 9 in × 3 ft 3 in (1·75 m × 0·99 m)
WEIGHT:
Normal gross weight   10 tons
PERFORMANCE (at normal gross weight at 15°C.):
Max water speed over calm water zero wind (cont power rating)   52 knots (96 km/hr)
Average service waterspeed in sheltered coastal waters 30·35 knots (55·65 km/hr)
Endurance at max cont power rating on 265 Imp gall of fuel   3·6 hours

SR.N6s of the Imperial Iranian Navy. The craft are employed on patrol and logistic support duties

WINCHESTER (SR.N6) CLASS— PASSENGER FERRY/GENERAL PURPOSE

Since the SR.N6 first entered service as a passenger ferry in 1965, it has carried well over three million fare-paying passengers and is now firmly established in certain areas as an integral part of surface transportation networks.

The popularity of these services subsequently led to the introduction of an SR.N6 with a larger carrying capacity, designated the SR.N6 Mk.1S. At 58 ft in length, the Mk.1S is 10 ft longer than the standard craft and can carry up to 56 passengers as opposed to 35/38 in the standard SR.N6.

Other modifications to this craft include additional baggage panniers, emergency exits and improved cabin ventilation. An additional bonus is a significant increase in ride comfort. To ensure that performance is maintained, the rating of the Rolls-Royce Marine Gnome gas turbine engine has been increased by 100 shp to 1,000 shp.

Two Mk.1S craft, Sea Eagle and Sea Hawk, are in service with British Rail Hovercraft Ltd, on the Seaspeed service linking Cowes and Southampton.

Apart from passenger services, commercial SR.N6s have also made successful inroads into other fields of operation in recent years and typical examples of such applications include freight-carrying, hydrographic/seismographic survey, offshore support operations, general communications, crash rescue and firefighting.

To undertake these duties, craft have been modified either with the fitting of specialised equipment or by structural alterations such as flat-decks.

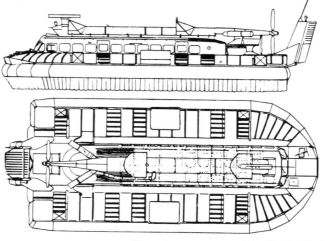

General arrangement of the SR.N6 Mk. 1S (one 1 000 shp Rolls-Royce Marine Gnome gas-turbine)

WINCHESTER (SR.N6) CLASS— MILITARY

Currently, variants of the SR.N6 are in service with eight of the world's military and paramilitary forces on coastal defence and logistic support duties.

The SR.N6 Mk.2/3, for logistic support, features a roof loading hatch and strengthened side-decks for carrying long loads of up to ½-ton. Lightweight armour may be fitted to protect troops being carried in the cabin, the engine and other vital systems. Defensive armament is provided by a roof-mounted light machine gun (7·62 mm or 0·5 in).

The craft can carry upwards of 20 fully-equipped troops or supply loads of up to 5 tons. A small auxiliary generator is installed to provide power when the main engine is stopped.

The SR.N6 Mk.4 for coastal defence duties may be fitted with 20 mm cannon or short-range wire-guided surface/surface missiles. Communications equipment is concentrated behind the rear cabin bulkhead.

The SR.N6 Mk.5, with a length of 53 ft, is 5 ft longer than the standard SR.N6 and differs greatly externally. Its main feature is a long central well-deck, strengthened for carrying vehicles including Snocats and landrovers and weapons including howitzers. A bow ramp is provided for loading. Twin cabins flank the well-deck, that on the starboard side housing the captain, navigator and controls, and that on the port the observer and vehicle driver.

To maintain high performance at the heavier loading—31,000 lb maximum gross weight—the Marine Gnome gas turbine has been uprated to 1,000 shp.

WINCHESTER (SR.N6) CLASS—Mk.6

The SR.N6 Mk. 6 is the latest development of the successful Winchester series and represents a significant step forward in terms of increased payload, all weather performance and a substantial reduction in external noise. These advances have been achieved by the introduction of twin-propeller propulsion, a more powerful engine, a redesigned skirt and an increase of 10 ft (3·04 m) in overall length.

The twin 10 ft (3·04 m) diameter propellers with which the craft is fitted turn at reduced rpm, resulting in lower external noise levels. The pitch of each can be varied independently giving the pilot greatly improved directional control at high and low speeds.

Power is supplied by a Rolls-Royce Gnome 1301 gas-turbine rated at 1,400 shp maximum and 1,285 shp continuous.

SR.N6 Mk 6A FAST INTERCEPTOR

This is a fast patrol version of the SR.N6 Mk 6, armed with a single Hispano Suiza A.32 30mm twin barrel cannon on the forward well deck, and a 7·62 mm machine gun on a ring mounting in the control cabin roof. Power is provided by a single Rolls-Royce Gnome gas turbine delivering 1,400 hp, and the maximum speed in calm conditions is 53 knots.

If required the craft can be adapted for various armed logistic support roles, including that of vehicle carrier, with troops in the main cabin, or troop carrier with a soft top extension above the well deck.

LIFT AND PROPULSION: Motive power is supplied by a single Rolls-Royce Gnome gas-turbine driving a centrifugal lift fan, and two 10 ft (3·04 m) diameter variable-pitch propellers.

ACCOMMODATION: Working accommodation for six crew members. Control cabin and main cabin air conditioned.

SYSTEMS, WEAPONS: Standard, one Hispano Suiza A.32 twin-barrel 30 mm rapid fire cannon with local control and stabilisation. Gun ring in cabin roof for 7·62 mm general purpose machine gun. Alternative systems: Two remotely operated multi-barrel 20 mm turrets, capable of individual or dual operation, or two McDonnell Douglas Harpoon surface-to-surface missiles. The fire control system employs a Decca 1626 navigation radar with appropriate weapon data display and output facilities. A passive EW system is used for target data acquisition.

DIMENSIONS, EXTERNAL:

Length, hard structure	58 ft 0 in (17·67m)
Beam, hard structure	23 ft 0 in (7·01m)
Height on cushion	21 ft 6 in (6·55m)
Well deck, length	19 ft 0 in (5·79m)
width	8 ft 0 in (2·43m)
Bow opening	8 ft 0 in (2·43m)

One of two SR.N6 Mk. IS hovercraft operated on the seaspeed service between Cowes and Southampton. This 'stretched' variant, 10 ft longer than the standard craft seats up to 56 passengers, compared with 35/38 in the earlier models

SR.N6 Mk 6 prototype, showing the twin-propeller arrangement and tapered skirt

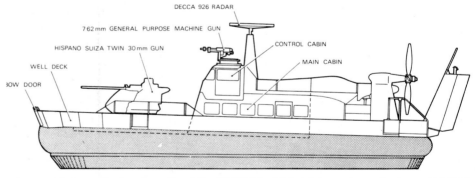

Above and below: Outboard profile of the SR.N6 Mk. 6A fast interceptor and cutaway showing interior layout and accommodation

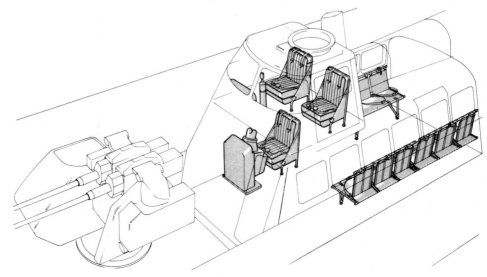

DIMENSIONS, INTERNAL:

Main cabin, length	15 ft 6 in	(4·72m)
width	8 ft 0 in	(2·43m)
Max headroom	6 ft 0 in	(1·82m)

WEIGHTS:

Starting all-up weight	35,000 lb
Weapon payload	5,000 lb

PERFORMANCE:

Max speed, calm conditions	53 knots
Max endurance at cruise power	4·7 hours
Typical range of operation	150-230 nautical miles

SR.N6 6B LOGISTIC

The Mark 6B is designed for the fast transport of military loads. It is fitted with a bow ramp for vehicle 'drive on/ drive off' to a strengthened well-deck (9·44 m × 2·33 m) which provides unobstructed stowage space. There are two cabins, one on each side deck. The starboard cabin is for the commander and navigator, the port for additional crewmen. Defensive armament consists of a ring-mounted machine gun mounted in the port cabin roof.

This craft has a carrying capacity of 45 fully equipped troops or one ¾ ton Land Rover with trailer or a Land Rover and 105 mm field gun. Alternatively it can be loaded with up to 6 tons of mixed stores.

SR.N6 MARK 6C GENERAL PURPOSE AND COMMAND VEHICLE

The Mark 6C is a development of the Mark 1. It is suitable for military and para-military roles and general coastal security work, and can carry up to 40 fully equipped troops or 5 tons of military stores.

WELLINGTON (BH.7) CLASS

BH.7 is a 50-ton hovercraft which was designed specifically for naval and military roles. The prototype, designated BH.7 Mk.2, has been in service with the Royal Navy since 1970 where it has been evaluated in a number of roles including Fishery Protection, ASW and MCM work.

The second and third craft, designated Mk. 4 and the fourth and fifth which are Mk. 5As, are all in service with the Imperial Iranian Navy. A further two Mk 5As are scheduled for delivery to Iran in 1975.

LIFT AND PROPULSION: Power for the integrated lift propulsion system is provided by a Rolls Royce/BS Marine Proteus 15M 541 gas-turbine with a maximum rating at 23°C of 4,250 shp. This drives via a light alloy driveshaft and bevel drive gearbox, a BHC 12-blade, centrifugal 11 ft 6 in (3·5 m) diameter lift fan and an HSD 4-blade, variable-pitch, 19 ft (5·79 m) diameter, pylon mounted propeller. Normal fuel capacity is 850 Imp gallons.

CONTROLS: Craft direction is controlled by swivelling the propeller pylon angle by a footpedal. Thrust ports are fitted at each quarter to assist directional control at low speed, and a hydraulically-operated skirt-shift system helps to bank the craft into turns, thereby reducing drift.

Fuel is transferred between forward and aft tanks via a ring main to adjust fore and aft trim.

The SR.N6 Mk. 5, with a central well deck for small armoured vehicles and weapons, including howitzers. The starboard cabin houses the controls and crew and the port cabin accommodates the vehicle and weapons crews. Payload is 7 tons

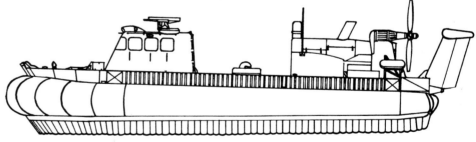

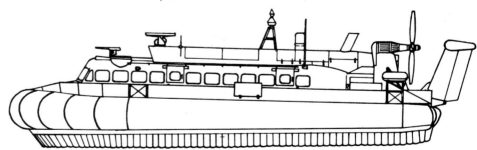

Outboard profiles of the SR.N6 Mk 6B, *above*, and 6C, *below*

HULL: Construction is mainly of corrosion resistant light alloy. Extensive use is made of components which were designed for the N4. The bow structure is a Plasticell base covered with glass fibre.

SKIRT SYSTEM: The fan delivers air to the cushion via a continuous peripheral fingered bag skirt made in neoprene coated nylon fabric. The skirt provides an air cushion depth of 5 ft 6 in (1·68 m). The cushion is divided into four compartments by a full length longitudinal keel and by two transverse keels located slightly forward of amidships.

ACCOMMODATION: The raised control cabin, located slightly forward of amidships on the hull centre line, accommodates a crew of three, with the operator and navigator in front and the third crew member behind. The driver sits on the right, with the throttle and propeller pitch control lever on his right, and the pylon angle footpedal and skirt-shift column in front.

The navigator, on the left, has a Decca 202 radar display and compass in front and Decometers in an overhead panel.

The large cabin area permits a variety of operational layouts. In a typical arrangement, the operations room is placed directly beneath the control cabin and contains communication, navigation, search and strike equipment and associated displays.

The craft has an endurance of up to 11 hours under cruise conditions but this can be extended considerably as it can stay 'on watch' without using the main engine.

Provision can be made for the crew to live aboard for several days.

SYSTEMS: Electrical: Two Rover IS/90 APUs provide via two 55kVA generators 3-phase 400Hz ac at 200 volts for ac and dc supplies.

DIMENSIONS, EXTERNAL

Length overall	78 ft 4 in (23·9 m)
Beam overall	45 ft 6 in (13·73 m)
Overall height on landing pads	
	34 ft 0 in (10·4 m)
Skirt depth	5 ft 6 in (1·67 m)

DIMENSIONS, INTERNAL (Mk 4 only):

Bow door size
13 ft 9 in × 7 ft 3 in (4·18 m × 2·20 m)
Headroom centre line   7 ft 10 in (2·38 m)

WEIGHT:

Normal gross weight	50 tons
Payload	14 tons

PERFORMANCE (at max operating weight at 15°C)

Max waterspeed over calm water (cont power rating)   60 kts

Average water speed in 4½ ft   (1·37 m) seas
35·50 knots

WELLINGTON (BH.7) Mk 4 LOGISTIC SUPPORT

ACCOMMODATION: In this role, the main hold floor area of 600 sq ft (56m²) of the Mk.4 provides an unobstructed space suitable for loading wheeled vehicles, guns and military stores.

Two side cabins, filled with paratroop-type seats, can accommodate up to 60 troops and their equipment.

Access at the bow is through a 'clamshell' door.

Machine guns can be fitted in gun rings on the roof on either side of the cabin and provision can be made for armour plating to

Above: One of two BH.7 Mk. 4s operated by the Imperial Iranian Navy. The craft are employed on logistics duties and have bow loading doors. *Below:* A BH.7 Mk. 5 coastal defence craft under construction for the Iranian Navy. The craft is equipped to carry medium range surface-to-surface missiles, such as the Exocet, on its side-decks

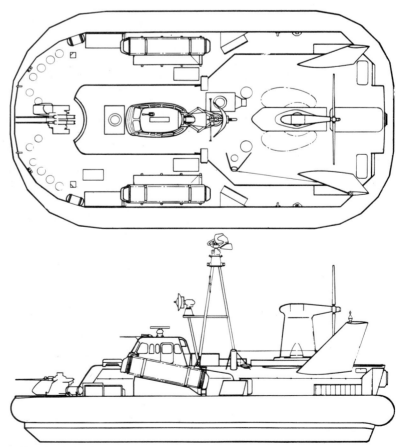

General arrangement of the Wellington (BH.7) Mk 5A Fast Attack/Logistic Support craft fitted with Exocet launchers and a twin 30 mm dual purpose mounting

protect personnel, the engine and vital electrical components.

SYSTEMS: Two Rover IS/90 gas turbine APUs provide electrical power independently of the main engine.

TYPICAL MILITARY LOADS: 170 fully equipped troops or 3 field cars and trailers plus 60 troops or two armoured scout cars or up to 20 NATO pallets.

DIMENSIONS, EXTERNAL:

Overall length	78 ft 4 in (23·85 m)
Overall beam	45 ft 6 in (13·8 m)
Overall height on landing pads	34 ft (10·40 m)

DIMENSIONS, INTERNAL:

Main cabin floor area	600 sq ft (56 m²)
Main cabin headroom—centreline	7 ft 10 in (2·38 m)
Access door aperture (height × width)	7 ft 3 in (2·20 m) × 13 ft 9 in (4·2 m)

WEIGHTS:

Normal gross weight	45 tons
Fuel load at 45 tons AUW	9 tons
Max fuel capacity	12·5 tons

PERFORMANCE (at normal gross weight at 15°C):

Max waterspeed, calm water, zero wind cont power rating 65 knots (120 km/hr)

Rough waterspeed in 4½ ft (1·37 m) seas depending on heading and wave length 35-50 knots (65-92 km/hr)

Endurance at max cont power rating with a 9 tons of fuel (with 10% reserve) 8 hours

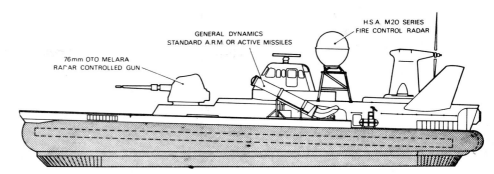

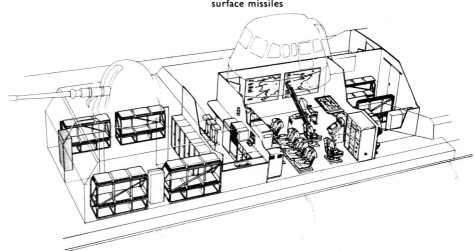

Above and below: Outboard profile and internal arrangements of the BH.7 Mk. 6 fast patrol hovercraft, equipped with a 76 mm Oto Melara cannon and four General Dynamics Standard surface-to-surface missiles

WELLINGTON (BH.7) MK. 5 FAST ATTACK

Designed for coastal defence operations, the BH. Mk.5 carries medium-range surface/surface missiles, such as Exocet, on its side-decks. Secondary armament consists of a twin 30 mm surface/AA radar controlled mounting situated on the foredeck forward of the main centre cabin.

The main central cabin, employed on the BH.7 Mk.4 for load-carrying, is equipped as an operations and fire control room. Since it is fully amphibious, the BH.7 Mk.5 can be operated from relatively unprepared bases on beaches and can head directly towards its target on interception missions regardless of the tidal state and marginal terrain. Also, since none of its solid structure is immersed, it is invulnerable to underwater defences such as acoustic, magnetic and pressure mines and to attack by torpedoes.

A full range of electronic navigational aids permit the craft to operate by day or night ensuring 'round-the-clock' availability.

WELLINGTON (BH.7) MK.5A FAST ATTACK/LOGISTICS

Similar to the Mk 5 above, with the exception that the bow door is retained, giving the craft a dual fast attack/logistic capability. Secondary armament can consist of 2 roof-mounted single 20 mm guns.

WELLINGTON (BH.7) Mk.6 FAST ATTACK/PATROL

This craft is designed to be powered by two 3,000 hp gas turbines driving a centrifugal lift fan and a 21 ft (6·40 m) diameter variable-pitch propeller. The craft illustrated is

A Wellington Mk 5A Fast Attack/Logistic Support craft

armed with four General Dynamics ARM (anti-radiation missile) or Active Standard surface-to-surface missiles and a single 76 mm Oto Melara dual-purpose cannon. If required it can be adapted for use as a hunter/killer ASW vessel or for employment as a mine-countermeasures craft, in conjunction with the Edo Mk 105 mine countermeasures system and other similar equipment.

ACCOMMODATION:

Air-conditioned working and living quarters for crew of 12.

WEAPON SYSTEMS:

As illustrated, 4 ARM or Active Standard surface-to-surface missiles, plus 76 mm Oto Melara radar-controlled dual-purpose gun. HSA combined fire control and surveillance radar. Alternative systems: Semi-active variant of Standard, Exocet or Seakiller, 35 mm twin Oerlikon or 30 mm twin Hispano Suiza.

DIMENSIONS:

Length overall, hard structure	108 ft 3 in (33·0 m)
Beam overall, hard structure	36 ft 4 in (11·2 m)
Height on cushion	36 ft 6 in (11·5 m)

WEIGHTS:

Starting all-up weight	90 tons
Weapons payload	17 tons
Fuel, including ballast	15 tons

PERFORMANCE:

Both engines running at max continuous rating of 6,000 shp.

Max speed, calm conditions	68 knots
Endurance	10 hours
Range of operation	400-550 nm

One engine running at 3,000 shp

Cruising speed (depending on weight and conditions)	16-40 knots
Endurance	18 hours
Cruising range	290-700 nm

CUSHIONCRAFT LTD
CC.7 LIGHT HOVERCRAFT

CC.7 is simple in design and of rugged construction to keep maintenance to a minimum. The hull construction is of corrosion-resistant alloy and the superstructure of tough glass-fibre reinforced resin. The few wearing items can be quickly and easily replaced in the field.

Two centrifugal fans driven by a gas turbine engine provide the air pressure for propulsion and lift through a system of ducts. This system enables the thrust power to be used for manoeuvring, stopping and reversing the craft and gives the pilot positive and accurate control. Moreover absence of an air propeller for propulsion makes CC.7 a silent craft in operation, a factor of great importance in the armed reconnaissance role. These qualities make CC.7 suitable for security and covert operations in harbours, rivers and sheltered waters. With a total disposable load of 1,245 kg (2,750 lb) CC.7 can transport up to 8 fully equipped troops or an equivalant quantity of military stores. CC.7 is readily transported by road or air. By deflating the side bodies the width is reduced to 2·52 m enabling it to be carried on a medium-sized truck.

A more detailed engineering description of this craft is given in the 1973/74 edition.

One of two CC-7s operated by the British Army

DIMENSIONS, EXTERNAL:

Length overall	25 ft 10 in (7·52 m)
Beam overall	15 ft 2 in (4·62 m)
Skirt depth	2 ft 0 in (0·60 m)
Height overall, hovering	8 ft 10 in (2·6 m)
Cushion area	233 sq ft (216 m²) app
Beam, deflated	8 ft 6 in (2·59 m)

DIMENSIONS, INTERNAL:

Cabin floor area	70 sq ft (6·50 m²) app
Door size 2 doors, each 2 ft 6 in (0·76 m) wide	

WEIGHTS:

Normal all-up weight	6,750 lb (3,060 kg)
Disposable load	2,750 lb (1,245 kg)
Basic weight, empty	4,000 lb (1,815 kg)

PERFORMANCE:

Max speed	35 knots
Cruising speed	30 knots
Max endurance	5 hours
Max gradient	1 : 9
Vertical obstacle clearance	2 ft (0·60 m)

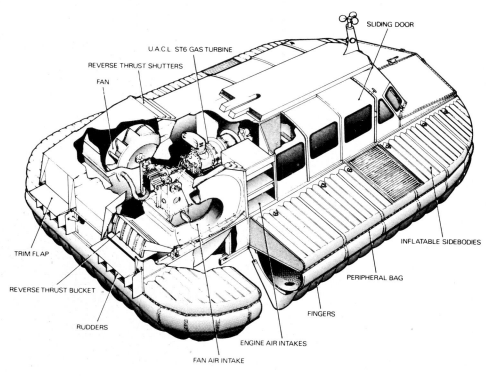

Cutaway showing the CC-7's engine installation, and the location of the centrifugal fans, multiple rudders and reverse thrust buckets

DAILY EXPRESS

HEAD OFFICE:
Fleet Street, London E.C.4
TELEPHONE:
Fleet Street 8000

Since September 1966 the Daily Express has been encouraging its readers to become hovercraft conscious by inviting them to become hovernauts. The two-seat Air Rider has been designed especially for construction by schools. Well over 100 British schools have built the craft and orders for plans have been received from nearly 5,000 overseas educational establishments and amateur constructors. The first inter-schools hovercraft building contest, organised jointly by BP and the Daily Express was in September 1968. Others followed in May 1970 and September 1972, staged at Hoverlloyd's hoverport, Ramsgate, Kent. School craft have reached 30 mph (48·28 km/h).

AIR RIDER

One of the most popular British light air cushion vehicle designs to date, the Express Air Rider is an amphibious two-seater capable of land speeds up to 50 mph and water speeds of up to 32 knots. The prototype was completed in April 1968. Trials are continuing with a variety of air cushion systems. In 1970-71 the craft was used to test an experimental skirt system for Enfield Marine Ltd. Piloted by John Vass, the newspaper's group information officer who manages this project, the prototype has won an overall rally championship and a home-built Air Rider won a major trophy in the Autumn of 1969.

LIFT AND PROPULSION: A single 300 cc Sachs Wankel engine mounted immediately ahead of the cockpit drives a 22 in diameter Multiwing axial lift fan. Aft of the cockpit are two more Sachs Wankel engines driving two ducted 2 ft 7½ in (800 mm) propellers.

FUEL: A single 3 gallon tank for the propulsion engine is located aft of the cockpit on the port side with the refuelling neck immediately above. Fuel for the lift engine is contained in a one gallon tank located beside the engine.

CONTROLS: An aerodynamic rudder operating in the propeller slipstream provides directional control. Braking is achieved by partially cutting off air to the cushion and increasing the skirt pressure. Throttle controls are fitted to the rudder handbar.

HULL: The boat-shaped hull is built up from ⅜ in (9·5 mm) ply formers with a 0·07 in (2 mm) ply skin. Buoyancy boxes are provided in the bow, stern and along both sides. The skirt is of the peripheral bag type.

ACCOMMODATION: Operator and passenger share a canvas seat in the central open cockpit.

SYSTEMS:

ELECTRICAL: An engine operated generator supplies 12 volts to an aircraft type battery for engine starting.

DIMENSIONS, EXTERNAL:

Length overall	12 ft 6 in (3·81 m)
Beam overall	6 ft 6 in (1·98 m)
Height overall on landing pads	3 ft 4 in (1·01 m)
Skirt depth	1 ft 0 in (0·30 m)
Draft afloat	3 in (77 mm)
Cushion area	70 sq ft (6·5 m²)

DIMENSIONS, INTERNAL:

Cockpit	4 ft × 3 ft (1·21 m × 0·91 m)

WEIGHTS:

Normal all-up weight	400 lb (181 kg)
Normal gross weight	700 lb (311 kg)
Normal payload	300 lb (136 kg)
Max payload	600 lb (272 kg)

Express Air Riders at the finals of the Inter-schools Hovercraft Contest, organised jointly by BP and the Daily Express at Harlow, Essex

PERFORMANCE (normal operating weight):

Max speed over calm water approx	32 knots (57 km/h)
Max speed over land	50 mph (80 km/h)
Cruising speed, calm water	25 knots (75·5 km/h)
Turning circle diameter at 30 knots	210 ft (64 m)
Still air endurance at cruising speed	45 minutes
Max gradient	15°
Vertical obstacle clearance	10 in (254 mm)

DEVON AIR CUSHION SYSTEMS LTD.

HEAD OFFICE:

Ringmore House, Shaldon, Devon

DIRECTORS:

Brian Holmes
Ken Harding
Eric Matkin

B. Godfrey
Major A. Gregson, MBE

Devon Air Cushion Systems Ltd was formed in September 1970, for the manufacture of light hovercraft and components. The company is at present fabricating components for the Canadian version of the Air Rider and developing a five-seater prototype, powered by a Hillman Imp engine.

During 1972 the company concentrated on the development of its 4-seater designs, one of which employs air-jet propulsion. All the craft are amphibious and have segmented skirts.

HOVERCRAFT DEVELOPMENT LTD

HEAD OFFICE:

Kingsgate House, 66-74 Victoria Street, London SW1E 6SL

TELEPHONE:

01-828 3400

DIRECTORS:

T. G. Fellows (Chairman)
M. W. Innes
Prof. W. A. Mair
J. E. Rapson
T. A. Coombs

SECRETARY:

P. N. Randell

TECHNICAL OFFICE:

Forest Lodge, West Fawley Road, Hythe, Hants SO4 6ZZ

TELEPHONE:

Hythe (Hants) 3178 STD Code 042 14

Hovercraft Development Ltd was formed by the National Research Development Corporation (NRDC) in January 1959 to develop and exploit the hovercraft invention. The company uses its large portfolio of patents as the basis of licensing agreements with the principal hovercraft manufacturers, and offers licensees access to work undertaken by its original Technical Group and current Technical Office at Hythe. In certain cases HDL may also assist new projects with financial backing.

The small technical team employed by the company makes assessments of new hovercraft designs and proposed operations in addition to providing a source of unbiased but informed technical information for official bodies, potential manufacturers, operators and backers of ACV enterprises.

Many of the patents held by the company result from the work undertaken by hovercraft inventor Christopher Cockerell and the HDL Technical Group, which investigated a wide range of marine and industrial applications and operated three research hovercraft for investigations into skirt and control systems.

HDL aims to promote the further use of the air-cushion principle for transport, industrial and recreational purposes.

HOVERKING LTD

HEAD OFFICE:

12, Clarendon Place, Leamington Spa, Warwickshire

TELEPHONE:

Leamington Spa 25766 and 28469

DIRECTORS:

C. Knight
R. T. Jackson
W. Gosling
D. Crowther
J. Jukes

Hoverking Ltd was formed in 1970 to design and develop the Ranger series of light hovercraft, initially for the amateur builder. The aim was to produce a luxury sports racing hovercraft that could be manufactured commercially to meet the wide demand for racing ACVs.

Ranger 1 has been intensively tested and developed to achieve the right combination of high performance, reliability, safety and stability. This included a series of tests conducted by Loughborough University which confirmed the machine's outstanding pitch and roll stability.

An amateur-built version of the Ranger 1, built by David Ibbotson, won the Hovercraft of the Year Award and David Ibbotson himself was Joint Hovernaut of the Year in 1973.

The manoeuvrability of the craft were tested to the full on the canals in Birmingham, where it featured in location shots for the film "Take Me High", starring Cliff Richard.

Widespread interest has been shown in the principles embodied in the design of the Ranger 1. A world-wide network of agents with complete spares and technical support is in the process of being established.

RANGER 1

A single-seater sports/racing hovercraft, Ranger 1 is easy to handle and its components are both simple and functional to ensure low maintenance and running costs.

LIFT AND PROPULSION: Lift air is provided by an 8 hp Sachs Wankel Rotary KM48 engine driving a 22 in (·55 m) diam. 8 blade Multiwing fan. Thrust is provided by a 21 hp Sachs Rotary MK914 engine driving a 27 in (0·68 m) diam. ducted Permali propeller. The fuel capacity is from 2 gal (9·02 l) (for racing) up to 8 gal (36·3 l) for cruising. The fuel tank is mounted inboard in a compartment behind the driver.

CONTROLS: Twin rudders mounted in the propeller slipstream provide directional control. The rudders are linked by teleflex cable to an ergonomically designed control column with handgrips set at 45%, permitting single or two-handed control. The thrust throttle lever can be operated by either hand.

HULL: Box-section, wood-laminated internal structure bonded into a light grp external skin. The four corners are foam filled to provide buoyancy and impact resistance.

SKIRT: Twin bag of lightweight polyurethene impregnated terylene/nylon. Skirt system permits safe operation of the craft even with extensive damage to the outer skirt. The lightweight material permits temporary repairs to be undertaken by hand. System maintains a higher pressure in the skirt than in the plenum, combining the advantages of a low cushion pressure with

Ranger I, winner of the 1973 Hovercraft of the Year Award, followed by an experimental version of the Ranger with twin Wankel thrust engines

resistance to skirt decay at high speeds.

ACCOMMODATION: Single-seat located just forward of the centre of gravity. Seating position is adjustable from a normal upright to full 'racing prone' position for maximum safety at high speeds. Adjustable footrest provided.

DIMENSIONS:

Length	11 ft 9 in (9·58 m)
Width	6 ft 7 in (2·00 m)
Height	4 ft 0 in (1·21 m)

WEIGHTS:

Weight empty	400 lb (181·42 kg)

Payload	400 lb (181·42 kg)

PERFORMANCE:

Max speed	55 mph (88·57 km/h)
Fuel consumption 1½-2 gal/hr	(6·81-9·0 l/hr)
Maximum cont. gradient	1 : 6
Obstacle clearance	9 in (228 mm)

PRICE: £1,400-£1,800 ex works subject to specification.

RANGER II

This is a 2-3 seat sports/cruising hovercraft. Tests are continuing. Details of the production model were expected to be available in late 1974.

HOVERMARINE TRANSPORT LIMITED

HEAD OFFICE AND WORKS:
   Hazel Wharf, Hazel Road, Woolston, Southampton SO2 7GB
TELEPHONE:
   Southampton 446831
TELEX:
   47141
DIRECTORS:
   Edward F. Davison, Managing Director and Chairman
   David W. Nicholas, Marketing Director
   Michael R. Richards, ACA, Financial Director and Company Secretary
   Peter J. Hill, Manufacturing Director
   Edward G. Tattersall, BSc(Eng), Technical Director
   W. Rathbone

Hovermarine Transport Ltd, a subsidiary of Hovermarine Corporation (USA), is currently manufacturing the HM.2 Mk III rigid sidewall craft. Two basic configurations are available: a 62-65 seat passenger ferry and a general purpose model, each capable of carrying a 5 ton payload. At the time of going to press it was understood that twenty-six vessels had been completed and that a further six were under construction.

HM.2 Mk III

A rigid sidewall craft designed for ferry operations, the HM.2 Mk III carries 62-65 passengers or 4·8 tons of freight at speeds up to 35 knots. The craft has a reinforced plastic hull, and is powered by three marine diesel engines.

HM.2 Mk III "Troiano", one of a fleet of four operated between Setubal and Troia, the Portuguese holiday resort south of Lisbon

The Mk III entered service early in 1971. Its features include an extended bow skirt which permits operations in waves up to 1·6 m (5 ft), mixed-flow fans to provide improved cushion characteristics; a new propulsion transmission system, modified engine components and the provision of sound insulation in the cabin to reduce internal noise levels.

HM.2 is type approved in the UK for Certificates of Construction and Performance and Hovercraft Safety Certificates issued by the Civil Aviation Authority, also for Operating Permits issued by the Department of Trade and Industry. In addition the HM.2 has been certified by Lloyds Register of

Shipping as a Class A1 Group 2 Air Cushion Vehicle.

In 1974 fleet services were running successfully in Setubal, Portugal; Rio de Janeiro, Brazil; and on the River Thames in London. In addition, HM.2s are operating in Australia, Belgium, Brazil, Canada, Greece, Italy, India, U.S.A. and elsewhere in the UK.

LIFT AND PROPULSION: Two turbocharged VT8-370M eight-cylinder V marine diesels, each developing 320 bhp at 2,800 rpm, provide propulsion power, and a single Cummins V8-504M diesel rated at 185 bhp at 2,800 rpm drives the lift fans. The lift engine drives two pairs of forward fans through toothed belts and one aft fan through a hydraulic system. Air for the forward fans is drawn through inlets at each forward cabin quarter and in the base of the wheelhouse structure while air for the aft fan is drawn through an inlet in the rear companion way. The lift fans are of glass fibre construction.

The two propulsion engines drive two 15 in (381 mm) diameter stainless steel propellers through a reversing gearbox and 1 : 1 ratio Vee box. Short skegs projecting from the base of the sidewalls protect the propellers from driftwood and grounding. Fuel is carried in reinforced rubber tanks, two beneath the aft companionway holding 640 litres (140 gal) and one under the main lift fan holding 182 litres (40 gal).

Two refuelling points are provided on the transom and one on the starboard side of the main air intakes.

CONTROLS: Craft direction is controlled by twin balanced stainless steel rudders, which are manually operated, with hydraulic assistance from the wheelhouse by a car type steering wheel. Additional control is provided by differential use of propulsion engine power.

HULL: The craft is built in glass reinforced plastic and grp sandwich panels. The hull is one homogeneous laminate into which are bonded grp panel frames. Bulkheads are provided aft.

ACCOMMODATION: Controls are all sited in an elevated wheelhouse with a 360° view, located at the front end of the passenger compartment. The captain is seated on the starboard side with the principal instrumentation. The radar and auxiliary instrumentation is located on the port side. The craft is operated by a crew of two.

Accommodation is normally for 62 seated passengers but the number can be increased to 65. Seats are normally three abreast in banks of three. Toilet and luggage compartments are located aft.

Passenger access is via a double width door aft. Crew and emergency access is provided forward via two hatch doors, one each side of the wheelhouse.

"Knock-out" emergency windows are provided in the passenger saloon. Safety equipment includes Beaufort life rafts, aircraft-type life jackets under the seats and Graviner fire detectors and extinguishers.

Heating for the passenger saloon and wheelhouse is from the freshwater circuits of the engine cooling system, via two heat exchanger blowers through ducts at floor level. Air conditioning can be fitted if required.

SYSTEMS: Electrical 24 volt dc from engine driven alternators (2 × 60 amp) with 128 Ah Dagenite batteries. Supplies instruments, radio, radar and external and interior lights.

HYDRAULICS: Systems used for the steering and rear fan operate at 800 lb/in² and 2,500 lb/in² max respectively.

SKIRT: Front and rear skirts are of loop and segment form and designed for a cushion height of 3 ft (914 mm).

COMMUNICATIONS AND NAVIGATION: Radar and radio: Decca Super 101 radar and Redifon GR674 VHF radio. Other navigational equipment: Smith E2B Compass and remote reading compass.

DIMENSIONS, EXTERNAL:
Length overall   51 ft 0 in (15·54 m)

Interior of the HM.2 Mk III's 62-65 seat passenger saloon

HM.2s under construction at the company's plant at Woolston, Southampton. At the time of going to press in July 1974 twenty-six HM.2s had been completed and a further six were on order

Beam overall	20 ft 0 in (6·10 m)
Height above hovering water line	13 ft 9 in (4·19 m)
Draft floating with water screws	5 ft 0 in (1·52 m)
Draft hovering with water screws	2 ft 0 in (0·81 m)
Cushion area	627 ft² (584·00 m²)

DIMENSIONS, INTERNAL:
Cabin (excluding wheelhouse, galley and toilet):

Length	22 ft 0 in (6·7 m)
Max width	16 ft 0 in (4·8 m)
Max height	6 ft 6 in (1·9 m)
Floor area	352 ft² (32·7 m²)

DOOR SIZES:
Rear door:
  4 ft 0 in (1·2 m wide) × 6 ft 3 in (1·9 m high)

Two forward doors
  2 ft 0 in (0·60 m wide) × 6 ft 3 in (1·9 m high)

BAGGAGE HOLDS:
Basic craft   60 ft³ (1·69 m³) aft of cabin

FREIGHT HOLDS:
None on standard passenger version
Freight carried in main cabin in freight version.

WEIGHTS:
Normal all-up weight   42,500 lb (19,300 kg)
Normal payload
    62 passengers or 4·8 tons (4,900 kg)
Max gross weight   44,500 lb (20,185 kg)

PERFORMANCE: (at normal operating weight):
Max service speed   35 knots
Water speed in 4 ft waves and 15 knot head wind   25 knots

Max wave capability on scheduled runs for reasonable passenger comfort 5 ft (1·52 m)

Endurance   4·0 hours

MH.2 MK III GENERAL PURPOSE CRAFT

Similar in basic design, construction and power plant to the HM.2 the general purpose version is suited to a variety of roles from police and customs patrol to hydrographic survey and search and rescue duties.

The craft is equipped with a revised superstructure to suit these applications. For para military roles, the craft can be equipped with conventional automatic weapons.

DIMENSIONS, EXTERNAL:

Length overall	51 ft 0 in (15·54 m)
Beam overall	20 ft 0 in (6·09 m)
Height above hovering waterline to wheelhouse top	10 ft 8 in (3·25 m)
Draft hovering	2 ft 10 in (0·86 m)
Draft afloat	4 ft 10 in (1·47 m)

WEIGHTS:

Max all-up weight (fully equipped)	42,500 lb (19,300 kg)
Normal disposable load	12,300 lb (5,830 kg)

HM5

Design of this new rigid sidewall craft was commenced in 1973. It is similar in concept to the HM.2 but significantly larger—seating between 140-160 passengers.

HM.2 Mk III general purpose sidewall craft equipped for hydrographic survey and operated on the River Scheldt by the Belgian Ministry of Public Works

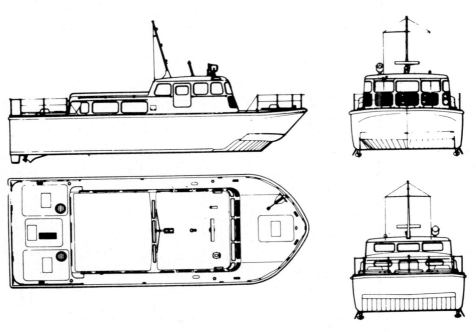

Hovermarine HM.2 Mk III, general purpose craft

K & B HOVERCRAFT

ADDRESS:
   20 Cotefield Drive, Leighton Buzzard, Bedfordshire, England.

TELEPHONE:
   Leighton Buzzard 67022

EXECUTIVES:
   G. Kent
   N. Beale

This organisation has developed a low-cost single-seat sports hovercraft designed by two of the most successful designers and builders of light hovercraft. Two prototypes of the Hoverfly have been completed and the second of these was undergoing final trials at the time of going to press. It is planned to manufacture Hoverfly in quantity at a price of approximately £400.00 per craft.

HOVERFLY

A simple single-seat design Hoverfly meets all the safety requirements of the Hover Club of Great Britain. It is capable of speeds of up to 25 mph (40·23 km/h) over land or water and employs an integrated lift/thrust propulsion system.

LIFT & PROPULSION: A single JLO 250 cc two stroke engine rated at 15 hp at 5,500 rpm drives via a toothed belt 24 in-dia, (609 mm) five-bladed, 45° pitch ducted fan. This unit supplies air for both lift and thrust, with about 40% of the fan duct diameter scooping air for the cushion and the remainder being used for thrust. With this system a static thrust of about 45 lb is achieved. Cushion pressure is about 9 lb/sq ft and the craft has a fuel capacity of 1½ gallons.

CONTROLS: A simple twist grip mounted on the steering handlebars operates the throttle for the single engine and an air rudder mounted in the fan duct gives directional control.

HULL: The complete hull structure is constructed from glass-reinforced plastics with polyurethane foam, providing about 150% buoyancy, contained in the underside of the hull. It is also possible to fit marine buoyancy bags along the open wells on the sides of the craft to give additional buoyancy if the craft operates with an overload weight.

SKIRT SYSTEM: A simple bag skirt giving about 6 in obstacle clearance is fitted to the hull. The skirt is made from polyurethane coated nylon fabric weighing 4 oz/sq yd.

ACCOMMODATION: Hoverfly is a single-seater with the driver sitting astride a central bench.

DIMENSIONS:

Length overall	9 ft 0 in (2·74 m)
Width overall	5 ft 0 in (1·52 m)
Height overall	3 ft 6 in app. (1·06 m)
Height at rest	3 ft 0 in app. (·91 m)

WEIGHTS:

Weight empty (dry)	120 lb (54·42 kg)
Normal payload	200 lb (90·71 kg)
Normal all-up	350 lb (158·75 kg)

PERFORMANCE:

Maximum speed over land	25 mph (40·23 km/h) approx.
over water	20 kt approx.

Hoverfly, single-seat sports ACV

LIGHT HOVERCRAFT COMPANY

HEAD OFFICE:
Felbridge Hotel & Investment Co Ltd, London Road, East Grinstead, Sussex

TELEPHONE:
East Grinstead 24424

EXECUTIVES:
L. H. F. Gatward, Proprietor
Richard Thomas, Consultant

Light Hovercraft Company has been active in the field of hoverpallets since 1969. It has entered the light sports ACV field with a fibreglass hulled-variant of Nigel Beale's Cyclone, which won the British National Hovercraft Championships in 1971 and was joint winner of this event in 1972. In August 1972 a production Cyclone crossed the English Channel from Pegwell Bay hoverport to Calais, a total open sea distance of 35 miles (56·32 km). In late 1973, the company introduced the Wasp, an ultralight runabout, and in April 1974, it introduced the Buzzard, a development of the Cyclone and available in two and four seat models.

At the time of going to press in June 1974, the company had sold five Buzzards and four Wasps.

The Light Hovercraft Buzzard sports ACV

BUZZARD

This lightweight amphibious sports craft is derived from the earlier Cyclone 274 (JSS 1973-74). Two and four seat and one light cargo model are available. The four basic variants are as follows:

Buzzard I. Two seats, one lift unit, one thrust unit.

Buzzard II. Two seats, one lift unit, two thrust units.

Buzzard III. Four seats, one lift unit, two thrust units.

Buzzard IV. Two seats, one lift unit, two thrust units, plus a cargo well.

LIFT AND PROPULSION: Lift is provided by a Rowena Stihl 137 cc engine rated at 9 bhp driving a 1 ft 7 in (482 mm) diameter fan. On the Buzzard Mk I a single Rowena Stihl 137 cc engine of identical type and output drives a ducted multiwing fan for thrust. On the Mk II, III and IV twin Rowena Stihl thrust units are fitted. Fuel capacity is 2·5 gals (12 litres).

CONTROLS: A single rudder hinged to the rear of the thrust fan provides directional control. A lever throttle operates the lift engine and a twistgrip throttle controls propulsion.

The Wasp ultralight hovercraft runabout

HULL: Single piece foam-filled glassfibre hull. Rigid structure. Light weight construction for roof rack or trailer.

SKIRT: Bag-type skirt in polyurethane

nylon, 1 ft 9 in (·5 m) deep at bow, and 1 ft 4 in (·4 m) at sides.

ACCOMMODATION: Open tandem seating for driver and up to three passengers.

DIMENSIONS:	BUZZARD 1	BUZZARD II		BUZZARD III	BUZZARD IV
Length	10 ft 8 in (3·3 m)	As I		14 ft 8 in (4·5 m)	As III
Width	6 ft 2 in (1·9 m)	As I		As I	As I
Height	3 ft 5 in (1·0 m)	As I		As I	As I
WEIGHT	180 lbs (80 kg)	220 lbs (100 kg)		250 lbs (115 kg)	260 lbs (120 kg)
Payload Normal	250 lbs (114 kg)	350 lbs (160 kg)		500 lbs (230 kg)	As III
Overload	350 lbs (160 kg)			700 lbs (320 kg)	As III
PERFORMANCE					
Speed (Optimum)	25 knots (50 khp)	40 knots (80 kph)		As II	As II
Range (Approx)	60 miles (100 km)	As I		As I	As I
PRICES—EXPORT	£	£	£	£	
Hovercraft Complete	1,000·00	1.300·00	1,600·00	1,700·00	
Hovercraft Kit	950·00	1.250·00	1,550·00	1,650·00	
Roof Rack	22·00	TYPICAL FREIGHT COSTS (KIT & COMP.)		I & II	III & IV
Trailer (Flat deck)	198·00	Case and Packing		100·00	120·00
		Freight in G.B.		40·00	50·00
		F.O.B. Costs		60·00	70·00
		Freight to European Ports		120·00	140·00
		Freight to Other Ports		240·00	280·00
		Air Freight to U.S.A.		450·00	550·00

WASP

This is a new ultralight runabout, based on the company's experience with the earlier Cyclone. The aim has been to produce a small craft of simple design which is both easy to operate and maintain.

LIFT AND PROPULSION: Integrated system, powered by a single Rowena Stihl 9 hp, 173 cc 2-cycle engine. This drives a 1 ft 7 in (482 mm) diameter axial fan, air from which is used for both lift and propulsion, at the ratio of 1:3. Total fuel capacity is ¾ gal (4 litre).

CONTROLS: Heading is controlled by a single aerodynamic rudder aft of the fan duct and operated by a handlebar. Engine output is controlled by a twist-grip throttle.

HULL: Single-piece foam-filled glassfibre structure.

SKIRT: Bag-type skirt in polyurethane nylon, 6 in (15 cm) deep.

ACCOMMODATION: Saddle-type seat in grp for driver.

DIMENSIONS:

Length	9 ft 1 in (2·8 m)
Beam	6 ft 1 in (1·85 m)
Height	2ft 10 in (·85 m)

WEIGHTS:

Empty weight	110 lb (50 kg)
Payload	175 lb (80 kg)

PERFORMANCE:

Speed	20 knots (40 km/h)
Range (app)	30 miles (50 km)

EXPORT PRICE: Craft complete £495.00.

Internal arrangements of the Wasp runabout: (a) handle bar steering; (b) twist grip throttle; (c) ignition cut out; (d) glove compartment; (e) grp saddle seat; (f) cleats; (g) grp duct unit; (h) rubber mounted 9 hp motor; (i) safety guard; (j) muffler; (k) polypropylene axial fan; (l) slipstream rudder; (m) fuel tank; (n) lift air duct; (o) polyurethane nylon skirt; (p) rigid foam buoyancy; (q) landing strake

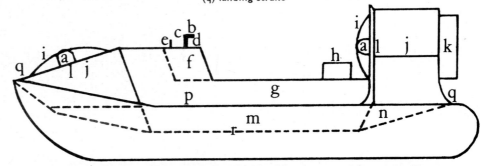

Internal arrangements of the Buzzard sports ACV (a) rubber mounted 9 hp engine; (b) twist grip thrust control; ((c) friction lever lift control; (d) handlebar steering; (e) ignition cut-out switches; (f) glove compartment; (g) g.r.p. seat; (h) portable fuel tank; (i) safety guard; (j) polypropylene axial fan; (k) slipstream rudder; (l) exhaust muffler; (m) rigid foam buoyancy; (n) 360° planing surfaces; (o) polyurethane nylon skirt; (p) footwells; (q) carry handles; (r) landing strake

MISSIONARY AVIATION FELLOWSHIP

ADDRESS:

3 Beechcroft Road, South Woodford, London E18 1BJ

TELEPHONE:

01-989 0838

DIRECTORS:

S. Sendall-King

B.Sc., C.Eng., A.F.R.Ae.S., F.S.L.A.E.T. General Director

T. S. Frank, B.A. UK Director

EXECUTIVE HOVERCRAFT PROJECT:

T. J. R. Longley, A.R.Ae.S.

The Missionary Aviation Fellowship is an international, interdenominational Christian organisation which operates a total of 75 light aircraft in support of missionary work in some of the world's more remote areas.

In the belief that a suitable hovercraft could make a valuable contribution to missionary work, M.A.F. began the design of a craft to its own specification, early in 1970. Design assistance was given voluntarily by several specialists in the field of hovercraft and aircraft engineering. The prototype was built at the Sir George Monoux School, London, as a community-service project, with generous help from industry, including two apprentice training schools.

The craft is now completing intensive trials at Gosport, based on the Royal Naval Aircraft Yard, Fleetlands. Apprentices there are building a hovercraft of this design for inshore rescue work.

On completion of trials, a probable destination will be Lake Chad, where African and foreign missionaries are together undertaking medical, evangelistic and famine-relief work. Difficulties of transportation, together with the extreme shallowness of the Lake, provide ample scope for evaluating the usefulness of a hovercraft.

In view of the very encouraging performance of the prototype, consideration is now being given to a production version of the design in order to satisfy future demand.

MISSIONAIRE Mk I

This is a lightweight amphibious hovercraft powered by two Volkswagen engines. Although originally designed as a five-seater, the craft has a spacious cabin and has demonstrated its ability to carry seven adults over hump speed into a 12 knot headwind without any difficulty. Cruising speed over calm water is 35 knots.

LIFT AND PROPULSION: An air-cooled Volkswagen 1,500 cc automotive engine, developing 53 bhp at 4,200 rpm, drives two 2 ft 0 in (609 mm) diameter aluminium centrifugal impellers for lift. Thrust is provided by a 68 bhp Volkswagen 1,700 cc engine driving a 5 ft 8 in (1·72 m) diameter fixed-pitch Sensenich airboat-type propeller. Power transmission and speed reduction on both units is by Stephens Miraclo-Meteor high-speed belting. Total fuel capacity is 35 Imp gallons (195 l), carried in a single welded aluminium tank located amidships. Recommended fuel is 95 octane automotive grade petrol.

CONTROL: An aerodynamic rudder operating in the propeller slipstream provides directional control under cruising conditions. Forward-located puff-ports are provided for low-speed directional control, though they can be used at high speed. This combination

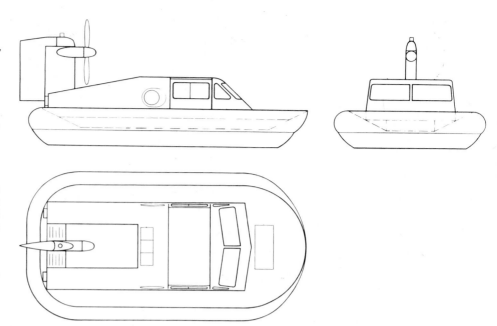

General arrangement of the Missionary Aviation Fellowship hovercraft prototype

Above and below: Missionary Aviation Fellowship's general purpose amphibious five-seater, the Missionaire. Powered by two Volkswagen engines, the craft has a top speed of 38 knots. The rear passenger seats can be replaced by a stretcher carried athwartships

of controls has been found to aid manoeuvrability and facilitate handling. The craft also possesses good high-speed ditching characteristics, with no tendency to plough-in.

Longitudinal trim and a certain amount of lateral trim is provided by two 8 gallon integral water-ballast tanks located side by side in the bows. Water can be pumped aboard while the craft is floating, and can

be off-loaded on or off cushion. No ballast is required when maximum payload is carried in the cabin.

HULL: The prototype hull is built in marine ply and spruce. For greater durability and ease of construction, a hull of composite GRP/aluminium alloy construction is planned for future craft. The hull incorporates ample reserve bouyancy.

SKIRT: Segmented type, 1 ft 6 in (458 mm) deep in neoprene/nylon.

ACCOMMODATION: Seats are provided in a fully enclosed cabin for a driver and four passengers. Access is via car-type doors (one each side) hinged to the forward door-posts. The entire cabin roof is hinged at its forward edge, providing unrestricted head-room for entry and loading. The three-place bench-type rear seat can be quickly converted into a stretcher, situated athwartships. A sizeable compartment for hand baggage and medical supplies is located behind the rear bench-seat. Cabin ventilation is provided by cushion air bleed ducts controlled by louvres.

SYSTEMS: Electrical: generator on the lift engine supplies 12 volts to a 60 a/hr battery for engine starting and other services.

Fire-detection and extinguishing: The engine bay is equipped with flame switches giving visual and audible warning on the instrument panel. A Graviner "Swordsman" BCF fire extinguisher adjacent to the driver's seat is plumbed into a distribution manifold in the engine bay. A quick-release connection makes it instantly useable as a hand-held extinguisher in the event of cabin, or other fires.

COMMUNICATIONS AND NAVIGATION: Provision for radio communications equipment. Magnesyn remote-reading compass.

DIMENSIONS, EXTERNAL:

Length overall, power off	22 ft 0 in (6·70 m)
Length overall, skirt inflated	22 ft 0 in (6·70 m)
Beam overall, power off	10 ft 6 in (3·20 m)
Beam overall, skirt inflated	12 ft 6 in (3·81 m)
*Height overall, on landing pads	7 ft 10 in (2·38 m)
*Height overall, skirt inflated	9 ft 4 in (2·84 m)
Draft afloat	10 in (254 mm)
Cushion area	170 sq ft (15·79 m²)
Skirt depth	1 ft 6 in (458 mm)

*Propeller horizontal.

DIMENSIONS, INTERNAL:

Cabin:	
Length	6 ft 3 in (1·90 m)

Max width	7 ft 0 in (2·13 m)
Max height	4 ft 2 in (1·26 m)
Floor area	43·75 sq ft (4·06 m²)
Baggage hold behind rear seats	15 cu ft (0·425 m³)
Freight hold (in place of rear seats)	45 cu ft (1·27 m³)
Door width	3 ft 6 in (1·06 m)

WEIGHTS:

Normal empty weight	2,200 lb (998 kg)
Normal all-up weight	3,200 lb (1,451 kg)
Maximum all-up weight	3,600 lb (1,633 kg)
Normal payload (with full tank)	1,000 lb (453 kg)
Maximum payload	1,400 lb (635 kg)

PERFORMANCE (at normal operating weight):

Max speed over calm water (max power) at 60 deg F	38 knots
Cruising speed, calm water	35 knots
Turning circle diameter at 30 knots	2,200 ft (670 m)
Max wave capability	2-3 ft (609-914 mm)
Still air range at cruising speed (without reserves)	280 nm
Max gradient, static conditions	1:10
Vertical obstacle clearance	1 ft 4 in (407 mm)

PINDAIR LIMITED

HEAD OFFICE:
16 Broom Lock, Teddington, Middlesex, TW11 9QP
TELEPHONE:
01-977 6435
WORKS:
The Albany Boathouse, Lower Ham Road, Kingston-upon-Thames, Surrey
TELEPHONE:
01-549 2317
DIRECTORS:
M. A. Pinder, BSc, CEng, MIMechE, (Managing)
A. M. Pinder
J. Holland, FCA
EXECUTIVES:
M. A. Pinder, Design and Sales
A. M. Pinder, Accounts
J. Johnstone, Administration
B. Oakley, Development
D. McClunan, Production

Pindair Limited was formed in May 1972. It is currently engaged in design, development, manufacture and sales of a range of inflatable light hovercraft for recreation, commercial and military use as well as supplying amateur hovercraft constructors in the United Kingdom with engines, fans, ducts, skirt materials and many other specialised components.

Four models are currently in production and three others are in the project or development stage,.

The use of folding inflatable hulls for the Pindair Skima range is claimed to have a number of advantages including ease of transport and storage, low weight, maximum safety and resistance to icing. In all cases efficient design has lead to low power requirements and consequently low fuel consumption. Special attention has been paid to simplicity of owner maintenance and use of components with worldwide spares availability. All four production models use Rowena Stihl 137 cc 2 stroke engines (See engine section) coupled to fully guarded, ducted Multiwing axial fans with replaceable polypropylene blades. In all cases HDL loop

Top: A Skima 2, two-seat inflatable light hovercraft at Poole Harbour. *Centre:* The Skima 3, powered by three Rowena Stihl 137 cc 2-stroke engines, and capable of 35 mph (56·32 km/h) over water. *Below:* The Skima 4, capable of carrying four people under favourable conditions, and recommended as an alternative to the Gemini inflatable boat where amphibious capability is required

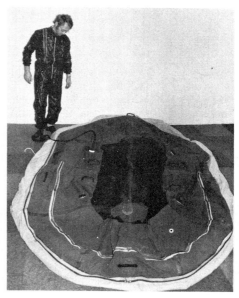
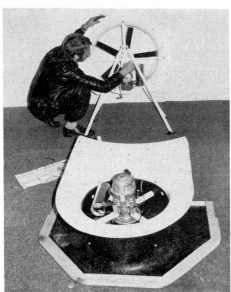

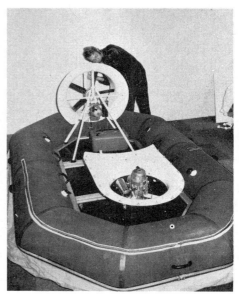

Above, left to right, top and bottom: Six stages in the assembly of the Pindair Skima 2. Packed
dimensions of the craft are 2 ft 6 in × 3 ft 6 in × 2 ft, and the total assembly time is 30 minutes

segment skirts are used. Controls are mounted centrally for operation by one hand from any front seat position. Seats are adjustable for trim purposes.

Prices compare with boats having a similar payload and performance.

SKIMA 1

This has been designed as a low cost one-man hovercraft which can be stowed in the luggage compartment of most cars, be light enough for easy portability by one man yet be capable of carrying one man on land or water in reasonable conditions. It is thus suitable as a first familiarisation with hovercraft, for amusement parks, for exploration or for class competitions.

In 1972 three single seat inflatable hovercraft prepared by the Pindair design team reached an altitude of 10,000 ft in the Himalayas by travelling along turbulent rivers.

SKIMA 2

This was the first craft marketed by the company and is the result of 7 years continuous development. Examples are now in use on every continent. Since it is light enough to be carried by two people and can carry two people in reasonable conditions it is called a two man hovercraft. It has separate lift and propulsions systems for accurate control and to allow it to be folded to fit onto a car roof rack on a small estate car or hatchback.

The Skima 2 can be used as an amphibious yacht tender-cum-runabout, for exploration or for class competitions.

SKIMA 3

This is derived from a special version of the Skima 2 which was raced successfully by Barry Oakely in the 1973 and 1974 Hover Club of Great Britain Championships, winning a number of open races and also speed, manoeuvrability and free style competitions outright.

Although capable of operating as a three man hovercraft it is mainly used for two people or by one person in competitions.

SKIMA 4

During proving trials in 1973 this hovercraft covered the longest journey so far by a light hovercraft on inland and coastal waters. The Interservice Hovercraft Unit has recommended it as an alternative to the Gemini inflatable boat used by the British armed services, particularly in cases where its amphibious qualities would be an advantage.

Examples of the Skima 4 are in use in various parts of the world as amphibious transport for two people plus their equipment in most conditions or four people in good conditions. Users include missionaries on Lake Chad, an aluminium company in the Arabian Gulf, a Pest Research Organisation and a Marine Biology research group. Other users include defence forces, subaqua organisations, exploration groups and flood and beach rescue organisations. The rear inflatable seat is instantly removable for stowing freight or equipment.

SKIMA 6 (projected)

A 6 man craft for inshore, on shore and offshore flood and crash rescue as well as various civil and military applications.

SKIMA 9 (projected)

A longer 9 man version of the above with space for stretcher cases.

SKIMA 20 (projected)

A 20 man/one car hovercraft for rescue as well as civil and military applications and featuring various propulsion options.

SKIMA PERFORMANCE DATA

Craft		Skima 1	Skima 2		Skima 3			Skima 4				Skima 6 (estimated)		Skma 9 (estimated)	
Payload	Units of 200 lb or 1 person	×1	×1	×2	×1	×2	×3	×1	×2	×3	×4	×2	×6	×2	×9
Max speed over water	mph	25	30	25	45	35	25	40	35	30	25	50	25	60	25
Max speed over grass	mph	25	30	25	45	35	25	40	35	30	25	50	25	60	25
Max speed over tarmac	mph	30	35	30	50	40	30	45	40	35	30	55	30	65	30
Max speed over ice	mph	35	45	35	60	50	40	55	50	45	40	75	45	80	45
Hump speed	mph	2	3	5	3	4	5	2	3	4	5	2	5	1	5
Max wind, Beaufort scale		3	4	2	6	5	4	6	5	4	3	8	4	9	6
Fuel consumption	Imp gal/hr	¾	1½	1½	2	2	2	2	2	2	2	6	6	10	10
Turning circle (low speed)	ft	8	10	10	15	15	15	20	20	20	20	25	25	30	30
Turning circle (high speed)	ft	70	100	150	70	100	150	100	150	200	250	100	250	100	250
Max short slope	°	45°	45°	30°	45°	35°	30°	45°	40°	35°	30°	45°	30°	45°	30°
Max continuous slope	°	10°	12°	8°	15°	12°	8°	20°	15°	12°	8°	20°	10°	20°	10°

SKIMA SPECIFICATIONS

Craft	Skima 1	Skima 2	Skima 3	Skima 4	Skima 6 (project)	Skima 9 (project)
Length	8 ft	10 ft	11 ft 6 in	13 ft 6 in	15 ft	18 ft
Width	5 ft	6 ft 4 in	6 ft 4 in	6 ft 4 in	10 ft	10 ft
Height off Cushion	3 ft 0 in	4 ft	4 ft	4 ft	5 ft	5 ft
Dry weight, lb	70	200	300	350	550	750
Skirt	HDL	HDL	HDL	HDL	HDL	HDL
Skirt depth	5 in	6 in	6 in	8 in	12 in	12 in
Obstacle clearance	9 in	2 in	12 in	14 in	20 in	20 in
Folded dimensions	30in × 36in × 14in	3ft × 5ft × 2ft	4ft × 5ft × 2ft	4ft × 5ft × 2ft	not determined	not determined
Packed dimensions	30in × 36in × 14 in	2 ft 6in × 3ft 6in × 2 ft	2ft 6in × 3ft 6in × 2 ft 6 in	2ft 6in × 3ft6in × 2ft6in	not determined	not determined
Assembly time, mins	15	30	40	40	50	60
Thrust, lb	35	55	95	95	180	360
Engines	1 Rowena	2 Rowena	3 Rowena	3 Rowena	Not Finalised	
Fans	1 Multiwing axial	2 Multiwing axial	3 Multiwing axial	3 Multiwing axial	Not Finalised	
Total engine power	8	12	20	20	55	110

HAROLD POISER LTD.

HEAD OFFICE:
967 Stockport Road,
Levenshulme,
Manchester M19 3NP
TELEPHONE:
061 224 5422
HOME TELEPHONE:
061 432 6636
DIRECTORS:
Donald Woolley
David Woolley

Harold Poiser Ltd is continuing the activities of Ajax Hovercraft Ltd, which had been engaged in ACV research and development since January 1971. The company's activities are centred chiefly on the production of the two-seat AH 5. It also offers a spares service for enthusiasts, including basic materials, skirts, fans, engines, ducts and complete thrust and lift modules.

AH 5

Series production of this amphibious two-seater began in June 1973. Features include a robust grp hull, enclosed luggage space fore and aft, and a wide, comfortable cabin for the driver and passenger.
LIFT AND PROPULSION: Lift air is provided by an 8·62 bhp Rowena Stihl single-cylinder two-stroke driving a 2 ft 0 in (609 mm) diameter, 10-bladed multiwing fan at 3,220 rpm. The fan blades are set at 30 degrees, and the hub has a steel bush mounted on a keyed, stainless steel shaft. At maximum auw, the cushion pressure is

Top: Ajax Hovercraft is building the new H5 amphibious two-seater in series. Lift and propulsion systems are powered by 8 bhp Rowena Stihl single-cylinder two-strokes
Bottom: Driver and passenger sit side-by-side in an enclosed cabin. The control stick operates twin sets of triple rudders attached to the rear of the two propulsion fanducts

12·52 lb sq ft. Cushion area is 67·88 sq ft. Propulsive thrust is supplied by two identical 8·62 hp Rowena Stihl 6507-JL single-cylinder two strokes, each of which drives a 2 ft 0 in (609 mm) diameter, 5-bladed multiwing fan with blades set at 45 degrees. Fuel is carried in two interconnected metal tanks installed in the sidebodies. Total capacity is 11 gallons (50 l). Manufacturer recommends 90-93 octane mixed 20 : 1 with outboard motor oil.

CONTROLS: Triple rudders hinged to the rear of each of the two thrust ducts control craft heading.

HULL: moulded grp structure.

SKIRT: 11 in (279 mm) deep bag-type skirt in 15 oz neoprene on nylon.

ACCOMMODATION: Driver and passenger sit side-by-side on a bench-type seat. Canopy is in grp and slides forward on nylon rails. Vents are provided in the side windows. Manual screen washer and electric wipers are standard. Plastic side windows can be pushed out in an emergency. Front screen is of laminated safety glass.

SYSTEMS: 6v lighting coils on each engine rectified to dc.

DIMENSIONS, EXTERNAL:

Length overall:
  power off   13 ft 7 in (4·14 m)
  skirt inflated   14 ft 4½ in (4·39 m)
Beam overall:
  power off   6 ft 7 in (2·00 m)
  skirt inflated   7 ft 11 in (2·41 m)
Height overall:
  on landing skids   3 ft 6¾ in (1·08 m)
  skirt inflated   4 ft 4 in (1·32 m)

Stern view showing the lift and propulsion fan ducts, rudder units and the aft stowage space for small baggage items

Draft afloat   2½ in (63 mm)
Skirt depth   11 in (279 mm)

DIMENSIONS, INTERNAL:
Cabin and forward stowage
  4 ft wide by 5 ft 8 in long (1·21 m wide by 1·72 m long)
Aft stowage
  19½ in by 23 in × 12 in deep (495 mm by 584 mm × 304 mm)

WEIGHTS:
Normal empty weight   350 lb (158·75 kg)

Normal all-up weight   850 lb (385·53 kg)
Recommended max payload
                     500 lb (226·78 kg)

PERFORMANCE:
Speed, calm water   about 35 knots
  sand, ice, short grass
           about 60 mph (96·56 km/h)
Max gradient   1 : 10

ROTORK MARINE LTD.

HEAD OFFICE:
Bath, BA1 3JQ
TELEPHONE:
0225 28451
TELEX:
44823
CABLES:
Rotomar Bath
DIRECTORS:
J. J. Fry
M. F. Briggs
J. Dyson
J. S. Fry
A. F. Garnett
G. Ruston

Rotork Marine is building and marketing a series of fast, flat bottom, multi-purpose workboats, the best known of which is the Sea Truck. A key feature of the design is the use of air lubrication to reduce hydrodynamic drag. A ram-air cushion, contained by shallow side skegs, raises the bow clear of the water at speed. As the pressurised air flows aft it generates air/foam lubrication for the remainder of the hull, permitting speeds of up to 50 mph (80·46 km/h) to be achieved. The performance depends upon the payload, installed power and sea conditions. A wide choice of power plants is available, and cabin modules can be supplied for passenger and work crew accommodation. Bow loading ramps are fitted for ease of access and operation from beaches. Typical operators and applications include: Royal Navy, range safety and diving craft; Canadian Army, tug/workboat, Mobil Oil; Singapore, off-shore

Above: A Rotork 12 m workboat *Below:* 8 m fast assault version of the Sea Truck. Armoured protection is provided for the helmsman's position.

rig crew transport; Gulf Lines, Saudi Arabia and Bahrein, waterbus, Egyptian government, assault craft.

The company offers a series of fast assault craft and patrol boats, tactical personnel carriers and logistic support craft, together with a range of general-purpose short haul passenger and vehicle ferries, from 8 m (25 ft 3 in) to 12 m (39 ft 4½ in) in length.

ROTORK 8M SEA TRUCK

This is a heavy duty, multi-purpose workboat designed for high performance and low running costs. It can operate safely in only 1 ft (304 mm) of water and is equipped with a bow ramp to facilitate the loading of passengers, freight or light vehicles from beaches. The maximum payload is 3 tons.

POWER PLANT: Dependant upon payload and performance requirements and whether the craft is to be employed for sheltered water or open sea operation. Engines recommended are: Outboard: 135 hp OMC OBMs, or 150 Mercury OBMs. These can be fitted as twin or triple installations. Inboard (diesel): which can be installed as either single or twin installations, 106 hp Volvo AQD 32/270. Supplied as standard with these units are the control console, and depending on the type of power unit, 50 gal (220 l) or 100 gal (440 l) bulwark or saddle tanks in welded mild steel, fuel lines, fittings and batteries.

HULL: Heavy duty glass fibre reinforced plastics. Star frame chassis integral with hull structure. 'Top hat' section. Bottom is in double thickness heavy duty grp and has five reinforced rubbing strips. Buoyancy is provided by closed cell polyurethane foam of TD 1 type. The skegs are in prestressed cold drawn stainless steel tube. The ramp, which is manually operated, is in 1 in (25·4 mm) thick, polyurethane-coated marine ply. It is housed in a galvanised steel frame with galvanised steel capping, and is counterbalanced by a torsion bar.

ACCOMMODATION: Up to four moulded grp cabin modules can be installed, together with passenger seats.

SYSTEMS, ELECTRICAL: Heavy duty 12 volt batteries housed in acid-resistant reinforced plastic battery box mounted at deck level

FUEL: Fuel is carried in one or more 50 or 100 gallon pannier type tanks, carried between the upper and lower fender tubes, port or starboard.

SCUPPERS: Scuppers for the removal of deck water are located in the transom. Discharge capacity is 180 gal/min (818·27 litres/min).

DIMENSIONS:

Length overall	24 ft 2 in	(7·36 m)
Length at waterline	20 ft 0 in	(6·09 m)
Beam	9 ft 10 in	(2·74 m)
Freeboard		
unladen, to deck level	5 in	(127 mm)
to top of bulwarks	3 ft 0 in	(0·914 m)
max load, to deck level	2 in	(50·80 mm)
to top of bulwarks	2 ft 7 in	(0·787 m)
Deck area (with outboard power)		
	170 sq ft	(15·79 m)

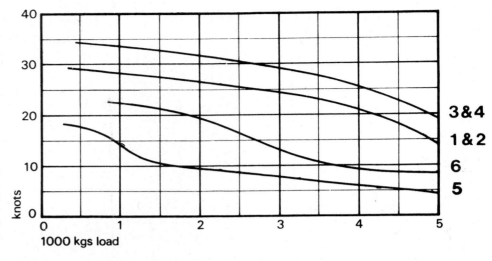

Approximate performance graph for Rotork 12 metre Sea Truck workboat

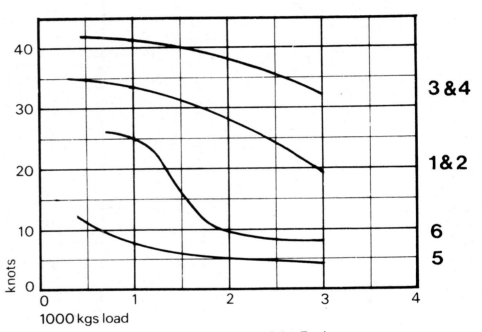

Performance graph for STW 8 Sea Truck

Propulsion
1 Two 135 hp OMC OBM's 282 kg (620 lb)
2 Two 150 Mercury OBM's 282 kg (620 lb)
3 Three 135 hp OMC OBM's 424 kg (932 lb)
4 Three 150 Mercury OBM's 424 kg (932 lb)
5 One 106 hp Volvo AQD 32/270 inboard
391 kg (861 lb)

6 Two 106 hp Volvo AQD 32/270 inboards
782 kg (1,721 lb)
Payload: Maximum normal loading in the 8 metre Sea Truck Workboat is 3,000 kg. This figure is dependent on choice of optional equipment and propulsion system. Individual weights are as indicated.

Draft
unladen, outboard drive up 7 in (177·8 mm) outboard drive down 1 ft 11 in (0·584 m)
Max load, outboard drive up
11 in (279 mm)
outboard drive down 2 ft 3 in (0·685 m)

WEIGHTS:
Basic hull, less engine 3,200 lb (1,451·49 kg)
Total integral foam buoyancy
11,500 lb (5,216·31 kg)
Payload, inshore 6,000 lb (2,721·55 kg)
sea conditions 3,000 kg

PERFORMANCE (8m):
Performance varies with rig, type of load, installed power and operating conditions. An approximate guide, based on the standard open deck-hull, is provided by the accompanying performance graph. This applies to the STW8 Sea Truck 8m workboat configuration.

ROTORK SEA TRUCK
12 METRE HULL

HULL: Glass-fibre reinforced plastic. Reinforcement: E glass chopped strand mat. E glass woven roving. Silane finish. Matrix:

Isophthalic polyester resins meeting Admiralty DG 180 specification for large ships, integrally coloured. Resins: Cellobond A2785 CV or Scott Bader 625 TV.

BUOYANCY: Closed cell polyurethane foam of the TDI type. Nominal density 43·64 kgf/cu m (2·4lb/cu ft) 98% closed cell. Method of manufacture: auto proportioning machine mix foamed in situ.

DECK: Non-slip bonded grit surface applied to special point load resisting composite structure.

CHASSIS: 'Star frame' chassis integral with hull structure. 'Top hat' section.

GLAZING: 6 mm perspex acrylic sheet. Triplex where wipers are used.

FENDER FRAMES: Hot-dip galvanized welded mild steel tube 101·6 mm (4 in) diam.

SKEGS: Prestressed cold drawn seamless steel tube. Anti-corrosion coated.

FENDERS: Rotating fender wheels are fitted as standard at bow and stern.

RAMP: 25·4 mm (1 in) thick marine plywood ramp. Polyurethane coated and grit bonded. Housed in galvanized steel frame with galvanized steel capping. Ramp counterbalanced by torsion bar.

RAMP LOCK: Ramp opened and closed by galvanized mild steel levers. Manually operated.

RAMP SEAL: 50·8 mm (2 in) diam neoprene tube in compression.

SCUPPERS: Scuppers for the removal of water from the deck are located in the transom.

TANKS: Welded mild steel, phosphate conversion coated, epoxide primed, 2-pack polyurethane finish enameled. Pressure tested.

FITTINGS: $\frac{1}{4}$ in and $\frac{3}{8}$ in BSP

FUEL LINES: 9·5 mm ($\frac{3}{8}$ in) ID rubber hose with integral steel braiding.

CAPACITY AND MOUNTING: Type 1—220 litre (50 gallon imperial) pannier for bulwark mounting. Type 2—440 litre (100 gallon imperial) saddle tank for athwartship mounting.

DIMENSIONS:
Length
  Overall   11·27 m (37 ft)
  At waterline   9·8 m (32 ft 2 in)
  Beam   2·74 m (9 ft 10 in)
Freeboards:
  Unladen to deck level   127 mm (5 in)
  Unladen to top of bulwarks
                 814·4 mm (36 in)
  With max load to deck level
                 50·8 mm (2 in)
  With max load to top of bulwarks
                 838·2 mm (33 in)
Height:
  Of top rail from deck 787·2 mm (31 in)
  Of metacentre above centre of gravity
                 5·51 m (18 ft 1 in)
Deck area:
  overall   30·85 sq m (287 sq ft)
Draft:
  Unladen, outdrive up   177·8 mm (7 in)
  Unladen, outdrive down 584·2 mm (23 in)
  With max load, outdrive up
                 279·4 mm (11 in)
  With max load, outdrive down
                 685·8 mm (27 in)
Weights:
  Less engine   2405 kg (4,500 lbs)
  Total integral foam buoyancy
                 886 kg (1,968 lbs)

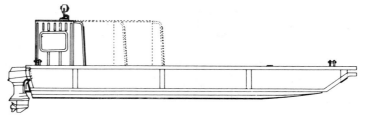
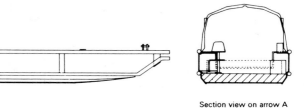

Section view on arrow A

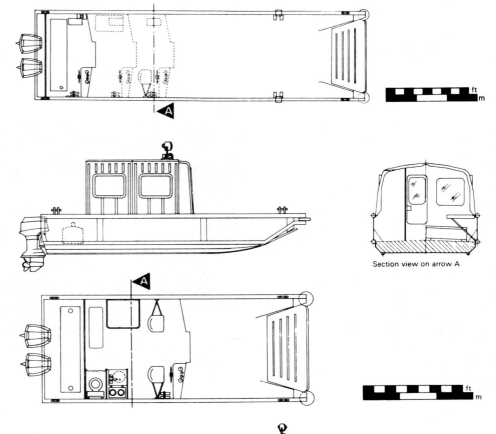

Section view on arrow A

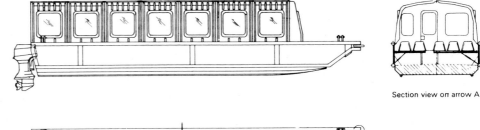

Section view on arrow A

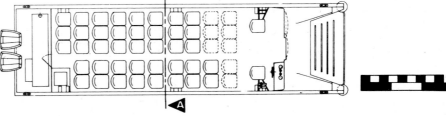

Three versions of the Rotork Sea Truck *Top:* the 12 m workboat configuration; *Centre:* the 8 m fast patrol boat and *bottom:* the 50-seat 12 metre shorthaul passenger ferry

ROTORK STW 12 SEA TRUCK WORKBOAT

HULL: Standard Rotork 12 metre hull.

COLOUR: Hull—high visibility orange. Metalwork—bright galvanized finish.

FIXING POINTS: Rotork military pattern eye bolts at modular fixing points on upper and lower mainframe.

ELECTRICAL: Navigation lights, klaxon and searchlight mounted on mast operable from helmsman's position are standard equipment.

FUEL: 445 litre (100 gallon imperial) capacity. Mild steel welded and pressure tested tanks fitted with drain cocks, quick release filler caps and sight gauges.

FIRE FIGHTING EQUIPMENT: 1·1 kg (2½ lb) rechargeable CO_2 hand extinguisher.
TOTAL WEIGHT: 2,045 kg (4,500 lb).
Optional items include:
NAVIGATION: Illuminated and fully gimballed compass mounted next to helmsman. Approx weight 2.7 kg (6 lb).
COMMUNICATIONS: VHF 8-channel transmitter/receiver. Approx weight 5·7 kg (13 lb) Small ship radar with range of 16 nm at 3kw. Approx weight 40 kg (88 lb).
CREW PROTECTION: GRP covered after-control position with all round vision. Nylon reinforced PVC dropscreen at rear. Approx weight: 143 kg (315 lb).
INSULATION: Heat resistant safari roof for

service in particularly high ambient temperatures. Approx weight 25 kg (55 lb).
SUPPLEMENTARY CREW AREA: 4 ft forward extension of control position providing additional covered crew space and GRP stowage lockers. Approx weight 65 kg (143 lb). Additional extension of cabin forming an enlarged crew compartment. Approx weight 130 kg (286 lb).
MOBILITY: Detachable short haul wheels for launching and landing. Approx weight 151 kg (333 lb).
PROPULSION: (Alterative power plants and weights)
1 Two 135 hp OMC OBM's
282 kg (620 lb)

2 Two 150 Mercury OBM's
282 kg (620 lb)
3 Three 135 hp OMC OBM's
424 kg (932 lb)
4 Three 150 Mercury OBM's
424 kg (932 lb)
5 One 106 hp Volvo AQD 32/270 inboard
391 kg (861 lb)
6 Two 106 hp Volvo AQD 32/270 inboards
782 kg (1,721 lb)
PAYLOAD: Maximum normal loading in the 12 metre Sea Truck Workboat is 5,000 kg. This figure is dependent on choice of optional equipment and propulsion system. Individual weights are as indicated.
See accompanying graph for approximate performance figures.

SEALAND HOVERCRAFT LTD

HEAD OFFICE:
2-5 Old Bond Street, London W1X 3TB
TELEPHONE:
01-493-7681
TELEX:
Dolphmart London, 24620
WORKS:
Devonshire Road, Millom, Cumbria
TELEPHONE:
Millom 2233
TELEX:
Sealhov Millom 65146
DIRECTORS:
E. Wise, Chairman
L. Landau, AICF, Managing Director
A. P. Freeman, MBIM, Works Director
L. M. Wise, FCA
J. A. Joseph
S. Marcelis
SENIOR EXECUTIVES:
B. A. M. Sewell, Works Manager
T. Raynor, Technical Liaison Executive
P. Seggar, Assistant Works Manager
L. D. Ackerley, Commercial Manager
P. H. Widdowson, Production Engineer
A. J. English, Senior Designer
M. Elliott, Manager New Projects
D. Long, Mechanical Designer

Sealand Hovercraft was formed in 1968 and completed its first craft—the SH-1 two seater—for systems evaluation the following year. In 1971 the Company built its first production craft, the SH-2 six seater. The craft was presented at the International Boat Show, Earls Court, January, 1972; Oceanology International Brighton, June, 1972; Europort '72 Amsterdam, November, 1972; and the Hovercraft and Hydrofoil Exhibition, Brighton May, 1974.

The SH-2 is now in full-scale production in a 20,000 sq ft (1,858 m²) factory at Millom, Cumbria, where the Company employs a staff of 151. By late May, 1973, twenty craft had been built for purchasers in Australia, Scotland, South America, Soviet Union, Nigeria, Pakistan and the United States of America.

SH-2

The SH-2 is an attractive, amphibious six seater designed for a variety of roles from water taxi and ambulance to patrol craft. Simplicity of operation and maintenance are keynotes of the design. Features include the use of a single 200 hp Chrysler automotive engine and transmission to power lift and propulsion system, and the incorporation of

The SH-2 amphibious six-seater

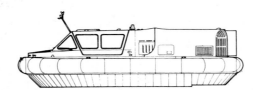
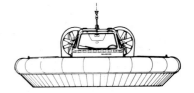

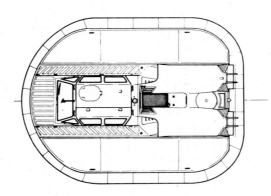

General arrangement of the Sealand SH-2

hinged sidebodies to facilitate transport. Overall beam with sidebodies folded is 7 ft 6 in (2·28 m). Trailer wheel units can be attached for towing along roads.

LIFT AND PROPULSION: Integrated system powered by a single 200 hp Chrysler 440 CD V8 automotive engine. Cushion air is supplied by a 3 ft 3 in (0·99 m) diameter Sealand Hovercraft grp fan driven via a clutch, shafting and a right-angled gearbox. Thrust is supplied by four 2 ft 8 in (0·81 m) diameter, four-bladed Permali axial-flow fans, mounted in pairs on a common shaft in each of the two propulsion air ducts. Each pair is driven via a toothed belt by a pulley on the power take-off shaft, aft of the clutch assembly. Air for the lift fan, located at the end of the hull, is drawn through an intake located between the two propulsion duct outlets. From the fan it is fed via a bag to individual fingers. Cushion area is 240 sq ft (22·29 m²) and cushion pressure is 17·9 lb sq ft. Engine, fans and transmission are built onto a steel sub-frame to form a single, easily removed unit.

Fuel is carried in two grp tanks located in the pannier sections, port and starboard, outboard of the main beams. Total capacity is 52 Imp gallons (236·39 litres). Refuelling points are provided at the centre of the craft, port and starboard. Fuel recommended, 95 octane. Oil capacity is 13 pints (7·38 l).

CONTROLS: Directional control is maintained by twin aerodynamic rudder vanes hinged to the rear of each of the propulsion ducts. Reverse thrust for braking is obtained by opening out the paired rudder vanes in opposing directions to block the propulsion duct outlets, forcing the air through louvres. The craft can be steered by use of the braking system. An electrically-powered water ballast system is used for longitudinal trim.

HULL: Main members are of sandwich form, employing Airex pvc foam cores faced with grp polyester. Hinged sidebodies are grp laminate, beneath which are two sectional buoyancy bags, inflated via an air induction system, controlled from the cabin. Structure is stressed to withstand forward impact loads of up to 6g, roughly the equivalent to driving into 3 ft waves at 43 knots.

SKIRT: 1 ft 6 in (457 mm) deep 50% fingered bag type, fabricated in pvc-coated nylon.

ACCOMMODATION: Basic version seats a driver and five passengers. The driver has an individual, adjustable seat, and to his right is a single bench seat for two abreast. Immediately behind is a bench seat for three abreast. Passenger seats can be quickly removed for the carriage of freight, for which anchor points are provided.

Access to the cabin is via a gull-wing canopy from the starboard side. In an emergency, the two-piece canopy can be jettisoned or alternatively all windows can be pushed out. One hand-held fire extinguisher is provided in the cabin. A fully automatic fire warning system is installed, together with a fire

The Sealand Skitabug two-seat recreational craft

extinguisher in the engine transmission bay. The cabin is both heated and ventilated.

SYSTEMS: Electrical: 12 volt alternator. 45 amp hr battery.

COMMUNICATIONS AND NAVIGATION: Optional extras: Viking Princess 10-channel marine radio; Decca 050 radar; Type E2A compass.

ARMAMENT: 7·65 mm machine gun and wire-guided missiles to order.

DIMENSIONS:

Length overall, power off	19 ft 4 in (5·89 m)
Length, power on	20 ft 10 in (6·35 m)
Beam overall, power off	7 ft 6 in (2·28 m)
Beam, skirts inflated	14 ft 4 in (4·36 m)
Height overall on landing pads	4 ft 4 in (1·32 m)
Height overall, skirt inflated	5 ft 10 in (1·77 m)
Draft afloat	4 in (101 mm)
Cushion area	240 sq ft (22·29 m²)
Skirt depth	1 ft 6 in (457 mm)

DIMENSIONS, INTERNAL:

Length	8 ft 0 in (2·43 m)
Max width	5 ft 0 in (1·52 m)
Max height	4 ft 0 in (1·21 m)
Floor area	40 sq ft (3·71 m³)

WEIGHTS:

Normal gross weight	4,650 lb (2,109 kg)
Payload, including driver	1,200 lb (544·28 kg)

PERFORMANCE:

Max speed over calm water	44 knots
Cruising speed	35 knots
Turning circle diameter at 30 knots	300 yards (274·32 m)
Still air range at cruising speed	200 miles (321·86 km)
Maximum gradient, static conditions	1 : 10

Vertical obstacle clearance
1, ft 6 in (457 mm)

PRICE AND TERMS: On application, according to specification.

SKITABUG

An ultralight recreational ACV, the Skitabug is an amphibious two-seater with a maximum speed of 35 mph (56 km/h). Built in glassfibre reinforced plastic, it is 9 ft 1 in (2·77 m) long, and is sufficiently small and light to be carried on the roof rack of a family car. Packed dimensions are 3 ft 3 in × 3 ft 3 in × 3 ft 6 in (1 m × 1 m × 1·1 m).

LIFT AND PROPULSION: Integrated system powered by a single 22 bhp Lloyd two-cylinder, two-stroke aircooled engine. Skirt is of bag type, in reinforced synthetic rubber.

CONTROLS: Craft heading is controlled by a single aerodynamic rudder hinged to the rear of the propeller duct and operated by a centrally positioned control column.

HULL: Deck power module package and propeller duct/roll bar are in glass reinforced plastics. Inflatable sidebodies are in reinforced synthetic rubber.

DIMENSIONS:

Length overall	9 ft 1 in (2·77 m)
Beam, on cushion	5 ft 6 in (1·68 m)
Height	3 ft 5½ in (1·05 m)

WEIGHTS

Weight empty	160 lb (73 kg)

PERFORMANCES:

Max speed over water	25 mph (40 km/h)
Max speed over land	35 mph (56 km/h)
Max gradient	1:6
Range	50 miles (80 km)

SURFACE FLIGHT LTD

HEAD OFFICE:
Vowels Lane, Kingscote, East Grinstead, Sussex RH19 4LD

TELEPHONE:
0342 28386

DIRECTORS:
A. C. Harrison
P. V. McCollum
G. R. Nichol
N. A. Old
Y. V. Ellis

Surface Flight Ltd is concentrating on the development of low-cost two-seat amphibious hovercraft, the first of which, the Sunrider, is due to go into production in October 1974.

SUNRIDER

Surface Flight's first production machine is

a glass-fibre-hulled two-seater powered by a single 48 bhp Kohler 2-stroke. Orders for the machine have been placed by clients in the United Kingdom, Western Europe, Middle East and North America. Noteworthy features include an extremely low noise level, simplicity of operation and rugged construction.

LIFT AND PROPULSION: Integrated system powered by a 48 bhp 2-cycle Kohler 440-2AS 2-stroke with electric starting and key ingition. Drive from the engine is transmitted forward via a flexible shaft to a 2 ft 0 in (0·60 m) diameter bow-mounted 5-bladed lift fan, and aft to a transverse fan shaft at the ends of which are two 2 ft (0·60 m) diameter single intake centrifugal fans for propulsion. Thrust deflectors are fitted to provide additional lift air when hovering or travelling at low speed. Fuel recommended is 2-stroke petrol oil mixture. Tank capacity is 5 Imp gallons (22·73 litres).

CONTROLS: Single control column operates twin rudders aft of the thrust ports.

HULL: Moulded glass-reinforced plastics. Manually-operated bilge pump; 3½ lb dry powder fire extinguisher.

SKIRT: Loop-segmented skirt in polyurethane nylon. Replaceable segments.

ACCOMMODATION: Single, two-place bench seat in open cockpit.

OPTIONAL EXTRAS: Tachometer, compass, ignition warning light. Fly-on/fly-off trailer. Boat type trailer also available. Electric horn and lighting, anchor, fend-offs etc.

DIMENSIONS:

Length	12 ft 8 in (3·86 m)
Beam	6 ft 6 in (1·98 m)
Height	3 ft 6 in (1·06 m)

WEIGHTS:

Empty weight	450 lb (204·10 kg)
Payload	450 lb (204·10 kg)

PERFORMANCE:

Cruising speed	35 mph (56·32 kmh)
Vertical obstacle clearance	9 in (228 mm)
Range	75 miles (120·70 km)

VOSPER THORNYCROFT LTD

HEAD OFFICE:
  Vosper House, Southampton Road, Paulsgrove, Portsmouth, England
TELEPHONE: Cosham 79481
TELEX: 86115
CABLES: Repsov, Portsmouth
DIRECTORS:

Vosper Thornycroft Limited (operating company)
  John Rix, MBE, CEng, FRINA, FIMarE, Managing Director
  Cdr C. W. S. Dreyer, DSO, DSC, RN
  P. D. P. Kemp, Managing Director (Shipbuilding)
  A. A. C. Griffith, OBE, BSc, FRINA, Development Director
  P. J. Usher, FRINA, Director in charge, Woolston Yard and Deputy Managing Director (Shipbuilding)
  K. D. C. Ford, FCA, MIMC, Financial Director
  J. E. C. Grant, FCA, ACWA, Director and Secretary
  D. P. E. Shepherd, VRD, Sales and Commercial Director
  D. E. Wilson, Ship Sales Director
  J. A. Wilde, CBE, MIMarE, Managing Director (Repairs)
SENIOR EXECUTIVES (HOVERCRAFT):
  A. E. Bingham BSc., (Tech), MIMechE, AFRAes, Chief Hovercraft Designer
  Arnaud de Cosson, Hovercraft Sales Manager

Vosper Limited is the holding company for a number of companies throughout the world, the most important of which are Vosper Thornycroft Ltd, with shipyards and repair yards at Portsmouth and Southampton and Vosper Thornycroft Private, Ltd in Singapore.

Vosper Thornycroft has a high reputation as builder of warships, including fast patrol craft, corvettes and frigates powered by diesel and gas turbine machinery singly or in combination. Vosper Thornycroft warships are in service with the Royal Navy and the navies of more than a dozen foreign and commercial countries.

With an annual turnover in the region of £42 million, derived mainly from warship and hovercraft building, Vosper Thornycroft also has a number of prosperous ancillary activities. These include the design and production of ship stabilizers, specialised electrical and electronic control equipment for marine and industrial use, oil burning equipment and furnishing.

In 1968, the decision was taken to enter

A 270-seat Vosper Thornycroft VT 1 hoverferry

Interior of one of the four corner passenger cabins flanking the VT 1's central deck area

the hovercraft field and shortly afterwards an order was received for the VT 1—an 87 ton hoverferry designed to carry 146 passengers and ten cars at speeds up to 40 knots. The VT 1 has been subjected to exhaustive trials to evaluate every aspect of its commercial viability and particularly its reliability and seakeeping, both in the English Channel and in the notoriously rough waters between the Channel Islands and the French coast. The first two all-passenger craft built by the company were operated in Scandinavian waters between Malmo, Sweden and Copenhagen, Denmark in 1972.

Operationally, the craft proved extremely successful. They carried more than 310,000 passengers and travelled more than 61,000 miles, with a mechanical reliability of 98·73 per cent.

In 1973 the company announced that it was building the VT 2, the first of a new class of fully amphibious hovercraft intended primarily for military applications. The prototype is expected to begin trials in late 1974. Design studies have covered a range of larger vessels, including a 170-ton ASW or MCM vessel and a 500-ton convoy escort.

VT 1

The VT 1 is an 87 ton ACV designed for fast, low-cost passenger/car/operation. It is built to the standards required by the British Civil Air Cushion Vehicle Safety Requirements. Power is supplied by two Avco Lycoming TF25 marine gas-turbines each driving four fixed-pitch lift fans and one controllable-pitch water propeller.

Cruising speed is 35-38 knots (65-70 km/h) and the craft will operate in complete safety in wave heights up to 10-12 ft (3-3·7 m). The VT 1 can be operated from existing terminals or alternatively, simple low-cost slipways or pontoon terminals can be established on beaches.

VARIANTS: Typical layouts include a car/passenger version for 146 passengers and 10 vehicles and a 250/270 passenger version which can be fitted with facilities for serving refreshments on route.

LIFT AND PROPULSION: Motive power is provided by two Avco Lycoming TF 25 marine gas-turbines, with power ratings between 1,675 and 2,000 hp for ambient temperatures between 80°-60°F. These are located in separate engine rooms amidships, port and starboard. Each engine is directly coupled via a transfer gearbox to four 5 ft diameter centrifugal lift fans and thence to a skeg-mounted water propeller via a Vee-drive gearbox.

The eight fans deliver air to the cushion via a continuous peripheral segmented skirt made in lightweight neoprene-proofed nylon material with full cushion depth segments. There are neither stability skirts nor other compartmentation arrangements. The skirt provides an air cushion depth of about 5½ ft (1·68 m).

The propellers are Stone KaMeWa 3-bladed controllable-pitch units and have a diameter of 2·1 ft (640 mm).

Fuel is contained in four integral tanks, located two each side in the raft structure amidships, beneath the lift fan rooms. Total fuel capacity is 3,480 Imp gallons (15,280 litres). One pressure refuelling point is fitted, on the starboard side forward. Types of fuel recommended are: Kerosene, AVTUR and Widecut; diesel, gas oil.

CONTROLS: The control cabin is located above the port side of the superstructure and provides a 360° view. Provision is made for two craft control positions abreast of each other forward, with radar located at a third seat position behind. Engine controls are on a central console within each reach of both front seat positions.

The main driving controls for course and attitude are positioned in front of the port seat, and duplicated in front of the starboard

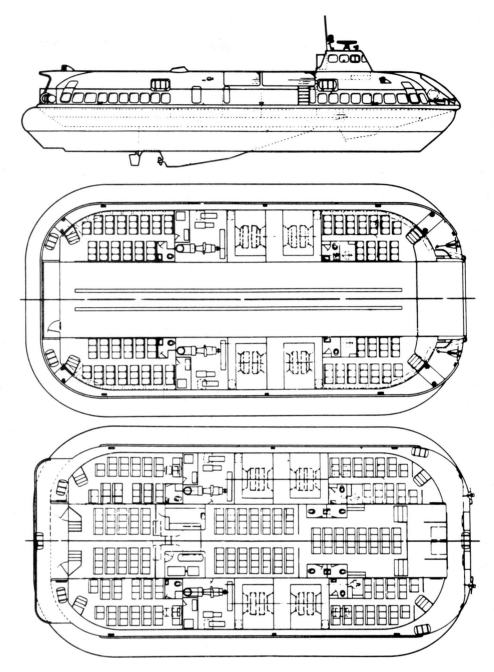

Profile of the VT I and (below) interior arrangements of the standard version for 146 passengers and 10 cars and the cruise variant for 270 passengers

seat. Directional control is provided by power-operated twin water rudders, controllable-pitch propellers and twin skegs. A water ballast system is provided for longitudinal and transverse CG adjustments.

OPERATING TECHNIQUES: The VT 1 is designed to operate like a conventional ship when at sea and when berthing alongside piers and moles. It can operate from simple concrete ramps or slips laid on any reasonably steep beach, an ideal arrangement for loading and off loading vehicles. By employing this technique for passenger car/ferry services, simple, inexpensive terminals can be built on beaches of suitable gradient (between 1 in 8 and 1 in 12) from which the craft can be operated in all tide states.

At its maintenance base, the beach landing technique is used to land the craft onto a trolley on which it is hauled out of the water

for maintenance.

HULL: Construction is mainly in marine corrosion-resistant aluminium alloys. Both the bottom and deck structures are of conventional stiffened plate. The craft bottom is designed to resist water impact pressures with closed-up framing in the bow where higher impact pressures are likely to be encountered. The deck structure in the central car bay will support axle loads up to 4,000 lb (1,814 kg)—an approximate gross vehicle weight of 3 tons (3·1 tonnes)—with lighter structure in the deck's side bays where only foot traffic is anticipated. Alternatively standard ISO 20 ft (6·1 m) containers of average weight (up to ½ ton per ft run) can be carried, using the car, guide tracks. The containers would be mounted on weight distributing rollers.

The bottom and deck structure are separated by longitudinal and transverse web frames which form a buoyancy raft of 31 separate watertight compartments including oil and fuel tanks. The raft provides the entire torsional strength of the craft. Reserve buoyancy is more than 100%.

Two main longitudinal vertically stiffened bulkheads run the length of the craft separating the central car bay from the outer machinery and the passenger bays. These provide the craft's resistance to overall longitudinal bending and shear. The outer bays are subdivided by four transverse bulkheads of similar construction linked across the central car bay by beams to provide the overall transverse strength of the craft.

The superstructure covering is of light gauge sheet with longitudinal stiffeners. It is supported on transverse roof and vertical side beams which are designed to resist aerodynamic loading in airspeeds up to 80 knots. The hull is designed for a maximum disposable load of 35 tons and a normal payload of 21 tons.

LANDING SKEGS: These are of stiffened plate construction similar to that of the buoyancy raft bottom. Loads due to beaching are diffused into the craft's longitudinal bulkheads via several main transverse frames.

ACCOMMODATION: The car/passenger version has four passenger compartments, one at each corner of the craft, and seats a total of 146 passengers. Each compartment has a toilet/washroom. There are two main entrances to each passenger compartment. For operations from a beach, passengers enter over the main ramp or may use the external superstructure doors via mobile embarkation steps.

The car bay, designed for 10 cars, has full width doors at the bow, which form an access ramp for loading and unloading. The craft always beaches bows-to, and cars must be driven off in reverse. To simplify the control and positioning of cars a guide track is provided for each lane of cars and runs the full length of the bay. This enables vehicles to be disembarked quite satisfactorily. As an alternative to cars, up to three ISO 20 ft containers can be carried.

Each passenger compartment has a sufficient number of approved emergency exits according to the numbers carried. A full range of safety equipment is carried. Both main engine rooms have individual fire warning and extinguishing systems monitored and controlled from the control cabin. The control cabin and each passenger compartment have hand-operated extinguishers.

One inflatable lifejacket of approved type is stowed under each seat in the passenger saloons, and in addition. liferafts catering for at least 100% of passengers and crew are stowed externally.

HEATING AND VENTILATION: Fresh air heating and ventilating is provided for the four passenger compartments and control cabin only. The heating plant is a separate combustion heater and blower unit. It supplies fresh air at ambient or higher temperatures and is thermostatically controlled. Complete air conditioning can be fitted if required.

A fast patrol variant of the VT 2

Impression of the 100 ton fast patrol boat, based on the VT1. Two 2,750 hp Avco Lycoming TF 35 gas turbines power the lift/propulsion system. Maximum speed is 46 knots.

SYSTEMS:
ELECTRICAL: 240 volt 50 HZ single-phase AC: 115 volt 400 HZ single-phase AC; 24 volt DC.

Provision for shore supply.

The 240 volt 50 HZ AC supplies are derived from diesel-driven alternators rated at 28 kVA continuous, giving 22·4 kW at 0·8 power factor, lagging. Other supplies are those met from transformer/rectifiers and solid state inverters. The medium voltage service supplies the following: lighting and heating; pumps for the fuel, propeller blade pitch and bilge systems; the transformer/ rectifiers for the 115 volt single-phase AC and main 24 volt DC supplies. The 115 volt. 400 HZ AC provides power for the following control systems: steering, speed (propeller blade pitch-adjustment), turbine power (throttle controls).

HYDRAULICS: A 3,000 lb/sq in (14,647 kgt/m²) hydraulic system is installed to operate the rudders, bow door and ramp when fitted. Propeller pitch is actuated by a separate system.

COMMUNICATIONS AND NAVIGATION: Standard equipment includes the following: VHF and standby VHF radio; crew intercom and public address system.
NAVIGATION: Decca 202 radar, Sperry CL.2 gyro compass and two repeaters standby magnetic compass, waterspeed indicator and log, and echo sounder.

Decca Navigator and Flight Log is optional. Alternative equipment can be fitted to customer specification.

DIMENSIONS, EXTERNAL:

Length overall	95 ft 6 in (29 m)
Beam	43 ft 6 in (13·26 m)
Base of skegs to masthead	
	41 ft 9 in (12·73 m)
Calm water level to masthead on hover	
	37 ft 5 in (11·41 m)
Cushion depth	5 ft 6 in (1·67 m)
Draft afloat	9 ft 9 in (2·97 m)
Draft hovering	3 ft 9 in (1·14 m)
Cushion area	3,487 sq ft (324 m²)

DIMENSIONS, INTERNAL:
Four passenger cabins with toilets, each with the following dimensions:

Length	24 ft 0 in (7·3 m)
Max width	13 ft 6 in (4·1 m)
Max height	7 ft 6 in (2·3 m)
Floor area	320 sq ft (29·8 m²) app

Vehicle bay (may also be used for passenger accommodation):

Length	79 ft 6 in (24·2 m)
Width, clear	16 ft 0 in (4·85 m)
Height, clear	9 ft 8 in (2·95 m)
Max axle load	4,000 lb (1,820 kg)

SIZE AND POSITION OF DOORS:
Forward loading door, 17 ft (5·1 m) wide × 9 ft 8 in (2·97 m) high. Four passenger external access doors to saloons, four further doors from saloons to car bay.

WEIGHTS:

Empty weight	55 tons
Normal maximum operating weight	87 tons
Normal operating weight	83 tons
Normal disposable load	27·5 tons
Normal payload	22 tons

PERFORMANCE (At maximum continuous power and normal operating weight), at ambient temperatures of 60°F:

Normal service speed 38 knots (70 km/h)

Turning circle diameter at 38 knots entry speed 2,000 ft (610 m)

Water speed in 4 ft waves and 15 knot headwind 35 knots (64 km/h)

Max wave capability at 15 knots 12 ft (3·6 m)

Max wave capability on scheduled runs 8 ft (2·44 m)

Still air range and endurance:

at normal fuel load 150 n miles, 4 hours

at maximum fuel load 340 n miles, 9 hours

VOSPER THORNYCROFT FAST PATROL HOVERCRAFT

Based on the VT 1, this gas-turbine powered hovercraft patrol boat has a floating displacement of 100 tons and a speed of 46 knots. Typical armament would comprise Exocet anti-ship missile launchers, and a twin-barrelled 35 mm Oerlikon cannon designed primarily for rapid and accurate fire against aircraft and guided missiles, but which is also extremely effective when directed against light surface craft. The missiles and cannon will be controlled by a Contraves fire control system or a similar system.

The craft offers a number of important advantages over conventional fast patrol boats of comparable size. In particular, due to the depth and flexibility of its fully peripheral skirt, the craft can maintain a high speed and provide a stable weapons platform in sea conditions in which many patrol boats would scarcely be able to operate.

LIFT AND PROPULSION: Motive power is provided by two Avco Lycoming TF 35 gas-turbines each rated at 2,750 shp at 60°F ambient temperatures located in separate engine rooms amidships port and starboard. Each engine is coupled via a transfer-gearbox to four g.r.p. lift fans and thence to a water propeller via a vee-drive gearbox. Total fuel capacity is 20 tons.

ARMAMENT. One 35 mm twin Oerlikon cannon and four Exocet missile launchers. Search radar, fire control radar, fire control systems for guns and missiles and electronic countermeasures equipment. Other suitable combinations can be installed.

HULL: Construction is mainly in marine corrosion-resistant light alloys.

ACCOMMODATION: Captain, three officers, three senior ratings and seven junior ratings are accommodated in air conditioned spaces, furnished to modern standards.

CONTROLS: The control cabin is located above the superstructure on the longitudinal centreline amidships and provides a 360° view. The control position is forward to port, with an engineer's position to starboard and navigator's and observer's positions behind.

Directional control is provided by power-operated twin water rudders, controllable-pitch propellers and twin skegs.

OPERATING TECHNIQUE: As for Vosper VT 1.

COMMUNICATIONS AND NAVIGATION: Decca TM626 navigational radar and full craft-to-air, craft-to-ship and craft-to-shore communications.

DIMENSIONS:

Length overall	93 ft 6 in (28·05 m)
Beam (hard structure)	43 ft 6 in (13·25 m)
Draft hovering	3 ft 6 in (1·07 m)
Draft hullborne	10 ft 0 in (3·05 m)

WEIGHTS:

Basic weight	66 tons
Armament and crew	24 tons
Fuel	20 tons
Total (in half fuel condition)	100 tons

PERFORMANCE:

Max speed	46 knots

Endurance

With 20 tons of fuel, the endurance is 14 hours at 43 knots, or 600 nautical miles

VT 2

First fully amphibious hovercraft to be built by Vosper Thornycroft, the VT 2 is intended for military applications. It employs air propulsion instead of water propellers, enabling the vessel to traverse shallows and operate from small coves and beaches. In overall size, configuration and payload, it is similar to the earlier VT 1 mixed-traffic ferry. Externally, the feature which immediately identifies the craft is the presence above the stern superstructure of two 13 ft 6 in (4·11 m) diameter ducted fans, which are powered by Proteus marine gas-turbines.

A number of variants are projected, ranging from a 65-knot logistic support vessel to a patrol craft armed with four surface-to-surface missiles and a rapid-fire cannon.

Normal load capacity of the logistic support variant is about 32 tons, but considerable overloading is acceptable, and with suitable deck reinforcing, a 50-ton Chieftain battle tank could be carried.

The ducted fans are designed to maintain a noise level far lower than that of earlier air-propelled craft. Its negligible water noise signature, combined with a low surface pressure and slight magnetic signature will render it less vulnerable to mines.

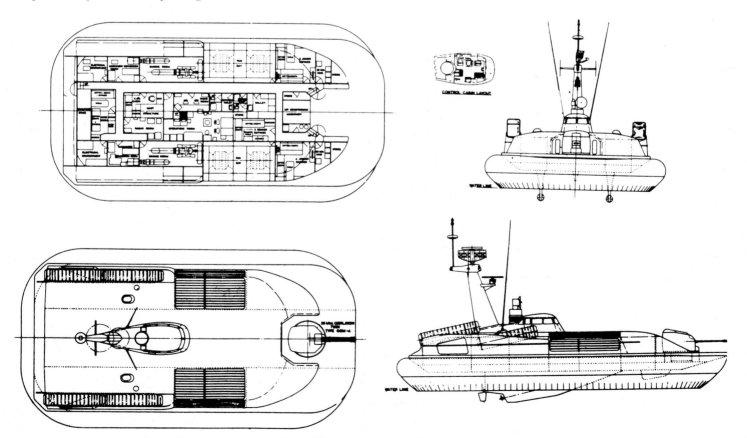

General arrangement of the Vosper Thornycroft hovercraft FPB equipped with four exocet anti-ship missile launchers and a twin-barrelled 35mm oerlikon cannon.

The vessel can either be shipped to a theatre of operations, or if required by a NATO country, it could be deployed to any point on the coastline of Europe or the Mediterranean under its own power. The longest 'stage' would be from the United Kingdom to Gibraltar, a distance of approximately 1,100 nautical miles, and to allow an adequate reserve en route for rough seas, the craft would carry an additional 10 tons of fuel, starting out at an all-up weight of 115 tons.

LIFT AND PROPULSION: Motive power for the integrated lift/propulsion system is supplied by two Rolls Royce Proteus marine gas-turbines rated at 4,500 shp maximum and 3,800 shp continuous. The gas turbines are installed in port and starboard engine rooms, amidship, and each powers two drive shafts via a David Brown gearbox. One shaft transmits power to a bank of four centrifugal lift fans, which absorbs about one third of the output, the other drives a ducted propulsion fan via an inclined shaft.

The 13 ft 6 in (4·11 m) diameter propulsion fans, made by Dowty Rotol, have variable-pitch blades and are housed in ducts manufactured by Vosper Thornycroft. Each engine/fan unit provides sufficient power to maintain the craft on full cushion and ensure adequate controllability in the event of a single engine failure.

The blade tip speed will be low so that the noise commonly associated with open air propellers will be substantially reduced.

CONTROLS: Control surfaces for vectoring thrust are fitted aft of the fans for normal steering, but differential pitch is used for steering at low speeds. Thrust can be varied for manoeuvring the craft without altering the engine speed or cushion depth.

HULL: Structure similar to that of VT 1. Built mainly in marine, corrosion-resistant aluminium alloys.

Preliminary details of the four main variants are summarised below, together with weights.

DIMENSIONS (all variants):

Length overall	99 ft 0 in (31·17 m)
Beam overall	43 ft 6 in (13·10 m)
Cushion height	5 ft 6 in (1·67 m)
Hand structure clearance when hovering	3 ft 7 in (1·09 m)
Draft in deplacement condition	2 ft 10 in (0·86 m)
Height (hovering to top of propulsion fan ducts)	30 ft 3 in (9·15 m)

PERFORMANCE:

Max speed, calm conditions
                 in excess of 60 knots
Max speed in 5 ft (1·52 m) waves 55 knots

VARIANTS:

VT 2 LOGISTIC SUPPORT (UNARMED)

Designed to carry a company of 130 fully-armed troops and their vehicles. The vehicle bay is approximately 16½ ft (5·02 m) wide, 9½ ft (2·89 m) high and 70 ft (21·33 m) long. It has a full width bow ramp and door together with an 8 ft (2·43 m) wide stern ramp and door for the through loading and unloading of vehicles. The craft can carry payloads of 30-33 tons, together with fuel for five hours. Considerable overloading of the craft is acceptable at reduced performance so that with suitable deck and entrance ramp reinforcing, a 50 ton Chieftain battle tank could be carried.

Above and below: Logistic support version of the new fully-amphibious VT 2. Two massive ducted fans, each 13 ft 6 in (4·11 m) in diameter, dominate the stern superstructure

Artist's impression of a missile-equipped fast patrol version of the VT 2

Impression of the Vosper Thornycroft 170 ton ASW or MCM vessel. Maximum speed would be in excess of 50 knots

WEIGHTS:

Operating weight	62·5	
Payload	32·0	
Fuel	10·5	
Starting auw	105·0 tons	

VT 2 MULTI-ROLE LOGISTIC SUPPORT AND GENERAL PURPOSE PATROL

Fitted with a rear loading door and ramp, enabling four 1-ton Landrovers and 60 troops to be loaded in the aft section of the central bay. The bow is the same as that of the lightly armed fast patrol version. The forward area of the central bay and the forward cabins on each side would be fitted out as a small operations room and crew quarters.

WEIGHTS:

Operating weight	65·5	
Armament and crew	5·0	
Payload	19·0	
Fuel	10·5	
Starting auw	100·0 tons	

VT 2 FAST PATROL, HEAVILY ARMED

This version can be equipped with two Otomat missiles and a 57 mm Bofors cannon or alternatively four Otomat missiles may be fitted in conjunction with a smaller rapid-fire cannon. Other armament of similar weight could be fitted to meet individual specifications. Armament and crew weight is 23½ tons, and with 10½ tons of fuel, the endurance is five hours or 300 nm at 60 knots. An additional 10½ tons of fuel for the overload case (giving a half fuel weight of 100 tons) results in a range of 600 nm.

WEIGHTS:

Operating weight	66·0	
Armament and crew	23·5	
Fuel	10·5	
Starting auw	100·0 tons	

VT 2 FAST PATROL, LIGHTLY ARMED

Armed with a twin Hispano-Suiza 30 mm cannon. At a starting weight of 100 tons, it has 24½ tons of fuel, providing a range of 700 nm or 11½ hours endurance at a speed of 60 knots. An additional 10½ tons of fuel (a total of 35 tons), increases the range to 1,000 nm.

WEIGHTS:

Operating weight	70·5	
Armament and crew	5·0	
Fuel	24·5	
Starting auw	100·0 tons	

170-TON ASW OR MCM VESSEL

This design for a 170-ton anti-submarine or mine countermeasures vessel is based on that of the 100-ton fast patrol boat. An increase in installed horsepower and length provides off-shore capability, and the larger deck area permits the installation of a wider range of weapons.

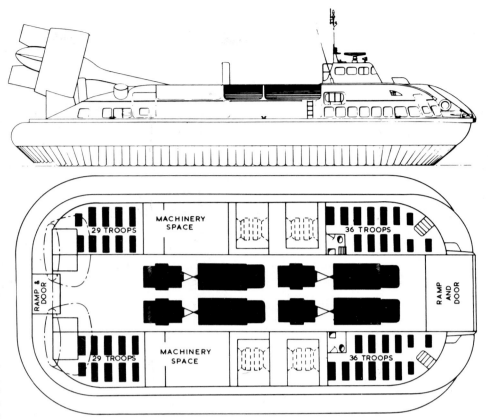

Outboard profile and accommodation plan of the VT 2 in logistic support configuration

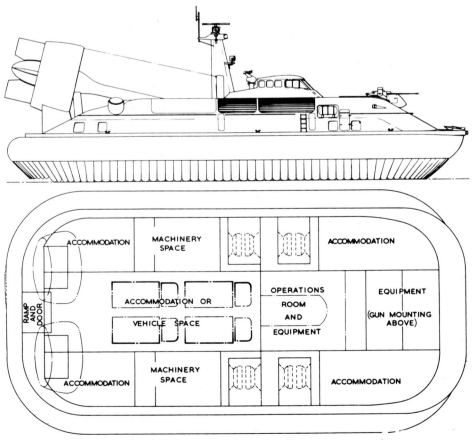

VT 2 equipped for lightly armed patrol and general purpose roles

Motive power is supplied by three Rolls-Royce Proteus gas-turbines driving lift fans and three axial-flow waterjet units. Alternatively the designers propose a CODAG arrangement in which diesel engines can be coupled to the integrated lift/propulsion system to provide increased range.

DIMENSIONS:

Length overall	37·1 m
Beam (hard structure)	12·25 m
Height, power on (sea level to top of control cabin)	8·1 m
Cushion depth	2·3 m
Hovering draught	1·0 m
Floating draught (gear retracted)	1·5 m

WEIGHTS:

All-up weight	170 tonnes
Armament load	29 tonnes

PERFORMANCE:

Range full power	700 nm
With diesels fitted for low speed cruising—at AUW 182 tonnes—15 knots	1,500 nm
Speed, maximum continuous	In excess of 50 knots

500-TON ASW OR CONVOY ESCORT

The main role for which this vessel has been designed is that of ocean convoy escort. Lift fans and waterjet units would be driven by a Rolls-Royce Olympus and two Avco Lycoming TF45 gas turbines.

DIMENSIONS:

Length overall	66 m
Beam (hard structure)	19 m
Height (sea level to top of control cabin— on cushion)	13·5 m
Cushion depth	3·5 m
Hovering draught	1·7 m
Floating draught (skeg folded)	2·8 m

WEIGHTS:

All-up weight	500 tonnes
Armament load	50 tonnes

PERFORMANCE:

Range full power	1,200 nm
Range at 23 kts	2,000 nm
Speed—maximum continuous	In excess of 50 knots

VT 1M

Built as a manned scale model of the VT1 hovercraft, the VT 1M has now completed its programme of development trials, including a test programme with waterjet propulsion.

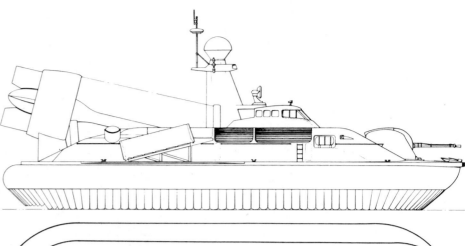

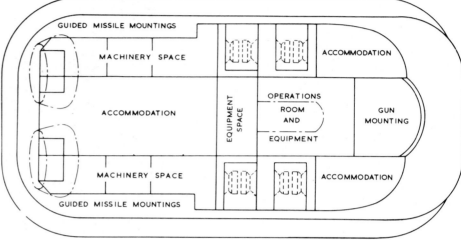

The VT 2 heavily-armed patrol craft carries either two Otomat missiles and a 57 mm Bofors cannon, or alternatively four Otomat missiles and a smaller gun

VT IM-001 equipped with a waterjet propulsion system

A 500-ton ocean-going escort designed by Vosper Thornycroft. A helicopter landing pad and hangar can be provided aft of the superstructure

UNITED STATES

AEROJET-GENERAL CORPORATION
(Subsidiary of the General Tire and Rubber Co)

HEAD OFFICE:
9100 East Flair Drive, El Monte, California 91734

TELEPHONE:
(213) 572-6000

WORKS:
Surface Effect Ships Division,
Aerojet-General Corporation,
PO Box 2173 Tacoma, Washington 98401

TELEPHONE:
(206) 597-6111

SENIOR EXECUTIVES:
Corporate:
J. H. Vollbrecht, President
Surface Effect Ships Division:
E. D. Ward, Vice President and General Manager

Aerojet-General began research and development programmes on both rigid sidewall and skirted amphibious air cushion configurations in June 1966. The company's research and development programmes include lift system development, skirt and structural materials investigations and development sub-scale and full-scale dynamic model testing, test laboratory development and full-scale vehicle operation. In addition, Aerojet has conducted government and company funded design and application studies on many rigid sidewall and skirted air cushion vehicle designs for military, non-military government and commercial roles. Work is at present concentrated on US Navy contracts for the development of large marine and amphibious vehicles including the SES-100A, 100-ton surface effect ship test craft, the 2,000-ton class SES operational combat ship prototype and the AALC Jeff(A) amphibious assault landing craft. In addition the company is undertaking the design of a 150-ton "soft sidewall" SEV under an Advanced Research Projects Agency contract.

SES-100A

Earlier contracts for preliminary design of a "less than 100-ton" SES craft and for the dynamic test programme for the US Navy's XR-3 research craft led to the award of a contract, in January 1969, for the detailed design, construction and test of a 100-ton rigid sidewall testcraft—the SES-100A—which is now under the sponsorship and management of the Surface Effect Ships Programme Office (SESPO), an agency of the US Navy.

Dockside testing began in August 1971 and deep water trials began in May 1972. Official US Navy test and evaluation trials began in September 1972 and were due to be completed in early 1974.

LIFT AND PROPULSION: Motive power for the integrated lift/propulsion system is supplied by four 3,500 shp Avco Lycoming gas-turbines. The transmission system couples the gas-turbines to two Aerojet-General two-stage axial/centrifugal waterjet pumps and three axial-flow lift fans through reduction gears. Power plant airflow is supplied through demisters from inlets located on the topside. The two waterjet pumps (port and starboard units) are installed on rail mounts that permit them to be removed through a port in the transom. The three axial-flow

Above and below: Aerojet-General's SES-100A during a series of high-speed test runs. The craft is powered by four 3,500 hp Avco Lycoming TF 35 gas-turbines and has a maximum speed of about 80 knots. Shown in these photographs are the forward skegs, used for directional control at high speeds, and the two engine air inlets on the topside, aft. The cabin accommodates four crew members and up to six test observers

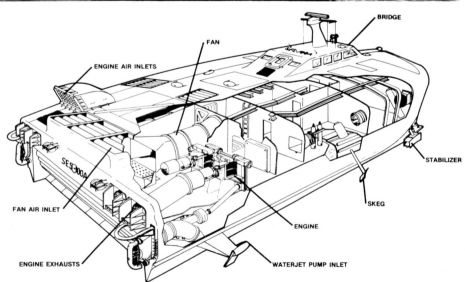

Cutaway drawing showing the positions of the waterjet pump inlets, skegs and bow stabilisers on the SES-100A

fans are located in compartments between the port and starboard engines. The four gas-turbines can be employed in any combination to drive the lift/propulsion system. For improved fuel consumption, the craft can cruise on two engines.

CONTROLS: At low speeds directional control is provided by waterjet thrust vector and at high speed by movable skegs, port and starboard. The fuel and fuel-trim subsystem comprises four fuel storage tanks—two in each sidewall; a service tank and bow and stern trim ranks. Trim is adjusted by transferring fuel from tank to tank by means of the fuel transfer pumps.

HULL: The hull, constructed by the Tacoma Boatbuilding Co., Tacoma, Washington, is a welded aluminium structure, built up from frames, stringers, beams, girders, bulkheads and plate aluminium skin. It is divided into compartments by transverse and longitudinal bulkheads. The weather deck, cargo deck and bridge are in glass-reinforced plastic.

ACCOMMODATION: The bridge, which is air-conditioned and sound-insulated, is located on the centreline forward. It accommodates four crew members and six observers. Crew safety during dockside and weatherdeck operations is provided by portable stanchions, life lines, and a non-skid surface on the weatherdeck. Emergency equipment includes inflatable life vests, life rafts, life rings, protective helmets and outer clothing, seat belts and harnesses. Fire detection and extinguishing systems consist of flame and smoke detectors and extinguishers located throughout the vessel.

SYSTEMS: Electrical: Power generation and distribution system supplies electrical and electronic operational equipment and the data acquisition subsystem (DAS). The primary purpose of the DAS is to measure selected testcraft performance parameters and record the resulting data on magnetic tape. The secondary purpose is to provide instantaneous data display.

COMMUNICATIONS AND NAVIGATION: Standard marine radio is carried and radar is included for collision avoidance. A gyro compass is fitted.

HYDRAULIC SYSTEM: 3,000 psig pressure and 100 psig return pressure.

COMPRESSED AIR: Engine bleed air is used for stern seal spring pressurisation. Stored compressed air is used for turbine starting and braking.

DIMENSIONS:

Length overall	81 ft 11 in (24·9 m)
Beam overall	41 ft 11 in (12·7 m)
Length-to-beam ratio	1·95
Cushion area	2,467 ft² (230 m²)
Height on cushion	23 ft 0 in (7·01 m)
Draft displacement condition	10 ft 7½ in (3·22 m)
Freeboard (design load waterline)	8 ft 7½ in (2·62 m)

WEIGHTS:

Light displacement	72·8 short tons
Loaded displacement design	100 short tons
Displacement fully loaded	123 short tons

PERFORMANCE:

Max speed, calm water 80 knots or more

2,000-TON OPERATIONAL SES WARSHIP

The success of the SES-100A testcraft programme resulted in the award of a SESPO preliminary design contract for a 2,000 ton operational prototype SES warship. The design will incorporate many of the SES-100A test craft systems, including waterjet propulsion.

The vessel will be equipped with ASW, AAW and SUW weapon systems and will be capable of about 80 knots. Preliminary estimates indicate that the vessel will be approximately 259 ft 0 in (78·9 m) long, will have an overall beam of 108 ft (32·9 m) and a height to the top of the bridge of 61 ft (18·6 m). It was anticipated that development and design would begin in early 1974, followed by detailed design and test.

ARCTIC SEV

Aerojet was awarded a conceptual and parametric study contract in April 1972 by the Advanced Research Projects Agency of the Department of Defense to study skirt and structure concepts and perform parametric design analyses necessary for the design of a skirted air cushion vehicle to operate in the Arctic. The work is being carried out under the technical management of the US Navy.

In early 1973, the study was augmented to include the preliminary design of an ACV with a nominal all-up weight of 150 tons. It is anticipated that the preliminary design will be based on the AALC Jeff(A), with modifications including the "winterizing" of systems and components, and the extension

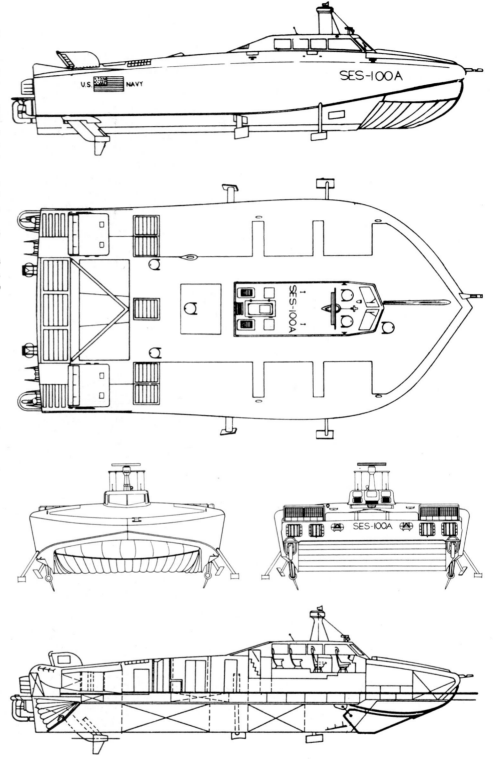

General arrangement of the Aerojet-General SES-100A, showing the revised loop-and-segment bow seal design

of the skirt depth to approximately 10 ft 0 in (3·04 m) to provide greater obstacle clearance capability.

AALC JEFF(A)

In 1970, Aerojet-General was awarded a contract by US Naval Ship Systems Command for the preliminary design of an experimental 160-ton 50-knot amphibious assault landing craft. This was followed in March 1971 by a further contract for the detail design, construction and test of the craft, which is designated AALC Jeff(A) Construction of Jeff(A) was scheduled to begin in 1974. Manufacturer's and US Navy

trials will be undertaken during 1976 and 1977.

The craft is designed to operate at a nominal speed of 50 knots in Sea State 2 and accommodate up to 75 tons in palletised supplies and/or equipment. It is designed primarily for use by the US Marine Corps, and will carry tanks, trucks, half-trucks and other equipment from an LPD, LSD or LHA mother ship to a point inland.

To ensure adequate world-wide operational capability, the specification calls for operation in temperatures from 0°-100°F.

Construction of the craft will be undertaken by Todd Shipyards Corporation, Seattle, Washington.

LIFT AND PROPULSION: Cushion lift is provided by two 2,800 hp Avco Lycoming TF40 gas-turbines, one in each of the two sidestructures, driving two sets of four 4 ft 0 in (1·21 m) diameter fans through lightweight transmission and shafting connections.

Thrust is supplied by four 2,800 hp Avco Lycoming TF40 gas-turbines each driving a 7 ft 5 in (2·26 m) diameter pylon-mounted shrouded propeller, located above the side-structure, and outside the cargo deck area to provide free access and uninterrupted air flow. Each propeller pylon rotates to provide both propulsion and directional control.

HULL: Constructed in marine aluminium with maximum use of corrugated structures to minimise total craft weight. The main hull is formed by a buoyancy raft with port and starboard side structures. Each side-structure contains three Avco Lycoming gas-turbines with associated air intakes, exhausts, shrouded propellers, lift fans, transmissions and auxiliary power systems.

The bottom and deck structures of the hull are separated by longitudinal and transverse bulkheads to form a number of watertight flotation compartments. The cargo deck area is 2,280 sq ft (211·82 m²); the bow ramp opening width is 21 ft 6 in (6·55 m) and the aft ramp width is 27 ft 4 in (8·33 m).

SKIRT: 5 ft (1·52 m) deep "Pericell" loop and cell type.

ACCOMMODATION: Two air-conditioned and sound-insulated compartments, each seating three crew members or observers. Access to each compartment is via the cargo deck.

DIMENSIONS:
Length overall, on cushion
                96 ft 1 in (29·30 m)
  on landing pads   92 ft 0 in (28·04 m)
Beam overall, on cushion
                48 ft 0 in (14·63 m)
  on landing pads   44 ft 0 in (13·41 m)
Height overall, on cushion
                23 ft 1 in (7·03 m)
  on landing pads   18 ft 9 in (5·71 m)
Bow ramp opening width
                21 ft 6 in (6·55 m)
Stern ramp opening width
                27 ft 4 in (8·33 m)
Cargo deck area   2,280 sq ft (211·82 m²)

WEIGHTS:
Gross weight   334,000 lb (154,221 kg)
Empty weight   180,000 lb (81,697 kg)
Fuel   40,000 lb (18,144 kg)
Design payload   120,000 lb (54,431 kg)
Design overload 150,000 lb (68,038 kg)

PERFORMANCE:
Max speed with design payload   50 knots
Range   200 nm
Max gradient, standing start   11½%
Nominal obstacle clearance
                4 ft 0 in (1·21 m)

Aerojet-General's preliminary design for a 2,000-ton ASW SES for the US Navy. Submarine detection equipment is located in bays beneath the helipad aft of the deckhouse. At the rear end of the deckhouse superstructure, hangar space is provided. Armament includes two four-cell Harpoon surface-to-surface missile launchers located forward on the weather deck, and one eight-cell Sparrow missile launcher above the hangar. Space for Standard missile launchers is provided amidships

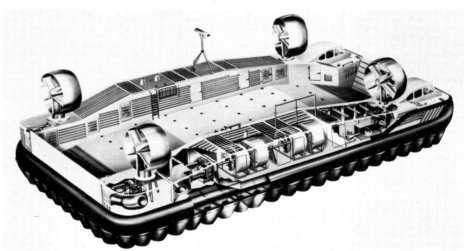

Above and below: The Aerojet-General Jeff(A) amphibious assault landing craft under construction for the US Navy. Designed primarily to meet the US Marine Corp's requirements in the 1980s, it will carry tanks, trucks, half tracks and other equipment from LPD, LSD or LHA mother ships to the shore at a speed of 50 knots

AEROMAR CORPORATION

HEAD OFFICE:
567 Fairway Road, Ridgewood, New Jersey
PRINCIPAL SHAREHOLDERS:
E. K. Liberatore
G. O. Rennerts
W. W. Kelly
PRESIDENT:
E. K. Liberatore
VICE PRESIDENT:
G. O. Rennerts

Aeromar Corporation was formed in 1964 on the initiative of E. K. Liberatore, the engineering consultant, who has been active in the ACV field since 1958.

Current activities include:

A joint engineering programme with Aerophysics Corporation on a 1,000-ton Arctic SEV; arctic environmental studies (see technical paper in this edition); negotiations with International Hydrolines Inc for a joint A-1 programme.

AEROMAR A-1 (Model 149)

Aeromar's first commercial design is the model A-1, a gas-turbine powered, amphibious passenger ferry with a cruising speed of 44 knots. A freight carrier version is being planned with a gross weight of 30,000 lb and a maximum payload of 9 tons.

LIFT AND PROPULSION: Power is provided by two separate lift/propulsion units, each comprising a Garrett 331 shaft turbine, a propeller, drive system and lift fan. The propellers are of standard, variable-pitch Hartzell type and the fans, which are driven through a right angle gearbox and shafting, are specially designed, solid fibreglass units and have a variable-pitch control.

The powerplant cowls are completely sealed to avoid water seepage into the nacelles. Engine air intake is from the pressurized duct plenum.

The fuel system consists of four flexible cells in the wall of the passenger well, one in each quarter. This permits balancing the craft with fuel, augmenting the ballast boxes provided fore and aft in the hull.

CONTROL: The operator uses a wheel for roll, column movement for pitch and rudder pedals for yaw. Two hydraulically-actuated aerodynamic rudders, operating in the airscrew slipstream, provide directional control. The horizontal stabilisers are used to balance out pitching moments in forward flight. Pitch and roll control are provided by raising the flexible skirt on the appropriate side. Hovering yaw control is produced by differential pitch of the propellers, and a slight amount of additional yaw can be produced by the impingement of exhaust gas on the rudders. An optional feature is an aircraft-

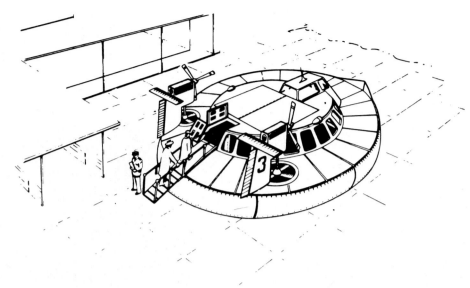

Aeromar's A-1 circular planform, amphibious ACV will be powered by two 600 shp Garrett 331 shaft turbines. Seating 45—56 passengers the craft will cruise at 50 mph

type tricycle landing gear. This permits taxi-ing with positive ground control.

HULL: The craft is of circular planform with two integrated lift/propulsion units at the rear. Passengers are accommodated in a central well which is covered by a glazed superstructure. Forward of the well and set slightly above the passenger compartment superstructure is the pilothouse.

The passenger well is a double wall cylinder of aluminium sheet, open at its upper end, and covered by a sheet aluminium structure containing plexiglas windows. Both the roof and the passenger floor are flat aluminium honeycomb structures built up from standard panels. The walls and floor are divided by bulkheads into watertight compartments.

The air duct around the passenger compartment is doughnut-shaped, and built from sub-assembled segments which are attached around the passenger well.

The flexible structure consists basically of a peripheral skirt and dividing members across the case.

ACCOMMODATION: Entrance to the passenger compartment, which will seat from 44 (standard) to 56 (maximum) depending on the operator's requirements, is from the rear, through a double doorway and down a flight of steps. The compartment can be converted to a cargo hold by removal of the roof and seats.

The pilothouse, which provides a 360° view, is located forward of the passenger well and accommodates a crew of two. Access is normally from inside the passenger compartment; a side door is provided for on-deck

activities.

Standard marine equipment is carried to meet US Coast Guard requirements.

DIMENSIONS:
Length overall	14·02 m (46 ft 0 in)
Width overall	13·04 m (43 ft 0 in)
Height	6·09 m (20 ft 0 in)
Cushion area	117 m² (1,260 sq ft)

WEIGHTS:
Gross weight	11,500 kg (25,200 lb)
Empty weight	5,450 kg (12,000 lb)
Useful load	6,000 kg (13,200 lb)

PASSENGERS:
Maximum	56
Crew	2

PERFORMANCE:
Max hover height (daylight clearance)	0·305 m (1 ft 0 in)
Max negotiable wave height	1·83 m (6 ft 0 in)
Max speed (calm water)	74 knots
Cruising speed	44 knots

AEROMAR SEV 1000-S

This is a design study of a 1,000-ton twin-duct Airjet intended for operations on the Arctic ice pack.

MODEL A-1S

This is a projected variant of the A-1 powered by two steam engines. The power plants are under development by Steamotive Inc of Tempe, Arizona.

Unit weight of the plant is under 1 lb/hp, with sfc in the ·35 lb/hr/hp range.

The plant uses a closed cycle water/steam system, with steam delivered at 1,000 psi and 800°F.

AIRCUSHION BOAT COMPANY INC

HEAD OFFICE:
401 Alexander Avenue, Building 391, Tacoma, Washington 98421
TELEPHONE:
(206) 272 3600
EXECUTIVES:
W. W. Buckley, President

The Aircushion Boat Company is responsible for the development of the Airboat—a concept described by the company as an air-cushion-assisted catamaran. Vessels of this series of sidewall craft are based on conventional fibreglass hulls and employ

water propeller or waterjet propulsion. Lift is supplied by an independent engine/fan system and flexible skirts are fitted fore and aft to contain the air cushion.

The company states that the cushion supports 75% of the loaded weight of the Airboats, and that as a result of the reduced drag the prototype uses 20% less fuel per mile. Another advantage is that when travelling at high speed, the air cushion softens the ride by preventing heavy slamming. Vessels of this type are being marketed by the company for a variety of applications including fast crew boats, water taxis,

patrol boats, survey and sports fishing craft.

AIRBOAT III

Airboat III is employed as a development craft and began trials in Puget Sound in January 1974.

It has performed in short 4 ft (1·21 m) waves at speeds up to 35 knots without undue discomfort to the crew due to slamming. Another characteristic is that it generates very little wash when executing full speed runs on smooth water in protected waterways.

LIFT AND PROPULSION: Two 330 Chrysler petrol engines driving twin water screws propel the craft. A third engine

powers a centrifugal fan for cushion lift.
HULL: Fine retardant foam and fibreglass
sandwich construction.

DIMENSIONS:

Length	38 ft (11·58 m)
Beam	13 ft 6 in (4·11 m)

WEIGHTS:

All-up weight	16,000 lb (7,257 kg)
Normal payload	3,000 lb (1,360 kg)

PERFORMANCE:

Cruising speed	35 knots
Maximum speed	40 knots plus

42 FT AIRBOAT

The 42 ft (12·8 m) long Airboat is a high
speed passenger ferry/freighter capable of
operating in 4·5 ft waves. In passenger configuration seating is provided for 21 plus a
crew of two.

A feature of the design is the extension of
the bow well ahead of the air cushion. When
rough water forces the bow down at speed
the broad area forward of the cushion planes
and raises the bow without slamming.

With the lift fan system off, the craft
operates as a conventional displacement
catamaran and has a top speed of 15 knots
With the lift system on, acceleration to the
cruising speed of 30 knots is easily attained
in ten boat lengths. In 8-10 ft (2·4-3·04 m)
following seas a stable, near horizontal
attitude is maintained while contouring
swells and no tendency to broach or lose
directional control is experienced.

LIFT AND PROPULSION: Motive power
is supplied by three GMC 6V-53 diesels, one
for lift and one for propulsion. The lift
engine drives a large low rpm centrifugal fan
contained in a reinforced box which is an
integral part of the hull structure. Power is
transmitted via a clutch and Spicer shaft to
a heavy duty, lightweight right-angle gearbox. Power delivered to the fan at cruise
condition pressure and airflow is 160 hp.
Each of the propulsion engines is turbo-
charged and drives a Hamilton 3⅞ in (10 cm)
diameter waterjet. The waterjet system has
been developed and is supplied by Stewart &
Stevenson, Houston, Texas. Each engine
delivers 220 hp to the two waterjets at
2,400 rpm. The standard fuel tank capacity
is 300 gallons, providing a cruising range of
more than 250 miles at 30 knots. Total fuel
consumption at 30 knots is 34 gph.

Marine propellers can be fitted to the vessel
instead of waterjets if required. The powerplant remains the same, but the propulsion
engines supply power through a reversing
gearbox to a shaft and marine propellers.
Hydraulically operated twin rudders are
mounted on the transom of each of the hulls.
The propeller-driven version is capable of the
same top speed, with slightly improved fuel
economy.

HULL: Robust, fire-retardant foam and
fibreglass sandwich structure, with unitized
beam tying the catamaran hulls. High

Airboat III during trials on Puget Sound

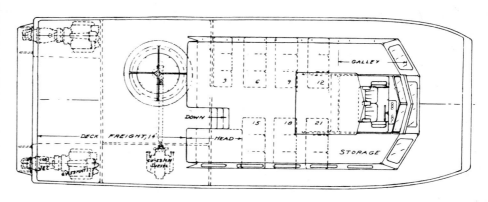

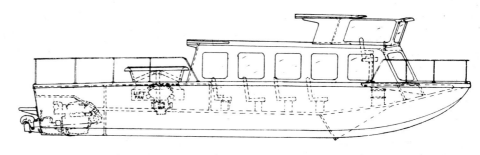

General arrangement of the waterjet-propelled 42 ft Airboat

freeboard, wide buoyant hull and low profile
for seaworthiness in rough seas and gale force
winds.

ACCOMMODATION: In passenger/crew boat
configuration, accommodation is provided for
21 seat passengers and a crew of 2. The
passenger saloon is completely enclosed with
6 ft 6 in (1·98 m) high headroom throughout.
The cabin contains a galley, head and large
storage area. The bridge is elevated for 360°
view and is located slightly aft of the bow.
A sliding hard top provides upward visibility

if required.

DIMENSIONS:

Length	42 ft (12·80 m)
Beam	17 ft (5·18 m)

PERFORMANCE:

Service speed	30 knots
Maximum speed	in excess of 33 knots
Max speed, displacement condition	15 knots
Fuel consumption at 30 knots	34 gph (154·56 l/ph)
Cruising range at 30 knots	over 250 miles (402 km)

AIR CUSHION VEHICLES, INC

HEAD OFFICE:
R.D.5., Box 85, Troy, New York 12180
TELEPHONE:
518 283-6200
EXECUTIVE:
William W. Haney, National Sales Manager

Air Cushion Vehicles Inc, is marketing a
lightweight, amphibious runabout, the Model
410 Air Cycle.

AIR CYCLE MODEL 410

LIFT AND PROPULSION: Power for the
integrated lift/propulsion system is provided
by a single, 33 hp twin-cylinder Rockwell

JLO engine, mounted immediately ahead of
the cockpit and driving a 3-bladed, ducted
axial fan. Air from the fan feeds into the
plenum below for lift and aft for propulsion.
CONTROL: Craft direction is controlled by
the movement of multiple rudder vanes
operating in the fan slipstream. Thrust

spoilers are provided for speed control, and horizontal stabilizers for trim.

ACCOMMODATION: Open cockpit with single seat. Craft will carry two sitting in tandem, but with reduced performance.

SYSTEMS: Electrical: 12 volts for engine starting and navigation lights.

DIMENSIONS:

Length	10 ft 6 in (3·20 m)
Beam	5 ft 6 in (1·67 m)
Height	3 ft 6 in (1·06 m)

WEIGHTS:

Weight empty	350 lb (158·75 kg)
Load capacity	300 lb (136·07 kg)

PERFORMANCE:

Max speed over land, water, snow and ice in excess of 40 mph (64·37 km/h)

Max gradient

Climbs 20% continuous gradient with one 170 lb (77·10 kg) adult aboard

PRICE:

Recommended retail price, FOB factory: $1,495·00

Controls on the Air Cycle include multiple rudders, thrust spoilers to vary the speed of the craft and horizontal stabilisers for trim

AIRSEAMOBILE COMPANY

HEAD OFFICE:
24706 Evereve Circle, El Toro, California 92630

TELEPHONE:
714 836-1192
714 586-4419

PROPRIETOR:
Arthur M. Jackes

AirSeaMobile Company was established by Arthur M. Jackes and a group of aircraft engineers to undertake on a part-time basis the design and development of ACV sports craft. Mr. Jackes' design concept is based on an integrated lift/propulsion system with a straight-through flow. Various aspects are incorporated in US patent 3,486,577. Several preliminary designs have been completed, two dynamic models have been tested, and the prototype of a two-seat sports ACV, the ASM-6, is undergoing trials.

Development of the ASM-6 is being undertaken in association with Palm Enterprises of Midland, Texas.

Northrop Corporation has sponsored a preliminary design study by the company of a 200-knot, 250-ton SES. A wind tunnel model of this design has been built and tested and has confirmed the high-speed characteristics predicted for this craft.

Technical papers based on this work have been prepared and will be presented as opportunity permits.

ASM-6

This fibreglass-hulled sports ACV is powered by a single Kiekhaefer Aeromarine two-cycle engine. The prototype provides side-by-side seating for two, but a four-seat model is planned. Speeds in excess of 30 mph (48·28 km/h) have been achieved but considerably better results are expected.

LIFT AND PROPULSION: A Kiekhaefer Aeromarine 525 two-cycle engine, rated at 45 hp, is located aft of the cabin and drives two 2 ft 3½ in (0·699 m) diameter aluminium-bladed lift fans mounted in ducts, one each side of the cabin. Power is transmitted to the

Airseamobile's ASM-6 two-seat sports craft. A Kiekhaefer Aeromarine 525 two-cycle engine, rated at 45 hp, powers the integrated lift/propulsion system

drive shaft of the starboard fan by direct coupling and to the port by an X-belt. The two fans, which are inclined downwards and rearwards, provide both lift and propulsive thrust. The cushion air propulsion system is augmented by cushion bleed ports.

Fuel is carried in two tanks, one each side of the cabin, with a total capacity of 4 US gallons (15·14 l). A filter cap is located over each tank. Fuel is 80 octane gasoline, plus lubricating oil.

CONTROLS: Directional control at cruising speed is provided by an aerodynamic rudder augmented by cushion air. Elevons, augmented by cushion air and skirt manipulation, provide pitch and roll control.

HULL: Fibreglass, with pvc foam core.

SKIRT: Vinyl-coated nylon fabric with vinyl plating for wear resistance.

ACCOMMODATION: Side-by-side seating for two in enclosed cabin. Access is through two doors, one each side. Heating will be provided on production models.

SYSTEM: 15 amp generator for starting and on-board power.

DIMENSIONS, EXTERNAL:

Length overall	17 ft 10½ in (5·43 m)
Beam overall	6 ft 0 in (1·82 m)
Height overall, power off	6 ft 6 in (1·98 m)
Draft afloat	6 in (152 mm)
Cushion area	56 sq ft (5·20 m²)
Skirt depth	7½ in (190 mm)

WEIGHTS:

Normal empty	550 lb (249·46 kg)
Normal gross	1,150 lb (521·60 kg)

PERFORMANCE:

Cruising speed, calm water	50 knots
Turning circle diameter	175 ft (53·34 m)

Maximum gradient, static conditions 1 : 10

Vertical obstacle clearance

1 ft 0 in (304 mm)

PRICE:
Approximate cost f.o.b. US $3,500

BEARDSLEY AIR CAR CO

HEAD OFFICE:
40, Windward Drive, Severna Park, Maryland

TELEPHONE:
301-647 0526

PRESIDENT:
Melville W. Beardsley

The Beardsley Air Car Co is basically a research and development operation conducted by Melville Beardsley. Details of the Fan-Jet Skimmer, the Beardsley Air Barrow and Flying Carpet can be found under the entries for Skimmers Incorporated, the company marketing these products.

BELL AEROSPACE
Division of Textron Inc.

HEAD OFFICE:
Buffalo, New York 14240

TELEPHONE:
Area Code 716 297-1000

OFFICERS:
William G. Gisel, President
Lawrence P. Mordaunt, Executive Vice

President—Operations
Norton C. Willcox, Executive Vice President—Administration
Joseph R. Piselli, Vice President—Marketing
Dr. C. F. Berninger, Vice President, Research and Engineering
Adolph Kastelowitz, Vice President—Manu-

facturing
John F. Gill, Vice President—Product Assurance
Delmar E. Wilson, Vice President—Western Region
John R. Clark, Jr., Vice President—Eastern Region (Washington, D.C.)
John W. McKinney, Controller

BELL NEW ORLEANS OPERATIONS

P.O. Box 29307, New Orleans, Louisiana 70189

TELEPHONE:
Area Code 504 255-5901

John J. Kelly, Vice President and General Manager
Donald F. Bonhardt, Director of Product Assurance
Joseph A. Cannon, Director of Marketing
John B. Chaplin, Director of Engineering
Roland Decrevel, 2KSES Project Manager
Hugh F. Farabaugh, Director of Employee Relations and Services
Clarence L. Forrest, SES-100B Project Manager
Donald E. Kenney, Director of Administration
Clifford F. Lennon, Director of Manufacturing
Robert S. Postle, LC JEFF(B) Project Manager
Murray Shabsis, Director of Material
Albert W. Spindler, Director of Public Relations

Bell Aerospace began its air cushion vehicle development programme in 1958. Craft built by the company range in size from the 18 ft XHS3 to the SES-100B, 105-ton surface effect ship test craft which is undergoing sea trials.

The company has rights to manufacture,and sell in the United States, machines employing the hovercraft principle through a licencing arrangement with the British Hovercraft Corporation and Hovercraft Development Ltd.

In addition to importing seven BHC SR.N5s, three of which were employed by the US Navy and later by the US Coast Guard for use and evaluation, Bell built three SK-5 Model 7255s—the company's first production ACVs—to a US Army specification. The craft were airlifted to Vietnam, where they performed a variety of missions, including high speed troop/cargo transportation and patrol. One SK-5 Model 7255 is employed in a research programme being conducted by the US Army's Weapons Command, St Louis Missouri.

In January 1969, the US Surface Effect Ships Project Office awarded Bell a contract for the detailed design of a 100-ton surface effect ship test craft. Construction began in September 1969 and the preparation of the craft for trials began early in 1971. An extensive test and evaluation programme began in February 1972 on Lake Pontchartrain, Louisiana.

In May 1973, the SES-100B was transferred to the Naval Coastal Systems Laboratory at Panama City, Florida, for deep water and high sea state testing in the Gulf of Mexico. In January 1974 the company announced that the SES-100B had successfully completed the testing necessary to confirm and expand the technology necessary for the design of a 2,000-ton ocean-going surface effect ship.

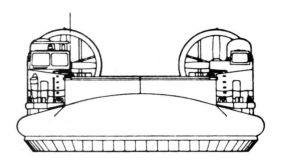

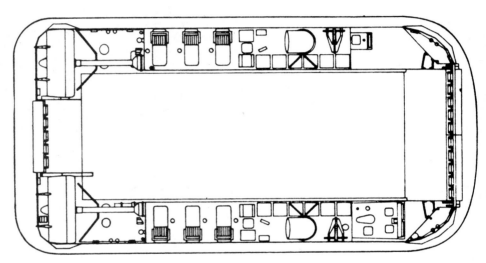

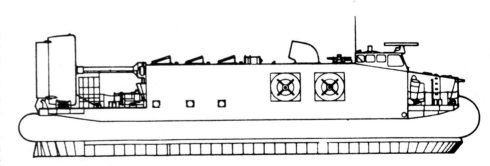

General arrangement of Bell's Amphibious Assault Landing Craft (AALC) JEFF (B). Power is supplied by six 2,800 hp Avco Lycoming gas-turbines driving four centrifugal impellers for lift and two 4-bladed ducted propellers for thrust

In March 1971 the company was awarded a Phase II contract by the US Navy authorising it to start work on a programme covering the detail design, construction and test of an experimental 160-ton AALC (amphibious assault landing craft), designated L. C. JEFF(B).

This work is being undertaken at the company's New Orleans Division, where all its SEV programmes have been consolidated. Construction of the prototype began in 1972.

In March 1972 the Advanced Research Projects Agency of the US Departments of Defense awarded Bell a contract under which the company will produce studies of nine different aspects of the ARPA's projected

1,000 ton, 120-knot arctic-based logistics vehicle.

In November 1972, it was announced that Bell had been awarded a $2·9 million contract by US Naval Ship Systems Command to conduct a preliminary design study for a 2,000 ton operational prototype surface effect ship. This study was completed in mid-1973, and a proposal was submitted to the US Navy in the autumn of 1973 for the detailed design and construction planning of the 2,000 ton ship.

Bell Aerospace Canada (see Canadian section) has built two prototypes of the Bell Model 7380 Voyageur heavy haul ACV, the second of which has been purchased by the Canadian Ministry of Transport for use by the Canadian Coast Guard. Production of additional Voyageurs is in hand. The company is also testing the prototype of a new craft, the 15-ton Viking, which has been designed to meet the need for a smaller but similar multi-purpose vehicle capable of handling a 5-ton payload. The prototype, equipped to Canadian Coast Guard requirements for inshore search-and-rescue duties, was completed early in 1974.

The company also initiated a programme for the USAF that covers the design, development, installation and test of an air cushion landing system aboard a De Havilland CC-115 Buffalo transport aircraft. Ground checkout was completed in November 1973 and the aircraft, redesignated XC-8A, was delivered to the USAF for landing trials which were scheduled to start in early 1974.

SK-5 Model 7255

Details of the SK-5 Model 7255 and its predecessor, the Model 7232, will be found in JSS 1972-73 and earlier editions.

AALC JEFF(B)

In March 1971, US Naval Ship Systems Command awarded Bell's New Orleans Operations a contract for the detail design, construction and testing of an experimental 160-ton, 50-knot air cushion assault landing craft.

Two companies are developing ACV test craft to the 150,000 lb (68,038 kg) payload. 50 knot specification—Bell and Aerojet-General. The Bell project is designated L.C. Jeff(B). Both craft will operate from the well-decks of landing ships and also alongside cargo ships.

The Bell contract involves mathematical and scale model investigations, interface and support system design, subsystem and component testing and design and systems analysis.

Detailed engineering began in 1971 and is continuing during 1974. Fabrication of the prototype started in 1972 at New Orleans. On completion the company will conduct a programme of technical trials and contractor's engineering tests. The craft will then be delivered to the US Navy, which will conduct a series of tests and trials with an emphasis on operational use.

A ⅛th dynamic scale model has been constructed and began an extensive series of engineering tests on Lake Pontchartrain in 1972. The model, which allows "free-flight" testing with radio control of all major craft functions, was used to confirm the final detailed design. A description of the craft, designated B-23, appears later in this entry.

L.C. JEFF(B) is designed to operate at a nominal speed of 50 knots in Sea State 2, and accommodate up to 75 tons in palletised supplies and/or equipment, up to the size of the 60-ton US Army main battle tank.

To ensure adequate world-wide operational capability, the specification calls for operation in temperatures from 0°-100°F and requires that the performance criteria can be met with a 25 knot headwind on a 100°F day.

Top: The helmsman's platform on the JEFF(B) amphibious landing assault craft is manned by two of the four-member operating crew and includes accommodation for an observer or wave commander. Helmsman and relief helmsman are located forward and occupy the right and left seats respectively. In addition to a set of controls and primary instruments that duplicate those of the helmsman, the relief helmsman's console also monitors radar information
Centre: Designed to fit within the dry well decks of the US Navy's LSD and LPD assault ships. JEFF(B) has fore and aft loading ramps for rapid on- and off-loading of troops, equipment and vehicles such as the 60-ton main battle tank. A typical LSD well deck can accommodate four JEFF(B)s and an LPD can take two
Bottom: Impression of a JEFF(B) coming ashore through surf with skirt inflated and bow and stern ramps raised

LIFT AND PROPULSION: Motive power is supplied by six 2,800 hp Avco Lycoming gas-turbines, driving four 5 ft 0 in (1·52 m) diameter double-entry centrifugal impellers for lift, and two 4-bladed 11 ft 9 in (3·58 m) diameter, Hamilton-Standard variable pitch, ducted propellers, for thrust. Fuel capacity is 6,400 gallons (29,094 l).

CONTROLS: Deflection of two aerodynamic rudders hinged at the rear of the propeller duct exits, differential propeller pitch, and the deflection of bow thrusters atop the side structures provide steering control. All controls are located in a raised bridge located well forward on the starboard superstructure. The helmsman's platform is raised to provide 360° vision for the two helmsmen, who have within easy reach all the necessary controls, navigation equipment and instruments. A third seat is provided at this level for another crew member or wave commander. On a lower level in the bridge is an engineer's station with monitoring instrumentation and a radar operator/navigator station. The crew will normally comprise four operating personnel and two deck supervisors.

HULL: Overall structural dimensions of the craft (80 ft length, 43 ft beam and 19 ft height) have been dictated by the well deck dimensions of the US Navy's LSDs (Landing Ships Dock), LPDs (Amphibious Transport Dock).

The main hull is formed by a 4 ft 6 in (1·37 m) deep buoyancy raft with port and starboard side structures. The main deck between the side structures forms the cargo deck, which is 66 ft long by 26 ft 4 in wide (20·11 m by 8·02 m), and provides an unobstructed cargo area of 1,738 sq ft (161·46 m²) A full width ramp is provided at the bow and a narrower ramp, capable of taking the main battle tank, at the stern.

The bottom and deck structures of the hull are separated by longitudinal and transverse bulkheads to form a buoyancy raft with a number of watertight flotation compartments. The craft fuel tanks and bilge system are contained within these compartments.

Plating at the bottom and side of the hull is stiffened by aluminium extrusions, and the main cargo deck is in mechanically fastened hollow truss-type core extrusions. The transverse bulkheads consist of sheet webs of aluminium alloy integrally-stiffened extrusions, with upper and lower bulkhead caps, also of aluminium extrusions.

The basic framing of the side-structures is aluminium back-to-back channels, which coincide with the transverse bulkheads and are spaced apart to straddle the hull bulkheads.

Each sidestructure contains three Avco Lycoming gas-turbines, and their associated air intakes, exhausts, lift fans, transmissions and auxiliary power systems.

SKIRT SYSTEM: Peripheral bag and finger type, with a 5 ft (1·52 m) high cushion compartmented by longitudinal and transverse keels. The upper seal bag attachment hinge line is raised high over the bow ramp area and the vertical diaphragm contains non-return valves similar to those fitted to the SR.N4.

The hull of the US Navy's JEFF(B) under construction at New Orleans. The hull bottom plating and most of the transverse and longitudinal bulkheads had been installed at the time of going to press. The craft is scheduled for completion in late 1975

Powered by two 30 hp JLO 2-cylinder petrol engines, the Bell Model B-23 is a one-sixth scale dynamic model of the JEFF (B) amphibious assault landing craft. Designed for "free-flight" testing, it is radio-controlled and provides data on safety, stability, manoeuvrability and performance

DIMENSIONS:

Length overall	86 ft 9 in (26·43 m)
stowed	80 ft 0 in (24·38 m)
Beam overall	47 ft 0 in (14·32 m)
stowed	43 ft 0 in (13·10 m)
Height	23 ft 6 in (7·16 m)
Cargo area	1,738 sq ft (160·71 m²)
Bow ramp width	28 ft 0 in (5·34 m)
Stern ramp width	14 ft 6 in (4·41 m)

WEIGHTS:

Normal gross weight	325,000 lb (147,416 kg)
Normal payload	120,000 lb (54,431 kg)
Overload payload	150,000 lb (68,038 kg)

PERFORMANCE:

Speed	50 knots in sea state 2
Range	200 nautical miles
Max gradient continuous	13%

BELL MODEL B-23

This is a one-sixth scale dynamic model of the Bell AALC JEFF(B). Powered by two petrol engines, it is designed for 'free flight'

testing under radio control. Data on safety, stability, manoeuvrability and performance is acquired by a lightweight instrumentation system and tape recorder installed aboard the craft.

With cushion inflated, the model is 14 ft 3 in (4·34 m) long, has a beam of 8 ft (2·43 m) and a height of 4 ft (1·21 m). Air cushion depth is 10 in (254·0 mm). The basic weight is 800 lb (362·85 kg), provision being made for the retention of lead ballast to increase the weight to a scale overload condition of 1,750 lb (793·75 kg). This will allow the model to be tested over the entire range of full-scale operating weights. The ballast can be located to allow any desired c.g. or inertia to be obtained.

HULL: The primary structure of the model is fabricated from aluminium honeycomb panels, with secondary structure incorporating fibreglass, styrofoam, and aircraft plywood. The seal system is fabricated in a coated nylon fabric of scale weight and bending stiffness. The model is painted in a bright red and yellow colour scheme. This was selected to provide maximum visibility for the operator and also to obtain the best cine camera coverage for engineering analysis.

LIFT AND PROPULSION: Motive power is provided by two 30 hp JLO two-cylinder, two-cycle petrol engines, one housed in each sidestructure. Each engine drives a scale propeller and a scale fan system through a transmission utilising a centrifugal clutch, tooth belts, and spiral bevel gearboxes. The engines are started electrically, and sufficient fuel is carried for two hours continuous operation.

CONTROLS: The remote control system provides simultaneous proportional control of the primary flight controls and switching of the instrumentation recorder. The ducted propellers are of controllable-pitch, the bow thruster direction and operating mode (forward/reverse) are controlled, the rudders and engine throttles are also included. In all cases, scale travel and scale rate have been maintained. The control system utilises two modified model aeroplane systems with a transmitter layout especially designed for ease of operation. A fail-safe system is arranged to cut the ignition of both engines if radio control is lost for any reason.

The instrumentation and recording system measures the behaviour of the model and the following characteristics: Model air speed (anemometer), cushion pressure in the fore and aft compartments, seal bag pressure, bow vertical acceleration, longitudinal acceleration, c.g. vertical acceleration, rate gyros for pitch, roll, and yaw, bow thruster position, rudder position, starboard propeller pitch, port propeller pitch, starboard side transmission rpm, port side transmission rpm.

The magnetic tape recorder is an environmentally-sealed, lightweight unit, designed originally for torpedo development. It conforms to IRIG standards and data reduction to oscillograph records will be performed at the Slidell Computer Centre.

PERFORMANCE: The model is capable of exploring the entire operational envelope over water, over land, and in surf. A model speed of approximately 20 knots will represent the full-scale design speed of 50 knots. In favourable conditions it is anticipated that model speeds greater than 30 knots will be obtained.

SES-100B TEST CRAFT

The SES-100B is the official designation for the 100-ton class sidehull surface effect ship (SES) test craft which has been built for the U.S. Navy by Bell Aerospace at New Orleans.

It is part of a long-range programme by the U.S. Navy to develop multi-thousand ton, ocean-going ships with speeds of 80 knots or higher.

This programme stems from research undertaken by the U.S Office of Naval Research in 1960, the U.S. Navy Bureau of Ships (now the Naval Ship System Command) and the U.S. Maritime Administration, which in 1961 sponsored the first programme for

the development of a 100-ton SES, known as the Columbia.

In 1966, based on the results of these early programmes, a joint office of the U.S. Navy and Department of Commerce was formed, known as the Joint Surface Effect Ship Programme Office (JSESPO), with the express purpose of determining the feasibility of building and operating large, fast, surface effect ships of 4,000-5,000 tons and capable of 80 knots or higher speed. Design studies conducted by industry for JSESPO (now SESPO, the US Navy having taken over the complete programme in 1971) over the period 1965-69 covered all aspects of SES design and operation—economic factors, performance characteristics, structural and material parameter and subsystem characteristics—and culminated in the award of two design and construction contracts. Bell Aerospace was awarded a contract to design, build and test a water propeller-driven 100-ton class surface effect ship test craft in January 1969. A similar contract was awarded to

Bell Model B-26, a 7 ft (2·13 m) long radio-controlled model employed initially to provide design data for the SES-100B, and which is now being used to investigate design proposals for Bell's 2,000-ton SES

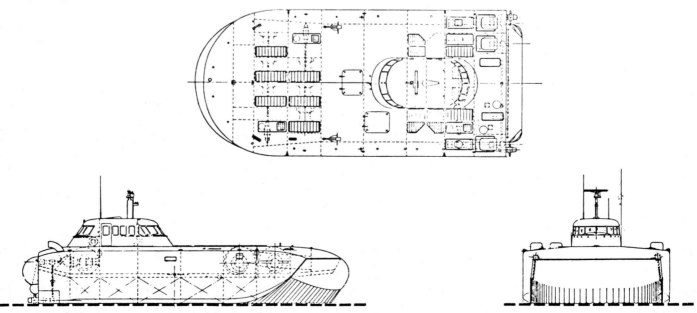

General arrangement of the Bell SES-100B 105-ton test craft

Aerojet-General Corporation for a waterjet-propelled test craft.

Construction of the Bell SES began in August 1970. The vessel was launched on July 22nd 1971 for hovering trials, and builder's trials, with the craft underway, began on February 4th, 1972. A test and evaluation programme encompassing performance trials, stability and seakeeping characteristics, structural load investigations, habitability and operational data, and other pertinent data necessary for the development of high speed surface effect ships, was conducted in the New Orleans area and in the Gulf of Mexico where a variety of sea conditions were experienced.

In January 1974, Bell Aerospace announced that the SES-100B had successfully completed the testing necessary to confirm and expand the technology necessary for the design of a 2,000-ton ocean-going SES. Although tests to accumulate additional data will continue in the Gulf of Mexico, off Panama City, the SES-100B has provided the information required in the areas of performance, stability and control, seal behaviour and sea keeping.

In tests, the craft achieved a speed of 80 knots. It operated for considerable periods of time in high sea states and demonstrated performance, stability and habitability exceeding expectations.

Development of SES systems will result in the production of very high speed, multi-thousand ton ships for a variety of missions. Such development would make it possible for the US Navy to have a smaller but more effective fleet which would revolutionise naval warfare.

HULL: The SES-100B is a single, all-welded continuous structure, incorporating two catamaran-style sidehulls and is constructed from high-strength, corrosion-resistant marine aluminium alloy sheet and plate. The hull carries an integral deckhouse welded to the after portion of the weather deck. The deckhouse is so positioned to optimize the ride quality and habitability of the ship's complement of personnel while retaining good visibility from the command station.

The sidehulls, which virtually skim the surface of the water, provide basic stability to the craft and also seal the air cushion and prevent leakage along the port and starboard sides of the ship. The sealing of the air cushion is completed at the bow and stern by flexible fabric seals. The bow seal is of pressurised bag type with convoluted fingers not unlike the proven design previously used on the Bell skimmers. The stern seal is of Bell design and capable of providing the necessary trim to the craft.

The hull was constructed to BAC design under contract by Levingston Shipbuilding Co. of Orange, Texas. Other major subcontractors for the SES-100B were the Buehler Corporation of Indianapolis, Indiana, for the propulsion transmission system; the Philadelphia Gear Corporation of King of Prussia, Pennsylvania, for the supercavitating controllable-pitch, partially-submerged propellers; Astrospace Labs of Huntsville, Alabama, for the lift fans built to BAC design; and EMR Telemetry of Sarasota, Florida, for the Data Acquisition Console. The remaining

construction of the craft, including outfitting, was undertaken by Bell Aerospace personnel in New Orleans.

LIFT AND PROPULSION: Power is supplied to the lift system by three United Aircraft of Canada (UACL) ST6J-70 marine gas turbines. The engine-fan systems provide pressurised air to seals and cushion in both normal modes of operation and in the event of system failure. An important feature of the design has been to ensure the safety of ship and crew since the craft is designed to investigate the boundaries of ship operation at high speed in rough seas.

The fans, constructed from marine aluminium, are of centrifugal design for ruggedness and stability of operation.

Power is supplied to the two marine propellers by three Pratt & Whitney FT 12A-6 marine gas turbines.

Auxiliary power for engine starting and emergency use is provided by a Solar T-62T-27 high speed turbine producing 100 shp at 8,000 RPM.

All engines are housed in engine rooms beneath the weather deck and take in air through appropriately placed demister screens to minimize sea water and spray ingestion.

Top: Propulsive thrust on the SES-100B is provided by two semi-submerged supercavitating propellers, each mounted directly on the stern of a side hull and positioned so that at high speeds the blades are only partially submerged. Each propeller has six variable pitch blades *Bottom:* The SES-100B, 105-ton surface effect ships test craft travelling at a speed in excess of 80-knots in St Andrew Bay, Panama City, Florida, on April 16th, 1974. The speed was attained during tests on an instrumented range and was recorded by the US Navy on high precision tracking radar

The fuel system, which also serves as a ballast system, is integral with the sidehulls.

ACCOMMODATION: The deckhouse houses all controls necessary for the operation of the craft and accommodation for four test crew and six observers. It is capable of sustaining the crew and observers for greater than 24 hour missions in life support functions. Navigation and communication equipment for all-weather operation is included in the crew subsystem and housed in the deckhouse.

SYSTEMS, EMERGENCY: Safety equipment in the form of fire detection and extinguishing equipment, life rafts, warning lights, etc, meet the requirements of the U.S. Coast Guard Rules of the Road, both International and Inland.

The characteristics of the SES-100B are as follows:

DIMENSIONS:

Length overall	77 ft 8½ in
Beam	35 ft 0 in
Height (top of radar)	26 ft 11 in

WEIGHTS:

Normal gross weight	105 tons
Normal payload	10 tons

POWER PLANTS:

Propulsion
    Three (3) P&W FT 12A-6 marine gas turbines
Lift:
    Three (3) UACL ST6J-70 marine gas turbines

PERFORMANCE:
Speed greater than 80 knots on calm water

PERSONNEL:

Crew (Test Mission)	Four
Observers	Six

MATERIALS:
Hull and Appendages
    Marine aluminium and titanium
Seals   Nylon supported elastainer

BELL MODEL B-26

This is a radio-controlled ⅛th scale free-flight model with sidehulls and seals hydrodynamically representative of the Bell SES-100B. Two contra-rotating air propellers are used for propulsion. A 14-channel tape recorder is installed to record engine speeds, rudder position, cushion and seal pressures, sideslip, pitch, yaw and roll rates. model air speed and accelerations.

The model is 7 ft 3 in (2·20 m) long with a 4 ft 3 in (1·29 m) beam. The basic weight is 480 lb (217·71 kg), with provision for up to 320 lb (145·14 kg) of lead ballast, permitting tests over a wide range of weight and trim conditions. Separate bow, stern and sidehull modules permit variations of seal and sidehull configurations.

HULL: Built into the centre module are four centrifugal lift fans, which are connected through gear belts to an 80 cc, single-cylinder, two-cycle petrol engine. The main structural elements are fabricated in aluminium and edge-grain balsa sandwiched with the bulk of the remaining elements which are built in aircraft plywood, wood and epoxy. All unassigned areas are filled with cast, rigid foam. Bow and stern modules are made of aircraft plywood and wood, and incorporate seal feed air passages. The sidehulls are designed as separate structures. Provision is made for the installation of strain gauges on the attachment linkages,

The deckhouse is at the aft end of the weatherdeck and accommodates a four-man crew and up to six observers. The engines—three FT12A-6s and three ST6J-70s—are located beneath the weatherdeck. Air is drawn through demister screens to minimise seawater and spray ingestion

Conceptual design of a 150-ton Arctic SEV employing many of the systems and components of AALC JEFF(B). The vehicle would have a 10 ft (3·04 m) deep cushion and would operate at speeds up to 80 knots over the Arctic icecap

permitting the measurement of hydrodynamic drag.

The seal system is in a coated nylon fabric of scale weight. The patterns were photoreductions of the Bell SES-100B seals.

PROPULSION: Power is provided by a 40 hp, two-cylinder, two-cycle JLO petrol engine, driving two propellers through a system of gear belts. The engine is started electrically from a battery aboard a chase boat. The model is released from the chase boat when started and recovered upon shutdown.

CONTROLS: An adapted six-channel model aircraft radio-control unit provides proportional control of the lift and propulsion engine throttles and scale rate control of the rudders, with on/off control of the recorder, event marker and shutdown. A fail-safe shutdown is incorporated to ground the ignition systems of both engines upon command or loss of radio signal.

PERFORMANCE: The model has explored the operational envelope of the SES-100B, at scale speeds, in excess of 70 knots. At the time of going to press it was being employed in the investigation of proposed designs for the Bell 2KSES, the modular construction permitting replacment of the hydrodynamic elements with new configurations of seals and planing surfaces.

ARPA ARCTIC SEV

In February 1972, Bell was awarded a US$983,900 contract to undertake a one-year study aimed at developing the technology on which to base the design of high-performance surface effect vehicles for use in the Arctic.

The study programme, for the Advanced Research Projects Agency (ARPA) of the Department of Defence, included nine separate, but interrelated tasks.

The first involved parametric and conceptual studies of total vehicle configurations. Several SEV concepts were developed which covered the gross weight from 100 to 1,000 tons. The vehicles are completely amphibious and equipped with relatively deep skirts to permit operation over the Arctic ice pack, open water, tundra and other Arctic terrain. Cruising speeds over typical rough Arctic ice surface vary between 60 and 90 knots, with maximum speed capabilities of 90 to 120 knots. The larger vehicles have a range of 2,000 nautical miles, with payloads of between 20 and 25%, and are capable of 'on station' operation of up to 40 days with a complement of 30 men.

Other tasks included: (1) Studies of skirt configurations and development of skirt materials in order to improve SEV operating capability and skirt life over Arctic terrain; (2) Vehicle dynamics studies to develop and utilize a computer simulation to investigate the effects of various cushion and lift system parameters on ride characteristics, structural loads, and obstacle clearance capability; (3) Manoeuvring and control studies; (4) Propulsion system studies; (5) Structural design studies; (6) Reliability and retainability studies; and (7) Surface traction studies to investigate means for improving grade climbing capability and low speed manoeuvring characteristics.

A further contract, for a 150-ton surface effect vehicle study, was awarded in May 1973. The duration of the study is 15 months, and the objective is to continue technological development of the Arctic surface effect vehicle by concentrating on areas specifically related to a vehicle in the 150-ton category.

The first phase of a two part study was completed in November 1973. During this phase, technological development was continued in the more critical areas, including skirt and lift system development, SEV vehicle dynamics and manoeuvring and control. Also several candidate SEV concepts were developed, trade-off studies were performed and a baseline configuration selected for further development during the second phase of the programme.

The selected baseline configuration illustrated employs many AALC JEFF(B) systems and components. The ARPA Arctic SEV has a 10 ft (3·04 m) deep cushion and can operate over the Arctic ice-cap at a speed of 60-80 knots.

BELL 2,000-TON SES

In November 1972 it was announced that Bell Aerospace had been awarded a US$2·9 million contract by US Naval Ship Systems Command to conduct a preliminary design study and define a total programme plan for a 2,000-ton operational prototype surface effect ship.

The vessel will have a complete combat system, including surface-to-air and surface-to-surface missiles, and anti-submarine sensors and weapons.

The accompanying impression shows one of the configurations under consideration—a vessel 250 ft (76·20 m) long, with a beam of 106 ft (32·30 m). Bell engineers and designers at Michoud, New Orleans, will undertake the major part of the nine-month study programme. About 65 employees are involved. Major subcontractors are: The Autonetics Division, North American Rockwell, for a role in combat systems integration; Gibbs & Cox Inc, naval architecture, crew

Above and below: In 1972, Bell was awarded a US $2.9 million contract by US Naval Ship Systems Command to conduct a preliminary design study and define a total programme plan for a 2,000-ton operational SES warship. These two artist's impressions show one of the design concepts completed by the company. Measuring 250 ft in length and with a beam of 106 ft, the craft, designated 2KSES, would carry a crew of 92, and have a top speed in excess of 70 knots. Cannisters for the two main batteries of McDonnell Douglas Harpoon RGM-84A-1 antiship missiles are seen at the forward end of the two sidedeck structures flanking the deckhouse. A launcher for Sea Sparrow surface-to-air missiles is located on the foredeck

support and auxiliary systems; Hydronautics Inc, hydrodynamic design and studies of propeller propulsion and waterjet inlets, the Rocketdyne Division of North American Rockwell for waterjet propulsion and the Avondale Shipyards Inc, for outfitting and fabrication, installation and furnishing of the deckhouse.

Bell Aerospace will devote its efforts to total ship design and to the fabrication and installation of those systems which are peculiar to SESs, such as the aluminium hull structure, propulsion system and the cushion seals.

This work will be undertaken at Michoud, where the National Aeronautics and Space Administration has allocated environmentally controlled manufacturing space to Bell for work on this project. This facility was designed specifically for the fabrication of high-integrity structures in welded aluminium.

VANGUARD

This is a projected mixed-traffic ferry based on the Jeff (B) assault landing craft configuration, but with twice the length and beam.

The design requirements call for a craft about 150 ft long by 68 ft wide, capable of carrying fifty-four North American size cars and 192 passengers. The cars would be carried on the open central deck, while the passengers would be accommodated in cabins in the port and starboard sidestructures flanking the deck.

Intended to operate in both coastal areas and coastal waterways, the Vanguard has been suggested as ideal for US and Canadian ferry routes including Portland, Maine—Yarmouth, Nova Scotia, Victoria Island—Vancouver, BC and to Prince Edward Island.

Typical cross-section of a 2,000-ton surface effect ship's centre hull constructed by Bell as part of its weld development programme. Constructed in 5456 aluminium alloy, the structure weighs 25 tons. Fabrication of the ships hull and bulkheads will require over 300,000 linear feet of high strength welding of aluminium plates up to ¾ in (19·05 mm) thick. The company has evolved a system which automates more than 60% of the welding in a flat position

Impression of the projected Bell Vanguard mixed-traffic ferry. The basic configuration is that of Jeff (B), but scaled-up to accommodate fifty-four cars on the open central deck and 192 passengers in cabins in the two sidestructures

Two preliminary design studies prepared by Bell for naval surface effect ships. *Top*: a multi-thousand ton ASW vessel propelled by ducted fans and capable of 100 knots, and *Bottom*, a large amphibious assault craft, designed for the direct to distant beachheads. A combined fanjet and waterjet propulsion system would be employed—deployment of assault forces from the US mainland the waterjets for long-range overwater cruising, and the fanjets for shallow water, surf and overland operations.

BERTELSEN MANUFACTURING COMPANY INC

HEAD OFFICE:
9999 Roosevelt Road, Westchester, Illinois 60153

WORKS:
113 Commercial Street, Neponset, Illinois 61345

and

4819 Cortland Street, Chicago, Illinois 60639

TELEPHONE:
312-681-5606, 309-594-2041

OFFICERS:
William R. Bertelsen, Chairman of the Board, Vice President and Director of Research
William C. Stein, President and Treasurer
Charles A. Brady, Secretary

Dr William R. Bertelsen, a general practitioner and talented engineer, was one of the first to build and drive an air cushion vehicle.

His interest was largely inspired by the difficulties he faced when trying to visit patients by car over icy roads. Having discovered that a helicopter would be too expensive to be a practical solution, he set to work to develop a vehicle that could be lifted free of the ground by air pumped beneath its base. Dr Bertelsen designed his first Aeromobile air cushion vehicle in 1950, and has since built and tested fourteen full-scale vehicles, ranging from simple plenum craft to ram-wings. One, the 18 ft long Aeromobile 200-2, was a star exhibit at the US Government's Trade Fairs in Tokyo, Turin, Zagreb and New Delhi in 1961. First design to be marketed by the company is the Aeromobile 13, a 4 passenger amphibious communications and light utility ACV. The prototype was built in 1968 and trials are complete. A description of this model will be found in JSS 1972-73 and earlier editions.

AEROMOBILE 14

Aeromobile 14 is a lightweight amphibious two or three-seater employing a single gimbal mounted lift fan/propulsion unit of similar design and construction to that introduced by Bertelsen on the Aeromobile 13.

The prototype was completed early in 1969 and trials ended in 1970.

LIFT PROPULSION AND CONTROLS: A single duct-mounted 55 hp (740 cc) JLO twin-cylinder engine driving a 36 in (914 mm) diameter eight-bladed axial-flow fan supplies lift, propulsion and control. The duct is spherical and gimbal-mounted at its centre so that it can be tilted and rotated as required in any direction. The discharge end of the duct faces a fitted aperture in the deck, from which air is fed into the cushion. When the fan shaft is vertical (no tilt), all the discharged air is fed into the cushion. By tilting the gimbal, the operator allows air from the fan to escape across the deck to provide thrust for propulsion and control.

Apart from the propulsion slipstream, there is no loss of lift air since the spherical duct fits closely into the deck aperture, and rotation of the sphere does not increase the air gap. Cushion pressure is 14 lb ft².

A simple mechanical linkage connected to handlebars enables the operator to tilt the fan duct fore-aft, right and left and make integrated movements. The only other controls are a throttle and a choke. Fuel is carried in a single 12 gallon (US) tank located in the deck structure at the CG, with a fuelling point in the centre deck. Recommended fuel is regular automotive gasoline mixed with two-cycle oil.

HULL: Moulded fibreglass with foam filling. Design load 1,100 lb gross weight.

SKIRT: Urethane nylon with conical exterior configuration. Depth 1 ft 0 in (304 mm).

ACCOMMODATION: Tandem seating for three, with operator forward with control handlebars.

SYSTEMS: Electrical: 12 volt alternator on engine for starting.

NAVIGATION: Magnetic compass.

DIMENSIONS:
Length overall, power off 13 ft 0 in (3·96 m)
Length overall, skirt inflated
13 ft 0 in (3·96 m)
Beam overall, power off 7 ft 0 in (2·13 m)
Beam overall, skirt inflated 7 ft 0 in (2·13 m)
Height overall on landing pads, power off
3 ft 0 in (0·914 m)
Height overall, skirt inflated
4 ft 0 in (1·21 m)
Draft afloat 4 in (101 mm)
Draft hovering 3 in (76 mm)
Cushion area 60 sq ft (5·57 m²)
Skirt depth 12 in (304 mm)

WEIGHTS:
Normal empty weight 700 lb (317 kg)
Normal all-up weight 1,100 lb (499 kg)
Normal gross weight 1,100 lb (499 kg)
Normal payload 400 lb (181 kg)
Max payload 500 lb (226 kg)

PERFORMANCE:
Max speed over calm water
50 mph (80·46 km/h)
Cruising speed, calm water
40 mph (64·37 km/h)
Turning circle diameter at 30 knots
·100 ft (30·4 m)
Max wave capability 3 ft (0·914 m)
Max survival sea state 5 ft waves (1·52 m)
Still air range and endurance at cruising
speed 2½ hours
Max gradient, static conditions 10%
Vertical obstacle clearance 1 ft (304 mm)
Price: On request.

AEROMOBILE 15

Employing the same lift, propulsion and control system as the Aeromobile 14, the Aeromobile 15 is a light amphibious four-seater powered by a single 125 hp Mercury outboard engine and capable of a speed of 60 knots over calm water.

The prototype is complete.

LIFT AND PROPULSION: A single duct-mounted 125 hp Mercury outboard engine driving a 36 in (914 mm) diameter, sixteen-bladed adjustable-pitch aluminium alloy fan, supplies lift, propulsion and control. The duct is spherical and gimbal-mounted at its centre so that it can be tilted and rotated in any direction. When the fan shaft is vertical, the total airflow is discharged into the cushion. By tilting the gimbal the operator allows air from the fan to escape across the stern to provide thrust for propulsion and control. At the maximum tilt angle of 90° for maximum thrust only 30% of the fan air is delivered to the cushion.

Propulsion and/or control forces, including braking thrust, can be applied throughout 360° from the stern by tilting the duct in the required direction.

The fan duct is controlled from the driver's position by servo system. The driver has a wheel on a control column. Turning the wheel tilts the duct sideways to produce yaw force, and fore-and-aft movement of the column tilts the duct fore-and-aft to produce forward propulsion or braking. Fuel is carried in one 18-gallon tank located on the cabin floor beneath the rear seat at the C of G. The fuelling point is located on the left deck outside the cabin. Fuel is automotive gasoline with two-cycle oil.

HULL: Moulded fibreglass.

SKIRT: Urethane nylon fabric, 1 ft 6 in (45·7 mm) deep.

ACCOMMODATION: Entry to the cabin is through a sliding canopy which moves from the windshield rearwards. Two bench type seats are fitted, one forward for the driver and one passenger, and one aft for two passengers. The cabin may be heated or air-conditioned if required. In emergencies the sliding canopy, windows and windshield may be kicked out.

SYSTEMS: ELECTRICAL: 12 volt alternator and 12 volt storage battery.

COMMUNICATIONS AND NAVIGATION: A magnetic compass is standard. Radio, radar and other navigation aids optional.

DIMENSIONS, EXTERNAL:
Length overall, power off 18 ft 0 in (5·48 m)
Length overall, skirt inflated
    18 ft 8 in (5·68 m)
Beam overall, power off 8 ft 0 in (2·43 m)
Beam overall, skirt inflated
    9 ft 10 in (2·99 m)
Height overall, on pads, power off
    4 ft 4 in (1·32 m)
Height overall, skirt inflated
    5 ft 9 in (1·75 m)
Draft afloat   5½ in (139 mm)
Draft hovering   4 in (101 mm)
Cushion area   90 ft² (8·36 m²)
Skirt depth   1 ft 6 in (457 mm)

DIMENSIONS, INTERNAL:
Cabin:
  Length   10 ft 6 in (3·2 m)
  Max width   4 ft 2 in (1·27 m)
  Max height   4 ft 0 in (1·21 m)
  Floor area   40 ft² (3·71 m²)
The sliding canopy opens 3 ft (·914 m) rearward from windshield.

Aeromobile 14 research platform employed by Bertelsen Manufacturing Co for the development of designs using single gimbal-mounted lift/fan/propulsion units.

Aeromobile 15, a 60-knot four-seater powered by a modified 125 hp Mercury outboard. The vehicle is at present being employed as a test-bed for the gimbal-mounted lift/propulsion system. The photographs show the gimbal duct in neutral and in high forward tilt

WEIGHTS:
Normal empty weight	1,300 lb	(589·64 kg)
Normal all-up weight	2,100 lb	(952·50 kg)
Normal gross weight	2,100 lb	(952·50 kg)
Normal payload	700 lb	(317·50 kg)
Max payload	1,000 lb	(453·57 kg)

PERFORMANCE (at normal operating weight, estimated):
Max speed over calm water,
  max power   60 knots
Max continuous power   50 knots

Cruising speed, calm water   50 knots
Turning circle at 30 knots 500 ft (152·4 m)
Max wave capability   3 ft (914 mm)
Max survival sea state 5 ft (1·52 m) waves
Still air range and endurance at cruising
  speed   3 hours
Max gradient, static conditions   10%
Vertical obstacle clearance
    1 ft 3 in (381 mm)

PRICE AND TERMS: On request.

DEPARTMENT OF DEFENCE, ADVANCED RESEARCH PROJECTS AGENCY

HEADQUARTERS:

1400 Wilson Boulevard, Arlington, Virginia 22209

ARPA ARCTIC SEV PROGRAMME

Brian K. Hannula, Programme Manager, Advanced Engineering Office

J. U. Kordenbrock, Technical Manager

In the spring of 1970, the US Defence Department's Advanced Research Projects Agency (ARPA) initiated a programme to develop the technology required to exploit the arctic military potential of the SEV. The ARPA SEV Programme, with technical management being provided by the Naval Research and Development Centre, Carderock, Maryland, was due for completion summer of 1974. By that time it was expected that the technology required to build an all-weather arctic SEV, with a gross weight as high as 600 tons and a cruise speed as great as 80 knots, would have been developed A vehicle with these or lesser specifications is considered adequate to perform most potential arctic SEV missions.

Major programme tasks have included quantitative arctic environment definition, mission analysis and vehicle and sub-system technology development. Primary emphasis during the remainder of the programme will be placed on the completion of preliminary design packages for nominally 150-ton and 500-ton SEVs. These design packages will include a review and specification of requirements, parametric analysis to identify basic vehicle configurations and performance characteristics, trade-off studies to select the most suitable vehicle sub-systems, model test data, layout drawings and cost estimates for detailed vehicle design and manufacture.

DEPARTMENT OF THE NAVY, NAVAL SEA SYSTEMS COMMAND (NAVSEA)

HEADQUARTERS:

Washington, DC 20360

PROGRAMME MANAGER, HOVERCRAFT AND HYDROFOILS:

James L. Schuler

OFFICE:

US Naval Ship Systems Command, Advanced Ship Development Programs Office, Code 032, National Center 3, Room 10E54, Washington, DC 20360

The US Naval Sea System Command (NAVSEA), formerly known as the Bureau of Ships, has the responsibility for the research, design construction and logistic support of all US Navy Ships. The Research Directorate of NAVSEA has been the primary technical sponsor of all US Navy hovercraft and hydrofoil programmes since 1960.

The Programme Manager responsible for the development of both types of vessel is Mr. James L. Schuler. Technical Managers have been appointed for each of the several research and development programmes managed and directed by NAVSEA. Technical Manager of the Amphibious Assault Landing Craft Programme is Mr. Melvin Brown of the Naval Ship Research and Development Centre, Carderock, Maryland, This programme includes the JEFF configuration, which is an ACV landing craft based on the designs prepared by Bell Aerospace and Aerojet-General Corporation. Details will be found under the respective entries for the two companies.

Technical manager for the Advanced Hydrofoil Systems Programme is Mr. Robert Johnston of the NSRDC at Carderock. This programme includes operation and trials of the PCH-1 and AGEH-1, as well as testing the PGH-1. Current emphasis is on the development of larger and faster hydrofoils.

DOBSON PRODUCTS CO.

HEAD OFFICE:

2241 South Ritchey, Santa Ana, California 92705

TELEPHONE:

(714) 557-2987

WORKS:

Santa Ana, California

DIRECTOR:

Franklin A. Dobson

Dobson Products Co was formed by Franklin A. Dobson in 1963 to develop and market small ACVs either in complete, factory built form, or as kits for private use. His first model, the Dobson Air Dart, won the first ACV race in Canberra in 1964. The company's Model F two-seater, available in plan form, has been described and illustrated in JSS 1973-74 and earlier editions.

The first Dobson craft designed for quantity production is the Model H. Features include a vacuum-moulded hull and a four-bladed reversible-pitch propeller. The company has now introduced a smaller version, the Model HK, which is available in kit form.

In May 1974, Mr Dobson stated that in the immediate future his company will be concentrating more on component development since it was felt that a more thorough engineering approach was needed in the field of small ACVs.

Specially designed components will be available to interested companies and individuals at competitive prices. Eventually they will be incorporated into Dobson

A smaller version of the Air Car Model H, above, is being introduced by Dobson Products. Known as the HK, it is being marketed in kit and component form

kits and complete vehicles.

The first project is a reversible pitch propeller of improved and simplified design, to be followed by variable-pitch fans and suitable intake ducts, screens etc.

Preliminary details of the former are given in the section devoted to power plants and propulsion systems.

Vehicles similar to the Dobson Model F and H are being employed for test purposes.

GEMCO INC

HEAD OFFICE:

PO Box 1191, Lynnwood, Washington 98036

TELEPHONE: (206) 743-3669

OFFICERS:

Gerald W. Crisman, President

A. J. Doug Nunally, Vice President

Edward J. Birney

Michael S. Curtis, Secretary

William D. Crisman, Financial Adviser

Gemco Inc has designed and built a number of light and ultra-light craft, including the first to cross the Mississippi (in 1959).

The company is now concentrating on the development of a new two-seat sports vehicle. the 4/5 seat Eagle, the prototype of which is under construction; two passenger ferries, one for 10-11 passengers the other for thirty, and the Alaskan, a utility vehicle with a payload capacity of 10-12 tons.

EAGLE

A glassfibre-hulled five-seater, the Eagle is currently under construction at Paine Field, Washington.

Power is provided by two 46 hp Volkswagen engines, one driving the lift fan system, the other driving a shrouded propeller. Craft direction is controlled by twin rudders aft of the propeller shroud, operated from the cockpit by a wheel.

Proposed derivatives include harbour and customs patrol craft and utility models.

DIMENSIONS:

Length overall	20 ft 0 in (6·09 m)
Beam overall	11 ft 0 in (3·53 m)
Height overall	7 ft 6 in (2·28 m)

WEIGHTS:

All-up weight	2,120 lb (961·57 kg)

PERFORMANCE:

Estimated cruising speed	50 knots

GEMCO 5300

This is a project for a 34 ft (10·36 m) long 10-11 seat passenger ferry or light freighter powered by two 250 hp Continental engines. A feature of the craft is an air cushion system employing two completely separate skirts 'split' longitudinally the length of the hull. The system is designed for improved stability in adverse weather.

DIMENSIONS:

Length overall	34 ft 0 in (10·36 m)
Beam overall	21 ft 0 in (6·40 m)
Height overall	11 ft 8 in (3·55 m)

WEIGHTS:

Empty weight	4,500 lb (2,033 kg)
All-up weight	7,000 lb (3,175 kg)

PERFORMANCE (still air):

Speed (estimated)	70 knots

5601 ALASKAN

An amphibious utility vehicle for the northern regions, the 5601 Alaskan features a flatbed hull which can be adopted to suit various requirements by adding equipment and/or superstructure. As a high speed ferry it will accommodate a crew of three and up to 70 passengers. In freight configuration, the payload capacity is 10-12 tons. During haulage operations in remote areas, the accommodation forward will provide sleeping and cooking facilities for up to ten crew members, eliminating the need for longshoremen at the end of each haul.

DIMENSIONS:

Length	64 ft 6 in (19·65 m)
Beam	40 ft 0 in (12·19 m)

5301 PIONEER VSS 89

This 30-seat passenger ferry is a scaled up Gemco 5300. The design is now complete and tests have been undertaken with a dynamic model. A feature of the craft is the employment of the company's 'split' skirt system, designed for improved stability.

Impression of the Gemco Eagle, a glass fibre hulled five-seater powered by two 46 hp Volkswagen engines

The Gemco 5300, a projected light passenger ferry for up to 11 passengers

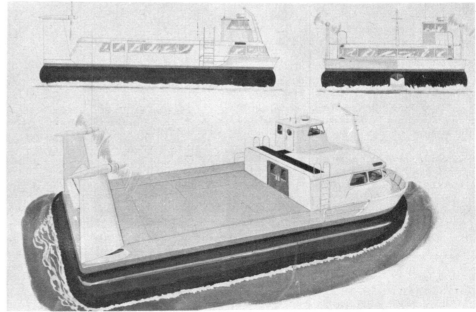

Impression of the Gemco Alaskan, a flat-deck utility vehicle for operation in the far north. A removable cabin module provides seats for up to 70 passengers

LIFT AND PROPULSION: Cushion air is supplied by a single 500 hp Williams Research gas-turbine driving two 6 ft 0 in (1·82 m) diameter centrifugal fans. A second engine of the same type, located aft of the cabin, drives two 4-bladed Hamilton-Standard reversible pitch propellers for thrust. Fuel is carried in four tanks with a total capacity of 400 US gallons (1,514 l).

CONTROLS: Craft heading is controlled by aerodynamic rudders hinged to the rear of the thrust augmentation ducts and differential pitch. Elevators provide pitch trim at cruising speed. Directional control at low speed is provided by thrust ports.

HULL: Built in conventional aircraft light alloys. Passenger cabin floor and sides built in standard aluminium honeycomb panels.

SKIRT: Fingered-bag system, 7 ft 0 in (2·13 m) deep, in patented dual plenum configuration.

ACCOMMODATION: Access to the cabin, which will seat thirty passengers and a crew of two, is via two gull-wing doors aft, one port, one starboard. Standard emergency equipment is carried to meet US Coast Guard requirements.

DIMENSIONS:

Length overall, power off
48 ft 0 in (14·63 m)
Length overall, skirt inflated
53 ft 0 in (16·15 m)
Beam overall, power off 30 ft 0 in (9·14 m)
Beam overall, skirt inflated
35 ft 0 in (10·66 m)
Height overall, skirt inflated
15 ft 6 in (4·72 m)
Craft afloat 2 ft 1 in (0·635 m)

Dynamic model of Gemco's Pioneer, a 30-seat high speed ferry derived from the smaller Gemco 5300

Cushion area	1,330 sq ft (123·55 m²)	
Skirt depth	7 ft 0 in (2·13 m)	

DIMENSIONS, INTERNAL:

Length	16 ft 6 in (5·02 m)
Max width	10 ft 6 in (3·20 m)
Max weight	6 ft 0 in (1·98 m)
Floor area	168 sq ft (15·60 m²)
Normal gross weight	up to 9 tons
Normal payload	6,000 lb (2,721·55 kg)

WEIGHTS:

Normal empty	16,000 lb (7,527·47 kg)
Normal all-up weight	21,000 lb (9,525·44 kg)

PERFORMANCES:

Cruising speed	65 knots
Max wave capability on scheduled runs	4 ft 0 in (1·21 m)
Still air range and endurance at cruisers speed	4 hours
Vertical obstacle clearance	3 ft 0 in (0·914 m)

EGLEN HOVERCRAFT INC

HEAD OFFICE:
801 Poplar Street, Terre Haute, Indiana, 47807
Telephone: 812-234 4307

DIRECTORS:
Jan Eglen, President
Alfred Brames, Secretary
O. Keith Owen, Jr, Treasurer
Lewis R. Poole, Controller
Woodrow S. Nasser, Counsel
Melvin McKibben, Asst Secretary
Paul Ferreira, Director
George Kassis, Director
Clarence Fauber, Director

EXECUTIVES:
Jan Eglen, General Manager
Lewis R. Poole, Works Manager
Lionel Saunders, Director of Production and Research
Terry Moore, Assistant Production Manager

MIDDLE EAST REPRESENTATIVE:
Al-Rodhan Trading & Contracting Est., PO Box 5020,
Kuwait, Arabian Gulf

Eglen Hovercraft Inc. was chartered in August 1969, to design and manufacture recreational hovercraft and other air cushion devices. The company is at present concentrating on the production of the Hoverbug, an amphibious two-seater with a moulded plastic hull. At the time of going to press the company was starting production of the new Mk 2 model and also four and six-seat

Eglen Hovercraft Hoverbug, a plastic-hulled two-seater powered by two Rockwell-JLO engines. Speeds of up to 60 mph (96·56 km/h) have been attained in this craft over water with one person aboard

ACVs which incorporate a number of design improvements, including the employment of shock-mountings for both the lift and thrust engines. A new product, the Terre-hover hoverplatform, is described in the section devoted to ACV Trailers and Heavy Load Carriers.

HOVERBUG Mk 2

A two-seat recreational ACV, the Hoverbug is powered by two Rockwell JLO engines and has a maximum speed of 30 mph (48·28 km/h) over water and 35 mph (56 km/h) overland. The standard version has an open

cockpit, but a cabin top to form an enclosed cockpit is available as an optional extra.

The craft is available in either fully assembled or kit form.

LIFT AND PROPULSION: A 22 hp Rockwell JLO-295 two-cycle engine, mounted immediately aft of the cockpit, drives a 2ft 0 in (609 mm) diameter, 10-bladed Multiwing fan for lift. Thrust is supplied by a 25 hp Rockwell JLO 395 driving a 3 ft 0 in (914 mm) diameter, Banks-Maxwell 2-bladed propeller. Both lift and thrust engines on the Mk 2 model have shock-absorbing mountings, reducing the vibration transmitted to the hull by about 90%. Similar mountings are also employed to attach the thrust duct to the thrust engine frame, resulting in a longer life expectancy for the duct and the rudders, which are now mounted directly onto the duct. The propeller is of laminated hardwood, tipped in stainless steel. The company is currently investigating the use of a 4-bladed propeller in order to reduce noise generation. Fuel capacity is 5 gallons (22·73 litres), representing about 2 hours running. Quick-release fittings to the fuel system facilitate maintenance.

CONTROLS: Directional control is provided by twin aerodynamic rudders hinged at the rear of the propeller duct and operating in the slipstream. Rudder installation on the Mk 2 has been modified to improve rate of turn. Additional pulleys have been introduced into the steering system for smoother steering. Cockpit controls comprise a steering wheel, two ignition switches, two throttles, two chokes, two emergency "kill" switches and a navigational lights switch.

HULL: High gloss, high impact plastics hull, formed by a thermovacuum moulding process developed by Hoosier Fibreglass Industries, Terre Haute, Indiana. Material used is Cycolacbrand ABS, supplied by the Marbon Division of Borg Warner Corporation. Hull side loading racks can be supplied as an optional extra. Two 6 in (152 mm) deep buoyancy chambers in the base of the hull are filled with foam plastic to provide 150% reserve buoyancy. Removable skids are fitted beneath.

SKIRT: Bag type, 1 ft 0 in (304 mm) deep, fabricated in neoprene-coated nylon. Skirt attachment system facilitates rapid removal and refitting.

ACCOMMODATION: Driver and passenger sit side-by-side in an open cockpit on a 4ft 0 in (1·21 m) wide bench-type seat. Optional extras include a cabin enclosure, windshield wipers and a custom upholstered seat.

SYSTEMS: Electrical : 12 volt, 75 watt system for engine starting instruments and navigation lights.

DIMENSIONS:

Length overall, power on	10 ft 0 in (3·04 m)
Beam overall, power on	6 ft 6 in (1·98 m)
Draft afloat	6 in (152 mm)
Skirt depth	1 ft 0 in (304 mm)
Cabin width	4 ft 0 in (1·21 m)

WEIGHTS:

Normal empty weight	400 lb
Payload	400 lb

PERFORMANCE:

Max recommended speed:

over water	30 mph (48·28 km/h)
over land	35 mph (56·32 km/h)
over ice	40 mph (64·37 km/h)

Wave capability (max)	1 ft 6 in - 2 ft 0 in (457-609 mm)
Max gradient at all up weight	1 : 6

PRICE:

Cost of complete craft, FOB Terre Haute:	US$2,495·00
Cost of standard kit	US$1,800·00

OFFSHORE SURVEY SIX-SEATER

This new Eglen utility hovercraft is designed for a variety of duties including off-shore surveys. Of mixed wood and fibreglass construction, it carries a payload of 1,625 lb (737 kg) and cruises at 35 knots. Construction time is 4-6 months depending on optional equipment or special features

New four-seater, developed from the Eglen Hoverbug, during trials in the late Spring of 1974

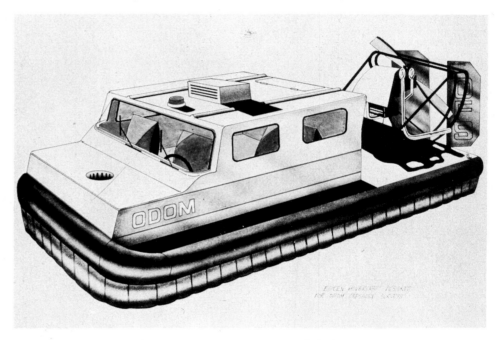

Impression of the new Eglen Hovercraft six-seat offshore survey and utility vehicle

required.

LIFT AND PROPULSION: Lift air is provided by a 90 hp Continental PC-60 aero-engine driving a 24 in (609 mm) diameter Rotafoil fan. Cushion pressure is 17-19 psf. Thrust is supplied by a 100 hp Lycoming air cooled piston engine driving a two-bladed Dobson reversible-pitch propeller.

CONTROLS: Craft heading is controlled by twin aerodynamic rudders hinged to the tubular metal guard aft of the propeller. Reversible and variable-pitch propeller provides braking and reverse thrust.

HULL: Wooden frame covered with fibreglass skin and finished with epoxy marine exterior paint. Cabin superstructure is in moulded fibreglass with 30 oz Durasonic ¼ in foam-backed sound proofing. Windows are of the "push out" type, in tinted plastic. Total fuel capacity is 55 gallons.

SKIRT: 14 in (355 mm) deep HDL type.

ACCOMMODATION: Seats provided for driver and five passengers. Optional items include seat belts, heating and air-conditioning and intercom system.

SYSTEMS, ELECTRICAL: 12 volt dc, with auxiliary outlets. Batteries: 2-12 volt, 72 amp hour capacity.

DIMENSIONS:

Length	24 ft (7·31 m)
Beam	10 ft (on cushion) (3·04 m)
Skirt depth	1 ft 2 in (355 mm)
Hover gap	¾ in (19 mm)

WEIGHTS:

Empty weight	2,500 lb (1,179·98 kg)
Payload (incl 400 lb fuel)	1,625 lb
Overload capacity	500 lb (226·79 kg)
Total weight in overload condition	4,625 lb (2,097·85 kg)

TERMS: On request. Domestic orders 50% payment with order, balance upon delivery. Overseas orders. Irrevocable letter of credit for full price placed with American Fletcher National Bank in Indianapolis, Indiana.

GLUHAREFF HELICOPTERS CO

HEAD OFFICE:

18518 South Broadway, Gardena, California 90248, USA

OFFICERS:

Eugene M. Gluhareff, President

Eugene Gluhareff is a former helicopter designer and project engineer at Sikorsky Aircraft Co. Gluhareff Helicopters was formed in 1952 to build and market small one-man helicopters equipped with G8-2 liquid propane pressure-jet engines. In recent years the company has designed two single-seat ACVs, the MEG-1H Yellow Jacket, powered by two go-cart engines and the MEG-2H Yellow Streak, a similar but larger craft propelled by Gluhareff pressure-jets.

MEG-1H YELLOW JACKET

The prototype of this single-seat triangular planform ACV was completed in November 1960. Trials continued until January 1971, when the company began marketing plans and component parts. More than 3,000 sets of plans have been sold. Maximum speed is 60 mph (96·50 km/h) over land and 20 mph (32·18 km/h) over water.

LIFT AND PROPULSION: Integrated system. Motive power supplied by two 10 hp Chrysler 820 go-kart engines located side-by-side aft of the open cockpit. Each drives a 2 ft 10 in (0·863 mm) diameter, six-bladed, solid spruce fan at 3,600 rpm. Fan blades are cambered. Fuel is carried in a cylindrical ¾ gal (US) go-kart tank mounted above the hull between the two engines. Propulsion air is expelled through twin thrust ports aft.

CONTROLS: At low speeds craft heading is governed by the differential movement of two pedal-operated thrust ports aft or kinesthetic control. By leaning in the required direction the craft can be made to spin, move backwards, forwards or sideways. Stick-operated aerodynamic rudders become effective at about 20-25 mph (32-40·2 km/h).

HULL: Triangular planform, designed to generate aerodynamic lift at speed. Welded structure, mainly in ⅞ in (22·22 mm) diameter 4130 thinwall steel tubing. Thin aluminium skin sections in 2924-T4.20 gauge are pop-riveted into place. Intake ducts and nose sections are in glass fibre. Cockpit box is in riveted aluminium. A tricycle undercarriage is fitted to assist ground handling.

SKIRT: Fabricated in canvas, with 4130 steel reinforcing tubes at hem.

DIMENSIONS:

Length overall	10 ft 7 in (3·22 m)
Max beam	7 ft (2·13 m)
Skirt depth	6 in (152 mm)

WEIGHTS:

Normal empty weight	165 lb (74·83 kg)
Normal gross weight	331 lb (150·13 kg)

PERFORMANCE:

Max speed, calm water	15-20 mph (24·1-32·8 km/h)
Max speed over land	60 mph (96·56 km/h)
Vertical obstacle clearance	6 in (152 mm)

PRICE:

Construction plans US $15·00 per set. Ready-made components available.

MEG-2H YELLOW STREAK

Similar in basic design to the Yellow Jacket, this developed model employs two fin-mounted G8-2-15 pressure-jet engines, each developing 18 lb st for propulsive thrust.

The Gluhareff MEG-1H Yellow jacket single-seat recreational ACV, powered by two 10 bhp Chrysler 820 go-kart engines. Each drives a six-bladed solid spruce fan. Propulsion air is expelled through twin thrust ports aft

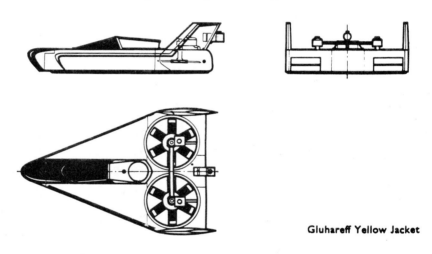

Gluhareff Yellow Jacket

Features of the MEG-2H Yellow Streak include propane pressure-jets atop the twin fins and a revised cockpit

HELIBARGE SYSTEMS INC

HEAD OFFICE:
10145 N. North Portland Road
Post Office Box 03159
Portland, Oregon 97203
TELEPHONE:
Area Code (503) 286-3661
SENIOR EXECUTIVES:
Glen Widing
Allan Bigler
Walter Crowley

Helibarge Systems was incorporated in 1971 to promote the use of "Helibarges" in commercial and military applications. The principle was conceived and developed by Walter A. Crowley and is described in US Patent No. 3,285,535. It combines a helicopter with an air cushion barge, employing the rotor downwash of the helicopter to pressurize the air cushion.

HELIBARGE MODEL HBX-150

The Helibarge is an amphibious ground effect machine designed to transport cargo over water, ice fields, marshland, tundra, deserts and other relatively flat areas Basically it is a flat-decked, cargo-carrying platform designed to be transported by helicopter, using the downwash air pressure developed by the helicopter rotor as the source of power for lift. Separate engine-driven propellers, in combinations with rudders, would provide propulsion, braking and steering.

Although the HBX-150 is designed specifically for the UH-1H, other Helibarges can be designed for transport by other helicopters, ranging from the Gyrodyne QH-50C drone to the Sikorsky S-64 series.

Some of the advantages claimed for the system include greater payload and daylight/obstacle clearance capabilities, improved operating range and lower first cost.

The overall dimensions of the Helibarge are approximately three times that of the diameter of the helicopter rotor. Thus, the Helibarge Model HBX-150 with UH-1H Helicopter would have a diameter of 150 ft (45·72 m).

The weight of the Helibarge would be dependent upon the engineering and design required to accomplish its intended transport function. The structural weight of the HBX-150 (UH-1H) is estimated at 5 lb sq ft (24·41 kg/m²).

Because of its fuel-carrying capabilities, the HBX-150 (UH-1H) could be transported over distances far greater than the normal operating range of the UH-1H Helicopter.

LIFT AND PROPULSION: Thrust is supplied by two 1,400 shp T53-L-13 propeller-turbines, each driving a 3-bladed, controllable-pitch propeller. Lift air is supplied by the helicopter rotor downwash which is blown via a collapsible diffuser duct into the plenum. A locking mechanism secures the duct in the open position. Remote actuators may be included in production craft. Louvres or other forms of covering surround the helicopter platform and are retained in the closed position while the helicopter is landing.

Fuel tanks have a total capacity of 28,000 lb (12,700·58 kg). An umbilical connection will be provided to extend helicopter capa-

Landing sequence prior to the operation of the Model HBX-150 Helibarge. *Top:* UH-1H helicopter approaches central platform of the Helibarge, which is resting on a solid, level surface. Duct is folded flat and louvres surrounding platform are shut. *Bottom:* Diffuser duct is raised and secured in place, louvres are opened and the vehicle is ready for work

Three 72 ft (21·94 m) diameter Helibarges combined to form a single 600-ton capacity unit for oil industry applications

bilities. APU centre is of modular type and removable for servicing.

HULL: Deck panels are light, buoyant structures of aluminium honeycomb, each 5 ft × 10 ft 6 in (1·52 m × 3·20 m) and mounted on a framework. They will be capable of supporting foot traffic or light cargo. Loads of up to 15 tons can be carried on each of the two load platforms, one each side of the craft. Inflatable landing pads will extend beneath the structure to provide support for concentrated loads and to protect the hard skirt air duct used to supply air to the flexible skirt stiffeners. The helicopter platform is adjustable for height and angle to enable the helicopter rotor shaft to be positioned accurately in relation to the diffuser duct. Slots in the platform align the helicopter skids in the direction of travel and a cargo hook attachment point anchors the helicopter.

SKIRT: Made in 32 oz/yd² neoprene-nylon material with inflatable stiffening "fingers" built-in. Skirt depth 7 ft 6 in (2·28 m). Replaceable sections fastened by air-tight zippers.

ACCOMMODATION: Control cabin is equipped with two seats, one for driver and one for engineer/navigator. Cabin is fully air-conditioned, heated and ventilated and has stowable sleeping accommodation for three.

CONTROLS: Craft direction is controlled by differential propeller pitch and aerodynamic rudders mounted aft of the propulsion engines. Pitch and roll trim is provided by four ballast tanks.

OPERATION: The Helibarge is designed to be loaded while resting on a solid level surface, with its landing pads inflated and the skirt stiffeners deflated. Payload and fuel are arranged so that the gross-weight centre-of-gravity is over the plenum centre-of-lift area. Final trim adjustment is made with the ballast tanks.

The check list prior to landing on the Helibarge will include: duct folded flat and secured, louvres closed, cargo secured to deck, thrust propellers and rudders secured, departure of unnecessary personnel from the deck.

The helicopter pilot then is signalled to approach and land on the platform (in the centre of the duct area) under the guidance of the Helibarge operator. When the helicopter has its landing gear correctly located in the grooves provided the rotor is stopped and the cargo-hook is lowered to be attached in the "eye" provided in the landing platform. Tension is applied as though the helicopter were to lift a 2-ton payload, and then the landing gear skids are locked in the platform grooves of the Helibarge.

The APU is started to provide electrical, pneumatic, and hydraulic power. The crewmen leave the duct area, the duct is raised and secured in place, louvres are opened and the thrust propellers and rudders are released from their secured condition.

To start transport operations, the two thrust engines are started up and checked while the helicopter rotor is brought up to speed at neutral collective pitch. (The cyclic pitch

A utility barge for applications involving the movement of heavy equipment

is normally kept neutral at all times). When the Helibarge operator is ready, he signals to the helicopter pilot to "take off". The collective pitch is then increased as for a normal helicopter take-off.

The rotor downwash blows into the duct-diffuser and expands into the plenum chamber under the deck of the Helibarge. At the same time, the Helibarge operator applies air pressure to the skirt stiffeners. The Helibarge lifts rapidly off the ground to a height where the air-escape-volume is equal to the air-input-volume from the helicopter rotor. The plenum is designed to provide good damping, so that any heave oscillation that would otherwise be induced is prevented. However, if the collective pitch were increased only slowly from zero to normal take-off position, there is a point where marginal heave stability might occur, just after the skirts barely cleared the ground.

As the Helibarge skirts clear the ground, the operator applies thrust, and controls the direction of travel, while the helicopter pilot merely maintains the designated fixed collective pitch position and keeps the cyclic pitch at neutral—unless the Helibarge operator requests a slight left or right motion to counter a cross wind, slope of the ground, or assistance in a turn; although this is normally achieved by "crabbing" sideways an appropriate amount.

The Helibarge is propelled forward immediately upon lift-off to prevent build up of a cloud of dust or water spray, although the expansion of the flow within the plenum causes precipitation of most heavier particles.

As the vehicle begins to move under its propulsive power, the operator deflates the landing pads and applies vacuum to retract them flat under the deck for minimum airflow interference.

The reversible pitch thrust units provide braking and aid in steering. Upon reaching its destination, the reverse procedure is used

to land, disconnect and take-off with the helicopter, and then unload.

Transporting an empty Helibarge with a helicopter follows the same procedure as for a loaded Helibarge, except that maximum allowable speed is reduced by half, due to a critical speed limit, at which the ram air pressure, due to speed, equals the plenum air pressure.

HEX-150 (UH-1H)
DIMENSIONS: EXTERNAL:

DIAMETER:	150 ft 0 in (45·72 m)

AREA:

Height overall on landing pads, power off	
	17 ft 0 in (5·18 m)
Height overall, skirt inflated (excluding daylight hover clearance)	
	23 ft 0 in (7·01 m)
Draft afloat	2 in (50 mm)
Cushion area	17,672 ft² (1,270·15 m²)
Skirt depth	7 ft 6 in (2·27 m)

DIMENSIONS, INTERNAL:

Length	10 ft 0 in (3·04 m)
Max width	20 ft 0 in (6·09 m)
Max height	8 ft 0 in (2·43 m)
Floor area	200 ft² (18·58 m²)

WEIGHTS:

Normal empty weight	50 tons
Normal all-up weight	94 tons
Normal payload (cargo)	30 tons
Max payload (incl fuel)	44 tons

PERFORMANCE:

Max speed over calm water	
	50 mph (80·46 km/h)
Cruising speed	40 mph;(64·37 km/h)
Water speed in 4 ft waves and 15 knot headwind	35 mph (52·32 km/h)
Still air range and endurance at cruising speed, 10% reserve	520 miles (804·67 km)
Range and endurance in 4 ft waves, 15 knot headwind	350 miles (10 hours at 35 mph)
Max gradient, static conditions	5%
Vertical obstacle clearance	8 ft (2·43 m)

HOVERMARINE CORPORATION
CORPORATE AND MARKETING OFFICES:
Three Gateway Center, Pittsburgh, Pennsylvania 15222

TELEPHONE:
(412) 288-0450
TELEX:
81-2479

MANUFACTURING AND ENGINEERING FACILITY:
805 Marina Road, P.O. Box R, Titusville, Florida 32780

TELEPHONE:
(305) 269-6712

SUBSIDIARY:
Hovermarine Transport, Ltd., Hazel Wharf, Hazel Road, Woolston, Southampton, SO2 7GB

TELEPHONE:
Southampton 446831

TELEX:
(851) 47141

DIRECTORS:
H. Arthur Bellows, Jr, Chairman
    The Triangle Corporation, New York, New York
Max W. S. Bishop, US Ambassador (Ret.), Ailey, Georgia
Charles C. Cohen, Partner,
    Reed Smith Shaw & McClay, Pittsburgh, Pennsylvania
Edward F. Davison, President
    Hovermarine Corporation
John H. Kennedy, Vice President
    Hovermarine Corporation
Jerry A. Whatley, Private Investor
    Dallas, Texas
William A. Zebedee, Chairman
    Hovermarine Corporation

OFFICERS:
HOVERMARINE CORPORATION:
William A. Zebedee, Chairman of the Board
Edward F. Davison, President
Bob L. Black, Vice President
Arnold M. Hall, Vice President
John H. Kennedy, Vice President
Dan E. Steigerwald, Controller

U.S. MANUFACTURE

Hovermarine Corporation completed its new 25,000 sq ft HM.2 production facility in Titusville, Florida in the Spring of 1974. Located on the Indian River adjacent to Cape Canaveral, it has the capacity to manufacture up to 24 HM.2 craft per year. The first U.S. built HM.2 was completed in June, 1974. Previously the craft was manufactured only by the company's English subsidiary, Hovermarine Transport Limited.

Prior to manufacture in the U.S., Hovermarine had been prohibited from offering the HM.2 in the U.S., due to legislation which restricts the domestic sale of foreign built craft. With the advent of U.S. production it is planned that the U.S. facility will produce craft for the North and Central American market and the U.K. facility will produce craft for other parts of the world.

In June, 1974, the first North American HM.2 commercial operation opened on Lake Ontario, providing regular commuter service between Toronto, Canada and Youngstown, New York.

In addition to its commercial ACV activities Hovermarine is engaged in surface effect ship research projects for both the U.S. and British governments. Hovermarine was also a sub-contractor to Lockheed Aircraft Corporation for component design for a 2,000 ton prototype surface effect ship for the U.S. Navy.

HM.2 HOVERFERRY

A rigid sidewall hovercraft, the HM.2 hoverferry carries 60 passengers in an air conditioned cabin fitted with aircraft style seats and has a maximum speed of 35 knots. It is propelled by marine diesel engines and twin underwater propellers.

Hovermarine Corporation HM.2 manufacturing facility at Titusville, Florida, on the Indian River, adjacent to Cape Canaveral

An HM.2 operating off the coast of Florida

Craft of this type has accumulated over 60 million passenger miles to date. A total of 28 HM.2 craft are in service or on order in thirteen countries around the world.

As a waterbus, the HM.2 provides competitive low-cost passenger travel at a cost of operation of 3 to 4 cents per passenger mile for a typical service. Its fuel consumption is 36 gal/hr (0·016 gal/passenger-mile).

DIMENSIONS:

Overall length	51 ft (15·54 m)
Overall beam	20 ft (6·09 m)
Overall height	13 ft 9 in (4·19 m)
Height above waterline—on cushion*	11 ft 10½ in (3·62 m)
Height above waterline—off cushion	8 ft 10½ in (2·71 m)
Draught on cushion*	2 ft 10½ in (0·87 m)
Draught off cushion	4 ft 10½ in (1·49 m)
Cabin size (length × width)	22 ft × 16 ft (6·70 m × 4·88 m)
Cabin height at centre line	6 ft 6 in (1·98 m)
Entrance size (height × width)	6 ft 3 in × 4 ft (1·90 m × 1·22 m)

*These heights and draughts take account of 2° bow up trim on cushion.

WEIGHTS:

Standard gross weight	43,500 lb (19,732 kg)
Normal pay-load	60 passengers
Freight	11,000 lb (4,990 kg)

PERFORMANCE: (at standard gross weight)

Max speed—calm water, no wind	35 kt (65 kph)
Acceleration—0-35 kt	36·5 secs
Deceleration—from max speed	
(normal)	270 ft (76 m)
(emergency)	150 ft (45 m)
Endurance	4·8 hours

HM.2 GENERAL PURPOSE CRAFT

The HM.2 general purpose craft utilizes the same hull and machinery as the HM.2 hoverferry. The superstructure and deck are designed to meet the needs of various special applications including:

Hydrographic survey craft; crew boat; oil spill recovery craft; air sea rescue; pilot cutter and patrol craft.

With a maximum speed of 35 knots and a payload of up to 11,000 lbs. it provides a high work output at low capital and operating cost.

The rigid sidewalls resist sideslipping in cross-winds and when turning. Positive directional control is maintained in all conditions and at all speeds. Relatively little wash is created by the craft on cushion.

Manoeuvrability is good throughout the speed range, permitting the HM.2 to operate safely in congested waterways or coastal areas. The twin rudders, mounted beneath the sidewalls, ensure banked turns. The craft has a turning circle of as little as 850 ft. (260 m) diameter at maximum speed. At low speeds, the widely spaced marine propellers allow the craft to be turned through 360° in its own length.

DIMENSIONS:

Overall length	50 ft 0 in (15·24 m)
Overall beam	19 ft 0 in (5·8 m)
Hull depth (base to deck)	6 ft 6 in (1·99 m)
Overall height (to top of cabin)	13 ft 4 in (4·10 m)
Draft on-cushion	2 ft 10½ in (0·87 m)
Draft off-cushion	4 ft 10½ in (1·49 m)
Wheelhouse area 14 ft × 14 approx	(4·3 m × 4·3 m)
After cabin area 14 ft × 14 ft approx	(4·3 m × 4·3 m)
Cabin at centre line height	6 ft 6 in (2·00 m)

WEIGHTS:

Total disposable payload including fuel and optional extras 11,000 lbs
Standard gross weight 42,500 lbs (19,300 kg)

An HM.2 general purpose craft

Max permissible gross weight	44,500 lbs (20,200 kg)

PERFORMANCE (at standard gross weight):

Maximum speed—calm water, no wind	35 knots
Acceleration—0·30 knots	45 secs
Deceleration—from max speed (normal)	250 ft (70 m)
Deceleration—from max speed (emergency)	150 ft (45 m)

HM.5

Hovermarine Corporation expects to complete the design of a larger craft, the HM.5, during 1974. It will be similar in concept to the HM.2 and will accommodate 140-160 passengers, It will operate at 40 knots. Features of the craft will include marine diesel engines, water jets and shallow draft. The first HM.5 craft is scheduled for completion in early 1976.

HOVERSPORT, INC

HEAD OFFICE:
313 Balsam Street, Palm Beach Gardens, Fla. 33403
TELEPHONE:
(305) 622-6568
EXECUTIVES:
Scott D. Thatcher, President
Donaldson A. Dow, Secretary and Treasurer

Hoversport was founded early in 1969 and was chartered in January 1971. Its first commercial design was the HS-1B Stingray, a circular-planform runabout which is sold either fully-assembled or in kit form. This was followed by the HS-1A single-seater and a two-seat model, the HS-11, both available as kits only. Two recent developments are the HS-IV, a 150 hp 4-5 seater with an enclosed cabin, and the HS-TR, a hovertrailer with a 1,500 lb (680·38 kg) payload capacity.

HS-1B STINGRAY

This single-seat recreational runabout for enthusiasts is designed to fit into the average station wagon or on top of a family car.

The craft is available in three different forms:

Basic: a starter or experimental kit for use in schools, or for individuals. Includes fibreglass shell with integral moulded fuel tank, engine, tool kit etc.

Standard: Complete with all materials required for flight, including neoprene impregnated skirt material.

Amphibian: In addition to the parts supplied with the standard version, this contains a fibreglass and foam flotation system which provides 150% buoyancy in the event of engine failure.

Hoversport HS-1B

LIFT AND PROPULSION: Integrated system powered by a 15·5 hp JLO L230 2-cycle engine driving a 2 ft 1¾ in (654 mm) diameter laminated wood fan. The primary air flow, used for direct thrust, is directed through a propulsive slot control flap aft of the fan duct. The secondary air flow, for cushion lift passes down into an open plenum. A fibreglass fuel tank, with a capacity of 2 US gallons is moulded into the back rest. Fuel is 20 : 1 petrol oil mixture.

Skirt is of "C" type, fabricated in abrasion resistant neoprene impregnated nylon.

CONTROLS: Craft heading is controlled kinesthetically and by a single aerodynamic rudder aft of the propulsive air slot. The rudder is operated by a single column on which is mounted a twist-grip for controlling forward speed.

HULL: Entire structure, including fuel tank, folding side panels, seats, lift duct, thrust duct and mount support, is fabricated in cloth reinforced fibreglass. Side panels are removable to simplify transport and storage. Craft will fit into the average station wagon or on top of a family car.

DIMENSIONS:

Hull diameter	8 ft 0 in (2·43 m)
Height overall, power off	1 ft 10 in (558 mm)
Folded length	8 ft 0 in (2·43 m)
Folded width	3 ft 6 in (1·06 m)
Folded height	1 ft 10 in (0·558 m)
Skirt depth	8 in (0·203 m)

WEIGHTS:

Normal empty weight	150 lb (68·03 kg)
Normal all-up weight	400 lb (181·42 kg)
Normal payload	250 lb (113·39 kg)

PERFORMANCE:

Max speed, calm water

	20 mph (32·18 km/h)
Max speed over land	33 mph (53·10 km/h)
Max speed over ice	40 mph (64·37 km/h)
Still air range	70 miles (112·65 km)
Gradient from static start	12·15%

Vertical obstacle clearance

8 in (203 mm)

PRICE AND TERMS: Basic version, §635·00; Standard, $795·00; Amphibian, $995·00. Terms: 50% with order, balance prior to shipment or COD. HS-1B assembly plans, $5·00.

HOVERSPORT HS-II

This is a twin-engined amphibious craft designed to carry a load of up to 400 lb (181·42 kg) over snow, swampland and water at speeds up to 40 mph (64·37 km/h).

LIFT AND PROPULSION: Cushion lift is supplied by a 15½ hp Rockwell JLO-230 air-cooled two-stroke engine driving a 2 ft 6 in (762 mm) diameter 6-bladed axial fan made in laminated wood. Fan air is delivered to the cushion via a peripheral bag type skirt. A second 15½ hp engine of the same type drives a 2 ft 6 in (762 mm) diameter Banks-Maxwell or Arrowcraft two-bladed propeller for thrust. A 2 US gallon (7·57 l) tank is located internally, forward of the lift engine.

SKIRT: Bag type, 8 in (203 mm) high. Annular slot for air entry to skirt, with slot for air exit and contact holes for laminar flow and ejection of dust.

CONTROLS: A control stick operates two aerodynamic rudders for directional control. Reverse thrust is not available, but the craft can be rotated easily for changes in direction. The control stick is located in front of the right hand seat, ahead of which are the master switches, choke actuators and twin throttles.

ACCOMMODATION: Driver and passenger sit side-by-side in a semi-enclosed cockpit on a bench type seat. A wind screen can be fitted if required.

HULL: Wooden structure with waterproof fabric covering.

DIMENSIONS:

Length	13 ft 0 in	(3·96 m)
Beam	8 ft 0 in	(2·43 m)
Height overall, power on	3 ft 10 in	(1·16 m)
Cabin width	2 ft 7 in	(0·787 m)

WEIGHTS:

Gross weight	750 lb (340·17 kg)
Payload	400 lb (181 kg)

PERFORMANCE:

Cruising speed over land

	35 mph (56·32 km/h)
Water speed	8·30 mph (13·48 km/h)

PRICE:

Generally costs between US$400·00 and $750·00 to build. Total materials package, $679·00. Special discounts for schools and quantity purchasers. Plans US$10·50.

HS-1V

This new 4-5 seater is still in the design stage and no illustrations were available at the time of going to press. The craft is fully amphibious and will be capable of speeds of up to 50 mph (80·46 km/h) over land and water. Production is expected to start early in 1974.

Hoversport HS-II, two seat light amphibious sports craft

HS-1B recreational ACV

LIFT AND PROPULSION: Motive power for the lift system is provided by a 45 hp Rockwell-JLO or Hirth engine driving twin 2 ft 0 in (0·60 m) diameter Multiwing axial fans. Air intakes are located on the sides of the craft. Two 45 hp engines, also of Rockwell-JLO or Hirth design, each drive a 2-bladed, 3 ft 0 in (0·91 m) diameter Banks-Maxwell propeller for thrust. Fuel tanks, with a total capacity of 18 US gallons (68·13 l) are located between the cargo compartment aft of the passenger cabin and the propulsion engine bays. Cushion area is 198 sq ft (18·39 sq m).

CONTROLS: Directional control is provided by aerodynamic rudders, differential thrust and reverse thrust. Thrust ports assist manoeuvring at low speeds.

HULL: Moulded glassfibre construction.

ACCOMMODATION: Enclosed, soundproofed cabin with operator forward. Side-by-side moulded bucket seats for three passengers behind. Thrust/reverse levers, throttles and switches located in arm rests at sides of operator's seat. Cabin access is via two gull-wing doors, one port and one starboard.

DIMENSIONS:

Height on landing pads	5 ft 3 in	(1·6 m)
Draft	4 in	(101 mm)

WEIGHTS:

Empty weight	800 lb (362·85 kg)
All-up weight	2,200 lb (1,000 kg)
Payload, approx	1,000 lb (453·59 kg)

PERFORMANCE:

Max speed over all surfaces

	50 mph : (80·46 km/h)
Max wave height	2 ft (0·60 m)
Max gradient, static conditions	22%

PRICE:

Approx US$8,000–$10,000.

Terms: 20% down, balance prior to shipment.

HS-1A

This single-seat recreational craft is similar in most respects to the HS-II, but with an emphasis on lower costs. Smaller engines (8 hp as opposed to 15·5 hp) and fans are used, and it has a lower payload. Cost of construction is about $150·00 less than the HS-II. PRICE: Plans, $6·00.

LIPPISCH RESEARCH CORPORATION

HEAD OFFICE:
   3450 Cottage Grove Avenue SE, Cedar
   Rapids, Iowa 52403
TELEPHONE:
   (319) 365-0175
SALES OFFICE:
   Ten Old Post Office Road, Silver Spring,
   Maryland 20910
TELEPHONE:
   (301) 588-3311
STAFF PERSONNEL:
   Dr Alexander M. Lippisch FRAeS, President
   George G. Lippisch, Vice-President
   Bryce M. Fisher, Treasurer
   Dr Herschel Shosteck, Director of Marketing

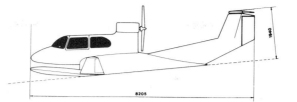 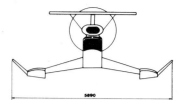

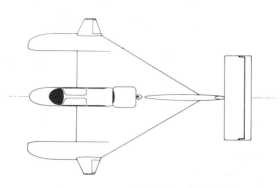

General arrangement of the Lippisch X-113B, a projected two-seat version of the X-113 Am

Lippisch Research Corporation was founded in 1966 to furnish engineering design and consultancy services to airframe manufacturers and others. In recent years, the Corporation has concentrated on the development of ram-wing and wingless vehicles based on research concepts originated by Dr Alexander M. Lippisch.

Dr Lippisch is renowned as "father" of the delta wing. His designs included the first delta-wing glider, built in 1928 and the first operational rocket-propelled fighter, the Me 163 of World War II.

The need for more reliable and efficient surface transportation for relatively under-developed areas of the world, most of which are either water-bound or water-traced, led Dr Lippisch to investigate air cushion concepts.

He determined that air cushion vehicles employing the dynamic ground effect principle offered greater speed, higher power efficiency, controllability, and flexibility in terms of the kinds of terrain which could be crossed, than aerostatic types. The primary problem, theoretically, lay in the pitch instability of

The "winged hull" ground effect vehicle concept originated by Dr. Alexander M. Lippisch has received extensive model, wind tunnel and prototype testing. The X-112, *upper left*, the earliest flying prototype, confirmed stability characteristics in and out of ground effect. Recent tests of the X-113 Am, *upper right*, in the North Sea, more than verified wind tunnel data on efficiency (50% less power required in ground effect). Projected configurations include a two-seat sports and utility craft, *lower left*, and a 6-ton river bus, *lower right*

conventional wings when flown at various distances from the surface; i.e., the centre of pressure travels rearward as the surface is approached, causing the nose of a craft to pitch downward.

Dr. Lippisch discovered that a low aspect ratio wing, properly designed, would solve this instability problem. The result of his studies was the "winged hull" concept.

The major research work has been performed under contract with or in cooperation with Rhein-Flugzeugbau GmbH and Dornier Gmbh

DESIGN: The "winged hull" combines the waterborne stability of the catamaran with the airborne stability of a unique, reversed delta wing with negative dihedral along the leading edge. The wing tips, or catamaran-type floats, and the wing's trailing edge are on the same plane. This special shape creates stable ground effect, enabling the craft to maintain a selected height from the surface automatically. Moreover, it solves the stability problem. The centre of pressure for the wing remains fixed whether the craft is in or out of ground effect.

The small-span, low aspect ratio wing design of the hull lends itself to simple, rugged construction which will withstand strong impacts without sacrificing loaded weight.

POWER PLANT: Conventional aircraft propulsion is employed.

CONTROLS AND PERFORMANCE: Control of the "winged hull" has proved in flight tests to be remarkably simple and safe. Conventional aircraft controls are used.

At low speeds, the craft operates as a planing boat. During take-off from the water, no control pressures are applied; gradual increase in speed develops the required lift and ground effect automatically. The craft is operated at a height above the surface of up to one-half the hull beam (wing span) for optimum performance.

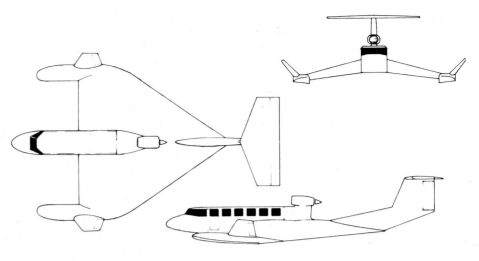

General arrangement of the projected 6-ton river bus

Flight testing has shown craft of this type to be extremely manoeuvrable. They can travel at speed along a river and negotiate turns of only a few hundred feet in radius.

Because of its inherent stability, the "winged hull" is not restricted to flying in ground effect. It can leave ground effect to fly above obstacles such as bridges, for example, or to operate above a fog bank. Prototype vehicles have converted from ground effect to altitude and back again with no difficulty.

It manoeuvres at altitude in much the same way as a slow-flying aircraft; however, it is least efficient when operated out of ground effect during the brief periods it might be required to do so.

Whilst resembling an aircraft in form and control, the "winged hull is designed, of course, for highest efficiency in ground effect. Flight tests, including a series performed over rough water in the North Sea near Bremmerhaven, have established

that 50% less power is required in ground effect, enabling operations in excess of 50 ton-miles per gallon of fuel at speeds in the 90-180 knot range.

APPLICATIONS: "Winged hull" designs ranging from small, two-seat sports and utility craft propelled by Volkswagen engines to river buses. Coastal transports of several tons have been initiated. A retractable wheeled undercarriage would permit amphibious operations in areas poorly suited for dock facilities.

No special depth of water is required when the craft is in ground effect; it will operate equally well over sand banks, beaches, deserts and arctic regions.

Military applications include fast river patrol boats, anti-submarine warfare (ASW) craft, as well as personnel and supply transports.

The Lippisch Research Corporation offers its design services to potential users and will undertake studies for specific applications.

LITTON INDUSTRIES INC.,
HEAD OFFICE:
2560 Walnut Avenue, Culver City,
California 90009, P.O. Box 92911,
Los Angeles
R. H. Du Bois, Vice President

In November 1972 Litton Industries received a $2·7 million contract from US Naval Ship Systems Command to conduct a preliminary design study for a 2,000-ton operational prototype surface effect warship capable of speeds in excess of 60 knots.

The contract was one of four competitive nine-month design contracts, and during the initial stages was undertaken by Litton in conjunction with Rohr Industries, Chula Vista, California.

In August 1973, Litton's contract was transferred to Rohr Industries, while certain Litton divisions retained sub-contract roles in support of the study.

In July, 1974, it was announced that the Rohr Industries study, and also that of Bell Aerospace, had been successful and that the company had received an 18-month contract worth $36 million for continuing the programme.

LOCKHEED MISSILES AND SPACE COMPANY INC
Ocean Systems Division

HEAD OFFICE:
Sunnyvale, California 94088

In November 1972, Lockheed Missiles and Space Company Inc was awarded a $2·3 million contract by US Naval Ship Systems Command to undertake a preliminary design study for a 2,000-ton operational prototype surface effect warship.

The contract was one of four competitive nine-month study contracts. the other recipients being Bell Aerospace, Aerojet General and Rohr Industries. In July 1974, Bell Aerospace and Rohr Industries each received 18 month follow-on contracts to conduct an advanced development programme for 2,000-ton ocean-going SESs.

Under a separate subcontract with Lockheed, the Rocketdyne Division of Rockwell International Corporation established the preliminary design for a high thrust waterjet system to propel the vessel.

At the time of going to press, the formation of a financial link between Textron (Bell Aerospace's parent company) and Lockheed Aircraft Corporation was being negotiated.

POWER BREEZE

HEAD OFFICE:
8139 Matilija, Panorama City, California
91402

TELEPHONE:
(213) 785-0197

EXECUTIVES:
Dan W. Henderson Jr, President/Designer

Power Breeze Air Cushion Vehicle Systems has been formed to stimulate public interest in ACVs, and is currently selling plans to home builders for a small, easily assembled amphibious single-seater.

A set of plans costs $5·00 and a ready made skirt costs $35·00.

Total cost of construction in the USA, including ply for the hull, skirt material, metal tubing, propeller and engine is about $400. Weight of the craft is 250 lb (113 kg) and the maximum speed is approximately 25 mph (40·23 km/h).

A number of craft have been built to this design in the United States and Australia.

Design of a more powerful craft is under way.

In 1974, the company became engaged in the sales of second-hand ACVs, and it now specialises in finding craft to meet the needs of its clients.

A recent survey conducted by the company showed that ACV enthusiasts in the United States prefer craft of their own construction to ready-built machines.

ROHR INDUSTRIES, INC
Marine Systems Organisation

HEAD OFFICE:
Foot of H Street, PO Box 878, Chula Vista,
California 92012

TELEPHONE:
(714) 426-7111

EXECUTIVES:
Burt F. Raynes, Chairman
Frank E. McCreery, Vice Chairman
Frederick W. Garry, President
Jerome J. Filiciotto, Group Vice President,
Aerospace & Marine Systems
Wilfred J. Eggington, Programme Manager,
2000-Ton SES

Rohr Industries, founded in 1940, is based in Chula Vista, California, adjacent to San Diego Bay. Its main plant comprises 130 acres of land with more than 2-million square feet of covered accommodation. It houses over 3,000 pieces of major production equipment representing a $31 million investment. Rohr employs about 11,000 people and holds a leading position in welded aluminium marine structures, manufacture and testing of boat hulls, offshore mooring systems for fuel transfer, specialised hydrostructures for oceanographic research.

Experience of SES technology to date has consisted of conducting a research and development programme for the US Navy, with the surface effect test craft, XR-1C. Rohr's responsibilities in this programme have included design, modification, testing and evaluation of equipment, methods and concepts relating to SES technology. Rohr recently completed a preliminary design study for a 2,000-ton operational prototype surface effect ship for the US Navy Surface Effect Ship Project Office and is currently competing for the next phase. Success in being awarded a contract for this could lead to construction of the vessel at Rohr's marine facility in Chula Vista, with test and evaluation in the San Diego area. As part of its expanding marine role, Rohr is engaged in studies, analysis and conceptual design of new commercial SESs to meet demands in mass urban transportation and the offshore oil industry.

Top: Impression of Rohr's proposal for a 2,000 ton operational prototype surface effect warship. The preliminary design of this vessel is now complete and further design and development is in hand. *Centre:* Design prepared by Rohr for a US Navy Coastal (Medium) Development craft. *Bottom:* The Company is evaluating several configurations for high-speed ferries to serve estuary, mainland-to-island and cross-bay routes

SESLAR AIR CUSHION VEHICLES

HEAD OFFICE:
3059 'A' Street, San Diego, California 92102

DIRECTORS:
Patrick and Linda Seslar

Seslar Air Cushion Vehicles was formed in 1969 to develop small, easily-built ACVs. SACV's latest prototype Scootair Mk. II, is now on permanent display in the San Diego Aerospace Museum, San Diego, California. Scootair Mk II was developed from an earlier design, Scootair Mk I, a 125 lb (56·69 kg) portable craft powered by a 3 hp engine.

SCOOTAIR MK II

Scootair Mk II features simplified and improved construction coupled with the use of an off-the-shelf propulsion unit.

LIFT AND PROPULSION: Power for lift is provided by a 3 hp, 2 cycle engine driving an axial fan, located in the centre of the platform. Thrust is provided by a modified 7 hp air-boat air drive engine bolted to the deck aft of the lift engine and fan.

CONTROLS: Craft heading is controlled by a column which activates a rudder in the thrust unit slipstream. The control column incorporates the thrust engine throttle.

HULL: The platform is built in ¼ in (6·35 mm) marine ply bonded to frame structural

members. Outer deck panels fold upwards
for transport reducing the beam to 3 ft 6 in
(1·06 m).

DIMENSIONS:

Diameter	9 ft 0 in (2·74 m)
Height (off cushion)	3 ft 0 in (0·914 m)
Height (on cushion)	3 ft 8 in (1·14 m)

WEIGHTS:

Empty	175 lb (79·37 kg)
Payload	220 lb (90·71 kg)

PERFORMANCE:

Speed	30 mph (48·28 km/h)

TURF BOARD

Development is underway of a new low-cost
recreational ACV designed to offer a counterpart to surfing or skate boarding. The
operator stands on the 4 ft (1·21 m) diameter
craft controlling direction by shifting his
weight and hover height by a foot-actuated
throttle.

Scootair Mk II

SURFACE EFFECT SHIPS PROJECT OFFICE

OFFICE:
PO Box 34401, Bethesda, Maryland 20034
CABLE ADDRESS:
SESPO, c/o Naval Ship Research and
Development Center, Bethesda, Maryland
EXECUTIVES:
Captain C. J. Boyd, USN, Project Manager

The Surface Effect Ships Project Office,
originally sponsored by both the Navy and
Commerce Departments, became a wholly
Navy sponsored operation on July 1, 1971.
In early December 1971, Captain Carl J.
Boyd, formerly Commanding Officer, USS
Springfield, Sixth Fleet Flagship, was assigned
to duties as Deputy Project Manager.
Captain Boyd became Project Manager in
February 1972.

With the change in sponsorship of the
project, there was also a change in programme
direction. This change is best described by
the following quote from remarks made by
Admiral Elmo R. Zumwalt, Jr., Chief of
Naval Operations: "It is my personal con-
viction that development of a large SES has
the potential for affecting other aspects of
naval warfare as profoundly as nuclear power
has affected submarine warfare".

The Surface Effect Ships Project Office is
developing the SES from the aspects of
"point design" and technological advancement across a broad front. Contracts were
let in January 1969 with Aerojet-General
Corporation and Bell Aerospace Company
for the detail design, construction and test of
100-ton testcraft. The 82 ft (24·99 m)
Aerojet-General craft is waterjet-propelled,
while the 72 ft (21·94 m) Bell Aerospace craft
has semi-submerged supercavitating propellers. Extensive testing of these two craft is
now under way.

Craft characteristics are:
Gross weight: 100 short tons
Speed: Excess of 80 knots
Propulsion: Gas turbine engine driving
supercavitating propellers or waterjets

SES-100B, built for SESPO by Bell Aerospace. SES-100A is waterjet-propelled and the SES-100B has semi-submerged propellers

SES-100A, built for the US Navy's Surface Effect Ships Project Office by Aerojet-General Corporation

A number of multi-thousand ton SES ship designs have been investigated and several point designs have been established as programme references. These studies confirm early expectations and indicate that large multi-thousand ton high speed surface effect ships are feasible.

On November 10th, 1972 contracts were awarded by SESPO to four companies to undertake preliminary nine-month design studies for a 2,000-ton surface effect warship prototype. The companies were Aerojet-General Corporation ($3·6 million); Bell Aerospace ($3·0 million); Litton Industries in conjunction with Rohr Corporation

($2·7 million) and Lockheed Missile and Space Company ($2·2 million).

The Litton contract was subsequently renewed with Rohr Corporation as main contractor, Litton being responsible for certain aspects of the design.

On July 2nd, 1974, SESPO announced that the design competition for the 2,000-ton SES had been won by Bell Aerospace and Rohr Corporation, Aerospace and Marine Systems Division. Cost-plus-fixed-fee awards were made to Bell Aerospace ($36,232,080) and Rohr ($35,219,933). Work will be performed by Bell at Michoud, New Orleans, La, and by Rohr at Chula Vista, California and at

selected subcontractor facilities.

The 18-month contract calls for the design development and testing of full-scale subsystems and components. Emphasis will be on the development of the SES propulsion system, including the transmission, waterjet inlet and pump, the air cushion lift fans, skirts and a system to control the ride characteristics in a variety of sea states.

It was indicated that work completed under this new design phase will put US Navy officials in a better position to judge the merits of large SES vehicles and their value in anti-submarine warfare.

SKIMMERS INCORPORATED

HEAD OFFICE:
  PO Box 855, Severna Park, Maryland, 21146
TELEPHONE:
  301-647-0526
DIRECTORS:
  M. W. Beardsley, President and General Manager
  H. L. Beardsley
  W. D. Preston

OVERSEAS REPRESENTATIVE:
  United Kingdom: Airhover Ltd, St. Osyth, Essex

Skimmers Inc was formed in April 1966 to produce plans and components for use by homebuilders in constructing the Fan-Jet Skimmer sport ACV. It is affiliated with the Beardsley Air Car Co.

FAN-JET SKIMMER

Fan-Jet Skimmer is one of the world's first practical solo sport ACVs. It was designed by Col. Melville Beardsley, a former USAF technical officer, and one of the pioneers in ACV development in the United States.

The Fan-Jet Skimmer was designed to be the simplest and cheapest one-man ACV that could be devised. More than forty craft of this type have been built to date. The company is now developing a two-seat sports ACV.

HULL: The main structural component is a tractor inner tube, giving 700 lb of buoyancy, around which is an aluminium framework of square tube, and L girders. The topside bow profile is in plywood. The structure is decked in vinyl-coated nylon fabric, which is also used for the self-extending skirt system.

LIFT AND PROPULSION: Power for the integrated, lift/propulsion system is provided by a Chrysler 2-cycle 6 hp engine, driving an 18 in axial flow fan. The fan has a marine

plywood hub with 9 sheet metal formed blades. The primary air flow, used for direct thrust is ejected through a propulsive slot control flap located aft of the fan duct. The area of the slot can be varied by a hinged-flap controlled by a lever. This and the throttle lever and ignition switch are the only controls. The secondary air flow, for cushion lift, passes into a rearward plenum chamber.

CONTROL: The craft is steered by kinesthetic control (body movement) which the designer feels is the ideal method of control for a craft of this size.

DIMENSIONS:
Length overall	9 ft 8 in (2·9 m)
Beam overall	6 ft 2 in (1·8 m)
Height overall on landing pads	
	36 in (0·9 m)
Skirt depth	9 in (0·2 m)
Draft afloat	5 in (0·12 m)
Cushion area	44 sq ft (4·0 m²)

WEIGHTS:
Normal all-up weight	250 lb (113 kg)
Normal payload (operating)	150 lb (68 kg)
Maximum payload	180 lb (397 kg) app

PERFORMANCE:
Max speed, calm water	18 mph (29 km/h)
Cruising speed, calm water	
	18 mph (29 km/h)

The Fan-Jet Skimmer

Max wave capability	6 in app (153 mm)
Still air range	35 miles app (56 km)
Max gradient, static conditions	5° app
Vertical obstacle clearance	5 in (127 mm)

For full over-the-hump performance with an operator weighing more than 175 lb the installation of two power plants is recommended each identical with the standard single power unit. With an operator weighing up to 225 lb the speed of the twin is approx 20% greater than the standard single engine.

With the overall length of the twin-engine model increased to 11 ft 2 in, it will carry a useful load of 350 lb at maximum speeds of approximately 35 mph over smooth land and 22 mph over calm water.

Price: USA, f.o.b. Severna Park, Maryland:
  $1,200·00 for complete vehicle
  $595 for kit
  Terms of payment   50% down

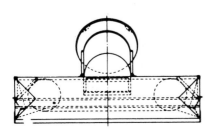

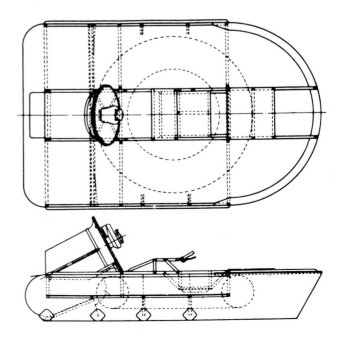

The Fan-Jet Skimmer, designed by Melville Beardsley

UNIVERSAL HOVERCRAFT

HEAD OFFICE:

2611 182nd Place, Redondo Beach, California 90278

TELEPHONE:
374 1904

DIRECTOR:
R. J. Windt

Formed in 1969, this company has designed and built fifteen different sports ACV prototypes, ranging from an ultra-light single seater powered by a model aircraft engine, to a six-seater powered by an engine of 110 hp. Plans of some of these designs are available to homebuilders.

The company is currently developing four different single-engine amphibious craft—an 8 ft single seater, a 10 ft two-seater, a 13 ft four-seater and a 16 ft six-seater. Work has also been undertaken on craft propelled by waterjets, outboard motors and sails.

UH-10

This single-seat amphibious runabout was one of the company's earliest designs. Construction of the prototype was completed in November 1969. The vehicle, which is of wooden construction, attains 30 mph (48·28 km/h) over land and 25 mph (40·23 km/h) over water.

LIFT AND PROPULSION: Integrated system employing a single McCulloch 101 2-cycle 116 cc engine, which drives a 1 ft 9 in (0·53 m) diameter, 12-bladed centrifugal fan mounted vertically on a shaft inside a transverse duct Air is drawn by the fan from each end of the duct. Propulsion air is expelled through an outlet nozzle aft and lift air is ducted into a plenum below. Maximum thrust is 32 lb (14·51 kg).

HULL: Frame is built from fir ribs and stringers and covered with ⅛ in ply.

ACCOMMODATION: Open cockpit with seat for driver. Craft will carry one person or a load of up to 170 lb (79·35 kg) over water, and up to 225 lb (102·05 kg) over land.

CONTROLS: Multiple rudders in the thrust air outlet provide directional control.

DIMENSIONS:

Length	10 ft 4 in (3·14 m)
Beam	6 ft 0 in (1·82 m)
Height, off cushion	2 ft 6 in (0·76 m)

WEIGHTS:

Weight empty	135 lb (61·23 kg)
Normal loaded weight	310 lb (140·14 kg)
Max loaded weight	360 lb (163·28 kg)

PERFORMANCE:

Max speed:	
Over land	30 mph (48·28 km/h)
Over water	25 mph (40·23 km/h)
Max gradient	10%

PRICE: Complete set of plans for homebuilding, US$6·00.

UH-12T

This amphibious two-seater is based on the company's original prototype which was built early in 1969. The new hull is easier to build and provides automatic pitch control. As thrust is increased, the aerofoil-shaped hull generates more lift, offsetting the pitching moment caused by thrust. The height of the centre of thrust has also been reduced.

UH-10, an amphibious single-seater powered by single McCulloch 101 2-cycle 116 cc engine

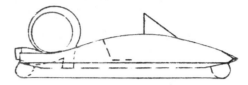
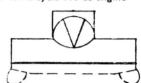

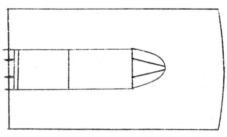

General arrangement of the UH-10 light ACV runabout. Of wooden construction, it attains 30 mph over land and 25 mph over water

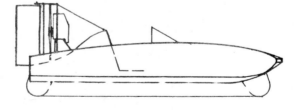
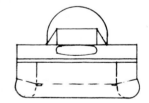

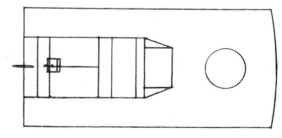

The UH-12T, an amphibious two-seater with a maximum speed of 55 mph (88·51 km/h)

LIFT AND PROPULSION: Motive power for the lift system is provided by 133 cc Chrysler 2-cycle petrol engine which drives a 2 ft 2 in (0·66 m) diameter, 4-bladed fan at 4,500 rpm. About 5% of the cushion air is employed to inflate the bag-type skirt. Thrust is provided by a 25 hp JLO 395 2-cycle engine driving a 3 ft 0 in (0·914 m) diameter 2-bladed ducted propeller.

HULL: Mixed wood and fibreglass construction. Structure comprises fir ribs and stringers covered with ⅛ in plywood. Cockpit floor and other highly stressed areas strengthened with fibreglass.

CONTROLS: Directional control is provided by a single aerodynamic rudder.

ACCOMMODATION: Single bench seat for driver and one passenger. Cockpit canopy can be fitted for use in cold weather.

DIMENSIONS:

Length overall	12 ft 6 in (3·81 m)
Beam overall	6 ft 0 in (1·82 m)

WEIGHTS:

Empty weight	275 lb (124·73 kg)
All-up weight	600 lb (272·14 kg)

PERFORMANCE:

Max speed:	
over land	55 mph (88·51 km/h)
over water	50 mph (80·46 km/h)
Max gradient	26%

PRICE AND TERMS: Plans US$15·00 per set.

UH-14T

A "stretched" version of the UH-12T, this model has a length of 14 ft (4·26 m) and a beam of 6 ft 6 in (1·98 m).

LIFT AND PROPULSION: Systems identical to those of UH-12T, but thrust engines with up to 25% more power may be installed.

SKIRT: 12 in (307 mm) bag skirt.

ACCOMMODATION: Single bench seat forward for driver and passenger; optional rear seat for one adult or two children.

WEIGHTS:

Empty weight	400 lb (181·42 kg)
All-up weight	950 lb (430·893 kg)

PRICE:

Complete set of plans, US$20.00.

UH-17S

Construction of the UH-17S, which has an integrated lift/propulsion system powered by either a Volkswagen or Corvair engine of 50-140 hp, was completed in May 1970. The craft, which seats a driver and up to three passengers, is said to be extremely quiet and control is precise. It is capable of towing water or snow skiers, sleds or ski boards.

LIFT AND PROPULSION: A single 75 hp Corvair automobile engine drives a 3 ft 6 in (1·06 m) diameter fan mounted vertically on a shaft inside a transverse duct. Air is drawn by the fan from each end of the duct. Propulsion air is expelled through outlets at the stern and lift air is ducted into a plenum below. The fan feeds air into the cushion at 240 cfs and provides 150 lb thrust.

ACCOMMODATION: Enclosed cabin seating driver and up to three passengers on two bench-type seats.

DIMENSIONS:

Length	17 ft 10 in (5·43 m)
Beam	7 ft 11 in (2·41 m)

WEIGHTS:

Empty weight	950 lb (430·89 kg)
Normal loaded weight	1,600 lb (725·71 kg)
Max loaded weight	1,900 lb (861·78 kg)

PERFORMANCE:

Max speed:	
over land	42 mph (67·59 km/h)
over water	35-40 mph (65·64 km/h)
Continuous gradient at 1,200 lb	12%

UH-18T

The prototype of this amphibious six-seater was built in 1971 and has accumulated over 200 operating hours, mainly on open seas. It was the first hovercraft to visit Catalina island, 26 miles (41·84 km) off the coast of California and the first to complete the journey from los Angeles to San Diego (105 miles (168·98 km) across open seas. It has also been employed extensively for water and snow skiing.

UH-14T—a stretched version of the UH-12T two seater

A feature of the UH-17S is the integrated lift/propulsion system powered by a 75 hp Corvair automobile engine

The UH-18T six-seater was the first hovercraft to visit Catalina Island, 26 miles (41·84 km) off the coast of California, and the first to complete the (105 mile 168·98 km) sea journey between Los Angeles and San Diego. It has a top speed over water of 60 mph (96·56 km/h)

The aerofoil shaped hull is similar to that of the UH-12T and UH-14T.

LIFT AND PROPULSION: Lift is provided by a 25 hp JLO 395 2-cycle engine driving a 2 ft 6 in diameter 4-bladed fan at 3,200 rpm. About 5% of the air is employed to inflate the bag skirt. Propulsive thrust is supplied by an 85 hp Corvair automobile engine driving a 5 ft 0 in (1·52 m) diameter 2-bladed propeller at up to 2,800 rpm.

SKIRT: 1 ft 6 in (0·46 m) diameter bag skirt, providing 1 ft 0 in (0·304 m) vertical clearance.

HULL: Mixed wood and grp construction. Hull frame is built from fir ribs and stringers and covered with ¼ in ply. Highly stressed areas covered with glass fibre.

ACCOMMODATION: Driver and up to five passengers seated on two 3-place bench seats. Cabin can be enclosed by canopy in cold weather.

CONTROLS: Craft heading is controlled by a single rudder operating in the propeller slipstream and two auxiliary rudders hinged to the rear of twin fins, one each side of the propeller guard. All three rudders are operated by a steering wheel. Separate throttle provided for lift and thrust engines.

DIMENSIONS:

Length	18 ft 3 in (5·56 m)
Beam	8 ft 0 in (2·43 m)
Height, off cushion	6 ft 0 in (1·82 m)
on cushion	7 ft 0 in (2·13 m)

WEIGHTS:

Empty weight	1,000 lb (453·57 kg)

Normal loaded	2,000 lb (907·14 kg)
Max loaded	2,400 lb (1,088 kg)

PERFORMANCE:

Max speed:	
over land	70 mph (112·65 km/h)
over water	60 mph (96·56 km/h)
Max gradient	31%

PRICE:
Complete set of plans for homebuilding,
US$ 25·00.

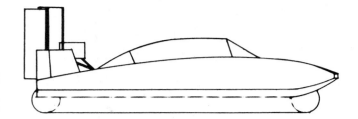

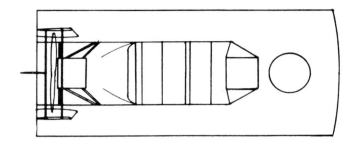
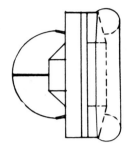

Universal Hovercraft UH-18T, a six seater of mixed wood and grp construction. Propulsive thrust is supplied by an 85 hp Corvair engine driving a 5 ft 0 in (1·52 m) diameter 2-bladed propeller

WATER RESEARCH COMPANY

HEAD OFFICE:
3003 North Central Avenue, Suite 600,
Phoenix, Arizona 85012

TELEPHONE:
(602) 265-7722

EXECUTIVES:
Richard R. Greer, President
John H. McMasters, Chief Engineer

(Members of American Society of Naval Engineers)

The Water Research Company was formed in 1972 to consolidate activities surrounding the patents held or applied for by Richard R. Greer relating to various aspects of water-borne vehicles. The company has subsequently prepared conceptual studies on a class of winged surface effect vessels (WSEV) intended to fill a variety of US Navy and commercial freight applications. The conclusions of this study were published in the Naval Engineers' Journal, April 1974. These vehicles are intended for use in conjunction with the patented Water Research Company hydrofoil/SES docking system. The company is able to undertake analytical studies on hydrofoil, SES and WIG systems, and can provide contract coordinating services for such systems. The company has no immediate plans for acquiring hardware development facilities.

THE UNION OF SOVIET SOCIALIST REPUBLICS

CENTRAL LABORATORY OF LIFESAVING TECHNOLOGY

HEAD OFFICE: Moscow
EXECUTIVES:
Yury Makarov, Chief Engineer
A. V. Gremyatskiy, Designer
V. P. Grunin, Designer
N. L. Ivanov, Designer

The Central Laboratory of Rescue Techniques, a division of OSVOD—the Rescue Organisation for Inland Waters—has designed a small aerodynamic ram-wing machine, capable of 75 mph (120 km/h), which will be used to answer distress calls on the Soviet lakes, rivers and canals. The vehicle, which is available in several versions, is the Eska—an abbreviation of Ekranolyetny Spasatyelny Kater-Amphibya (Surface-effect Amphibious Lifeboat). It has also been referred to as the Ekranolet and the Nizkolet (skimmer).

Apart from meeting emergency situations on waterways, the craft, which is amphibious, is capable of operating in deserts, tundra, arctic icefields and steppland. It has been suggested that it could be employed as a support vehicle for geologists, communications engineers and construction groups.

In Russian publications emphasis has been given to the potential value of such craft

One of the first three prototypes of the Eska-1 operating at its maximum flying height of about 33 ft (10 m). Normal operating height, in ground effect, is between 5-11 ft. The vehicle, a two-seat aerodynamic ram-wing, is employed as an experimental high-speed rescue craft on Russian inland waterways

in opening up the mineral wealth of Siberia, the Soviet Far East, Far North and other virgin territories.

As with the X 113 Am and other machines of this type, the vehicle operates on the principle that by flying in close proximity to the ground, the so-called image flow reduces drag by about 70%. Whereas an average aircraft at normal flight altitude carries about 9 lb (4 kg) per hp of engine output, the wing-in-ground effect machine, on its dynamic air-cushion is expected to carry up to 44 lb (20 kg).

For maximum effectiveness, the Ezka has to fly very close to its supporting surface. If the vertical distance between the vehicle and the surface beneath is equal to half the span, lift is increased by 3-4%. If the distance between the wing and the ground is reduced to ¼ span, lift is increased by more than 10%.

Control of the Ezka is said to be easy and pilots require no special training. Within ground effect it is no more complicated to control than a car.

The design, which has been strongly influenced by the Lippisch "aerofoil boat" concept, employs an almost identical short span, low aspect ratio reversed delta wing with anhedral on the leading edge, dihedral tips and wing floats. Preliminary details are given below.

ESKA-1

Designed initially as an amphibious high-speed rescue craft for use on Russia's inland waterways, the Eska has been developed into a general utility vehicle with a wide range of applications in underdeveloped areas. Three prototypes, similar to the craft illustrated, had been built by mid-February 1974. Two other models, one with fabric-covered rear hull and flying surfaces, the other a four-seater, were under construction in March 1974. Variants with larger cabins and more powerful engines are being developed.

In the summer of 1974, the four-seat model was due to be flown from Moscow to Sochi and Pitsunda, with sea trials in Imeretinsk Bay. The flight, via the Volga-Don canal and the Sea of Azov, was expected to take 10-12 days.

POWER PLANT: Single 30 hp M-63 motor-cycle engine, on strutted dorsal mounting aft of cockpit, drives via shafting a two-bladed fixed-pitch propeller.

CONSTRUCTION: Forward hull design based on that of a two-seat sports boat. Corrosion resistant aluminium alloy construction employed for first three craft. Heavy fabric covering employed on wings inboard of tips and hull aft of crew compartment on one later model.

CONTROLS: Single aircraft-type control stick, incorporating engine throttle, located in the centre of the cockpit. Conventional

Top: The strong Lippisch influence on the design is particularly evident in this view. Note the anhedral, reversed delta wing, dihedral tips and wing floats
Bottom: Design of the forward hull and cockpit is based on that of a two-seat sports boat. Power is supplied by a 30 hp motorcycle engine. Cruising speed is 75 mph (120 km/h)

foot-operated bar to control rudder.

ACCOMMODATION: Enclosed cabin for two, seated side-by-side. Access is via hinged hood. Initial arrangement is for rescuer/pilot, with one seat available for the person being rescued. Three and four seat models are under development.

DIMENSIONS:

Wing span, overall	22 ft 5⅝ in (6·9 m)
Length overall	24 ft 7 in (7·5 m)

WEIGHTS:

Max all-up weight	992 lb (450 kg)

PERFORMANCE:

Take-off and landing speed	50-60 km/h (31-37 mph)
Cruising speed	120 km/h (75 mph)
Optimum height in ground effect	1 m (3 ft 3¾ in)
Max operating height	10 m (32 ft 9¾ in)
Endurance	2 hours
Limiting weather conditions	can operate in force 5 winds

KHARKOV AVIATION INSTITUTE

ADDRESS: Kharkov

In August 1973, it was reported in Pravda that the Institute of Aviation, Kharkov, had built two amphibious ACVs. At the same time, it was mentioned that ACV research and development was being undertaken at forty national enterprises, in Moscow, Tomsk, Gorki, Gorlovka, Ufa and Volgograd.

KRASNOYE SORMOVO

ADDRESS:

Gorky

OVERSEAS REPRESENTATIVES:

United Kingdom, Western Europe and British Commonwealth: Airavia Ltd, 20 North Road, Shanklin, Isle of Wight.

This shipyard began work in the ACV field by building a five-passenger air cushion river craft known as the Raduga in 1960-61.

Since then it has built the Sormovich, a 30-ton peripheral jet ACV for 50 passengers, the Neva, a plenum-chambered type craft seating 38 and the Gorkovchanin, a 48-seat sidewall craft for shallow, winding rivers.

The latter is now in service on a number of rivers, together with a derivative, the Zarnitsa.

The design of an 80-seat rigid sidewall ferry the Orion, was approved by the Soviet Ministry of Inland Waterways in 1970. Construction of the prototype began in 1972 and trials began in October 1973. Preparations are being made to put the craft into production.

In 1969, prototypes of two new fully skirted hovercraft made their debut, the Breeze, a light utility craft, and the Skate, a 50-seat passenger ferry with an all-up weight of 27 tons and a cruising speed of 57·5 mph. Military versions of the Skate are now in production in addition to the passenger ferry model. Development of the Skate and its naval and army counterparts is believed to have been undertaken in conjunction with the Leningrad Institute of Marine Engineers, also thought to be responsible for the design and construction of the Soviet Union's biggest skirted hovercraft, which is generally similar in shape, size and performance to the SR.N4.

The Sormovo yard is likely to have been responsible for building of the world's largest air cushion vehicle—a wing-in-ground effect machine capable of carrying 800-900 troops at speeds up to 300 knots. In April 1972 it was announced that plans were in hand to build wing-in-ground effect machines capable of navigating rivers at a speed of about 155 mph (250 km/h). A number of these craft are understood to be in experimental service and one, with catamaran hulls, is illustrated.

BREEZE

This interesting light amphibious ACV has external features which are reminiscent of the Vickers VA-2 and VA-3.

It was developed by an amateur design group led by German Koronatov, a graduate of the Leningrad Shipbuilding Institute.

The design incorporates the cabin and propulsion system of the Kamov KA-30 Aerosled. The craft performed well across ice and water during trials, and in August 1973 it was reported that it had undergone successful tests on the Vuoksa river.

LIFT AND PROPULSION: Thrust is provided by a 260 hp A1-14RS radial piston engine driving an AV-59 three-bladed metal, controllable and reversible pitch propeller. Lift is supplied by two Moskvich 407 automotive engines mounted aft on the side-structures, one port and one starboard, each driving a set of four centrifugal fans mounted on a common shaft.

CONTROLS: Directional control over most of the speed range is provided by twin rudders. Low speed control is assisted by puff ports fore and aft.

HULL: Riveted corrosion-resistant aluminium alloy.

SKIRT: Fingered bag type, in rubberised fabric.

ACCOMMODATION: In standard form the craft accommodates a driver and 8 passengers.

DIMENSIONS:

Length overall, power off

approx 30 ft (9·14 m)

WEIGHTS:

All-up weight   4 tons

PERFORMANCE:

Hard structure clearance   1 ft 8 in (50 cm)

Maximum speed, over land and water

62 mph (100 km/h)

GORKOVCHANIN

The Gorkovchanin is a waterjet-propelled, 48-seat, rigid sidewall ACV, designed for water-bus services on secondary rivers with

The Gorkovchanin rigid sidewall waterbus

Top: The Breeze light amphibious ACV for ten-passengers. Thrust is supplied by a radial aircraft engine driving a 3-bladed airscrew, and lift by twin Moskvich 407 automotive engines, each driving a set of four centrifugal fans mounted in series on a common shaft. Fan air is drawn through fixed louvres

Bottom: Passengers boarding the Breeze. To facilitate access to the cabin a panel is removed from the lift fan cowl ahead of the engine and a handrail and steps are slotted into position.

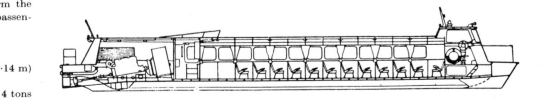

General arrangement of the Gorkovchanin sidewall craft, powered by a single 265 hp 2D12AL diesel

a guaranteed depth of 1 ft 8 in (0·5 m). In view of the winding nature of these rivers, the craft operates at the relatively low speed of 19-22 mph (30-35 km/h). No marked reduction of speed is necessary in water up to 1 ft 8 in (50 cm) deep.

The craft has been developed from a ten seat scale model built at the experimental yard of the Institute of Water Transport Engineers at Gorky in 1963, and the pre-production prototype was completed in September 1968. Design was undertaken by a team at the Volgobaltsudoproekt special design office.

Preliminary trials were conducted in September and October 1968, and official trials were completed on the Sura river in May and June 1969. During speed tests over a measured mile with a full complement of passengers aboard, 22·75 mph (36·6 km/h) was attained. The main engine developed 265 hp of which approximately 30 hp was used to drive the centrifugal fan.

The craft has covered the journey from Gorky to Moscow (622 miles (1,016 km)) and back in 31 and 27 running hours respectively at an average speed of approximately 22 mph (35 km/h) and has good manoeuvrability when running both ahead and astern. The craft is in production and large numbers are in service. The type is now being superseded by an improved model, the Zarnitsa.

LIFT AND PROPULSION: Integrated system powered by a 3D6H diesel engine rated at 250 hp continuous. The engine is mounted aft and drives a 3 ft 1¾ in (960 mm) diameter six-bladed centrifugal fan for lift, and a 1 ft 4½ in (410 mm) diameter single stage water-jet rotor for propulsion. Fan air is taken directly from the engine compartment. Skirts of rubberised fabric are fitted fore and aft. The bow skirt of production craft is of segmented type. Cushion pressure is 180 kg/cm².

The waterjet intake duct is located 4 in (100 mm) below the displacement water level to prevent air entry, with a consequent reduction in the navigable draft.

CONTROLS: Vanes located in the waterjet stream provide directional control. Thrust reversal is achieved by the use of waterflow deflectors.

HULL: Similar in appearance to that of the Zarya, the hull is in riveted D16 corrosion resistant aluminium alloy. The hull bottom and sides have transverse frames and the sidewalls and superstructure top longitudinal frames. Thickness of plating on sides and bottom is $\frac{1}{16}$ in (1·5 mm) ($\frac{3}{32}$ in, (2·5 mm) in the bow section); and on the sidewalls $\frac{3}{64}$ in (1 mm) (up to $\frac{13}{64}$ in (5 mm) in the bow section).

Deck plates are $\frac{3}{32}$ in (1 mm) thick and the top of the superstructure is in $\frac{1}{64}$ in (0·8 mm) plating.

Acoustic and thermal insulation includes use of 4 in (100 mm) thick foam polystyrene sheeting.

ACCOMMODATION: Seats are provided for a crew of 2, who are accommodated in a raised wheelhouse, and 28 passengers. Access to the passenger saloon, which is equipped with airliner-type seats, is through a single door located at the bow in the centre of the wheelhouse. The craft runs bow-on to flat sloping banks to embark and disembark passengers.

SYSTEMS: Electrical: One 1·2 kW, 24 volt dc, engine-operated generator and batteries.
COMMUNICATIONS: Car radio in wheelhouse and speakers in passenger saloon.

Military derivatives of the 27-ton Skate passenger ferry at speed on the Volga

This 15-ton research craft has been employed by the Soviet Navy to assess the potential of the skirted air cushion vehicle for naval applications

DIMENSIONS:

Length overall	73 ft 2 in (22·30 m)
Beam overall	13 ft 3¼ in (4·05 m)
Hull beam	12 ft 7⅝ in (3·85 m)
Height of hull to top of wheelhouse	10 ft 9⅞ in (3·3 m)
Height of sidewalls	1 ft 5¾ in (0·45 m)
Draft afloat	2 ft 1⅝ in (0·65 m)
Draft cushion borne	1 ft 4⅞ in (0·43 m)

WEIGHTS:
All-up weight with 48 passengers, crew and fuel   14·30 tons

PERFORMANCE:
Normal service speed
19-22 mph (30-35 km/h)

Distance and time from full ahead to full astern   65·6 yards (60 m) and 14 seconds

NAVAL RESEARCH HOVERCRAFT

A 15-ton experimental ACV has been employed by the Soviet Navy since 1967 to assess the potential of hovercraft for naval applications and investigate controllability and manoeuvrability. Lift is provided by a single 350 hp radial aircraft engine driving a centrifugal fan and propulsion by two pylon-mounted radials of the same type driving controllable-pitch airscrews.

DIMENSIONS:

Length	70 ft 0 in (21·33 m)
Beam	30 ft 0 in (9·14 m)

WEIGHTS:
Displacement.   15 tons

PERFORMANCE:
Max speed   50 knots

SKATE

This 50-seat amphibious passenger ferry, designed for services on sheltered estuaries, rivers and bays, is now in production. The craft has an all-up weight of 27 tons and cruises at 57·5 mph (92·5 km/h).

Two military variants are in production, one for the Soviet Navy and one for the Army.
LIFT AND PROPULSION: Motive power is provided by three 780 hp TVD 10 marine gas turbines mounted aft. Two drive three-bladed variable and reversible-pitch propellers for thrust and the third drives an axial lift fan. Cushion air is drawn through a raised intake aft of the passenger cabin superstructure.

CONTROLS: Craft direction is controlled by differential propeller pitch, twin aerodynamic rudders and forward and aft puff ports. Elevators provide pitch trim at cruising speed.

HULL: Hull and superstructure are in conventional corrosion-resistant marine light alloy. Basic structure comprises a central load-carrying platform which incorporates buoyancy tanks and outer sections to support the side ducts and skirt. The cabin, fuel tanks, lift fan bay engines and tail unit are mounted on the platform.

ACCOMMODATION: Up to fifty passengers are accommodated in an air-conditioned cabin in airliner type seats. Commander and navigator are seated in a raised wheelhouse.

DIMENSIONS, EXTERNAL:
    Length overall, power on 67 ft 7 in (20·6 m)
    Beam overall, power on 23 ft 11½ in (7·3 m)
WEIGHTS:
    Normal operating weight   27 tons
PERFORMANCE:
    Cruising speed   57·5 mph (92·5 km/h)
    Normal cruising range   230 miles (370 km)

SKATE (MILITARY)

Military versions of the Skate are in production for the Soviet Army and Navy. Variants built so far appear to be employed as fast amphibious transports for Soviet marine's and infantry units.

ORION

Design of the Orion, a rigid sidewall ACV with seats for 80 passengers, was approved in Moscow in the Autumn of 1970. The prototype built in Leningrad, began trials in October 1973.

Cruising speed is about 37 mph (60 km/h).

Unlike the smaller Zarnitsa, Orion is designed for service on both secondary and major rivers, estuaries, lakes and reservoirs.

NAVAL ASSAULT LANDING CRAFT

The first large Soviet amphibious hovercraft is undergoing proving trials with the Soviet Navy. The craft has an all-up weight of about 200 tons and is similar in size and general appearance to the SR.N4 Mountbatten.

EKRANOPLAN EXPERIMENTAL

A giant Soviet experimental wing-in-ground-effect machine, with a span of about 125 ft (38·1 m) and a length of nearly 400 ft (122 m), is undergoing tests on the Caspian sea.

The machine, which operates at heights of 25-50 ft (7·62-15·24 m) above the water, has a speed of about 300 knots. Power is supplied by eight marinised gas-turbines mounted above a stub wing forward, and two 'booster' turbines installed at the base of the dihedral tailplane aft. All ten engines

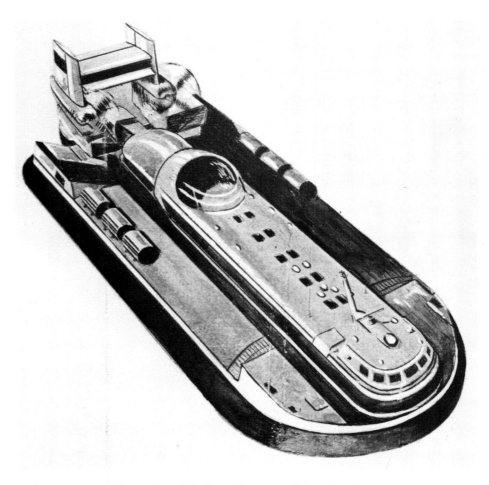

Impression of the Skate 50-seat amphibious hoverferry

Artist's impression of an Orion type sidewall craft

are employed at take-off, when thrust has to be 2·5-3·5 times greater than that required to maintain cruising conditions in flight.

It is reported that the thrust from the eight forward engines is deflected downwards on take-off to create additional cushion pressure beneath the wing and that after take-off the jet exhaust is directed above the upper surface of the wing to create additional lift.

Western WIG specialists, commenting on an artist's impression published in the United States in January 1974, say, first the wing design does not facilitate pitch stability during its transition from ground-effect to free flight and back again. Thus the machine is probably intended to fly only in close proximity to the surface. This means it may not be able to operate safely either in extremely turbulent weather conditions or in areas where it would encounter projections higher than 50 ft (15·24 m) above the surface. Secondly, as presented by the artist, the machine has relatively wide span wings. Because it has to operate close to the surface its banking capabilities, and thus its manoeuvrability, appear limited. It is therefore much more likely that it has shorter span wings of lower aspect ratio, as shown in the illustration.

Soviet experts maintain that craft of this type should be able to negotiate sand spits, shallows, marshes, ice, snow, relatively even and gently sloping banks and low obstacles.

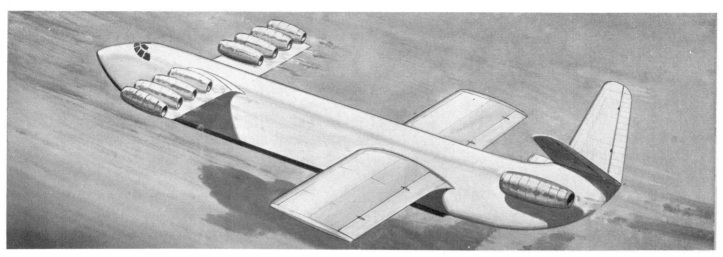

The giant Soviet ten-jet experimental Ekranoplan which is currently undergoing tests on the Caspian Sea

Low bridges have been mentioned. They are also stated to be sufficiently seaworthy to operate in rough seas. Wide employment of this type of vessel is foreseen, particularly in the Soviet Navy, which has suggested that they will be invaluable in amphibious operations.

Large numbers of troops could be carried to the selected landing zones with little regard to the condition of the sea, tidal currents, underwater obstacles and minefields, none of which would constitute a hazard.

Advantages in the battle zone will include high speed manoeuvring, and a considerable reduction in the time taken to undertake a mission compared with conventional landing craft.

The capacity of the WIG craft, Ekranoplan machines as they are known in the Soviet Union, will enable them to carry the biggest items of military equipment. Other likely applications (according to Soviet sources) are ASW patrol, minesweeping, missile-armed patrol ships and fast supply vessels for surface warships and submarines.

References have been made in Soviet technical publications to vehicles with chords of 30-40 m (98 ft 6 in—131 ft 2 in) and speeds of 400 knots being under consideration.

Impression of a new catamaran-hulled Ekranoplan research craft now under development in the Soviet Union. Designed for high speed long distance passenger services along the main Soviet rivers, it rides on a dynamic air cushion formed between its wings and the supporting surface below. Seats are provided for forty passengers in each of the twin hulls. Top speed is likely to be between 150-200 knots

The Raduga experimental air cushion vehicle

EKRANOPLAN RIVER BUSES

The Ministry of the River Fleet announced in April 1972 that it planned to build craft of the Ekranoplan (WIG) type "which will travel within several metres of a river surface at speeds of some 155 mph (250 km/h)".

It seems probable that in order to avoid navigation problems in busy river port areas these craft will be of smaller overall dimensions than the 170 ft (57·81 m) span machine described earlier. Low aspect ratio wings are likely to be employed and it is possible that these early production craft are of 5-6 tons displacement. A number of these machines were reported to be in experimental service in 1973.

On Moscow television in July, 1973, a programme commemorating Soviet Navy Day traced the progress of high speed water transportation and confirmed that ekranoplanes are being developed in the Soviet Union. The craft were described by the commentator as "ground gliders", capable of operating

over land, water, snow and ice. A small machine built in Odessa in the early 1960s was shown to viewers, together with a completely new research craft of much larger size.

The craft is of catamaran configuration and carries up to forty passengers in each of the two hulls. The crew and operating controls are accommodated in a central pod carried on the forward wing.

Thrust is provided by six marinised gas-turbines mounted in pairs on the triple fins aft. Length of the craft is about 100 ft.

RADUGA

This experimental amphibious ACV was completed at the Krasnoye Sormovo shipyard in the summer of 1962 and is reported to have attained a speed of 100 km/h (62 mph) during trials.

Built originally as a peripheral jet type, it is now being used to develop control techniques, and provide amphibious experience and data

on skirt design.
LIFT AND PROPULSION: The craft is powered by two 220 hp air-cooled radial engines. One, mounted amidships, drives a 5 ft 11 in (1·8 m) 12-bladed lift fan; the second, mounted on a pylon at the stern, drives a two-bladed propeller for propulsion. The fan delivers air to the cushion via a continuous peripheral skirt, the bow and side sections of which are of the fingered bag type.
HULL: Riveted aluminium construction.
ACCOMMODATION: The cabin seats five.
CONTROLS: Directional control is provided by an aerodynamic rudder operating on the propeller slipstream.
DIMENSIONS:
Length   30 ft 10 in (9·40 m)
Beam   13 ft 6 in (4·12 m)
WEIGHTS:
Operating weight   3 tons
PERFORMANCE:
Maximum speed   75 mph (120 km/h)
Endurance   3 hours

RASSVET (DAWN)

A derivative of the Zarnitsa, the Rassvet is designed for local sea routes and appears to be an offshore counterpart to the Orion sidewall ACV which is intended for river services.

Features include shallow draft, good manoevrability and seagoing qualities and simple construction.

LIFT AND PROPULSION: Total output of engines driving the lift fans is 150 hp. Propulsive thrust is thought to be supplied by twin 520 hp diesel engines, driving two waterjets.

ACCOMMODATION: Up to eighty passengers are accommodated in an air-conditioned cab in airliner-type seats. Captain and engineer are accommodated in an elevated wheelhouse, forward.

DIMENSIONS:

Length overall	86 ft 11·7 in (26·51 m)
Beam overall	23 ft 3½ in (7·10 m)
Height	29 ft 8·6 in (9·06 m)
Draft on cushion	2 ft 3·6 in (0·7 m)

WEIGHTS:

Displacement fully loaded	44 tons (44·7 tonnes)

PERFORMANCE:

Cruising speed	25 knots
Endurance at cruising speed	6 hours

SORMOVICH

Launched in October 1965, the Sormovich is a 50-passenger ACV designed by Mr Valeri Schoenberg, Chief Constructor of the Krasnoye Sormovo Shipyard, with the assistance of the N. E. Zhukovski Central Institute of Aerodynamics.

In general layout, the craft represents a "scale-up" of the configuration tested with the Raduga.

In 1970 the craft was equipped with a 4 ft deep flexible skirt. Several experimental services have been operated with the craft. It is not yet in production, although orders are expected from the Ministry of the River Fleet.

TESTS: Rigorous acceptance trials included a special programme of runs between Gorky and Gorodets, Gorky and Lyskovo, Gorky and Vasilsursk, and also on the Gorky Reservoir.

These trials confirmed the craft's ability to operate across shoals, sandy spits and dykes, and run on to dry land for cargo handling and repairs.

In the air-cushion mode, her ability to maintain course up- and downwind is satisfactory, and controlled entirely by the rudders. In sidewinds, control is by combined rudder movement and differential propeller pitch. Steering during turns by rudders alone is unsatisfactory, the turning-circle diameter being 2,734-3,280 yds (2,500-3,000 m) with substantial drift. Turning is improved if the manoeuvre is accomplished by varying propeller pitch. The distance from the inception of the manoeuvre to securing a 180 deg. course then drops to 765-1,093 yards (700-1,000 m) and the diameter of the sub-

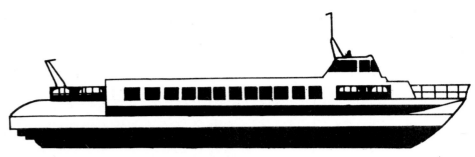

Rassvet (Dawn), a new 80-seat sidewall-type ferry for short sea routes

sequent turning circle falls to 164 yards (150 m.)

Collision avoidance manoeuvres with a floating object employing rudder deflection, showed that avoidance is feasible at a distance of not under 546 yards (500 m). This distance can be reduced, however, if the manoeuvre is accomplished with variable propeller pitch. Successful undertaking of this manoeuvre depends largely on the skill of the operator.

In the air-cushion mode, while accelerating to 37-43 mph (60-70 km/h) and turning through 180 deg in both directions, stability is adequate in any of the load conditions investigated, and passengers may move about freely.

In addition to the basic flight-trial programme, tests were made to check vehicle response to sudden splash-down in case of the emergency shutdown of the main engine while underway. The splash-down tests were conducted at various speeds and drift angles, and showed that the loads imposed are not excessive and that the passengers were not alarmed. In 4 ft (1·2 m) waves the craft operates at reduced speed, but steering control and satisfactory passenger comfort are maintained.

Since late 1970, Sormovich has been in experimental service with the Volga United Steamship Company.

While operating on the Gorky-Cheboksary run in light conditions and with passengers aboard during the 1971 season, various problem areas were identified. In particular, it was found necessary to improve the reliability of the airscrew and fan drive transmission; improve the design of flexible-skirt and select a stronger material from which it can be manufactured; find ways of reducing engine noise and improve its operation and maintenance; render more effective the devices employed to reduce craft drift during high-speed turns; and raise the overall economic efficiency of the craft.

After modification, the vehicle returned to experimental service on the Gorky-Cheboksary-Gorky passenger run in 1972, with flights scheduled for daylight hours only, in winds not over 32-39 f/sec (10-12 m/sec) and at speeds not above 50 mph (80 km/h). The route selected was generally beyond that negotiable by a conventional vessel, with

depths not less than 1 ft 8 in (0·5 m).

Two crew training flights and 42 passenger flights were undertaken during this particular service. Some 5,655 people were carried a total of 15,534 miles (25,000 km).

However, experimental operation of the craft during the 1972 season was a financial loss. The economic viability of Sormovich, as in the previous season, was impaired by the craft being withdrawn from service to eliminate main transmission reduction gear defects and attend to various other repair and maintenance jobs.

A passenger survey indicated that noise levels in the rear of the saloon are acceptable, but high exterior noise levels are a nuisance to shore personnel and members of the public in the vicinity.

Experimental operation of the Sormovich has indicated the possibility of its being used on inland waterways.

During the 1972/73 off-season period, measures were being taken to eliminate the shortcomings revealed, replace the reduction gear, improve flexible-skirt nozzle elements, and undertake various other modifications found necessary. There are grounds for believing that these measures will make Sormovich into a viable economic proposition.

LIFT AND PROPULSION: All machinery is located aft behind a sound-proof bulkhead to keep down the noise level in the passenger compartments. A single 2,300 hp Ivchenkc AI-20K shaft-turbine, at the extreme stern, drives the integrated lift/propulsion system. Its output shaft passes first to a differential gearbox from which shafts extend sideways to the two four-blade ducted variable pitch propellers. A further shaft runs forward from the differential to a bevel gearbox from which a drive-shaft runs vertically upward to the 12-blade variable pitch lift-fan mounted under the intake on the rear of the roof of the vehicle. The gas-turbine operates on diesel fuel. Cushion area is 220 m².

CONTROLS: Each propeller duct contains two hydraulically-actuated rudders, working in the slipstream.

HULL: Light alloy buoyancy type, with air feeding to the cushion through a peripheral slot. There is a fore and aft stability slot on each side parallel to and about 5 ft (1·50 m) inboard of the peripheral slot.

ACCOMMODATION: The crew compartment, forward, contains two seats and is separated from the main cabin by a partition containing a door. The front two rows of seats in the cabin are only four-abreast to facilitate entry through the forward door on each side. The remaining 42 seats are six-abreast, in three-chair units with centre aisle. Aft of the cabin is a wardrobe on the port side, with a buffet opposite on the starboard side. Then comes the main entry lobby, with a passenger door on the port side and service door opposite, followed by a toilet (port) and baggage hold (starboard).

An unusual feature of the Sormovich is that it is fitted with retractable wheels which can be lowered to avoid damage to the hull when the craft operates over uneven ice or rough country. The wheels are carried on lightly-sprung legs, enabling them to ride easily over obstructions.

The craft is equipped for navigation at night.

DIMENSIONS:
Length	96 ft 0 in (29·2 m)
Beam	32 ft 9½ in (10·00 m)
Height to top of hull, on cushion (7 m)	

WEIGHTS:
Normal loaded weight	36·5 m tons

PERFORMANCE:
Max cruising speed	74·56 mph (120 km/h)

ZARNITSA

Evolved from Gorkovchanin, the Zarnitsa is a 48-50 seat waterjet-propelled rigid side-wall ferry designed to operate on shallow rivers, some less than 2ft 3in (0·70m) deep. Series production has begun and at least twenty were scheduled for delivery during 1973.

The prototype was put into trial service on the Vyatka river, in the Kirov region, in the summer of 1972, and the first production models began operating on shallow, secondary rivers later in the year. During 1973-74, Zarnitsas entered service on tributaries of the Kama, Lena and Volga. In March 1974, Zarnitsa-7 was reported to have been delivered to the Kama River Shipping Line which will employ the vessel on the upper shallow reaches of the Vishera and Chusovaya rivers.

LIFT AND PROPULSION, CONTROLS, HULL: Arrangements almost identical to those of the Gorkovchanin.

ACCOMODATION: Seats are provided for two crew members, who are accommodated in the raised wheelhouse, forward, and 48-50 passengers. Access to the passenger saloon is via a single door located at the bow in the centre of the wheelhouse. The craft runs bow-on to flat sloping banks to embark and disembark passengers.

DIMENSIONS:
Length	72 ft 3 in (22·3 m)
Beam	12 ft 8 in (3·85 m)
Skeg depth	1 ft 6 in (0·45 m)

WEIGHTS:
Light displacement	9 metric tons

Above and below: The Sormovich ACV passenger ferry, powered by a single 2,300 hp Ivchenko AI-20K gas turbine

All-up weight, with 48 passengers, crew and hull	15 m tons

PERFORMANCE:
Service speed	20-22 mph (33-35 km/h)

ZARYA (DAWN)

Experiments with high speed "aeroglisseur" (literally air skimmer) water buses, capable of negotiating the many shallow waterways in the Soviet Union, began in 1961.

The object was to develop a vessel for services on shallow waters, with depths of only 20 in (0·5 m), at speeds of at least 21·5 knots. The prototype Zarya, called the

Opytnye-1 (experimental), was put into experimental operations on the river Msta in 1963. During trials the craft attained a speed of 26 mph (42 km/h) and proved to have a turning radius of 44·76 yards (40·70 m). The craft runs bow-on to any flat, sloping bank to embark passengers.

Built with a strong aluminium alloy hull and equipped with a well protected waterjet, the craft is unharmed by floating logs, even when they are encountered at full speed.

Variants include models with a flat load deck in place of the passenger cabin superstructure amidships, and used as light freight vessels.

Zarya was designed by a team at the Central Design Office of the Ministry of the River Fleet Gorky, working in conjunction with the Leningrad Water Transport Institute. Series production is under way at the Moscow Shipbuilding and Ship Repair Yard of the Ministry of the River Fleet.

The latest model is distinguished by its trimaran bow configuration, which gives improved performance in waves and enables the craft to be routed on major waterways.

LIFT AND PROPULSION: Power is provided by a single M-400 watercooled, supercharged, 12-cylinder V-type diesel with a normal service output of 830 hp at 1,650 rpm and a maximum output of 1,100 hp at 1,800 rpm. This drives a single 2 ft 2½ in (0·7 m) diameter waterjet impeller.

The waterjet is of single-stage type, with a semi-submerged jet discharge. The impeller sucks in water through an intake duct which is covered by a protective grille. The discharged water flows around two steering vanes which provide directional control. Waterjet reversal deflectors are employed to reverse the craft or to reduce the waterjet thrust when variations in speed are necessary.

A localised ram-air cushion, introduced by an upswept nose and contained on either side by shallow skegs, lifts the bow clear of the water as the craft picks up speed. The airflow also provides air/foam lubrication for the remainder of the flat-bottomed hull.

HULL: All metal construction in corrosion resistant magnesium alloy.

ACCOMMODATION: The craft seats a crew of two in a raised wheelhouse forward and 65 passengers in a single saloon aft. An additional 15 standing passengers are accommodated on short routes. Access is through two entrance doors, one each side of the wheelhouse.

DIMENSIONS:
Length	72 ft 3¼ in (22·1 m)
Beam	12 ft 10¾ in (3·93 m)
Moulded depth	3 ft 11½ in (1·2 m)
Draft	1 ft 5¾ in (0·45 m)

WEIGHTS:
Displacement	25 metric tons

PERFORMANCE:
Speed (in channel of 0·8 m depth)	27·96 mph (45 km/h)
Range suitable for service distances of 93 miles (150 km) and above	
Endurance at cruising speed	4 hours

Top: A Zarya, 80-seat, air-lubricated hull passenger ferry during demonstrations in the German Federal Republic
Centre: Stern view of a Zarya in service on one of the shallow tributaries of the Volga. The vessel is powered by an 830 hp M-400 12 cylinder diesel driving a single-stage waterjet. Cruising speed is 27·96 mph (45 km/h)
Bottom: Compared with earlier variants, this new model of the Zarya is distinguished by its trimaran bow, introduced for improved seakeeping. The new bow design allows the vessel to be routed into major waterways

UFA AVIATION INSTITUTE

An experimental circular planform ACV, the Skat, has been designed and built by students of the UFA Aviation Institute. The vehicle was displayed in 1970 in Moscow at the USSR National Economy Achievements Exhibition.

OIIMF (ODESSA ENGINEERING INSTITUTE OF THE MERCHANT FLEET)
OIIMF-2

This is one of a number of experimental wing-in-ground-effect machines built at the institute by a group of students under the direction of Y. Budnitskiy.

The craft is a single-seater with an all-up weight of 926-992 lb (420-450 kg) and a payload of 176-220 lb (80-100 kg). The wings, floats and hull are of semimonocoque construction and built in duralumin.

Power is supplied by two 18 hp aircooled motorcycle engines driving two 3 ft 11 in (1·2 m) diameter two-bladed airscrews.

Special flaps have been designed to improve the starting characteristics of the craft by creating a static air cushion through the utilisation of the airscrew slipstream. The flaps are located between the wings and are secured by special shock absorption cables in the operating position at the moment of starting the craft. As speed increases so the flaps hinge upwards automatically.

Tests indicate that the flaps noticeably decrease the leakage of air from the high pressure area under the aft wing, thus increasing wing lift and unloading the floats.

A vertical tail assembly and flap are provided for steering and stabilisation. The flap on the aft wing is designed to balance the craft during starting and control it in pitch. The leading wing barely generates any lift at low speeds, therefore a pitching moment, obtained by deflecting the flap upwards, must be created during the initial period of its run in order to balance the craft. As speed increases and the forward wing comes into operation, the centre of pressure shifts forward, which requires a diving moment (deflection of the flap downward) in order to balance the craft.

Static stability in pitch is provided by constant contact of the aft section of the floats with the water surface and the corresponding stabilising effect of the forward wing.

The vehicle has good manoeuvrability, and the turning diameter, at a speed of 20 mph is approximately 32 ft.

DIMENSIONS:

Length overall	16 ft 5 in (5·0 m)
Hull beam	10 ft 6 in (3·2 m)
Wing span	9 ft 2¼ in (2·8 m)
Chord, forward lower wing	3 ft 4 in (1 m)
Chord, upper wing	9 ft 10 in (3 m)

The Zarnitsa, a derivative of the Gorkovchanin, is now in series production and at least twenty of this type were scheduled for delivery during 1973

The Skat on display in Moscow

The OIIMF-2 single-seat wing-in-ground effect research craft.

ACV OPERATORS

THE AMERICAS
NORTH AMERICA AND CANADA

CANADA

CANADIAN COAST GUARD HOVERCRAFT UNIT

HEADQUARTERS:

Canadian Coast Guard, Canadian Marine Transportation Administration, Ministry of Transport, Hunter Building, Ottawa, Ontario

UNIT ADDRESSES:

Canadian Coast Guard Hovercraft Unit, P.O. Box 68, Vancouver A.M.F., B.C., Canada

TELEPHONE:

604-273-2383

Canadian Hovercraft Unit, Ministry of Transport, P.O. Box 310, Parry Sound, Ontario P2A 2X4, Canada

TELEPHONE:

705 746-2196

Capt. W. J. H. Stuart, Commandant, Canadian Coast Guard Marine Operations, MoT

ADMINISTRATION:

Mr. H. Buchanan, Regional Director Marine Services (Western)

Mr. R. A. Wiseman, OIC, CCG Hovercraft Unit

The Canadian Coast Guard Hovercraft Unit was formed on August 5th 1968, to evaluate the use of hovercraft in search and rescue and other Coast Guard duties.

OPERATIONS:

The normal area of patrol is the Straits of Georgia and Gulf Islands—an area of approximately 500 square miles. The unit is often called upon outside this area on search and rescue missions.

The average patrol distance is 80 n.m.

Since April 1st, 1969, unit has carried out well over 400 S.A.R. missions, directly involving some 478 persons. These included marine, aircraft distress and mercy missions.

Other operations included the checking, servicing and repairing of marine navigational aids within the patrol area; aircraft accident inspection; water pollution investigation; carriage of Steamship Inspectors for spot safety checks of tugs; working with police departments, exercises with the Royal Canadian Navy; training and familiarisation of selected Government personnel, and

experimental work with other Government agencies.

In January 1974 the Canadian Coast Guard took delivery of a refurbished Voyageur 002, which it is operating from the CCG Base, Parry Sound, Georgian Bay, Lake Huron, The craft is undergoing a one-year trial in the aids to navigation (A to N) and search and rescue (SAR) roles. In early ice-breaking trials passages were cleared in 15 in thick ice. The crew assigned to the craft includes two operators, one of whom serves as first officer, two engineer technicians and three deck-hands.

EQUIPMENT: One SR.N5, registration CH-CCG, modified to Coast Guard requirements, Equipment includes 2 × 25 man inflatable liferafts, 2 × 100 gal auxiliary fuel tanks (extending endurance to 7 hours at max power), stretchers, first aid kit, fire fighting equipment, towing gear and other S.A.R. equipment.

One Bell Aerospace Voyageur, registration CH-CGA.

KAPS TRANSPORT LTD.

Inuvik, N.W.T.

Kaps Transport Ltd, of Edmonton, Alberta, has been operating the first Bell Aerospace Voyageur under charter. It has been carrying freight and providing various other services for locations that are otherwise inaccessible prior to the winter freeze.

CRAFT OPERATED:

Bell Voyageur (Model 7380) 001 (CH-BAC)

Voyageur 001 hauling three 20 × 8 × 8 ft cargo containers during its 1972 overland and overwater trials. The vehicle is now under charter to Kaps Transport Ltd, Edmonton, Alberta

NORTHERN TRANSPORTATION COMPANY LIMITED

OPERATIONS OFFICE:

9945-108 Street, Edmonton, Alberta T5K 2G9

TELEPHONE:

(403) 423-9201

TELEX:

037-2480

DIRECTORS:

W. M. Gilchrist (President)

L. R. Montpetit (Executive Vice President)

W. B. Hunter (Vice President, Operations)

P. L. P. Macdonnell

H. Basil Robinson

Murray Watts

J. H. Parker

A. B. Caywood

DIRECTOR OF AIR CUSHION VEHICLE OPERATIONS:

Bert W. Mead

Northern Transportation Company Limited (NTCL) is a wholly-owned subsidiary of Eldorado Nuclear Limited and was formed in 1931. It is Canada's largest Western Arctic marine transportation operator—and serves approximately 4,800 miles of water routes throughout the Mackenzie River Basin and the Western Arctic. The fleet

One of two SR.N6s operated by Northern Transportation Co. Ltd. during operations in the Mackenzie Delta

includes three ocean-going ships, 28 diesel tugs, 163 all steel dual purpose barges with varied capacities up to 1,500 tons, 4 thruster barges and the fleet has a reported capability of some 560,000 tons of cargo in any one season.

To supplement its Marine, Trucking and Aviation Divisions, NTCL has acquired two SRN6 Air Cushion Vehicles which are now available for charter and commercial operations including seismographic and hydrographic survey work.

One of these vehicles has been operating in the Beaufort Sea since September 1973, providing logistic support to off-shore drill rigs.

TORYOUNG CANADA LTD.

Niagara Falls, Canada
PRESIDENT:
Harold Logan

This company recently took delivery of two HM2 Mk III sidewall hovercraft to operate a commuter service between Toronto and Niagara to Youngsville in New York State, U.S.A. The service operates on an hourly basis with departures in both directions until late at night. Journey time is about 45 minutes.
Craft employed: HM2 Mk III 311, HM2 Mk III 3001 (U.S. built).

UNITED STATES

BELL AEROSPACE COMPANY

Bell Aerospace Company continued in 1973 operational trials of its 100-ton surface effect ship test craft at New Orleans. The craft was designed and constructed for the U.S. Navy's Surface Effect Ships Project Office Started on Louisiana's Lake Pontchartrain, near New Orleans. The test programme moved into the Gulf of Mexico late in 1973.

UNITED STATES ARMY

In 1972, a Bell SK-5 Model 7255 of the U.S. Army's Cold Region Research Laboratory, Houghton, Michigan, was operated in Alaska for extended tests over varying arctic terrain and waterways. In early 1973 the SK-5 was shipped to the U.S. Army's Weapons Command, St Louis, Missouri, for continued operations.

SCIENCE APPLICATIONS INC
HOVERLIFT APPLICATIONS INC

McLean, Virginia
It is intended to operate Voyageur 003 and 004 on logistics operations in Alaska. So far only one craft, 003, has been purchased but the company hopes to convert its option on a second craft into a firm order providing they are permitted to import the craft by the US authorities. They will be operated by a subsidiary of Science Applications Inc, Hoverlift Applications Inc.

SOUTH AMERICA

BRAZIL
COMPANHIA DE NAVAGACAO BAHIANA

ADDRESS:
Po Box 1406, Av. Franca, Salvador, Bahia.
A Hovermarine HM. 2 sidewall hovercraft operates out of Salvador (Bahia) to the site of a large oil refinery on the opposite side of the bay. During off-peak hours the craft operates sightseeing tours.

Craft operated; HM.2 Mk111 306 "Hovermarine One"
Route(s): Commuter service out of Salvador and routes in Todos os Santos Bay.

SERVICOS DE TRANSPORTES DA BAIXA DA GUANABARA (STBG)

This company operates three HM2 Mk III sidewall hovercraft on a 3 n. mile route between communities and business areas in the Bay of Guanabara, Rio de Janeiro.
Craft employed:

HM2 321 "Gavea"
HM2 322 "Gragoata"
HM2 323 "Guarativa"

ASIA

BRUNEI:
GOVERNMENT OF BRUNEI

Craft operated: SR.N5 019 (AMBD 110)
Reports suggest that this craft may not be in an operational state.

ROYAL BRUNEI MALAY REGIMENT

Berakas Camp
Bandar Sevi Begawan
Brunei
Craft operated: SR.N6 037 (AMBD 120)

PAKISTAN

The Pakistan Coast Guard authority is understood to have purchased two SH-2 five or six seat craft for patrol and interception duties.
Craft employed: SH.2 009, SH.2 010

THAILAND:

Thai Customs Authority
Klong Toly
Bangkok
Craft operated: MV-PP1 001 "Customs Hovercraft 1"

TOUR ROYALE

Bangkok, Thailand
This company has on order 3 HM2 craft for delivery towards the end of 1974 and these will be used to operate a series of tours from Bangkok to Pattoya Beach and other locations.

INDIA:

City and Industrial Development Corp of Maharashtra Ltd
Nirmail
2nd Floor
Nariman Point
Bombay 1
Craft operated: HM.2 Mk III 314 "Jalapriya"
Route(s): Between Old and New Bombay linking Appollo Bunder and Ferry Wharf with Uran, Belapur and Elephanta.

AFRICA

AFRICA:
ZAIRE
SOCIETE MINIERE DE BAKWANGA

Mbujimayi
R. C. Lulubourg 10,424
Craft operated: CC.7 002

NIGERIA
PIPELINE CONTRACTORS INCORPORATED

Craft operated: Sealand SH.2 007 (The operator of this craft is an oil exploration company and the craft will assist in this activities.)

AUSTRALASIA

AUSTRALIA
DOLPHIN FERRIES
Sydney

Formed in August 1973, this company operates a single HM2 Mk III craft on regular commuter and tourist services from Circular Quay in Sydney Harbour and began operations in November of that year. Managing director of the firm is Mr Bjarne J. Halvorsen. Craft employed: HM2 319 "Blue Dolphin".

MUNDOO PASTORAL COMPANY
ADDRESS:

Mundoo Island, South Australia

A Hovergem G-6 agricultural ACV is employed by this company for carrying personnel, cattle and equipment to various islands in the Mundoo group.

THE NATIONAL PARKS COMMISSION
ADDRESS:

Flinders House,
17 Flinders Street,
Adelaide, S. Australia 5000

The Commission employs a Taylorcraft Skimmer for patrol and supervisory work in the Coorong National Park. The Coorong is a large shallow lake within the park. It is about 90 miles long by ½-1 mile wide and connects with the Murray River and the sea. Illegal poaching of water fowl is a problem and the Skimair is employed to overcome this. Patrols are undertaken about twice a week and total about 7-8 operating hours. The craft operates at up to 70 miles from base.

NOOSA HEADS HOVERCRAFT CO.
Noosa Heads
Brisbane
Queensland
Craft operated: SH.2 005
NEW ZEALAND:
DEPARTMENT OF CIVIL AVIATION

The New Zealand Department of Civil Aviation is operating one SR.N6 Winchester for crash rescue services at Mangere Airport, Aukland.

Craft operated: SN.N6 014 "Whakatopa"

EUROPE

ITALY:
ITAL HOVER SpA
Zaltere 66
Venice
Craft operated: HM.2 Mk III 302 "Mare 3"
Route(s): Venice-Sattomarina-Grado
CASA NAVI SOC. NAVIGAZIONE SpA
Via Felice Venezian 2
TRIESTE
Craft operated: Denny D.2 003 "Sortilege"
Route/s: Lignano-Sabbiadoro-Trieste
ITALIAN INTERFORCE UNIT
Ancona
Craft operated: SR.N6 036 (HC 9801)
PORTUGAL:
SOCIEDADE TURISTICA PONTA DO ADOXE SARL
Avenida Casal Ribeiro 46-6
Lisbon
CHAIRMAN:

Commander H. Noronha

Craft operated: HM2. Mk III 301 "Torralta" HM.2 Mk III 308 "Soltroia" HM.2 Mk III 316 "Troiamar" HM.2 Mk III 318 "Troiano"
Route(s): Setubal-Troia/Sesimbra
GREECE:
HELLENIC HOVERCRAFT LINES ("HOVERLINES")
Piraeus
MANAGING DIRECTOR:

Mr A. N. Vomvoyiannis

Craft operated: HM.2 Mk III 304 "Natouro" 2" HM.2 Mk III 307 "Natouro"1
Route(s): Piraeus-Hydra-Spetsai-Porto Heli

NORWAY:
De Bla Omnibusser A/S
Stromsveien 196
Oslo 6
DIRECTOR:

Dahlseide

Craft operated: HM.2 Mk III 317 "Fjordbuss 1"
Route(s): Oslo-Horten, with calls at Drobak, Filtvet and Tofte
BELGIUM:
Ministry of Works
Antwerp
Craft operated:
HM.2 Mk III 315 "Kallo" (Employed as River Scheldt survey craft).
FRANCE:
LANGUEDOC-ROUSILLON REGIONAL DEVELOPMENT BOARD
Montpellier & Perpignan
Craft operated: 2 × N.102 craft
FRENCH NAVY
Toulon
Craft operated: 2 × N.102
GIRONDE PORT AUTHORITY
Bordeaux
Craft operated: N.300 001 and N.300 002
Route(s): Blaye-Lamarque

SOVIET UNION:
MINISTRY OF THE RIVER FLEET

The 50 seat Sormovich ACV has been operating experimental services on the Volga and Oka rivers and a derivative is expected to go into production in 1975. The most widely used commercial ACV at present is the 48-50 seat Zarnista sidewall craft. This is expected to be enlarged into production by an enlarged 80-seat waterjet-propelled vessel now in the final stages of development. The new 50-passenger gas-turbine-powered Skate was introduced into service in 1971. Well over one hundred Zarya air-lubricated hull craft have been completed and many of these are in service on shallow rivers in the eastern areas of the Soviet Union. Wing-in-ground effect machines are being developed for high-speed ferry services along the main rivers. These are described as being capable of travelling within several metres of river surface at speeds of some 155 mph (250 km/h).
SOVIET NAVY
Several experimental ACVs are being evaluated by the Soviet Navy, and a military version of the Skate is now in limited service with the Soviet naval infantry as high speed transport.
SOVIET ARMY
A military version of the Skate 50-seat fast ferry is in limited service with the Soviet Army.

UNITED KINGDOM

BRITISH RAIL HOVERCRAFT LIMITED (Seaspeed Hovercraft)
HEAD OFFICE:

Royal London House, 22/25 Finsbury Square, London EC2P 2BQ
TELEPHONE:

01-628-3050
TELEX:

883339

DOVER ROUTE HEADQUARTERS
Seaspeed Hoverport, Eastern Docks, Dover
TELEPHONE:

Dover (0304) 203574
TELEX:

965079
RESERVATIONS:

7 Cambridge Terrace, Dover

The Princess Margaret, one of two SR.N4 hovercraft operated by British Rail Hovercraft Ltd on its Seaspeed cross-channel routes, Dover-Boulogne and Dover-Calais.

TELEPHONE:
01-606 3681
TELEX:
96158
SOLENT ROUTE HEADQUARTERS
Marine Court, The Parade, Cowes, I.O.W.
TELEPHONE:
Cowes (098 382) 2303
TELEX:
86252

DIRECTORS:
D. McKenna, CBE, Chairman
J. M. Lefeaux, Managing Director
Lord Black of Barrow-in-Furness
G. R. Hill
J. Posner
SENIOR EXECUTIVES:
P. A. Yerbury, Chief Engineer
A. Tame, Commercial and Planning Manager
A. H. Thorne, Route Manager, Dover Strait
R. B. W. Gladstone, Route Manager, Solent

British Rail Hovercraft Ltd, a wholly-owned subsidiary of British Railways Board, was formed in March 1966 and launched its first commercial service in July, 1966, between Southampton and Cowes. The cross-channel service for passengers and cars between specially constructed hovercraft terminals at Dover and Boulogne began in August, 1968 using an SR.N4 'The Princess Margaret'. A year later the service was augmented by the introduction of a sister craft 'The Princess Anne' and in October 1970 a service was initiated between Dover and Calais.

In association with British Rail and French Railways the Company operates a through London/Paris service taking about 6 hours, using special trains operating from a platform alongside the Boulogne hovercraft terminal. At Calais a coach connection with Ostend and Brussels is provided, enabling the through London/Brussels service to be performed by rail/hovercraft/coach in 7 hours.

A further coach service from Calais to Lille was introduced in May 1974, giving a London/Lille journey time of 5½ hours.

Investment plans were well advanced last year (1973) to "stretch" the two SR.N4 craft to Mk. 3 standard. This modification involved the lengthening of each craft by 47 ft, providing a capacity for up to 396 passengers and 53 vehicles. The four marine Proteus gas turbines were to be up-rated to 3,800 shp each and each would drive a propeller/fan unit with a 21 ft (6·40 m) diameter propeller. The additional power would have ensured that the performance of the current craft would be maintained.

Craft motion would have been considerably less than that experienced on the standard SR.N4 and for similar comfort levels the larger craft would have been capable of operating in waves up to 2 ft (0·61 m) higher than the present craft.

Unfortunately, because of the economic situation at the time of the investment submission these modifications had to be shelved for the time being.

REPRESENTATION OVERSEAS:
SNCF, Armement Naval, 51 rue de Londres, Paris VIIIe, France.

Top: The Princess Anne, sister craft to the Princess Margaret, arriving in front of the Seaspeed terminal building at Boulogne. In the foreground is one of the fast "Autotrains" which enable the company to operate a through London/Paris service taking about 6 hours.
Bottom: Vehicles loading at Dover. During 1973, the two SR.N4s carried 607,000 passengers and 106,000 cars on the two cross-channel services

Sea Hawk, one of the two lengthened SR.N6s employed by British Rail Hovercraft Ltd on the Southampton-Cowes route. A total of 252,500 passengers were carried by the Sea Hawk and its sistercraft, Sea Eagle, during 1973

OPERATIONS:

Dover-Boulogne:

26 n miles. Winter service 2 flights daily, increasing to a peak of 8 in summer. Journey time 35 minutes.

Dover-Calais:

23 n miles. Winter service 1 flight daily increasing to peak of 8 in summer. Journey time, 30 minutes.

Southampton-Cowes:

10 n miles. Hourly service with 12 flights daily. Journey time, 20 minutes.

1973 CARRYINGS:

Dover-Boulogne:

394,000 passengers, 59,000 cars.

Dover-Calais:

213,000 passengers, 47,000 cars.

Southampton-Cowes:

252,500 passengers.

CRAFT IN SERVICE:

Dover-Boulogne-Calais:

BHC Mountbatten class SR.N4s, GH 2006 and 2007.

Southampton-Cowes:

BHC Winchester class SR.N6s, GH 2014 and 2015.

DEPARTMENT OF TRADE AND INDUSTRY (DTI).

CRAFT OPERATED:

CC.7 001 (XW249)

HM.2 Mk III 310 (XW555)

HD.2 001—Held by National Physical Laboratory for R & D purposes.

HOVERLLOYD LIMITED

ADDRESS:

International Hoverport, Sandwich Road, Ramsgate, Kent

TELEPHONE:

Thanet (0843) 54881/54761 499-9481

TELEX:

96323

LONDON OFFICE:

Board of Chief Executive, Sales Administration, 49 Charles Street, London, W1

TELEPHONE:

01-493 5525

TELEX:

262374

DIRECTORS:

Ingemar Blennow (Swedish) Chairman

James A. Hodgson, Deputy Chairman and Managing Director

James Clement

Hans Pihlo (Swedish)

Hoverlloyd was formed by two shipping companies, Swedish Lloyd and Swedish American Line (now both members of the Broström group) to operate a cross-Channel car and passenger ferry service between Ramsgate and Calais. The company operates three BHC SR.N4 Mk.II widened Mountbattens.

The crossing between Ramsgate and Calais takes 40 minutes and there are up to twenty-one return trips a day in summer and a minimum of four a day in winter. On May 1st, 1969, the company opened coach/hovercraft/coach services between London and Paris. This service takes eight hours and a single fare costs £7·20. There are up to five daily departures during summer and two during winter.

On April 1st 1974, Hoverlloyd opened

Hoverlloyd's three SR N4's, operating on the Pegwell Bay (Ramsgate)/Calais route carried 800,000 passengers and 120,000 vehicles across the English Channel in 1973. The craft above converted from a standard SR.N4, carries 280 passengers and 37 vehicles, compared with 254 passengers and 30 vehicles on the standard craft. This increase in capacity was achieved by removing the two inner passenger cabins to increase the car deck area and by widening the outer passenger cabins

coach/hovercraft/coach services between London/Kortrijk and Brussels. The service takes seven hours to Brussels and a single fare to either destination costs £6·50. There are two daily services in the summer peak and a daily departure is maintained year-round.

Passengers are able to buy tickets from travel agents, or by making a booking direct from Hoverlloyd or at the Hoverport Those travelling with a car pay only for their car, according to its length. The car charge covers the driver and up to six passengers. For vehicles there are three tariffs; 'A', 'B' and 'C'. 'A' tariff is more expensive and is applied in peak hours during summer, in either direction, according to a detailed traffic analysis. 'B' tariff is cheaper and accounts for the balance of the departures listed for the summer. The 'C' tariff applies during the winter (except over Christmas when tariff 'B' applies) and this represents reductions of up to 30% on normal vehicle fares. The tariffs have been designed so as to encourage a balance in the origin of cross-channel traffic, and to spread the daily peaks of traffic.

The company's hoverport covers 12½ acres below the cliffs at the north end of Pegwell Bay, Ramsgate. The site is raised 8 ft above the level of the beach, so that operations are not affected by tides. It consists of a group of long low buildings running parallel to the cliffs. Between the buildings and the cliffs is a car park and the car reception area which is joined to the main Ramsgate-Sandwich road by an access road built up the cliff face.

In front of the buildings is a large square concrete apron with a ramp at both corners leading down into the sea. The SR.N4 comes up one ramp, parks on the apron in front of the building while it loads and unloads, then leaves down the other ramp.

These buildings contain the main passenger and car terminal area which includes the inspection halls for customs and immigra-

tion, duty free shops, cafe, bar, restaurant, banks and other passenger facilities. Next to this area are the administrative offices.

Craft operated:

"Swift" (SR.N4002) registration GH 2004

"Sure" (SR.N4003) registration GH 2005

"Sir Christopher" (SR.4005) registration GH 2008

HOVERWORK LIMITED

(Wholly owned subsidiary of Hovertravel Limited)

HEAD OFFICE:

12 Lind Street, Ryde, Isle of Wight

TELEPHONE:

Ryde 5181

TELEX:

86513

CABLE:

Hoverwork Ryde

DIRECTORS:

D. R. Robertson (Chairman)

C. D. J. Bland (Managing Director)

E. W. H. Gifford

A. C. Smith

SENIOR EXECUTIVES:

J. M. Youens (Company Secretary)

Hoverwork Limited is a subsidiary of Hovertravel Limited and was formed in 1966. The company provides crew training and charter facilities for all available types of ACVs, thus bridging the gap between the operators and manufacturers.

The company has trained over 35 hovercraft captains and has received some 36 charter contracts, including film sequences and the operation of the SRN6 craft for mineral surveys all over the world. The company operated the hovercraft passenger service during Expo'67 at Montreal and a service at the 1970 Algiers Exposition.

Hoverwork is the largest international operator of hovercraft, having access to Hovertravel's two 38 seater SRN6s as well as their own five ton flat deck-freighter and a multi-purpose SRN5 GH-2009. Hoverwork has undertaken operations in areas from the Arctic to the equator. These have included logistics operations in the northern part of Svalbard and in equatorial parts of South America. To date Hoverwork has operated in the following countries: Canada, South America, Mexico, Brunei, Holland, Bahrain, Kuwait, The Trucial States, Saudi Arabia, Algeria, Tunisia, English North Sea and Spitsbergen.

Craft Operated:
SR.N6 024   Maplin Sands charter
AV.2 002   Dutch Water Resources Board
SR.N5 GH. 2009

HOVERTRAVEL LIMITED

HEAD OFFICE:
12 Lind Street, Ryde, Isle of Wight
TELEPHONE:
Ryde 5181
TELEX:
86513
CABLE:
Hovertravel, Ryde
TERMINAL OFFICES:
Quay Road, Ryde, Isle of Wight (Tel: 3051)
Clarence Pier, Southsea (Tel: 29988)
DIRECTORS:
D. R. Robertson (Chairman)
C. D. J. Bland (Chief Executive & Managing Director)
E. W. H. Gifford
D. E. Webb
SENIOR EXECUTIVES:
J. M. Youens (Company Secretary)
R. G. Clarke (General Manager)
G. Tarrant (Manager, Middle East)

Hovertravel Limited, formed in 1965, is a £120,000 company whose main activity has been the operation of two SRN6 Winchester class hovercraft in the Solent, primarily between Ryde and Southsea. The distance is just over four miles and the frequency varies between one return trip per hour in the winter and five return trips per hour in the summer.

Approximately 400,000 passengers are carried per year, together with fifty tons of freight. The service has gained in popularity and the total number of passengers carried by July 1973 was well over 2·6 million. The maximum number of passengers carried in one day (using both hovercraft) was over 3,600.

On 16th July 1971 Hovertravel carried its two millionth passenger on the Solent service.

Hovertravel operates a year-round service and during 1972 reliability was in excess of 99%. The average crossing time throughout the year is less than seven minutes for the four mile route. Hovertravel Limited is now the most experienced profit making ACV operator in the world and together with Hoverwork employs a staff of fifty, including 12 Captains and 18 maintenance engineers.

The SRN6s available on the Solent service are normally SRN6 GH-2013 and SRN6 GH-2012. A total of 42,000 hours of ACV operation had been accumulated by Hovertravel and Hoverwork by the end of April 1973. The craft owned by the two companies are SRN6s GH-2013, GH-2012, GH-2011 and GH-2010.

BH.7 from the Interservice Hovercraft Unit during cold weather trials in the Baltic

One of the three HM 2 Mk III rigid sidewall ACVs employed by London Hoverservices Ltd on its Thames commuter service between Greenwich and Westminster

INTERNATIONAL HOVERSERVICES LIMITED

HEAD OFFICE:
138 Rownhams Lane, North Baddesley
TELEPHONE:
0421 23 2588
OPERATIONAL OFFICE:
(Operational matters and advance bookings) Greenland Dock, Guilliver Street, Rotherhithe SE16 1LT
TELEPHONE: 01 237 9025/6
DIRECTORS:
Capt A. S. Hands, MRIN, Chairman and Joint Managing Director
Lt Cdr M. D. Dawson, RN, Retd, Secretary and Joint Managing Director
L. R. Colquhoun, DFC, GM, DFM

International Hoverservices was formed in January, 1969 to operate hovercraft and the first service, which opened in July 1970, was between Bournemouth and Swanage. This was maintained each year until 1973, when the demand for short excursion trips at Bournemouth superseded this service enabling the company to expand into the charter market. This was an extension of a major contract for an industrial commuter service between Cowes, Isle of Wight and the Vosper Thornycroft shipyard in Southampton, believed to be the first in the world of its type, and which IHL continue to operate.

With three years experience in the field of hovercraft operation, the company began a consultancy service to both prospective and existing operators. These were, in turn, an extension of the company's ex-

perience in training of both craft commanders and engineers. The accumulated knowledge of both scheduled and charter operations has now been applied to the associate company, London Hoverservices Limited, formed to operate commuter/tourist service on the Thames.

During the summer of 1973 IHL operated trips round the bay at Bournemouth and lunchtime visits to Poole with "Lady Montagu" one of its HM2 Mark III rigid sidewall craft.

Craft Operated:
HM.2 Mk III 305 "Lady Montagu" Solent route and charters

International Hoverservices craft are also employed in operations with its subsidiary operating company, London Hoverservices Ltd, on the River Thames.

INTERSERVICE HOVERCRAFT UNIT

ADDRESS:
HMS Daedalus, Lee-on-the-Solent, Hampshire, PO13 9NY
TELEPHONE:
Lee-on-the-Solent 550143 (STD0705)
COMMANDING OFFICER:
Commander W. R. Hart, AFC AFRAeS RN

The Interservice Hovercraft Unit at Lee-on-the-Solent is responsible for the assessment of hovercraft in various military roles and the training of all service hovercraft pilots.

With the withdrawal of Army and RAF personnel from the Unit by January 1975 the Royal Navy is expected to take over IHU as a single service Unit.

In September 1973 the BH.7 returned to UK from the United States of America where it was demonstrated to the US Navy, Marine Corps and Army as well as the Department of Transportation, City of New York.

Craft Operated:
SRN5 002 (XT 492)
SRN5 006 (XT 246)
SRN6 027 (XV 859)
SRN MK V 005 (XT 657)
*BH7 001 (XW 225)
*modified to MK 4 version embodying bow door.

LONDON HOVERSERVICES LIMITED

OPERATIONAL OFFICE: (operational matters and advance bookings)
Greenland Dock Entrance, Gulliver Street Rotherhithe SE16 1LT

TELEPHONE:
01 237 9025/6

TICKET OFFICES:
Westminster   Tel: 01 839 5532
Greenwich   Tel: 01 858 9633
Tower Pier   Tel: 01 237 9025

DIRECTORS:
Lt. Cdr. M. D. Dawson, RN (Ret'd) (Chairman and Joint Managing Director)
Capt. A. S. Hands, MRIN (Secretary and Joint Managing Director)
L. R. Colquhoun, DFC, GM, DSM
R. A. Bambrough
B. Levy
N. Olivares (Italian)
R. Morhaim

EXECUTIVES:
P. E. Marzetti, Passenger Sales Manager
Capt. J. Penn, Senior Captain
W. T. Hague, Chief Engineer

This company was formed by International Hoverservices Limited in 1972 to exploit the potential for rigid sidewall hovercraft on the Thames. The decision to operate the route from Greenwich Pier to Tower Pier and Westminster Pier was taken after extensive trials which included a six week period in the Spring of 1972 when the manufacturers, Hovermarine Transport Limited, ran a trial scheduled service on this route. Further trials were conducted by the company and the manufacturers in conjunction with the Port of London Authority.

A commuter service run in conjunction with daily scheduled tourist services started on Monday, 23rd July between Greenwich and Westminster via Tower Pier using two HM2 Mark III rigid sidewall hovercraft.

A third craft joined in March 1974 and a summer schedule, including calls at Charing Cross, was started in May 1974, operating from 07·15 until 20·15.

All LHL hovercraft are available for charter on the Thames.

Craft operated:
HM2 Mk III 320 Argonaut GH 2033
HM2 Mk III 303 GH 2024
HM2 Mk III 312 GH 2019

Craft operated by the Interservice Hovercraft Unit, Lee-on-the-Solent. *Top left:* the BHC SR.N5. *Top right,* the prototype SR.N6 Mk 5 with a central well deck for small armoured vehicles and weapons or 50 armed troops, *Bottom left:* the 60-knot SR.N6 Mk 2. Using radar and optical navigation aids, the craft can be employed for high speed coastal surveillance in low visibility and at night. *Bottom right:* The 50-ton BH.7 which in 1973 was demonstrated in the United States to the US Navy, Marine Corps and Army. The previous year this particular vessel participated in a two-month arctic exercise in the Baltic. It travelled over 5,000 miles under its own power and operated to within 60 miles of the Arctic circle

MIDDLE EAST

IRAN
IMPERIAL IRANIAN NAVY
Hovercraft base: Khosrowabad

Eight BHC Winchesters are being operated by the Imperial Iranian Navy on logistics duties and coastal patrol.

Two BH.7 Wellingtons are also in service and four more—Mk 5s—are under construction. The first two craft, BH.7 Mk.4s are operated in the logistic support role. The Mk 5 is designed as a multi-role craft and is designed to carry surface-surface, surface-air missiles on its side decks.

IMPERIAL IRANIAN NAVY

Craft operated:		
SR.N6 040(IIN 01) Mark 4	SR.N6 045(IIN 06) Mark 4	BH.7 004(IIN 103) Mk 5
SR.N6 041(IIN 02) Mark 4	SR.N6 046(IIN 07) Mark 4	To be delivered 1974-75
SR.N6 042(IIN 03) Mark 3	SR.N6 047(IIN 08) Mark 4	BH.7 005(IIN 104) Mk 5
SR.N6 043(IIN 04) Mark 3	BH.7 002(IIN 101) Mk 4	BH.7 006(IIN 105) Mk 5
SR.N6 044(IIN 05) Mark 4	BH.7 003(IIN 102) Mk 4	BH.7 007(IIN 106) Mk 5

SAUDI ARABIA
Saudi Arabian Coastal and Frontier Guard
Ministry of the Interior
   Airport Road
   Riyadh
   The Saudi Arabian Coastal and Frontier Guard operates a number of SR.N6 Win-chesters on patrol, contraband control, search and rescue and liaison duties. The craft are attached to bases at Jeddah and Aziziyah on the east and west coasts.
Craft operated: SR.N6 038
SR.N6 048
SR.N6 049
SR.N6 050
SR.N6 051
SR.N6 052
SR.N6 053
SR.N6 054

PACIFIC

JAPAN
Meitetsu Kaijo Kankosen K. K.
99-1, Shin-miyazaka-cho, Atsuta-ku, Nagoya City
   Began regular services across the Mikawa and Ise Bays between Gamagori and Toba in September 1969 with an intermediate stop at Nishiura. The craft employed is MV-PP5 002 which has been named "Hakucho".

Oita Hoverferry Co. Ltd
1309 Nishi-shinchi, Imatsura, Oita City
   Operating three MV-PP5 craft, numbers 004, 005 and 006, named "Hobby 1, 2 and 3" on a service between Oita Airport, Oita and Beppu cities. Service began in 1971.

Japanese National Railways
Kokutetshu Building, 625 Marunouchi 1-chome, Chiyoda-ku, Tokyo
   A service between Uno in Okayama Prefecture and Takamatsu in Kagawa Prefecture was inaugurated in November 1972, using MV-PP5 007, named "Kamome" (Sea Gull).

Kagoshima Airport Hovercraft Service Co. Ltd.
   Started in July 1972, using MV-PP5 009, "Angel No. 1", on a service linking Kajiki and Ibusuki in the Kagoshima Bay. The route currently takes over two hours to accomplish by car but with the hovercraft the 60 km route is achieved in less than an hour. A second craft, MV-PP5 010—"Angel No.2"—has been added to the service.

Yaeyama Kanko Ferry K. K.
No 1 Aza-ohkawa, Ishigaki City, Okinawa
   Delivered to her owners in the spring of 1972, MV-PP5 008-"Koryu"-operates a service linking Ishigaki and Iriomote Island, a distance of about 30 km, taking about 20 minutes, compared with the 2½ hours taken by the ships used previously. Yaeyama Kanko Ferry K. K. is a joint investment of Taketomi City, Ryuku Kaiun and several other local shipping concerns.

Kinki Nippon Tetsudo K. K.
6-chome, Uehommachi, Tennoji-ku, Asaka
   Operating SR.N6-029 which was imported by Mitsubishi several years ago and is now redesignated SR.N6-M, Kinki Nippon Tetsudo is believed to be engaged in operating sightseeing tours in the Ise Bay region.

ACV TRAILERS

AND

HEAVY LIFT SYSTEMS

AUSTRALIA

TAYLORCRAFT TRANSPORT (DEVELOPMENT) PTY LTD

HEAD OFFICE:
Parafield Airport, South Australia 5106

TELEPHONE:
(08) 258 4944

DIRECTORS:
R. V. Taylor
J. Taylor

Taylorcraft has built an ACV trailer unit for carrying loads of up to 1¼ tons over a wide range of soft or wet surfaces. A smaller version is being built for carrying fruit and vegetables from the point of harvesting to the point of dispatch.

TRAILAIRE I

This air cushion assisted trailer is intended for use in situations where the ground is too soft or wet to allow the use of normal trailers. One or more may be towed by a tractor or single units may be man-handled as required. The skirt and lift unit are removable allowing operation as a normal trailer in good conditions. Lift engine is a Kawasaki KT 300.

Towbar and tow ball are interchangeable to simplify handling in confined spaces.

Operation as conventional trailer:
DIMENSIONS:
Length overall (including towbar)
                  18 ft 0 in (5·49 m)
Width   6 ft 0 in (1·83 m)
Load Space 6 ft × 12 ft (1·83 m × 3·66 m)
              (Wheel arches at centre)
Loading Height   2 ft (0·61 m)
TYRES: 6·40 × 13
WEIGHTS:
Tare   330 lb (150 kg)
Payload (Max)   30 cwt (1,524 kg)
TRACK: 5 ft (1·52 m) centres
Operation as air cushion assisted trailer:
DIMENSIONS:
Length overall   18 ft 6 in (5·54 m)
Width   8 ft (2·24 m)
Load space
   2 each of 6 ft × 4 ft (1·83 m × 1·22 m)
Loading height   2 ft (0·61 m)
WEIGHTS:
Tare   580 lb (263 kg)
Payload (Max)   24 cwt (1,219 kg)
Cushion pressure (Max) 45 lb/sq ft
FUEL:
25 : 1 petrol oil   2·1 gals (10 litres)

TRAILAIRE II

The basic Trailaire unit is an 8 ft × 16 ft (2·43 × 4·87 m) platform capable of lifting 1¼ tons on its deck. At the rear of the platform an enclosed 127 air-cooled engine and fan assembly provides lifting power. At its gross weight the Trailaire loads the surface beneath to only 30 lb sq ft—less than one hundredth of the loading of an equivalent tracked or wheeled vehicle. Drag is very low and the unit may be used over a wide range of soft or wet surfaces, including mud banks and sandbars.

Units may be coupled together to provide load platforms of 24 ft × 8 ft (7·31 m × 2·43 m), 16 ft × 12 ft (4·87 m × 3·65 m) (2½ tons payload) or 16 ft × 24 ft (4·87m × 7·31 m) (5 tons) or spaced to carry long loads, such as pipes. They can be towed by light vehicles or winched over land. Over water an outboard motor or a water pump unit may be used for propulsion.

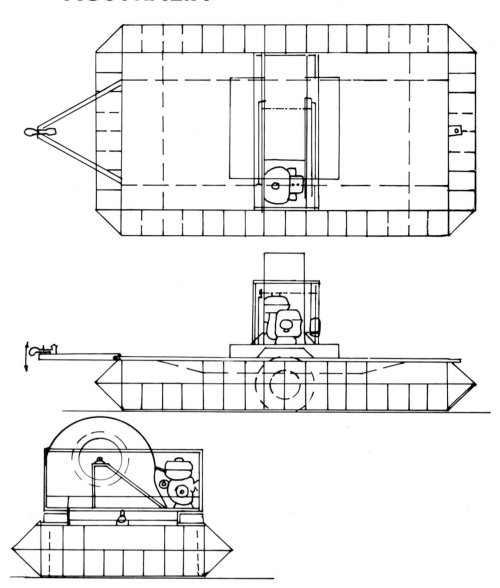

Taylorcraft Trailaire I, intended for use in situations where the ground is too wet to permit the use of conventional trailers. Both skirt and lift systems can be removed to allow operation as a normal wheeled trailer in good conditions

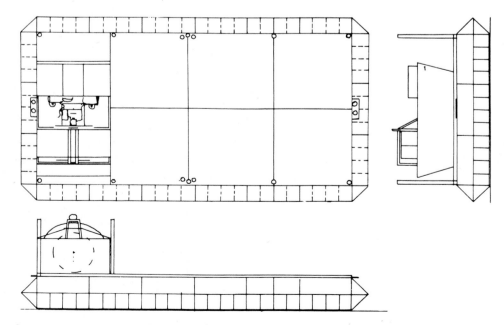

General arrangement of the Trailaire II, an 8 ft × 16 ft (3·43 × 4·87 m) air cushion trailer. Cushion air is generated by a VW 126A air-cooled automotive engine driving a 2 ft (609 mm) diameter centrifugal fan

Space alongside the lift engine allows an operator to ride on the platform clear of the load space. Sockets around the platform edge are provided to accept posts to fence-in the load area.

Ground clearance of the standard unit is 10 in (254 mm) but greater clearance can be provided if required. For amphibious operation buoyancy tanks can be fitted, though the standard unit can be operated over water as long as the engine maintains lift.

DIMENSIONS: (Single Unit)	Hard Structure	Overall on Cushion
Length	16 ft 9 in (5·10 m)	17 ft 8 in (5·38 m)
Width	8 ft 1 in (2·46 m)	9 ft 8 in (2·94 m)
Height of Deck	10 in 254 mm	20 in (0·50 m)
Height of Lift Unit	4 ft 0 in (1·21 m)	4 ft 10 in (1·47 m)
Load Space	12 ft 4 in × 8 ft 0 in (3·75 m	2·43 m)
Fence Height (Posts)	4 ft 10 in (1·47 m)	

CANADA

JOHN N. BROCKLESBY TRANSPORT LTD

11175 Parkway Boulevard, Ville d'Anjou, Montreal, Quebec H1J 1S2

EXECUTIVES:

B Gauthier, Eng, Vice-President

G. E. Simard, General Manager

TELEPHONE: (514) 352-0700

TELEX:

01 2746

Brocklesby, a member of the Canada Steamship Line Group of companies, is licensee for Air Cushion Equipment Ltd's industrial skirt system.

The company has employed the system to move a 500-ton oil tank in Quebec City. The tank, which was 150 ft (45·72 m) in diameter, was raised 14 in (355 mm) on its segmented skirt and moved a distance of one mile (1·60 m) over a variety of surfaces to the tank farm of a storage firm, St Lawrence Stevedoring Co. Ltd.

HOVER-JAK LTD.

HEAD OFFICE:

169 Centre Street East, Richmond Hill, Ontario, Canada L4C 1A5

OFFICERS:

See ACV section.

This company is the Canadian licence holder for the Bertin system of independently fed multiple plenum chambers. The Hover-Jak HJ-15, a 15-ton payload ACV trailer employing this system is currently undergoing trials

HJ-15

The HJ-15, 15-ton capacity air cushion trailer, is of rugged simple construction and can be dismantled easily for transportation by conventional highway truck or cargo plane. The platform folds to a size of 40 ft × 9 ft × 5 ft 6 in (12·97 m × 2·74 m × 1·67 m). Engine and fan assemblies are removable as two separate units.

Lift is provided by two centrifugal fans mounted at the rear and driven by two Deutz B/F 8L413 diesel engines. The HJ-15 is designed for amphibious applications and has a buoyancy at gross weight of 150%.

Propulsion is provided by swamp crawler vehicles, boats, winching or by helicopter.

DIMENSIONS:

Length overall	40 ft (12·2 m)
Width	18 ft (5·5 m)
Height, base of hardstructure to top of fan assembly	9 ft (2·75 m)

WEIGHTS:

Empty weight	8 tons
Payload	15 tons

PERFORMANCE:

Towing speed (helicopter at full load	20 mph plus (32·18 km/h)
Clearance height	2 ft 5 in (74 cm)
Endurance, normal tanks	10 hours

Hover-Jak HJ-15 15-ton capacity air cushion trailer being towed by a Sikorsky S-55 helicopter

The Hover-Jak HJ-15 air cushion trailer. Air for the Bertin multiple plenum lift system is provided by two centrifugal fans aft, powered by twin Deutz diesels

TERRACROSS LIMITED

HEAD OFFICE:

985 Notre Dame Street, Lachine 640, Quebec

TELEPHONE:

(514) 634-3551 Extensions 505 and 595

TELEX:

05-25536

DIRECTORS:

T. C. A. Horn

R. J. A. Fricker

O. D. Blankenship

D. K. Smith

EXECUTIVES:

Rowland D. Hunt, General Manager

Terracross has been formed in Canada under a four company partnership agreement involving Air Cushion Equipment Limited, Southampton, England; Dominion Bridge Limited, Montreal; Global Marine Inc., Los Angeles and Raymond International Inc., of New York.

It will market HTI cross-country hover-trailers and Mackace amphibious hover-platforms in Canada for a wide range of industrial and transportation purposes. These products, which are capable of moving loads of 100-tons and more, have been successfully introduced to the British and European markets by Hovertrailers International Limited (HTI) and Mackley Ace Limited (Mackace), both of which are associate companies of Air Cushion Equipment Limited.

Terracross expects to manufacture the air cushion vehicles under licence in Canada and also to develop its own products for the Canadian market.

It will make available both specialised and general purpose, non-self-propelled air cushion transporters with payload capacities of 10 to 100-tons and more for cross country and amphibious purposes. These transporters will be marketed initially for operation in Canada, with particular emphasis on the Arctic and Sub-arctic regions, where mineral exploration, civil engineering, construction, hydro-electric, forestry and manufacturing projects are hampered by climate and difficult terrain.

FRANCE

SEDAM

HEAD OFFICE:
80 Avenue de la Grande Armé, 75 Paris 17 eme
TELEPHONE: 380-17-69

TELEX: 29-124 Paris

Sedam is developing a range of air cushion trailers for carrying loads across uneven ground, particularly marshland, agricultural areas and construction sites. One of the first vehicles, with a payload capacity of 25 metric tons, will be employed to transport prefabricated building sections from the storage areas on construction sites to the point of work.

UNITED KINGDOM

This 620-ton, 175 ft diameter oil storage tank is the largest ever moved by Air Cushion Equipment's hover flotation method. The resiting of this and seven other tanks, is part of a modernisation scheme being undertaken at the Esso refinery, Antwerp, by Fluor Belgium NV.

AIR CUSHION EQUIPMENT LTD

HEAD OFFICE:
360 Shirley Road, Southampton
TELEPHONE:
Southampton 776468
TELEX:
477258
CABLES: HOVERACE, SOTON
WORKS:
35 Randolph Street, Shirley, Southampton
DIRECTORS:
L. A. Hopkins, Chairman and Technical Director
T. T. A. Horn, Managing
W. A. Melhuish, Finance
O. J. Colman
J. M. Horn
P. B. A. Hopkins
B. H. Wright

Air Cushion Equipment Ltd specialises in design, consulting and manufacturing work in the application of hover principles to the industrial and medical fields. Its chairman, Mr L. A. Hopkins, was one of the original team led by Sir Christopher Cockerell at Hovercraft Development Ltd, Hythe, Southampton. Specialising in the industrial applications at Hythe, Mr Hopkins left to develop his ideas on industrial hover devices by setting up Air Cushion Equipment in April, 1968.

Now associated with the company (see separate listing) are: Hovertrailers International Ltd (37% owned); Mackley-Ace Ltd (20% owned); Air Cushion Engineering (USA) Ltd (100% owned); Terracross Ltd (Canada) (26% owned).

A significant part of Air Cushion Equip-

ments' expansion policy has been the formation of new companies in Britain and abroad to take on design, manufacture and sale of industrial hover vehicles. These are partnership companies and their objective is to exploit the many applications of the ACE air cushion system in as wide a market as possible. Latest is Terracross Ltd, a company formed with Global Marine Inc (Los Angeles), Raymond International Inc (New York), and Dominion Bridge Ltd (Montreal) as partners. It will make and sell a range of industrial air cushion vehicles for the Canadian market, and will carry the agency for Hovertrailers International Ltd.

LOW PRESSURE AIR INDUSTRIAL SYSTEMS

Design and consulting services are offered in the application of the hover principle, utilising low-pressure air for the movement of heavy and awkward loads over unprepared ground and to the solution of industrial lifting and transporting problems in general. This embraces air cushion systems engineering, and the design and manufacture of skirts. Out of this design development capability emerged the hovertrailer concept which has been developed significantly since 1971. Many hovertrailers have been built and sold in Europe, West Africa, Pakistan, Canada and elsewhere for pipelaying, movement of contractors plant and carriage of materials stores and equipment.

In conjunction with Hovertrailers, Air Cushion Equipment Ltd designed and built a system for the recovery of crashed aircraft on behalf of British Airways. This was demonstrated for the first time in March 1970.

The system of aircraft recovery equipment has been developed further and is now available for all jet aircraft in commercial use, up to Boeing 747, DC-10 and Concorde size.

The company is also working with Global Marine, the Los Angeles exploration, oil, gas and drilling contractors, on a project to float a complete oil drilling rig on air for use in the Canadian Arctic and Alaska. This development has resulted in the ACT 100, a 100-ton capacity (264-ton AUW) amphibious transporter, built in Edmonton, Alberta, Canada in 1971 and successfully tested there during the summer of that year. Subsequent Arctic trials at Yellowknife, Canadian N.W. Territories have been extremely successful and the skirt system, designed and built by ACE, worked without fault at temperatures below —50°F. Global Marine Inc (Los Angeles) handled the design of the air cushion transporters, while ACE designed and built the skirt system. The sales and operational aspects with respect to the arctic, are handled by Arctic Engineers & Constructors, a joint venture between Global Marine and Raymond International, New York City.

Larger transporters are under development by Arctic Engineers and Constructors.

In January 1973, it was announced that Air Cushion Equipment had been awarded a £50,000 contract by the U.K. Government to design, build and test a high pressure air cushion skirt system capable of lifting and moving a 1,000-ton load—the heaviest ever to be moved by this method. The object is to prove the ability of the system for handling such loads under conditions and in areas typical to the heavy construction, steel fabrication, civil engineering and shipbuilding industries.

Co-operating with ACE in the development of this new heavy lift system is Redpath Dorman Long, who are currently building a new yard at Methil on the Firth of Forth for the construction of North Sea oil rigs. They made available the required load in the form of a 50 ft sq by 20 ft high prestressed concrete structure.

The test programme has now been completed.

The latest development in air cushion technology, based on the ACE system, is a range of modular amphibious pontoon units with payloads of 30, 50, 75 and 100 tons. Available through Mackley-ACE Ltd, they provide transport equipment for container handling and other loads between ship and shore. These platforms make the transition between land and water without prepared slipways or other landing ramps. Mackley-ACE Ltd has also developed a launch and recovery air cushion system for dredgers, barges and other similar vessels.

AIR CUSHION MOVEMENT OF HEAVY INDIVISIBLE LOADS

The weight of large heavy loads such as transformers, stators, petro/chemical pressure vessels etc, has increased to the 300-500 ton range. This creates a major transport problem, whether in movement along the highway, in crossing weak bridges or in movement over unprepared surfaces. This is a universal problem, although the loads vary considerably in size and shape and the application can vary from crossing bridges and flyovers, to transferring from water to beach and grassland.

For operating on roads and bridges, Air Cushion Equipment have, in conjunction with Central Electricity Generating Board, developed a segmented skirt system, which can be clamped beneath a standard girder trailer and will operate at cushion pressures in excess of 5 psi. The neoprene/nylon skirt is assembled on a light framework which can be built up to any planform to suit the trailer. Skirt wear and dust are kept to a minimum by inserting a drag sheet (of polyurethane) between the segments and the road. Air, supplied by high pressure blowers, is fed directly into the cushion space to provide the cushion pressure, and adjustable vent valves enable multiple blowers to operate together at their optimum efficiency.

A typical load is a 350 ton transformer mounted on a fourteen axle girder trailer. A cushion system, acting at approximately 5 psi, gives an axle relief of 125 tons, significantly reducing the stresses in bridge structures. A system of this size is under development for the Central Electricity Generating Board, Two small gas turbines are being developed to provide the lift power for this equipment.

For operating over unprepared ground, the cushion pressures must be very much reduced. ACE is experimenting with a simplified form of skirt, which can be attached to a simple framework, with wheels on an oleo pneumatic suspension system at each corner, to provide stability and lateral control. With this platform, loads can be hovered off a simple barge onto a firm beach and winched directly onto a waterside site.

An air cushion supported road trailer. Employment of this equipment reduces axle loadings by as much as 50 per cent

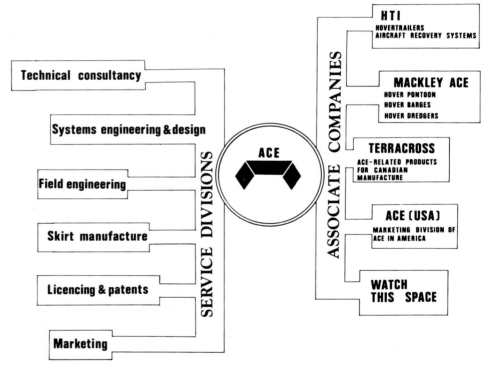

Air Cushion Equipment's operating divisions, associates and subsidiaries.

Cushion pressures will vary from 0·6 psi to 2·5 psi depending on the texture of the terrain to be crossed. Air is supplied by high grade centifugal fans, or mixed flow fans, according to the cushion pressure required and these are mounted directly on the platform.

Besides the movement of heavy factory-made equipment, other possible applications include hovering large concrete dock structures from the land into the sea, launching very large barge structures and positioning bridge components.

MOVEMENT OF OIL STORAGE TANKS

The fundamental component of the air cushion support system is the segmented skirt which not only maintains an air seal to contain the air cushion but also provides the necessary stability to enable the tank to be moved when on cushion. Advantage

has been taken of the individuality of the segments of the skirt to design a system which is adaptable to a large variety of tank, sizes, and within very broad limits, any size of tank may be accommodated within the scope of a standard skirt kit. The limiting factor is the ratio between tank diameter and hoverheight, as with increase in diameter a greater hoverheight is required to obtain the same capacity for negotiating changes in gradient. To some extent, this can be resolved by the introduction of a little more site preparation when a large tank is to be moved. Current design practice is to nominate the limiting diameters and use the skirt applicable for that size for all tanks below that datum. The largest tank moved to date was a 620-ton, 175 ft diameter oil storage tank at the Esso refinery in Antwerp. The operation, which entailed the resiting of this and seven other tanks, began in March 1973. The 620-ton tank was moved a distance of over 2,000 ft.

The method of attachment of the skirt is very simple and a fundamental concept of the design is that no welding is required to be done on site during any part of the move. A lower attachment rail is tensioned round the base of the tank in sections and to this the individual segments of the skirt are bolted. When more than one tank is to be moved on the same site. the attachment rails may be transferred from one tank to the next with all the segments in situ, thus making a considerable time saving. The tops of the segments are retained by a wire bond tensioned round the tank. Special segments are provided at appropriate intervals in the skirt to receive the air feed hoses. All manholes, outlets and drains can be accommodated within the skirt system and these are blanked off to prevent air transfer from the cushion into the tank.

When the setting up has been completed, air is fed into the skirt from mobile fans driven by diesel engines. Pressure is slowly built up in the skirt round the tank, and under this pressure, the air slowly percolates under the tank until sufficient pressure is obtained to lift the tank from its foundation. No jacking of the tank by mechanical means is required. Once lift off has been achieved and the tank has obtained the appropriate hoverheight, it is ballasted, if necessary, to compensate for out of balance items such as ladders, manholes and swing arms.

The tank, when ready, may be winched or towed to the new site. Changes of direction during the move are simple, it being necessary only to set the tank down, realign the towing bridle and the fans and travel in the new direction. Final location to within ± 2 in can be achieved without difficulty. While setting down, or at any other convenient time during the move, the tank may be rotated about its axis to align pipework.

Air Cushion Equipment Ltd is now initiating a world-wide service through licenced contractors. Appointed contractors include:

Mears Construction Ltd (UK and W. Europe) Sydenham, London, and Brocklesby Transport Ltd (Canada, of Toronto and Montreal)

TANK ROOF LIFT SYSTEM

Air Cushion Equipment Ltd, in conjunction with Whessoe, has developed an application of the segmented seal which enables large unsupported arched tank roofs to be raised pneumatically after the construction of the tank's sidewalls.

The system allows the free span roof to be constructed at ground level prior to the erection of the tank. On the completion of the tank shell the roof is lifted pneumatically to the top, where it is held on a cushion of air while the roof rafters are bolted or welded onto the stub connections already attached to the shell of the tank.

The low air loss and fine control permit movements up and down by increments of $\frac{1}{8}$ in, allowing holes in the rafters and stubs to be aligned.

As a safety precaution in the event of engine failure while the roof is being raised, four special segmented non-return valves are built into the feedlines at the point of air entry into the tank shell. These close automatically when the pressure under the roof exceeds the pressure of the air delivered from the fan.

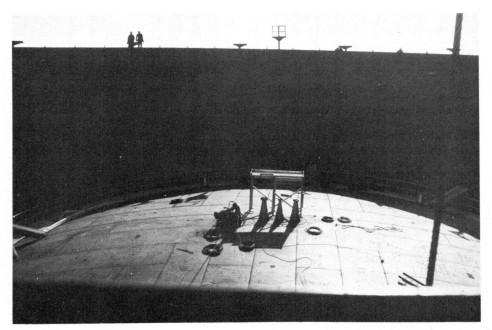

Top: Roof of a liquid petroleum gas tank approaching the top. The roof of this particular tank roof weighed 230 tons.
Centre: Seen in this photograph is the skirt seal and one of the stub connections on the inner face of the tank shell onto which the roof rafters are bolted or welded. Fine control of the cushion pressure permitted the roof to be raised or lowered by increments of $\frac{1}{8}$ in to facilitate bolting
Bottom: Segments of neoprene/nylon mounted on special frames suspended from the inner roof

The first application of this system was the raising of the 148 ft diameter roof on a 150 ft high LPG (liquid petroleum gas) tank.

BHC
BRITISH HOVERCRAFT CORPORATION

HEAD OFFICE:
Osborne, East Cowes, Isle of Wight

DIRECTORS:
See ACV Section

AIR CUSHION HEAVY LOAD TRANSPORTER (AIR CUSHION EQUIPMENT SERIES I)

The development of this equipment was prompted initially by the Central Electricity Generating Board, which is constantly faced with route-planning problems caused by the high weights of laden transporters.

Transformer units now going into service weigh between 155 and 250 tons and 400-ton units are in prospect. On occasion the CEGB has been involved in the heavy expense of strengthening and even rebuilding bridges to accept these loads when no alternative route has been available.

The use of air-cushion equipment, however, provides a practical and economic alternative. By providing an air-cushion under the centre section of an existing transporter it is possible to support a high proportion of its gross weight. Distributing the gross load over the whole length of the transporter reduces the bending movements and sheer force imposed on bridges so that these heavy transformers can be transported without risk over existing bridges.

The investigation into and development of this air-cushion transporter has been supported by the CEGB with the co-operation of the Ministry of Transport and the road haulage companies that operate the transporters.

The transporter illustrated has a length of 90 ft (27·4 m) and a maximum width of 16 ft 10 in (5·13 m). The payload is normally supported between two bogies each of which may have up to 48 wheels.

The skirt containing the air cushion is an easily handled unit which is fitted under the load and side beams of the trailer. Any spaces between the load and trailer frame are 'timbered -in' to take the upward thrust.

This type of skirt system can be built to suit any size of transporter and the one illustrated measures 32 ft (9·57 m) × 14 ft (4·26 m). It is constructed largely of nylon/neoprene sheet extending across the underside of the load platform and formed into a bellows around its periphery. To the bottom of the bellows is attached a series of plates

The CEGB Heavy Load Transporter crossing Felin Puleston Bridge, Wrexham, with a 155-ton load

each about 1 ft (0·30 m) long, which make contact with the road surface. Thus, the only escape route for air from the cushion is through the small gap formed between the plates and the ground by the roughness of the surface.

Any general unevenness of the surface, such as the camber of a road or the hump of a bridge, causes the bellows of the 'skirt' to flex so that the plates can remain in contact with the road.

The cushion was designed for a 155-ton lift, when the cushion pressure reaches 5·4 pounds per square inch. At this pressure, when moving over the roughest road surfaces, the volume of air escaping from underneath the shoes is approximately 13,200 cu ft/min (373·5 m³/min) (free air volume flow).

The power to maintain the air cushion is provided by four Rolls-Royce B81SV petrol engines delivering 235 hp (gross) at 4,000 rpm. Each engine drives, through a gearbox, its own centrifugal compressor, with engine, gearbox and compressor mounted together on a steel underbed as a complete working unit. The four units supplying the power are

built onto a road vehicle chassis. This vehicle, which also contains stowage space for the folded cushion container, is attached to the rear of the transporter train whenever it is required for a bridge crossing. It is connected to the air cushion through four, 1 ft diameter air ducts, each connected to a power unit. The ducts are connected by sections of flexible hose to allow for relative movement between the vehicles.

The first commercial load carried by the transporter was a 155-ton transformer for delivery to the Central Electricity Board's sub-station at Legacy, near Wrexham, from the A.E.I. Transformer Division Works at Wythenshawe, Manchester. The route involved crossing the Felin Puleston Bridge which, under normal circumstances, was incapable of withstanding the combined weight of the transporter and the transformer. By using the air cushion to relieve the load on the transporter's wheels the stress on the bridge was reduced by about 70 tons.

Had a conventional transporter been used the bridge would have had to be strengthened at a cost equal to about half the cost of developing and equipping the transporter.

HOVERTRAILERS INTERNATIONAL LIMITED

HEAD OFFICE:
Lower William Street, Northam, Southampton, SO9 2DN

TELEPHONE:
Southampton 21271

CABLES:
47106 Hovetrail Soton

DIRECTORS:
C. S. Richards, Managing Director
J. F. Dibben
G. P. P. Schwerdt
T. C. A. Horn
G. M. Parkes

SENIOR EXECUTIVES:
D. Williamson, Marketing Manager
I. R. Bristow, Technical Manager

System of hover platforms and inflatable air bags being employed to recover an RAF Hastings transport aircraft

Hovertrailers International was formed early in 1970 under a joint venture agreement between United Builders Merchants Limited and Air Cushion Equipment Limited. Its purpose is to specialise in the development, construction and marketing of a range of non-self propelled air cushion vehicles capable of traversing undeveloped ground, particularly marsh, bog, mudflats, ploughland and construction wayleaves.

Hovertrailers convey heavy loads over terrain impassable to wheeled and tracked vehicles under load, and can be used in widely varying application fields, from civil engineering, pipe or cable laying, forestry work, geological and mineral surveying to agricultural, conservation or drainage schemes.

The basic structure is a rigid rectangular steel platform, with a strong welded subframe, to which a flexible segmented skirt is attached. The vehicle is supported by low pressure air, the lift power being provided by a centrifugal fan coupled to a petrol or diesel power unit mounted at the rear of the hovertrailer.

Hoverheight varies between 0·46 m (1 ft 6 in) and 0·71 m (2 ft 5 in), depending on the design of the vehicle. The units are easily manoeuvred, and the drawbar pull is very low. All types of terrain can be negotiated, including side slopes. Wheels fitted to swinging arms at the rear of most models give directional control on slopes and when reversing.

All vehicles are designed so that they may be linked together side by side in order to transport awkward loads with a high centre of gravity, and special purpose vehicles, such as pipe carriers, are available. Trailers of up to 100 tons capacity can be supplied for general purpose use in the civil engineering, contracting and allied industries.

Since the company was formed, hovertrailers have been sold in the United Kingdom, Europe, Africa, Asia, North America and South America.

AIRCRAFT RECOVERY SYSTEM

The company also markets an aircraft recovery system capable of recovering civil and military aircraft up to the size and weight of the Boeing 747. The system is of modular construction so that it can be transported in a standard Boeing 707 airfreighter. The advantage of the system is that the recovery can be undertaken quickly, regardless of the condition of the ground surface, also secondary damage to the aircraft is reduced to a minimum, and in some cases is non-existent.

The prototype system was demonstrated at London Heathrow Airport in 1970, and production units were evaluated by the Ministry of Defence at Bicester RAF station in 1973. During these tests a Hastings aircraft was manoeuvred over soft ground and hovered across the airfield at speeds of up to 16 km/h (10 mph).

In March 1974 the system was demonstrated

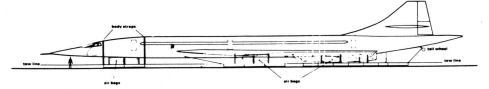

Drawing showing how hover platforms and air bags would be positioned to recover a Concorde airliner

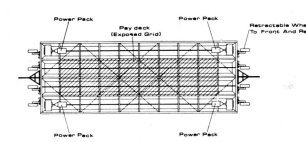

SPECIFICATION

Overall Length (Structure)	105' 0" 32·00m
Overall Width (Structure)	40' 0" 12·19m
Payload	224,000 lbs 101,605 kg
Power	four diesel engines and fans

A standard 100-ton capacity hovertrailer

A hovertrailer loaded with six 12·19 m (40 ft) by 0·68 m (3 ft) diameter pipes crossing soft sand

at Gatwick Airport under operational conditions. A Britannia airliner was hovered over soft ground for nearly a mile, and at one point crossed a 20 ft (6·09 m) wide drainage ditch on a bridge constructed of light steel beams and plywood sheets. This was possible because of the low ground bearing pressure of the air cushion system. Both

hovertrailers and aircraft recovery systems operate at less than 1 psi.

Almost any form of towing vehicle or winching equipment may be used in conjunction with the range of hovertrailers and the aircraft recovery system. For extremely marshy conditions, the use of fully-tracked low ground pressure vehicles is advised.

MACKLEY-ACE LTD

HEAD OFFICE:
421/427 Millbrook Road, Southampton
SO1 3HY
TELEPHONE:
0703 781844
TELEX:
477434 Mackace Soton

DIRECTORS:
D. G. W. Turner (Managing)
J. R. Mackley (Chairman)
F. R. Mackley, CEng, FICE
L. A. Hopkins, CEng. AFRAeS
W. A. Melhuish (Secretary)
Mackley-Ace Ltd specialises in the design and construction of hoverplatforms and has

helped to build the world's first hover dredger.

In May 1974 it was announced that this company is designing and building two air cushion transporters for operation in the Arabian Gulf. The craft will have an all-up weight of 730-750 tons and a 250-ton payload capacity.

750-TON ACT

Two of these craft have been ordered by Bechtel International Ltd, London, in association with Chiyoda Chemical Engineering & Construction Co Ltd.

They are being built in the sheikdom of Abu Dhabi and the first was due to be launched in June 1974. The second craft will follow in September.

They will be employed to carry prefabricated sections of a liquid natural gas plant (LNG) from a fabrication site at Abu Dhabi, to the installation site at Das Island, a distance of 110 miles (177·02 m).

The work is being undertaken on behalf of the Abu Dhabi Gas Liquification Co Ltd.

The ACTs will be towed from the mainland to the island, and then pulled by crawler tractors half a mile (0·81 km) inland across rocks and sand to the construction site, where the prefabricated components will be lifted directly on to their foundations by crane.

LIFT SYSTEM: Cushion lift will be supplied by two 890 hp MWM TBD 602 V12 diesels, each driving a 4 ft 7 in (1·39 m) diameter Alldays Peacock 1,400 BA DIDW centrifugal fan. Each fan delivers 135,000 cu ft (3,823 cu m) of air per minute, giving a cushion pressure of 1 lb sq in (0·7 kg m²).

SKIRT: 4 ft (1·21 m) deep, open segment type, with double segments aft and an anti-spray flap.

BALLAST: A seawater ballast system is fitted to permit the craft to be employed as ship-to-shore transporters.

DECK EQUIPMENT: Two 10-ton hydraulic winches are fitted at the bow for loading plant components, which will either be mounted on rollers or hoverpallets. Twin hydraulic capstans are located amidships for use during mooring, manoeuvring and anchoring.

ACCOMMODATION: Elevated bridge and quarters forward for a five-man crew.

DIMENSIONS:

Length overall	180 ft 0 in (58·46 m)
Beam overall	80 ft 0 in (24·38 m)
Length, load deck	158 ft 0 in (48·16 m)
Beam, load deck	52 ft 0 in (15·85 m)
Height on cushion	32·70 ft (9·94 m)
Height off cushion	28·70 ft (8·72 m)

WEIGHTS:

All-up weight	730-750 tons
Payload	250 tons

PERFORMANCE, FULLY LOADED:
Calm water, towing force of 15 tons
7 knots
In 9 ft (2·74 m) high by 250 ft (76·20 m) long waves
3 knots

HOVERPLATFORMS

Mackley-Ace hoverplatform designs have ranged in payload capacity from 30-95 tons.

Based on the standard Uniflote pontoon, each platform can be expanded or contracted to suit particular requirements.

Specially fabricated skirt frames are cantilevered off the side of the Uniflote pontoons. The neoprene-coated nylon weave is attached beneath these frames to protect it against accidental damage.

Each frame has its own skirt section attached and is quickly replaced if damaged. The self-contained power packs to power the lift system are also mounted on the skirt frames, leaving the deck area clear.

Unskilled contracting labour can handle

A Mk I Hoverplatform working over deep mud in the Wash estuary

Impression of the new 250-ton capacity hover transporter designed and built by Mackley-Ace for operation in the Arabian Gulf. Two of these craft will be employed to carry LNG plant modules from Abu Dhabi to Das Island

A hover platform, carrying surveying equipment, being towed ashore

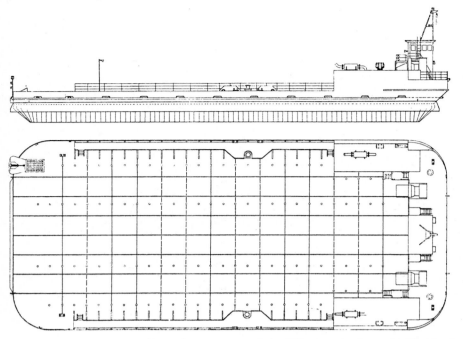
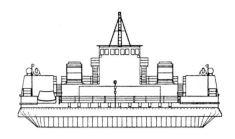

General arrangement of the 250-ton payload capacity Mackley-Ace hover transporter

and assemble the platforms on site. The platforms are normally winched or towed, although it is possible to propel them with suitable outboard motors such as Harbormasters. During 1975, specifications of a new range of self-propelled hover platforms should be completed.

HOVERDREDGERS

Further development work is being undertaken on larger cutter suction hover dredgers.

Mackley-Ace's original air cushion dredger was a 114 ton purpose-built machine with a 12-in cutter. Capable of dredging to a depth of 25 feet, it could dredge 250 cu yds of sludge an hour, discharging through a 12 in pipe to a maximum distance of 3,000 ft.

The company is also able to convert conventional dredgers to air cushion types and now offers a specialist consultancy service in this field.

MEARS CONSTRUCTION LIMITED

HEAD OFFICE:
  154-158, Sydenham Road, London, SE26 5LA
TELEPHONE:
  01-659-3371
TELEX:
  947157
EXECUTIVES:
  R. W. Bale, BSc, CEng, FICE, Director-in-Charge Air Cushion Division
  P. F. Morgan, Manager, Air Cushion Division

Mears Construction Limited holds the franchise for Air Cushion Equipment Ltd's system of tank moving throughout the U.K., Western Europe and part of the Middle East.

The service is available on a four-phase basis, comprising a desk study, and a site survey followed by the shipment of equipment and the moving operation.

The equipment consists of a wrap-around segmented skirt, together with air supply fans, motors and ducting, all of which can be readily shipped to sites anywhere in the above territories.

Site surveys are undertaken by a Mears engineer in conjunction with an appointed local contractor. The local contractor provides non-specialist plant and equipment for the move, Mears provides the lift equipment, and each move is undertaken as a joint venture under the direct control of a Mears engineer.

A 175 ft (53 m) diameter tank, weighing 620 tons, relocated for Esso at their refinery in Antwerp in 1973. This is the largest and heaviest load lifted and solely supported by air during movement to date. The technique employed by Mears Construction Ltd is shown in the accompanying diagram

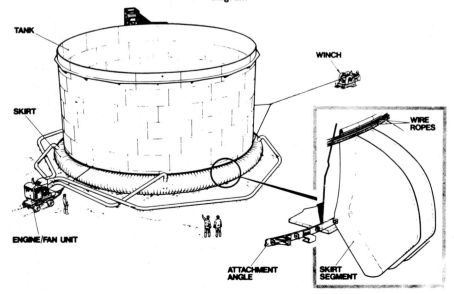

ROBERT TRILLO LIMITED

HEAD OFFICE:

Broadlands, Brockenhurst, Hampshire
SO4 7SX

TELEPHONE:

Brockenhurst 2220

Robert Trillo Limited is UK representative for A/S Seiga Harvester Company Limited, Copenhagen, manufacturer of the Seiga Tortoise multiterrain vehicle. The vehicle is suitable not only as a tug for hovertrailers, but also as a support vehicle for large hover-platforms.

SEIGA TORTOISE

The Seiga Tortoise is an amphibious transporter capable of negotiating swamps, soft earth, mud banks, sand, snow and open water. Special low pressure tyres are fitted to avoid damage to vegetation and enable the vehicle to roll fully-loaded from land to water or vice versa. The vehicle has hydraulic load tilting facility.

POWER PLANT: Motive power is supplied by either a 30 hp Volkswagen VW Type 124 petrol engine or Lombardini Type LDA 673 diesel, air-cooled, 3 cyl engine, delivering 36 hp at 3,000 rpm. Clutch is of dry single plate type. Gear rear-axle assembly is Type VW Type 002 300 041 D, with 4 forward and 1 reverse gear. Gear ratio is 1: 3·80; 2: 2·06; 3: 1·22; 4: 0·82; R: 3·88. A gear-wheel pump, 3 cm³/rev is fitted.

SYSTEMS: Electrical: 12 volt, two headlights 5·1 in (130 mm), Oil pressure control, battery charging control, light switch (ignition switch), push-button starter, hourmeter, battery.

CONTROLS: The front wheel drive is directly from a differential box by chain-drive, a 1 in (2·5 cm) roller-chain. Gear ratio 1:9. Rear-wheel drive is synchronized hydraulically by two closed circuit systems. Steering is hydraulically assisted and employs two pistons working on turn-tabled back-wheels. Each front wheel is braked separately by conventional drums and linings.

DIMENSIONS, EXTERNAL:

Length	16 ft 5 in (5·0 m)
Width	10 ft 2 in (3·1 m)
Height	5 ft 7 in (1·7 m)

Seiga Tortoise, a multiterrain vehicle which is to be employed as a tug for hovertrailers and as a support vehicle for large hover platforms

DIMENSIONS, PLATFORM:

Length	13 ft 1 in (4·0 m)
Width	10 ft 2 in (3·1 m)
Height above ground	4 ft 7 in (1·4 m)

DIMENSIONS, WHEEL:

Diameter	3 ft 11 in (1·2 m)
Width	3 ft 3½ in (1·0 m)
Cubage	46 ft³ (1·3 m³)

All 4 wheels with 1·38 in (35 mm) tread (rib) tubeless tyres, repaired externally.

Wheelbase	8 ft 2½ in (2·5 m)

WEIGHTS:

Weight	1·275 tons (2,860 lb) (1,300 kg)

Ground pressure:

unloaded	0·6 lb/in² (0·04 kg/cm²)
loaded	1·2 lb/in² (0·08 kg/cm²)
Ground clearance	1·3 ft (0·40 m)

Load capacity   2,200 lb (1,000 kg) over water; greater over land

PERFORMANCE:

Towing capacity on soft grass field, unloaded, 2,530 lb (1,150 kg) tow-bar pull on soft grass field, loaded with 1,096 lb (500 kg) on front wheels, 3,070 lb (1,400 kg) tow-bar pull

Speeds over land: at 3,000 rpm (centrifugal regulator)

1st gear 2·3 mph (3·6 km/h) 16 wheel rpm 400 rev/mile 250 rev/km

2nd gear 4·3 mph (6·7 km/h) 30 wheel rpm 400 rev/mile 250 rev/km

3rd gear 7·0 mph (11·0 km/h) 49 wheel rpm 400 rev/mile 250 rev/km

4th gear 10·6 mph (17·0 km/h) 75 wheel rpm 400 rev/mile 250 rev/km

Rev gear 2·5 mph (3·8 km/h) 17 wheel rpm 400 rev/mile 250 rev/km

THE UNITED STATES OF AMERICA

ARCTIC ENGINEERS AND CONSTRUCTORS

HEAD OFFICE:

1770 St. James Place, Suite 512, Houston, Texas 77027

TELEPHONE: (713) 626-9773

CABLES: ARENCO

TELEX: 762587

EXECUTIVES:

O. D. Blankenship, General Manager

E. O. Anders, Chief Engineer

R. G. Longaker, Manager Icebreaking Systems

ASSOCIATED COMPANIES:

Arctic Systems, Calgary, Alberta, Canada

Terracross Limited, Montreal, Quebec, Canada

Arctic Engineers and Constructors, a joint venture of Global Marine Inc of Los Angeles and Raymond International Inc of Houston, was formed to create a single company with the capability and experience to offer a complete construction and drilling service to the petroleum industry in the arctic.

The ACT-100 air cushion transporter operating north of Inuvik on the Mackenzie River in March 1974

Prior to the formation of Arctic E&C, engineers of the two parent companies had conducted an extensive environment, design, equipment and engineering study of the problems involved in the search for and production of petroleum in the arctic. The study's objective was to analyse and define the operational problems encountered both onshore and offshore. It included analyses of climate, ice properties and distribution, land and air transport vehicles, drilling and construction, transportable arctic housing, and past and present arctic drilling operations.

It was concluded that air cushion transporters, used on a year-round basis, would offer substantial economic and technical advantages in arctic drilling, construction, and transportation.

The company's air cushion transporters are designed to transport heavy equipment and as a foundation support for drilling and construction equipment. The transporters are non-self-propelled and of simple robust construction for ease of operation and maintenance. The company designs air cushion transporters to suit specific operations. It owns and operates the transporters under contract to its clients.

Apart from its activities in the development and exploitation of air cushion transporters, the company has also developed an air-cushion assisted Arctic Marine Pipelay System (AMPS) and a unique ice breaking attachment for conventional ships. By linking a VIBAC craft (Vehicle, Ice Breaking, Air Cushion) to the bow of a conventional ship, the ship's ice passage ability is greatly enhanced.

A further development is the company's Pneumatically Induced Pitching System (PIPS) which significantly improves a vessels icebreaking ability by inducing large amplitude pitching at the natural frequency of a given hull.

The company is licenced by Hovercraft Development Ltd and retains Air Cushion Equipment Ltd of Southampton as consultants for skirt design.

ACT-100

Construction of the prototype ACT-100 was completed in April 1971. The craft is essentially an ACV barge designed to transport 100-ton payloads throughout the year across arctic tundra, muskeg and marsh without unduly disturbing the soil and vegetation. It will also traverse offshore ice and open water.

Five months of testing under arctic winter conditions on the Great Slave Lake at Yellowknife during 1971-72 demonstrated that the craft is able to operate in temperatures of —50 deg F without difficulty. It proved extremely stable and manoeuvrable when travelling over level terrain, slopes, water, and over varying thicknesses of ice. It also showed unusual icebreaking ability in thicknesses up to 660 mm (26 in) and had no difficulty in traversing broken ice.

The Canadian Ministry of Transport employed the ACT-100 under contract to investigate the feasibility of operating air cushion ferries in the Mackenzie River highway system. Initial trials were conducted at Tuktoyaktuk, NWT, in November 1972. The craft was towed 322 km (200 miles) up the Mackenzie for final ferry trials at Arctic Red River in June 1973.

Impression of the 3,840-ton ADS, designed to carry a complete offshore drilling system

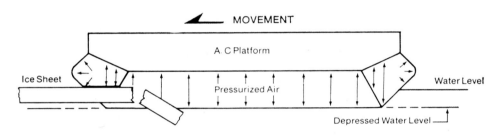

Action of the air cushion platform when an ice sheet is encountered. On contact, the skirt rises above the ice, continuing to act as an air seal. The ice sheet then loses its flotation support from below as the water beneath it is depressed by the cushion of pressurised air within the skirt zone. The ice sheet then becomes a cantilevered ledge and on reaching its critical length breaks, and the overhang section falls off into the displaced water below. The arrows in the drawing above show the force vectors within the skirt

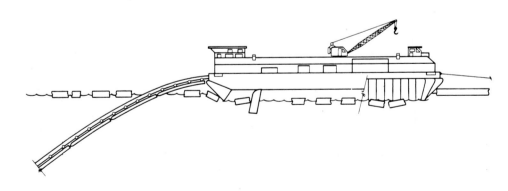

Side view of the Arctic Marine Pipelaying System, which will act as a combined ice-breaker and pipelaying barge. Conventional pipelaying barges are unable to operate in ice covered water. The AMPS will be able to operate in ice, thus greatly extending the limited northern working season

In December 1973 the ACT-100 was employed by Imperial Oil Ltd to transport drill rig supplies and equipment from Langley Island to Adgo Island. Adgo is an expendable artificial island constructed by Imperial in the Beaufort Sea to support an exploratory drilling operation. The ACT-100 carried loads of up to 99·8 tons over ice, broken ice, and water.

LIFT: Cushion air is supplied by two 640 hp Caterpillar D-348 diesel engines driving two 4 ft 6¼ in (1·37 m) diameter Joy 5425 N.O.L. steel centrifugal fans. Air is fed directly into the cushion without ducting. Cushion pressure is 144 psf. Diesel is contained in a single 500 US gal integral tank in the main hull amidships.

CONTROLS: Towing cables to pull vehicle and wheels beneath center of hull. A liquid ballast is provided for trim.

HULL: Box-type hull in A537 low temperature alloy steel. Hull is designed to support

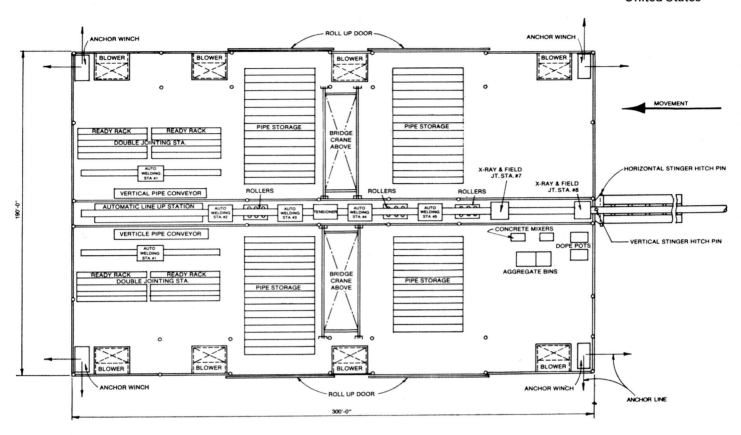

Operating deck of the Arctic Marine Pipelayer System (AMPS) showing the pipe handling equipment located beneath the winterisation covering which will maintain the work area at temperatures well above freezing

a 100-ton payload.

SKIRT: 1·52 m (5 ft) deep fully segmented skirt in rubber-coated nylon.

CREW: Control cabin accommodates one operator and assistant. A third member of the operating crew is the towing vehicle operator.

ACCOMMODATION: A "habitat" unit, with complete camp facilities for 35-40 men and storage facilities, can be mounted on the hull.

SYSTEMS: 110/220 volt, 60 cycle 30 kW generator for lighting, control and pumping.

COMMUNICATIONS: None permanently installed.

DIMENSIONS:

Length overall:	
power off	23·71 m (75 ft 3⅜ in)
skirt inflated	24·15 m (79 ft 3 in)
Beam overall:	
power off	13·74 m (57 ft 0⅜ in)
skirt inflated	18·59 m (61 ft 0 in)
Height overall:	
power off	1·98 m (6 ft 6 in)
skirt inflated	3·20 m (10 ft 6 in)
Draft afloat	1·04 m (3 ft 5 in)
Cushion area	308·068 m² (3,316 sq ft)
Skirt depth	1·52 m (5 ft 0 in)

CONTROL CABIN:

Length	2·43 m (8 ft 0 in)
Max width	2·74 m (9 ft 0 in)
Max height	2·43 m (8 ft 0 in)
Floor area	6·89 m² (72 sq ft)

FREIGHT HOLDS: Open deck, with tankage available beneath.

WEIGHTS:

Normal empty weight	150 US tons
Normal all-up weight	250 US tons
Normal payload	100 US tons
Max payload	130 US tons

PERFORMANCE (at normal operating weight):

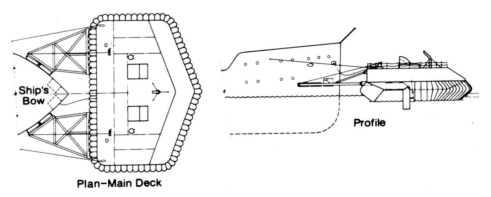

Plan–Main Deck

Profile

The VIBAC air cushion ice-breaking applicator unit designed for attachment to conventional ships travelling through Arctic waters. The unit was an outcome of experience with the ACT-100 in the Mackenzie River where it continuously broke ice as thick as 27 in (0.685 m)

Speed (dependent on tow vehicle)
    6 mph (9·65 km/h) plus
Still air range and endurance at cruising speed: 12 hours at average speed of 9·65 km/h (6 mph) = 115·87 km (72 miles)
Vertical obstacle clearance
    1·21 m (4 ft 0 in)

ADS

The company's latest vehicle—the ADS (Arctic Drilling System) combines a large air cushion barge with modern offshore drilling equipment and an ice-melting positioning system. It is designed for arctic offshore use.

The system offers two important advantages: (1) the complete drilling system can move between locations at any time during the summer or winter, and (2) the unit can remain over the well bore in ice moving at moderate speeds.

The three basic components of the ADS are:

(1) a large 70·4 by 43·7 by 4·5 m (231 by 143·5 by 15 ft) self-contained, shallow-draft aluminium drilling hull.

(2) an air-cushion system capable of lifting the hull—complete with drilling, crew, and drilling expendables—2·59 m (8·5 ft) above the surface.

(3) an external hull heating system capable of melting a ledge of ice moving from any direction at a rate of 4·57 m (15 ft) per day, using waste heat from the engines.

Design of the ADS is 95% complete. The unit, with a gross weight of 3,840 long tons, is designed to operate in land-fast ice in water depths from 0-183 m (0 to 600 ft) during the 7-8 month arctic winter season and in water depths of 9·14-183 m (30 to 600 ft) during the open-water summer season. The ADS is designed to operate in nearshore conditions in the Beaufort Sea at the Mackenzie Delta, the Alaskan North Slope, and the inter-island areas of the Canadian Arctic Islands. It could be used in any arctic land-fast ice areas including the continental shelves of Greenland and Siberia.

ARCTIC MARINE PIPELAYER SYSTEM (AMPS)

A combined air cushion pipelaying barge and icebreaker is being designed by Arctic Engineers and Constructors for Arctic operations.

The concept is the result of extensive tests which proved that air cushion platforms are able to carry exceptionally heavy loads over all types of arctic surfaces and break ice over water.

The barge, which will have a gross weight of 6,000 tons, will be capable of laying pipes of up to 48 in (1·21 m) diameter in waters that are either covered in ice up to 7 ft (2·13 m) deep—or ice-free. Typical areas in which craft of this type could be employed are Prudhoe Bay, Mackenzie Delta, the Canadian Archipelago and the continental shelves of Siberia and Greenland.

The barge, known as the Arctic Marine Pipelay System, will operate at an air pressure of 2 psi and the total lifting force will be in excess of 7,000 tons.

LIFT AND PROPULSION: Cushion lift will be provided by diesel engines developing in excess of 8,000 hp and driving eight fans rated at 85,000 cfm. The skirt, fabricated in rubber-coated nylon, will be 8 ft 6 in (2·59 m) deep. During ice-free periods the skirt and cushion lift system would be removed and the craft would be operated as a conventional pipelaying barge.

Propulsion would involve the use of an on-board winch pulling a cable attached to a conventional bottom anchor system in open

water and an ice-anchor system while operating over ice. These will provide the forward pull rate which will be governed by the speed needed for welding joints.

Forward speed when travelling without pipelaying in progress would be 1-2 mph (1·60-3·21 km/h).

HULL: Aluminium barge-type construction 300 ft long, 190 ft wide and 15 ft deep (91·44 m × 57·91 m × 4·57 m). A centreline lay system would be employed using a gantry or bridge-type crane handling pipe joints from storage to the double-joint make-up line.

ACCOMMODATION: Entire operating deck will be protected by a winterisation enclosure which will maintain the work area at temperatures well above freezing. Complete crew quarters for a full complement of more than 100 men will be located within the hull structure.

SYSTEMS, PIPE LAYING:

It is estimated that 48 in pipe could be laid at 2,400 ft per 24 hour day using manual welding. This could be increased by 30-40% if automatic welding processes were introduced. Provision would be made to employ double-jointing before setting out, so that the craft would move 80 ft at a time instead of the normal 40 ft.

The use of two ACV barge units in tandem is envisaged, with a connecting gantry bridge, to control the lowering of pipelines in waters with depths below 400 ft.

The ACV system permits pipe-laying when the water depth is less than the barge's floating depth. This means it can be employed over marshland, swamps and inland areas where the terrain is reasonably flat.

DIMENSIONS:

Length overall	300 ft (91·44 m)
Beam overall	190 ft (57·91 m)
Depth, hull	

structure	15 ft (4·57 m)
cushion depth	8 ft 6 in (2·59 m)

WEIGHTS:

Hull-to-deck	1,100 tons
Superstructure	250 tons
Power plant	350 tons
Supplies	400 tons
Service and misc. equipment	600 tons
Pipeline equipment	500 tons
Stored pipe, 48 in diameter	2,800 tons
Gross weight	6,000 tons
Safety margin for overload including ice and snow	1,000 tons
Lifting force	7,000 tons

VEHICLE, ICE-BREAKING, AIR-CUSHION (VIBAC)

The icebreaking characteristics of the ACT-100 has led to the development of a new vehicle designed specifically to aid the passage of a conventional ship through ice-bound waters.

The craft, known as the VIBAC system, is attached to the bow of the ship as soon as it enters an ice-field. Close visual observation and films have revealed what happens when air cushion platform approaches an ice sheet, and how the air cushion ice-breaking phenomenon takes place.

On making contact with the ice sheet the skirt rises up over the ice while continuing to maintain its air seal. The ice sheet then penetrates the zone of pressurized air beneath the craft, where the water level with the skirt area is depressed to a lower level than the bottom of the ice layer. The ice has now become a cantilevered ledge without water support beneath. When the cantilevered section reaches its critical length, failure occurs and the overhanging section breaks off and falls in to the depressed water below.

A plough like deflector attached to the VIBAC unit will thrust the ice aside as the vessel progresses through the ice sheet.

EGLEN HOVERCRAFT INC

HEAD OFFICE:
   801 Poplar Street, Terre Haute, Indiana
   47807
TELEPHONE:
   (812) 234 4307

TERREHOVER

In February 1973 Eglen Hovercraft Inc designed and built a prototype hover platform, in order to investigate possible agricultural applications. Particular attention is being given to its use for transporting heavy loads, including fertilizer tanks, over wet and muddy fields which cannot be negotiated by conventional farm equipment.

The prototype Terrehover is built in wood and measures 16 ft (4·87 m) long by 8 ft (2·43 m) wide. Air is put under pressure by two 2 ft (0·60 m) diameter axial-flow fans, driven by two JLO Rockwell L395 two-cycle engines. An H.D.L. type segmented skirt is used and the hoverheight is 9 in (228 mm).

Although designed originally to lift 2,000 lb (907·18 kg) the platform has successfully lifted 4,000 lb (1,814·37 kg), and has applied fertilizer in conditions normally considered too severe for conventional fertilizing equipment. The prototype is towed by another vehicle with low pressure tyres, but the production version will be self-propelled, with the operator housed in a cab mounted

The prototype Eglen Terrehover, a 16 ft (4·87 m) long hover platform, designed for carrying agricultural equipment over wet and muddy terrain. Production models will be self-propelled, with the operator seated in an enclosed cabin

on the platform. Two centrifugal fans, powered by a small diesel engine, will be used and the engine will also drive an hydraulic pump which will power a hydrostatic motor for propulsion.

The vehicle will be capable of highway

operation, riding on wheels which will be retracted while in the hovering mode.

At the time of going to press negotiations were under way for a joint development programme with an agricultural equipment company.

UNION OF SOVIET SOCIALIST REPUBLICS

ALL-UNION OIL MACHINERY RESEARCH INSTITUTE, WEST SIBERIA
(VNII neftmash)

HEAD OFFICE: Tyumen

DIRECTOR:
  A. V. Vladimirskii

EXECUTIVE:
  V. A. Shibanov, Head of Air Cushion Vehicle Department

Air cushion platforms with load capacities of up to 200 tons have been under development in the West Siberian lowlands since 1965. Some 80% of the gas and petroleum sites in this area are located amidst almost impassable swamps, salt marshes, taiga and stretches of water.

In the Tyumensk area, where deep wells are being drilled, more than 200 tons of support equipment are required at each site in addition to between 130-180 tons of drilling gear. In 1965, a group of ACV engineers and designers headed by V. A. Shibanov left the Urals for Tyumen to apply their efforts to the design of a hoverplatform capable of carrying a complete oil rig across tundra and taiga, and also to the design and construction of an all-terrain vehicle capable of towing the drilling rig, on hover, to the drilling sites.

Small scale models were employed by the group during the development stages, and several attempts were made before a completely satisfactory design was conceived.

The most successful arrangement—the BU-75-VP—is illustrated. It comprises a rectangular, all-metal buoyancy raft (the load carrying member), with side structures to carry a bag-type skirt. A derrick, derived from a standard BU-75 drilling rig, was mounted on the central raft, and the drilling pump, generally delivered to sites separately, was also installed on board. Apart from specialist items of oil drilling gear, the platform is equipped with lift fans and drilling engines which serve a dual purpose by driving the lift fans when the platform is changing location.

Two tractors are normally required to tow the platform in a fully loaded condition.

Transport and routing problems are now greatly simplified as the need to detour virtually impassable lakes, marshes, and snow or water-filled ravines no longer arises. The rig has been employed in oilfields at Shaimskoye, Urai and Samotlor.

A more recent design has been undergoing tests at the Strezhevoye workings at Alexandrov field in the Tomsk region. Large ACV rigs with a capacity of several thousand tons are under development.

BU-75-VP

DIMENSIONS:
  Length   98·43 ft (30 m)
  Width   65·62 ft (20 m)
WEIGHTS:
  All-up weight   170 tonnes
PERFORMANCE:
  Speed (depending on towing vehicle)
                   About 6 mph (9·65 km/h)

ACV TRAILERS

Three ACV trailers are being developed by the organisation—a six-ton platform, the PVP-40 with a cargo capacity of 40 tonnes and a larger derivative with a capacity of

Line cutaway of the BU-75-VP oil rig, the first in the world to be mounted on an air-cushion platform

PVP-40 air cushion trailer undergoing field tests. The trailer, which has a load capacity of 40-tons, is designed for carrying heavy, single-piece cargoes and machines, drilling and oil-production equipment in the difficult and marshy terrain of Russia's Northern regions·

60 tonnes. The PVP-40 has been undergoing state acceptance trials in Surgut and the Soviet Far North and if put into production will be employed in the construction of oil installations, pipelines, by geological surveys and on drainage and irrigation schemes.

The PVP-40 is powered by a single diesel engine driving two centrifugal fans. Its 60-ton counterpart is powered by a single gas-turbine driving twin axial-flow fans. Discs or wheels fitted to swinging arms at the rear provide directional control when reversing. "Trains" of ACV trailers can be employed to carry heavy loads and a further development is an articulated trailer, several times the length of platforms like the PVP-40, with one tractor forward and another at the rear.

ACV TRACTORS

Towing requirements for the rigs and ACV Trailers built in Tyumen were at first met by conventional GTT amphibious crawler tractors. Since these were unable to cope with very soft terrain, development of a true multi-terrain tractor was undertaken, and this led to the construction of the Tyumen I. This was the first of a completely new ACV type and combined crawler propulsion with air cushion lift. The first model, now relegated to Tyumen's ACV museum, carried a 2-tonne load at speeds up to 25 mph (40 km/h) in off-road conditions. It is described as a broad, squat vehicle on long narrow caterpillor tracks, with a flexible skirt between its crawlers. The second was the MVP-2 which was upgraded soon afterwards to the MVP-3 5-tonne capacity model. The policy at Tyumen is to standardise on composite crawler ACV systems rather than air propeller or endless-screw type propulsion

Rear view of the PVP-40 air-cushion trailer showing the unusual arrangement of varied length segments on the bag skirt

A 8-ton capacity air cushion trailer towed by a five-ton capacity MVP-3 combined ACV/crawler tractor. Both vehicles have been developed by the West Siberian Branch of the All-Union Oil Machinery Research Institute. The first vehicle of this type built in the Soviet Union had completed 621 miles (1,000 km) crossing swamps and other difficult terrain by September 1973

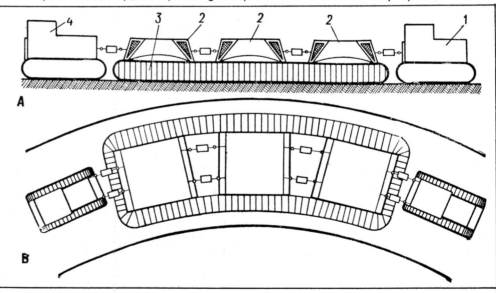

Articulated ACV trailer.

A, Operating arrangement.
B. How turns are negotiated
1, tractor;
2, cargo areas;
3, flexible skirt;
4, second tractor to stabilise trailer motion.

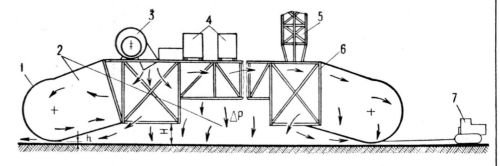

Diagram of a typical Soviet-designed ACV oil rig platform.

1, flexible bag skirt;
2, air cushion;
3, fan;
4, drilling rig engines (employed to drive fans during moves);
5, derrick;
6, drilling rig base;
7, tractor.
h—air gap;
H—hard structure clearance;

AIR CUSHION LANDING SYSTEMS

FRANCE

BERTIN & CIE

OFFICE AND WORKS:
  BP 3, 78370 Plaisir, France
TELEPHONE:
  462.25.00
TELEX:
  26 619 AVIATOM PLAIS
DIRECTORS:
  M. Jean Bertin, President Director General
  M. Benjamin Salmon, Director General
  M. Michel Perineau, Director General

Bertin & Cie is now developing air cushion landing systems based upon the company's technique of separately-fed multiple plenum chambers.

ATTERROGLISSEUR

The Atterroglisseur is an air cushion drop platform for damping both vertically and horizontally the landing of heavy loads dropped by parachute. The system comprises a platform carrying the load and an air cushion system which includes inflatable balloons fitted on the underside of the platform, a light tray at the base of the balloons, and flexible skirts beneath the tray connected to the balloons.

While in the aircraft, the complete air cushion system is tightly packed beneath the platform and secured in position by a plate. When the platform is dropped, the securing plate detaches itself automatically and both the flexible skirts and the balloons inflate.

On landing the balloons deflate first, thus feeding the skirts continuously. It is only when the balloons are empty that the skirts slowly collapse to bring the platform to a standstill.

AIRCRAFT LANDING SYSTEM

The same basic system but incorporating air generators is being developed as an air cushion landing system for heavy cargo aircraft and wing-in-ground-effect machines, providing them with multi-terrain landing and take-off capability.

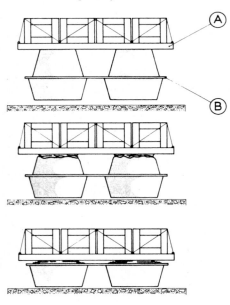

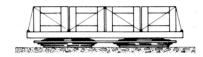

Bertin Atteroglisseur in action. The system is designed to prevent loads dropped by parachute from turning over on hitting the ground. As the loaded platform lands, balloons beneath it cushion the impact as they deflate. Air from the balloons is then fed below into a series of multiple skirts, inflating them and creating an air cushion. This allows the platform to skim the terrain in the dropping zone while the parachutes settle, thus reducing the possibility of the platform and load overturning. When the balloons are finally deflated, the skirts collapse and friction brings the platform to a standstill

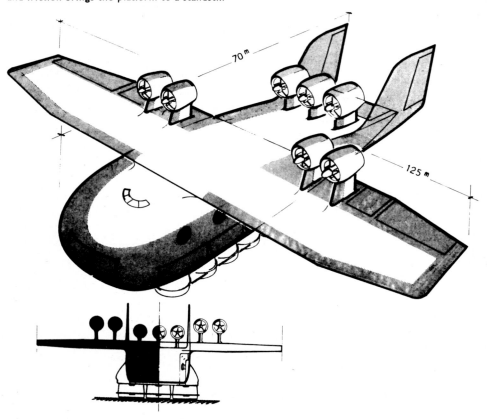

Bertin air cushion landing system employed on a giant cargo carrying wing-in-ground-effect machine, providing multi-terrain landing and take-off capability

Four phases during an air drop employing an Atteroglisseur skirted platform: 1, During descent, balloons above the multi-skirt cells are fully inflated; 2. On hitting the ground the balloons are gradually crushed and eject air below to inflate the skirts; 3. Balloons are deflated and collapse; 4. Skirts are flattened and increased friction through surface contact brings the platform to a halt. The platform comprises: A. The load platform with balloons fitted below and B. a light tray, to which the lower ends of the balloons are secured. The multi-cell skirts are hung beneath the tray

THE UNITED STATES OF AMERICA

BELL AEROSPACE

HEAD OFFICE:
Buffalo, New York 14240

TELEPHONE:
Area Code 716 297-1000

OFFICERS:
See ACV Section

The air cushion landing system is designed by Bell to replace wheels, skis, or floats on any size or type of aircraft, with a single system combining the functional capabilities of them all.

This application of the air cushion principle is an outgrowth of work in the field of air cushion vehicles. The system minimises airstrip requirements and enables aircraft to take-off and land on unprepared surfaces, in open fields, on open water, ice, snow, marsh, sand or dirt. Factors contributing to this feasibility are the very low pressure in the bag supporting the aircraft, the elimination of friction because of the air jets, and the increased area of contact during braking.

It has proved to be an ideal gear for crosswind take-off and landing.

The first aircraft to be fitted with ACLS was a Lake LA-4 light amphibian. In November 1970 Bell was awarded a USAF contract to install this equipment on a de Havilland CC-115 Buffalo.

The aircraft, so modified, was redesignated XC-8A and delivered to the USAF in November 1973. USAF landing trials were scheduled to take place in the late summer of 1974.

ACLS-EQUIPPED LA-4

Preliminary tests have been undertaken with the aid of a specially equipped LA-4 amphibian, details of which are given below.

The ACLS consists primarily of a doughnut-shaped bag inflated to a thickness of approximately 2 ft (·60 m) by an axial fan. The fan, powered by a separate engine, forces air down into the bag. This flow of air escapes through thousands of small jet nozzles on the underside of the bag, providing a cushion of air upon which the aircraft floats. The bag is elastic, fabricated from multiple layers of stretch nylon cloth for strength, natural rubber for elasticity and coated with neoprene for environmental stability. When deflated during flight it fits snugly against the underside of the aircraft.

At touchdown, six brake skids on the underside of the bag are brought into contact with the landing surface by pneumatic pillows. When fully inflated for maximum braking, these pillows are each slightly larger than a basketball. For parking on land or water a lightweight internal bladder seals the air jets, thus supporting the aircraft at rest, or providing buoyancy to keep it afloat indefinitely.

Above: the ACLS-equipped LA-4 taking off from an airfield and below: taxiing across a muddy, ice-strewn farmfield near Wheatfield, New York

Impression of the ACLS-equipped De Havilland 'CC-115 being developed by Bell for the USAF Flight Dynamics Laboratory. The air cushion system will permit the CC-115 to operate from terrain completely unsuitable for conventional wheeled landing gear aircraft

DIMENSIONS:

Aircraft

Wing span	38 ft 0 in (11·58 m)
Overall length	24 ft 11 in (7·59 m)
Gross wing area	170 sq ft (15·79 m²)

Air Cushion

Length	16 ft 0 in (4·87 m)
Width	3 ft 10 in (1·16 m)
Area	45 sq ft (4·18 m²)

LOADINGS:

Wing loading	15 lb per sq ft
Air cushion pressure	55 lb per sq ft

WEIGHTS:

Gross operating weight
2,500 lb (1,113·92 kg)

Air cushion system weight   258 lb (117 kg)

POWER PLANTS:
Propulsion engine rating:

Lycoming Model 0 360 01A   180 bhp

Air Cushion Engine rating:
Modified McCulloch Model 4318F (driving 2-stage axial fan)   90 bhp

PERFORMANCE:

Cruising speed	125 mph (201 km/h)
Stalling speed	54 mph (86·9 km/h)
Take-off run	650 ft (198·12 m)
Landing run	475 ft (144·78 m)

SPACE SHUTTLE VEHICLE WITH ACLS

In 1970 Bell Aerospace completed a seven-month preliminary design study to determine the applicability of its Air Cushion Landing System (ACLS) to Space Shuttle System booster and orbiter vehicles.

Work was sponsored by the National Aeronautics and Space Administration's (NASA) Langley Research Center, Hampton, Va.

Investigations of ACLS applicability to Space Shuttle boosters and orbiters with landing weights of 200,000 and 700,000 lb have indicated that the relative weight of an air cushion system would be at least competitive, and possibly lower, than conventional wheeled gear for these vehicles.

Under the seven-month study, Bell refined its preliminary weight estimates. The company also studied means of providing cushion air, plus the effects of an ACLS on the aerodynamic characteristic of a shuttle vehicle, the feasibility of ACLS installations on shuttle vehicle configurations, and the suitability of both internal and external stowage during re-entry.

ACLS-EQUIPPED XC-8A BUFFALO

In November 1970, the USAF Flight Dynamics Laboratory awarded Bell a $4·6 million contract authorising the company to embark on a programme for the design, fabrication, installation and test of an ACLS-equipped de Havilland CC-115 Buffalo STOL transport aircraft, provided by the Canadian Defence Department. The objective of this joint US/Canadian programme is to demonstrate through tests on the ground and in the air the capabilities of an ACLS-equipped military transport aircraft.

United Aircraft of Canada Ltd developed and qualified the auxiliary power system and de Havilland Aircraft of Canada Ltd modified the CC-115 testbed aircraft for the ACLS installation. The Canadian Government funded this portion of the project.

Running concurrently with the Programme Definition Phase (PDP), completed by Bell Aerospace on July 1st 1971, was an air cushion trunk fabrication phase, which was completed in 1972. ACLS installation was completed in February 1973. Ground checkouts were completed in November 1973 and the aircraft, redesignated XC-8A, was delivered to the USAF. Landing trials were scheduled for the late summer of 1974.

ACLS employs a layer of air instead of wheels as the ground contacting medium. The system's trunk, a large inner-tube like arrangement, encircles the underside of the fuselage, and, on inflation, provides an air duct and seal for the air cushion.

The underside of the rubberised trunk is perforated with hundreds of vent holes through which air is allowed to escape to form the air cushion. Cushion air pressure is provided by an on-board auxiliary compressor.

Because the ACLS distributes the weight of an aircraft over a considerably larger area than conventional wheeled systems, and itself exerts a ground pressure of less than 3 lb sq in (06·45 sq cm) it permits operations on surfaces with very low bearing strength.

Earlier aircraft modifications include the addition of two engine fan systems to supply air to the ACLS, changes that permit the fuselage to accept the elastic ACLS trunk,

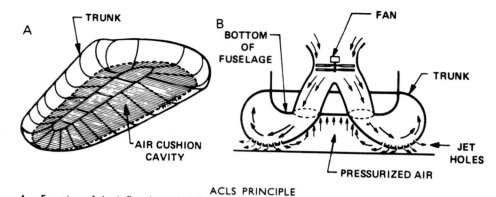

ACLS PRINCIPLE
A. Function of the inflated trunk, left, is to contain the pressurised air in the air cushion cavity. This cushion of air supports the weight of the craft.
B. Air continuously forced through the jet holes pressurises the air cushion cavity, and also provides air bearing lubrication between the trunk and its supporting surface.

Loaned for tests by the Canadian Department of National Defence, this Bell ACLS-equipped De Havilland CC-115 Buffalo will operate from a range of surfaces including rough ground, marshland, water and grass

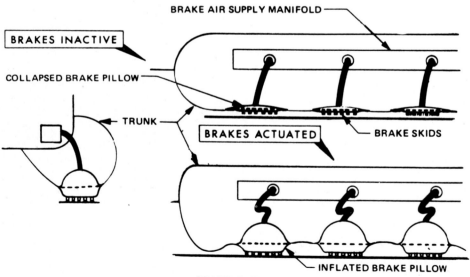

BRAKE SYSTEM
Inflation of the brake pillow of the ACLS-equipped plane brings multiple brake skids into ground contact, drawing the aircraft to a halt

and installation of wing outriggers equipped with spring skids.

The two ST6F-70 gas turbine engines that drive the two-stage fan system to supply air

to the ACLS trunk were developed by United Aircraft of Canada, Ltd.

Hamilton Standard Division of United Aircraft Corp. has modified the standard

Buffalo propellers to give the pilot direct control of the blade angle. This allows precise speed and directional control during landings and ground manoeuvres on the air cushion.

Six skids on the bottom of the trunk operate when the pilot applies the aircraft brakes. The braking action pushes the skids, of tyre tread-type material, against the ground and stops the aircraft. Stopping distance is comparable to that of conventional wheel and brake landing systems.

The Buffalo will be able to operate from a range of surfaces including grass, unprepared rough ground, snow and water as well as paved surfaces.

In flight, the ACLS engines may be shut down or used for additional propulsive thrust. The engines are mounted on each side of the fuselage beneath the wing in a manner similar to those used on some other aircraft for jet assisted take-off (JATO).

The trunk is a highly elastic rubber-nylon composite developed by Bell for the ACLS programme. It is designed to contract to a snug aerodynamic fit against the underside of the aircraft when not in use.

Considered far more flexible than conventional landing systems, the ACLS also provides increased safety on landing and takeoff. It is simpler to deploy and is an ideal crosswind landing gear.

XC-8A BUFFALO

DIMENSIONS:
Aircraft:

Wing span	96 ft 0 in (29·26 m)
Overall length	77 ft 4 in (23·57 m)
Gross wing area	945 sq ft (22·63 m²)

Air Cushion:

Length	32 ft 2 in (10·25 m)

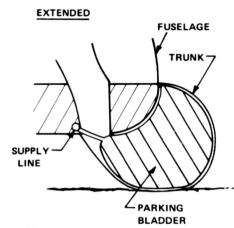

RETRACTED — FUSELAGE — TRUNK — PARKING BLADDER

EXTENDED — FUSELAGE — TRUNK — SUPPLY LINE — PARKING BLADDER

PARKING SYSTEM
A separate bladder within the rubberised air cushion trunk is inflated to support the weight of the aircraft when parked

Width	14 ft 0 in (4·26 m)	Stalling speed, 40 degree flap	
Area	228 sq ft (21·18 m²)	at 39,000 lb	66 knots
LOADINGS:		Take-off run on level surface	1,130 ft
Wing loading	14·8 lb per sq ft	to 50 feet from level surface	1,640 ft
Air cushion pressure	170 lb per sq ft	Landing run	
WEIGHTS:		from 50 feet on level surface	1,130 ft
Gross operating weight		on level surface	650 ft

Gross operating weight
41,000 lb (18,597 kg)
Air Cushion system weight
2,220 lb (1,006·92 kg)

POWER PLANT:
Propulsion engines:
Two General Electric Model CT64-820-1, rated at 3,055 eshp
Air cushion engines:
Two United Aircraft of Canada ST6F-70, rated at 800 bhp

PERFORMANCE:
Cruising speed at 10,000 ft   230 knots TAS

ACLS F-8 CRUSADER

In 1972 Bell Aerospace completed a study of the adaption of the ACLS to the Vought F-8 Crusader carrier-based jet fighter.

ACLS FOR UNMANNED AIRCRAFT

In July 1972, Bell Aerospace completed a study of air cushion landing systems for recovery of unmanned aircraft for the USAF.

In early 1974 the company completed another USAF study of air cushion landing systems for the Australian Jindivik unmanned aircraft.

UNION OF SOVIET SOCIALIST REPUBLICS

BARTINI

Robert Oros di Bartini, a 75-year-old Soviet aircraft designer of Italian birth, has indicated that air cushion landing systems are under development in the Soviet Union, and will possibly replace conventional wheeled undercarriages on aircraft by the end of the century.

His Stal-6, of 1933, was the first in the Soviet Union with a completely retractable undercarriage.

Bartini is former head of the group of designers at the Scientific Research Institute of the Civil Air Fleet. His Stal-7 was shown at the 15th Paris Aviation Salon and achieved a world speed record in 1939. He worked with Lavochkin and Myasishchev on fighter development and his later designs include the ER-2 long-range night bomber. In recent years he has participated in the development of VTOL aircraft.

TRACKED SKIMMERS

BRAZIL

FEI
FACULTY OF INDUSTRIAL ENGINEERING
ADDRESS:

Research Vehicle Department (DEPV), Faculty of Industrial Engineering, São Bernado do Campo, Aviendo Oreste Romano 112, São Paulo

TELEPHONE:

443 1155

SENIOR EXECUTIVES:

Baj. Rigoberto Soler Gisbert, Director of Vehicle Research

The Vehicle Research Department of the FEI, founded in 1968, has designed a number of small air cushion vehicles, one of which is about to be put into production.

The Department's first and most ambitious project to date has been the design and construction of the TALAV tracked air cushion vehicle, development of which is being supported by the Ministry for Industry and Commerce through FUNAT—a government fund for sponsoring new technological developments.

The prototype, an all-metal vehicle propelled by twin Marbore VIs, and seating 20 passengers, displays several novel features, including the siting of the main passenger access door at the front. The whole of the front section moves forward telescopically to provide space for entry and exit. This arrangement facilitates the loading of freight when necessary, and should an emergency stop occur when carrying passengers on a narrow elevated guideway, walking out through the front will be far safer than through the sides, say the designers.

It is also stated that passenger handling will be simplified at termini, where the vehicles can be drawn up side-by-side without the need to devote valuable space for platforms.

The main application foreseen for vehicles of this type is that of city centre to suburbs or city centre to airport links.

To enable construction to be undertaken without difficulty in developing areas where manpower is available, the structure is based on easily-handled sub-assemblies and standard panels of aluminium honeycomb.

LIFT AND PROPULSION: Cushion air is delivered by fans powered by a 70 hp engine. Cushion pressure, 40 lb ft², cushion area 3,250 ft². Two 900 lb st Turbomeca Marbore VI gas-turbines supply propulsive thrust.

DIMENSIONS, EXTERNAL:

Length   51 ft (15·54 m)

Above and below: Prototype of the FEI, 20-seat TALAV tracked air cushion vehicle. Designed to cruise at 200 mph (321·86 km/h), the vehicle is powered by twin Turbomeca Marbore VI gas-turbines

Width	7·4 ft (2·26 m)	WEIGHTS:	
Height	9 ft 5 in (2·87 m)	Empty weight	6,500 lb (2,948·35 kg)
DIMENSIONS, INTERNAL:		Loaded weight	13,000 lb (5,896·70 kg)
Internal height, passenger saloon		PERFORMANCE:	
	7 ft 0 in (2·13 m)	Cruising speed	200 mph (321·86 km/h)

FRANCE

SOCIÉTÉ DE L'AEROTRAIN
HEAD OFFICE:

Tour Anjou, 33, quai National, 92806 Puteaux

TELEPHONE:

776 43 34

TELEX:

61385 Bertrin Puteau

PRESIDENT DIRECTOR GENERAL:

Jean Bertin

DIRECTOR GENERAL:

André Garnault

Jean Berthelot, International Division

Originally named "Société d'Etudes de l'Aerotrain", this company was formed on April 15, 1965 to develop a high speed transportation system based on air cushion support and guidance principles conceived by Bertin & Cie.

The Aerotrain has completed its experi-mental phase as far as the air cushion technique is concerned. The 01 half-scale prototype, after nearly three years of test runs at speeds up to 215 mph (346 km/h), has successfully attained its phased design requirements, namely the verification of dynamic behaviour, the development of integrated suspension systems, and the accumulation of data for the design and costing of full-scale operational vehicles.

The 02 half-scale prototype has undergone similar tests in order to produce data for vehicles operating at speeds above 200 mph (322 km/h). A speed of 263 mph (322 km/h) was attained by the vehicle in January 1969.

There are three families of Aerotrain systems, Interurban, with a speed of 225 mph (360 km/h); Suburban, with a speed of 113 mph (180 km/h) and the new Tridim system, designed for speeds of up to 50 mph (80 km/h) as the distance between stations generally ranges between several hundred yards and one or two miles. The speeds selected will be based on economic considerations. Suburban systems will cover a variety of routes from city centres to airports and city centres to satellite towns and suburban areas. The size, speed and control system of each vehicle will be decided according to the route.

Current studies are aimed primarily at developing associated techniques including propulsion modes for the various speeds and environments, controls, signals and stations. A mathematical model has been developed in order to computerise the various parameters for both families of applications. This will enable operating costs to be obtained, in an optimised form, for given traffic requirements.

Two full-scale vehicles, the 80-seat Orleans inter-city Aerotrain and the 40-44 seat suburban Aerotrain have undergone extensive trials. During trials between 1969 and 1971, the 80-seat 1-80 "Orleans" Aerotrain has completed more than 700 hours of operation on its 18 km (11·2 mile) track north of Orleans, carrying more than 10,000 people at a speed of 160 mph (260 km/h). In January 1973, the vehicle was taken to the UTA maintenance facility at Le Bourget airport where it was equipped with a 15,000 lb st JT8D-11 turbofan, permitting its speed to be studied in the 220-250 mph (360-400 km/h) range.

In November 1973, a speed of 250 mph (400 km/h) was attained and by May 1974, 150 hours of operation had been logged in this configuration, during which 2,000 professionally interested passengers had been carried.

All these programmes, completed or under way, represent a financial development effort of roughly $22 million. The French Government, which has extended its support at every stage by means of various loans, subsidies and orders, decided at a Cabinet meeting in July 1971 to build a rapid transit line from the new business centre of Paris, La Défense to the New Town of Cergy-Pontoise, using the Aerotrain air cushion technique and propelled by linear induction motor.

A substantial amount of the land for the track has been acquired and construction will begin in 1975.

In November 1969, the company formed a US subsidiary, Aerotrain Systems Inc, to build and market Aerotrains in the United States and Mexico. The company is jointly held by Rohr Industries Inc, Bertin et Cie and Société de l'Aerotrain. Rohr's interest is 80%. The company's first prototype was completed in December 1972 and will be tested in 1974 on an experimental line built at the US Department of Transport centre at Pueblo, California.

The experimental Aerotrain 01 running at 215 mph over its 4·2 mile long test track, located south-west of Paris, near Gometz-la-Ville.

Turntables are installed at each end of the present Aerotrain test track, but they will not be used normally on operational lines. In service Aerotrains will be able to manoeuvre independently on the flat floor surfaces of stations

In 1971, another subsidiary was formed, Aerotrain Scandinavia AB, in which the Salen Group has a 50% interest. A third company, formed in Brazil with the support of four French banks, is Aerotrain Systems de Transporte.

In December 1973 an agreement was signed between Bertin & Cie, Aerotrain, Spie-Batignolles, Jeumont-Schneider, SGTE MTE and Francorail-MTE, who will cooperate in the promotion and operation of Aerotrain systems and various aspects of production.

EXPERIMENTAL AEROTRAINS
AEROTRAIN 01

An experimental, half-scale prototype, this vehicle was operated along a test track 4·2 miles (6·7 km) long. The track has an inverted T cross section, the vertical portion being 1 ft 10 in (55 cm) high and the horizontal base 5 ft 11 in (1·80 m) wide. A turn-table is fitted at each end.

The vehicle is of light alloy construction. The slender body has seats at the front for six people, and an engine compartment at the rear. Lift and guidance are provided by two centrifugal fans, driven by two 50 hp Renault Gordini motor car engines, linked by a shaft. The fans supply air to the guidance and lift cushions at a pressure of about 0·35 lb/sq in (25 gr/cm²), the maximum airflow being 350 cu ft/sec (10 m³/sec). Propulsion is provided by a 260 hp Continental aero-engine, mounted at the top of a 3 ft 11 in (1·20 m) tail pylon and driving a

reversible-pitch propeller, which is also used for normal braking. There are brake pads at the rear of the vehicle which grip the vertical track section like a disc brake.

The first test run on the track was made on December 29, 1965. The prototype was intended to evaluate and demonstrate the Aerotrain principle on a small scale, and was developed with the active support of the French Government and French Railways.

Although the vehicle was designed for a maximum speed of 125 mph (200 km/h) tests have been undertaken at higher speeds with the help of booster rockets to supplement the propulsive airscrew. In December 1967, the vehicle reached the top speed of 215 mph (345 km/h) several times with a jet engine assisted by two booster rockets.

DIMENSIONS:

Length overall	32 ft 10 in (10·00 m)
Width overall	6 ft 7 in (2·00 m)
Height overall	12 ft 2 in (3·70 m)
Height to top of body	5 ft 3 in (1·60 m)

WEIGHTS:

Basic weight	5,500 lb (2,500 kg)

PERFORMANCE:

Cruising speed	125 mph (200 km/h)
Top speed	188 mph (303 km/h)

EXPERIMENTAL AEROTRAIN 02

Aerotrain 02 is an experimental half-scale prototype designed for high speed tests on the track at Gometz used by the first proto-type.

Due to the track's relatively short length, a more powerful thrust engine, a Pratt & Whitney JT 12, is installed in order to maintain high speeds over a distance of 1·3 miles (2 km) for performance measurements.

During its first series of test runs, the Aerotrain 02 attained 235 mph (378 km/h). A booster rocket was then added, and a series of tests followed, culminating in a record speed of 263 mph (422 km/h) being attained. The average speed recorded over the 2/3 mile track was 255 mph (411 km/h).

The air cushions for lift and guidance are provided by fans driven by a Turbomeca Palouste gas turbine. At high speed, the dynamic pressure is sufficient to feed the air cushions.

The internal space has been devoted in the main to test instrumentation. Seats are provided only for the pilot and a test engineer.

Aerotrains 01 and 02 were both equipped with propulsion engines which were readily available from the aviation market and capable of giving high speed on a short test track. Operational vehicles use quieter power arrangements.

FULL-SCALE AEROTRAINS
I-80 ORLEANS INTERCITY PROJECT

This medium range inter-city vehicle (the Orleans-Paris line will be 70 miles (113 km) long) was designed originally with airscrew propulsion for speeds up to 186·41 mph (300 km/h), but has now been equipped with a silenced turbofan engine which has increased its speed to 250 mph (400 km/h). The vehicle carries 80 passengers in airline comfort in an air-conditioned and sound-proofed cabin.

The lift and guidance air cushions are fed by two axial fans driven by a 400 hp Turbomeca Astazou gas turbine. At high speeds, they will be fed by dynamic intake pressure.

On the original model thrust was supplied by a shrouded propeller, driven independently by two 1,300 hp Turmo 111 gas-turbines.

In January 1973, the vehicle was taken to the UTA maintenance facility at Le Bourget, where it has been fitted with a 15,000 lb thrust Pratt & Whitney JT8D-11 turbofan, which will permit the systematic study of the I-80 and its components at speeds in the 220-250 mph (354-426 km/h) range.

Hydraulically retractable tyred wheels are incorporated to help to achieve silent operation near and in stations, and also to assist in manoeuvring and switching the vehicle on station floors. The vertical rail of the inverted T track is unnecessary at low speeds.

A very low empty-weight-to-payload ratio has been possible because of the lack of concentrated loads inherent in the vehicle. This permits the use of lightweight supporting structures—tracks and stations.

Vehicles will not be coupled, so that very high frequency services can be maintained throughout the day. With headways as low as one minute, simple or articulated vehicles

The Aerotrain 02, a research vehicle built for tests up to and above 250 mph on the No. I track at Gometz

The I-80HV Aerotrain with its new turbofan thrust unit

offer a range of capacities which largely cope with the peaks of traffic expected in known intercity lines.

Two articulated cars with seats for up to 160 passengers and luxury models with a wider aisle and reduced seating capacity are being considered in feasibility studies being undertaken for several projected routes.

DIMENSIONS:

Length overall	101 ft 8 in (30·50 m)
Length at track level	92 ft 6 in (27·75 m)
Height at fan jet air intake	
	17 ft 0 in (5·10 m)
Width	10 ft 8 in (3·20 m)

WEIGHTS:

Gross weight	24 metric tons

PERFORMANCE:

Test speed range
220-250 mph (354-426 km/h)

THE GUIDEWAY

The first leg of the future Orleans to Paris line—a track 11·5 miles (18·5 km) long— was completed in July 1969. It includes turntables at both ends and a central platform for manouevring and switching.

In mid-1973 the French Government confirmed that the line is to be completed in due course, but did not announce details.

The track has been designed for a service speed of 250 mph (402 km/h). It is mounted on pylons along the entire route. The prefabricated concrete beams, of 67 ft (20 m) span, have a minimum ground clearance of 16 ft (4·90 m). This allows the track to be constructed across roads and cultivated land.

Due to the low stresses produced by the Aerotrain vehicles it has been possible to design a lightweight elevated track structure,

which is less expensive than an equivalent ground track. Local ground subsidence, which may occur during the first years after erection, will be countered by adjusting the pylon heads. This will be limited to a simple jacking operation using built-in devices in the pylon structure.

The radii of curves and gradient angles will depend upon the accelerations admissible without causing discomfort to passengers. Banking can be provided if necessary. Banking of 7% is in fact incorporated in three curves in the Orleans track. The radius requirements are therefore the same as for other guided systems of transport for similar speeds. The advantage of the Aerotrain track is that there are no gradient limitations and it can therefore be constructed with a much smaller number of curves.

Aerotrain guideway track beams can be adjusted at the pylon heads in the event of ground subsidence

TESTS

By May 1974, the vehicle had completed more than 850 hours of operation, during which it logged more than 30,000 miles and carried nearly 13,000 passengers.

During the investigation tests, over one hundred technical parameters were systematically measured under various configurations and throughout the entire performance envelope.

Speed, acceleration and braking characteristics have confirmed expectations, and the riding comfort has proven to be highly satisfactory. Under all operating conditions, including propeller reverse braking, negotiating curves and in cross winds of 31 mph (50 km/h), the average accelerations were less than 0·6 m/s² at all times, with values of 0·3 to 0·5 m/s² during normal cruising conditions.

Since the interior noise level in the passenger compartment is between 75 and 78 dBA, it is possible to converse in normal tones. A level 70-72 dBA will be reached on series production vehicles.

External noise, 90-95 dBA at 65 yards (60 m) compares favourably to that of a modern electric train, with a much shorter duration.

During the 850 hours of operation there was no breakdown which caused the vehicle to stop on the guideway, with the exception of a single incident involving hydraulic circuits to the propeller, which were repaired

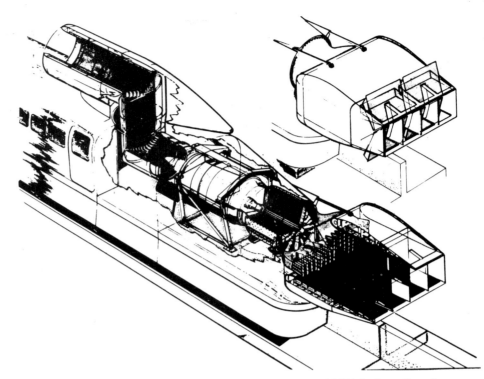

The I-80HV Orleans Aerotrain after being fitted with a 15,000 lb thrust Pratt & Whitney JT8D-11 turbofan, which will permit the behaviour of the vehicle's systems to be studied at speeds of 220-250 mph (354-426 km/h). Considerable attention has been given to sound attenuation. As seen in the cutaway drawing, the air intake has been designed for the maximum effectiveness, and a special high dilution ejection system suppresses the noise of the exhaust gases

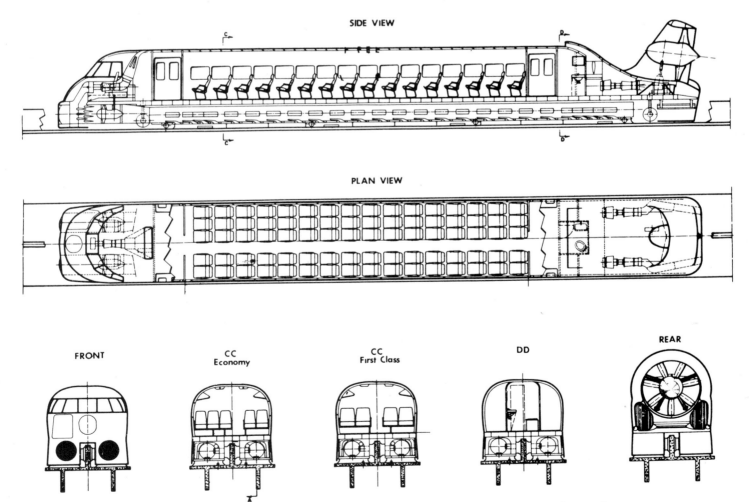

The Aerotrain I-80—a typical Aerotrain configuration for medium-range inter-city traffic, carrying 80 passengers at a cruising speed of 180 mph and a top speed of 190 mph

The prefabricated concrete beams of the Orleans track have a minimum ground clearance of 16 ft (4·87 m). This allows the track to be constructed across roads and agricultural land without causing obstruction *Photo: P. M. Lambermont*

in less than an hour. Only three items, other than the air cushions, have necessitated a major repair since the vehicle was put on the guideway. The air cushions have been completely trouble-free.

The third phase of the test programme consisted of an endurance, or accelerated service test involving 200 hours of running time. Thirty-six operating days were utilised and during the average six hours of continuous operation were completed. The cruising speed established was 154·33 mph (250 km/h). Since this involved acceleration and deceleration between 0 and 154·33 mph (250 km/h) every six minutes, a commercial operation of 1,000-2,000 hours or 200,000-400,000 km in terms of wear on the vehicle was simulated. The rate of air cushion lip wear experienced indicates a useful lip life of 40,000 to 50,000 km and a practically negligible cost factor of ·001 to ·002 francs per passenger/kilometer.

It is to be noted that cultivation has been resumed around and underneath the guideway which, in sharp contrast with the high permanent way maintenance costs experienced by the railways, has required no maintenance whatsoever since it was built.

SUBURBAN AEROTRAIN
AEROTRAIN S-44

The prototype 40-44 passenger suburban vehicle is equipped with a linear induction motor. The vehicle underwent trials at Gometz between 1969 and 1972, where its 2 mile (3 km) test track runs parallel to that used by the Aerotrain 01 and 02 experimental vehicles. During its test programme the vehicle was operated at speeds up to 105 mph (170 km/h). The S-44 is currently undergoing modification as part of the company's development programme for the new 15 mile (24 km) La Défense—Cergy line.

The power for the two axial lift fans is provided by a 525 hp GM Chevrolet V-8 car engine. Practically silent operation is achieved since there is no noise of rolling wheels. No vibration is communicated to the track structure which can therefore be erected in urban areas without fear of any noise disturbing local communities, even if steel is used for the longer spans of the guideway.

This vehicle is equipped with an electrical linear motor developed by the Société Le Moteur Linéarie (Merlin & Gerin Group). It provides a thrust of 18,000 N at 85 mph (137 km/h) and has been currently operated at speeds above 100 mph (160·93 km/h).

Electric current is collected from the three-phase 1,000 V power line set alongside the track.

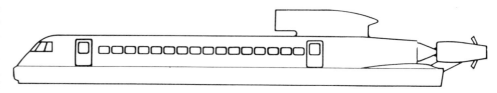

Side view showing the revised configuration of the I-80HV Aerotrain with its new turbofan thrust unit

Artist's impression of the Cergy-Défense suburban Aerotrain

Braking performance is particularly efficient. During normal operation braking is obtained either by dephasing the linear motor supply (or in the case of failure of this supply by feeding it with DC current from the battery), or by a hydraulic braking system equipped with friction pads which grip the vertical portion of the track.

The passenger cabin is divided into four ten-seat compartments, each provided with two doors. An additional half-compartment forward can accommodate four passengers seated on folding seats.

Automatic doors are provided on both sides of each passenger compartment which will help to reduce stopping time. The coupling of several of these vehicles will be possible, but this should only be necessary at peak hours for heavy commuter traffic.

The seating arrangement is optional; each of the various layouts is optimised to provide the maximum possible space for passengers.

DIMENSIONS:

Length	47 ft 0 in (14·4 m)
Beam	9 ft 4 in (2·75 m)
Height	10 ft 2 in (3·10 m)

WEIGHTS:
  Loaded weight:

linear motor weight	25,000 lb (11,500 kg)
automotive version	22,000 lb (10,000 kg)

PERFORMANCE:

Cruising speed	113 mph (180 km/h)

A lower speed system is being designed for urban lines with stations only ½ mile apart.

THE GUIDEWAY

In this programme the track is at ground level. The horizontal support is an asphalt carpet and the upright is an aluminium beam which is used for both guiding the vehicle and as an induction rail for the linear motor. A 1·9 mile (3 km) long track has been constructed at the company's base at Gometz.

Operational suburban lines will generally

Prototype of the 40-44 seat suburban Aerotrain seen on its 1.9 miles (3 km) test track at Gometz

be supported on pylons in order to leave the ground free. The use of an elevated track will reduce the construction time and avoid costly tunnelling on many sections of urban/suburban projects.

PROJECT STUDIES

Société de l'Aérotrain has conducted detailed studies of a dozen projects. The technical and operational characteristics of the vehicles may substantially differ from those of the two prototypes, particularly as regards capacity and cruising speed.

The mathematical model, which has enabled the company to examine technico-economical optimisation procedures, an approach to operations, station design, and baggage handling has produced data based on a number of projected situations. The two major fields which are being investigated are inter-city services and suburban links, mainly between city centres and airports.

Suburban links require, in some cases, a higher capacity than the one provided by the Gometz-type vehicle. Capacity can be increased by widening the vehicles, or coupling them, to provide an hourly capacity of around 10,000 passengers each way.

Projects of an almost urban nature are also being investigated with the Tridim version.

CERGY-PONTOISE—LA DEFENSE SUBURBAN AEROTRAIN

The French government decided in July 1971 to build an Aerotrain rapid transit line from the new business centre of La Défense, just outside Paris, to the new town of Cergy-Pontoise. The line is to be opened in early 1979. Detailed studies are under way and on-site works will begin before the end of 1974.

The travel time between Cergy-Pontoise and La Défense will be less than 10 minutes. The line will connect with a new express metro linking La Défense with Etoile, and the Opéra, the journey times being 4 and 7 minutes respectively.

Cergy-Pontoise will have a population of 200,000 by 1975 and between 350,000 and

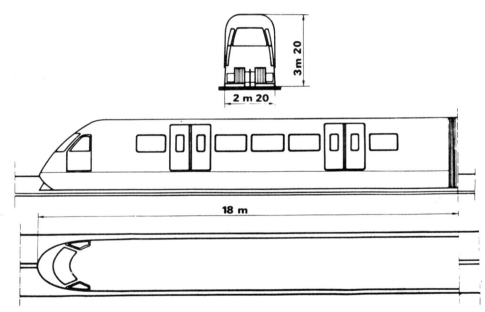

A unit of the suburban Aerotrain. Two of these 80-seat units are coupled to form a vehicle, and on the Cergy-Défense line, two vehicles will be coupled to form each train—providing a total seating capacity per train of 320 passengers

400,000 by the year 2000. It is to be a satellite town of the capital and is about 30 km west of Paris.

TRACK: The length of the route will be 15 miles (24 km). Later it may be extended to cater for urban developments. A part of it will be laid alongside freeways to be constructed during the next 5 years, necessitating a few additional land acquisitions.

The track will be elevated for most of the distance, providing a clearance of 16 ft (5 m) above ground. Supporting pylons will be 66 to 83 ft (20-25 m) apart. The track itself will be 17 ft 8 in (5·30 m) and will be double. Each side will have an aluminium alloy vertical centre rail providing both guidance for the vehicles and the secondary, or induction element, for the linear motor. Electric power is supplied by wayside rails carrying 1500v dc.

The horizontal radii of curves are kept above 1,200 m to allow a high cruising speed. The steepest slope is 6% and occurs when climbing a cliff after a crossing of the Seine.

The Aerotrain vehicle to be used on this service will be supported and guided by air cushions, and propelled by a linear induction motor.

The vehicles will each comprise two units, and on the Cergy-Défense line a train will consist of two coupled vehicles.

SUPPORT AND GUIDANCE: Each unit has its own air cushion guidance and support systems, air for which is put under pressure by electrically driven fans.

PROPULSION: Each unit will be equipped with a linear induction motor of variable voltage and frequency which will be regulated by on-board power-control equipment.

BRAKING: Two systems will be employed:

reversion of propulsion power and by friction brakes gripping the vertical centre rail.

DIMENSIONS:

Length overall (2 units)	240 ft (72 m)	
Width	7 ft 4 in (2·20 m)	
Height	10 ft 8 in (3·20 m)	

WEIGHTS:

	Vehicle	Unit
Gross weight	73 US tons	36·5 US tons
Capacity	160 seats	80 seats
	(max 180)	(max 90)

PERFORMANCE:

Cruising speed	113 mph (180 km/h)

CAPACITY: Capacity requirements, as they are set up by the Paris Regional Authority, are 4,000 passengers per peak hour in each direction in 1978, rising to 8,000 by 1985. This capacity is met by the system with headways of 160 seconds during the initial peak phase and 60 seconds afterwards. Stations are equipped with switching systems to distribute incoming vehicles on to two platforms for each direction.

A three-phase powerline alongside the track at ground level provides electric current for the linear motor

COST: Cost of infrastructure and equipment is slightly over 300 million francs.

Half is devoted to work on the track, a quarter to right-of-way, stations and workshop cost, and a quarter to track equipments, electric distribution and wayside signalling equipment. Cost of the vehicle fleet for the opening year is around 100 million francs. Total cost of the project is in the region of 400 million francs.

OPERATING COSTS: Operating costs, including amortisation of the vehicles, are around 12 to 16 French cents per passenger-km or about 4 US cents per passenger-mile. Load factor is likely to be no more than 50%, due to the nature of the traffic which will be mainly commuting. More balanced traffic is expected when the growth of Cergy leads to increased local employment and could lower the cost to 3 US cents per passenger mile.

TIME TABLE: The line is expected to be opened at the beginning of 1979. Construction time is estimated to be 2½ years, to be preceded or overlapped by acquisition of rights-of-way which could take one to two years. A prototype vehicle will be tested on the first constructed leg of the line at the beginning of 1976. Construction of the vehicle fleet will take about 18 months.

Construction of the line and vehicles will be undertaken by a consortium comprising the following companies:

Société de l'Aérotrain
Société Bertin & Cie
Francorail—MTE
GMT Bâtiments & Travaux Publics
Jeumont Schneider
Spie-Batignolles

The Authority responsible for the project and future operator is Société Aeropar (an SNCF-RATP joint venture).

A 4-seat Tridim urban transport vehicle on its "switchback" test track

Rush-hour capacity of this 65 mph Tridim vehicle would be 52 passengers, 36 of whom are seated

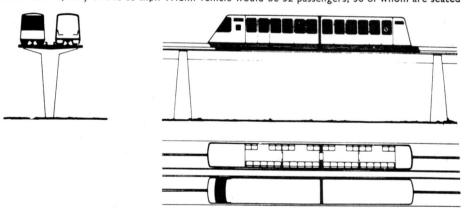

Elevation and plan views of the Aerotrain Tridim VM I vehicle and its track.

TRIDIM URBAN TRANSPORTATION SYSTEM

The Tridim system has been designed to solve the transportation problem in urban areas or suburbs where the distance between stations ranges from a few kilometres down to several hundred metres.

It is believed that the solution to this problem lies in an overhead transportation system adapted to passenger flows ranging from a few thousand to 10-15,000 per hour and offering appreciable comfort, speed and frequency. To transport 6,000 passengers per hour, trains of 3 vehicles of 50 seats each every 90 seconds will be sufficient. If a larger module is adopted, 20,000 passengers

can be carried hourly.

The Tridim system is designed to meet these requirements through the use of an air cushion for suspension and a flexible rack-and-pinion system, rubber-tyred traction-wheels, or linear induction motor for propulsion.

It consists of small-size self-powered air-cushion vehicles moving on a lightweight overhead track.

The capacity of each vehicle can be between 4 and 100 seats according to customer requirements. The required capacity can be obtained by varying the width and the length of the vehicles or grouping any number of vehicles to form a train. Since June 1973, a 4-6 seat prototype vehicle has been under test at a research centre of the French National Electricity Company (E.D.F.) located at Les Renardières, near Fontainebleau, on a 1,000 ft (305 m) track which includes a straight section, grades, curves and points.

Characteristics of this vehicle are as follows:

Loaded weight	1·2 tons
Nominal propulsion power	15 kW
Lifting power	4 kW
Max speed	50 km/h
Max slope	20%
Power supply	cc 160V
Number of air cushions	8
Air pressure	900 kg/m²

The Tridim vehicle is built on a modular basis, with additional modules being added as required to provide the desired capacity.

In the case of the type VM 1 (designed for a specific client), the passengers are transported in modules measuring approximately 10 ft by 6 ft and equipped with 9 seats placed along the longitudinal walls. There is also room for a minimum of 4 standing passengers, which brings the rush-hour capacity to 13 passengers for each module, i.e. 52 per vehicle, 36 of whom are seated (the vehicle consists of 4 modules).

Propulsion and lift are obtained from electric energy collected from a "third" rail (direct-current power supply).

The vehicle is guided by a low metal rail fixed on the track in line with the vehicle axis. This is the inverted-T track fundamental to the Aerotrain technique. Besides its guidance function, this rail carries the propulsion rack and keeps the vehicle retained on the track, which makes overturning impossible in the event of incident or abnormal operating conditions.

LIFT: The basic advantages of employing the air-cushion principle are:

Suspension of concentrated loads and shocks, hence possibility of a lightweight vehicle structure on the one hand, and of the overhead track on the other; the absence of rolling noise and vibration; vehicle maintenance drastically reduced, and virtually non-existent for the track; and finally low total cost of the transportation system due to the simplicity and the lightweight of the track.

The air cushion system requires a power supply of only 4 to 5 hp per supported metric ton. This is expected to be reduced to the order of 2 hp per metric ton. The air cushion supply is operated by sound-insulated electric fans.

PROPULSION: In the case of the VM 1 the vehicle is propelled by a patented rack-and-pinion system. But alternative methods include rubber-tyred traction wheels acting on the centre guidance rail or linear induction motor, according to requirements. The former consists of a dual rack fixed on the guiding rail and two pinions carried by the vehicles and driven by electric propulsion motors. It allows operation on tracks with steep slopes and maintain acceleration and braking performance in any weather including conditions of snow and ice.

The ability to climb steep slopes enables the stations to be built at street level or at the level of another transportation system for ease of transfer.

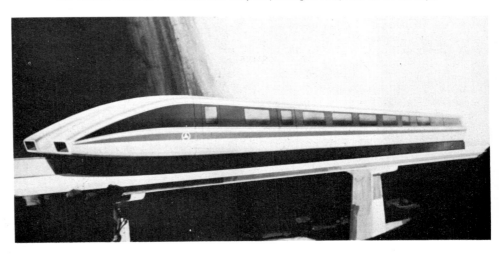

Above and below: The Rohr-built Aerotrain, built under a US Department of Transportation contract. The vehicle, which is 94 ft long, will carry 60 passengers at speeds up to 150 mph

OVERHEAD TRACK: The system is intended primarily for an overhead track but it can also be used at ground level or as an underground system. In the case of an overhead track, the viaduct can be made of metal or of reinforced concrete, the choice between the two materials being dictated mainly by the line layout.

This consists of pylons supporting beams of 66 ft to 100 ft span carrying the guideway which has a width of about 7 ft 4 in for single track or 15 ft 6 in for dual track in the case of the VM 1 system. The track itself consists mainly of the guiding rail with its rack.

The absence of concentrated loads, either static or dynamic, allows the use of a light viaduct, which leads to less cost.

As an example, with metal construction, a dual track viaduct weighs approximately 1,300 lbs per metre (VM 1).

VM1 SPECIFICATION:

The system can be adapted to client specification.

Capacity of the VM 1 is 52 passengers, 36 of whom are seated.

DIMENSIONS:

Length	53 ft 4 in
Width	6 ft 4 in
Height	8 ft 6 in

WEIGHTS:

Empty weight	13,000 lb
Loaded weight	21,800 lb

PERFORMANCE:

Nominal speed	40/50 mph
Maximum speed	50/65 mph
Average acceleration between 0 and 40 mph	0·12 g
Emergency deceleration	0·2 g
Allowable slope at 40 mph	3%
Maximum allowable slope at reduced speed	15% to 25%
Minimum turning radius	80 ft approx.

MOTOR POWER:

for propulsion	150 kW approx.
for cushion	35 kW

OVERHEAD TRACK:

Span	66 ft to 100 ft for normal span
Height above ground	16 ft on the average

Width of track:

single track	7 ft 4 in
dual track	15 ft 4 in

Electrical power supply by conductor rail

URBA

Compagnie d'Energetique Lineaire mb

HEAD OFFICE:

5 Rue Monge, 92 Vanves, France

OFFICERS:

M. E. Barthalon, ScMMIT, Ecole Polytechnique, President Director General

UK REPRESENTATIVE:

mBm Powercels Ltd,
25 Bedford Row, London WC1

P. Watson, BA MIMarE, Managing Director

The URBA mass transport system, invented
in 1960 by M. Maurice Barthalon, aims at
providing a means of urban transport which
combines absence of noise, vibration and
atmospheric pollution with low capital and
maintenance costs and a high degree of flexibility of installation and operation. The
vehicle, which may operate singly or in trains,
is suspended from its track by an air lift
system in which the pressure is sub-atmospheric, and propulsion is by electric linear
induction motors. The cabin of the vehicle is
suspended from a number of Dynavac air
bogies which run within an elevated track the
section of which is like a flattened, inverted
U, with inward facing flanges on the bottom
edges of the sides, on which the air bogies sit
when at rest. The Dynavac air bogies
house the lift fans which draw air from the
space between the track and the top of the
bogie, so producing a pressure difference
which causes the air bogie to lift off the track
flanges.

Special sealing arrangements provide a
controlled leak into the lift chamber which
decreases as the weight of the vehicle increases, so increasing the pressure difference.
The air bogies therefore remain in a stable,
floating condition without being in contact
with the track.

Lateral guidance is provided by similar but
smaller Dynavac cushions between the sides
of the bogie and the sides of the track. The
air bogies also house the linear induction
motors which react with a reactor rail
projecting downwards from the centre of the
track. This effectively divides the lift
chamber into two independent halves, thus
providing a degree of roll control. The
suspension between the cabin and the air
bogie acts as a secondary suspension system
(the air cushion being the primary) and
provides for articulation of the air bogies so
that the vehicle can take curves of small
radius.

In order to carry the development of
URBA from a vehicle to a fully integrated
public transport system, the Société d'Etudes
de l'URBA (SETURBA) has been formed by
the Caisse des Dépöts et Consignation, the
Enterprise Bouygues and the Gazocéan-
Technigaz Group.

The registered office of the Society is at
4 Place Raoul Dautry, Paris 15.

SETURBA has accelerated the application
of URBA by confirming, technically and
economically, the best means of applying this
new method of transport and has prepared
the constitution of a new company charged
with the industrial and commercial development of the URBA system.

A technical and financial appraisal of
URBA, undertaken by the SETURBA study
group, proved favourable, and this has led
to the establishment of Société de l'URBA
(S.U.), supported by former associates of
SETURBA, finance companies, banks and

The URBA 4 prototype seats 6/12 passengers and has a cruising speed of 50 mph (80 km/h)

Impression of a single-track URBA 30 line, with supporting columns located in the centre of a highway

URBA 20, a light urban transport vehicle with a service speed of 45 mph (72 km/h) and seating 20 passengers

investors. Capital investment will be between F10-15 million. SETURBA has also launched a marketing programme to communities in France where likely applications are foreseen.

The company states that public funds are being made available in the form of research and development grants, and that the next phase of URBA's development programme is budgeted at F 30 million.

URBA has been specially designed to satisfy the transport needs of medium-size towns of 200,000 to 1,000,000 inhabitants, and the suburbs of large cities.

The prototype URBA 4, and later two URBA 8s coupled together, were demonstrated at Lyon during 1968. The prototype has been in daily use for almost four years at the Ecole Centrale of Lyon, where research and development has been supported by D.G.R.S.T., D.A.T.A.R., A.N.V.A.R. and the Ministry of Transport. To date it has carried 30,000 visitors. The computer analysis of its dynamic behaviour has confirmed its stability, its comfort and its ability to take small radius curves.

Several recent international assessments, including a searching study by Eurofinance, consider URBA as one of the most promising of the new means of transport for the years 1970 to 1990. A certain number of towns in France and abroad, including Rouen, Bordeaux and Montpellier, are already at the stage of serious preliminary studies. Three different lines located in the outskirts of Paris have been studied. A special study has also been undertaken for the new business centre of La Défense, on the western side of Paris. These bring out the favourable capital and operating costs which should place the price per passenger per kilometre of URBA at a level comparable with that of the bus today.

URBA 8

A prototype urban and suburban monorail URBA 8 is an improved version of the URBA 4, with three linear motors instead of two, and seats for eight passengers. Two URBA 8s were demonstrated at Lyon on December 4th, 1968, on an 87 yard (79 m) track. They operated singly and coupled, with acceleration and deceleration in the range 0·25 to 0·35 g (with 0·5 g deceleration in an emergency), and at speeds up to 30 mph (48·28 km/h). It consists of a rectangular-framed cabin seating up to eight passengers and suspended from three Dynavac air bogies running in an experimental 260 ft (80 m) track.

PROPULSION: Propulsion and normal braking is by three Merlin Gerin linear motors of 25 kW, weighing 176 lb (80 kg) and providing a thrust of 220 lb (100 kg) at starting. 66 lb (30 kg) at normal service speed. Supply is from 380 volt, 3-phase, 50 cycle mains. The motor is the first to be designed as an industrial unit for vehicle propulsion. An aluminium conductor fin runs down the centre of the track and a set of coils is mounted in each bogie. Conductor rails for current supply to the linear motor and lift fans are in the base of the fin.

CABIN: The cabin is rectangular and measures 14 ft 10 in (4·5 m) long, 5 ft 3 in (1·6 m) wide and 4 ft (1·2 m) high. It is built from 4 cm square section tube and diecast corners of a type normally used for the framework of holiday bungalows.

The floor is of light alloy and the sides are perspex. Suspension between the cabin and the three air bogies is by rubber cord springs and hydraulic automobile shock absorbers.

Tests have demonstrated that the air bogie concept is suitable for sharp curves, can climb steep slopes and provides good acceleration and braking. It cannot be derailed.

URBA 20

An enlarged version of the URBA 4, this model will seat 20 passengers in a cylindrical cabin and have a top speed of 45 mph (72 km/h). More efficient lift fans will be employed on this model which will require a total of 12 kW for lift power. All-up weight will be 10,470 lb (4,750 kg).

URBA 30

This is the first model designed to go into service as a public transport system and will seat 30 passengers in rows, three abreast. The initial design will have 5 special, lightweight automatic doors on one side. Overall dimensions of the cabin will be: length 29 ft 6 in (9 m), width 6 ft 3 in (1·9 m), height 6 ft 7 in (2 m) overall, loaded weight 5·3 tons. Propulsion will be by linear motors.

Cost of the double overhead track for the URBA 30 will be in the region of £200,000 per mile excluding wayleaves.

FIRST COMMERCIAL LINE

Bids have been submitted by the Société de l'URBA for two projects, the most promising being a line between the centre of a new town to the south of Paris, and the nearby railway station. The line will be about 3·21 km (2 miles) in length and will have gradients of 10%.

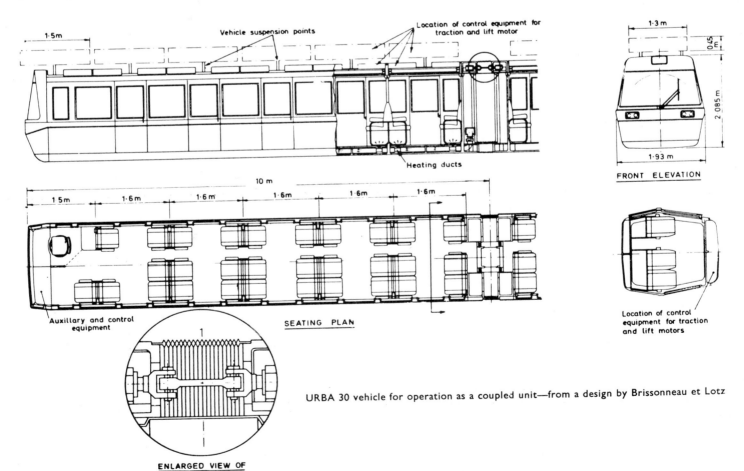

URBA 30 vehicle for operation as a coupled unit—from a design by Brissonneau et Lotz

GERMAN FEDERAL REPUBLIC

KRAUSS-MAFFEI AG

HEAD OFFICE:

8000 München 50, Krauss-Maffei Strasse 2, Munich

TELEPHONE:

(089) 88 99 1

TELEGRAMS:

Kraussmaffei Münchenallach

In 1969, Krauss-Maffei AG built the world's first working model tracked vehicle with electromagnetic support and guidance and a linear induction motor for propulsion. Two years later a 1:30 scale functional mock-up of the Transrapid high-speed transportation system was presented to illustrate the concept. Supported and guided electro-magnetically and propelled by a linear induction motor, it runs on a curved track and conveys a realistic impression of the vehicle in its final configuration.

In addition to its experiments with the manned model of the Transrapid vehicle, the company is conducting a series of tests with a prototype of its Transurban short distance, tracked system, which is also equipped with magnetic support, guidance and propulsion systems.

TRANSRAPID 02 RESEARCH VEHICLE

In October 1971 Krauss-Maffei started operating an experimental 39 ft 4 in (12 m) long vehicle on a 1,093 yard (1,000 m) test track. So far, it has reached a maximum speed of 99 mph (160 km/h). A novel power pick-up system ensures troublefree transmission of electric energy at high speeds. A secondary suspension system with pneumatic shock absorbers and vibration dampers constitutes the link between the vehicle superstructure and the hovering chassis.

Guideway and vehicle concepts provide realistic test data. The test results obtained so far have revealed that the system requirements can be fulfilled without difficulty.

TRACK:

Length	1,093 yards (1,000 m)
Radius of curvature	875 yards (800 m)

EXPERIMENTAL VEHICLE:

Length	38 ft 4½ in (11·70 m)
Width	9 ft 6 in (2·90 m)
Height above track surface	6 ft 8¾ in (2·05 m)
Number of seats	1 × 7/9
Weight	appr 11 Mp
Payload	appr 2 Mp
Design speed of vehicle	appr 220 mph (350 km/h)

PROPULSION BY LINEAR INDUCTION MOTOR:

Thrust (transient)	appr 3·2 Mp
Present vehicle speed (due to short track length)	appr 100 mph (160 km/h)
Synchronous speed LIM at 50 cps	appr 112 mph (180 km/h)

SERVICE BRAKES:

Brake retardation by LIM	appr 2·5 m/sec/²
by jaw brake	appr 8·5 m/sec/²
by friction brake	appr 8·0 m/sec/²

ELECTROMAGNETIC SUPPORT AND GUIDANCE SYSTEM:

Specific carrying capacity
appr 800 kp/m magnet length (25 mm air gap)

Air gap	½ in 1 in (10·25 mm)

POWER SUPPLY:

Support and guidance system:

Voltage 380 V three-phase current, 50 cp	
Output	32 kW

Krauss-Maffei's Transrapid research vehicle in 02 configuration, with magnetic support, guidance and propulsion systems

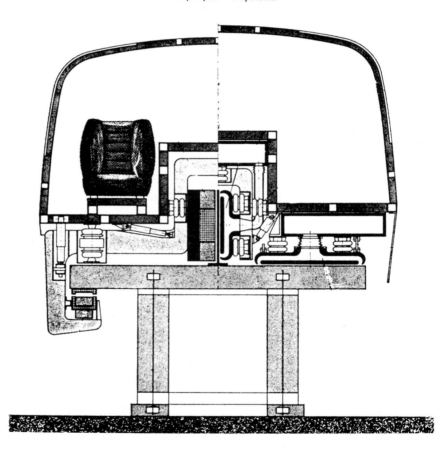

LIM:

Voltage 2·6 KV three-phase current, 50 cps	
Output	5 MVA

TRANSRAPID 03 RESEARCH VEHICLE

In October 1971, the company started operating a dual-purpose test facility which allows a comprehensive system comparison between magnetic cushion and air cushion techniques using same vehicles on the same track with completely identical operating conditions. Vehicles and track have been designed for a maximum speed of approximately 220 mph (350 km/h). The track length is 0·6 miles (1,000 m) allowing the attainment of a speed of about 100 mph (160·93 km/h), which has already been reached with the magnetic cushion vehicle. This experimental system provides realistic

information since it subjects the support, guidance and propulsion system to extreme loads both during straight runs and cornering.

Transrapid 03 is the basic Transrapid 8-ton research vehicle adapted for tests as a tracked air cushion vehicle. The payload of two tons and overall dimensions are identical to those of the vehicle in its earlier configuration. The programme, which is supported by the Federal Ministry of Research and Technology, is enabling the TACV and Maglev concepts to be compared under identical conditions for the first time.

Tests with aircushion support began at the end of 1972 and finished in 1973.

As a TACV, the vehicle is supported and guided by a total of 14 air cushion pads. Six, each with a cushion area of 3 m², support the vehicle on its elevated concrete guideway, and eight, mounted in pairs, each of about

1 m² cushion area, provide lateral guidance along the LIM reaction rail. The air cushion lift system is of plenum type and each pad has a rubber skirt. Cushion air is supplied by a two-stage compressor.

The vehicle is propelled by a French-made LIM system, which accelerates the vehicle to 90 mph (145 km/h) on its 1,093 yard (1,000 m) guideway.

Comparisons covered the following areas: vehicle dynamics; weight; load tolerances; vertical air gap tolerances; specific power requirements for support and guidance; effects on the environment (noise level); reliability; life; reaction to weather influences; maximum speed; aerodynamic drag; investment, operating and maintenance costs.

Result of the comparison: Magnetic levitation technology is superior.

TRACK:

Length	1,093 yards (1,000 m)
Radius of curvature	875 yards (800 m)

EXPERIMENTAL VEHICLE:

Length	38 ft 4½ in (11·7 m)
Width	9 ft 6 in (2·9 m)
Height above track surface	6 ft 8¾ in (2·05 m)
Number of seats	10
Weight	appr. 8 mp
Payload	appr. 2 mp
Design speed of vehicle	appr. 220 mph (350 km/h)

PROPULSION BY LINEAR INDUCTION MOTOR:

Thrust (transient)	appr. 3·2 Mp
Present vehicle speed (due to short track length)	appr. 100 mph (160 km/h)
Synchronous speed LIM at 50 cps	appr. 112 mph (180 km/h)

SERVICE BRAKES:

Brake retardation by LIM	appr. 2·3 m/sec²
by jaw brake	appr. 8·5 m/sec²
by friction brake	appr. 8·0 m/sec²

ELECTROMAGNETIC SUPPORT AND GUIDANCE SYSTEM:

Specific carrying capacity appr. 800 kp/m magnet length (25 mm air gap)

Air gap	½ in 1 in (10·25 mm)

POWER SUPPLY:

Support and guidance system:

Voltage 380 V three-phase current, 50 cp	
Output	32 kW

LIM:

Voltage 2·6 KV three-phase current, 50 cps	
Output	5 MVA

TRANSRAPID 04 RESEARCH VEHICLE

In March 1974 Krauss-Maffei started operating an experimental 18 m long vehicle —first of the new Transrapid generation— on a 2,400 m test track elevated on 6 m high pylons and including two curves. Three different tracks are being constructed to permit the selection of the most favourable configuration. The objective is to achieve speeds up to 350 km/h.

This project is being performed by Krauss-Maffei jointly with MBB. As agreed with Federal Minister of Research and Technology, the managements of Krauss-Maffei and MBB have decided to conduct their future development of a track-guided high-speed transportation system on a joint basis.

TRACK:

Length	2,400 m
Radius of curvature	800-3100 m

A 12-seat test vehicle employed in Krauss-Maffei's Transurban programme. The support and propulsion systems are similar to those employed on the Transrapid system. Transurban vehicles, which are to be employed on short-distance passenger transport services will have a cruising speed of 62·5 mph (100 km/h)

Model of a 144-seat Transrapid, inter-city vehicle. Cruising speed will be about 312 mph (500 km/h)

Transrapid 04 research vehicle

EXPERIMENTAL VEHICLE:

Length	18·4 m
Width	3·2 m
Height above track surface	2·45 m
Number of seats	8
Weight	appr. 15 Mp
Payload	appr. 5 Mp
Design speed of vehicle	appr. 350 km/h

TRANSRAPID OPERATIONAL VEHICLE

The 148 ft (45 m) long Transrapid high-speed transportation system will carry passengers, cars, general and containerised freight. The standard vehicle will have 144 passenger seats and will cruise at 312 mph (500 km/h). A 43·4 mile (70 km) guideway is being built to the north of Augsburg, and is designed for vehicle cruising speeds of this order. The first section of the national test facility will be completed in 1977.

TRANSRAPID PERFORMANCE CHARACTERISTICS AND TECHNICAL DATA:

Length	appr 147 ft 8 in (45 m)
Width	appr. 10 ft 10 in (3·3 m)
Height	appr. 14 ft 1 in (4·3 m)
Total weight	appr. 90 Mp
Payload (incl in total weight)	appr. 25 Mp
Cruising speed	312 mph (500 km/h)

Power input for continuous operation appr. 7,500 kW (at 500 km/h)
Average acceleration   appr. 0·8 m/sec²
Average brake retardation appr. 2·5 m/sec²
Passenger transportation capacity per day and direction, with single vehicles, 20-hour operation and 3 minute intervals   57,600 passengers
or freight equivalent to a volume of 600 40 ft ISO-containers

* *The above data applies to a vehicle with 144 seats.*

TRANSURBAN SYSTEM

Development of the totally automatically controlled train-system concept is being partly financed by the Federal Ministry of Research and Technology. Its low energy consumption and completely automatic operation suggest lower operating costs than any of the more conventional means of short-distance public transport. Underground, elevated or ground-level guideways can be provided, and the system is adaptable to all transportation capacity requirements from 1,000 to 20,000 passengers per hour.

The first 12-seat vehicle is being tested on a level, straight guideway at Munich-Allach. Phase two of the test programme began in mid-1974 on an extended, oval guideway, supported by 16 ft 5 in (5 m) high pylons.

The system allows the operation of a net-work by using rigid points. Changes in direction are accomplished by magnets which can be controlled from the vehicle.

The Transurban System can be easily adapted to individual capacity requirements. On major traffic lines, where there is heavy demand, several vehicles can be connected to form trains. When the major line branches off to serve suburban areas, the trains are automatically separated into individual vehicles. Each vehicle is pre-programmed for a specific line. At the time of departure, the passenger picks the vehicle that will serve his or her point of destination. Thus the need to change vehicles is avoided along the major arteries of a network.

The company's current R & D programme is aimed at the development and optimization of all components by testing the magnetic support and guidance systems at speeds up to 60 km/h; magnetic motors; magnetic switches; automatic coupling and precision-stopping.

Based on the present state of development, Krauss-Maffei believes that this urban transportation system will be operational towards the end of 1974.

TRANSURBAN SYSTEM *

Passenger space/person in sq ft (m²)	8·6 (0·8)
Average cruising speed in mph (in km per hour)	12·5-38 (20-60) **
Max capacity person/hour and direction	1,000 to 20,000
Power requirements in KWh per pass mile (KWh per pass km)	0·32 (0·2)
Average investment costs in Mill US $ per mile (in Mill DM/km)	3·8 *** (12)
Costs cents/pass mile cents/pass km (Dpf/Pass km)	25 **** (5)
Profile for double track ft (m)	10·7 × 14 (3·2 × 4·2)

INSTALLED POWER:
per vehicle in KW	25-200
per station in KW	100

* *Estimated projection of performance*
** *Dependent on station distance*
*** *Costs are valid for elevated construction.*
**** *At a load factor of 30%*

TORONTO-PROJECT

The first Transurban system in the world is at present under construction in Toronto, Canada. In 1971 the Government in Ontario decided to make a study of modern intra-urban transportation systems and selected 8 out of 100 systems and submitted them to a thorough test. The manufacturers of three of these systems were invited to submit an offer for the construction of a demonstration installation. On May 1, 1973 Krauss-Maffei was awarded the contract.

The installation, which will be erected in the National Exhibition Park in Toronto on the shores of Lake Ontario and will consist of an oval 4 km long elevated guideway with 4 branch-line stations, provides for an extension of the network to the Ontario Place pleasure ground.

The first vehicles will be in operation by the end of 1974 and by the middle of 1975 15 vehicles will be available for tests by the government. It is the purpose of this installation to prove to Canadian towns the effectiveness of the system.

HEIDELBERG STUDY

The city of Heidelberg is planning to improve its traffic situation, especially in its historical quarter. It intends to declare the main street a pedestrian zone and remove the main system of public transport.

The Federal Ministry of Transport had awarded Krauss-Maffei a contract for a feasibility study on the introduction of the

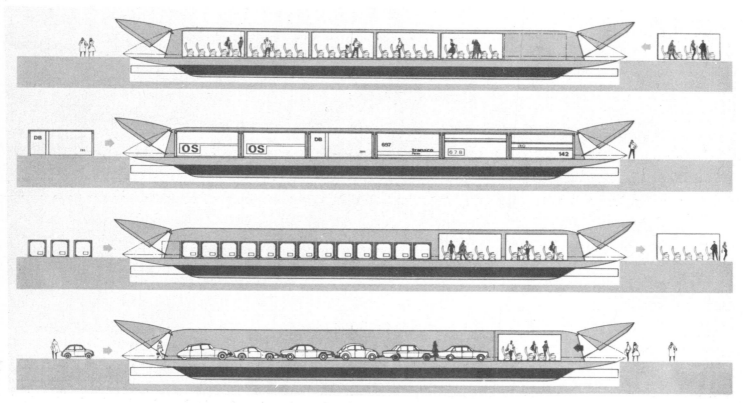

Payload of the standard Transrapid vehicle will be 25 metric tons. Full-width clam-shell doors will permit straight-through loading and off-loading of vehicles and containers

Transurban system in this area of the city.

The study was finished in December 1973 and proved that an underground transurban line is able to replace the tramway. Based on a project proposal requested by the Municipal Council of Heidelberg, the plan initially provides for 1·24 miles (2,000 m) line including 6 stations between Karlstor in the east and Bismarckplatz in the west with extensions to the main railway station. The line runs along the main street of Heidelberg in two directions connecting the two terminal stations with four intermediate stations Pharmakologie, Theaterstrasse, Marktplatz, Leyergasse.

The proposal provides for fully air-conditioned 14 passenger vehicles with wide automatic doors on the right side and wide windows on the left side. During peak traffic periods, four of the (7·5 m) long vehicles can be coupled together to form a train. The maximum speed between stations is 27 mph (45 km/h). The main distance between stations is to be 437 yards (400 m) which means less than 3 minutes walking time to the next station. The vehicle stopping time in the 98 ft (30 m) long stations is 20 seconds. The next vehicle arrives within 45 seconds of the departure of the previous one, ensuring practically no waiting time.

MESSERSCHMITT-BOLKOW-BLOHM

HEAD OFFICE:

Neue Verkehrssysteme, 8000 München 80, Postfach 801265

TELEPHONE:

(089) 60 0034 19

TELEX:

522 279 MBBO

The MBB Transport System Division (Waggon und Maschinenbau GmbH, Donauworth) has been working for many years on the design, development and manufacture of railway locomotives. Since 1946 it has delivered more than 1,000 to railways in all parts of the world. The growing need for transit systems offering higher speeds and a greater degree of automation led to the formation within the company of an advanced transport systems department, which has the task of analysing, defining and developing advanced, high-speed track-guided systems for the future.

The company is a member of a study group—Hochleistungs-schnellbahn-Studiengesellschaft GmbH— formed in conjunction with German Federal Railways and Strabag Bau-AG. One of the first tasks undertaken by the group was a general study on the future of track-guided long-distance transport systems for the government of the Federal Republic, and concluded late in 1971. The results form the basis for the possible decision by the Federal Republic to establish an advanced high-speed transportation system.

The study showed that improvement and rationalisation of transportation and traffic in general can be achieved by a new transport system having the following three characteristics:

Connection of the high density centres of industry and population in the Federal Republic—at first by a main route;

Facilities to transport trucks, cars, and containers, in order to relieve the freeways and highways;

Straight-to-destination service, without interim stops and vehicle changes.

A rapid transit system of this type could be the point of departure for an inter-European transport network between the economic centres of the Common Market and other European countries.

SUSPENSION AND GUIDANCE SYSTEM

After intensive studies, a rapid transit system travelling at speeds up to 310 mph (500 km/h) with no-contact magnetic track guidance was found to be the most favourable when engineering, power requirements, and environmental protection were taken into account.

Of the possible magnetic suspension and

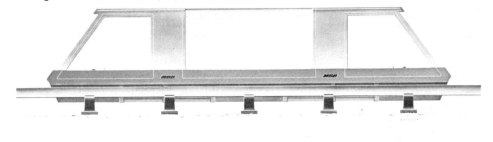

Above and below: First full-scale test vehicle to employ magnetic suspension guidance and propulsion was MBB's basic experimental craft. Weighing 5·6 metric tons, and 23 ft (7 m) in length, it has reached 62 mph (100 km/h) on a 766 yard (700 m) track

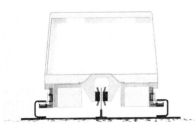

guidance systems—permanent magnets, attracting electromagnets, repelling inductive system,—the attracting electromagnetic system has been given development priority, partly for reasons of economy and partly for reasons relating to the state of the art. With this system, a control of the magnets is required to maintain a nearly constant air gap. This also allows the riding quality to be maintained.

DRIVE

A vehicle that is carried and guided by electromagnetic fields must be provided with an adhesion-free propulsion system.

The use of impulse drive systems is not feasible because of environmental considerations (noise, exhaust gases). The most promising method by which the requisite thrust could be produced is by the use of a linear motor, which has been developed from the rotating electric motor. Of the various possible linear motor principles, the asynchronous type is being used at present because of lower track cost (simple aluminium rail mounted in the track).

However, the synchronous linear motor design cannot be completely ruled out since it is more efficient in certain operational ranges.

POWER TRANSMISSION

With respect to the present state of the art, for reasons of weight and environmental protection, power produced externally to the vehicle and transmitted to the vehicle from the track by means of a current pickup system is preferred to a system in which the energy is produced within the vehicle itself.

Of the various possibilities for power transmission, mechanical gliding current collectors and controlled electric arc collectors are the two most promising methods, the company considers. A great deal more development work has to be undertaken, in this area, however.

In April 1974 it was announced that Krauss-Maffei (KM) and Messerschmitt-Bolkow-Blohm (MBB) are to develop jointly a high-speed transportation system.

As agreed with the Federal Minister of Research and Technology, the corporate managements of both companies have decided to conduct their future development activities for a track-guided high-speed transportation system—started in the late sixties—on a joint basis.

In 1971 both companies presented to the public the world's first large-scale test vehicles supported, guided, and driven by magnetic fields. In the meantime extensive testing performed on test rigs and test tracks at Munchen-Allach and Ottobrunn has demonstrated that contact-free magnetic suspension using controlled electromagnets can be achieved and is practical for high-speed ground transportation systems.

Both companies, using different approaches, arrived at very similar research results.

The chief objective of the joint venture group is to develop a uniform high-speed transportation system for Europe for economic long-haul passenger and freight transportation. To achieve this aim, international links, such as co-operation with DAF Netherlands began in 1973, and plans for the formation of an international management corporation for high-speed transportation are under way.

Research work is being financed by the Federal Minister of Research and Technology as well as by funds from the two companies.

During 1974 speeds up to 248 mph (400 km/h) will be attained by the magnetic suspension test vehicles of the joint venture group.

TRACK

The track for a rapid transit system based on the principle of magnetic suspension and guidance would consist of the supporting concrete pylons and beams, the ferromagnetic support and guidance rails, the secondary part of the linear motor, and the power rails.

In order to ensure the safe operation of a rapid transit system on the one hand, and not to endanger the environment by its operation on the other, the track will be supported on pylons spaced approximately 52 ft 6 in (16 m) apart with the elevation (clearance) of the track being at least 14 ft 9 in (4·50 m). This eliminates to a large extent, the need for special structures at intersections with roads,

The MBB STS 2000 rapid transit system, designed for a maximum block speed of 280 mph (450 km/h) over distances of 30-310 miles (50-500 km)

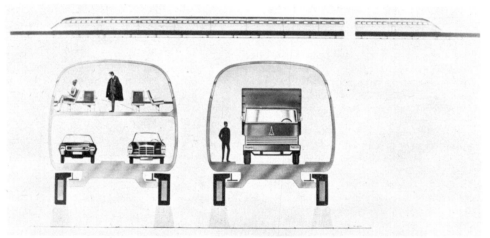

In designing the STS 2000, MBB examined the possibility of employing the system for the carriage of trucks, cars and containers as well as passengers. These sectional views indicate the variations in vehicle superstructure that would be available

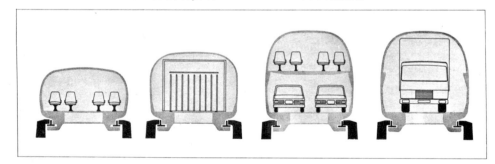

rail tracks, etc.

A fast and reliable switching system for traffic diverging from and merging with the main line is necessary for smooth and safe operation of a rapid transit system. To meet this need, MBB has developed an electromagnetically controlled switching device that has no moving parts situated on the track.

TEST STAND MODELS

By 1970 the company had developed and built a fixed dynamic test stand for studying the behaviour of electromagnets and the corresponding control circuits.

By coupling the simulation of the system with a hybrid computer, the development of

the control circuits and the electromagnets can be adapted to the changing requirements during the development phase.

In this manner the suspension and guidance magnets and the control of the experimental vehicle were investigated with respect to the effects of forces and track irregularities, and the simulation of the overall model was thus adapted to the actual behaviour of such a system.

The test stand model was designed so that system components of a later date may also be tested on it.

EXPERIMENTAL MAGNETIC CUSHION VEHICLE

The experimental vehicle developed by

MBB for magnetic field suspension and guidance research in combination with linear motor propulsion is the first large-scale test vehicle to be raised and guided solely by magnetic fields. The development of this vehicle is being supported financially by the Federal Ministry for Research and Technology.

Work on the vehicle and the test track began in July of 1970. On February 4, 1971, the first suspension tests of the experimental vehicle took place in the test laboratory. On April 2, 1971, the first test runs were made on MBB's special test track.

On May 5, 1971, the experimental vehicle was presented to the public for the first time in the presence of the Federal Minister for Educational Science and the Federal Minister for Transportation.

It demonstrated the feasibility of magnetic suspension and guidance with linear motor propulsion, and it provided information on those parameters not covered during simulation of the system and development of the components.

Weighing 5·6 metric tons and with a length of 23 ft, it has an asynchronous linear motor with 200 kW nominal power which is capable of accelerating the vehicle on the 766 yard (700 m) test track to a speed of 62 mph (100 km/h).

Four controlled suspension magnets and two guidance magnets on each side of the vehicle lift it and guide it during operation with a nominal air gap of $\frac{1}{2}$ in (14 mm) between the magnets and the rails.

FOURTH RESEARCH VEHICLE

Before prototype or operational vehicles can be realised, the interaction of all components and subsystems must be tested under more realistic, semi-operational conditions.

This vehicle is to run on a projected national test track of 75 km length, near Augsburg, and will allow extensive study of the following: riding comfort, safety systems, operational facilities and environmental effects.

In addition, detailed aerodynamic tests will be made, so that the performance characteristics of this vehicle will correspond closely to future operational requirements.

STS 2000

The MBB rapid transit vehicle STS 2000 has the goal, among others, of providing the prerequisites for the construction of fast, economic connections for passenger service between various business centres and vital transportation points.

The design is such that solely through variations in the superstructure—while retaining the essential system parameters along with the dimensions of the track and the vehicle's bogie—it will be possible to develop passenger versions of the vehicle. This will ensure that vehicles will be developed that are capable of meeting the respective transport requirements of any particular operational system.

CARS

As regards the cases where the transport of automobiles and their occupants is necessary (tourism), the MBB rapid transit system STS 2000 may be adapted to individual requirements.

TRUCKS AND CONTAINER TRAFFIC

In designing the system, the possibility of transporting trucks "piggy-back" was given special consideration, since this type of

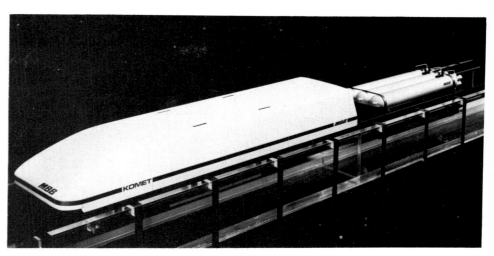

Model of the MBB Komet, a rocket-propelled MAGLEV test vehicle due to start tests during the summer of 1974. The vehicle is designed to test magnets, linear motors, braking systems and MAGLEV tracks at speeds up to 248 mph (400 km/h)

transport has several advantages over other types of transportation. For example, much higher speed (and transport performance) per vehicle is possible, in comparison to free transport of goods on the roads, resulting in a considerable gain in time for the shipping company. Furthermore, the highways are freed from obstruction by slow trucks and the risk of accidents is thus lowered. With respect to pure container traffic, appreciably better it will provide appreciably improved transport facilities for the collection and distribution of goods. This factor could affect the economy of the overall system decisively.

Since there is the possibility that in limited cases the transport of containers in special vehicles built for this purpose would be economically sound, this type of transportation was also taken into consideration. Here, too, by varying the superstructure while retaining the basic system parameters of the vehicle the track and their dimensions, optimised vehicles for this particular task can be constructed.

COMBINATIONS

In the case that the objectives of a future rapid transit system also require combinations of the aforementioned transport possibilities, the door will be open for the realisation of these combinations. Thus it will be possible to adapt freight-carrying vehicles to passenger transportation by means of installing rows of quick-mounting seats.

In addition, mixed traffic variants can be implemented by proper determination of the railway loading gauge, corresponding to the transport tasks required.

MBB STS 2000

This system is in the process of testing and development. While basic technologies have been decided upon, there are as yet many details (such as exact vehicle size, number of passengers, top speed) which have to be finally specified. The following refers to the concept as it is currently described by MBB.

High-speed ground transport system based on tracked vehicles capable of transporting passengers and/or freight (trucks, cars, containers, etc). Vehicle superstructure to be adapted to respective requirements, while essential system parameters, including guideway technology and dimensions, will be retained (50-150 passenger vehicles being examined). Automatic vehicle spacing will allow close headways, thus permitting frequent operation. Expected to operate at speeds of up to 280 mph (450 kp/h). Suspension and guidance by attracting electromagnets, propulsion by LIM. Track consists of ferromagnetic support/guidance rails, reaction rails, power rails and beams supported by pylons in most cases. Braking by LIM and mechanical means. Great advantages claimed in safety, comfort environmental aspects and maintenance costs.

Experimental vehicle known as the "MBB Magnetmobile". No switching in prototype. Driver operated. Max speed 56 mph (90 kp/h).

TECHNICAL DATA:

Block Speed	217 mph (350 kph)
Max	280 mph (450 kph)
Capacity:	
Average	5,000 pph
Max	10,000 pph

Cross section	2·1 m × 2 m (1-way)
Type of operation:	
Max grade	8% (planned)
Min curve	3,000 m (at max speed)
Headway	60 seconds (planned)
Station size	"much smaller than train"
Ave trip leg	31-310 miles (50-500 km)

COST DATA:

Guideway—$2 million/km (including control system, 2-way).

Vehicles—$400,000 each

Terminals—$500,000 each

Fare—will have to be comparable to air economy.

PRESENT STATUS: Prototype (Magnetmobile) under test since May 1971. Single vehicle on 410 miles (660 m) track. 124 mph (200 km) test vehicle has been in operation since spring 1972. Advanced 249 mph (400 kph) experimental vehicle, the Komet, to be tested in 1974.

CHIEF PROBLEMS/BARRIERS:

Switching (apparently solved but has yet to be tested under realistic conditions).

Necessity for international agreements as to guideway specifications.

Power collection at high speeds.

AVAILABILITY: Early eighties, given continuance of the recent rate of development.

REMARKS: Joint development programme on guideway for planned national test track together with other German partners within the "Gesellschaft für Bahntechnische Innovationen (GBI)" currently under way. Plan is to agree on and standardise common guideway configuration. Greatly expanded joint test facility built at Augsburg. Programme has substantial support by the German Government.

KOMET

In June 1973, MBM announced that it was constructing a rocket-propelled MAGLEV vehicle in order to test critical components which will be employed in "close to application" vehicles that are scheduled to start tests in 1977.

The vehicle, which is 24 ft 7 in (7·50 m) long, will operate along a 1,421-yard (1,300 m) linear test track at speeds of up to 248

The power for the electromagnetic supporting and guidance system is supplied by onboard batteries. The supporting and guidance magnets are located and controlled separately. The reaction rails (T-profile) are encircled by the supporting structure of the magnets. In the test track the control of the propulsion-free vehicle receives the gap-dependent values from a test rail in the centre of the track, in order to ensure undisturbed measurement of the test components located on the underside of the vehicle. PCM telemetry transmits the measurement values from the vehicle to the ground. The vehicle is equipped with an emergency support and guidance system. Deceleration is effected by friction brakes on the vehicle which act on the rails.

COMPONENT TEST VEHICLE:

Length	24 ft 7 in (7·5 m)
Width	8 ft 3 in (2·5 m)
Height	4 ft 11 in (1·5 m)
Weight	7 ton 7 cwt (7,500 kg)
Payload	1 ton 9 cwt (1,500 kg)
Design speed	248 mph (400 km/h)
Engine thrust (external drive)	20 t

TRACK:

Max length	1,421 yards (1,300 m)
Track gauge	7 ft 2 in (2·2 m)

SIEMENS AG

HEAD OFFICE:

Wittelsbacherplatz 2, D-800, Munchen 2

The Federal German government has funded a joint programme by AEG, Siemens and Brown-Boveri for the design and construction of a repulsive magnetic levitation system which aims at being efficient, economical to operate, comfortable, clean and silent. Self-stabilising lift and guidance forces produced by superconducting magnets provide levitation heights of between 10 and 20 cm. The magnetically suspended vehicles are driven by linear induction motors which can be controlled over their entire speed range with low losses. Tests have recently begun on a special test track at the Siemens Research Center in Erlangen. The track is laid out in a circle 306 yards (280 m) in diameter to enable individual components of the system to be subjected to endurance tests, using telemetric equipment, in both the rolling and suspended positions. The power supply equipment, the asynchronous linear motor and the magnet bearers, are currently being subjected to detailed tests in the rolling position. Test runs with full magnetic levitation are planned for Autumn 1974.

Testing will later be transferred to a large test track at Donauried financed by Federal funds.

A prototype vehicle designed jointly by AEG, BBC and Siemens is to be demonstrated on this 984 yard (900 m) long test track, built in the grounds of the Siemens Research Centre at Erlangen. The vehicle is scheduled for completion early in 1974

ITALY

PALERMO UNIVERSITY

HEAD OFFICE:

Aeronautical Institute, University of Palermo, Viale delle Scienze 90128, Palermo

TELEPHONE:

222748-317172-227439

DIRECTOR:

Professor Ennio Mattioli

The Aeronautical Institute, Palermo University began its tracked ACV research programme in 1967. Development of the I.A.P.2 manned model began in 1969, and the vehicle has undergone low speed tests. During 1970-71 the Institute undertook a series of theoretical studies and investigations in the TACV field and began the construction of the I.A.P.3. Designed for speeds up to 155 mph (250 km/h) the I.A.P.3 is a half-scale prototype TACV and is now being tested on a track built in conjunction with Ferrovie dello Stato, at Trapani-Milo airport. Assist-ance has also been given by the Aeronautica Militare.

The Institute is now engaged in research in the field of magnetic levitation and SLIM (single face linear induction motor) propulsion.

I.A.P. 2

The I.A.P. 2 tracked air cushion research vehicle has been constructed as part of a research programme which is aimed at the development of high speed tracked vehicle system with the following features: a speed of 250 mph (400 km/h) propulsion by propeller-turbine or linear induction motor, active and passive suspensions, modular construction and an elevated double track guideway.

I.A.P. 3

A half-scale TACV prototype, the I.A.P. 3 began its trials in May 1972 along a U-shaped concrete guideway.

The vehicle can be operated from either forward or rear driving positions and the basis design permits the coupling of a number of units to form a train

Lift is provided partly by air cushion pads and partly by an electro-magnetic system.

Propulsion is by single-faced linear induction motor. An electronically controlled suspension system is fitted at present, but the vehicle can be converted to a magnetic suspension system.

DIMENSIONS:

Length	43 ft 3½ in (13·20 m)
Beam	10 ft 0½ in (3·06 m)

WEIGHTS:

Loaded	10 tons

PERFORMANCE:

Designed for speed tests up to

155 mph (250 km/h)

I.A.P. 2 tracked air cushion vehicle research craft designed and built by the Aeronautical Institute, Palermo University, Sicily

The I.A.P. 3 half-scale TACV prototype in its guideway at Trapani-Milo airport

THE UNITED STATES OF AMERICA

AEROTRAIN SYSTEMS, INC

A subsidiary of Rohr Industries, Inc
HEAD OFFICE:
Chula Vista, California 92012
TELEPHONE:
(714) 426-7111
DIRECTORS:
B. F. Raynes, Chairman
F. E. McCreery
K. W. Tantlinger
A. K. Openchowski
L. Kaplan
J. Bertin
M. F. Millard
A. Garnault
EXECUTIVES:
K. W. Tantlinger, President
N. J. Beck, Vice-President and General
Manager
A. K. Openchowski, Vice-President
T. T. Brekka, Treasurer

Aerotrain Systems, Inc (formerly Aeroglide Systems, Inc) is a jointly held subsidiary of Rohr Corporation, Bertin & Cie, and Societe de l'Aerotrain. Rohr's interest in Aerotrain Systems, Inc is 60 per cent. Rohr will manufacture and market in the United States and Mexico, the high speed, guided air cushion transportation systems developed by the two French companies. Research, development and testing will be undertaken by Rohr, at the company's main plant at Chula Vista.

Aerotrain Systems, Inc is currently studying the application of tracked air cushion vehicles of various capacities, speeds, and modes of propulsion for fast passenger services between central metropolitan areas and airports, and also between cities. The former will probably travel at speeds below 200 mph (322 km/h) and the latter will operate at speeds over 200 mph (322 km/h). Either gas turbines driving propellers or linear induction motors may be used for propulsion, the choice depending on routes and noise restrictions.

The company has been given a DoT contract for a first-place engineering design study of a tracked ACV for urban applications. This is valued at about $1·5 million and involves the building of a full-scale 150 mph vehicle plus the design of tracks and terminals.

SYSTEM SPECIFICATIONS(1)

The following specifications are representative of prototype vehicles and are subject to change based on continuing vehicle development.

VEHICLE:	M-60	M-80	M-100
Model number	**M-60**	**M-80**	**M-100**
Passenger Capacity	60	80	100
DIMENSIONS:			
Overall length	94·0 ft	110·0 ft	124·2 ft
Overall height	10·8 ft	10·8 ft	10·8 ft
Overall width	10·7 ft	10·7 ft	10·7 ft
Interior cabin height	6·8 ft	6·8 ft	6·8 ft
Interior cabin width	9·5 ft	9·5 ft	9·5 ft
WEIGHT:			
Net vehicle weight	46,000 lb	54,000 lb	60,000 lb
Passengers and Baggage	14,000 lb	16,000 lb	20,000 lb
Gross vehicle weight	60,000 lb	70,000 lb	80,000 lb
POWER:			
LIM propulsion	3,415 KW	3,415 KW	3,415 KW
Maximum electrical load	4,100 KW	4,199 KW	4,298 KW
Average electrical load (cruise)	2,800 KW	3.899 KW	2,998 KW
PERFORMANCE:			
Cruising speed	150 mph	150 mph	150 mph
Maximum speed	170 mph	170 mph	170 mph
Acceleration distance to cruising speed	2 mi	2·3 mi	2·7 mi
Normal stopping distance	1·5 mi	1·5 mi	1·5 mi
Emergency stopping distance	0·5 mi	0·5 mi	0·5 mi
Allowable grade at cruise speed	5·5%	4·7%	4·2%
GUIDEWAY:			
Elevated roadbed width	135 in	135 in	135 in
Reaction rail height (overall)	33 in	33 in	33 in
Surface waviness		⅛ inch in 25 feet	
Minimum vertical turn	10,000 ft	10,000 ft	10,000 ft
Minimum horizontal turning radius	500 ft	500 ft	700 ft
ELECTRIFICATION:			
3 phase ac power supplied from wayside			
Frequency	60 Hz	60 Hz	60 Hz
Voltage	4,160 volt	4,160 volt	1,460 volt
Substation spacing	5·0 mi	4·0 mi	3·3 mi

Details of the 60-100 seat Aerotrain prototype are given on the previous page.

AEROTRAIN 150 mph AIRPORT ACCESS SERIES

The Aerotrain vehicle represents the adoption of the tracked air cushion vehicle technology developed by Société de l'Aérotrain and Bertin et Cie to the requirements of US applications.

The inverted "tee" guideway and K type air cushion have been fully developed and are available for operational úse.

Linear induction propulsion and high speed three phase power collection systems have been demonstrated at the facilities of Société de l'Aérotrain and are available for revenue producing TACV systems.

AEROTRAIN VEHICLE: The Aerotrain vehicle, featuring a 60 to 100 passenger size cabin and lightweight construction, operates on an inverted "tee" shaped guideway by linear induction motor propulsion at

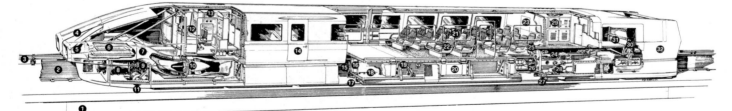

1 PRESTRESSED CONCRETE GUIDEWAY BEAMS	11 AUXILIARY DRIVE WHEELS	22 AIRCRAFT QUALITY SEATS
2 ALUMINIUM REACTION RAIL	12 AUTOMATIC TRAIN CONTROL CONSOLE	23 EMERGENCY EXIT DOORS
3 3-PHASE WAYSIDE POWER DISTRIBUTION SYSTEM	13 AUXILIARY TRAIN EQUIPMENT	24 LINEAR INDUCTION MOTOR
4 FRANGIBLE SAFETY FOREBODY	14 FLUSH PASSENGER DOORS	25 LIM SUPPORT SYSTEM
5 SUSPENSION AIR INLET	15 GUIDANCE AIR CUSHIONS	26 LIM GUIDANCE WHEELS
6 SOUND SUPPRESSOR	16 SUSPENSION AIR DISTRIBUTION DUCTS	27 AUXILIARY SUPPORT SKIS
7 INLET AIR DUCTING	17 LIFT AIR CUSHIONS	28 PROPULSION COOLING DUCTS
8 COMPRESSOR MOTOR	18 AIR DISTRIBUTION ORIFICES	29 PROPULSION CONTROL BAY
9 COMPRESSOR SPEED REDUCTION	19 EMERGENCY STOP BY PASS DOORS	30 MECHANICAL BRAKE
10 LIFT COMPRESSOR	20 AIR CONDITIONING UNITS	31 BAGGAGE COMPARTMENT (OPTIONAL)
	21 PASSENGER COMPARTMENT	32 FRANGIBLE SAFETY AFTERBODY

speeds up to 150 mph. Electric motor driven compressors supply pressurised air for the lift and guidance air cushion suspensions.

POWER COLLECTION: A power collection unit, mounted on one side of the vehicle, collects 3-phase, 4,160 volt, electrical power from the wayside power distribution rails. Power is collected by sliding contact with the power distribution rails and the collection unit is articulated from the vehicle to accommodate relative motion.

ELECTRICAL PROPULSION: A polyphase linear induction motor provides the thrust required to accelerate, maintain speed, and dynamically brake the vehicle. The LIM primary is mounted in the vehicle afterbody. The LIM secondary is the reaction rail which is mounted on the guideway. Separate motor fans provide both LIM cooling by forced convection and LIM guidance by a set of air bearing units attached to opposite ends of the LIM. A Thryistor variable voltage power control unit is used to limit acceleration onset. A power supply furnishes controlled dc current for dynamic braking. Static power factor correction capacitors compensate for the LIM reactive power.

AIR CUSHION SUSPENSION: The low pressure air cushion suspension system raises the vehicle from the guideway providing relatively friction-free motion. The secondary suspension integrates with the air cushion to damp the effects of dynamic disturbance from guideway irregularities and cross winds. The associated air supply system contains an air inlet with guide vanes, a forward plenum, two compressors, supply ducts, and cushion supply scoops. Two constant speed, 3-phase, induction motors drive the compressor units.

BRAKING: LIM dynamic braking reduces vehicle speed to approximately 50 mph, whereupon a hydraulic system circuit applies frictional braking at the reaction rail for final stopping. In an emergency, the air cushions can be vented to rest the vehicle on skids for additional braking which is controlled to not exceed 0·4 g deceleration. A pneumatic system applied to the hydraulic system frictional brakes provides redundancy.

PASSENGER CABIN: The typical seating arrangement illustrated features 22 inch seat width and 34 inch seat pitch. Each seat contains a seat belt and protective padding. Exposed hard metal surfaces are avoided. The cabin interior acoustical treatment maintains the noise level below 65 dB(A). The vehicle external acoustical treatment maintains the noise level below 73 dB(A) at 50 feet to the side of the vehicle (measured on the dB(A) scale with a reference of 0·0002 microbars). Multiple air conditioning units modularly mounted in the undercar area maintain the passenger and crew compartment environment at 65° to 75°F.

(1) Automatic Train Control and other Sub-systems available to individual application requirements.

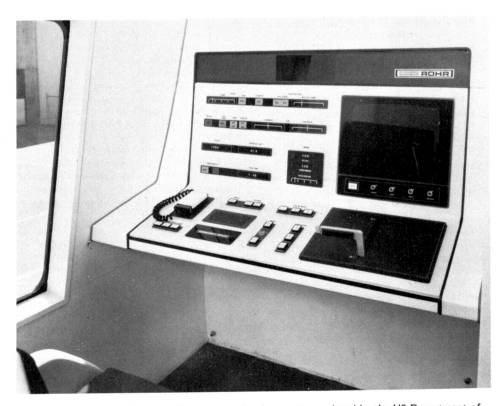

Top: The Rohr-built Aerotrain, a 60-seat operational prototype ordered by the US Department of Transportation. This particular model is propelled by a linear induction motor, and rides on a Bertin air cushion suspension system *Centre:* Interior of the Aerotrain Systems Inc M-60 prototype Automatic air conditioning is provided *Bottom:* The vehicle, designed to operate at 150 mph, is controlled by computer, but has provision for a manual override. The driver monitors the track at the front and rear by a closed circuit television system. Seen in this photograph is the automatic control console

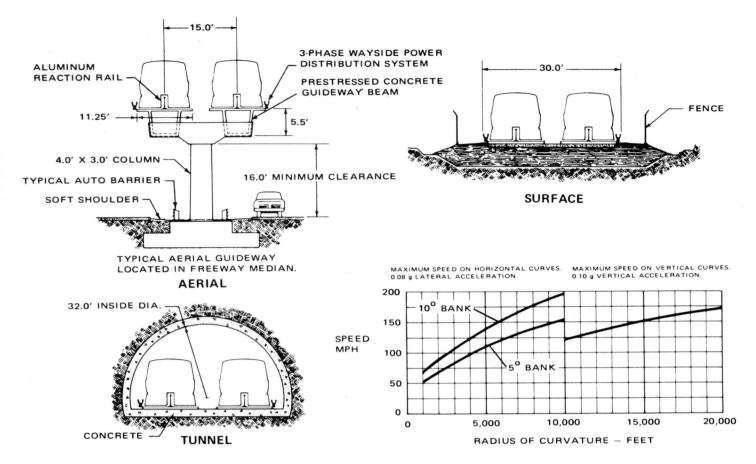

Types of guideway envisaged for the Aerotrain and graphs showing the radius of track curvature and the maximum speed on horizontal and vertical curves

AIRESEARCH MANUFACTURING COMPANY A division of the Garrett Corporation

2525 West 190th Street, Torrance, California 90509

TELEPHONE:

(213) 323-9500

EXECUTIVES:

John A. Teske, Vice President and Manager

Dan W. Derbes, Assistant Manager

William L. Bowler, Manager Ground Transportation Systems

AiResearch Manufacturing Company is a division of the Garrett Corporation, Los Angeles. It is engaged primarily in the design, development and manufacture of sophisticated systems and components for aerospace and ground transportation. Products include environmental controls, electronics, electromechanical and turbomachinery, heat transfer and cryogenics and ground transportation and industrial power systems. Located in the Los Angeles suburb of Torrance, AiResearch employs approximately 4,500 persons. The firm pioneered the concept of air conditioned and pressurized aircraft for high-altitude flight, and today more than 90 per cent of the aircraft built in the free world are equipped with AiResearch systems.

In the field of surface transportation AiResearch has developed and built a linear induction motor research vehicle (LIMRV) for the US Department of Transportation. The LIMRV runs on standard railroad track with a reaction rail mounted in the centre of the track. It is designed for 402·336 km/h

(250 mph) and has achieved speeds in excess of 234 mph to date. AiResearch also developed and built the LIM propulsion system for the Grumman-built tracked levitated research vehicle (TLRV) tests of which were scheduled to begin in 1974.

Other surface transportation systems under development include a dual power, gas-turbine/electric propulsion system for commuter cars, a flywheel energy storage system for subway and commuter cars, a wayside electric power collection system for high speed vehicles (this system has been tested at 482·80 km/h (300 mph)), and the Advanced Concept Train (ACT-1).

LINEAR INDUCTION MOTOR RESEARCH VEHICLE (LIMRV)

Starting in 1966, AiResearch performed a study for the U.S. Department of Transportation, Federal Railroad Administration, aimed at proving the feasibility of using linear induction motors as propulsion systems for high-speed ground transportation vehicles.

Subsequently, AiResearch was selected to build a demonstration LIM and a vehicle to test the propulsion system. The vehicle was completed in December 1969. In January 1970 a year-long slow speed test programme was started in Torrance, California on a one-quarter mile (0·40 km) test track. In May 1971 the vehicle was moved to Pueblo, Colorado, site of the Department of Transportation High Speed Ground Test Centre, where high-speed track and 6·2 miles (10·05 km) of reaction rail were installed. The track is standard gauge railroad track.

In September 1971 AiResearch personnel began testing the LIM propulsion system for the Federal Railroad Administration. In incremental steps the vehicle was operated at successively higher speeds. The vehicle and LIM are designed for a top speed of 250 mph (402·33 km/h). Test runs of more than 234 mph had been demonstrated by April 1974. The vehicle has been equipped with two gas-turbines so that it can be accelerated to 402·336 km/h (250 mph) in a shorter distance than is possible with LIM propulsion alone. The faster rate of acceleration will permit data to be obtained on the LIM propulsion at its top speed and at the same time provide adequate safety margins for braking and stopping within the limits of the track available 9·67 km (6·2 miles).

LIM FOR TRACKED LEVITATED RESEARCH VEHICLE (TLRV)

Under a US Department of Transportation contract, AiResearch has designed and constructed a LIM propulsion system for the second-generation tracked levitated research vehicle built by Grumman Aerospace Corporation.

The LIM propulsion system will produce 10,000 pounds of thrust continuous at 300 mph (8,000 hp) and was delivered for installation in the TLRV in early 1974.

The LIM propulsion system will be supported and guided by its own air cushion system which was designed and fabricated by AiResearch. The vehicle will be suspended with a separate air cushion system.

AiResearch has also designed a wayside power collection system for this 300 mph vehicle under a separate Department of Transportation contract. Both DOT contracts are under the auspices of the Federal Railroad Administration. The vehicle will be tested at Pueblo, Colorado.

To propel the TLRV at 300 mph (482·80 km/h) AiResearch has designed the propulsion system to include two identical LIM power modules each to provide one-half of the maximum vehicle thrust requirements, only one of which will be installed for the initial test phases. The two LIMs have a combined system rating of 10,000 lb of thrust continuous at 300 mph (8,000 hp). The two LIM modules are mounted in tandem under the TLRV.

Since the TLRV is a research vehicle, the propulsion system was sized primarily to attain high acceleration. Initial acceleration is about 6·0 mph/sec and even at 250 mph the acceleration is still about 3·3 mph/sec. With thrust at full acceleration, a speed of 300 mph is reached in about one minute. By way of comparison, the average initial acceleration of conventional trains is only one-sixth that of the LIM-propelled TLRV due to passenger comfort limits.

Above and below: Linear induction motor research vehicle built by AiResearch Manufacturing Co. Twin gas-turbines have been fitted enabling the vehicle to accelerate to 402·336 km/h (250 mph) on the existing 9·67 km (6·2 mile) US Department of Transportation's high-speed test track, near Pueblo, Colorado

LINEAR INDUCTION MOTORS

The LIM horseshoe shaped windings in the vehicle straddle and react electromagnetically with an aluminium reaction rail mounted vertically in the centre of the guideway. Thrust and speed of the LIM are controlled by a power conditioning unit which varies the voltage and frequency applied to the LIM.

Input power for propulsion is obtained from a wayside power pickup at 8,250 volts, 3 phase 60 Hz. The wayside power collector was designed and built by AiResearch.

Much of the experience in design, fabrication, and testing of the company's first LIM system has been incorporated in the TLRV LIM. Significant differences include a higher output-to-weight ratio and fully independent suspension for the TLRV LIM. The improvement in specific thrust is achieved principally by direct liquid cooling and the use of high strength-to-weight structural materials such as titanium.

Independent suspension of the LIM is achieved by the use of air cushions for both support and guidance and a first-degree-of-freedom thrust link connection with the vehicle chassis. Only the thrust axis is restrained.

LIM REACTION RAIL

The LIM reaction rail serves a dual purpose in the TLRV propulsion system: (1) it provides the electrical secondary for the LIM and functions as a continuous reactive thrust element, and (2) it provides a surface suitable for the vertical air cushions which laterally guide the LIM.

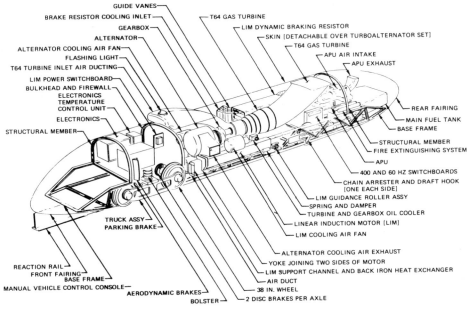

Garrett/AiResearch linear induction motor research vehicle

POWER CONDITIONING UNIT (PCU)

The LIM propulsion system power conditioning unit converts 3 phase, fixed voltage, 60 Hz wayside power into 3 phase, variable voltage, variable-frequency output power suitable for operating the LIM at various speed conditions. The PCU is comprised of five main components: a phase delay rectifier, a high voltage inductor, an inverter, a synchronous condenser, and field power supply. Two PCU's are required for the full LIM propulsion system, one for each LIM.

FORD MOTOR COMPANY

North American Automotive Operations
HEAD OFFICE:
  20000 Rotunda Drive, Dearborn, Michigan 48121
MAILING ADDRESS:
  PO Box 2053, Dearborn, Michigan

Since 1969, Ford has been conducting a research programme aimed at answering a number of questions concerned with magnetic levitation. In 1971, the US Department of Transportation awarded the company a research contract to study the feasibility of magnetic support in greater depth. In particular, the company was asked to look at problems related to system stability and the cryogenics of superconducting magnets.

Ford's first-phase contract is reported to have been $130,000, and a second-phase contract, awarded in 1972, was for $200,000. A third phase, awarded in 1973, was for $75,000.

Conceptually, the simplest levitation scheme is one in which the vehicle contains a large number of permanent magnets, and the track is also made of permanent magnets, arranged in such a way that the magnets in the vehicle are repelled by the magnets in the roadbed. This scheme has serious drawbacks, however, because the weight of the permanent magnets is so large that a clearance of only a fraction of an inch can be achieved. Furthermore the system is unstable and active control devices would be needed.

A much better scheme uses several high-strength electromagnets in the vehicle and no magnets in the track. Instead the track is covered with an aluminium sheet or plate. There is no magnetic levitation when the vehicle is at rest, but when the vehicle moves it generates electrical currents in the aluminum. These in turn produce a magnetic field which pushes up on the electromagnets in the vehicle. The magnetic field gets stronger as the vehicle speeds up, but it levels off at speeds of 50 to 100 mph. Thus the vehicle moves on wheels at low speeds, but lifts off as the speed increases.

Ordinary electromagnets in the vehicle require a lot of electrical power to maintain them. In the past ten years, however, there has been a very great development in superconducting magnets. These magnets must be maintained at cryogenic temperatures, but do not require additional electrical power once they are energised. They require some refrigerator power on a continuous basis, but this is small compared to the amount of electrical power required by a conventional electromagnet.

Detailed calculations and experiments with superconducting magnets situated over a rotating aluminium wheel have shown that this magnetic levitation concept is a sound one. Lateral guidance can also be provided magnetically. Some active control is needed to help stabilise the system against perturbations, but the control power needed is quite small.

As part of its programme, the company has

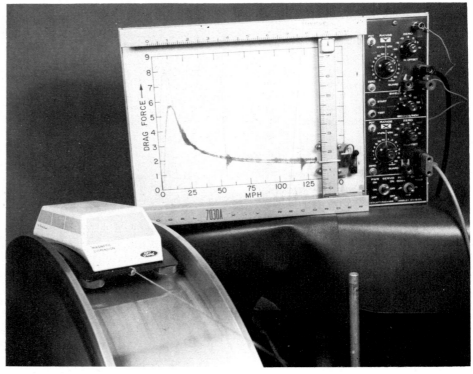

Tests being undertaken with a model equipped with superconducting magnets over a rotating aluminium wheel in Ford's Scientific Laboratory

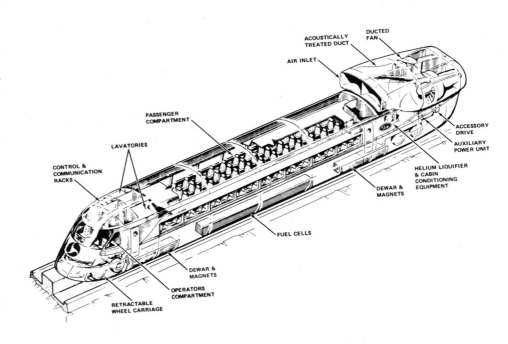

Cutaway of a Ford project for a MAGLEV vehicle propelled by gas-turbine-driven ducted fans

built superconducting magnets and subjected them to simulated conditions they would encounter when employed operationally. The company has also tested a servo-controlled, attraction magnetic system, and investigated problems likely to arise from the use of superconducting magnets, including shielding of passengers from magnetic fields.

Another area of investigation at Ford, is passenger comfort. A suspension damping system will be necessary to ensure a comfortable ride. The company believes that this can be achieved at speeds up to 482·78 km/h (300 mph) by employing either an active control system or, with passive damping, a secondary suspension system.

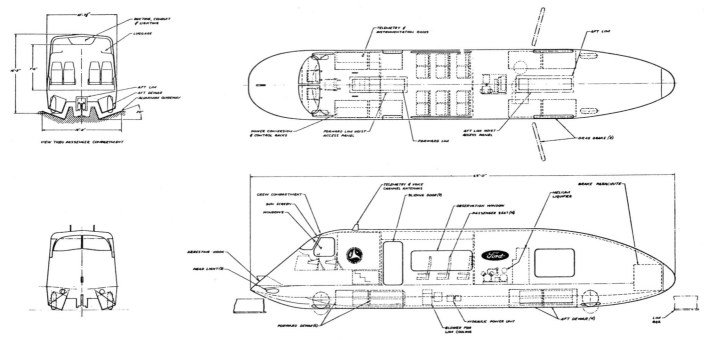

Conceptual layout of a Ford magnetically-levitated and propelled research vehicle. The vehicle would move on wheels at low speeds, and lift off the surface as the speed increased

GRUMMAN AEROSPACE CORPORATION

HEAD OFFICE AND WORKS:
South Oyster Bay Road, Bethpage, Long Island, New York 11714

CHAIRMAN OF THE BOARD AND CHIEF EXECUTIVE OFFICER:
J. G. Gavin, Jr.

PRESIDENT:
G. M. Skurla

SENIOR VICE-PRESIDENT:
I. G. Hedrick

Grumman has completed the detail design and fabrication of a 300 mph (483 km/h) tracked levitated research vehicle TLRV under contract to the US Department of Transportation. Testing is underway at the Department of Transportation High Speed Test Centre, Pueblo, Colorado.

GRUMMAN TLRV

The Grumman TLRV is a 51 ft (15·54 m) long air cushion research vehicle designed to ride in a U-shaped track at speeds up to 300 mph (483 km/h). The maximum use is made of developed aerospace hardware and the materials and processes used in the construction of the vehicle are conventional.

The craft is being used to investigate aerodynamic performance and stability, dynamic response of both vehicle and guideway members, secondary suspension requirements, air cushion design and the wearability of flexible skirt material. During certain tests, sections of the guideway will be misaligned deliberately in order to study vehicle safety and reliability when variations are introduced.

LIFT AND PROPULSION: Three externally mounted JT15D turbofans are employed as compressors for cushion air. Air from the bypass fans is ducted to four lift pads and four guidance pads. During 1973 the vehicle was operated up to 90 mph (144·84 km/h) using only residual thrust from the JT15Ds for propulsion and is expected to reach 125 mph (201·16 km/h) in that mode.

Grumman's 51 ft (14·54 m) research vehicle in its guideway at the Department of Transportation's High Speed Test Centre, Pueblo, Colorado

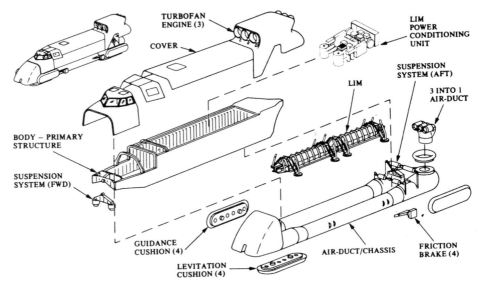

Exploded drawing of the Grumman TLRV, showing the turbofan installation linear induction motor, and body and cover structure

With the linear motor installed, the vehicle is expected to attain speeds in the region of 300 mph (483 km/h).

SECONDARY SUSPENSION SYSTEMS: The body is connected to the chassis by elements which can be operated in an active or passive mode. The entire body can also be banked with respect to the chassis to substantially eliminate lateral acceleration during turns. The levitation and guidance cushions are connected to the chassis by elements which can also be operated actively or passively.

ACCOMMODATION AND SAFETY FEATURES: The vehicle requires only one operator. Three additional seats are provided, however. One seat is for use by a test instrumentation engineer, and the other two will provide observer accommodation. The cabin is surrounded by a strong primary structure and has a 'bird proof' windshield. Both entrance doors are accessible to all crew members. Fire protection includes detection and suppression systems, foam-filled fuel tanks, fire walls and fuel tanks located remotely from the cabin.

BRAKING SYSTEM: Normal braking is applied by aero-brake, reverse thrust and friction pads. Provision for emergency braking includes a form of arresting system built into the guideway, and a 7 ft (2·13 m) diameter drag chute.

DIMENSIONS:

Length overall	51 ft 0 in (15·54 m)
Width overall	12 ft 0 in (3·65 m)
Height overall	13 ft 2 in (4·01 m)

OPERATING WEIGHT:

Aero propulsion	34,000 lb (15,422 kg)
Linear induction motor	62,000 lb (28,123 kg)

PERFORMANCE:

Max speed	300 mph (483 km/h)
Min acceleration distance, 0-300 mph (0-483 km/h)	1·9 miles app (3·1 km)
Min braking distance	1·5 miles app (2·4 km)

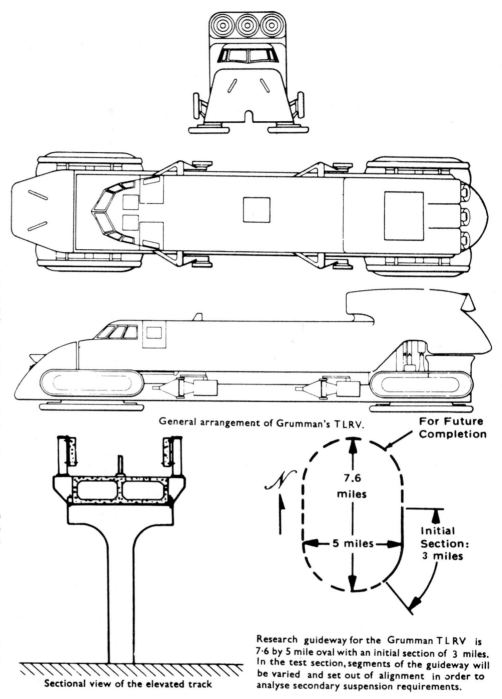

General arrangement of Grumman's TLRV.

For Future Completion

7.6 miles

5 miles

Initial Section: 3 miles

Sectional view of the elevated track

Research guideway for the Grumman TLRV is 7·6 by 5 mile oval with an initial section of 3 miles. In the test section, segments of the guideway will be varied and set out of alignment in order to analyse secondary suspension requirements.

STANFORD RESEARCH INSTITUTE
HEAD OFFICE:
Menlo Park, California 94025
TELEPHONE:
(415) 326-6200
CABLES:
Stanres, Menlo Park/TWX 910-323-1246
EXECUTIVES:
Charles A. Anderson, President
Don R. Scheuch, Ph.D., V.P., Research Operations
Weldon B. Gibson, Ph.D., Executive V.P., SRI International

Stanford Research Institute (SRI) completed a three phase contract with the U.S. Department of Transportation, Federal Railroad Administration in 1974. This contract provided for the analysis of the various forms of magnetically levitated vehicles that could be used for high speed passenger transportation.

A 500 ft (152·40 m) guideway was built by SRI and used initially to investigate the forces generated on a rectangular superconducting magnet moving in it. Lift, drag and guidance forces, sensitivity to small guideway misalignments and electrical imperfections were measured.

Tests were conducted in 1972 with a vehicle which was 14 ft (4·26 m) long, 3 ft 4 in (1·01 m) wide and weighed 650 lb (244·82 kg). These tests assessed the levitation characteristics of the vehicle and confirmed analytic predictions of the vehicle's performance.

The vehicle is magnetically levitated and guided by four super-conducting magnets in the white dewars on the corners of the vehicle. During 1972, the test vehicle was levitated more than twenty times at speeds up to 30 mph (48·28 km/h). It is supported by four wheels underneath when at rest and levitates at a speed of about 10 mph (16·09 km/h). It is accelerated and braked by an endless cable powered by a winch at the end of the guideway.

The vehicle and guideway were modified during 1973 to investigate its stability and ride quality and evaluate analytic predictions of these features. Both active and passive damping coils were used in these experiments. These controls, the on-board recorder and the additional power supplies increased the vehicle's weight to 1,070 lb (485 kg). More than thirty-five tests were performed including the levitation of the vehicle over a variety of guideway offsets that were as great as 25% of the suspension height. No instabilities were observed in any of the five degrees of freedom measured in any of these tests using passive or active damping. The ride quality was improved by the use of active damping.

Stanford Research Institute's 14 ft (4·26 m) long Maglev research vehicle, which employs super- conducting magnets for support

AIR CUSHION APPLICATORS, CONVEYORS and PALLETS

AUSTRALIA

AUSTRALIA
SOUTHERN HYDRO-HOVER
HEAD OFFICE:
   P.O. Box 23, Walkerville, South Australia

5081
OFFICERS:
   Trevor de V. Webb
   Southern Hydro-Hover is engaged in the development of an air cushion conveyor system originated by the late Thomas W. Webb. His son, Trevor de V. Webb is now continuing the development of the system in conjunction with a local company, Rotor-Lift.

TAYLORCRAFT TRANSPORT PTY LTD
HEAD OFFICE:
   Box 127, Elizabeth, South Australia 5112
TELEPHONE: 584944
DIRECTORS:
   R. V. Taylor
   D. C. Bartell
In addition to a series of light air cushion vehicles, Taylorcraft Transport Pty Ltd has built a small load-carrying platform, the Portaire, which is available to order. Two larger platforms, the Trailaire and the Utilaire—a 1 ton vehicle with road suspension—are in the planning stage.

PORTAIRE
This is a pedestrian operated load-carrying platform for use in soft, wet or sandy locations where the use of wheeled carriers is precluded. It may be used with pallets where the 6 in (152 mm) lift permits easy loading. A payload of up to 600 lb (272 kg) may be carried, depending on the slope of the ground to be traversed.

Lift is provided by a Wisconsin HS-8D engine driving a 20 in (508 mm) diameter centrifugal fan.

DIMENSIONS:

Length	5 ft (1·52 m)	Height	2 ft 6 in (0·762 m)	WEIGHT:	
Width	3 ft 6 in (1·06 m)	Hard structure clearance	8 in (204 mm)	Empty	135 lb (61·23 kg)

A Portaire pedestrian-operated load-carrying platform equipped for spraying

FRANCE

SOCIÉTÉ BERTIN & CIE
OFFICE AND WORKS:
   BP No. 3, 78370 Plaisir, France
TELEPHONE:
   462.25.00
TELEX:
   26.619
DIRECTORS:
   Jean Bertin, President Director General
   Benjamin Salmon, Director General
   Michel Perineau, Director General
Air Cushion Handling Division
OFFICER:
   M. Croix-Marie
ADDRESS:
   Centre d'Essais Aérotrain, Gometz la Ville
   91400 Orsay, France
TELEPHONE:
   592.03.18
TELEX:
   60.090
Research on ground effect and air cushion principle applications has been undertaken by Bertin et Cie since 1956. The company developed the original technique of separately fed plenum chambers surrounded by flexible skirts—see entries for SEDAM (ACVs) and Société de l'Aérotrain (Tracked Skimmers). The same basic technology is being applied extensively to industrial materials handling.

In the past, developments in this field have mainly covered special applications. A stage has now been reached where standard equip-

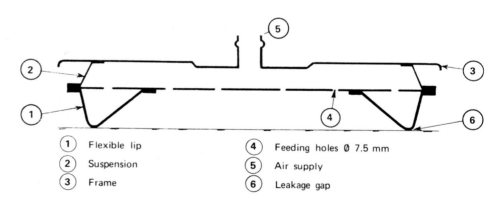

(1) Flexible lip	(4)	Feeding holes Ø 7.5 mm
(2) Suspension	(5)	Air supply
(3) Frame	(6)	Leakage gap

Basic configuration and components of a Bertin circular cushion

Standard Bertin circular cushion

ment can be made available for a large number of handling applications.

Bertin has now made available standard components and, according to the type of problem to be solved, offers clients 'do-it-yourself-kits'', plus advice, technologyical assistance or full design services.

STANDARD DO-IT-YOURSELF KITS

These are available in the following configurations:

1. Circular Cushions

These form the basis of the handling platforms. Their positioning and number is determined by function, the weight and nature of the loads (height, position of centre of gravity etc.).

Three cushions at least must be employed to ensure stability.

The cushions can be fitted on to a chassis with spring fastenings.

The flexible lips will not suffer wear under normal conditions but are interchangeable in cases of accidental damage.

Circular cushions are produced as standard units in three sizes: ϕ 300, ϕ 450, ϕ 600.

General characteristics are given in the accompanying table.

2. Standard Modules

Standard Modules complete with chassis and a standard circular cushion can be supplied, ready for use. The lift capacity of these modules is comparable to that of the corresponding circular cushion. Chassis can be modified as required.

3. Honeycomb Cushions

Honeycomb cushions are available in three standard sizes. Fully stable, these cushions allow full use of the load bearing surface for lift. In addition they are very thin but can bear very heavy loads when at rest.

These cushions employ inflatable joints to seal off adjacent square cells which are fed separately through vents from a single plenum. The plenum itself is fed from any suitable compressed air source.

STANDARD UNITS FOR SPECIAL APPLICATIONS

For moving and positioning loads in fac-

Metal air cushion skids fitted beneath a platform used to feed loads of up to 3,000 kg to a press Off-cushion, beneath the press, the platform withstands pressures of up to 26,000 kg.

Circular Cushions	ϕ 300	ϕ 450	ϕ 600
Overall diameter	0,364 m	0,540 m	0,680 m
Height at rest	0,035 m	0,050 m	0,050 m
Weight	5,5 kg	8,5 kg	14 kg
Lift area	0,07 m²	0.16 m²	0.28 m²
Load capacity	500 kg	1,200 kg	2,500 kg
Air Supply	through connection to a compressed air network from an adapted low pressure compressor		

Honeycomb Cushions Major characteristics:	Type 1	Type 2	Type 3
Length × width (mm)	626 × 329	416 × 768	590 × 590
Height at rest (mm)	22	32	30
Lift area (m²)	0,162	0,250	0,250
Load capacity (kg)	1,000	1,700	3,000

Standard module, ready assembled, comprising chassis and one circular cushion.

Chassis can be modified as required

tories and buildings with low ceiling heights air cushion skids have been designed. These metal pads have no flexible seals, and used over a very even surface, they operate without surface contact on an air film a few hundredths of a millimetre deep.

Applications include a 3,000 kg payload platform—for feeding a press-mounted on seven skids 200 mm in diameter. This unit can withstand a pressure of 26,000 kg when at rest beneath the press.

MACHINERY HANDLING IN FACTORIES

Typical examples of air cushion applicators for handling machinery within factories and workshops are four 30-ton profiling units in a metallurgical centre. Each is fitted with 16 circular cushions each 0·600 m diameter to enable a rapid changeover in function to cope with fresh production orders. Air flow required to move each unit reaches 80 litres/ second and traction effort is limited to 40 kg.

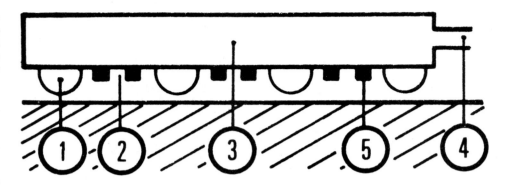

1 *joint*
2 *aperture*
3 *chamber*
4 *air supply*
5 *resting pads*

Diagram showing the basic structure of the Bertin honeycomb air cushion pallets

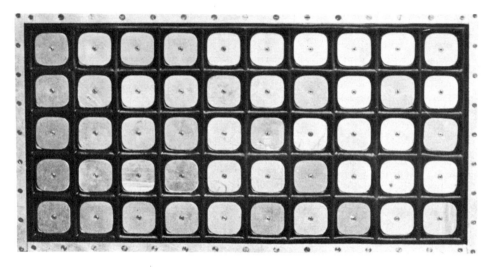

Underside of standard honeycomb cushion showing the inflatable joints which seal off adjacent square cushion cells

One of four 30-ton profiling units in a metallurgical centre, each of which is fitted with sixteen Bertin circular cushions. Only 88 lb (40 kg) of traction effort is needed to reposition each unit in readiness for production change overs

ETABLISSEMENTS NEU

HEAD OFFICE:
Sac Postal No. 28, 59 Lille, France
Etablissements NEU is a licensee of Jet-
stream Systems Co of Hayward, California.
Details of the conveyor system built by the
company can be found under the entry for
Jetstream Systems Company, USA.

GERMANY

HELMUT FRANK BLECHVERARBEITUNG

HEAD OFFICE:
Laufdorferstrasse, D-6331 Bonbaden, West
Germany

This company manufactures Jetstream
conveyor systems under licence.

ITALY

DEL MONEGO

HEAD OFFICE:
Piazza della Republica 8, Milan

Del Monego produces Jetstream conveyor
systems under licence.

JAPAN

EBARA MANUFACTURING COMPANY

HEAD OFFICE:
11 Haneda Asahicho, Ota-Ku, Tokyo

This company produces Jetstream conveyor
systems under licence.

TRINIDAD

COELACANTH GEMCO LTD

HEAD OFFICE:
1 Richardson Street, Point Fortin, Trinidad,
West Indies
DIRECTORS:
Nigel Seale
Kelvin Corbie
Teddy Watson
SECRETARY:
R. Varma

Coelacanth Gemco Ltd., the first company
to specialise in the design and construction
of air cushion vehicles in the West Indies,
has developed a hover conveyor system and
a hover pallet.

The pallet, measuring 3 ft × 4 ft, is capable
of lifting and moving 1,000 lb, while operated
by one man and great potential is seen for
the use of these units within Trinidad
factories.

The hover-conveyor system is designed in
modules of 10 ft and 15 ft, enabling a system
of any length to be devised to suit changing
production line requirements.

Coelacanth Gemco is also working on a
self-contained unit, powered by a 100 hp
diesel engine driving a 36 in eight-blade
axial fan at 2,500 rpm to produce 30,000 cu
ft of air per minute at 6 in w.g. pressure.

This will be used in the movement of oil
company tanks between various locations.
Multiples of this unit will enable tanks of any
size to be moved after attaching the skirt
system.

A Coelacanth hoverpallet employed in a workshop to move air-conditioning equipment. This
particular model lifts loads up to 1,000 lb (453·592 kg). Other models, operating on factory air
supplies of 80 lb sq in, will carry loads of up to 15 tons. The model seen above operates on either
115 or 230 volts ac

UNITED KINGDOM

AIRAVIA LTD

HEAD OFFICE:
20 North Road, Shanklin, Isle of Wight
TELEPHONE:
Shanklin 3643, 2580

DIRECTORS:
H. H. Snowball, Managing Director
A. A. Godbold
K. M. Wainwright

R. Croft, Secretary
Airavia is consultant to British Hovercraft Corporation on matters affecting the supply of hoverpallets to the USSR.

AIRMATIC ENGINEERING LTD

HEAD OFFICE:
King Street, Sileby, Leicestershire
TELEPHONE:
Sileby 2816 (STD Code 050 981)
EXECUTIVES:
P. Lucas. Marketing Manager

This company is manufacturing and marketing the Pneu-move air bearing system under licence from the National Research Development Corporation of the United Kingdom.

PNEU-MOVE

The Pneu-move system has been developed by the National Engineering Laboratory to enable heavy loads to be moved by hand without necessitating an expensive, high precision, operating surface.

Its low friction, small size, and low power requirement suit it for the movement of heavy machinery, particularly where man-handling in confined spaces may be necessary. It is also suitable for use in the production lines of heavy components where it eliminates the need for powered conveyors, allows accurate positioning because of the low friction, and gives secure parking by switching off the air supply.

The system consists of an air bearing, mounted on a ball to allow some pivoting, and a track of a compliant material. It can be operated from a normal workshop air supply of 85 psi.

Applications include:

The installation of machines where suitable lifting facilities do not exist in the hosiery, printing, and carton-making industries.

A production flow line, e.g. final assembly of machine tools.

The movement of heavy raw materials, including steel plate.

The handling of components during manufacture, e.g. large fabrications between operations.

Assembly of mining machinery on site.

The movement of heavy loads without damage to floors, in machine tool showrooms and lecture theatres.

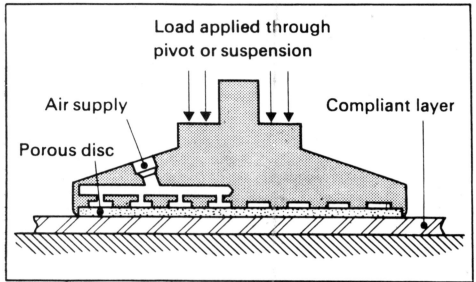

Sectional view of a Pneu-move air bearing pad. The undersides of the pads have porous stainless steel surfaces which ride on the air flow created between the porous surface and a layer of compliant material below, such as neoprene sheet

Pneu-move air bearing pads enable heavy loads to be moved quickly by hand, without damaging floors

PNEU-MOVE AIRMATS

Derived from the company's air bearing pads, the Pneu-move air-mats are designed for the movement of heavy moulds, fixtures and work-pieces across machine tables. Air pressure and flow requirements are low and existing workshop air lines can be used. A range of standard sizes is available but other sizes and special designs can be produced by the company, the standard air supply connector is ¼ in (6·35 mm) BSP.

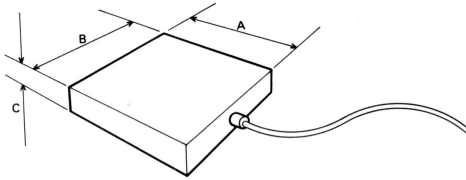

Pneu-Move-Air-Mat. Designed to carry heavy loads over holes and slots on machine tables, the Air-Mat is suitable for moving components in drilling, tapping, milling, rubber and plastics moulding and many other machine operations

The above tables give typical performance for a supply of pressure 6kp/cm². (85 psig) of Pneu-Move Air-Mats when used on an average machine tool table with a continuous surface. For loads less than those shown, lower supply pressures may be used, with correspondingly lower airflow rates. Where holes and slots are to be traversed, or if the table is badly worn, some allowance must be made for increased airflow and reduced maximum load.

Ref.No.	Dimensions in mm (inches)			Max.load kgf (lbf)		Airflow m³ / min(scfm)	
	A	B	C				
AM 1	150(6)	150(6)	25(1)	450	(1000)	0.085	(3)
AM 2	150(6)	300(12)	25(1)	900	(2000)	0.170	(6)
AM 3	200(8)	150(6)	30(1¼)	675	(1500)	0.127	(4.5)
AM 4	200(8)	300(12)	30(1¼)	1350	(3000)	0.255	(9)
AM 5	200(8)	600(24)	30(1¼)	2700	(6000)	0.51	(18)
AM 6	300 (12)	300(12)	40(1½)	1800	(4000)	0.34	(12)
AM 7	300(12)	450(18)	40(1½)	2700	(6000)	0.51	(18)
AM 8	450(18)	450(18)	50(2)	4500	(10000)	0.85	(30)
AM 9	600(24)	600(24)	45(1¾)	7200	(16000)	1.36	(48)

BRITISH HOVERCRAFT CORPORATION

HEAD OFFICE:
East Cowes, Isle of Wight
DIRECTORS:
See ACV section

FLOATLOAD (1 Ton)

The 1-ton Floatload hoverpallet consists of a load-carrying, steel and plywood sandwich platform with four easily removable rubber diaphragm assemblies underneath. Air is supplied through a 1 in BSP connector and control valve.

Designed for moving loads of up to 1 ton on smooth floors, the hoverpallet can also be used in conjunction with standard fork lift trucks, pallets and stillages, which can easily be modified for this purpose. Single man operation of the loaded pallet is easily effected.

Loads may be placed directly on to the platform of the Floataload hoverpallet, but a simple bridge system allowing the units to be slid under the load is more economical. When this is done the centre of pressure

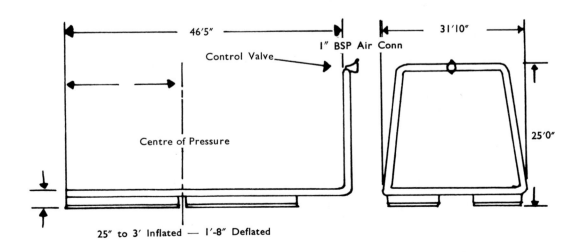

BHC 1-ton Floataload hoverpallet

should be approximately under the centre of the load.

Operation is by opening the control valve until the load is airborne. The load can then be pushed, pulled or spun with minimum effort, the valve being closed and Floataload withdrawn when the load reaches the required position.

Floataload will operate satisfactorily over any smooth non-porous surface. Sheet metal, linoleum, vinyl, sealed concrete, plywood, smooth asphalt, and similar surfaces are all suitable.

DIMENSIONS:
Max length of pallet   3 ft 10 in (1·16 m)

Width of pallet   2 ft 8 in (0·81 m)
AIR PRESSURE:
Working air pressure for 100 lb (45·3 kg) load   3 lb sq in (0·21 kgf/cm²)
Working air pressure for 1,000 lb (453·5 kg) load   6 lb sq in (0·42 kgf/cm²)
¾ in BSP connection, 1 ton load   8 lb sq in (0·56 kgf/m²)

LIGHT HOVERCRAFT COMPANY
HEAD OFFICE:
   Felbridge Hotel & Investment Co Ltd, London Road, East Grinstead, Sussex
TELEPHONE:
   0342 24424
EXECUTIVES:
   Lindsay H. F. Gatward, Proprietor
   Richard Thomas, Consultant

This company markets a pedestrian controlled hoverpallet which has a payload capacity of 3 cwt (150 kg).

Lift power is provided by an 8 hp Briggs & Stratton petrol engine which drives a plastic/alloy axial fan mounted beneath a close mesh safety guard. Since the power unit is of the lawn mower type, the general noise level is low.

The pallet which is built in glassfibre can be used over a wide range of unprepared surfaces including snow, ice, mud, water, grass, swamp and sand. Ploughed fields with ridges of up to 6 in (152 mm) can be traversed with a reduced payload. The over-water and swamp applications are restricted by the amount the operator is prepared to become immersed, or the degree by which this ability to control the vehicle is impaired. Machines can be winched across areas of deep water. Working under these conditions, however, applications such as wildfowling, reed collection, slurry control and insect spraying in swamp areas are possible.

Two directional wheels are fitted and these can be adjusted or removed according to the degree of directional control or ground contact pressure required.

A clip-on spraying unit, manufactured by E. Allman & Co Ltd, Birdham Road, Chichester, Sussex, has been developed for use in conjunction with the pallet.

Skirt is of HDC segmented type in nylon-coated polyurethane. Depth is 5 in (127 mm).

SPECIFICATIONS:
Length with handle	9 ft 6 in (2·89 m)
Width	4 ft (1·21 m)
Height with handle	3 ft (0·91 m)
Weight (approx)	160 lb (72·57 kg)
Skirt depth	5 in (127 mm)
Fuel capacity	6 pints (3·40 l)
Engine	319 cc (4-cycle)
Endurance (approx)	2 hrs per gallon
Payload	3 cwt (150 kg)
Payload area	28 sq ft (2·6 m²)

SUPER SUCKER
This hoverpallet variant combines the features of hovercraft and the industrial vacuum cleaner.

Air escaping beneath the front of the skirt raises litter which is then sucked through a forward intake nozzle, located above the skirt line, into a 1·5 cu yd sack carried the load chamber. The sweep path is 5 ft (1·37 m)

Light Hovercraft Co. hoverpallets can be used over a wide range of unprepared surfaces including mud flats. A clip-on attachment is available for crop spraying

Super Sucker industrial vacuum unit

Light Hovercraft Co. hoverpallets can be used over a wide range of unprepared surfaces including mud flats. A clip-on attachment is available for crop spraying

wide. It will operate over kerbs, ledges and root outcrops and is effective in wet conditions.

The entire vacuum unit can be removed in one piece if the basic platform is required as a hoverpallet.

DIMENSIONS:

Length, with handle	10 ft 0 in	(3·04 m)
Width	5 ft 0 in	(1·37 m)
Height	3 ft 9 in	(1·2 m)
Sucking nozzle width	5 ft 0 in	(1·37 m)

WEIGHTS:

Total weight		220 lb (96 kg)

OTHER SPECIFICATIONS:

Engine	319 cc 4-cycle
Fuel	6 pints (3 l)

Speed according to material collected.

BASIC PRICES:

Hoverpallet, £350·00; Super Sucker, £550·00
Spraying attachment, £140·00.

ROLAIR SYSTEMS (UK) LTD

HEAD OFFICE:
56 Brompton Square, London, SW3 2AG
TELEPHONE:
01 584 8511, 01 584 8010
CABLES:
Projectser London SW3
TELEX:
888941 Chaincom: for Projectser

DIRECTORS:
B. H. Wright, RD, BSc, BCom, CEng, MIEE, Chairman
D. L. Campbell, MC
R. H. Lacey CEng, MIMechE
N. F. Haycock, CEng, MIEE
All contracts for equipment designed, developed and built by Rolair Systems Inc,

Santa Barbara, California, in the United Kingdom is now handled by the above company, which started operating in early 1974. Equipment is being supplied to a number of companies including British Steel Corporation, CEGB and IBM and the first installations were expected to be operating by late July or early August 1974.

UNITED STATES

AERO-GO INC

HEAD OFFICE AND WORKS:
5800 Corson Avenue South, Seattle, Washington 98108
TELEPHONE:
Area Code 206 RO 3-9380
GENERAL MANAGER:
K. G. Wood
EUROPEAN DISTRIBUTORS:
United Kingdom:
Applied Technology Co. Ltd., London (Heathrow) Airport, England
Telephone: SKYport 2811
Sweden:

ASEA, Mechanical Products Division, Helsingborg 1, Sweden
Telephone: 042-13 93 00

Aero-Go was founded in April, 1967 to commercialise air film and air cushion devices developed by the Boeing Company. It holds the exclusive world licence for products and patent rights of Boeing in this field.

The company has developed and is selling the Aero-Caster air film bearing in eight sizes ranging from 1½ in to 48 in diameter. These are manufactured in neoprene impregnated nylon material and are thus highly resistant to tearing damage and capable of supporting very large loads. Lifting capacity ranges from 1,000 lb in the 12 in (304 mm) size to 80,000 lb in the 48 in (1·21 m) size. Individual Aero-Casters are employed in combinations to transport heavy loads. Load module systems are available, complete with portable blowers, hose manifolds and air controls.

Aero-Casters are also incorporated in standard pallets designed for a wide range of applications, including loading and unloading trucks, movement of loaded scissor-lift tables, wire and cable reel carriers, paper and fabric rolls and production machinery. The Company builds Aero-Trucks and Aero-Turntables to meet customer requirements.

Aero-Turntables are available for use in factory production lines or such applications as paint booths and product shipping/receiving points. Multi-ton capacity air film turntables have been installed for lifting and rotating Boeing 747 jumbo jets during pre-flight testing and compass calibration.

Underside view of an Aero-Truck, used to lift and float 18-ton loads, showing its four 36 in (0·914 m) diameter Aero-Casters

Test transformer weighing 264,000 lb (119,743 kg) being moved on air film to its site in ASEA's High Voltage Hall, Sweden. Four 48 in (1·21 m) Heavy Duty Aero-Casters provide the lift

In 1971 Aero-Go installed three air turntables for rotation of rapid transit rail cars for the Bay Area Rapid Transit (BART) system in Northern California. The turntables have been constructed to ride on water film should there be an electrical power failure.

In effect, the Aero-Caster is an open-ended piston with a dynamic end-seal that conserves the volume of air required to lift and float loads. The thin air film under this peripheral seal lubricates the bearing and allows it to float freely only ·005 in above the floor surface. As the caster moves across the surface, the flexible seal automatically con-

tours to provide a constant gap and thus maintain a uniform air flow. When the air is shut off, the captured air bubble within the caster escapes, slowly lowering the load gently and safely to the ground. The casters are self pressure-regulating systems that may be operated without separate line regulators.

AIRFLOAT CORPORATION

HEAD OFFICE:
1304 North 20th Street, Decatur, Illinois 62521

TELEPHONE:
Area Code 217, 422-8365

GENERAL MANAGER:
David R. Snoeyenbos

OVERSEAS REPRESENTATION:
Airfilm Luftkissenlagertechnik GMBH, 41 Duisburg, Moselstrasse 37, West Germany

H. Englebert NV., Dobbeweg 2-3, Voorschoten/Holland

Airfloat Corporation was formed in October, 1967 to develop and apply air bearing technology, based on a licence granted by General Motors, and on experience gained by the principal when working on the G.M. air bearing development programme.

Airfloat offers a line of air bearing cells, standard products mounted on air bearings, and also engineers and fabricates special-purpose equipment utilising air bearing technology. A summary of standard products follows:

AIR BEARINGS: A wide variety of types and sizes range from 6 in (152 mm) diameter to 43 × 67 in (1·09x1·70 m) racetrack shape bearings, with capacities from 200 lb to 24,000 lb (90·71 to 10,886 kg) each.

SMALL PLATFORMS: A line of standard general-purpose air bearing platforms for loads up to 8,000 lb (3,629 kg). Each consists of four bearings mounted to a structural panel, with necessary air controls.

LARGE PLATFORMS: Similar, but for movements of heavy loads, from 8,000 lb to 120,000 lb (3,629 kg to 54,430 kg). Air motor powered drive wheels available for self-propelled operation.

TURNTABLES: 3 ft to 9 ft (·914-2·74 m) in diameter, up to 40,000 lb (18,143·68 kg) capacity.

AIR SKIDS: Two-bearing structural platforms. Two or more used together can move loads of most any size on a film of air, for almost frictionless handling. They are frequently used for moving and relocating machinery in the plant, for die handling, and for assembly line movement of large machines.

Engineered system applications pursued by Airfloat include the following:

Equipment for moving very heavy equipment or machinery by use of special very large air bearings, for loads from 50 tons to thousands of tons.

High density mobile storage systems, where rows of storage racks are mounted on air

bearing bases. Groups of rows of racks can be stored close together with no aisles, and can be moved aside on air to create an aisle where needed. Allows savings in floor space of 40-50%.

A variety of forms of conveyors have been designed, for flowthrough storage of heavy palletised loads, assembly line movement of heavy equipment, shuttle conveyors, etc.

Airfloat air bearings use a continuously flowing film of air between a flexible diaphragm and floor surface to allow virtually friction free movement. Thus large loads can be moved on air bearings with considerably less force than on conventional wheels or rollers.

Air bearing cells have a flexible diaphragm which is sealed around the circumference and attached to the centre of a top plate. Air supplied to the bearing inflates the diaphragm and passes through communicating holes in the diaphragm to the space below. A continuous air film is formed between the diaphragm and floor surface as air escapes to the atmosphere.

The area that is pressurised below the diaphragm is referred to as the effective "Support Area"; the "Seal Perimeter" is the outer boundary of the support area and the point where the pressurised air escapes to the atmosphere.

The pressure inside an air bearing depends upon the load applied to the bearings. Bearing pressure can be determined for any given load by dividing the load by the bearings' support area.

Air bearings operate at maximum efficiency, on smooth, good quality floor surfaces—rough or porous floors cause excessive air consumption. The flexible diaphragm will conform to gradual floor undulations of ¼ in to ½ in over an eight foot span without a noticeable decrease in efficiency. Smooth surfaces such as terrazo, tile, linoleum, steel sheet, and sealed concrete allow excellent performance. Cracks or expansion joints must be filled or bridged to provide a continuous floor surface. Poor concrete surfaces that are rough, worn, or pitted can be improved with readily available patching or topping materials.

AIRFLOAT CORPORATION
GLASS SHEET TRANSPORTER

ASG Industries, Kingsport, Tennessee, is employing a specially designed Airfloat transporter to carry up to 66 ton loads of glass sheet at a time from in-process storage to production lines.

The transporter, which uses four air bearing diaphragms, is operated entirely by remote control with a "joy stick" on a hand-held control box connected to the platform by a 12 ft long cable.

Airfloat utility platform, showing four air bearings, guide wheels and controls

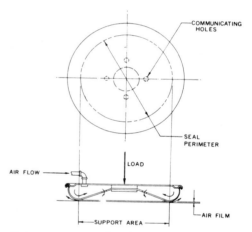
Basic construction of an Airfloat air bearing cell

The operator guides the transporter beneath the rack, the air bearings are deflated and the transporter lowered to the floor. The platform support frame is then raised to the base of the A-frame rack holding the 11 ft × 20 ft glass sheets and locked in place. The air bearing diaphragms on the transporter are then reinflated and the rack is lifted off the floor.

The steerable drive wheel is then used to manoeuvre the rack out of the storage area and then guide it down an aisle to the production area.

After a short period of familiarisation, operators can steer the load down narrow aisles. By shifting the steering axis, the transporter can move the rack at right angles into the bay with only a few inches of clearance either side.

JETSTREAM SYSTEMS COMPANY

HEAD OFFICE:

3486 Investment Boulevard, Hayward, California 94545

OFFICERS:

Stanley Lenox, General Manager

Warren P. Landon, Vice-President, Marketing

Eugene S. Batter, Vice-President, Operations

Stanley E. Hurd, Manager, Research and Development

Jetstream Systems Company holds the world-wide rights for Jetstream conveyors. The company is currently producing and developing Jetstream conveying and processing equipment and Jetsweep storage and drying systems.

Jetstream uses low-pressure air delivered to a plenum by a fan or fans and introduced to the conveyor surface through various types of orifices along the full length of the conveyor, to maintain a belt of air flowing close to the conveyor surface. It conveys granular materials, such as sand, iron pellets, grain, etc; paper and metal trim and scrap; cartons; webs or sheets of paper or metal; and practically any other material within reason.

The air can be heated or cooled to condition the product while it is being conveyed. Extremely good results have been attained, especially in the heating, cooling and drying field. Longer or shorter dwell time can be obtained by using different configurations of the conveyor.

Objects are moved by a succession of angularly disposed openings. The system provides constant controlled power around curves and up inclines including vertical faces. Entry points and spurs, inputs and outputs, can be added easily anywhere along the conveyor.

The objects can be moved upwards along an inclined conveyor and can be discharged into a hopper or other receptacle. The conveyor membrane may be used for moving solid objects by air-jet action and as a support and walkway for workmen while adjusting, operating or maintaining an associated machine.

POWER SUPPLY: Pressure of air necessary: $\frac{1}{10}$ inch water gauge to $\frac{1}{2}$ psi. Air ducting and centrifugal fans are generally fitted as an integral part of the conveyor.

CONVEYOR SYSTEM: Units are designed to suit product. The length can run to 1,000 ft or more and the width from 1 in to 10 ft or more as necessary.

BLOWER H/P: Power requirements for loadings up to 7 lb sq ft ($34 \cdot 17$ kgt/m²) $\frac{1}{500}$ hp/sq ft—$\frac{1}{10}$ hp sq ft

ROLAIR SYSTEMS, INC.

ADDRESS:

P.O. Box 3036, Santa Barbara, California

TELEPHONE:

(805) 968 1536

DIRECTORS:

Henry W. Huthsing, Vice-President

Terry Baker, Vice-President

Robert Kieding, Vice-President

E. Douglas Reddan, President

Roger Kenyon

Rolair Systems Inc. manufactures a range of equipment making use of compliant air bearings for moving heavy or large loads. The company began operations in March 1968 and now markets air flotation systems, incorporating air bearing caster jacks and pallets.

The basic compliant air bearing device comprises a membrane holding compressed air which conforms to the floor. Controlled escape of this air in a thin layer between membrane and floor forms a frictionless air film which 'floats' the load, enabling it to be moved in any horizontal direction by a force only one-thousandth of the weight of the load. Air pressure is self-regulating according to the bearing size and its load. Typically a 2 ft diameter bearing will lift 4,000 lb; four 2 ft bearings will carry a truck.

Several typical applications are described below.

SHIPYARD PANEL LINE

Rolair has constructed and installed a complete air-film panel handling system for a major US shipyard. Comprising several hundred, pylon-mounted upturned air-bearings, it permits the omnidirectional movement of steel plates measuring 3·65 m by 12·19 m (12 ft by 40 ft) for welding. The plates, which can be positioned with great accuracy, are tack-welded five at a time into 100-ton 'blanket' sections, each measuring 12·19 m by 18·28 m (40 ft by 60 ft). Axis positioning is accomplished through the use of low-horsepower, steerable electric drives.

After all five plates have been tacked together, they are driven by linear casters to an overhead welding station, where they are seam welded on both sides, have channels added, and are then driven to the crane pick-up area.

Above and below: Rolair-designed panel line for a major US shipyard. It enables steel plates, weighing up to 100 tons, to be accurately positioned for welding and then transports them down the line to a crane pick-up area. The plates are used in the construction of giant tankers

OMNIMOBILE CRANE

Gantry and top-running bridge cranes are available in this line. They can be pushed to the load and deliver it without the expense of overhead or ground rails. The company has standard designs available of up to 60-tons and will design and build larger units to customer requirements.

VARIABLE-PLAN SPORTS STADIUM

Rolair air-bearings will be used to vary the seating configurations of a new 28,000-seat stadium under construction in Honolulu.

The stadium comprises four 7,000-seat sections, and the air-bearings will be employed to rotate each through a 45 degree arc to provide ideal seating patterns for either football or baseball games.

Located under each of the four stadium sections will be twenty-six Rolair transporters, each incorporating four air-bearings. These will be inflated by three main air compressors, each with a capacity of 1,250 cfm. The sections will be moved by a system of lightweight hydraulic jacks. A rail guideline will prevent the sections drifting when 20-knot Pacific tradewinds are blowing. Each stadium section has a fixed pivot point and it is estimated that only 20 minutes will be required to move each one through its 45 degree arc—a total distance of 53·34 m (173 ft).

In baseball configuration the stadium will have an open double "horseshoe" look. For football the four sideline sections will be moved inward to form straight sidelines. In the football position the spectators on the 50 yard line will be only 12·19 m (40 ft) from the sideline, and only 7·62 m (25 ft) away from the goal line.

Ramps connecting the stadium sections extend and retract on air film with each move.

AUTOMATIC MODULAR HOME PRODUCTION LINE

Rolair has designed and installed a fully-automated air-film walking beam conveyor system which moves factory built home modules simultaneously through eighteen assembly stations several times an hour.

The system can handle modules with lengths of up to 60 ft (18·28 m) and widths up to 14 ft (4·26 m).

ASSEMBLY LINE FOR CRAWLER TRACTORS

The assembly operation begins on a 175-ft-long section of track immediately preceding the air pallet area. There, drive assemblies are built on manually-propelled transfer carts.

First, the tractor's two planetary gears are aligned on a stationary fixture. A housing is then lifted into position by an overhead crane. After the housing has been connected to the axles, the unit is lifted onto a transfer cart. Small components are then added to the housing as the cart is moved to the end of the track. The sub-assembly and cart now weighs about 18,000-lb and requires two men to push it. At this point the sub-assembly is lifted by the overhead crane and positioned on one of the air pallets. Now one man can easily move the 9-ton load.

Components are brought to the air pallet line on flat-bed trucks and lifted by crane onto the pallets. Workers climb portable step ladders to perform the necessary welding and bolting operations. The same

A Rolair unit specially designed for Caterpillar Tractor Co's excavator production line. The Rolair transporters automatically move the chassis to various work stations where major sub-assemblies are added. At the end of the line, the excavator is driven off its transporter

Production line movement for Waukesha diesel generators. Two men can easily move this 20-ton generator, supported by standard Rolair transporters

Left: Stadium positioned for football, and *right*, for baseball. Rolair air-bearings are employed to rotate each of the four 7,000-seat sections through a 45-degree arc to provide ideal seating patterns for both games

air source that supplies the pallets is used to power air-articulated assembly tools.

Between moves, the air supply is cut off and the pallet rests on the steel cross members; the air bearings do not support the pallet or load. Because there are no rails or tracks, the pallets can be positioned anywhere on the concrete floor. Thus, one tractor can easily pass another, by simply pushing one pallet to the side and moving another forward.

At the end of the line, the pallet is removed from the tractor by means of an air-powered lifting device. This is made up of three parallel lifting platforms, each about 2 ft wide by 14 ft long. Mounted on the under-surface of each platform are sixteen 10-in-diameter diaphragms. These are connected to a separate air source via a series of air valves.

The centre platform and either outside platform can be raised or lowered simultaneously. When lowered the platforms are flush with the concrete slab.

Before a tractor reaches the end of the line, its treads are laid out on top of two of these platforms. The pallet is then pushed between the two platforms so that the tractor's wheels straddle the platforms. A worker then opens the air valves to lift the platforms and raise the treads so that they can be attached to the drive wheels. When this is done, the platforms are raised 6 in and the pallet is removed.

AIRCRAFT GROUND TESTING INSTALLATION

An air flotation system has been installed by Vought to allow quicker positioning of each plane for testing operational equipment. The system uses an air film and replaces hand-operated tripod-type jacks. It has provided not only a saving in time, but a safer environment for testing. Twelve Corsair II light attack aircraft can be closely positioned within a single hangar.

Three air bearings, connected directly to a T-shaped dolly, make up the casters for each of six "sets" of bearings in use in the hangar. Their design is such that they easily handle the 19,000-pound aircraft. On-off air valves for the bearings are operated quickly by a single employee. The bearings have their own stabilizing chamber, eliminating any throttling of incoming air. Inlet air pressure is supplied at 75 psig from standard 1-inch plant lines.

Usually three men hand-manoeuvre the dolly for directional accuracy, although one man can easily push the 9 tons of aircraft supported on the air film. In most cases, the flotation system is used in conjunction with a crane for fine positioning of the craft during equipping and testing its gears, wheels, and other systems and components.

UNION OF SOVIET SOCIALIST REPUBLICS

LENINGRAD INSTITUTE OF ENGINEERING AND CONSTRUCTION

An air cushion vibrating platform designed to improve the rate of setting and uniformity of concrete has been designed and built by the Leningrad Institute of Engineering and Construction. It oscillates vertically, horizontally and diagonally.

The idea of employing an air cushion in constructing vibrating platforms for the production of prefabricated reinforced concrete was proposed and introduced by technologists in the Byelorussian Ministry of Construction.

Conventional vibrating platforms require considerable quantities of metal in their construction and costly foundations, the weight of which can be 18-20 times the load capacity of the platform. The concentrated dynamic loads frequently lead to the breakdown of the platform's framework, and during operation the vibration and noise cause severe discomfort to plant personnel.

The operating principle of vibrating platforms using air cushions is as follows. Beneath the vibrating platform, which is a framework with a metal bottom, air is fed by a fan to form an air cushion between the foundation and the bottom of the vibrating platform. As a result, the vibrating platform (along with a form filled with mixed concrete) is lifted into the air. The vibrating system is then switched on and the mixture is allowed to set under the influence of vertical oscilla-tions with an amplitude of 0·3-1 mm. To limit power expenditure, the cushion forms a closed system with an elastic apron. The pressure in the air cushion is 600-800 kg/m^2 with a lift of 6-10 tons.

These platforms have a load capacity of 2-3 tons. They do not require special concrete foundations and are mounted on a sandy base 100-150 mm thick. The power consumption of existing mass-produced platforms with load capacities of 4·6 and 8 tons are 14,20 and 40 kW, respectively, in contrast to 10,14 and 28 kW for air cushion vibrating platforms. Use is made of the ability of an air cushion to distribute pressure evenly over the entire reaction surface and of its outstanding shock absorbing qualities.

HYDROFOILS

CANADA

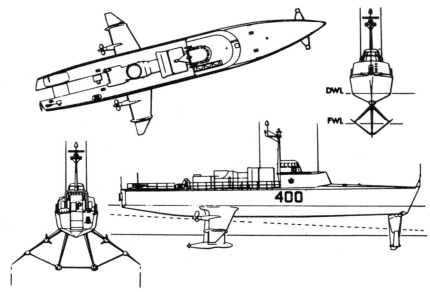

De Havilland FHE-400 ocean going ASW warship

DE HAVILLAND AIRCRAFT COMPANY OF CANADA, LIMITED

HEAD OFFICE AND WORKS:
Downsview, Ontario, Canada
TELEPHONE:
633-7310 Area Code 416
TELEGRAMS:
Moth Toronto
DIRECTORS:
A. Stewart Kennedy, Chairman
B. B. Bundesman, President & Chief Executive Officer
D. B. Annan, Vice-President, Operations
D. L. Buchanan, Vice-President, Marketing
W. T. Heaslip, Vice-President, Engineering
D. N. Kendall
F. A. Johnson, Vice-President, Contracts and Programmes Administration
A. J. MacIntosh, QC
Sir Harry Broadhurst
SENIOR EXECUTIVES:
S. B. Kerr, Vice-President, Finance
F. H. Buller, Chief Designer
S. Morita, Hydrofoil Project Manager

In early 1961 the Canadian Department of Defense contracted De Havilland Aircraft of Canada Ltd for a feasibility and engineering study based on the NRE ASW hydrofoil report. The company's recommendations were approved in April 1963 and led to the construction of the FHE-400 fast hydrofoil escort warship. The programme had two fundamental objectives: (a) to establish in practice the feasibility of an ocean-going hydrofoil of the proposed size and characteristics (b) to evaluate the prototype as an ASW system.

FHE 400 was commissioned as HMCS Bras d'Or in Halifax and was tested in brief displacement mode trials in September 1968. The foilborne transmission was fitted during the winter of 1968 and the first foilborne trial took place on April 9, 1969. The craft attained a speed of 63 knots during calm water trials in July 1969. Rough water trials during the winter of 1971 culminated in a 2,500 mile "shake down" cruise from Halifax to Bermuda and Norfolk, Va.

Foilborne trials were conducted in 10-15 ft (3·04-4·57 m) waves (sea state 5) at speeds in excess of 40 knots. Hullborne trials were conducted in higher sea states.

While objective (a), to confirm operations feasibility in open ocean conditions, was met, objective (b), ASW system operation, was suspended because of a change in Canadian defence priorities, requiring priority attention to territorial and coastal surveill-

ance. The craft was therefore put into store, although research in this field continued. In May 1974 it was reported that the craft is to be reactivated. In the meantime the company reports that wide interest is being shown in a smaller and similar design—the DHC–MP–(Maritime Patrol) 100—which will have the same seakeeping capability. Possible civil applications include oil-rig re-supply, coastguard work and fisheries patrol.

FHE-400

FOILS: The foil system is a canard configuration of the surface piercing type and non-retractable. The steerable bow foil is super-cavitating and designed for good response in a seaway. The subcavitating main foil carries 90% of the static weight and is a combination of surface-piercing and submerged foils. The centre high speed foil section is protected from ventilation by the struts and the dihedral foils have full-chord fences to inhibit ventila-

tion. Anhedral foils provide reserve lift at take-off and their tips provide roll restoring forces at foilborne speeds. All foil elements are in welded 18% nickel maraging sheet steel and forgings.

The struts are a compromise to provide the optimum fin effect in yaw in conjunction with the steerable bow foil.

HULL: Hull and superstructure are fabricated from ALCAN D54S, and extensive use is made of large extrusions with integral stringers for the plating.

A crew of twenty is carried, comprising eight officers and twelve men. In order to maintain crew alertness at all times, comfortable crew quarters and good messing facilities were considered essential features. Both were intensively studied by the Institute of Aviation Medicine. The study included the testing of crew bunks on a motion simulator at NCR Ottawa, and the use of a simulator

The FHE 400 fast hydrofoil escort warship

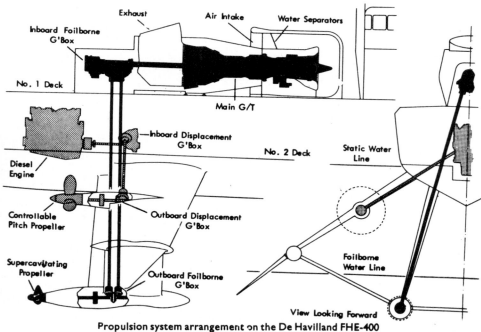

Propulsion system arrangement on the De Havilland FHE-400

to assess crew efficiency under foilborne conditions.

POWER PLANT: Continuous search for a useful period demands economical operation in any sea state at displacement speeds and the ability to attack at high speeds. For this reason there are two propulsion systems —the foilborne marinised gas-turbine, a 22,000 shp Pratt & Whitney FT4A-2, and a 2,000 bhp Davey-Paxman 16YJCM diesel engine for hullborne power.

The FT4A-2, a marine version of the shaft-turbine engine developed from the JT4 and 5 gas turbine, is enclosed by a protective cowling aft of the bridge.

Shaft power is transmitted to the inboard gearbox directly aft of the engine exhaust elbow and is then transmitted via dual shafts through each of the two inner struts to the outboard gearboxes in the streamlined pods at the intersection of the struts and foils. The dual shafts are combined at the outboard gearboxes into a single drive then taken through an over-running clutch to each of the two 4 ft (1·22 m) diameter fixed-pitch supercavitating propellers.

A governor prevents overspeed if the propellers leave the water in rough seas.

The Paxman Ventura 16YJCM diesel-engine is sited in the engine room, on the ship's centreline. Power is transmitted to the variable pitch hullborne propellers through a dual output gearbox and thence through shafts to gearboxes located in the pods.

The KMW controllable-pitch displacement propellers of 7 ft (2·13 m) diameter are novel, since they are feathered when the craft is foilborne so as to minimise the appendage drag penalty. Slow speed manoeuvring is effected by control of individual propeller pitch settings.

CONTROLS. Diesel power, propeller pitch, main gas turbine speed and individual displacement propeller pitch are all normally controlled by lever from the bridge. Dual wheels are provided to steer the bow foil which acts as the rudder for both foilborne and displacement operation. It is also adjustable to rake enabling the best angle of attack to be selected for foilborne or hullborne operation. An engineer's console is located in the operation room and starting and stopping of all engines is undertaken from this position. Engine and propeller pitch controls duplicating those on the bridge are provided on the console.

Turns are fully or partially coordinated, depending on speed, by the variable incidence anhedral tips. The tips are also coupled to an auto-pilot and act as stabilisers to supplement the foil system's inherent roll resistance.

SYSTEMS:

AUXILIARY POWER: An auxiliary gas-turbine, a United Aircraft of Canada ST6A-53 rated at 390 hp continuous at 2,100 rpm is used to power electric generators, hydraulic pumps and a salt-water pump. It can also be used to increase the available displacement propulsion power and for emergency propulsion power at reduced speed.

EMERGENCY POWER: The emergency power unit is an AiResearch GTCP-85-291 shaft-coupled turbine rated at 190 hp continuous. In the event of the auxiliary gas turbine becoming unserviceable or being

HMCS Bras D'Or during calm water trials

in use for the displacement propulsion, this turbine will power the ship's system. Alternatively bleed air may be drawn from the compressor for main turbine starting.

DIMENSIONS, EXTERNAL:

Length overall, hull	151 ft 0 in (45·9 m)
Length waterline, hull	147 ft 0 in (44 m)
Hull beam	21 ft 6 in (6·5 m)
Width across foils	66 ft 0 in (20 m)
Draft afloat	23 ft 6 in (7·16 m)
Freeboard, forward	11 ft 0 in (3·3 m)

WEIGHTS:

Gross tonnage (normal)	212 tons
Light displacement	165 long tons
Max take-off displacement	235 long tons
Useful load (fuel, crew and military load)	over 70 tons

PERFORMANCE:

Maximum speed, foilborne
50 knots rough water, 60 knots calm water
Cruising speed, hullborne over 12 knots
Sea state capability
Sea State 5 significant wave height 10 ft

DHC-MP-100

De Havilland Canada's latest hydrofoil design is the DHC-MP-100, a multi-duty vessel of 104 tons displacement and a maximum speed of 50 knots. Twin gas-turbines power the foilborne propulsion system instead of the single turbine employed in the FHE-400, the foil system has been simplified, and although the craft is smaller than its predecessor the same outstanding sea-keeping performance is maintained.

A worldwide market survey has been undertaken to determine the needs of potential customers outside Canada and reports indicate that considerable interest is being shown in the craft particularly for the following applications: oil rig re-supply, coastguard patrol, search and rescue, customs and excise, gunboat, missilecraft and ASW patrol.

In general the configuration and construction follows that of the FHE-400.

FOILS: Canard, surface-piercing configuration with approximately 90% of the weight carried by the main foil and 10% by the bow foil. The bow foil is of diamond-shape and acts as the rudder for both foilborne and hullborne operations. The main foil, of

trapeze configuration combines a fully submerged central section with dihedral surfaces outboard.

POWER PLANT, FOILBORNE: Foilborne propulsion is supplied by two 3,100 shp gas-turbines each driving a fixed-pitch super-cavitating three-bladed propeller. Power is transmitted via dual shafts through each of the two inner foil struts to gearboxes at the intersections of the struts and foils.

Among the engines likely to be specified are the Rolls Royce Marine Proteus, the Marine Tyne and the Avco Lycoming TF 40.

POWER PLANT, HULLBORNE: Hullborne propulsion is supplied by two 400 hp diesels driving two two-bladed propellers through outdrive units.

Data for the basic craft and the main variants are given below.

DHC-MP-100 GENERAL PURPOSE

In this configuration, the craft can be equipped for coastguard, search and rescue, fisheries and environmental patrol, customs and excise duties and oil-rig re-supply.

DIMENSIONS, EXTERNAL:

Length	118 ft 1 in (36 m)
Beam	21 ft 0 in (6·4 m)
Width across main foil	50 ft 9¾ in (15·5 m)
Draft hullborne	17 ft 5⅞ in (5·33 m)
Freeboard, hullborne	8 ft 0 in (2·44 m)

WEIGHTS:

Crew and supplies	2,930 kg
Roll equipment and fuel	26,800 kg
Total payload	29,730 kg
Basic weight	75,740 kg
Displacement	105,470 kg
	(104 tons)

PERFORMANCE:

Maximum speed, est. 50 knots (90 km/h)
Range:
18,000 kg fuel capacity
at 11·5 km/h (10 knots)
3,500 km (1,910 nm)
at 74 km/h (40 knots) 1,180 km (642 nm)
27,000 kg fuel capacity
at 18·5 km/h (10 kt) 5,250 km (2,865 nm)
at 74 km/h (40 kt) 1,770 km (963 nm)

GUNBOAT

For coastal patrol, interdiction or for escorting larger ships or convoys, a 57 mm Bofors gun can be fitted. For self-defence a Vulcan gun is mounted on the afterdeck.

Other armament installations can be fitted within weight and c of g limits.

Overload fuel will extend the range in displacement condition to a maximum of 4,600 km (2,500 nm). In the maximum overload condition take-off may be restricted to moderate sea states.

The foil system stabilises the vessel and gives it the seakeeping characteristics of a ship of 1,000/1,500 tons, thus improving accuracy of shot and crew performance for a craft of this size.

DIMENSIONS:

As for basic craft

WEIGHTS:

Crew and supplies	2,930 kg
Bofors gun and ammunition	7,140 kg
Vulcan gun system	1,540 kg
Fuel	18,150 kg
Total payload	29,760 kg
Basic weight	75,740 kg
Displacement	105,500 kg
	(104 tons)

PERFORMANCE:

Range at 18·5 km/h	3,500 km (1,910 nm)
Range at 74 km/h	1,180 km (642 nm)

MISSILECRAFT

To complement the gunboat role, the MP-100 may be fitted with missiles like the Harpoon and Exocet. The fire control system is located in the large operations room.

For self-defence a Vulcan gun system is mounted aft between the missile containers. An alternative arrangement is the mounting of the gun on the foredeck and its detection system above the bridge.

DIMENSIONS:

As for basic craft

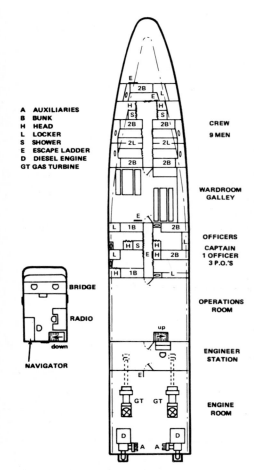

A   AUXILIARIES
B   BUNK
H   HEAD
L   LOCKER
S   SHOWER
E   ESCAPE LADDER
D   DIESEL ENGINE
GT GAS TURBINE

Typical accommodation arrangement on a patrol escort version of the MP-100 hydrofoil

Designed to meet a variety of both military and commercial requirements, the DHC-MP-100 is available in a variety of different configurations, three of which are depicted above
Top: The basic 100-tonne configuration, suitable for coast guard, fisheries and environmental patrol and oil rig servicing. *Centre:* Operated as a missile-equipped patrol craft, the MP-100 would carry two launchers aft—Harpoon and Exocet missiles are two choices—and for self-defence a Vulcan gun pack is mounted aft between the missiles. An alternative arrangement would be to mount the gun on the forward deck and its detection system above the bridge. *Bottom:* An ASW version equipped with lightweight VDS gear and torpedoes mounted in multiple tubes. Full sonar and fire control systems are provided in the operations room

WEIGHTS:

Crew and supplies	2,930 kg
Missile system	4,530 kg
Vulcan gun system	1,540 kg
Fuel	20,400 kg
Total payload	29,400 kg
Basic weight	75,740 kg
Displacement	105,140 kg
	(103·5 tons)

PERFORMANCE:

Range at 18·5 km/h	3,960 km (2,150 nm)
Range at 74 km/h	1,340 km (723 nm)

ASW PATROL CRAFT

The craft can cruise at convoy speed on its displacement propulsion units while using variable-depth sonar to search for submarines. On making contact it can attack at high speed.

Lightweight VDS gear is installed. This has a low-drag body and cable and can be towed at over 55 km/h (30 kt). The system is of modular construction and can be quickly installed or removed. Torpedoes can be mounted in multiple tubes. Sonar and fire-control systems and fitted in the operations room. A Vulcan gun can be mounted on the foredeck with sensors above the bridge.

DIMENSIONS:
As for basic craft

WEIGHTS:

Crew and supplies	2,930 kg
VDS gear	5,080 kg
Torpedoes	3,035 kg
Vulcan gun	1,540 kg
Fire control	4,080 kg
Fuel	15,860 kg
Total payload	32,525 kg
Basic ship	75,740 kg
Displacement	108,265 kg
	(106·8 tons)

PERFORMANCE:

Range at 18·5 km/h	3,150 km (1,710 nm)
Range at 74 km/h	1,040 km (565 nm)

WATER SPYDER MARINE LTD

HEAD OFFICE AND WORKS:
157 Richard Clark Drive, Downsview, Ontario, M3M 1V6

TELEPHONE:
244 5404, Area Code 416

DIRECTORS:
J. F. Lstiburek, President
G. A. Leask, Secretary/Treasurer
A. Lstiburek, Vice President

SENIOR EXECUTIVES:
L. Civiera, Sales Manager
J. F. Lstiburek, Designer

Water Spyder Marine Ltd is a wholly-owned Canadian company operating under charter issued by the Government of the Province of Ontario. It produces three fibreglass-hulled sports hydrofoils which are available either ready-built or in kit form.

WATER SPYDER 1-A

The Water Spyder 1-A is a single-seat sports hydrofoil powered by long-shaft outboard of 10-25 hp.

FOILS: The foil system comprises a split W-type surface piercing main foil supporting 98% of the load, and an adjustable outrigged trim tab which supports the remaining 2%.
HULL: Two-piece fibreglass reinforced plastic construction, foam-filled for flotation. Standard fittings and regulation running lights.
ACCOMMODATION: Single fibreglass seat.
POWER PLANT: Any suitable outboard engine of 10-25 hp (Mercury, Evinrude or Chrysler) with long shaft.
CONTROLS: Controls include joy-stick and rudder pedals.
DIMENSIONS:

Length overall, hull	6 ft 0 in (1·828 m)
Beam overall, foils retracted	
	4 ft 0 in (1·219 m)
Beam overall, foils extended	
	7 ft 0 in (2·133 m)

WEIGHTS:

Weight empty	80 lb (36·24 kg)

PERFORMANCE:

Maximum speed	40 mph (64·37 km/h)
Max permissible wave height in foilborne condition	1 ft 6 in (457·2 mm)
Turning radius at cruising speed app	10 ft (3·04 m)

Cost of standard craft and terms of payment: US$1,000·00. Terms: cash. Delivery 3 weeks app from date of order, f.o.b. Toronto.

WATER SPYDER 2-B

The Water Spyder 2-B is a two-seat sports hydrofoil powered by a long-shaft outboard of 20-35 hp.

FOILS: The foil system comprises a split W-type surface piercing main foil supporting 98% of the load and an adjustable outrigged trim tab which supports the remaining 2%.
HULL: This is a two-piece (deck and hull) moulded fibreglass construction and incorporates buoyancy chambers. Standard fittings include a curved Perspex windshield and regulation running lights, fore and aft.
ACCOMMODATION: The craft seats two in comfortably upholstered seats. Foils and the trim tab assembly are adjustable from inside the cockpit.
POWER PLANT: Any suitable outboard engine of 20-35 hp (Mercury 200L or 350L Chrysler Evinrude) with long-shaft extension.
CONTROLS: Controls include steering wheel with adjustable friction damper and trim tab control.
DIMENSIONS:

Length overall, hull	12 ft 0 in (3·6 m)
Beam overall, foils retracted	
	5 ft 4 in (1·6 m)
Beam overall, foils extended	
	7 ft 4 in (2·2 m)

WEIGHTS:

Weight empty	220 lb (99·7 kg)

PERFORMANCE:

Max speed	up to 40 mph (64 km/h)
Max permissible wave height in foilborne mode	1 ft 6 in
Turning radius at cruising speed	10 ft (3 m) app

Cost of standard craft and terms of payment: US$1,600·00. Terms: cash. Delivery: 3 weeks from date of order, f.o.b. Toronto.

WATER SPYDER 6-A

An enlarged version of the Water Spyder 2. Model 6-A is a six-seat family pleasure hydrofoil boat, with a two-piece moulded fibreglass hull.

The seats, located immediately over the main foil, are arranged in two rows of three abreast, one row facing forward, the other aft.

Power is supplied by a long-shaft outboard motor of 60-115 hp.
DIMENSIONS:

Length overall, hull	19 ft 0 in (5·79 m)
Beam overall, foils retracted	
	8 ft 3 in (2·5 m)
Beam overall, foils extended	
	13 ft 0 in (3·96 m)
Height overall, foils retracted	
	4 ft 6 in (1·37 m)
Floor area	30 sq ft (2·78 m²)

WEIGHTS:

Gross tonnage	1 ton app
Weight empty	980 lb (444 kg)

PERFORMANCE:

Max speed	35-40 mph (56-64 km/h)
Cruising speed	32 mph (51 km/h)
Max permissible wave height in foilborne mode	2 ft 6 in (0·76 m)
Turning radius at cruising speed	20 ft (6·09 m)

Cost of standard craft and terms of payment: US$3,500·00. Terms: cash. Delivery: Three weeks from date of order f.o.b. Toronto.

Water Spyder 1-A, single-seat pleasure craft

Water Spyder 2-B

Water Spyder 6-A is a six-seat hydrofoil. The main foil, trim-tab support and engine fold upward so the craft can be floated on and off a trailer

CHINA   (People's Republic of)

HUTANG SHIPYARD

HEAD OFFICE AND YARD:

Shanghai

Hydrofoil torpedo boats of the Hu Chwan (White Swan) Class have been under construction at the Hutang Shipyard, since about 1966. Some 60-70 are in service with the navy of the Chinese People's Republic and another twelve have been lent or leased to the Albanian navy.

One of four Hu Chwan-class torpedo/fast attack craft built by the Hutang Shipyard, Shanghai, and supplied to the Pakistan Navy in 1973.

HU CHWAN (WHITE SWAN)

FOILS: The foil system comprises a bow subfoil to facilitate take-off and a main foil of trapeze or shallow vee configuration set back approximately one-third of the hull length from the bow. At high speed in relatively calm conditions the greater part of the hull is raised clear of the water. The main foil and struts retract upwards when the craft is required to cruise in displacement condition.

HULL: High speed V-bottom hull in seawater resistant light alloy.

POWER PLANT: Thought to be two 1,100 hp M-50 watercooled, supercharged 12-cylinder V-type diesels, each driving its own inclined propeller shaft.

ARMAMENT: Two 21 in torpedo tubes, plus four machine guns in two twin mountings.

DIMENSIONS: (approximate):
Length overall	70 ft (21·33 m)
Beam overall	16 ft 6 in (5·02 m)
Hull beam	13 ft (3·96 m)

WEIGHTS:
Displacement full load	45 tons

PERFORMANCE:
Max speed foilborne calm conditions	55 knots

FRANCE

SOCIETE NATIONALE INDUSTRIELLE AEROSPATIALE

HEAD OFFICE:

37 Boulevard de Montmorency, 75781 Paris-Cedex 16, France

TELEPHONE:

224-8400

525-5775

CABLE/TELEX ADDRESS:

Aerospatiale-Paris, AISPA 62059F

WORKS:

Marignane, B.P.13, 13722 Marignane

TELEPHONE:

(91) 89.90.22

In 1966 the Direction des Recherches et Moyens d'Essais (Directorate of Research and Test Facilities) initiated a basic hydrofoil design and research programme with the object of building a prototype hydrofoil ferry with a displacement of 55 tons and a speed of 50 knots.

The companies and organisations cooperat-

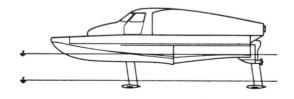

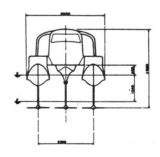

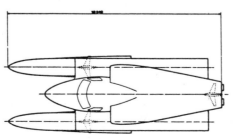

Foil configuration on the H.890 can be changed from canard to conventional (aeroplane) as required

ing in this programme are: Aerospatiale, project leader: STCAN, the hull test centre; several French government laboratories of the DTCN; SOGREAH, and Constructions Mecaniques de Normandie.

The main headings of the programme are: Hydrodynamics (foils, struts and hull) Foil hydroelasticity data and flutter phenomenon Automatic pilot Material technology relative to foils, struts and hull

The design and research programme is nearly complete and the results will be processed and refined using a 4 ton submerged foil test craft, the H. 890, designed by Aerospatiale.

The craft, which was launched on June 16th, 1972 is employed in a comprehensive test programme which is under the control of Aerospatiale and DTCN, a French government agency.

In addition to the SA 800 55-ton hydrofoil ferry, preliminary designs have been completed for a missile-carrying 118-ton hydrofoil combat vessel, the H. 851, and a commercial variant, intended for mixed-traffic ferry services.

The H.890 4-ton submerged foil test vehicle is being employed by the Aerospatiale to develop automatic control systems and gather data for the design of larger vessels. It has attained 50 knots during high speed runs on the Etang de Berre

H.890

This 4·5 seagoing test vehicle is being employed to gather data for foil systems and accelerate the development of autopilot systems for large hydrofoils.

The combination of catamaran hull and pure jet propulsion allows the foils to be arranged in either conventional configuration—two foils forward and one aft—or canard configuration, with one foil forward and two aft.

The vessel was developed and built under contract to the French government agency DTCN by Aerospatiale's Helicopter Division in conjunction with Constructions Mecaniques de Normandie and SOGREAH of Grenoble. It has been undergoing tests on the Etang de Berre since it was launched on June 16th, 1972. A speed of 50 knots has been reached during trials.

FOILS: Fully submerged system with facilities for changing from conventional (aeroplane) to canard configuration as required. In aeroplane configuration about 70% of the weight is supported by the twin bow foils, which are attached to the port and starboard pontoons, and 30% by the single tail foil, mounted on the central hull section aft.

The stern foil rotates for steering and all three struts are fixed (non-retractable). Lift variation of the three foils is achieved by an autopilot system, developed by Aerospatiale and SFENA, which varies the incidence angles of all three foils. During the first series of tests the foils were tested in conventional configuration. During the second series the canard configuration was adopted.

HULL: Catamaran type, constructed in corrosion-resistant light alloys. Central hull, which incorporates control cabin, engine bay and test instrumentation, is flanked by two stepped pontoons.

ACCOMMODATION: Seating is provided for two—pilot and test observer.

POWER PLANT: Twin 480 daN Turbomeca Marbore VIc gas-turbines, mounted in the central hull structure aft of the cabin, power the craft when foilborne. Hullborne propulsion is supplied by a 20 hp Sachs 370 engine driving via a hydraulic transmission a folding-blade Maucour waterscrew located at the top of the aft foil strut. The waterscrew rotates through ±90° for steering.

DIMENSIONS:
Length overall	34·97 ft (10·66 m)
Length waterline	30·51 ft (9·30 m)
Beam overall	12·80 ft (3·90 m)
Draft afloat	5·64 ft (1·72 m)
Draft foilborne	1·21 ft (0·37 m)

WEIGHTS:
Normal take-off	4·5 m tons

PERFORMANCE:
Cruising speed, foilborne, calm conditions
50 knots
Cruising speed, hullborne, calm conditions
6 knots
Craft is designed to cross waves up to 2·62 ft
high without contouring (0·80 m)

SA 800

The SA 800 is a design study for a mixed-traffic hydrofoil powered by two Turmo 111C turbines driving a waterjet propulsion unit. Conventional marine light alloy construction is employed and the craft will have incidence-controlled, fully-submerged foils operated by a sonic/electronic sensing system.

A number of variants of the basic design are being studied for alternative applications, including prospecting, marine research, coastal surveillance and naval patrol. Trials conducted with dynamic models have been successful and are continuing. Preliminary design studies are now complete.

FOILS: The foil system is fully submerged

and of "aeroplane" configuration. All three foil struts retract hydraulically completely clear of the water. An SNIAS sonic auto-pilot system controls the incidence angle of the two bow foils and adjustable control flaps on the rear foils.

HULL: The hull is of conventional marine corrosion-resistant aluminium alloys. Features include a deep vee bow, designed to minimise structural loadings due to wave impact, and a flat W section aft for good directional control when hullborne.

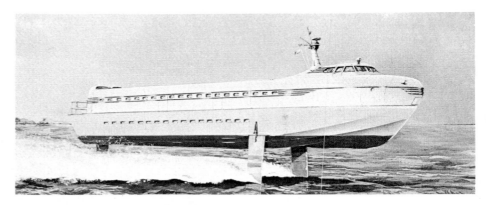

Artist's impression of the SNIA SA-800 waterjet propelled hydrofoil ferry

POWER PLANT: Foilborne propulsion is supplied by two 1,300 shp Turboméca Turmo 111C gas turbines driving a SOGREAH waterjet propulsion unit mounted at the base of the aft foil strut.

Output from the transmission shafts of the two turbines, which are mounted end-to-end, intakes outwards, athwart the stern, passes first to a main bevel drive gearbox, then to a drive shaft which extends downwards through the aft foil strut to a waterjet pump gearbox located in a nacelle beneath the aft foil. Air for the turbines is introduced through intakes at the top of the cabin aft. Filters are fitted to the intakes to prevent the ingestion of water or saltspray into the gas turbine. There is a separate hullborne propulsion system, with a 400 hp diesel driving twin water propellers beneath the transom.

ACCOMMODATION: The elevated wheel-house forward of the passenger compartment seats the captain and engineer. All instru-mentation is located so that it can be easily monitored. Navigation and collision avoidance radar is fitted. Accommodation is on two decks, each arranged with three seats abreast on either side of a central

aisle. As a passenger ferry the craft will seat 200—116 on the upper deck and 84 on the lower; and in mixed traffic configuration, it will carry 8-10 cars on the upper deck with the lower deck seating capacity remaining at 84. Cars are loaded via rear door/ramps. Baggage holds are provided forward of both upper and lower saloons.

DIMENSIONS:

Length overall	88 ft 0 in (26·88 m)
Max beam, deck	18 ft 0 in (5·40 m)

WEIGHTS:

Displacement, fully loaded
55 tons (56 m tons)
Payload (200 passengers with luggage or 84 passengers with luggage and 8-10 cars)
40,300 lb (18,300 kg)

PERFORMANCE:

Max speed, calm conditions	55 knots
Cruising speed	50 knots
Cruising speed, Sea State 5	48 knots
Range, at 50 knots, calm sea	250 nm
at 48 knots, Sea State 5	200 nm

Craft is designed to platform over 10 ft (3 m) high waves, crest to trough, and contour 13 ft (4 m) high waves.

H.851

The H.851 is a preliminary design for a missile-equipped combat hydrofoil capable of all-weather operation. Initially it will have a displacement of 118 tons (120 m. tons) and cruise at 45 knots, but later models, with increased power, are expected to attain nearly 60 knots. Development is being undertaken in conjunction with the French Navy. A civil version employing the same foil system and basic hull is projected.

FOILS: Fully submerged canard arrangement with about 80% of the weight supported by the twin aft foils and 20% by the bow foil. The bow foil strut, which rotates for steering, retracts forwards and upwards ahead of the stem, and the two aft struts rotate rearwards

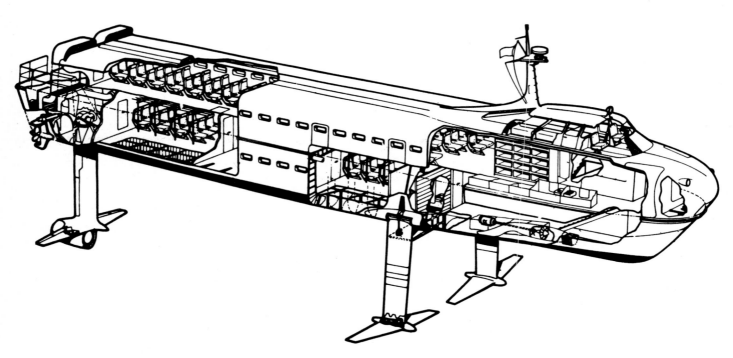

Cutaway showing internal arrangements of the 200-seat passenger ferry

and upwards. The strut locking system is designed to dampen shocks resulting from encounters with floating wreckage. Struts and foils have NACA Series 16 profiles.

Lift variation is achieved by an Aerospatiale autopilot system which varies the incidence angles of all three foils. Trailing edge flaps on the foils augment lift during take-off.

HULL: Constructed in marine corrosion-resistant aluminium alloys.

ACCOMMODATION: Berthing, galley and toilet arrangements for crew of 21.

POWER PLANT: Foilborne propulsion is supplied by a single 5,200 kW SNECMA THS 2000 gas-turbine driving two SOGREAH water pumps, one at the base of each foil strut, via mechanical right-angle drives. Hullborne propulsion is provided by a single 770 kW diesel engine driving a single variable-pitch propeller.

ARMAMENT: Four Exocet MM 38 missiles and one 40 mm Bofors rapid-firing cannon.

DIMENSIONS:

Length overall	114·83 ft (35 m)
Beam overall	49·21 ft (15 m)
Draft hullborne	5·90 ft (1·80 m)
Draft foilborne, foils lowered	27·23 ft (8·30 m)

WEIGHTS:
Displacement, full load
115 tons (117 m. tons)

PERFORMANCE:

Max speed calm conditions	48 knots
Cruising speed, calm conditions	45 knots
Cruising speed, sea state 5	45 knots

Range and endurance :
at 45 knots, calm conditions
1,300 nm or 29 hrs
at 45 knots, sea state 5
1,165 nm or 26 hrs
hullborne at 13 knots
2,130 nm or 163 hrs

H.851 CAR/PASSENGER FERRY

A direct derivative of the H.851 fast patrol vessel, this 65-ton mixed-traffic vessel utilises the same basic hull, foils and propulsion system, but has a completely redesigned interior and superstructure. Up to 200 passengers and 15 cars can be carried over short-medium route lengths at a normal service speed of 45 knots.

POWERPLANT: Arrangements similar to those of the H.851. Either one or two engines can be installed for hullborne propulsion, depending on the route(s) operated and the payload requirements. Hullborne power on models projected so far will be provided by either a single 1,100 kW Turbo-meca Turmo 111 or a single 600 kW Hispano Suiza diesel. The engine room, at the aft end of the lower deck, is thoroughly sound-proofed.

ACCOMMODATION: Up to 200 passengers are accommodated in a large single saloon on the upper deck. The bridge, which is on a separate level above and forward of the upper deck, is reached by a companionway from the passenger saloon. Four WC/washbasin units are provided. Access to the saloon is via two doors, one port, one starboard, at the forward end of the super-structure on the main deck. Eleven cars

Impression of the Aerospatiale H.851 missile-equipped combat hydrofoil, being developed in conjunction with the French Navy

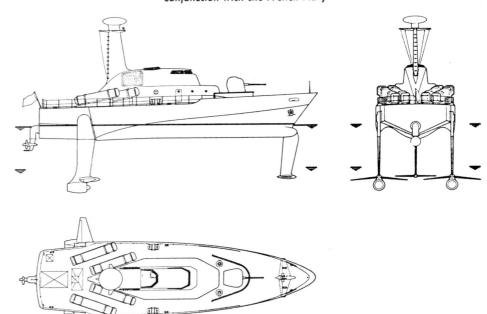

The H.851, 48-knot naval hydrofoil powered by a single SNECMA THS 2,000 gas-turbine driving two SOGREAH water pumps

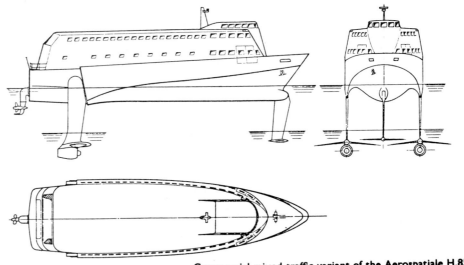

Commercial mixed-traffic variant of the Aerospatiale H.851

are carried on the main deck, and four on the lower deck, access to which is provided by two vehicle lifts.

A bar and a small promenade deck are located at the forward end of the main deck. The vessel will normally carry a crew of eight.

DIMENSIONS:

Length overall	114·83 ft (35 m)
Width across foils	49·21 ft (15 m)
Draft hullborne	5·90 ft (1·8 m)
Draft hullborne, foils lowered	
	27·23 ft (8·3 m)

WEIGHTS:

Displacement, fully loaded
115 tons (117 m. ton)

Useful load (Divided as required between fuel and payload) 50·2 tons (51 m. tons)

The version to which these figures apply carries 11·8 tons (12 m. tons) of fuel and 38·4 tons (39 m. tons) of payload.

PERFORMANCE:

Max speed, calm sea	48 knots
Normal service speed, calm sea	45 knots
Normal speed, sea state 5	45 knots

Range with 11·8 tons (12 m. tons) of fuel:

Foilborne at 45 knots, calm sea	550 nm
Foilborne at 45 knots, sea state 5	485 nm
Hullborne at 13 knots (Turmo 111 gas turbine)	520 nm
Hullborne at 11·5 knots (diesel engine)	920 nm

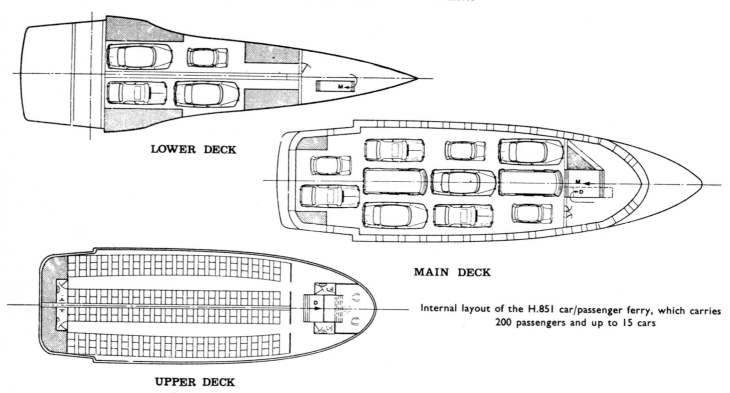

LOWER DECK

MAIN DECK

Internal layout of the H.851 car/passenger ferry, which carries 200 passengers and up to 15 cars

UPPER DECK

HONG KONG

SUPRAMAR PACIFIC SHIPBUILDING CO LTD

HEAD OFFICE:
505 Pedder Building, Pedder Street, Hong Kong
TELEPHONE:
5 227 131
TELEX:
HX 5042 TFOK

YARD:
32 Ko Fui Road, Yau Tong Bay, Kowloon. Hong Kong
TELEPHONE:
3-478 326
OFFICERS AND EXECUTIVES:
Timothy Fok, Director
Charles Choy, Project Manager
Vincent Schweizer, (Supramar Ltd,

Lucerne) Resident Engineer
This company is a licensee of Supramar Ltd, Lucerne. Under the current agreement between the two companies, Supramar Pacific Shipbuilding Co Ltd is permitted to build craft of the following designs—PT 20, PT 20B, PT 50, PTS 75 Mk III and PT 150.

Under construction in the Kowloon yard at present are two PTS 75 Mk IIIs.

ITALY

ADVANCED MARINE SYSTEMS—ALINAVI S.p.A

HEAD OFFICE AND WORKS:
Via Privata Oto, 1, 1902 Termo (La Spezia)
TELEPHONE:
(0187) 505.393
TELEX:
27489 Alinavi
DIRECTORS:
Dr. Publio Magini (Boeing), Chairman
D. A. Cole
H. J. McClellan (Boeing)
R. A. Young
Ing. Enrico Bocchini (Fincantieri)

Com. te Pietro Notarbartolo (Fincantieri)
Ing. Carlo Rodriquez (Rodriquez)
MANAGEMENT:
Dr. Publio Magini, President
Ing. Richard A. Young, Chief Executive Officer
Ing. Francesco Cao, General Manager
Ing. Fabrizio Antonucci, Chief Engineer
Ing. Alberto Bellini, Project Engineer
Ing. Fulvio Biasi, Production Manager
Ing. Giorgio Cortini, Purchasing Manager
Com. te Franco Rodriquez, Manager, Trials and Customer Support
This company was formed in 1964 to

develop, manufacture and market military and commercial advanced marine systems, primarily in Europe and the Mediterranean areas. It is owned jointly by the Boeing Company (60%), Sviluppo e Promozione Industriale (30%) and Carlo Rodriquez (10%).

Under the terms of a Boeing-Alinavi licensing agreement, Alinavi has access to Boeing technology in the fields of military and commercial fully-submerged foil hydrofoil craft.

In October 1970, the company was awarded a contract by the Italian Navy for the design

and construction of the P 420 class hydrofoil missilecraft. Named Swordfish, the craft
is an improved version of the Boeing PGH-2
Tucumcari. Delivery to the Italian Navy
took place in the Spring of 1974.

SWORDFISH

The Swordfish missile-launching hydrofoil
gunboat displaces a maximum of 64·5 metric
tons and is designed for both offensive and
defensive missions. Its combination of speed,
firepower, and all-weather capability is
unique in a ship of this class.

The vessel has fully-submerged foils arranged in canard configuration and an automatic
control system. A gas turbine powered
waterjet system provides foilborne propulsion and a diesel-driven propeller outdrive
provides hullborne propulsion. A typical
crew comprises two officers and eight enlisted
men.

FOILS: Fully-submerged canard arrangement, with approximately one-third of the
dynamic lift provided by the bow foil and two-
thirds by the two aft foils. The aft foils retract
sideways and the bow hydrofoil retracts
forwards into a recess in the bow. Bowdoors
preserve the hull lines when the forward
hydrofoil is either fully extended or retracted.
Foils and struts are built in corrosion-
resistant stainless steel.

Anhedral is incorporated in the aft foils to
enhance the directional stability of the craft
at shallow foil depths. In addition, the
anhedral assures positive roll control by
eliminating tip broaching during rough
water manoeuvres.

CONTROLS: Automatic system incorporating two aircraft-type gyros, one to sense pitch
and roll and the other to sense yaw, plus three
accelerometers to sense vertical movements
(heave) of the craft. An utlrasonic height
sensor is used to detect and maintain flying
height above the water's surface. Information from the sensors is sent to a hermetically-
sealed solid-state computer, which calculates
movements of the control surfaces necessary
to maintain boat stability, and/or pre-selected
flying height, and sends appropriate commands to the servo-mechanisms that control
flap movement.

Foilborne steering: Helm commanded
automatic control system controls hydraulic
servo-actuated hydrofoil flaps and steerable
forward hydrofoil strut to produce coordinated (banked) turns in design sea conditions.

Hullborne steering: Helm commanded
steerable outdrive unit. Helm-driven
potentiometer sends signals to a servo-valve
controlling steering hydraulic motor. Manual emergency hullborne steering is provided
on the aft deck.

HULL: Both hull and superstructure are
built entirely in corrosion-resistant aluminium, the hull being welded and the superstructure riveted and welded.

BERTHING: Two fixed berths in the compartment under the bridge, plus eight folding
berths in the forward crew space. One
toilet and one sink. A folding table with
benches in the forward crew space.

Above: The Swordfish missile-equipped hydrofoil gunboat during foilborne firing tests of its 76 mm Oto Melara cannon. *Below:* Swordfish hullborne with foils extended

Swordfish hullborne with foils retracted

POWERPLANT, FOILBORNE: Power for the waterjet is supplied by one Rolls-Royce Proteus 15M/553 gas-turbine. At the customer's option the craft may be fitted with the "sprint" model of this gas-turbine, which incorporates water injection. The "sprint" model ("wet") develops 5,000 shp maximum versus the 4,500 shp of the normal ("dry") Proteus. Adoption of the "sprint" model permits take-off at higher displacements and therefore, more fuel and/or military payload to be carried. It also provides better craft performance in very high sea states, particularly in conditions of high ambient temperatures. The respective performance characteristics of the Swordfish equipped with 'dry' and 'wet' models of the Proteus are shown in the accompanying performance table.

Engine output is transferred to a single double-volute, double-suction, two impeller centrifugal pump, rated at 28,000 US gpm at 1,560 rpm and absorbing app 4,700 shp (4,766 CV). Water is taken in through inlets on the nose of each aft foil at the foil/strut intersection and passes up through the hollow interiors of the struts to the hull, where it is ducted to the pump. From the pump, the water is discharged through twin, fixed-area nozzles located beneath the hull under the pump.

POWERPLANT, HULLBORNE: A General Motors 6V-53 diesel engine, rated at 160 shp (162 CV) at 2,600 rpm, powers a Schottel-Werft SRP-100 steerable propeller outdrive unit, which is mounted on the centreline of the transom. The unit is retractable and rotates through 360°. Propeller is fixed-pitch. Power is delivered to the outdrive at about 1,700 rpm.

FUEL: Fuel oil is NATO 76, carried in three tanks located amidships and integral with the hull, side keelson and platform deck. Total capacity is about 2,900 gallons (11,000 litres).

Fuel oil system: Three primary 208 volt 400 Hz 7 gpm (26·5 l/min) submerged pumps (one for each tank), and three standby 28 volt d.c. 7 gpm (26·5 l/min) external pumps (one for each tank). The d.c. pump is started automatically by a pressure switch in the fuel supply line if a.c. pump power is lost.

Craft may be refuelled through main deck connection at dock or at sea. The fuel tanks are equipped with fuel level indicators and vents.

AUXILIARY SYSTEMS: HYDRAULICS: Two independent systems: foilborne and ship service. Systems pressure, 3.000 psi. Systems fluid, MIL-H-5606.

Foilborne system: normal and standby 21·8 gpm pumps serve hydraulic control system.

Ship service system: normal and standby 32·5 gpm pumps serve other uses including hydrofoil retracting and locking, bowdoor, hullborne outdrive retraction and steering, foilborne turbine starting, foilborne turbine exhaust door, cannon loading, and the fixed saltwater fire pump.

ELECTRICAL: Turbine generator sets: At customer's option, either two or three identical sets, one installed in forward machinery space, the other(s) in the aft machinery space.

Each set consists of a Solar T-62 T-32 gas turbine engine capable of developing a maximum output of 150 shp (152 CV) under standard conditions and driving: a General Electric 208 volt 400 Hz 3-phase alternator rated at 75 KVA; a 30 volt d.c. starter-generator with 200 amp generating capacity; and one hydraulic pump for ship service and hullborne steering.

Starting battery sets: One 24 volt, 34 amp-hr capacity starting battery is provided for the hullborne diesel engine and for each solar turbogenerator set.

Emergency battery set: Two additional 24 volt batteries in parallel provide 68 amp-hr capacity to power in emergency conditions, radios, intercommunications system and navigation lights.

Shore power: Craft requires up to 30 KVA of 200 volt 3-phase 4 wire 400 Hz power.

Intercommunication system: The system consists of one station in each space and three external stations allowing complete craft machinery and weapons coordination.

Every station is a control unit and has a reversible loudspeaker with press-to-talk switch.

Main station is equipped with radio operation access control.

Emergency announcements can be made to all stations simultaneously.

Selective communications are available between any two or more stations.

Electrical alarm, safety and warning system: Systems installed to indicate conditions of smoke or fire in the two machinery rooms or flooding in any compartment. Systems indicate normal or malfunction conditions of machinery, auxiliary systems, hydrofoil craft automatic control system and hydrofoil extension/retraction position control mechanism.

A portable battery-powered electronic megaphone with provision for connection to an external power supply is stowed on the craft.

NAVIGATION AND COMMUNICATIONS: Navigation light system: All lights are small boat type. Lights are: 2 white masthead signalling lights, one white, one green and one red side navigation light: white stern and bow anchor lights, and 2 red and 1 white man overboard, breakdown and task lights on main mast.

Navigation horn: One electrically operated horn mounted on forward top of deckhouse.

Signal searchlight: One portable incandescent signal searchlight mounted on the deckhouse canopy.

Depth sounder: Transducer on the hull bottom 6 inches (0·152 metres) above the keel and a recorder at the navigation station measure and record water depth from echo soundings. Recorder may be set for sounding depths of 0-20, 20-45, 40-65, 0-60, 50-110, 100-160 fathoms (0-38·6, 38·6-86·9, 77·2-125·4, 0-115·8, 96·5-212, 193-309 metres). Recorder contains electronic circuits and a two-speed mechanism with a stylus which burns a black mark on moving chart paper. A white line mode of recorder operation eliminates false traces below the true bottom line on the chart and allows detection of small objects close to the bottom and an indication of hard or soft composition of the sea bottom.

Navigation set: The shipboard navigation system (ShipNav) automatically performs, independently of all external aids, precise dead reckoning navigation for both foilborne and hullborne operations. It continuously computes and displays the craft's current position, true heading, true course, and true speed. Actual position is displayed digitally on counters in latitude and longitude co-ordinates and pictorially on standard charts having local coordinate information. Indicators display true heading, course, and speed.

Speed log: Hull rodmeter, foil rodmeter, rodmeter selector switch and calibration unit, transmitter and remote indicator set measures craft hullborne or foilborne speed, computes the distance travelled and displays both at the navigation station and helm..

IFF system: The system consists of an IFF/ATC transponder (APX 72) and an IFF interrogator coupled to the radar.

Navigation and search radar: SMA Model 3RM7-250B radar performs navigation and search operations with master indicator, rayplot with variable range marker (VRN) bearing control unit and remote indicator.

Set operates in "X" band and is tunable from 9,345 MHz to 9,405 MHz. Set has two different transmitters and it is possible to select the proper one by a RF switch unit. Peak power output is 7 kW for navigation purposes and 250 kW for search purposes.

Performance includes a minimum range less than 200 yards (182 metres), range discrimination better than 11 yards (10·00 metres), azimuth discrimination less than 1·2 degrees and maximum range of 40 nautical miles.

HF-SSB radio system AN/ARC-102: The AN/ARC-102 uses the Collins 618T/3 HF single-sideband transceiver for long range voice, CW, data or compatible AM communication in the 2,000 through 29,999 MHz frequency range. It is automatically tuned in 28,000 1-kHz channel increments by means of an operator's remote control unit. The operating frequency is indicated directly in a digital-type presentation. Nominal transmit power is 400 watts pep. in SSB or 125 watts in compatible AM. The system is tuned through the antenna coupler Collins 490T-1 to a helical monopole antenna.

UHF radio system AN/ARC-109: Two identical units are provided. The AN/ARC-109 transceiver has two separate receivers: a main tunable receiver and a guard receiver. Common circuit design is maintained in the two receivers. Each receiver uses carrier-to-noise ratio squelch system. Receiver selectivity is ±22 kHz at —6 db and ±45 kHz at —60 db.

The 20-channel present memory in the frequency control utilises a magnetic core storage system with solid-state drivers and interrogators.

DAMAGE CONTROL: Bilge pumps: Pumps are mounted in the bilge of each water-tight compartment and controlled from engineer's station.

A portable, emergency gasoline motor-driven pump and hose are stowed on deck. Freon flooding systems: Two 53 pound (24 kg) freon FE1301 (CBR F_3) storage cylinders are provided in the engineer's compartment. Fire in forward or aft machinery room extinguishable by total flooding of room through fixed piping. One 5 pound (2·27 kg) freon cylinder is piped to Proteus turbine shroud. Systems manually controlled by engineer.

Portable fire extinguishers: A 2 pound (1 kg) dry chemical extinguisher is mounted in each of the seven manned compartments. The portable gasoline motor driven bilge pump is fitted with a nozzle for fire fighting with sea water.

VENTILATION AND CONDITIONING: Unit air conditioners (6 units) are distributed throughout the manned spaces to provide heating and cooling.

DECK EQUIPMENT: One 60 lb (27 kg) Danforth anchor with 2 fathoms (3·66 metres) of ½ in (13 mm) galvanised chain and 75 fathoms (137·25 meters) of 2 in (51 mm) circumference nylon anchor line. Bitts and chocks where necessary for mooring and anchoring. Two six-man life rafts.

ARMAMENT: A typical military payload consists of:
One dual purpose 76 mm automatic OTO Melara gun and ammunition
Two fixed missile launchers and two ship-to-ship missiles, e.g., Sea Killers, OTOMAT or Exocet
Gunfire and missile launch control system(s)
Other military electronics, e.g. ECM
A variety of other payloads may be accommodated according to customer needs.

DIMENSIONS:
Length overall	75 ft 4 in (22·95 m)
Length overall, foils retracted	
	80 ft 7 in (24·6 m)
Width across foils	35 ft 4 in (10·8 m)
Deck beam, max	23 ft 0 in (7·0 m)

WEIGHTS:
Max displacement	64·0 metric tons

PERFORMANCE:
Exact craft performance characteristics depend upon the choice of foilborne gas turbine by the customer and operating conditions which, in turn, can affect the quantity of fuel carried. Performance figures shown below, therefore, are representative:

Foilborne intermittent speed in calm water	50 knots
Foilborne continuous speed in calm water	45 knots
Foilborne continuous speed in Sea State 4	40 knots
Hullborne continuous speed	8 knots
Foilborne range at maximum continuous speed	up to 400 nm
Hullborne range, up to	1,150 nm
Turning radius at maximum foilborne continuous speed less than 410 ft (125 m)	
Endurance	5 days

PARAMETER	Without water injection		With water injection	
	15°C/59°F	22°C/80°F	15°C/59°F	22°C/80°F
Displacement (metric tons)	62·5	60·0	64	64
Military payload (metric tons)	11·7	11·7	14	14
Fuel (metric tons)	9·4	6·9	9·4	9·4
Max foilborne intermittent speed in calm sea (knots)	50	48	50	48
Max foilborne continuous speed in calm sea (knots)	45	43	45	43
Max foilborne continuous speed in Sea State 4 (knots)	41	39	41	39
Hullborne continuous speed (knots)	8	8	8	8
Foilborne range at max continuous speed (n.m.)	400	300	400	400
Hullborne range (n.m.)	1,050	920	1,150	1,050
Turning radius at 40 knots	less than 125 metres			
Foilborne stability: max vertical acceleration	·25 g (rms) in Sea State 4			
Hullborne stability with foils up*	stable in 50 knot wind			
Hullborne stability with foils down*	stable in 70 knot wind			
Endurance	5 days			

The Swordfish, the first missile-launching hydrofoil vessel to be built for the Italian Navy.

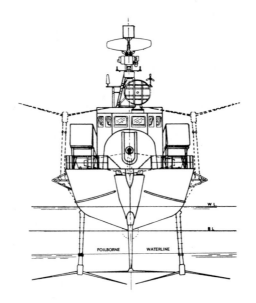

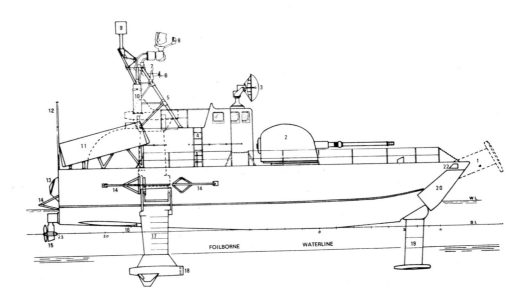

1	Forward hydrofoil retracted	5	Main mast	9	Antenna
2	OTO Melara 76 mm cannon	6	Anemometer	10	Antenna
3	Fire control radar	7	Antenna	11	Surface-to-surface missile launchers (P/S)
4	Vertical ladder	8	Navigation and search radar	12	Ensign staff
				13	Turbine exhaust: foilborne propulsion

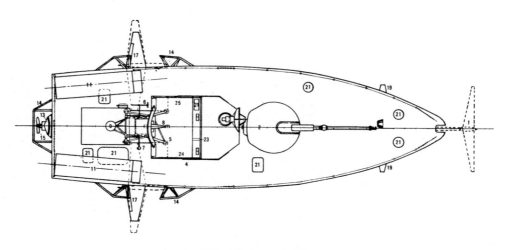

14	Guards	18	Water inlet (P/S): foilborne propulsion	22	Height sensors: automatic control system (P/S)
15	Propeller outdrive: hullborne propulsion	19	Forward hydrofoil extended	23	Optical putter-on
16	Waterjet nozzle (P/S)	20	Bow doors (P/S)	24	Starboard gyrocompass readout
17	Aft hydrofoil extended (P/S)	21	Watertight hatches	25	Port gyrocompass readout

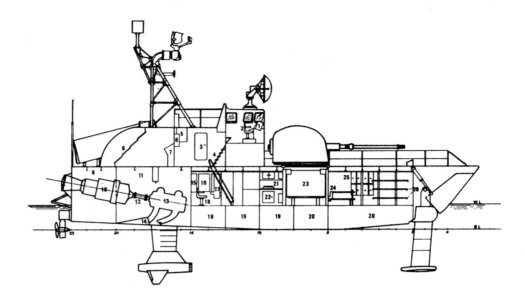

1	Helm/main control console
2	Helm station (starboard)
	Conning station (port)
3	Combat Operations Centre,(C.O.C.) door
4	Companionway ladders
5	C.O.C. electric power distribution panel
6	Combat Operations Centre electronics (speed log, radios, etc)
7	Air intake forward machinery room
8	Demister panels for combustion air
9	Aft machinery room
10	Gas turbine engine: foilborne propulsion
11	Forward machinery room
12	Pump drive coupling
13	Waterjet pump
14	Waterjet nozzle (P/S)
15	Main electrical switchboard
16	Main electrical power distribution panel
17	Engineer's console
18	Engineer's station
19	Fuel oil tanks (3)
20	Void
21	Electric hot plate
22	Refrigerator

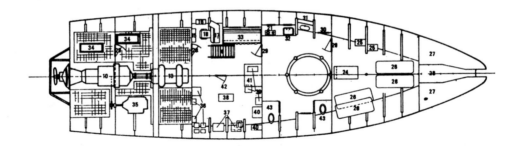

23	Cannon revolving feeding magazine
24	Folding mess table with benches (2)
25	Crew lockers (8)
26	Crew berths (8)
27	Rope locker (P/S)
28	Forward hydrofoil retraction well
29	Watertight doors
30	Galley stores locker
31	Lavatory
32	Sink
33	Officers' stateroom
34	Turbine generator set
35	Diesel engine: hullborne propulsion
36	Search and navigation radar electronics
37	Fire control radar components
38	Fire control radar computer
39	Gyrocompass and Stable element
40	Electronic equipment
41	Automatic control system
42	Electronic equipment bay (unmanned)
43	Water closet

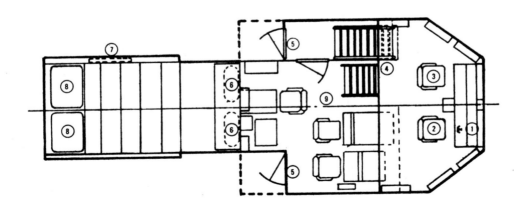

1	Helm/main control console
2	Helm station
3	Conning station
4	Companionway ladders
5	Watertight doors (P/S)
6	Air-inlet plenums: forward machinery room (P/S)
7	Exhaust duct
8	Machinery combustion air inlets
9	Combat operations center

LEOPOLDO RODRIQUEZ SHIPYARD

HEAD OFFICE:
Molo Norimberga, 24 Messina
TELEPHONE:
44801 (PBX)
TELEX:
98030 Rodrikez
OFFICERS AND EXECUTIVES:
Cav Del Lavoro Carlo Rodriquez, President
Dott. Ing. Leopoldo Rodriquez, Managing Director
SENIOR EXECUTIVES:
Dott. Ing. Giovanni Falzea, Yard Director
Ing. Frederick Leobau, Design Office Director

The Leopoldo Rodriquez Shipyard was the first in the world to produce hydrofoils in series, and is now the biggest hydrofoil builder outside the Soviet Union. On the initiative of the company's president, Carlo Rodriquez, the Aliscafi Shipping Company was established in Sicily to operate the world's first scheduled seagoing hydrofoil service in August 1956 between Sicily and the Italian mainland.

The service was operated by the first Rodriquez-built Supramar PT 20, Freccia del Sole. Cutting down the port-to-port time from Messina to Reggio di Calabria to one-quarter of that of conventional ferry boats, and completing 22 daily crossings, the craft soon proved its commercial viability. With a seating capacity of 75 passengers the PT 20 has carried between 800-900 passengers a day and has conveyed a record number of some 31,000 in a single month.

The prototype PT 20, a 27-ton craft for 75 passengers, was built by Rodriquez in 1955 and the first PT 50, a 63-ton craft for 140 passengers, was completed by the yard in 1958.

By the end of 1973, the company will have built and delivered more than 100 hydrofoils. The new RHS models, the only craft now built by the company, are fitted on request with a Hamilton Standard electronic stability augmentation system.

At the time of going to press, the company had under construction three RHS 70s, two RHS 140s and three RHS 160s. Additionally, the company has on order two RHS 70s, three RHS 140s and one RHS 160. Construction of the company's first RHS 200 is expected to be under way by the end of 1975.

Apart from these standard designs, the company offers a number of variants, including the RHS 70/M and 110/M fast patrol craft, and the RHS Hydroil series of mixed passenger/freight hydrofoils based on the RHS 70 and 140, but adapted for servicing offshore drilling platforms.

RHS 70

This is a 32-ton coastal passenger ferry with seats for 71 passengers. Power is supplied by a single 1,350 hp MTU diesel and the cruising speed is 32·4 knots.

FOILS: Surface-piercing type in partly hollow welded steel. During operation the angle of the bow foil can be adjusted within narrow limits from the steering position by means of a hydraulic ram operating on a foil support across the hull.
HULL: V-bottom hull of riveted light metal alloy construction. Watertight compart-

Shearwater 3, a 71-seat Rodriquez RHS 70 hydrofoil passenger ferry operated by Red Funnel Steamers Co on the route Southampton-Cowes

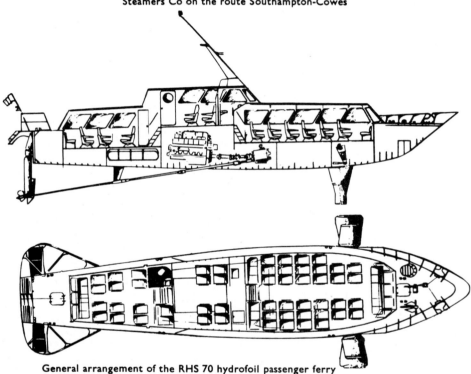

General arrangement of the RHS 70 hydrofoil passenger ferry

ments are provided below the passenger decks and in other parts of the hull.

POWER PLANT: A single MTU MB 12V493 Ty 71 diesel, developing 1,350 hp at 1,500 rpm, drives a 3-bladed bronze aluminium propeller through a Zahnradfabrik W 800 H 20 gearbox.
ACCOMMODATION: Forty-four passengers are accommodated in the forward cabin, nineteen in the rear compartment and eight aft of the pilot's position, above the engine room, in the elevated wheelhouse. A W/C washbasin unit is provided in the aft passenger compartments. Emergency exits are provided in each passenger compartment.
SYSTEMS, ELECTRICAL: 24 volt generator driven by the main engine; batteries with a capacity of 350 Ah.
HYDRAULICS: 120 kg/cm³ pressure hydraulic system for rudder and bow foil incidence control.

DIMENSIONS:

Length overall	72 ft 2 in (22 m)
Width across foils	24 ft 3 in (7·40 m)
Draft hullborne	8 ft 10 in (2·70 m)
Draft foilborne	3 ft 9 in (1·15 m)

WEIGHTS:

Displacement fully loaded	31·5 tons
Useful load	6 tons

PERFORMANCE:

Cruising speed, half loaded	32·4 knots
Max speed, half loaded	36·5 knots

RHS 110

A 54-ton hydrofoil ferry, the RHS 110 is designed to carry a maximum of 110 passengers over routes of up to 300 miles (485·7 km) at a cruising speed of 37 knots.
FOILS: Surface-piercing type, in partly hollow, welded steel . Hydraulically operated flaps, attached to the trailing edges of the bow and rear foils, are adjusted automatically by a Hamilton Standard stability augmenta-

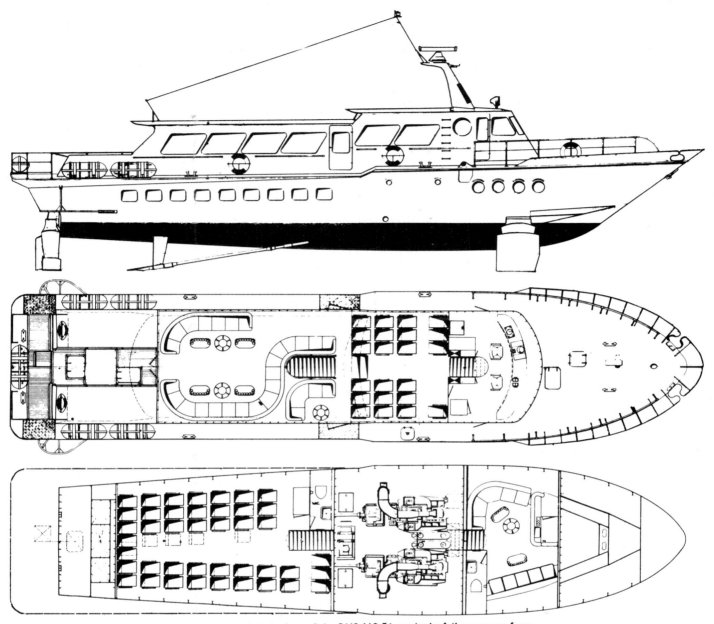

Outboard profile and deck plans of the RHS 110 54-ton hydrofoil passenger ferry

tion system for the damping of heave, pitch and roll-motions. The rear foil is rigidly attached to the transom, its incidence angle being determined during tests.

HULL: Vee-bottom of high-tensile riveted light metal alloy construction, using Peraluman plates and Anticorrodal profiles. The upper deck plates are in 0·137 in (3·5 mm) thick Peraluman. Removable deck sections permit the lifting out and replacement of the main engines. The superstructure which has a removable roof is in 0·078 in (2 mm) thick Peraluman plates, with L and C profile sections. Watertight compartments are provided below the passenger decks and other parts of the hull.

POWERPLANT: Power is supplied by two 12-cylinder supercharged MTU MB 12V493 Ty 71 diesels, each with a maximum output of 1,350 hp at 1,500 rpm. Engine output is transferred to two 3-bladed bronze-aluminium propellers through Zahnradfabrik W 800 H20 gearboxes. Each propeller shaft is 3·5 in (90 mm) in diameter and supported at three points by seawater

lubricated rubber bearings. Steel fuel tanks with a total capacity of 792 gallons (3,600 litres) are located aft of the engine room.

ACCOMMODATION: The wheelhouse/observation deck saloon seats 58, and the lower aft saloon seats 39. Additional passengers

are accommodated in the lower forward saloon, which contains a bar.

In the wheelhouse, the pilot's position is on the port side, together with the radar screen. A second seat is provided for the chief engineer. Passenger seats are of lightweight

RHS 110, a 110-seat passenger ferry equipped with a Hamilton Standard stability augmentation system

aircraft type, floors are covered with woollen carpets and the walls and ceilings are clad in vinyl. Two toilets are provided, one in each of the lower saloons.

SYSTEMS:

ELECTRICAL: Engine driven generators supply 220 volts, 50HZ, three-phase ac. Two groups of batteries for 24 volt dc circuit.

HYDRAULICS: Steering, variation of the foil flaps and the anchor windlass operation are all accomplished hydraulically from the wheelhouse. Plant comprises two Bosch pumps installed on the main engines and conveying oil from a 13 gallon (60 litre) tank under pressure to the control cylinders of the rudder, foil flaps and anchor windlass.

FIREFIGHTING: Fixed CO_2 plant for the main engine room, portable CO_2 and foam fire extinguishers of 7 lb (3 kg) and 2 gallon (10 litres) capacity in the saloons, and one water fire fighting plant.

DIMENSIONS, EXTERNAL:

Length overall	84 ft 0 in (25·60 m)
Width across foils	30 ft 2¼ in (9·20 m)
Deck beam, max	19 ft 2 in (5·95 m)
Draft afloat	10 ft 9⅞ in (3·30 m)
Draft foilborne	4 ft 1 in (1·25 m)

WEIGHTS:

Displacement, fully loaded	54 tons

PERFORMANCE:

Max speed	40 knots
Cruising speed	37 knots
Range	300 miles (485·7 km)

RHS 140

This 65-ton hydrofoil passenger ferry seats 125-140 passengers and has a cruising speed of 32·5 knots.

Condor 3, an RHS 140 operated by Condor Ltd, the Channel Islands hydrofoil ferry company, between Guernsey, Jersey and St Malo

FOILS: Surface-piercing V foils of hollow welded steel construction. Lift of the bow foil can be modified by hydraulically-operated trailing edge flaps.

HULL: Riveted light metal alloy design framed on longitudinal and transverse formers.

ACCOMMODATION: 125-140 passengers seated in three saloons. The belvedere saloon, on the main deck above the engine room, can be equipped with a bar, W/C washbasin units can be installed in the forward and aft saloons.

POWER PLANT: Power is provided by two MTU 12V493 Ty 71 12-cylinder super-charged engines, each developing 1,350 hp at 1,500 rpm. Engine output is transmitted to two 3-bladed 700 mm diameter bronze propellers through Zahnradfabrik gearboxes.

SYSTEMS, ELECTRICAL: Two engine-driven generators supply 24 volt d.c. Two battery sets each with 350 Ah capacity.

HYDRAULICS: Steering and variation of foil flap incidence is accomplished hydraulically from the wheelhouse. Plant comprises two Bosch pumps installed on the main engines and conveying oil from a 15·4 gal (70 litre) tank under pressure to the control cylinders of the rudder and foil flaps.

FIREFIGHTING: Fixed CO_2 plant for the

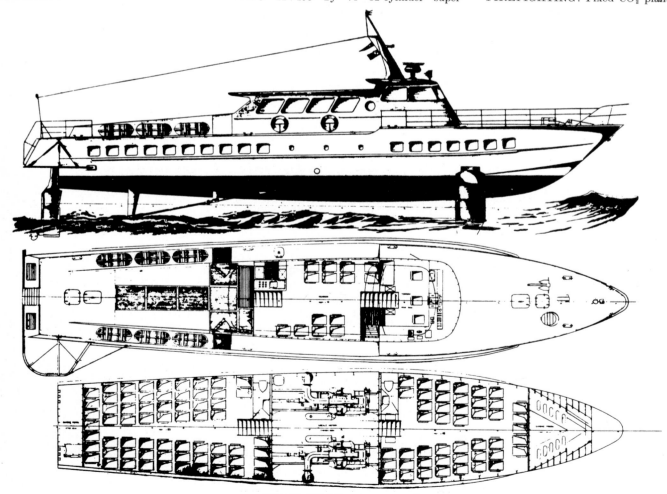

RHS 140, 125-140-seat passenger ferry

engine room; portable CO_2 and foam fire extinguishers in the saloons. Water intake connected to bilge pump for fire hose connection in emergency.

DIMENSIONS:

Length overall	94 ft 1½ in (28·70 m)
Width across foils	35 ft 2¼ in (10·72 m)
Draft hullborne	11 ft 5¾ in (3·50 m)
Draft foilborne	4 ft 11 in (1·50 m)

WEIGHTS:

Displacement, fully loaded	65 tons
Carrying capacity, including 3 tons bunker, and 5 tons fresh water, lubricating oil and hydraulic system oil	12·5 tons

PERFORMANCE:

Max speed, half load	36 knots
Cruising speed	32·5 knots
Range at cruising speed 900 miles (550 kms)	

RHS 160

One of the latest additions to the Rodriquez range is the RHS 160, an 82-ton passenger ferry with seats for 160-180 passengers and a cruising speed of 36 knots.

FOILS: Surface-piercing W foils of hollow welded steel construction. Craft in this series feature a bow rudder for improved manoeuvrability in congested waters. The bow rudder works simultaneously with the aft rudders. Hydraulically-operated flaps, attached to the trailing edges of the bow and rear foils, are adjusted automatically by a Hamilton Standard electronic stability augmentation system, for the damping of heave, pitch and roll motions in heavy seas.

HULL: Riveted light metal alloy longitudinal structure, welded in parts using inert gas. The hull shape of the RHS 160 is similar to the RHS 140 series. In the manufacture of the hull, plates of aluminium and magnesium alloy of 4·4% are used whilst angle bars are of a high-resistant aluminium, magnesium and silicon alloy.

ACCOMMODATION: 160-180 passengers seated in three saloons. Fifty-seven passengers are accommodated in the forward cabin, fifty-seven in the rear compartment and forty-six in the belvedere. Forward and aft saloons and belvedere have a toilet, each provided with W/C washbasin units and the usual toilet accessories.

POWER PLANT: Power is provided by two supercharged MTU MB 12V 652 TB 71 4-stroke diesel engines each with a maximum output of 1,950 hp at 1,460 rpm under normal operating conditions. Engine starting is accomplished by compressed air starters. Engine output is transmitted to two 3-bladed bronze propellers through two Zahnradfabrik 900 HS 15 gearboxes.

SYSTEMS, ELECTRICAL: Two 35 KVA generating sets, 220 v, 60 cps, 3-phase. Three insulated cables for ventilation, air-conditioning and power. Two insulated cables for lighting, sockets and other appliances, 24 v d.c. for emergency lighting, auxiliary engine starting and servocontrol. A battery for radio telephone supply is installed on the upper deck. Provision for battery recharge from a.c. line foreseen.

HYDRAULICS: Steering is accomplished hydraulically from the wheelhouse. Plant comprises a Bosch pump installed on the main engines and conveying oil from a 10 gallon (45 litre) tank under pressure to the control cylinders of the rudder and anchor windlass, whilst a second hydraulic pump, which is also installed on the main engines, conveys oil under pressure to the flap control cylinders.

FIREFIGHTING: Fixed CO_2 plant of four CO_2 bottles of about 20 kg each for the engine room and fuel tank space; portable extinguishers in various parts of the craft. Water intake connected to fire pump for fire connection in emergency.

DIMENSIONS:

Length overall	101 ft 6 in (30·95 m)
Width across foils	41 ft 4 in (12·60 m)
Draft afloat	12 ft 6 in (3·70 m)
Draft foilborne	4 ft 6 in (1·35 m)

WEIGHTS:

Displacement, fully loaded	82 tons
Pay load, passengers and luggage	13·5 tons

PERFORMANCE:

Speed, max	39·0 knots
Speed, cruising	36·0 knots
Cruising, range	300 miles

RHS 200

Construction of this 116-ton, 200-seat fast ferry is expected to start in 1975. Power will be provided by two supercharged MTU MB 16V 652 TB 71 4-stroke diesel engines. The designed cruising speed is 37·5 knots.

FOILS: Surface-piercing vee foils of hollow welded construction. Hydraulically-operated flaps are fitted to the trailing edge of the bow foil to balance out longitudinal load shifting, assist take-off and adjust the flying height. The craft can also be equipped with the Hamilton Standard electronic stability augmentation system, which employs sensors and servomechanisms to automatically position flaps on the bow and stern foils for the damping of heave, pitch and roll motions in heavy seas.

HULL: Vee-bottom hull of high tensile riveted light metal alloy construction, employing Peraluman plates and Anticorrodal frames. The rake of the stem is in galvanised steel.

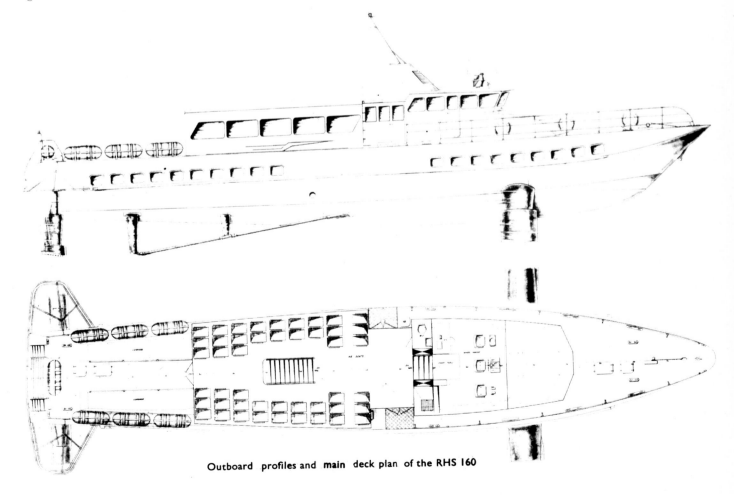

Outboard profiles and main deck plan of the RHS 160

ACCOMMODATION: Seats can be provided for up to 200 passengers, according to the route served. There are three main passenger saloons and a bar. The standard seating arrangement allows for 60 in the main deck saloon, 75 in the aft lower saloon and 51 in the bow passenger saloon. Seating is normally four-abreast in two lines with a central aisle. The bar, at the forward end of the wheelhouse belvedere superstructure, has either an 8-place sofa or 19 chairs.

The wheelhouse, which is raised to provide a 360° view, is reached from the main deck belvedere saloon by a short companionway. Controls and instrumentation are attached to a panel on the forward bulkhead which extends the width of the wheelhouse. In the centre is the steering control and gyro-compass, on the starboard side are controls for the two engines, gearboxes and controllable-pitch propellers, and on the port side is the radar. Chairs are provided for the captain, chief engineer and first mate. At the aft of the wheelhouse is a radio-telephone and a chart table.

POWER PLANT: Motive power is supplied by two supercharged MTU MB 16V 652 TB 71 4-stroke diesel engines, each with a maximum output of 2,415 hp at 1,485 rpm under normal operating conditions. Engine output is transferred to two supercavitating, controllable-pitch propellers.

SYSTEMS, ELECTRICAL: Two generating sets. One 220 volt, 3-phase a.c., for all consumer services, the second for charging 24 volt battery sets and operating fire-fighting and hydraulic pumps. Power distribution panel in wheelhouse for navigation light circuits, cabin lighting, radar, RDF, gyro compass and emergency circuits.

Above and below: The new Rodriquez RHS 160, an 82-ton passenger with seats for 160-180 passengers and a cruising speed of 36 knots

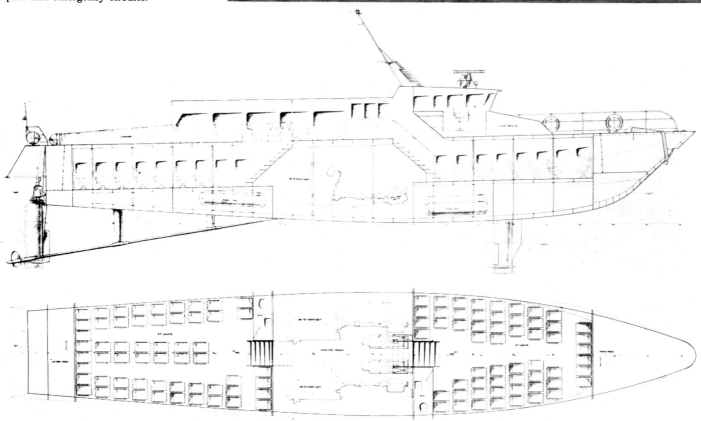

Inboard profile and lower deck plan of the RHS 160

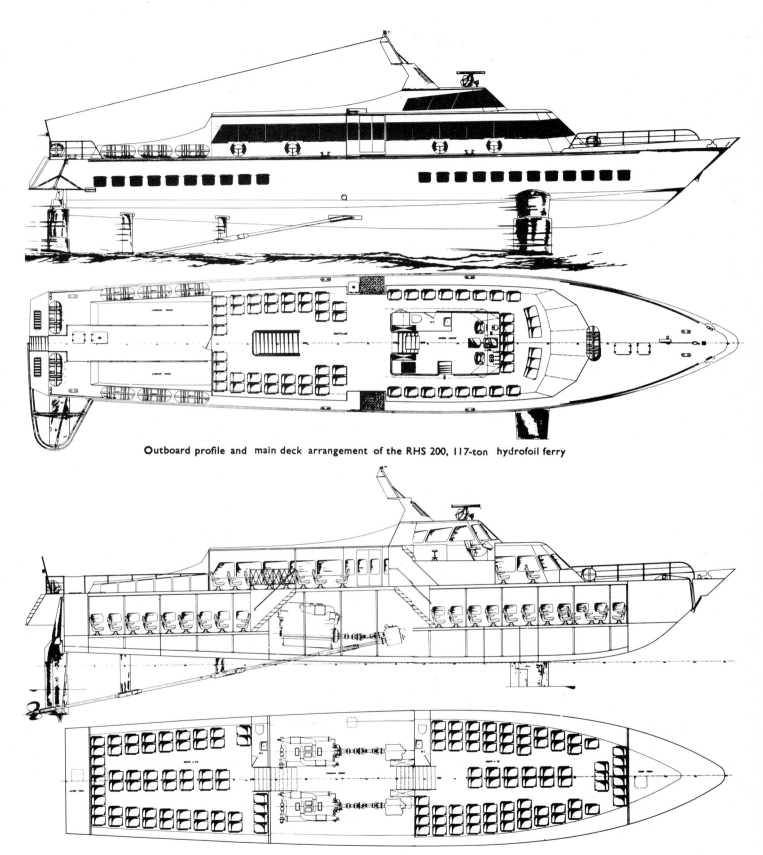

Outboard profile and main deck arrangement of the RHS 200, 117-ton hydrofoil ferry

Inboard profile and lower deck arrangement of the RHS 200

FIREFIGHTING: Fixed CO_2 self-contained automatic systems for power plant and fuel tank spaces, plus portable extinguishers for cabins and holds.

DIMENSIONS:

Length overall	116 ft 5⅝ in	(35·50 m)
Width across foils	46 ft 6⅞ in	(14·20 m)
Draft afloat	14 ft 2⅛ in	(4·32 m)
Draft foilborne	5 ft 3¾ in	(1·62 m)

WEIGHTS:

Displacement fully loaded	117 tons

PERFORMANCE:

Cruising speed	37·5 knots
Maximum speed	41 knots
Cruising range	275 n. miles

RHS ALIYACHT

A luxury hydrofoil yacht of light alloy construction, the RHS Aliyacht is derived from the RHS 110 passenger ferry. It is powered by two 1,350 hp Maybach MB 12V493 Ty 71 diesel engines and has a cruising speed of 38 knots.

The craft is equipped with the Hamilton Standard electronic stability augmentation system, which is designed to provide a smoother ride in heavy seas. The system uses sensors and servomechanisms to automatically position foil flaps for the maximum damping of heave, pitch and roll motions.

FOILS: Bow and rear foils are of surface-piercing type, and constructed in partly hollow, welded steel. Two hydraulically-operated flaps, attached to the trailing edges of the bow foil, are adjusted automatically by the stabilisation system for the damping of heave, pitch and roll motions. The rear foil is rigidly attached to the transom, its incidence angle being determined during tests.

HULL: The vee-bottom hull is of high-tensile riveted light metal alloy construction, using Peraluman (aluminium and magnesium alloy) plates and Anticorrodal (aluminium, magnesium and silicon alloy) profiles. The rake of the stem is in 0·137 in (3·5 mm) thick galvanised steel. The superstructure is constructed in 0·078 in (2·0 mm) Peraluman plate, and the roof is detachable to facilitate the removal and replacement of the main engines.

ACCOMMODATION: Main deck accommodation comprises the wheelhouse and radio cabin, a comfortably furnished saloon and a galley. The saloon will be fitted with two four-seat sofas, armchair, tea-table, a meal table with four chairs, and a bar. Below deck, from aft peak forward, is a large cabin for the owner, with its own bathroom and small private drawing room; two double cabins for guests with adjacent WC/wash-basin/shower units, and beyond the engines, a cabin for the captain and engineer, and two single cabins for guests.

The wheelhouse is reached via a companion-way from the saloon and is connected by a door with the upper deck. The pilot's position, controls and instruments are on the port side, together with the radar screen.

POWERPLANT: Power is supplied by two supercharged 12-cylinder MTU MB 12V 439 Ty 71 diesels, each rated at 1,350 hp at 1,500 rpm. Engine output is transferred to two 3-bladed bronze aluminium-propellers through Zahnradfabrik BW 800 H20 gearboxes.

SYSTEMS: Two 10 kW, 220 volt, three-phase ONAN generating sets, coupled to batteries, provide 24 volts dc for engine starting, instruments, lighting radio etc.

DIMENSIONS, EXTERNAL:

Length overall	78 ft 9 in (24·50 m)
Beam overall	20 ft 0 in (6·10 m)
Hull beam	19 ft 2¼ in (5·85 m)
Draft afloat	9 ft 8⅛ in (2·95 m)
Draft foilborne	4 ft 1¼ in (1·25 m)

WEIGHTS:

Displacement, loaded	52 tons

PERFORMANCE:

Max speed	41 knots
Cruising speed	38 knots
Range	400 miles (644 km)

RHS HYDROILS

These are derivatives of RHS passenger-carrying hydrofoils, and are designed to ferry personnel, materials and equipment between offshore oil rigs and shore bases. Vessels in this series feature an open cargo deck aft of the bridge superstructure instead of an aft passenger saloon. The two main types are the RHS 70 Hydroil and the RHS 140 Hydroil.

RHS 70 HYDROIL

The first of the new series of RHS 70 Hydroil offshore drilling platform supply vessels has been built for ENI Oil Corporation, which is employing the craft in the Adriatic. A mixed passenger/cargo version of the RHS 70 passenger ferry, this variant has an open cargo deck aft of the bridge superstructure in place of the Caribe's main passenger cabin. Dimensions of the cargo deck are: length, 24 ft 7 in (7·50 m); width, 11 ft 6 in (3·50 m) and height, 3 ft 5 in (1·05 m).

FOILS: Bow and rear foils are of surface-piercing vee configuration, with about 66% of the weight supported by the bow foil and 34% by the rear foil. Each foil, together with its struts and horizontal supporting tube, forms a rigid framework which facilitates the exchange of the foil structure. The foils are of hollow-ribbed construction and fabricated from medium Asera steel. The forward foil can be tilted within narrow limits by means of a hydraulic ram acting on the foil strut supporting tube. The angle of attack can therefore be adjusted during operation to assist take-off and counteract the effect of large variations in loading.

HULL: The hull is of riveted light metal alloy (Peraluman) and framed on a combination of longitudinal and transverse formers. Watertight compartments are provided in the bow and stern, and a double-bottom runs from immediately aft of the engine room, beneath the full length of the cargo deck, to the after peak. Contained within the double-bottom are six cylindrical

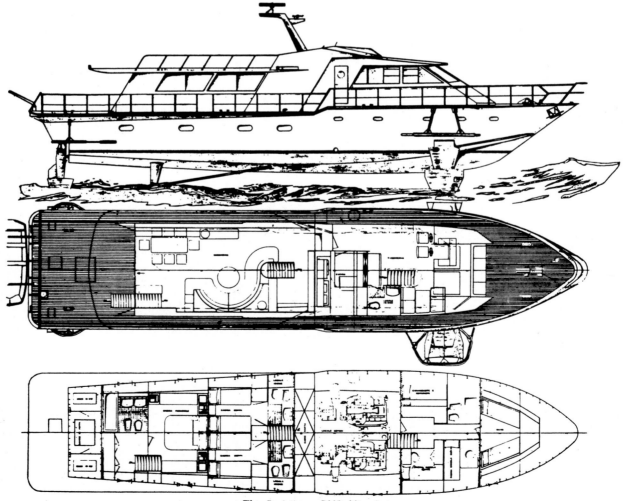

The Rodriquez RHS Aliyacht,

The Rodriquez RHS Aliyacht, powered by two MTU diesels each rated at 1,350 hp. Cruising speed is 38 knots and the range 400 miles

Porto Corsini, first of the RHS 70 Hydrofoil 33-ton off-shore drilling platform supply vessels. The craft has been built for ENI, the Italian oil company and is seen operating from one of the company's drilling platforms. Loads of up to 3 tons can be carried on the open cargo deck aft of the bridge structure. Cruising speed with normal payload is 32 knots

aluminium fuel tanks with a total capacity of 495 gallons (2,250 litres). Access to the fore and aft compartments is via removable deck hatches. The deck is of 0·196 in (5 mm) Peraluman, suitably reinforced to withstand heavily concentrated loads. Two 4·9 in (125 mm) diameter scuppers are provided aft for rapid drainage. Heavy rubber fenders are provided at the bow and stern.

POWER PLANT: Power is supplied by a 12-cylinder supercharged MTU 12V493 Ty 71 with a maximum output of 1,350 hp at 1,500 rpm. Engine output is transferred to a 3-bladed 27·5 in (700 mm) bronze-aluminium propeller through a Zahnradfabrik BW 800 H20 gearbox. The propeller shaft is 3·5 in (90 mm) in diameter, and supported at three points by seawater lubricated rubber bearings. In an emergency, hullborne propulsion is provided by a 105 hp Mercedes OM 352 diesel with a Mercruiser Z-drive. The engine is installed in the aft peak and propels the craft at about 5 knots.

ACCOMMODATION: The craft has a crew of

two, and seats up to 12 passengers in a comfortably appointed saloon, immediately aft of the wheelhouse. Passengers have a choice of six armchairs and two three-place settees, one of which converts into a bed for transporting sick or injured personnel. All seats are equipped with safety belts. Aft of the saloon is a fully equipped galley, with refrigerator, a gas cooker with two gas rings, cupboards, plate rack and sink unit. Two folding wooden tables permit up to eight passengers to take meals at one sitting. A toilet/washbasin unit is provided opposite the galley on the port side. The engine room, wheelhouse and passenger saloon are fully heated and ventilated. A full range of safety equipment is carried including inflatable rafts and lifebelts for each passenger and crew member.

SYSTEMS: Electrical: 220 volt 50 H2 three-phase a.c., 24 volt dc; provision for 220 volt 50 H2 three phase shore supply. The dc supply is from a 24 volt generator driven by the main engine and feeding a 235 Ah battery. AC supply is derived from a 4-stroke Onan diesel generator set, located in the engine

room.
HYDRAULICS. One Bosch Hy/ZFR 1/16 AR 101 for steering and bow foil incidence control.

COMMUNICATIONS AND NAVIGATION: Radio: VHF radio-telephone to customers' requirements.
Radar: Decca, Raytheon etc., to customers' requirements.
DIMENSIONS:

Length overall, hull	68 ft 9 in (20·95 m)
Hull beam	16 ft 7 in (5·06 m)
Width over foils	24 ft 3 in (7·40 m)
Draft afloat	8 ft 10 in (2·70 m)
Draft foilborne	3 ft 9 in (1·14 m)

WEIGHTS:

Max take-off displacement	33·12 tons
Max load on open cargo deck	3 tons

PERFORMANCE (with normal payload)

Cruising speed	32 knots
Range	300 miles (480 km)

RHS 140 HYDROIL

Latest in the Rodriquez Hydroil range is a mixed passenger/cargo version of the 65-ton RHS 140. As with the smaller RHS 70 Hydroil, the main passenger saloon is

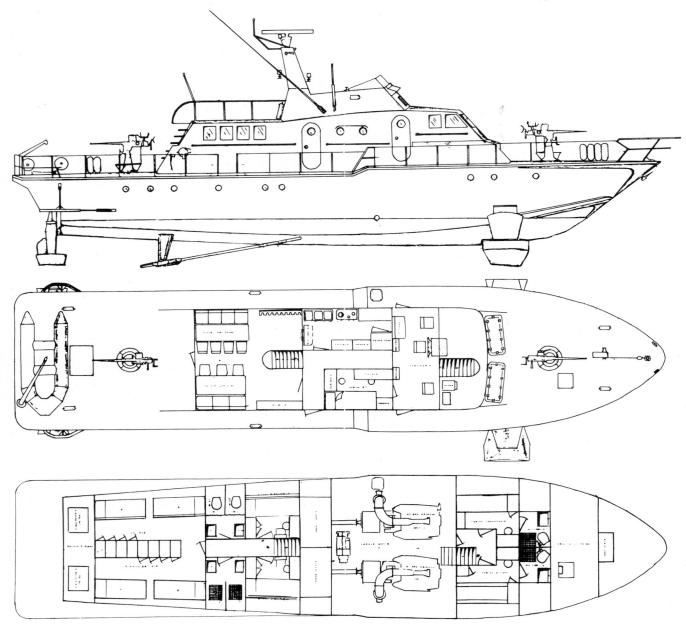

General arrangement of the fast patrol variant of the RHS 110

replaced by a large open cargo deck for loads up to 6 tons. The deck is 31 ft 2 in (9·5 m) long, 15 ft 9 in (4·8 m) wide and 6 ft 4 in (1·9 m) high.

The craft will carry a crew of two and up to 14 passengers. Power will be supplied by two 12-cylinder supercharged MTU 12V493 Ty 71, with a maximum output of 1,350 hp.

DIMENSIONS:

Length overall, hull	93 ft 6 in (28·50 m)
Hull beam	20 ft 0 in (6·10 m)
Width over foils	35 ft 2 in (10·72 m)
Draft hullborne	11ft 6 in (3·50 m)
Draft foilborne	4 ft 11 in (1·50 m)

WEIGHTS:

Normal take-off displacement	64 tons

PERFORMANCE:

Cruising speed	32-34 knots
Range at cruising speed	300 miles (480 km)

RHS/M PATROL CRAFT

Derived from RHS passenger vessels, the RHS/M series craft are designed for coast guard and anti-contraband patrol. Suitably armed, they can undertake various naval duties, ranging from patrol to minelaying. The armament shown in the accompanying drawings can be augmented or substituted by sea-to-air and sea-to-sea missiles according to requirements.

RHS 70/M

The RHS 70/M is similar in design and performance to the two PAT 20 patrol hydrofoils built by Rodríquez for the Philipine Navy.

FOILS: Bow and rear foils are of surfacing piercing V configuration and identical to those of the standard PT 20. About 59% of the total weight is borne by the bow foil and 41% by the rear foil. The foils are of hollow ribbed construction and made from medium Asera steel.

Total foil area is 112 sq ft (10·4 m²). The angle of incidence of the forward foil can be varied during flight by means of a hydraulic ram acting on the foil strut supporting tube.

HULL: The hull is of riveted light alloy construction with Peraluman (aluminium and magnesium alloy) plates and Anticorrodal (aluminium, magnesium and silicon alloy) profiles.

ACCOMMODATION: The crew comprises a captain, two officers and eight NCO's and ratings. The pilot's position is on the left of the wheelhouse, with the principal instrumentation; and the radar operator sits on the right with the auxiliary instrumentation. The pilot is provided with an intercom system connecting him with the officer's cabin, engine room and crew cabin. The internal space has been divided as follows:

(a) The forward or bow room, subdivided into two cabins, one for the captain, the other for two officers, and including a WC with washstand and a storeroom with a refrigerator.

(b) The stern room, with eight berths for the NCOs and ratings, a WC with washstand and a galley equipped with a gas stove and an electric refrigerator.

(c) The deck room, aft of the wheelhouse, with tilting sofa and table for R/T equipment.

Air conditioning is installed in the captain's and officer's quarters.

POWER PLANT: Power is supplied by a supercharged 12-cylinder MTU 12V493 Ty 71 with a max continuous output of 1,350 hp at 1,500 rpm. Engine output is transferred

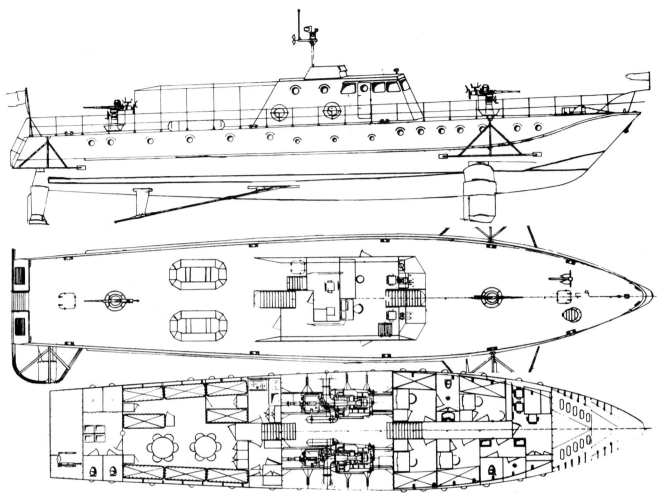

General arrangement of the Rodriquez RHS 140/M

to a 3-bladed bronze aluminium propeller through a Zahnradfabrik BW 800/S reversible gear. Fuel (total capacity 2,800 kg) is carried in ten cylindrical aluminium tanks located in the double bottom beneath the bow room and the stern room. Dynamic and reserve oil tanks in the engine room give a total oil capacity of 120 kg. An auxiliary engine can be fitted in the stern for emergency operation.

ARMAMENT AND SEARCH EQUIP-MENT: Single 12·7 machine-gun mounted above well position in bow, and two searchlights.

SYSTEMS:

ELECTRICAL: 220v, 10 kW, diesel generator with batteries. Supplies instruments, radio and radar and external and internal lights, navigation lights and searchlights.

HYDRAULICS: 120 kg/cm² pressure hydraulic system for steering and varying forward foil incidence angle.

APU: Onan engine for air conditioning when requested.

DIMENSIONS:

Length overall, hull	68 ft 6 in (20·89 m)
Hull beam	15 ft 8¾ in (4·79 m)
Beam overall	24 ft 4 in (7·4 m)
Draft afloat	9 ft 1 in (2·76 m)
Draft foilborne	4 ft 0 in (1·20 m)
Height overall:	
hullborne	21 ft 0 in (6·44 m)
foilborne	26 ft 3 in (8·00 m)

WEIGHTS:

Net tonnage	28 tons
Light displacement	26 tons
Max take-off displacement	32·5 tons
Useful load	7·6 tons
Max useful load	8·1 tons

PERFORMANCE:

Max speed foilborne	38 knots
Max speed hullborne	13 knots
Cruising speed foilborne	34 knots
Cruising speed hullborne	12 knots
Max permissible sea state foilborne mode	Force 4
Designed range at cruising speed	540 miles (869 km)
Number of seconds and distances to take-off	20 secs, 328 ft (100 m)
Number of seconds and distances to stop craft	12 secs, 164 ft (50 m)
Fuel consumption at cruising speed	145 kg/h
Fuel consumption at max speed	180 kg/h

RHS 110/M

This is the fast patrol boat version of the RHS 110 passenger ferry. Modifications include a revised cabin superstructure with an upper bridge; the installation of two rapid firing cannon, and provision of fuel tanks of additional capacity increasing the operating range to 560 miles (347.96 km).

FOILS, HULL, POWERPLANT: Arrangements similar to those of the RHS 110.

ACCOMMODATION: Berths provided for eight officers and non-commissioned officers and eight ratings.

DIMENSIONS:

Length overall	83 ft 2 in (25·40 m)
Beam overall	27 ft 6¾ in (8·40 m)
Height of hull structure	9 ft 4 in (2·85 m)
Draft foilborne	4 ft 1 in (2·15 m)
Draft hullborne, fully loaded	9 ft 10 in (3·00 m)

WEIGHTS:

Displacement, empty	36 tons
Displacement, loaded	50 tons

PERFORMANCE:

Max speed	41 knots
Cruising speed	38 knot
Cruising range	560 miles (896 km)

RHS 140/M

Derived from the RHS 140 passenger ferry this fast patrol variant is armed with two rapid firing cannon and has a maximum speed of 37 knots. Above the wheelhouse is an open bridge with duplicate steering, engine controls and instrumentation.

FOILS, HULL, POWERPLANT: Arrangements similar to those of the RHS 140.

ACCOMMODATION: Berths, living accommodation for eight commissioned and non-commissioned officers and sixteen ratings.

DIMENSIONS:

Length overall	95 ft 2 in (29 m)
Width across foils	31 ft 6 in (9·60 m)
Height of hull structure	11 ft 8⅛ in (3·56 m)

WEIGHTS:

Displacement loaded	64 tons
Displacement empty	50 tons

PERFORMANCE:

Max speed foilborne	37 knots
Cruising speed	34 knots
Minimum foilborne speed	23·3 knots
Range	736 miles (1,127 km)

SEAFLIGHT SpA Cantiere Navale

HEAD OFFICE:
Via della Munizione 3, Messina
TELEPHONE:
46100
TECHNICAL OFFICE:
Villagio Torre Faro, Messina
TELEPHONE:
811200
DIRECTOR AND SENIOR EXECUTIVES:
Professor Felice Siracusano, President and Director
Ing. Gregorio Alberto Costa, Director
Dott Ing Giuseppe Zuffo, Director
Dott Ing Cesare Vinciguera, Director
Ing Giuseppe Giuffrida, General Manager
Dott Ing Emanuele Midolo, Technical Manager

The Seaflight series of hydrofoils use a variable-incidence foil system introduced by Giuseppe Giuffrida who formed this company in 1961. The company is backed by a group of Messina industrialists and currently employs a staff of about sixty.

Construction of the company's yard on the beach at Torre Faro, began in 1962, and the Seaflight P 46 prototype, the C 44, was launched in January 1965. The company has since built eight 30 seat P 46s and six H 57s, the latter being a larger and more powerful development of the P 46, seating 60 passengers. The first of the company's 60-ton L 90 hydrofoils is now in service with Societe Sarda per Navigazione Veloce on the route Civitavecchia—Olbia. The company is at present conducting studies aimed at the further development of the Seaflight variable incidence foil system and the design of a gas-turbine powered waterjet propulsion system for commercial hydrofoils.

Descriptions of the P 46 and military variants of this craft and the H 57 appeared in JSS 1972-73 and earlier editions.

SEAFLIGHT L 90

The L 90, latest passenger ferry hydrofoil in the Seaflight series, seats 118-123 passengers and cruises at 35 knots. The prototype was built under the supervision of Registro Italiano Navale.

FOILS: The foil system is of aeroplane configuration with surface-piercing bow and rear foils. Approximately 60% of the load is supported by the bow foil and 40% by the rear foil.

The bow foil, of W type, is attached to a supporting tube inside the hull by a central and two lateral struts. The foil pivots around the axis of the supporting tube between positions of maximum and minimum incidence. The lift and drag generated by the foil tends to rotate it backwards, particularly during take-off and in rough seas, but this movement is opposed by a spring attached to an arm on the foil assembly shaft. The system is designed to produce the same amount of lift, whether the speed varies or the foil's submerged surface varies in a wave crest or cavity.

Foils, struts and the supporting tube are fabricated in steel. Four shear points are provided, two inside the hull at the attachment points of the support tube arm and the automatic incidence control system, and two externally, at the point of attachment of the two subfoils to the central strut. In the event of damage, the affected foils and their supporting structure can be quickly and easily repaired.

The rear foil combines a horizontal submerged centre section with inclined surface-piercing areas. It is attached to the hull by two struts and the two rudder supports and the angle of incidence is fixed.

HULL: Riveted light alloy construction is employed throughout. The structure is of the transverse type with frames spaced 1 ft 0 in (300 mm) apart. Full-length longitudinal members reinforce the hull bottom and the decks and run from stem to stern. All plates and sections are specially treated by the company for added protection against corrosion. Braking load of the plates is 30·35 kg/sq mm. The hull is designed for two compartment sub-division and will remain afloat with any two adjacent compartments flooded.

ACCOMMODATION: The standard version accommodates a crew of 3-4 and 118-123 passengers, who are seated in three large saloons. Entry is through one of two side doors, one port, one starboard, in the central saloon, which provides access via a companionway to the aft saloon, the forward saloon and the wheelhouses. There are two WC washbasin units in the aft saloon and one in the forward saloon.

The pilot's position, instruments and controls are on the starboard side of the wheelhouse and there is a crew member's observation position on the port side. Access to the

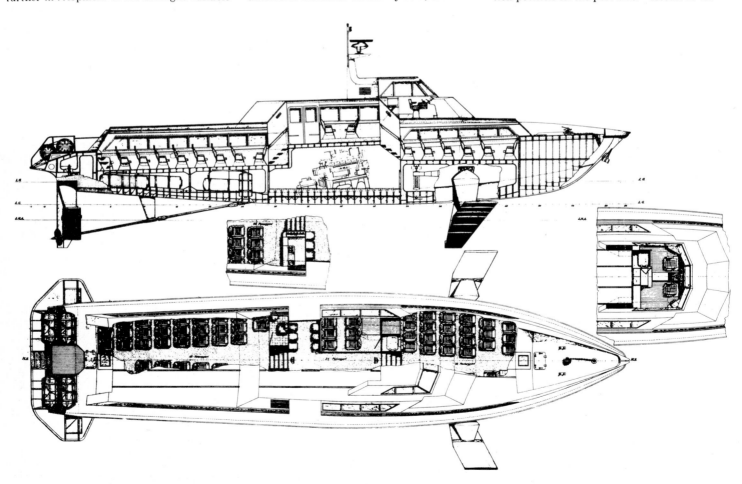

Inboard profile and plan views of the Seaflight L90 passenger ferry hydrofoil. Power is supplied by two 1,100 hp MB 820 DC diesels

engine room is from the wheelhouse via a watertight hatch.

POWER PLANT: Power is supplied by two supercharged 12 cylinder Mercedes-Maybach MB 820 Dc diesels, each with a maximum continuous output of 1,100 shp at 1,400 rpm. Engine output is transferred to two high tensile bronze propellers through Zahnradfabrik BW 800/s reversible gears.

SYSTEMS:

ELECTRICAL: Two engine driven generators coupled to two battery sets provide 24 volts dc for engine starting, instruments, lighting, radio, etc. Separate diesel ac generating plant can be installed if required.

COMMUNICATIONS AND NAVIGATION: Ship-shore vhf and radar to customer's requirements.

Seaflight's L. 90 prototype undergoing trials in April 1973. The vessel is now in service with Societe Sarda per Navigazione Veloce on the route Civitavecchia—Olbia

DIMENSIONS, EXTERNAL:

Length overall	89 ft 4 in (27·24 m)
Length waterline, hull	74 ft 6 in (22·70 m)
Draft afloat	10 ft 1 in (3·07 m)
Draft foilborne	4 ft 1¼ in (1·25 m)
Hull beam	19 ft 9¾ in (6·04 m)
Width across foils	32 ft 9¾ in (10·00 m)
Freeboard	5 ft 5 in (1·35 m)
Height overall	26 ft 3 in (8·00 m)

DIMENSIONS, INTERNAL:

Aft passenger saloon compartment, including WC:

Length	28 ft 6½ in (8·70 m)
Max width	15 ft 5 in (4·70 m)
Max height	5 ft 6 in (1·95 m)
Floor area	398 sq ft (37 m²)
Volume	2,472 cu ft (70 m³)

Main deck saloon, excluding wheelhouse:

Length	16 ft 8¾ in (5·10 m)
Max width	15 ft 9 in (4·80 m)
Height	6 ft 5 in (195 m)
Turning radius at cruising speed	392 ft (120 m)
Take-off distance	427 ft (130 m)
Max-height	6 ft 5 in (1·95 m)
Floor area	258 cu ft (24 m³)
Volume	1,589 cu ft (45 m³)

Wheelhouse

Length	6 ft 2¾ in (1·90 m)
Width	9 ft 10 in (3·00 m)
Height	6 ft 2¾ in (1·90 m)
Area	64 sq ft (6 m²)
Volume	423 cu ft (12 m³)

WEIGHTS:

Light displacement	45 tons
Max take-off displacement	59·5 tons
Deadweight (incl fuel, water, passengers, crew)	14 tons
Payload	10 tons

PERFORMANCE (Designed):

Cruising speed foilborne	32·4-35 knots
Max wave height in foilborne mode	5 ft 3 in (1·60 m)
Range at cruising speed	270 nautical miles (500 km)
Turning radius at crusing speed	328 yards (300 m)
Take-off distance	218 yards (200 m)
Take-off time	30 seconds
Stopping distance	87 yards (80 m)
Stopping time	10 seconds
Fuel consumption at cruising speed	300 kg/h

JAPAN

HITACHI SHIPBUILDING & ENGINEERING CO

HEAD OFFICE:

47 Edobori 1-chome, Nishi-ku, Osaka, Japan

TELEPHONE:

Osaka 443-8051

CABLES:

Shipyard, Osaka

TELEX:

J 63376

WORKS:

Mizue-cho 1, Kawasaki-ku, Kawasaki City, Japan

TELEPHONE:

Kawasaki 28-1111

DIRECTORS AND EXECUTIVES:

Takao Nagata, President

Nobuo Inoue, Executive Vice-President, General Manager of Shipbuilding Division (Sales Director)

Giichi Miyashita, Manager of Kanagawa Shipyard

Hitachi, the Supramar licencee in Japan, has been building PT 3, PT 20 and PT 50

Kondoru, a 123-passenger Hitachi-built PT 50 operated by Setonaikai Kisen Co Ltd on the route Hiroshima-Kure-Matsuyama

hydrofoils since 1961.   The majority of these have been built for fast passenger ferry services across the Japanese Inland Sea, cutting across deep bays which road vehicles might take two-to-three hours to drive round, and out to offshore islands.   Other PT 20s and 50s have been exported to Hong Kong and Australia for ferry services.

Specifications of the PT 3, PT 20 and PT 50 will be found under Supramar (Switzerland). The Hitachi-built craft are identical apart from minor items.

By the end of March 1974, Hitachi had built a total of eighteen PT 50s and fourteen PT 20s.

A special military hydrofoil, based on the Schertel-Sachsenburg foil system, and designated PT 32, has been designed by the company and two are in service with the Philippine Navy.

Hankyu Lines of Kobe City operates this 131-seat Hitachi PT 50 between Kobe and Naruto

POLAND

GDANSK SHIP RESEARCH INSTITUTE
ADDRESS:
Technical University, Gdansk
TELEPHONE:
41-47-12
DIRECTORS:
Prof Dr Lech Kobylinski

Research on problems connected with hydrofoil design and construction have been conducted by the Department of Theoretical Naval Architecture at Gdansk Technical University since 1956.

Experience with various dynamic test models led to the construction of the K-3 four-seat runabout which, powered by an FSC Lublin converted auto-engine, has a top speed of 27 knots (50 km/h).

In 1961 the Department was invited by the Central Board of Inland Navigation and United Inland Shipping and River Shipyards Gdansk, to design a hydrofoil passenger ferry for service in the Firth of Szczecin. Designated ZRYW-1 the craft seats 76 passengers and cruises at 35 knots.   It was completed in 1965.   A second craft, the W-2, intended for passenger services in the Baltic, is under development.

During 1966 the Ship Research Institute designed two hydrofoil sports craft, the WS-4 Amor and the WS-6 Eros.   The prototypes were completed in 1967 and both types were put into series production during 1972.

In 1971, a catamaran-hulled research hydrofoil, the Badacz II, was built for the Ship Hydrodynamics Division of the Institute.   The vessel is employed to tow models of ACVs and hydrofoils in coastal waters and provide data and performance measurements.

It is also being employed to test new propulsion systems.

The largest hydrofoil craft to be designed by the Institute is a 300-ton passenger/car ferry.

BADACZ II
Designed for hydrodynamic research in coastal waters, the SP-04 Badacz II is a 40 ft 4 in (12·60 m) long catamaran-type hydrofoil powered by two 110 hp Volvo Penta Aqua-

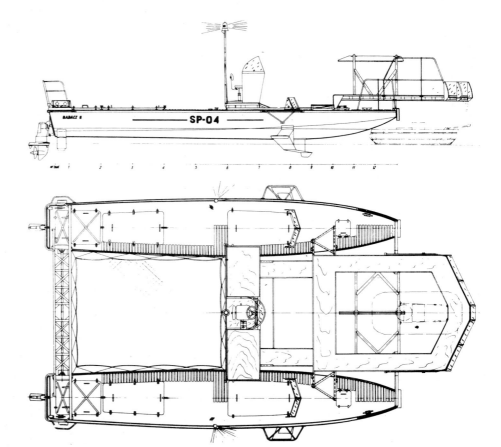

General arrangement of the Badacz II, showing a dynamic model of a skirted ACV suspended beneath the test platform

matic outboard engines.

Models of hydrofoils and SEVs undergoing tests are suspended beneath the observer's platform extension at the bow, and towed by the craft at speeds up to 59 f/s (18 m/s). Measurements made during the towing tests include resistance, height at the bow, trim angle and behaviour in various wave conditions.

FOILS: Split "trapeze" foil forward, combining surface piercing and shallow submerged areas with additional vertical stabilising areas. Twin surface piercing W foils aft. 58% of the load is carried on the bow foils and 42% on the rear foils. Bow and rear foils are all-welded in seawater-resistant aluminium alloy.

HULL: Catamaran type.   All-welded construction in welded seawater - resistant aluminium alloy.

ACCOMMODATION: Crew of three and two test observers.

POWER PLANT: Motive power is supplied by two stern-mounted Volvo Penta Aquamatic 110/200 marine outboard engines, each developing 110 hp. Each transmits power through a right-angle drive to a standard 3-blade propeller at the base of a strut-and-pod assembly which rotates for steering. Fuel is carried in two tanks, one in each hull.

DIMENSIONS:

Length overall	40 ft 4 in (12·60 m)
Length waterline hull	29 ft 6⅜ in (9 m)
Hull beam	5 ft 3 in (1·60 m)
Beam overall, across foils	24 ft 3⅜ in (7·40 m)
Draft afloat	2 ft 8¼ in (0·82 m)
Draft foilborne	1 ft 3⅜ in (0·39 m)
Freeboard	1 ft 9⅜ in (0·55 m)

WEIGHTS:

Light displacement	6,064 lb (2,750 kg)
Normal take-off displacement	7,938 lb (3,600 kg)
Max take-off displacement	8,269 lb (3,750 kg)

PERFORMANCE:

Max speed foilborne	40 mph (64·80 km/h)
Cruising speed foilborne	36 mph (57·60 km/h)
Max permissible wave height in foilborne mode	20 in (0·50 m)
Turning radius at cruising speed	98 ft (30 m)
Number of seconds and distance to take-off	20 secs 656 ft (200 m)
Number of seconds and distance to stop craft	10 secs 164 ft (50 m)

ZRYW-1

The ZRYW-1 was completed in May 1965, and sea trials were initiated the following month. On scheduled passenger services between Szczecin and Swinoujscie, a distance of 36 nautical miles (67 km), the average operating speed has been in excess of 39 knots (73 km/h). The journey has been covered successfully in Sea States 2-4, with wave heights up to 5 ft 0 in (1·5 m).

FOILS: The foil configuration is a combined surface piercing and submerging type. The foils are welded assemblies fabricated from 0·2 to 0·28 in (5·7 mm) thick stainless steel. The configuration is subcavitating and is designed to be inherently stable in any expected combination of heave, pitch, roll and yaw.

HULL: This is a light alloy structure of almost fully welded construction, riveting being applied mainly to the joints of the longitudinal and transverse framings with the outer plating of the vessel's roof, and also the joining of steel elements, such as the foil foundations and stern tube, with light alloy members.

POWER PLANT: Provided by a single Russian-built M-50F4 diesel, rated at 1,000 hp continuous and 1,200 hp maximum, driving a fixed-pitch, three-blade propeller.

The engine room, sited amidships, houses the main engine together with reversible gear, auxiliary set, tanks, and pumps serving the engine room system.

Badacz II, Gdansk Ship Research Institute's hydrofoil test craft. Dynamic models of hydrofoils and ACVs are towed by the vessel to gather design and performance data in open coastal waters

The ZRYW-I, first Polish-built hydrofoil passenger ferry to enter service

The WS-4 Amor, a four-seat runabout designed by Gdansk Ship Research Institute and powered by a Mercury 350 outboard motor

ACCOMMODATION: Forty passengers are carried in the forward passenger saloon, and thirty-six passengers in the aft saloon.

Comfortable, upholstered seats are fitted and the floors are covered with vinyl.

The wheelhouse, crew cabin and toilet are situated forward. Passenger entrance doors are provided on both sides of the craft and lead to a small vestibule forward of the crew's cabin. The two passenger compartments are provided with heat and acoustic insulation, and are electrically heated when stationary (shore supplied) and when in motion.

DIMENSIONS:

Length overall, hull	90 ft 7 in (27·60 m)
Length waterline, hull	75 ft 6 in (23·00 m)
Hull beam	14 ft 6 in (4·40 m)
Width across foils	24 ft 10 in (7·56 m)
Draft afloat	8 ft 1 in (2·45 m)
Freeboard	4 ft 3 in (1·30 m)

WEIGHTS:

Light displacement	22·7 tons
Max take-off displacement	30·7 tons
Useful load (fuel, water, passengers, baggage and crew)	8·0 tons

PERFORMANCE

Cruising speed:

foilborne	35 knots (65 km/h)
hullborne	16 knots (30 km/h)
Sea State max capability	State 3
Design foilborne range	250 miles (460 km)
Fuel consumption at cruising speed	330 lb/hr (150 kg/h)
Fuel consumption hullborne	176 lb/hr (80 kg/h)

WS-4 AMOR

A four-seat sports hydrofoil designed by E. Brzoska, the WS-4 is of moulded fibreglass construction and powered by an outboard engine. It was put into series production in 1972.

FOILS: The foil system is of combined surface-piercing and submerging type and non-retractable. It comprises a shallow draft surface-piercing bow foil and a fully submerged rear foil. Both are made of solid aluminium alloy. The foil arrangement is tandem in the sense that when foilborne the load is balanced between bow and rear foils.

ACCOMMODATION: Comfortable upholstered seats are provided for a helmsman and three passengers. The hull is of moulded fibreglass construction and incorporates a step to facilitate take-off.

POWER PLANT: The standard model is equipped with a Mercury 350 outboard, with single lever throttle and gearshift control. The engine propeller unit turns for steering. Fuel is contained in a 6 gallon tank.

DIMENSIONS, EXTERNAL:

Length overall, hull	15 ft 4 in (4·67 m)
Length waterline, hull	13 ft 2 in (4·0 m)
Hull beam	5 ft 0 in (1·5 m)
Width across foils	5 ft 11 in (1·8 m)
Draft afloat	1 ft 8 in (·05 m)
Draft foilborne	9 in (0·23 m)
Height overall	3 ft 4 in (1·0 m)

DIMENSIONS, INTERNAL:

Length	7 ft 3 in (2·2 m)
Max width	4 ft 0 in (1·2 m)
Floor area	27 sq ft (2·5 m²)

WEIGHTS:

Light displacement	1,521 lb (686 kg)
Max payload	881 lb (400 kg)

PERFORMANCE (with normal payload):

Max speed foilborne	34 mph (55 km/h)
Max speed hullborne	19 mph (30 km/h)
Cruising speed foilborne	80 mph (50 km/h)

Max permissible wave height in foilborne mode   6 in (0·15 m)

Designed range at cruising speed   31 miles (50 km)

Number of seconds to take-off (theoretical, approx)   15 sec

Number of seconds to stop craft (theoretical, approx)   10 sec

WS-6 EROS

A six seater hydrofoil runabout, the WS-6 Eros, like the smaller WS-4, was put into series production in 1972.

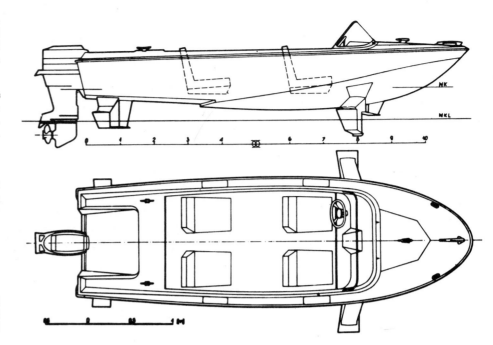

The Gdansk Ship Research Institute WS-4 Amor. The standard model is powered by a Mercury 350 outboard with single lever throttle and gearshift control

HULL: The prototype is built of marine plywood, but the hull of the production models will be moulded fibreglass.

FOILS: The foil system is similar to that of the WS-4. It is a combined surface-piercing and submerged configuration with a shallow draft surface-piercing bow foil, central "keel" and a fully submerged rear foil. Foils are of solid aluminium alloy. About 52% of the load is carried by the bow foil and 48% by the rear foil. Total foil area is 11·5 sq ft (1·07 m²).

ACCOMMODATION: Upholstered seats are provided for a helmsman and five passengers.

POWER PLANT: The production model will have a Volvo Penta Aquamatic 110/200. Power is transmitted through a right-angle drive transmission to a 3-blade propeller at the base of a strut-and-pod assembly which rotates for steering. Total fuel capacity is 100 litres.

DIMENSIONS, EXTERNAL:

Length overall, hull	23 ft 9 in (7·25 m)
Length waterline, hull	20 ft 2 in (6·15 m)
Hull beam	7 ft 4 in (2·24 m)
Beam overall, foils extended	8 ft 6 in (2·6 m)
Draft afloat	3 ft (0·9 m)

WS-6 Eros, six-seat sports hydrofoil

Draft foilborne	1 ft 2 in (0·36 m)
Freeboard	2 ft 2 in (0·65 m)
Height overall	5 ft 1 in (1·55 m)

DIMENSIONS, INTERNAL:

Cockpit length	10 ft 2 in (3·1 m)
Max width	6 ft 7 in (2 m)
Floor area	67·2 sq ft (6·2 m²)

WEIGHTS:

Light displacement	1·05 tons
Normal take-off displacement	1·6 tons
Max take-off displacement	1·75 tons
Normal payload	0·55 tons
Max payload	0·7 tons

PERFORMANCE:

Max speed foilborne	35 mph (56 km/h)
Cruising speed foilborne	31 mph (50 km/h)
Max permissible wave height in foilborne mode	10 in (250 mm)
Number of seconds and distance to take-off	10 sec, 394 ft (120 m)
Number of seconds and distance to stop craft	8 sec 329 ft (100 m)
Turning radius at cruising speed	820 ft (250 m)

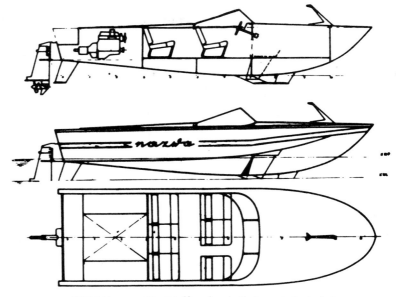

WS-6 Eros, a six-seat fibreglass-hulled sports hydrofoil

SINGAPORE

VOSPER THORNYCROFT PRIVATE LTD, SUPRAMAR LING HYDROFOIL DIVISION

HEAD OFFICE:
GPO Box 95, Singapore 1
TELEPHONE:
499121
TELEX:
RS 21219
WORKS:
200 Tanjong Rhu, Singapore 15

DIRECTORS:
John Rix, Chairman
R. Du Cane, Managing Director
R. G. Bennett
D. W. Sitwell
P. Joyce
D. S. Allpress
Prof. Yeoh Ghim Seng,
A. A. C. Griffith
S. N. Houghton
EXECUTIVES:
Paul Bakmand, Hydrofoil Sales

Vosper Thornycroft Private Limited, the Singapore subsidiary of the British warship design and construction specialists, have been appointed sole builder in South East Asia of the Supramar range of hydrofoils. The parent company in the UK has an agreement with Supramar AG of Lucerne, Switzerland and one PT5 Mk III has been built at the Portchester shipyard for Far East Hydrofoils, Hong Kong. The new agreement in Singapore is between Vosper Thornycroft Private and Supramar-Ling Private Limited, a company established after the signing of a licence agreement between Supramar and Mr Charles Tow Siang Ling, a Singapore businessman.

The Supramar-Ling Division of Vosper Thornycroft Private will build the craft and market them jointly with Supramar-Ling Private. This will be Vosper Thornycroft's first joint venture with a Singapore company and the first time any Singapore shipyard has built hydrofoils.

There are more than 160 Supramar hydrofoils, from 38 to 134 in length, operating around the world. The biggest carries up to 300 passengers at 38 knots. Applications foreseen for Supramar design in South East Asia are high-speed passenger transport, logistic support and patrol duties.

SWITZERLAND

SUPRAMAR AG
HEAD OFFICE:
Denkmalstrasse 2, 6006 Lucerne
TELEPHONE:
041-36 96 36
TELEX: 78228
MARKETING DEPARTMENT:
Supramar Trade Ltd, Denkmalstrasse 2, 6006 Lucerne

MANAGEMENT:
Hussain Najadi, Chairman and Managing Director
Ing Volker Jost, Technical Director and Assistant Managing Director
Baron Hanns von Schertel, Technical Director

DESIGN:
Dipl Ing Ernst Jaksch, Chief
Section Heads:
Dipl Ing Ernst Jaksch, Foil Design
Ing Volker Jost, Hull
RESEARCH AND DEVELOPMENT:
Baron Hanns von Schertel, Head of Development
Section Heads:
Dipl Ing Georg Chojka, Analysis and EDP
Dipl Ing Eugen Schatté, Propulsion and Tests
Dr Ing Hermann de Witt, Hydrodynamics

Supramar was founded in Switzerland in 1952 to develop on a commercial basis the hydrofoil system introduced by the Schertel-Sachsenberg Hydrofoil Syndicate and its licensee, the Gebruder Sachsenberg Shipyard.

The co-operation between the companies started in 1937 and led to the development of the VS6, a 17 ton hydrofoil, which in 1941 attained 47·5 knots, and the VS8 an 80-ton supply hydrofoil completed in 1943 which attained 41 knots. The inherently stable, rigid V-foil system used on these and subsequent Supramar vessels, stems from experimental work undertaken by Baron Hanns von Schertel between 1927-1937.

In May 1953, a Supramar PT 10, 32-passenger hydrofoil began the world's first regular passenger hydrofoil service on Lake Maggiore, between Switzerland and Italy. In August 1956, the first Rodriquez-built Supramar PT 20 opened a service across the Straits of Messina and became the first hydrofoil to be licenced by a marine classification authority for carrying passengers at sea.

Established originally as a research and design office, Supramar has recently been reorganised and will produce hydrofoils of its own design at shipyards independently of the arrangements with its licencees.

The Marketing Department provides, in addition to its normal marketing functions, consultancy service covering financing, leasing and operating.

Supramar employs a staff of over 40, mainly highly qualified scientists and engineers specialising in hydrodynamics, marine engineering, foil design, propulsion and shipyard production. In addition to building its own hydrofoils it licenses other shipyards to produce its hydrofoil designs.

Supramar hydrofoils being built by these companies are referred to elsewhere in this section under the respective company headings.

The latest Supramar design is the PTS 75 Mk III, a development of the PT 50 with increased engine power and full air stabilisation. The prototype is under construction at the Vosper Thornycroft yard, Paulsgrove, Portsmouth and was due for completion in November 1973. The company has also completed designs for a modernised PT 50 which is available as the PT 50 Mk 11. A new version of the PT 150 D, the PTS 150 Mk 111, is being introduced with improved air stabilisation and a higher cruising speed. Supramar is now concentrating on the development of second generation hydrofoils

with improved performance and greater passenger comfort.

The company is also developing a fully submerged foil system with air stabilisation. First craft to use this system is the Supramar ST 3A, a 4·9 ton experimental boat built under a US Navy contract. During tests in the Mediterranean it demonstrated promising stability and seakeeping qualities and reached a speed of 54·5 knots. Supramar has completed the design of a patrol boat hydrofoil which meets the tactical requirements of the NATO navies. The vessel, the MT 250G, has an operational displacement of 250 tons and a maximum intermittent speed of 60 knots.

PT 20 Mk 11

The PT 20 Mk 11, a 27-ton boat for 72 passengers, is considered by Supramar to be the smallest size hydrofoil suitable for passenger-carrying coastal services. The first of this very successful series was built by the Rodriquez shipyard at Messina in 1955 and since then nearly 70 PT 20s of various types have been built in Sicily, Japan, Holland and Norway. The design has been approved by almost every classification society. Fast

patrol boat variants, the PT 32 and the PT 20, are described under the entries for Hitachi (Japan) and Leopoldo Rodriquez (Italy) respectively.

FOILS: Foils are of standard Schertel-Sachsenberg, surface-piercing type, with 58% of the load supported by the bow foil and the remaining 42% by the rear foil. Submerged foil area in foilborne condition is 5·50 m². Together with the struts and a horizontal guide, each foil forms a uniform framework which facilitates the exchange of the foil elements. The medium steel foils are of partly hollow, welded construction. The angle of incidence of the bow foil can be adjusted within narrow limits from the steering stand by means of a hydraulic ram operating on a foil support across the hull. To counteract the effects of large variations in passenger load and to ensure optimum behaviour in sea waves the angle of attack can be adjusted during operation.

HULL: The hull has a V-bottom with an externally added step riveted into place. Frames, bulkheads, foundations, superstructure and all internal construction is in corrosion-proof light alloy. Platings are of AlMg 5 and the frames, bars and other members are made in AlMgSi. Watertight

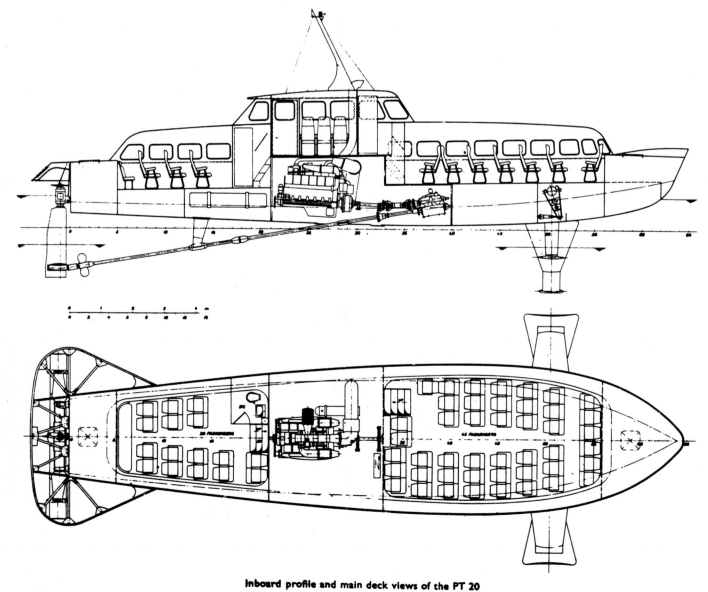

Inboard profile and main deck views of the PT 20

compartments are provided below the passenger decks and in other parts of the hull.
POWER PLANT: Power is supplied by a supercharged, 12-cylinder Daimler-Benz MB 820Db with an exhaust turbo-compressor. Maximum continuous output is 1,100 hp at 1,400 rpm. A BW 800/HS 20 reversible gear, developed by Zahnradfabrik Friedrichshafen AG, is placed between the engine and the drive shaft.
ACCOMMODATION: The boat is controlled entirely from the bridge which is located above the engine room. Forty-six passengers are accommodated in the forward cabin, twenty in the rear compartment and six aft of the pilot's stand in the elevated wheelhouse. There is an emergency exit in each passenger compartment, and the craft is equipped with an inflatable life raft and life belts for each person. A crew of four is carried.

SYSTEMS:
ELECTRICAL: 24 volt generator driven by the main engine; batteries with a capacity of approx 250 Ah.

HYDRAULICS: 120 kg/cm² pressure hydraulic system for rudder and bow foil incidence control.
COMMUNICATIONS AND NAVIGATION: VHF ship-shore radio is supplied as standard equipment. Radar is optional.

DIMENSIONS, EXTERNAL:

Length overall, hull	68·07 ft	(20·75 m)
Length over deck	67·50 ft	(19·95 m)
Hull beam, max	16·37 ft	(4·99 m)
Width across foils	26·39 ft	(8·07 m)
Draft hullborne	10·10 ft	(3·08 m)
Draft foilborne	4·59 ft	(1·40 m)

DIMENSIONS, INTERNAL:

Aft cabin (inc toilet)	145 sq ft	(13·5 m²)
Volume	954 cu ft	(27·0 m³)
Forward cabin	280 sq ft	(26·0 m²)
Volume	1,766 cu ft	(50·0 m³)
Main deck level (inc wheelhouse)		
	129 sq ft	(12·0 m²)
Volume	847 cu ft	(24·0 m³)

WEIGHTS:

Gross tonnage	approx 56 tons
Max take-off displacement	32 tons
Light displacement	25 tons
Deadweight (inc fuel, oil, water, passengers, baggage and crew)	7 tons
Payload	5·4 tons

PERFORMANCE (with normal payload):

Cruising speed, foilborne	34 knots (63 km/h)
Max permissible wave height in foilborne mode	4·25 ft (1·29 m)
Designed range at cruising speed	216 nautical miles (400 km)
Turning radius	427 ft approx (130 m)
Take-off distance	493 ft approx (150 m)
Take-off time	25 sec
Stopping distance	230 ft (70 m)
Fuel consumption at cruising speed	150 kg/h

SEA TEST: Prototype tests were undertaken in the Mediterranean in every kind of sea condition, and further tests have taken place off Japan. Acceleration measurements have shown maximum values below 0·5g when accelerometer had been fitted above the bow foil. Maximum lateral acceleration was 0·32g. Measurements were made in wave heights of approx 1·2 to 1·5 m. These are the maximum measurements obtained and subsequent tests have seldom equalled these figures.

PT 20B Mk 11

In this model of the PT 20, the engine room and bridge are arranged in the foreship. This improves the pilot's vision in waters likely to have an influx of driftwood and provides a large main passenger cabin with seats for 55 and an upper deck cabin with seating for 16 passengers.

The layout of this craft has been based on experience gained with the Supramar PT 27 which was designed for servicing the offshore drilling platforms on Lake Maracaibo. This design has been slightly modified to meet the requirements of passenger services.
FOILS: The foil design is similar to that of the PT 20 Mk 11. About 66% of the total weight is borne by the bow foil and 34% by the rear foil. Submerged foil area in foilborne condition is 6·2 m². The forward foil can be tilted within narrow limits by means of a hydraulic ram acting on the foil strut supporting tube. The angle of attack can therefore be adjusted during operation to assist take-off and to counteract the effect of large variations in passenger loads.

HULL. This is of riveted light metal alloy design and framed on a combination of longitudinal and transverse formers. Watertight compartments are provided below the passenger decks and in other parts of the hull, and some are filled with foam-type plastic.
POWER PLANT: Power is supplied by a 12 cyl Mercedes-Benz Mb 820 Db with a max continuous output of 1,100 hp at 1,400 rpm. Average time between major overhauls is approx 10,000 hours. Engine output is transferred to a 3-bladed 700 mm diameter bronze subcavitating propeller through a BW 800/H 20 reversible gear made by Zahnradfabrik. The propeller shaft is supported at three points by seawater lubricated rubber bearings.

ACCOMMODATION: The PT 20B Mk 11 has a crew of 4 and seats 71 passengers. The main passenger compartment seats 55, and the small cabin behind the pilot's stand seats a further 16. Access to the main compartment is through either of two doors, located port and starboard, to the rear of the wheelhouse. An emergency exit is provided at the rear of the main passenger compartment.

A full range of safety equipment is carried, including inflatable rafts and lifebelts for each passenger and crew member.
SYSTEMS:
ELECTRICAL: An MWM AKD412E single-phase, 220 volt, 7·1 kVA, 50 c/s generator is provided.
HYDRAULICS: 120 kg/cm² pressure hydraulic system for operating rudder and bow foil angle of incidence control.
COMMUNICATIONS AND NAVIGATION: A vhf ship-shore radio is supplied as standard equipment. Radar is an optional extra.

A Supramar PT 20 72-seat hydrofoil passenger ferry of Compagnie General de Navigation sur le Lac Leman on Lake Geneva

DIMENSIONS, EXTERNAL:

Length overall, hull	67·50 ft (20·58 m)
Length over deck	63·00 ft (19·80 m)
Hull beam, max	17·05 ft (5·30 m)
Width over foils	26·40 ft (8·05 m)
Draft hullborne	10·04 ft (3·06 m)
Draft foilborne	4·56 ft (1·39 m)

DIMENSIONS, INTERNAL:

Main passenger compartment (inc toilet):	
Length	30 ft 7 in (9·3 m)
Width	12 ft 6 in (3·8 m)
Height	6 ft 7 in (2·0 m)
Floor area	237 sq ft (22·1 m²)
Volume	1,553 cu ft (44·0 m³)

WEIGHT:

Gross tonnage	60 tons, app
Max take-off displacement	32·5 tons
Light displacement	25·4 tons
Deadweight (inc fuel, oil water, passengers, luggage, crew)	7·1 tons
Payload	5·44 tons

PERFORMANCE (with normal payload):

Cruising speed	34 knots (63 km/h)
Max permissible wave height in foilborne mode	4·25 ft (1·29 m)
Turning radius	426 ft (app 130 m)
Take-off distance	492 ft (app 150 m)
Take-off time	app 30 sec
Stopping distance	231 ft (app 70 m)
Stopping time	app 10 sec
Fuel consumption at cruising speed	150 kg/h

PTL 28

The PTL 28 is derived from the PT 27 utility and oil rig supply vessel, three of which have been in service for more than

Oyfoil, a Supramar PT 20B owned by Hydrofoilrutene A/S, Oslo, seen in the Oslofiord

ten years with the Shell Oil Company on Maracaibo Lake, Venezuela.

Features of the new craft include facilities for loading across the bow as well as the stern, twin rudders for improved manoeuvrability, and a variety of structural and mechanical modifications to simplify and reduce maintenance. The Schottel drive now has only two bevel gears, the hull is of welded construction, and the foil and

propeller mounting arrangements have been redesigned to facilitate servicing. All components of a non-essential nature have been omitted.

Normally seats are provided for 54, but the number of passengers can be increased if the range is reduced. The weather deck above the engine room is available for cargo; heavy loads are compensated by a reduction in passenger capacity. A cargo compart-

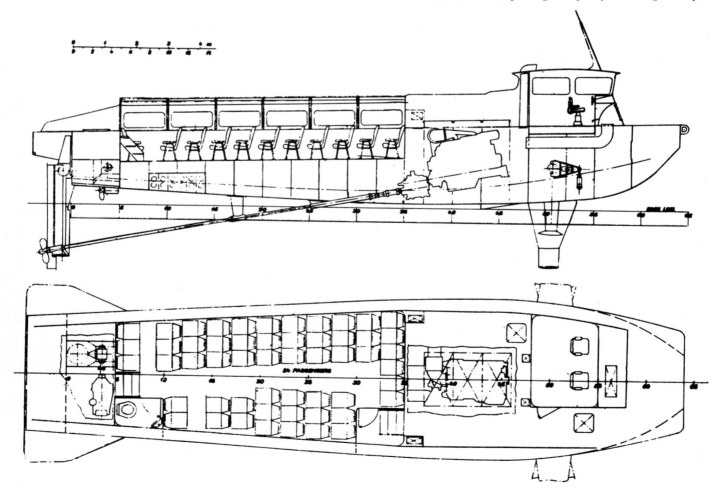

Inboard profiles and passenger deck plan of the Supramar PTL 28 utility craft and supply vessel

ment can be made available at the rear of the passenger cabin (up to frame 17), a typical load being 4,023 lb (1,825 kg) of cargo combined with 33 passengers.

FOILS: Schertel-Sachsenburg surface-piercing system similar to that of the PT 20 Mk 11. Bow foil of hollow welded stainless steel. Foil, vertical struts, inclined fins and horizontal supporting tube form a framed structure which can easily be detached when necessary. The complete assembly divides into two to facilitate transport. Once the angle of incidence is adjusted no further alteration is necessary.

The rear foil is similar to the bow foil in type and construction. The complete system is mounted on its bearings at the transom by four bolts.

HULL: Constructed in seawater-resistant light metal alloy, the V-bottomed hull is of hard chine type and framed longitudinally. All joints are welded. Hoist fittings are provided to facilitate maintenance.

POWER PLANT: Power is supplied by a 12-cylinder supercharged Mercedes-Benz MB 820 Db, rated at 1,100 hp at 1,250 rpm continuous and 1,350 hp at 1,500 rpm maximum.

Engine output is transferred to a 3-bladed bronze propeller through a Zahnradfabrik BW 800 128 reverse gearbox. Hullborne propulsion is provided by a 150 hp diesel engine directly coupled to a Schottel Z-drive unit which can be rotated through 360°. During take-off and when foilborne, the lower bevel gear and hullborne propeller are retracted hydraulically into a recess in the hull bottom.

ACCOMMODATION: The PTL 28 has a crew of three and seats 54 passengers in a single saloon aft of the engine room. The bridge is located forward and provides a 360° view. The captain's seat, together with the operating controls and instrumentation, is located on the hull centreline.

DIMENSIONS, EXTERNAL:

Length overall	68·08 ft (20·75 m)
Length over deck	66·93 ft (20·40 m)
Beam over deck	16·73 ft (5·10 m)
Width over foils	26·25 ft (8·00 m)
Draft hullborne	9·68 ft (2·95 m)
Draft foilborne	4·92 ft (1·50 m)

WEIGHTS:

Displacement fully loaded	27·56 tons (28·00 t)
Disposable load	5·51 tons (5·60 t)
Light displacement	22·05 tons (22·40 t)

PERFORMANCE:

Speed max	39·00 knots (72·00 km/h)
Speed cruising	35·00 knots (65·00 km/h)
Range	140 nm approx (260 km)

PT 50 Mk II

The successful and profitable operation of the PT 20 led to the development of the PT 50, a 63-ton hydrofoil passenger ferry designed for offshore and inter-island services. The prototype was completed early in 1958, and more than thirty are now operating regular passenger services in areas ranging from the Baltic and Mediterranean to the Japanese Inland Sea.

The craft has been approved by almost every Classification Society including Registro Italiano Navale, Germanischer Lloyd, Det Norske Veritas, American Bureau of Shipping and the Japanese Ministry of Transport. The requirements of the SOLAS 1960 convention for international traffic can be met by the type if required.

FOILS: Both rear and forward foils are rigidly attached to the hull but the lift of the forward foil can be modified by hydraulically operated flaps, which are fitted to assist take-off and turning, and for making slight course corrections and adjustment of the flying height. The foils are of hollow construction using fine grain and MSt 52·3 steel throughout. Foils in stainless steel construction are optional.

The bow foil comprises the following elements:

Two fins, forming connecting links between the foil and the supporting structure which

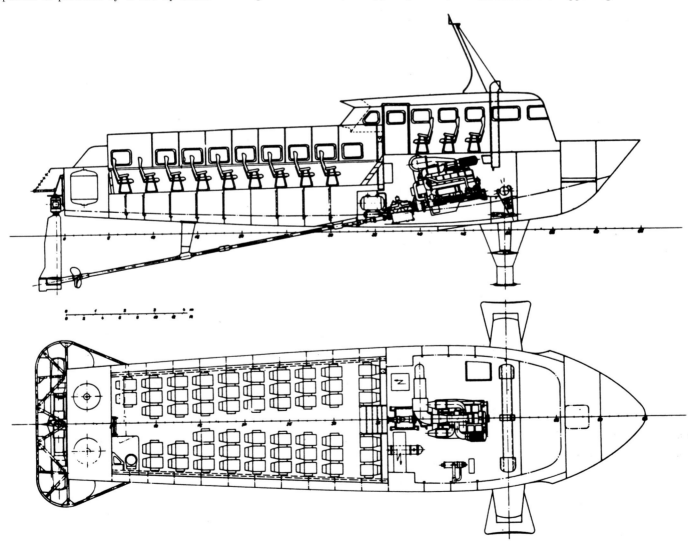

Inboard profile and main deck view of the PT 20B

is riveted to the hull.

The hydrofoil which (according to its foil section characteristics) generates the lift and, with the stern foil, provides transverse stability in foilborne conditions.

Two struts, which transmit the main lift loads to the supporting structure.

The rear foil system comprises the following elements: the hydrofoil, which generates the lift, two side struts, and the single rudder which transmits the lift to the supporting structure.

HULL: Of hard chine construction, the hull is of partly riveted, partly welded light metal alloy design and framed on longitudinal and transverse formers. Steel is used only for highly stressed parts such as the foil fittings, and the shaft brackets and exits.

ACCOMMODATION: On long distance operations 105 passengers are carried in forward (45) and aft (60) lower saloons. A foyer and bar is located on the main deck, amidships. On shorter operations and ferry services the bar is omitted and seating can be provided for up to 115 passengers. The crew varies from 6-8 members, depending mainly on local regulations.

Passenger seats are of lightweight aircraft type and the centre aisle between the seat rows has a clear width of 30 in (0·76 m). Ceilings are covered with lightweight plastic material and the walls, including web frames, are clad in luxury plywood or artificial wood. Toilets are provided in the rear and forward passenger spaces. Floors in the passenger compartments are provided with thick carpets. Each passenger compartment has an emergency exit. Inflatable life rafts and lifebelts are provided for 110% of the passenger and crew capacity.

POWER PLANT: The craft is powered by two Maybach-Mercedes-Benz MB 820 Db diesels each with a continuous output of 1,100 hp at 1,400 rpm. Engine output is transmitted to two 3-bladed 700 mm diameter bronze propellers through two inclined stainless steel propeller shafts, each supported at four points by seawater lubricated runner bearings. Average operation period between overhauls is 10,000 hours. Compressed air starting is provided. Reverse and reduction gear with built-in thrust is manufactured by Zahnradfabrik Friedrichshafen, Germany. The reverse clutches are solenoid-operated from the bridge.

Eight cylindrical fuel tanks with a total capacity of 3,650 litres are located in the aft peak and below the tank deck. Oil capacity is 320 litres.

SYSTEMS, ELECTRICAL:
One diesel generator set with a capacity of 24 KVA, 50 cps, 3-phase is placed in the engine room. An emergency generator of the same capacity is installed on the main deck aft.

HYDRAULICS: 120 kg/cm² pressure hydraulic system for operating twin rudders and front foil flaps.

AIR CONDITIONING: Air conditioning can be provided as optional equipment.

COMMUNICATIONS AND NAVIGATION: Standard equipment includes UHF and VHF

Osho, a Hitachi-Zosen built Supramar PT 50, operating in Japanese coastal waters

radio telephone. Radar and Decca Navigator is optional.

DIMENSIONS, EXTERNAL:

Length overall, hull	91·55 ft (27·90 m)
Length overall	89·50 ft (27·23 m)
Hull beam, max	20·05 ft (6·11 m)
Width across foils	35·40 ft (10·80 m)
Draft afloat	11·50 ft (3·55 m)
Draft foilborne	4·65 ft (1·42 m)
Fuel consumption at cruising speed 300 kg/h	

DIMENSIONS, INTERNAL:

Aft passenger compartment (inc toilet):

Length	29 ft 7 in (9·0 m)
Width	16 ft 0 in (4·9 m)
Height	6 ft 7 in (2·0 m)
Floor area	474 sq ft (44·1 m²)
Volume	3,108 cu ft (88·0 m³)

Forward passenger compartment (inc toilet):

Length	23 ft 3½ in (7·1 m)
Width	17 ft 9 in (5·4 m)
Height	6 ft 7 in (2·0 m)
Floor area	412 sq ft (37·3 m²)
Volume	2,703 cu ft (67·6 m³)

Main deck foyer:

Length	12 ft 9½ in (3·9 m)
Width	13 ft 1½ in (4·0 m)
Height	6 ft 7 in (2·0 m)
Floor area	161 sq ft (15·0 m²)
Volume	2,030 cu ft (57·6 m³)

WEIGHTS:

Max take-off displacement	63·3 tons
Light displacement	49·3 tons
Deadweight (inc fuel, oil, water, passengers, baggage and crew)	14·0 tons
Payload	9·5 tons

PERFORMANCE (with normal payload):

Max speed foilborne	36·5 knots (67·5 km/h)
Cruising speed foilborne	34·0 knots (63 km/h)
Range	325 nm (600 km)
Turning radius	1,542 ft (470 m)
Take-off distance	819 ft (250 m)
Take-off time	35 sec
Stopping distance	264 ft (80 m)
Time to stop craft	10 sec
Fuel consumption at cruising speed	710 lb/h (300 kg/h)

PTS 75 Mk III

The Supramar PTS 75 Mk III is an advanced derivative of the PT 50. It seats up to 160 passengers and is designed for higher speed, improved seaworthiness and greater riding comfort. By increasing the specific PT 50 engine power of 43 hp/t to 50 hp/t a top speed of about 38 knots is obtained with the vessel fully loaded, and sufficient power is provided for operation in tropical waters.

An improved Schertel-Supramar air stabilisation system is fitted, and this, combined with a new W-foil configuration, considerably reduces rolling, pitching and vertical accelerations. The vessel can operate foilborne in waves up to 6 ft (1·82 m) in height with full power.

The prototype was completed at the Vosper Thornycroft, Paulsgrove, Portsmouth yard in May 1974, and two further craft of this type are being constructed by Supramar's licencee in Hong Kong—Supramar Pacific Shipbuilding Co Ltd.

FOILS: The foil configuration is surface piercing and incorporates the Schertel-Supramar air stabilisation system. The bow foil assembly forms a rigid framework which facilitates the exchange of the foil structure. The foil is of hollow steel construction. It has three supporting struts, one on the centre line and one on either side. These are bolted to welded steel suspension points on the keel and chine respectively. Hydraulically operated flaps are fitted to the trailing edges to assist take-off, facilitate course corrections and provide automatic stabilisation when low frequency disturbances are encountered.

The rear foil is of surface-piercing Schertel-Supramar type and attached to the transom. Method of construction is the same as that employed for the bow foil. The complete assembly—foil, rudder sternpost, rudder, and two inclined struts—forms a rigid frame unit which is attached or detached as necessary. The aftermost propeller bearings are attached to the foil, the propellers being sited aft of the foil.

HULL: Hard chine type, constructed in partly riveted, partly welded corrosion resistant light metal alloy. A longitudinal frame system is employed, with transverse frames 900 mm apart. Steel is used only for highly stressed parts such as the foil

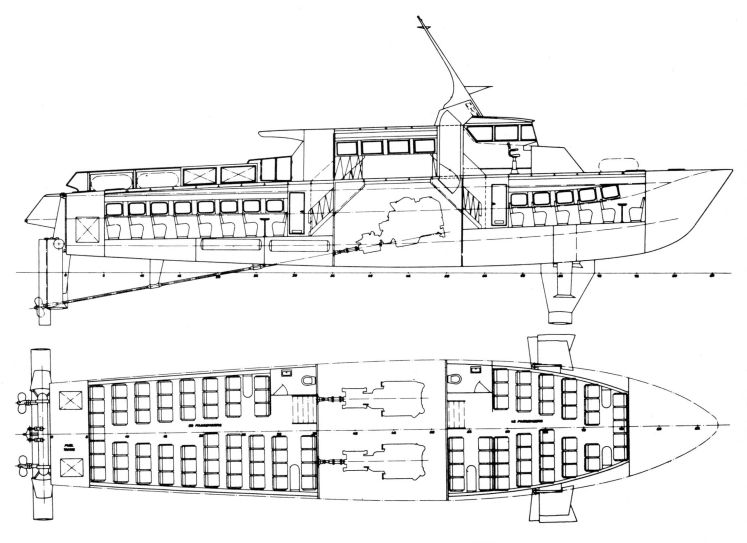

Inboard profile and main deck view of the Supramar PT 50 Mk II

fittings and shaft exits. A new hull construction method is being employed for this design. The hull is built in the inverted position and turned upright after the plating is completed.

ACCOMMODATION: Depending on operating requirements, between 130 and 160 passengers can be accommodated in three saloons. In the standard version airliner type seats are provided for 135 passengers, 19 in the upper aft saloon, 61 in the lower aft saloon and 55 in the lower forward saloon.

Ceilings are covered with lightweight plastic material, walls including web frames, are clad in luxury ply or artificial wood, and the floors are provided with thick carpets.

Three toilets are installed on the upper deck, within easy reach of all three saloons.

Passengers board the craft through wide side doors on the upper deck opening to a central foyer from which companionways lead to the lower passenger saloons. A promenade deck is available aft of the upper saloon and can be reached by passengers from the lower saloons via the foyer. Sufficient space for luggage is provided in the foyer. The upper aft saloon can be modified into a small dining room, if required, reducing the passenger capacity by 19.

All passenger saloons have emergency exits. A lifebelt is stowed beneath each seat and most of the inflatable life rafts are stowed aft and on the forward main deck.

POWER PLANT: Power is supplied by two 12 cylinder, 4-cycle Maybach-Mercedes-Benz MB 12V 652 SB7 supercharged diesels, each with a normal continuous output of 1,650 hp at 1,380 rpm, and 1,950 hp at 1,460 rpm maximum. Under tropical conditions normal continuous rating is 1,590 hp at 1,380 rpm and 1,810 hp at 1,460 rpm maximum. Engine output is transferred to two 3 ft 1⅜ in (950 mm) diameter 3-bladed bronze propellers through a Zahnradfabrik BW 900 HS 15 reversible gearbox, which is hydraulically operated and remotely controlled from the wheelhouse. The propeller shafts are in stainless steel and supported at four points by seawater lubricated rubber bearings. Fuel is carried in integral tanks beneath the lower deck in the bottom compartments.

SYSTEMS, ELECTRICAL: Two 37 KVA water-cooled 60 c/s diesel-driven 380 V generators installed in the engine room. An emergency generator of similar capacity is provided at main deck level.

HYDRAULICS: 120 kg/cm² pressure hydraulic system for operating all hydraulic driven consumers.

AIR CONDITIONING: An air conditioning system is provided. Capacity is sufficient for adequate temperature and humidity conditions in all passenger saloons and on the bridge when operating the craft in tropical conditions.

COMMUNICATIONS AND NAVIGATION: UHF radio, VHF radio-telephone and magnetic compass are standard. Radar, Decca Navigator and gyro compass to customer's requirements.

DIMENSIONS, EXTERNAL:

Length overall, hull	98·5 ft (30·0 m)
Length overall, deck	96·0 ft (29·2 m)
Hull beam max	19·1 ft (5·8 m)
Width across foils	38·1 ft (11·6 m)
Draft afloat	13·1 ft (4·0 m)
Draft foilborne	6·7 ft (1·96 m)

DIMENSIONS, INTERNAL (Standard version)

Aft lower saloon:

Length	9·0 m
Width	4·6 m
Height	2·15 m
Floor area	42·0 m²

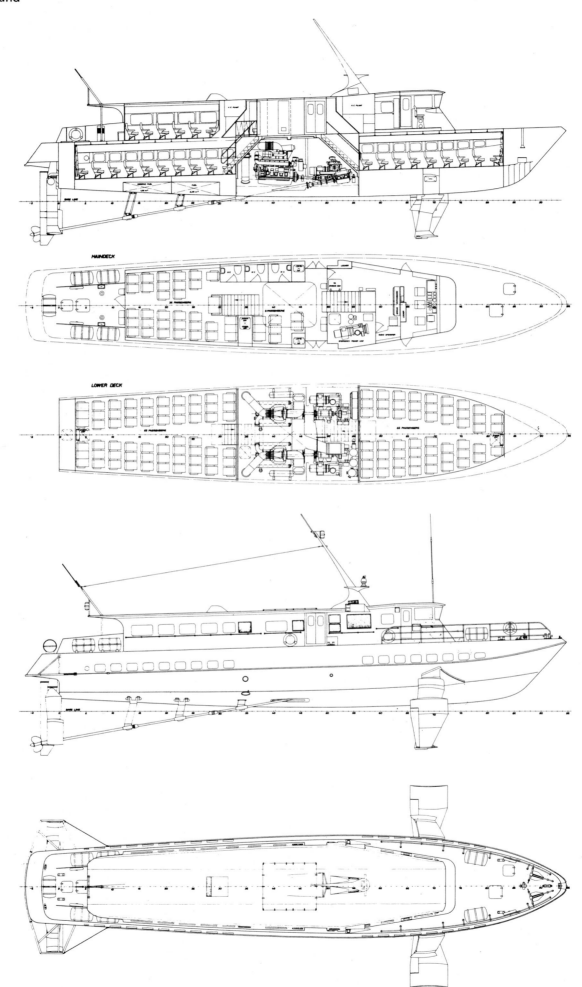

Inboard and outboard profiles and deck views of the new Supramar PTS 75 Mk III

Volume	92·0 m³
Forward lower saloon:	
Length	8·1 m
Width	4·7 m
Height	2·15 m
Floor area	37·0 m²
Volume	82·0 m³
Upper aft saloon:	
Length	4·5 m
Width	4·2 m
Height	2·1 m
Floor area	18·0 m²
Volume	38·0 m³
Foyer:	
Length	5·1 m
Width	4·2 m
Height	2·1 m
Floor area	20 m²
Volume	42 m³

WEIGHTS:

Max take-off displacement	85·0 tons
Light displacement	68·5 tons
Disposable load	16·5 tons

(incl fuel, oil, water, passengers luggage and crew)

PERFORMANCE (with normal payload):

Cruising speed	36·0 knots (66·5 km/h)
Max speed	39·0 knots (72·5 km/h)
Range	180 nm
Turning radius approx	2,350 ft (700 m)
Take-off distance approx	1,600 ft (500 m)
Take-off time approx	50 sec
Stopping distance approx	330 ft (100 m)
Time to stop the craft approx	20 sec
Fuel consumption at cruising speed	
	approx 600 kg/h

SUPRAMAR PTS 150 Mk III

The Supramar PTS 150 Mk III carries 250 passengers and is the world's largest seagoing hydrofoil. The vessels fulfil SOLAS requirements, and have been built under the supervision of Det Norske Veritas, which has granted the class designation IA2-Hydrofoil-K.

FOILS: The foil configuration is a combined surface piercing and submerged system. The bow foil, which provides the necessary static transverse stability, is of the Schertel-Sachsenburg surface-piercing V design and carries 6% of the load. The rear foil, which bears about 40% is of the submerged, Schertel-Subramar air-stabilised type. In foilborne conditions the boat is inherently stable.

Hydraulically-actuated flaps are fitted at the trailing edges of the bow foil to assist take-off and adjust the flying height.

The rear foil is fully submerged.

Air stabilisation is fitted to the rear foil which gives the necessary transverse and longitudinal stability and improves passenger comfort under heavy sea conditions. Separate port and starboard systems are installed to stabilise rolling and pitching.

The system feeds air from the free atmosphere through air exits to the foil upper surface (the low pressure region) decreasing the lift. The amount to lift is varied by the quantity of air admitted, this being controlled by a valve actuated by signals from a damped pendulum and a rate gyro. The stabilising

First of the new Supramar PTS 75 Mk III series during trials on the Solent in May 1974. The vessel was built by Vosper Thornycroft Ltd at the company's Portchester shipyard for Far East Hydrofoil Co. Ltd. of Hong Kong

moment is produced by decreasing the available air volume for the more submerged side and increasing that of the less submerged one.

The rear foil includes the lift-generating sections, rudders and the rear suspension structure which serves as a connecting element with the hull. Struts for the aftermost propeller bearings are also attached to the rear foil, the propellers being sited beneath the foil. The complete assembly is a framed structure which can easily be detached from the transom. The angle of attack of the rear foil can be controlled hydraulically both during take-off and when foilborne.

The surface piercing bow foil is provided with air exits on the upper surface (the low pressure region) in order to vary lift and control pitch and heave motions by the quantity of air admitted. This is released by a valve which is actuated by amplified signals taken from a vertical accelerometer and a rate sensor.

Front and rear foil are of hollow construction and by the extensive use of welding, the number of connecting parts requiring screws, bolts or similar means of attachment is reduced to a minimum.

HULL: Partly riveted and partly welded construction and a system of longitudinal and transverse frames has been adopted. It has fairly high deadrise and hard chine sections for performance as a planing hull and for structural impacts in a seaway while foilborne. A step is provided to facilitate take-off. While the main or structure deck is continuous from bow to stern, the lower deck is interrupted by the engine room, sited amidships. The superstructure, which is also longitudinally and transversally framed, is not included in the load bearing structure. Several expansion joints have therefore been provided.

ACCOMMODATION: The PTS 150 Mk III carries 250 passengers in four saloons, two on the main deck and two on the lower deck.

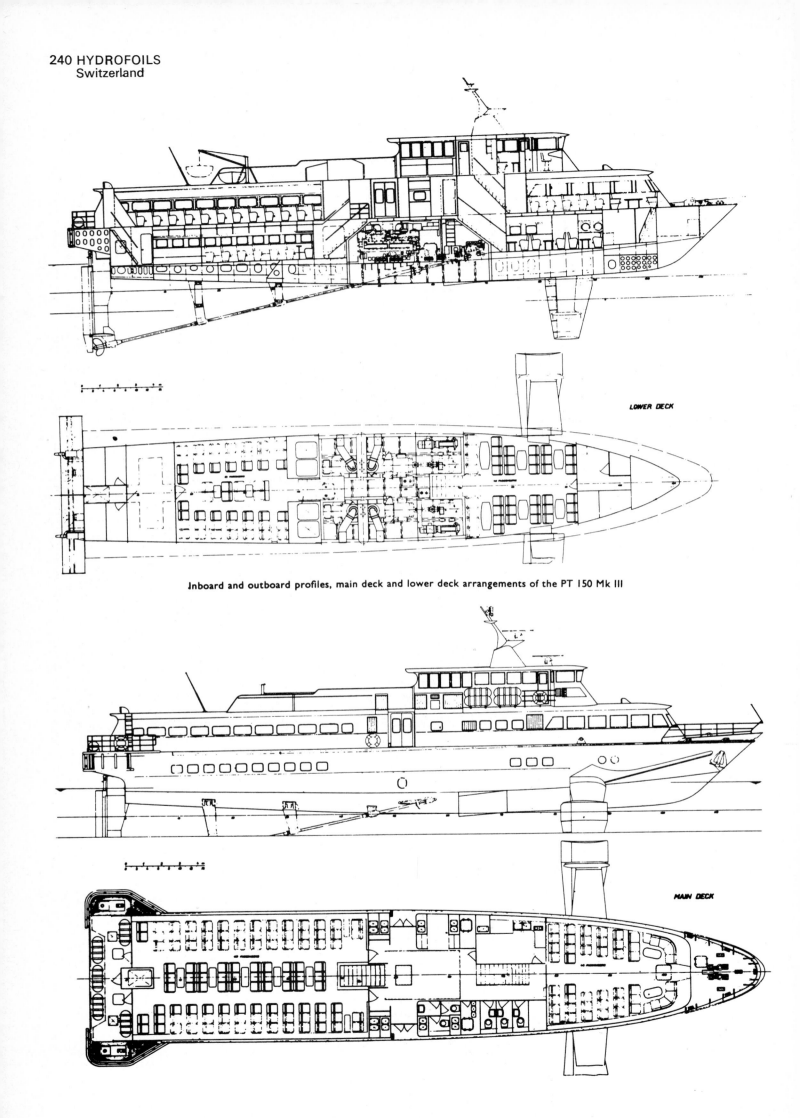

LOWER DECK

Inboard and outboard profiles, main deck and lower deck arrangements of the PT 150 Mk III

MAIN DECK

The forward compartment main deck, seats 48, and the aft compartment 110. On the lower deck the forward compartment seats 40 and the aft compartment 52.

Passengers board the craft through double doors to the single centralized foyer, from which doors and companion ladders lead to the respective passenger saloons on the upper and lower decks.

Provision is made for all passengers to be served in their seats with cold meals and drinks as in an airliner.

Passenger seats are of lightweight aircraft type. Floors and ceilings are covered with lightweight plastic material and the walls are clad in luxury plywood. Each passenger saloon has fitted carpets. Each room has an independent ventilation unit. Six toilets are provided.

The bridge, which is on a separate level above the main deck, slightly forward of midships, is reached by a companion ladder at the aft of the forward passenger compartment. All passenger saloons have emergency exits.

The craft carries 12 inflatable RFD liferafts (for 110% of the classified number of passengers and crew) which are stowed along both sides of the superstructure deck, and on the aft maindeck. Lifebelts are arranged beneath the seats.

POWER PLANT: Power is supplied by two 20-cylinder Maybach MD 20V 538 TB8 supercharged and intercooled diesels each rated at 3,400 hp continuous. To improve torque characteristics during take-off two engine-mounted Maybach torque converters are provided.

Reverse and reduction gears are of the lightweight Zahnradfabrik BW 1500HS22 hydraulically-operated type, and incorporate the propeller thrust bearings. They have three shafts and two gear trains, one of which has an idler. The output shafts rotate either in the same direction as the input shaft or the opposite direction, depending upon the gear through which power is directed. Selection is by pneumo-hydraulic double-plate clutches on the input shafts. A mechanical lock-up is provided so that the gear can transmit full torque in the event of clutch slip while in service. This takes the form of a dog clutch which is effective in one direction, and can only be engaged in the "stop" condition. The gearboxes each have integral oil pumps for lubrication and clutch operation.

The angle between the engine crankshaft and the parallel shaft of the gearbox is accommodated by a cardan shaft with universal joints. The converter gear main shaft bearings, as well as those on the reverse gear primary shaft, are proportioned in such a way as to resist the forces and couples imposed by the cardan shaft universal joints. As a protection against accidents the cardan shaft is installed within a substantial removable tunnel.

SYSTEMS, ELECTRICAL:
The total electrical system is supplied by three diesel generators with an output of 65 KVA each, one of them being

Interior of the PT 150 DC showing *above* the forward saloon on the upper deck and *below* the aft saloon on the upper deck

an emergency generator installed on the upper deck.

In the event of an electrical failure the emergency generator is switched on automatically. The engines are started by fresh air and are fresh-water cooled. The following systems are supplied by the electrical plant. For power and permanently installed heating and cooling equipment: 380 V rotary current, 50 cps. For light, pockets and instrumentation: 220 V ac, 50 cps. For remote control and monitoring: 24 V ac.

HYDRAULICS: Steering, variation of the front foil flap angle and the angle of attack of the rear foil are all operated hydraulically. Each system has its own circuit which is monitored by a pressure controlled pilot lamp.

CONTROL: Starting, manoeuvring and operation of the craft is controlled from the bridge, but in cases of emergency the main engines may be controlled from the engine room.

The two main engines are each controlled by an operating lever designed for single-handed control. Propeller reversal is also by means of these levers, the reverse gear being actuated by pneumatic remote control between bridge and main engines.

To start the boat both operating levers must be put in the "full ahead" position simultaneously. The engine mounted torque converter gear is actuated automatically. Foilborne speed can be regulated by fine adjusting of the operating levers. No other control devices are necessary for the main engines.

Levers for variation of the front foil flap

angle and the angle of attack of the rear foil are actuated only before and after starting. During foilborne operation these can be used for trim compensation. All instrumentation and monitoring equipment is installed on the bridge.

AIR CONDITIONING: The vessel is equipped with air conditioning and heating plant which guarantees a room temperature of between 20 and 25°C, dependent upon the relative humidity. Air rate is 25 m³/h, person.

COMMUNICATION AND NAVIGATION: Standard navigation equipment includes a gyro master compass with transformers, rectifiers and one multiple steering repeater positioned ahead of the helmsman, Loran or Decca Navigator and radar.

Communications equipment includes radio telephone equipment for normal and emergency use.

DIMENSIONS, EXTERNAL:

Length overall, hull	124·2 ft (37·9 m)
Length overall, deck	121·8 ft (37·10 m)
Hull beam, max	24·6 ft (7·50 m)
Deck beam, max	24·2 ft (7·40 m)
Width across foils	52·45 ft (16·0 m)
Draft afloat	18 ft (5·5 m)
Draft foilborne	8·5 ft (2·6 m)

WEIGHTS:

Displacement, fully loaded	165 tons
Disposable load (payload plus consumable stores)	23 tons
Passenger capacity	250

PERFORMANCE:

Cruising speed at 6,880 hp 36·5 knots (67·5 km/h)
Range 250 nm (400 km)
Max permissible wave height in foilborne mode at full power (head seas) for passenger acceptability 10 ft (3·0 m)

"Queen of the Waves", a Westermoen-built PT 150DC operated between Malmo and Copenhagen by Nordo Rederi AB

Supramar ST 3A

ST 3A FULLY SUBMERGED FOIL RESEARCH CRAFT

In 1965 the US Navy awarded Supramar a contract for the construction and testing of a 5-ton research craft with fully submerged air stabilized foils. The object of the tests was the investigation of the effectiveness and reliability of the Schertel-Supramar air stabilization system under a variety of wave conditions.

FOIL SYSTEM: The craft is fitted with two fully submerged bow foils and one fully submerged rear foil. The load distribution is 62% on the bow foils and 38% on rear foil. The centre of the front foils is 3 ft 11 in (1·20 m) from the craft centre line. Normal submergence depth for the bow foils is 1 ft 8 in (0·50 m) and for the rear foil 1 ft 2 in (0·35 m). Foil outlines are tapered. The foils are in solid stainless steel "Remanit" 2604 Mo S (standard German designation: X4 Cv Ni Mo Nb 25 7).

The front foils are connected by 5 ft 3 in (1·6 m) long struts to a supporting tube to which they are flanged. The tube pivots to enable the angle of attack to be adjusted. The struts are of welded stainless steel plate and have solid leading edges. At their top is a casing which accommodates the devices for transmitting signals from the sensors to the air valves which are located in the foil centres. On the outer faces of the front foil struts are small auxiliary fins which give added stability during the transition from displacement condition to the onset of air stabilization. The rudder flap is attached to the end of the rear foil strut.

AIR FEED SYSTEM: Lift variation is achieved without movable foil parts. Each foil has two air ducts with outlets on the suction side. Air is drawn through these apertures from the free atmosphere via the foil suspension tube and the hollow struts. Air valves, controlled by sensors, govern the quantity of air admitted to the respective ducts. Lift is normally only influenced by the air emitting from the rearward row of outlets. No power is required for a change in lift. The forward row, which is fed by overpressure, is automatically engaged for attaining very low or negative lift. For this purpose, a comparatively small quantity of air is drained off from the last stage of the turbine compressor, reduced by a valve to about 1 atm, and then accumulated in a reservoir before it is led to the control valve. The slight power loss in the turbine is compensated by a drag reduction of the foil which takes place in the pressure fed condition.

CONTROLS: The signals of a depth sensor, a rate gyro and damped pendulum are added and amplified. The pneumatic follow-up

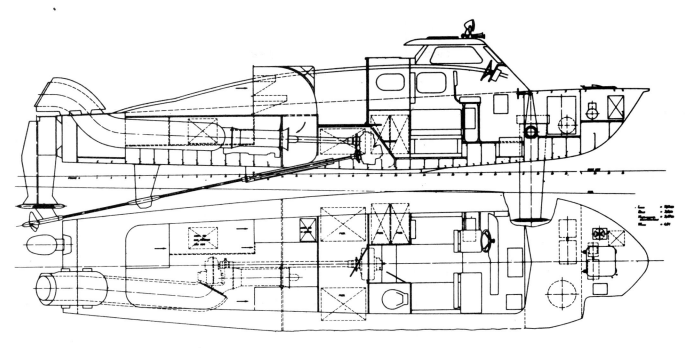

Inboard profile and deck plan of the ST 3A foil research craft

amplifier draws its propulsion power from the subpressure which is produced at a suction opening at the strut near the foil. The amplifier output is connected with the air valve. The depth sensor probes the submergence depth digitally by means of suction orifices at the front struts. No motor-driven power source is required for the control system which, as well as the air feed system for lift variation of the foils, is designed for simplicity and reliability.

HULL: The hull, which is of hard chine construction, is basically that of a standard Supramar ST 3, modified to accommodate a new foil system, gas turbine and test equipment. To facilitate take-off, a step is provided at frame 24 (see inboard profile) and a ram wedge is fastened to the stern bottom.

The hull clearance (tip of step to water surface) of only 1 ft 2¼ in (0·36 m) was due to the requirement that an existing ST 3 hull, with an inclined propeller shaft, should be used for the tests.

Hull, transverse framing and superstructure are of riveted light metal alloy. The main engine, ducting for fresh air, exhaust pipe and most of the auxiliary units are positioned between frames 0-16½.

Above the Vee-drive, between frames 16½ and 20, there is an observation platform which lies 8 in (200 mm) lower than the turbine casing. From this platform the outer section of the front foils can be observed. A short staircase at frame 20 leads to the wheelhouse which extends forward to bulkhead 31. At the front of the wheelhouse are two seats for pilot and observer, controls and the steering wheel which is hydraulically connected with the rudder flap. In the rear section two benches are arranged in longitudinal direction. The stabilization control device is located direct behind bulkhead 31 so that it can be easily watched by the observer. The sequence and control system for the gas turbine is arranged on the port side, between frames 20 and 23.

The ST 3A showing the fully-submerged air-stabilized foils. Two small dihedral fins are attached to the outer sides of the struts of the two bow foils to provide additional stability during the transition from hullborne to foilborne mode

POWER PLANT: The craft is powered by a 1,000 hp GE 7LM100 PG 102 gas turbine. Engine output is transferred to a 1 ft 3 in (0·38 m) diameter S·C bronze propeller through a reduction gear, a Vee-drive and an inclined stainless steel shaft. A 35 hp Mercury outboard is installed on the port side of the transom to provide auxiliary propulsion. To feed the stabilization gyros a 6 hp gasoline engine is installed in the forepeak and coupled to a 3-phase ac generator.

DIMENSIONS:

Length overall (hull)	33 ft 10 in (10·32 m)
Breadth over foils	11 ft 10 in (3·6 m)
Breadth over hull	8 ft 10 in (2·7 m)
Draft hullborne	5 ft 1 in (1·55 m)
Draft foilborne (front foil)	1 ft 7½ in (0·5 m)
Hull clearance	1 ft 2¼ in (0·36 m)

WEIGHTS:

Displacement	4·9 tons

PERFORMANCE:

Max measured test speed	54·5 knots (101 km/h)
Max. speed (design)	56 knots (104 km/h)
Take-off time	14·5 sec
Stopping distance (50 kt to 5 kt)	390 ft (120 m)
Turning radius at 40 kt	750 ft (230 m)

SEA TEST: Sea trials along the Mediterranean coast revealed that the craft, despite a small hull clearance, is capable of taking waves 3-4 ft (0·9-1·2 m) high, and with a minimum length of about 100-120 ft (30·4-36·4 m), at 45 kt in all courses from head to beam seas, partially contouring. In waves over 4 ft (1·2 m) the hull periodically touches

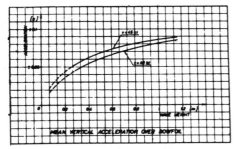

Graph showing mean vertical accelerations over the ST 3A's bow foil in a seaway

Impression of the Supramar MT 250 G, 250 ton missile-equipped hydrofoil patrol boat. Gasturbine-driven waterjets will propel the craft. Maximum intermittent speed will be 60 knots

wave crests, which is accompanied by a marked speed reduction (very high froude number) during water contacting. In a following sea, and in all courses up to about 60° to a following sea, foilborne operation was limited to 2½ ft (0·76 m) waves due to the control system, which at that time had no heave sensor. A further improvement will be achieved when the lower foil side feeding, which is still under development, materialises.

The smooth run in waves can be seen in the accompanying table of mean vertical acceleration over the bow foil. At a wave height of 3 ft (0·91 m) (1/10 of boat length), vertical accelerations of only 0·08 g have been measured, which compares very favourably with the sea test results of other craft with fully submerged foils.

SUPRAMAR MT 250G

This is a design concept for a 250 t patrol boat hydrofoil which meets the tactical requirements established by the West German and other NATO navies. It conforms to the fast patrol boat standards of the West German Navy and has a max intermittent speed of 60 knots.

Main dimensions of the vessel are similar to those of the Swedish Spica class, Vosper Tenacity, Israeli Sa'ar class and the West German Type 148. It is designed for all-weather operation in the western Baltic, the Skagerrak and other areas with similar operational conditions.

Foilborne propulsion is supplied by gas-turbine powered waterjets. The foil system is of fully-submerged type employing the Schertel-Supramar air stabilisation system.

FOILS: Canard system with a single fully submerged bow foil and two fully submerged rear foils. The foils are of welded hollow shell construction in stainless steel. All three are retracted hydraulically. The design avoids the use of hinged doors or panels to raise the bow foil.

CONTROLS: The lift forces generated by the foils are varied by air drawn from the free atmosphere and fed through air exits to the foil upper surface. The airflow decreases lift and the flow is deflected away from the foil section with an effect similar to that of a deflected flap.

The stabilization system smooths the vessel's foilborne flight by controlling the lift of the foils. It consists of four units: the sensors, a computer (for automatic flight control), a command unit and the actuators.

The sensors measure the boat's attitude relative to the water surface and the horizon.

The flight sensor is responsible for the maintenance of the correct height of the craft above the surface. It is a digital system with detectors positioned along the strut of the front foil. The main advantage of this system over analog sensors (sonic height sensors or capacitive sensors) is its higher reliability. Should one detector fail, the mean height of flight is changed and the range of the sensor decreases slightly but the vessel continues to operate in the foilborne mode. Special sensors have been developed for pitch and roll angles, using the minimum number of moving parts. The application of these sensors to hydrofoils is possible because ships have narrow limits of pitch and roll angles and the frequency range to be dealt with is limited. The sensors need a run-up time of only about twenty seconds. The sensors for vertical and lateral acceleration are of conventional strain-gauge type.

The computer, used for automatic flight control, computes the appropriate command signals to the actuators from the signals received from the sensors. It is an electronic, all-transistorized unit comprising a number of sealed watertight modules.

The command unit is located on the bridge, and from here the vessel can be trimmed in pitch, height and roll to the required attitude. The desired response of the stabilization system to the waves (platforming or contouring) can be selected on a sea state selector switch, whilst the indicator display gives an overall view of the whole stabilization system.

The actuators (electro-hydraulic servo actuators) control the air valves which regulate air flow to the apertures on the foils.

HULL: Welded seawater resistant aluminium construction with longitudinal foaming system and integral tanks for fuel oil.

INTERNAL LAYOUT/ACCOMMODATION

Accommodation and operations rooms are located almost entirely below deck leaving a relatively large free deck area. Crew would normally comprise twenty-two officers and ratings with three in reserve.

Operating and control rooms are all fully air-conditioned. Minelaying equipment conforming to NATO standards can be installed as an alternative to missile launchers. Stand-by space is available for a substantial number of Mk 55 mines. There are three officers cabins and two crew rooms, two toilets with wash basins, one pantry, store rooms, operating and control rooms for ship and machinery. The control and operations room have direct access to the bridge and the radio room. The engine has two subdivisions and contains two separate generator sets.

POWER PLANT: Foilborne propulsion is supplied by a marinized gas turbine driving waterjets. Hullborne propulsion is supplied by a diesel engine driving a propeller.

ARMAMENT: Four MM38 Exocet missiles, 1, 76 mm OTO-Melara gun with 250 rounds, 2, 20 mm Rheinmetall cannon with 4,000 rounds.

FIRE CONTROL SYSTEM: Thomson-CSF Vega-Pollux or Hollandse Signaal.

DIMENSIONS:

Length overall	127 ft 11 in (39·0 m)
Max beam across deck	26 ft 3 in (8·0 m)
Draft, foilborne	8 ft 2 in (2·5 in)
Draft, hullborne,	
Foils extended	22 ft 3 in (6·8 m)
Foils retracted	5 ft 10 in (1·8 m)

WEIGHTS:

Operational displacement	250 t

PERFORMANCE:

Max intermittent speed foilborne	60 knots
Max intermittent speed hullborne	25 knots
Max continuous speed foilborne	53 knots
Max continuous speed hullborne	20 knots
Range at maximum speed	400 nm
Sea endurance	3 days

SUPRAMAR 500-SEAT PASSENGER FERRY

In August 1972, Supramar revealed that it is undertaking studies for the design of a 500-seat passenger ferry.

UNITED KINGDOM

AIRAVIA LTD

HEAD OFFICE:
  20 North Road,
  Shanklin,
  Isle of Wight
TELEPHONE:
  098-386-3643
  098-386-2850
LONDON OFFICE:
  Ivory House,
  World Trade Centre,
  St. Katharine's Way
  London, E1 9LD
TELEPHONE:
  01 790 7979
DIRECTORS:
  H. S. Snowball
  K. Wainwright
  R. Snowball
  Count A. de Lasta
  General H. Alexander

Airavia Ltd is the first company outside the Soviet Union to specialise in the sales, servicing, maintenance and operation of Soviet hydrofoils. Founded in January 1968, it is the appointed sales and marketing representative for passenger vessels of Sormovo design in the United Kingdom, British Commonwealth, Western Europe and other Western countries. World sales rights are being negotiated. In 1968 a standard Kometa was employed by Airavia in a 3,700 mile sales tour of Europe, which included a voyage up the Thames to the Port of London.

The company has sold Volga hydrofoils in Western Europe and the USA, and through its operating subsidiary, Speed Hydrofoils Ltd, has operated these high speed runabouts as in-shore pleasure craft in the United Kingdom and Mediterranean.

In April 1974 the company took delivery of two 58 seat Raketa T's (tropicalised model) which underwent immediate modification to meet British Department of Trade and company operating requirements. After modification and trials the vessels were each issued with British Civil Passenger Operating Certificates and licenced to carry up to 100 passengers on approved routes. The first of the Airavia-modified craft was then shipped to Manila where it is in service with Bataan Manila Ferry Services. The second is operating on the River Thames with Speed Hydrofoils Ltd.

Airavia is currently negotiating sales of Kometas, Meteors, Raketas, Voshkods and Volga 70s, together with ancillary equipment to a large number of operating companies based principally in the United Kingdom, Western Europe, Mediterranean, Pacific, Africa and South America. Adaptation of these vessels to meet British Department of Trade Requirements is undertaken in the United Kingdom and each will carry a British Civil Passenger Operating Certificate. At the time of going to press the company had on order eleven Kometa Ms and MTs, two Meteors and eight Raketas.

In addition to outright sales of these and other Soviet-built hydrofoil craft, the company also leases vessels on wet or dry charters and provides technical and marketing

Top: HS Raketa Greenwich, an Airavia-modified Raketa TA operated on the Thames by Speed Hydrofoils Ltd (Photo: Weekend).
Centre: Interior of the Raketa TA's wheelhouse. A hydraulic remote control system is installed for the main and auxiliary engines, reverse gear and fuel supply. (Photo: Weekend).
Bottom: Passenger access is via either a plateform to the upper deck or through detachable "gates" on the promenade deck, port and starboard, combined with upward hinging roof panels.

consultancy, servicing, and crew training support for new services.

The description below applies to the Raketa TA—the Airavia modified version and issued with a British Passenger Certificate.

RAKETA TA

This is the standard tropicalised Raketa 58-seat passenger ferry adapted to meet British Department of Trade operating requirements and licensed to carry up to 100 passengers on approved routes. Power is supplied by an M-401A supercharged diesel giving a service speed of 35 knots.

The crew comprises a captain, mate/engineer, deckhand and a hostess.

FOILS: The foil system comprises one bow foil, one aft foil and a pair of planing subfoils located immediately aft of the bow foil. Foils, subfoils and struts are all in welded stainless steel. The bow foil, which incorporates sweepback, and the straight aft foil are both supported by three vertical struts. The base of the centre strut aft forms the end bearing for the inclined propeller shaft.

HULL: The hull is framed on longitudinal and transverse formers, with all the main elements—plates, bulkheads, partitions, platforms and decks—in riveted duralumin. The stern is in interwelded steel strips. Below the freeboard deck the hull is divided into six watertight compartments employing web-framing.

ACCOMMODATION: The passenger saloon seats 58 in aircraft-type reclining seats. Six Norris Warming air-conditioning units and two electric fan heaters are installed in the saloon and one in the wheelhouse. Cool air is distributed through the saloon by eight electric fans mounted on the ceiling, four each side. One fan is installed in the wheelhouse. A ram-air intake provides ventilation when the craft is under way.

At the aft of the saloon is a bar, on either side of which are doors leading to the promenade deck. At the forward end of the saloon is a door leading to the forecastle. Aft of the bar is the engine room, storerooms, two toilets and a companionway leading up to the wheelhouse.

Features of the TA model include the substitution of three fixed windows on either side of the saloon, by three hinged to open fully outwards to allow passenger escape in an emergency. Hand holds for standing passengers in the backs of the aisle seats in the saloon are provided. Additional handrails are fitted in the side gangways and at the foot of the companionway leading to the upper deck. In the interest of child safety a net is fitted across the promenade deck, aft.

Passenger access is via either a platform to the upper deck or through detachable "gates" combined with upward hinging roof panels on the promenade deck, port and starboard.

Since life jackets are not required under British regulations for a Class 5 Passenger Certificate, life rafts have been substituted. Five 20-place Salter buoyant rafts are stowed in open trays above the passenger saloon superstructure ahead of the wheelhouse. Four lifebelts are carried, two on the lower deck, and two on the upper deck.

A British made CO_2 firefighting system is installed, with controls in the wheelhouse. Freestanding fire extinguishers are all of British design and manufacture.

POWER PLANT: The main engine is an M-401A, watercooled, supercharged 12-cylinder V-type diesel, with a normal cruising output of 1,100 hp. This drives, via a reverse gear and inclined steel shaft, a 3-bladed cast bronze propeller. Fuel (low sulphur content diesel) is carried in two steel tanks with a total capacity of 190 Imp gallons. Copper or stainless steel fuel lines are employed throughout.

A compressed air system, comprising a propeller-shaft-driven air compressor and two 40 l compressed air bottles is provided for main engine starting, emergency stopping, operating the foghorn and scavenging the water intake.

The diesel generator unit comprises a Perkins P3.152 diesel engine employed in conjunction with a Stamford C20 alternator. In addition to the fire suppression system in the engine room, the walls are covered in Rocksil asbestos matting which will contain a fire outbreak for 15 minutes, allowing passengers ample time to escape from the vessel in an emergency.

CONTROLS: The wheelhouse is equipped with a hydraulic remote control system for the main engine and auxiliary engines, reverse gear and fuel supply. The balanced rudder, in aluminium-magnesium alloy, is controlled hydraulically by turning the wheel. A hand tiller is employed in an emergency. Employment of exhaust gas as a side thruster to assist mooring is permitted at 850 rpm.

SYSTEMS, ELECTRICAL:

A 3 kw generator, rated at 27·5V and coupled to the main engine is the main power source while the vessel is under way. A 50 cycle, 230V, 1,500 rpm 3-phase alternator supplies ac power. Four 12 volt acid storage batteries, each with a 132 ah capacity and connected in series to give 24 volts, supply power during short stops.

HYDRAULICS: The system for controlling the main engine, reverse gear and fuel supply consists of control levers located in the wheelhouse and on the main engine, power cylinders located on the main engine, a filter tank, pipelines and fittings.

HEATING AND VENTILATION: Passenger saloon and wheelhouse are provided with natural ventilation using ram inflow when the boat is in motion. Norris Warming air-conditioning is fitted for hot weather.

NAVIGATION:

LIGHTS: A rotating yellow light, range 5 miles and flashing 60 times a minute is carried on the masthead and operated at all times when the vessel is under way. In addition a masthead light, range 5 miles, and port, starboard and stern lights are fitted for night operation.

AUDIO NAVAIDS: A foghorn is mounted above the wheelhouse and an 8-in bell is carried in the bow.

RADIO: Marconi vhf radio is carried for ship-ship and ship-shore communication.

RADAR: Decca radar is fitted for night operation.

INTERCOM: A public address system is installed and intercom speakers link the wheelhouse with the engine room and forecastle.

DIMENSIONS:

Length overall	88 ft 5 in (29·96 m)
Beam amidship	16 ft 5 in (5·0 m)
Freeboard	2 ft 7½ in (0·8 m)
Height overall (excl mast)	14 ft 8 in (4·46 m)
Draft hullborne	5 ft 11 in (1·8 m)
Draft foilborne	3 ft 7¼ in (1·1 m)

WEIGHTS:

Displacement, fully loaded	27·09 tonnes
light	20·31 tonnes

PERFORMANCE:

Service speed	35 knots
Max speed	38 knots
Max wave height	
foilborne	2 ft 8 in (0·8 m)
hullborne	4 ft 11 in (1·5 m)
Turning diameter	
hullborne	3-4 boat lengths
foilborne	15-16 boat lengths

NEW HYDROFIN LTD

HEAD OFFICE:

Burfield Flat, Bosham Lane, Bosham, Sussex

MANAGING DIRECTOR:

Christopher Hook

Christopher Hook's early Hydrofins demonstrated for the first time the stability and excellent seakeeping qualities of incidence-controlled, submerged foil craft, and marked a turning point in hydrofoil design.

Nearly seventy Hydrofins of various types have been built since 1949 in Norway, the USA, Poland and Israel. The company's latest design is the 22 ft Channel Skipper, a four-seat fibreglass-hulled runabout.

CHANNEL SKIPPER

Developed from the earlier K2 Hydrofin, the K2D Channel Skipper is a four-seat sports hydrofoil fitted with mechanical wave sensors to control the incidence angle of the fully submerged main foils.

FOILS: The fully submerged foil system is of "aeroplane" configuration with 65% of the weight carried on the two main foils and the remainder on the aft foil. All three foils have swept back leading and trailing edges. A high-riding crash preventer plane is mounted ahead of and beneath the bow. The plane is also used as a platform for mounting a lightweight pitch sensor which is hinged to the rear. The sensor rides on the waves and continuously transmits their shape through a connecting linkage to vary the incidence angle of the main foils as necessary to maintain them at the required depth. A filter system ensures that the craft ignores small waves and that the hull is flown over the crests of waves exceeding the height of the keel over the water.

Two additional sensors, trailing from port and starboard beams immediately aft of the

main struts, provide roll control. The pilot
has overriding control through a control
column, operated in the same manner as that
of an aircraft.

All three foils and the crash plane arm are
retractable. The crash plane arm retracts
into a hull slot: the two main foils swing
forward above the displacement waterline
and the rear foil strut assembly retracts
upwards into the hull at the same time
raising the propeller and drive shaft.

POWER PLANT: Motive power is provided
by a single 80 hp Ford diesel engine, driving
a 3-bladed propeller through a Z-drive.

DIMENSIONS:

Length overall	22 ft 0 in (6·71 m)
Length waterline, hull	18 ft 0 in (5·48 m)
Hull beam	6 ft 7 in (2·00 m)
Length overall, foils extended	
	19 ft 7 in (5·96 m)
Max beam, foils retracted	10 ft 9 in (3·27 m)
Max beam, foils extended	13 ft 5 in (4·09 m)
Draft afloat, foils retracted	1 ft 7 in (0·48 m)
Draft afloat, foils extended	5 ft 3 in (1·60 m)
Freeboard	2 ft 6 in (0·78 m)

WEIGHTS:

Gross tonnage	1·8 tons

A, New Hydrofin Channel Skipper; B, Hydrofin conversion kit employing a standard long-shaft outboard; C. Hydrofin craft propelled by a ducted fan

Net tonnage	1·2 tons
Light displacement	1·2 tons
Useful load (fuel, water, passengers, baggage and crew)	1,300 lb (598 kg)

PERFORMANCE:

Cruising speed, foilborne 32 knots (51 km/h)

Cruising speed, hullborne	
	8-12 knots (14-21 km/h)

Sea state capability   Unlimited in seas
corresponding to Barnaby's "average
rough sea" providing they conform as
regards proportions

Turning radius at cruising speed
150 ft (45·7 m) fully banked on turns.

UNITED STATES OF AMERICA

BOEING AEROSPACE COMPANY
Naval Systems Division

HEAD OFFICE:
PO Box, 3999 Seattle, Washington 98124
TELEPHONE:
Area 206, 237-2710
EXECUTIVE:
Darrell A. Cole, Vice-President and General
Manager, Naval Systems Division

The Boeing Advanced Marine Systems
Organisation, now part of the company's
Naval Systems Division, was formed in
1959 to conduct research, development,
design, manufacture and the testing of high
performance marine vehicle systems. Boeing
also has a 60 per cent interest in Alinavi SpA,
the Italian hydrofoil company, with headquarters in Rome. Boeing's entry into the
hydrofoil field was announced in June 1960,
when the company was awarded a $2 million
contract for the construction of the US Navy's
120-ton PCH-1 High Point, a canard design
which was the outgrowth of experiments
with a similar arrangement in the US Navy
test craft Sea Legs.

Boeing has also built a jet-driven hydroplane, the HTS, for testing foil models at
full-scale velocity; the Fresh-1, a manned
craft for testing superventilating or supercavitating foils at speeds between 60-100
knots and a water-jet test vehicle, Little
Squirt. Descriptions of Fresh-1 and Little
Squirt appears in JSS 1970-71 and earlier
editions. The company has also completed
a highly successful water–jet propelled gunboat, the PGH-2 Tucumcari, for the US
Navy's Ship Systems Command. Its operational trials included several months of
combat evaluation in Vietnam as part of the
US Navy's coastal surveillance force. Data
provided by the vessel has assisted the design
and development of the NATO/PHM and
the Jetfoil passenger ferry.

High Point was modified by Boeing

The Tucumcari during a tight turn at 40 knots

during 1972 to incorporate a new automatic
control system, new struts and foils, a
new diesel for hullborne propulsion and a
steerable forward strut to provide improved
manoeuvrability. The craft was returned to
the US Navy in a new configuration identified
as Mod-1 in March 1973. In its revised
form it is employed as a weapons testbed
and as a training vessel for crews for the
projected PHM-class vessels.

On January 19th, 1973, the keel was laid
for the first 106-ton 250-seat Jetfoil passenger
ferry. The hulls are being assembled in a
former 727 assembly building at Renton,
Washington, and the first craft was launched
on March 29th, 1974 on Lake Washington,

which is adjacent to the plant.

In April 1973, US Naval Ship Systems Command awarded the company a $42,602,384
contract for the design and development of
the 235 metric ton NATO PHM missile-
equipped patrol boat, under the terms of
which Boeing is building two lead craft for the
US Navy for evaluation. The first PHM will
be launched in late 1974 and the second will
follow three months later. Delivery of the
two craft to the US Navy is scheduled for
the summer of 1975. Participating in the
NATO PHM programme with the US Navy
are Italy and the Federal Republic of
Germany. Early on in the programme
participating countries are expected to

purchase Boeing-built PHMs for their own navies. The contract calls tentatively for twenty-eight craft to follow the two lead vessels. Design studies are now being completed on bigger and faster hydrofoils including the 1,300-1,500 ton Destroyer Escort Hydrofoil (DEH), a vessel capable of open ocean missions and of crossing the Atlantic without refuelling.

PCH-1 HIGH POINT

General design of the PCH-1 High Point was specified by the US Navy's Bureau of Ships, with responsibility for detail design and construction assigned to Boeing. The ship was accepted by the US Navy in August 1963 and based at the Puget Sound Naval Shipyard at Bremerton, Washington. Since then it has been undergoing a wide range of tests to evaluate the performance of an inshore hydrofoil ASW system.

High Point had a major modification and overhaul by Boeing in 1972 and was returned to the US Navy in March 1973. The new configuration is identified as Mod-1. In its revised form it is employed as a weapons test-bed to evaluate PHM missile ship equipment and weapons and ASW devices. Two RGM-84A-1 Harpoon blast test vehicles were successfully launched from the deck of the vessel while foilborne at 40 knots off British Columbia on the US-Canadian Nanoose range during December 1973-January 1974.

Both firings were conducted in normal sea conditions and moderate winds, the first being made while foilborne with the vessel straight and level, and the second while turning foilborne at 5 deg/sec. The dynamic stability of the craft was measured throughout the tests and the gas turbine was monitored to establish any possible harmful effects caused by the blast of the Aerojet-General 300 lb solid-propellant booster employed in the launch. The success of the test confirmed the suitability of the launch canister design for use on the PHM and other hydrofoils.

FOILS: Submerged fixed incidence canard foil system, with 68 per cent of the foil area located aft, and trailing-edge flaps on all foils for lift control, is a scaled-up version of that employed on Sea Legs. The foil struts retract vertically into the hull. Foils are of built-up construction in HY-80 weldable steel, and struts are in HY-130 steel.

HULL: Hull and superstructure are of all-welded, corrosion resistant 5456 aluminium. Integral plate stiffener extrusions are extensively used for decks and portions of the sides not having excessive curvature.

ACCOMMODATION: A crew of 18 is carried to provide a three-section watch: on duty at any given time are one officer of the deck/helmsman, one lookout on bridge, one radar operator and one navigator required in combat information centre, and two engineers on watch in main control. The wheelhouse seats two operators—OOD on port and the helmsman on the starboard side. In addition there are seats for two observers. Crew accommodation is ventilated and heated only. Entry is via four watertight doors in the deckhouse and two watertight hatches on main deck.

POWER PLANT: Foilborne propulsion is provided by two Proteus Model 1273 gas

Above: The PCH-1 High Point launching a McDonnell Douglas RGM-84A-1 Harpoon anti-ship missile during tests on the joint US-Canadian Range, Nanoose, Canada, in January 1974. *Below:* Employed initially to evaluate the performance of an inshore hydrofoil ASW system, the High Point is now used as a test bed for PHM weapons and equipment, and as a training vessel for crews of the new PHM-class hydrofoils

turbines, each rated at 4,250 hp max and 3,800 hp continuous. The turbines are located aft and take air through the two towers housing the retracted foil struts. The exhaust is discharged directly aft through the transom. Each gas-turbine is coupled to a pair of contra-rotating, subcavitating five-bladed propellers, 34 in. in diameter, through two right-angle gearboxes one at the top of each aft strut and the others in each of the underwater nacelles.

Hullborne propulsion is supplied by a single GM 12-V-71 (N75) rated at 525 hp for continuous operation. The engine is coupled to a 43 in (1,092 mm) diameter propeller through a retractable outdrive unit, which is steerable through 360 degrees and rotates

about the axis of the horizontal shaft for retraction.

CONTROLS: Altitude and foilborne stability are controlled by an automatic control system, the heart of which is a computer. This governs motion of the trailing edge flaps and the steerable forward strut in response to inputs from ultrasonic height sensors, position and rate gyros, accelerometers, feedback on control surface positions and helm commands. The system is active and all control surfaces are continuously moving in response to computer commands. On the bow foil, which is of single inverted tee (T) configuration, lift is varied by two trailing edge flaps driven by a single actuator. The aft foil, of shallow M configuration, has two ailerons

and two trailing edge flaps. Each flap and
its corresponding aileron is driven by a
single hydraulic actuator.

Pitch is controlled by the flaps on the
forward and aft foils. The gains in the
control system were selected to provide automatic trim. Roll is controlled by differential
operation of the flaps on the aft foil system.
A roll to steer system causes the vessel to
perform banked turns. Hullborne steering is
accomplished by rotation of the hullborne
propulsion unit about a vertical axis. This
unit can also be rotated upward 87° about a
longitudinal axis to eliminate its drag during
foilborne operation.

The attitude control is entirely automatic
except for steering. The take-off procedure
on the PCH-1 is simply to set the desired
flying height, then advance the throttles.
At a gross weight of 117 tons take-off occurs
at 24 knots with 3,750 total horsepower
delivered to the transmission system, the
speed stabilizing at 40 knots at that power
setting. Minimum foilborne speed is 24
knots. At a cruising speed of 44 knots
4,400 hp is required, with propellers turning
at 1,350 rpm.

SYSTEMS: ELECTRICAL: 100 kw (450
volts, 60 cycles 30).

HYDRAULICS: 3,000 psi ship's service for
hullborne steering, strut and foil extension/
retraction, engineering auxiliaries, and separate 3,000 psi system for foilborne control
surfaces.

ELECTRONICS: Raytheon Pathfinder 1605,
radar, UHF and HF radio transceivers.

ARMAMENT: Two fixed twin-tube Mk 32
torpedo tubes mounted on main deck at
waist of ship.

DIMENSIONS:
Length overall, hull   115 ft 9 in (35·28 m)
Length waterline, hull 110 ft 5 in (33·65 m)
Hull beam   30 ft (9·14 m)
Beam overall with foilguards
                         38·42 ft (11·71 m)
Draft afloat   8·58 ft (2·62 m)
Freeboard   8·75 ft (2·67 m)
WEIGHTS:
Light displacement   99·6 long tons
Normal take-off displacement
                         127·2 long tons
Useful load (fuel, water, etc)   27·6 tons

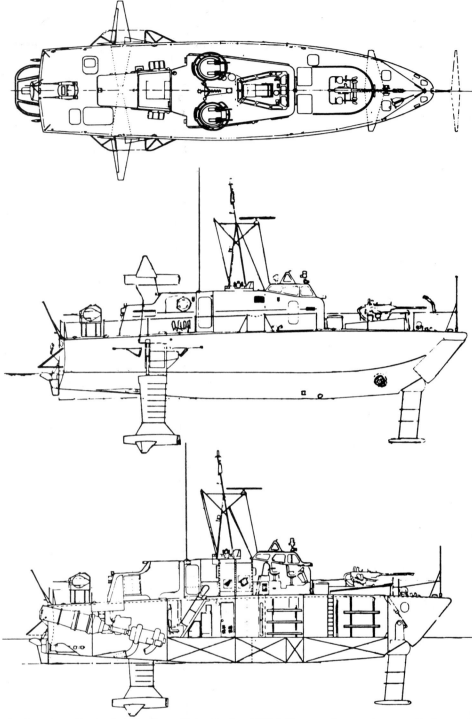

Outboard profiles and deck view of the Boeing PGH-2 Tucumcari, waterjet propelled patrol
gunboat hydrofoil

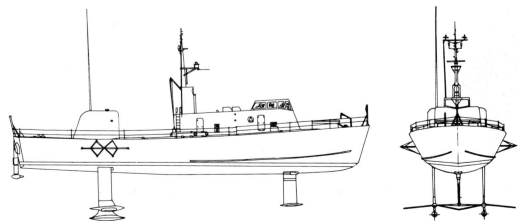

Outboard profile and bow-on view of the PCH-1 High Point in its new Mod-1 configuration.
Note the shallow M aft foil, which has two ailerons and two trailing edge flaps. Output of each
of the two Proteus 1273 gas-turbines has been uprated to 4,000 shp

PERFORMANCE:

Max speed foilborne	50 knots
Cruising speed foilborne	30-40 knots
Max speed hullborne	25 knots
Cruising speed hullborne	8 knots

PGH-2 TUCUMCARI

A 58-ton waterjet-propelled hydrofoil gunboat, the PGH-2 was ordered from Boeing by the US Navy's Ship Systems Command in 1966, under a $4 million, fixed price PGH (Patrol Gunboat Hydrofoil) programme. The craft was designed, constructed and tested in 23 months and delivered on schedule to the US Navy on March 7, 1968.

The craft has operated with both the US Navy Pacific Fleet Amphibious Command, San Diego, and the Atlantic Amphibious Forces, Norfolk, Virginia. Its operational trials included several months of combat evaluation in Vietnam as part of the US Navy's 24-hour coastal surveillance force in Operation Market time.

In 1971 the craft was deployed to Europe for operation with the US Sixth Fleet in the Mediterranean following a series of demonstrations for officials of NATO navies.

In November 1972, Tucumcari ran aground in the Caribbean, seven miles east of Puerto Rico, while conducting nightime operations with amphibious forces. No crewmen were killed or seriously injured. Due to damages sustained while removing the craft from the coral reef, the craft was struck from the list of active US Navy vessels and sent to the US Naval Research and Development Center for structural evaluation.

FOILS: Like High Point, Tucumcari has a fully submerged canard arrangement with retractable foils. Unlike High Point however, the aft foils are divided for sideways retraction, instead of retracting vertically, and the single forward strut retracts forward into a slot in the bow. Doors preserve the hull lines when the strut is either fully extended or retracted. Foils and their struts are fabricated in 17 4PH steel and have thin sections to avoid cavitation within the speed design range. Control flaps on the three foils are of marine aluminium alloy.

Both aft foils have anhedral to reduce their tendancy to ventilate in banked turns.

CONTROLS: A Boeing automatic control system stabilizes the craft in foilborne operation. This system consists of dual sonic height sensors; an inertial sensor package with vertical gyro, yaw rate gyro and vertical accelerometer; command signal equipment, control system computer and the hydraulically actuated control surfaces. The computer also controls steering to a large extent. Using signals received from the helm, it adjusts the foil flaps so the craft banks into a turn, much the same as the banking manoeuvres performed by aircraft. This procedure allows the vessel to turn sharply at high speeds without a corresponding loss of stability. At 40 knots the craft can turn a full circle in a diameter of 700 ft (213 m). The front strut is also steerable, giving added turn control. Height command is the only other manual input and this control is used primarily during take-off and landing.

The Tucumcari's forward strut retracts into a slot in the bow. Doors preserve the hull's lines when the strut is either fully extended or retracted

HULL: The hull shape is designed to minimise the structural loadings due to wave impact. It has a 25 degree deadrise, rounded chines, a flaring bow and straight runs aft. Construction is entirely of welded aluminium and careful design has resulted in a relatively low hull weight of 10 tons. The deckhouse includes both welded and mechanically fastened aluminium structures. Four watertight bulkheads are incorporated.

ACCOMMODATION: Crew of 13—comprising one officer and 12 enlisted personnel. Berthing arrangements comprise one officer stateroom with single berth and twelve berths, three high, in crew berthing compartment. Galley equipped with 120 volt electric stove, two WCs, two lavatories and one shower.

POWER PLANT: (foilborne) The waterjet propulsion system consists of a 3,200 hp Rolls Royce Proteus gas turbine driving through a direct coupling a Byron Jackson double volute, double suction, two impeller centrifugal pump rated at 4,800 shp, 29,300 gpm, 1,545 rpm and 550 ft head.

Water is drawn into the system through two ports in the two aft foil/strut intersection pods then ducted up through the hollow struts to the pump's intakes, each strut supplying one pump element. From the pump outlets the water is discharged to twin-fixed area nozzles beneath the transom. The system ejects about 29,300 US gallons of water a minute, providing 24,000 lb (10,000 kg) thrust.

Four normal and one alternate fuel tank are integral with hull below platform deck amidships. Normal (95% full) fuel capacity is 3,953 gallons. Alternate tank may be filled (95% full) to increase capacity to total of 5,440 gallons.

POWER PLANT (hullborne): A Buehler centrifugal pump, powered by a General Motors 6V-53 160 hp diesel propels the vessel when hullborne. Steering and reversing are accomplished by vectoring the water jet exit flow, eliminating the need for reverse gearing.

The propulsion machinery space is divided into two watertight compartments. The hullborne diesel is located in one compartment and the Proteus in the other, permitting the craft to operate with either engine

Impression of the Boeing PHM (Patrol Hydrofoil Missile) class vessel, which will be employed in the counter-missile craft role by the United States Navy. The craft is a 'scaled up' Tucumcari designed for greater speed, range and weapons capability

compartment flooded. Both foilborne and hullborne waterjet pumps are designed to operate under water in an emergency.

ARMAMENT: Main armament comprises a 40 mm gun forward of the bridge and a twin 20 mm gun mount aft. Two twin 20 mm cannon are mounted in port and starboard gun tubs in top of deckhouse outboard of the main mast.

SYSTEMS: ELECTRICAL, Diesel generator set: Governor controlled GM 4-53N diesel engine rated at 75 shp at 1,800 rpm, driving a GE generator rated for 50 kw (62·5 kva) 450 volt 60Hz 3-phase service. Standby turbine generator set: Governor-controlled Solar T-62T-12 gas-turbine rated at 88 shp at 8,216 rpm driving a standby 50 kw GE generator. Starting battery set comprises two 12-volt batteries in series to provide 24v 204 Ah capacity to start two diesel engines and turbine of standby generator set. It also provides emergency power source for limited supplementary lighting, navigation lights, gyro compass and hydrofoil automatic control systems.

HYDRAULICS: Two independent systems— foilborne and ship service. Foilborne system: 4 electro-hydraulic servo actuators for foil control, normal and standby 21·8 gpm pumps. Ship service system: 15 linear actuators, one hydraulic motor (foilborne turbine starter), normal and standby 17·9 gpm hydraulic pumps. Linear actuators retract/extend and lock hydrofoils, open/close bow doors and foilborne turbine exhaust door. Pressure settings 600 or 3,000 psi.

COMMUNICATIONS: Fourteen stations with two intercom channels for complete craft,

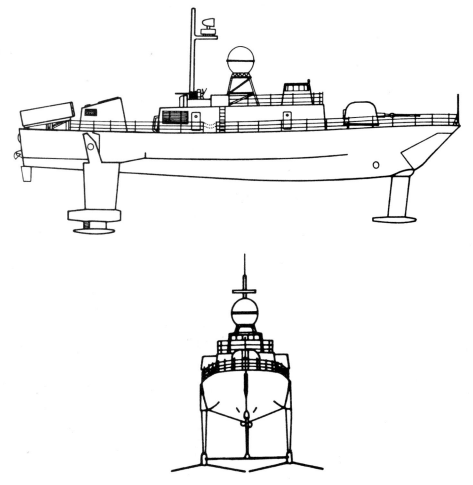

Outboard profile and bow-on view of the NATO PHM

machinery and weapons co-ordination. Electrical alarm, safety and warning systems, weapon control system providing audible signals at all weapon mounts, and public address (loud hailer) set. HF, VHF (surface) and UHF (surface-to-air). Infra red signal system AN/SAT-2, comprising two beacons, a control panel and two telegraph keys, for a secure means of signalling at night under darkened conditions.

NAVIGATION, ELECTRONIC: Depth sounder (echo sounder), navigation set LNS-101 providing continuous craft heading and position information; radio direction finder, speed log, identification radar, navigation radar (anti-collision).

DIMENSIONS, EXTERNAL:

Length overall:	
foils retracted	80 ft 4 in (24·38 m)
foils extended	74 ft 7 in (22·71 m)
Hull beam	19 ft 6 in (5·94 m)
Max beam:	
foils retracted	28 ft 3 in (8·61 m)
foils extended	35 ft 4 in (10·77 m)
Draft afloat (foils retracted) 4 ft 8 in (1·42 m)	
Freeboard	7 ft 0 in (2·13 m)

WEIGHTS:

Light displacement	40·8 tons
Max take-off displacement	64 tons
Useful load (fuel, water, equipment, armament and crew)	18·7 tons

PERFORMANCE:

Speed, foilborne	in excess of 50 knots

BOEING NATO/PHM

The NATO Hydrofoil Fast Patrol Ship Guided Missile (NATO/PHM) originated in mid-1969 when C-IN-C South presented to NATO a requirement for a large number of fast patrol boats to combat the threat posed by missile-armed fast patrol boats in the Mediterranean.

The concept of a common fast patrol boat was studied, and in September 1970 it was decided that the submerged foil craft of 140-tons proposed by the US Navy was the vessel most suited to NATO mission requirements. In October 1971, the United States indicated that it would proceed at its own expense with the design of the vessel and share the results of the studies with those nations wishing to purchase PHMs. It also offered to conduct all aspects of design and development, contracting and management in co-operation with governments entering into project membership. Costs would be reimbursed only by those nations engaged in the project.

Letters of intent, acknowledging design and cost scheduled obligations, were provided by Italy and the Federal Republic of Germany in April and May 1972, respectively. Although only three governments have decided to participate actively, future project membership is not restricted. Interested observers include Canada, Denmark, the Netherlands, France and the United Kingdom.

In November 1971, the US Navy awarded Boeing a $5·6 million contract for the preliminary design of a 230-ton craft and the purchase of mechanical and electronic components for at least two of the vessels. Seventeen months later, Boeing was awarded a $42,607,384 contract for the design and development of the PHM for NATO navies.

Impression of the Boeing NATO/PHM, hullborne with foils retracted. When hullborne the craft is propelled by twin waterjets powered by two 800 hp Mercedes-Benz 8V33ITC80 diesels

Above and below: PHM-I under construction by Boeing at Renton, Washington. These photgraphs were taken in January 1974, when the hull structure was 75% complete. The PHM-I was due to be launched in late 1974, and the second of the two lead craft was scheduled for completion three months later. Delivery of the first two craft to the US Navy is due to take place in the summer of 1975

Under the terms of the contract the first two craft will be built for the US Navy, the first to be launched in late 1974 and the second to follow three months later. Delivery of the two vessels is scheduled for the summer of 1975. The contract calls, tentatively, for 28 craft to follow and these are expected to become operational with the US Navy over the next seven years. It is the first US navy vessel designed and built on the metric system.

On May 3rd 1974, Boeing announced the receipt of a $3,809,235 cost plus fixed fee contract from US Naval Sea Systems Command for the preliminary design of a Patrol Hydrofoil Missile ship for the Federal Republic of Germany. The company stated that the design will be essentially the same as that of the two lead vessels scheduled for delivery to the US Navy during the summer of 1975. Later in May it was announced by General Electric that the first two LM2500 marine gas-turbines had been delivered to Boeing for the US Navy vessels. Rating of the LM2500 was given at 16,000 shp.

Cooperative production will be founded upon a production data package, which will be available after the trials and operation of the first two craft. A competitive procurement from a United States shipbuilder will be available to prospective NATO purchasers, in addition to which each participating nation will receive a complete production data package should they wish to build PHM in their own shipyards. However, it is envisaged that lead ship acquisition will be under a US production contract, on a commercial basis between Boeing and individual NATO shipbuilders or governments.

The PHM has sufficient design flexibility to allow for individual variations by any country. These variations will be primarily in the weapons systems installed, and the participating nations, current and future, can acquire the standard PHM carrying whatever combat equipment is determined necessary to meet national requirements.

The standard PHM is approximately 132·8 ft (40·5 m) long, has a beam of 28·2 ft (8·6 m) and a full load displacement of about 231 tons (235 tonnes). Foilborne range is in excess of 500 nautical miles at speeds in excess of 40 knots in 8-12 ft seas. The hull form and size, the major structural bulkheads and decks, foils and struts, waterjets, pumps, controls and main propulsion machinery are identical. The auxiliary equipment and arrangements, deckhouse and crew accommodation are also of standard design, but variations in the latter are possible to suit the manning requirements of individual countries.

The PHM is designed on similar lines to the 64-ton Tucumcari, a development of which is being built by Advanced Marine Systems—Alinavi SpA for the Italian Navy. The primary peacetime missions of the craft are to patrol straits and exits through restricted waters, support task force operations and shadow potentially hostile forces. Employment will, in general, depend on national defence requirements and each country's responsibility within NATO. The mission of the PHMs employed by the US Navy will be to conduct surveillance, screening and special operations, with the following contingent tasks: Patrol and blockade in coastal

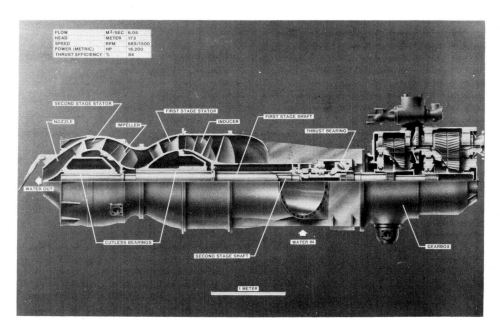

FLOW	M³/SEC	6.05
HEAD	METER	173
SPEED	RPM	685/1500
POWER (METRIC)	HP	16,200
THRUST EFFICIENCY	%	84

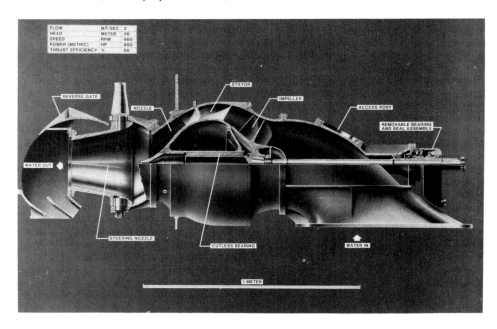

FLOW	M³/SEC	2
HEAD	METER	26
SPEED	RPM	965
POWER (METRIC)	HP	800
THRUST EFFICIENCY	%	86

Sectional drawings of the PHM's foilborne waterjet system, *above*, and hullborne propulsion system, *below*, The twin waterjet pumps of the hullborne system, powered by two Mercedes-Benz 800 hp diesels, propel the craft during long-range cruising and slow speed manoeuvring. Both the waterjet propulsion systems were developed and manufactured by Aerojet Liquid Rocket Company, Sacramento, California

areas, island waters and inland sea areas; augment screening of local convoys against surface attack; fast transport of lightly equipped troops, augment screening ships during arrival and departure of convoys or amphibious task forces.

FOILS: Fully-submerged canard arrangement with approximately 32% of the dynamic lift provided by the bow foil and 68% by the aft foil. The aft foil retracts rearwards and the bow foil retracts forward into a recess in the bow. Bow doors preserve the hull lines when the forward foil is either fully extended or retracted. The foils and struts are in 17-4 PH stainless high strength steel. Both forward and aft foils are welded assemblies consisting of spars, ribs, and skin. Flaps are fitted to the trailing edges to

provide control and lift augmentation at take-off and during flight. The bow foil system incorporates a strut that rotates to provide directional control and reliable turning rates in heavy seas.

The shallow 'M' or inverted double pi configuration of the aft foil is designed for improved hydroelastic and turning characteristics. The primary strut structure consists of spars, ribs and skin welded into watertight assemblies. The struts are designed as beam columns, and rigidly attached to the foil support structure at the hull.

The struts are attached to the hull with pivot pins that allow the foils to rotate clear of the water. Hydraulic actuators are used for retraction and extension, mechanical stops and position locks being employed to secure the foils in either position.

CONTROLS, FOILBORNE: The helm, throttle and an automatic control system (ACS) provide continuous dynamic control during take-off, foilborne operation and landing. Once take-off is complete, the ACS requires no attention on the part of the crew. It controls the craft by sensing craft attitude, motion rates and acceleration, then comparing them electronically with desired values. Any deviations are processed by analog control computer which generates electrical commands causing hydraulic actuators to reposition the control surfaces, thus minimising detected errors. The foilborne control surfaces are trailing edge flaps on each of the foils, plus the rotating bow foil strut which acts as the foilborne rudder.

Manual controls and displays for both hullborne and foilborne conditions are concentrated at the helm station and include the wheel, a foil-depth selector, a foil-depth indicator, a ship-heading indicator and a heading holding switch.

CONTROLS, HULLBORNE: Steering control in the hullborne mode is provided by stern rudders which rotate electrohydraulically in response to the wheel. An automatic heading control, similar to that employed for foilborne operation is incorporated, together with the necessary heading reference provided by the gyrocompass.

POWER PLANT, FOILBORNE: The foilborne propulsion system comprises a single waterjet pump driven through a power-splitting reduction gear by a General Electric LM 2500 gas-turbine. The LM 2500 is a 2-shaft, simple-cycle engine developed from the GE TF39 which powers the USAF's C-5 transport and the DC-10 Trijet.

In April 1973, Aerojet Liquid Rocket Company, Sacramento, California, was awarded a $1·5 million contract by Boeing to manufacture and test the waterjet propulsion pumps. The single foilborne propulsion pump is capable of handling 90,000 gpm and the two hullborne pumps will each operate at approximately 30,000 gpm.

Engine installation and removal for overhaul is accomplished through hatches located in the main deck between the deckhouse and exhaust outlet.

The vessel is capable of operation on JP-5 or diesel fuel.

POWER PLANT, HULLBORNE: Twin waterjet pumps powered by two 800 hp Mercedes-Benz 8V331TC80 diesels propel the vessel when hullborne. The hullborne system provides long-range cruising and slow speed manoeuvring, while the gas turbine is available when required for high-speed foilborne operation.

HULL: Hull and deckhouses are all-welded structures in AL 5465 alloy.

ACCOMMODATION: Crew will average 21 officers and men, but will vary according to the armament carried. Accommodation on the US Navy version is provided for four officers — the CO has a separate cabin, three chief petty officers and fourteen enlisted men. The superstructure accommodates the bridge, which contains steering and engine control consoles and is elevated to provide a 360 degree view. A short ladder from the bridge leads down to the command and surveillance

The first Boeing Jetfoil was launched on March 29th 1974. The vessel was due to be tested on Puget Sound and in the Pacific before being delivered to Far East Hydrofoil Co of Hong Kong.

deckhouse that accommodates the fire control, radar, communications and navigation equipment The size of the deckhouse provides flexibility in accommodating various national equipment requirements. The space aft of the superstructure and forward of the foilborne engine exhaust is used to erect rigging for replenishment and refuelling.

Below the main deck, about one third of the PHM's length is devoted to crew accommodation, the forward third is occupied by the primary gun, automatic loader mechanism, ammunition storage and forward foil, and the after third is occupied by the unmanned machinery spaces.

All manned spaces are equipped with a recirculating air conditioning system to give a maximum air temperature of 27 deg C at 55% relative humidity in summer, and a minimum inside temperature of 18 deg C in winter. The officer staterooms, crew quarters and lounge/messing area are fully air-conditioned, the temperature being controlled by individual thermostats in the spaces concerned.

SYSTEMS, ELECTRICAL: Ship's service electric plant comprises two 200 kw generator sets providing 450 volt 3-phase, 400 Hz AC power. One is capable of handling entire electrical load, the second is provided as a standby. Through the use of static power conversion equipment, limited 3-phase, 60HZ AC power and 28 volt DC is available for equipment requirements. In port, the craft can utilise shore power, or use its own auxiliary power unit for this purpose as well as battery charging and emergency use of navigation and radio equipment.

HYDRAULICS: 3,000 psi to actuate the hullborne and foilborne controls, foil retraction and hullborne engine starting. Dual hydraulic supply is provided to each service with sub-system isolation fore and aft in the event of major damage.

FIRE EXTINGUISHING: Dry chemical equipment throughout craft, and a fixed total flooding-type Freon 1301 system.

WEAPONS/FIRE CONTROL: Either WM-28 radar and weapons control system or American model, the Mk 92. Both systems embody a combined fire control and search antenna system, mounted on a single stabilised platform, and enclosed in a fibreglass radome. The Italian Argo system can also be installed.

GUNS: Standard primary gun is the Oto Melara 76 mm gun, which is unmanned and automatically controlled by the fire control system. The craft can also be delivered with secondary guns. If specified two Mk 20 Rh 202 20 mm AA cannon can be provided, one each, port and starboard, adjacent to the fire control antenna structure.

MISSILES: The two prototypes will carry Harpoon missiles with eight launchers, but Exocet, Otomat, Tero or any smaller missile system can be installed. Space is provided aft to accommodate the four launchers, port and starboard, in parallel pairs. The launchers are deck-fixed in elevation and azimuth.

Armament of the standard US Navy version will be eight McDonnell Douglas Harpoon anti-ship missiles in lightweight container launchers; one Mk 75 Mod 1 76 mm cannon and one Mk 92 Mod 1 GFCS.

The following details apply to the model under construction for the US Navy.

DIMENSIONS:

Length overall,		
foils extended	132·8 ft	(40·5 m)
foils retracted	147 ft 6 in	(45 m)
Beam maximum, deck	29 ft 0 in	(8·9 m)
Max width across foils	47 ft 6 in	(14·5 m)
Draft:		
hullborne, foils retracted	9ft 5 in	(2·9 m)
hullborne foils extended	23·2 ft	(7·1 m)
foilborne, normal	8·9 ft	(2·7 m)

WEIGHTS:

Displacement, full load including margins
235 metric tons

PERFORMANCE:

Max speed foilborne	in excess of 50 knots
Cruising speed foilborne,	
sea state 0-5	in excess of 40 knots
hullborne	in excess of 10 knots

Sea state:
can negotiate 8-12 ft seas at speeds in
excess of 40 knots
Foilborne range   in excess of 600 n miles
hullborne range   in excess of 1,000 n miles

BOEING JETFOIL 929-100

This is a 106-ton waterjet-propelled commercial hydrofoil for services in relatively
rough waters. It employs a fully-submerged,
automatically-controlled canard foil arrangement and is powered by two 3,780 hp
Allison 501-K20A gas turbines. Normal
foilborne cruising speed is 45 knots.

Typical interior arrangements include a
commuter configuration with 250 seats, a
tourist layout for 190 tourists plus baggage,
a mixed traffic variant for 190 plus up to
four compact cars, and an all-cargo variant.
The company is also evaluating various
utility models with open load decks suitable
for search and rescue duties, offshore oil-rig
support and firefighting. Two utility derivatives for offshore rig crew and priority/
emergency cargo support are showing great
potential. They are 50 and 100 seat crew/
supply boat versions with considerable cargo
capacity for supporting rigs within 50-250
nautical miles from shore.

At the time of going to press five Jetfoils
were on order: two for Far East Hydrofoil
Co, Hong Kong and three for Pacific Sea
Transportation Ltd, Hawaii.

Keel-laying of the first Jetfoil took place
at the company's Renton, Washington, plant
on January 19th 1973, and the craft was
launched on March 29th, 1974. After testing
on Puget Sound and in the Pacific, the craft
was due to be delivered to Pacific Sea
Transportation Ltd for inter-island services
in Hawaii. High speed foilborne tests began
in Puget Sound in mid-July and it was
reported that the vessel attained a speed of
37 knots during its initial runs.

FOILS: Fully submerged canard arrangement with a single inverted tee strut/
foil forward and a three-strut, full-span
foil aft. The forward foil assembly is
rotated hydraulically through 7 degrees
in either direction for steering. All foils
have trailing edge flaps for controlling
pitch, roll and yaw and for take-off and
landing. Hydraulically-driven foil flap actuators control the variation in flap positions
through linkages between actuators and flap
hinge points. Foils and struts retract
hydraulically above the waterline, the bow
foil forward, and the rear foil aft. All
structural components of the foil/strut
system are in 15·5 PH corrosion resistant
all-welded steel construction.

CONTROL: The craft is controlled by a three-
axis automatic system while it is foilborne
and during take-off and landing. The system
senses the motion and position of the craft
by gyros, accelerometers and height sensors,
signals from which are combined in the
control computer with manual commands
from the helm. The resulting computer
outputs provide control-surface deflections
through electro-hydraulic servo actuators.
Lift control is provided by full-span trailing
edge flaps on each foil. Forward and aft
flaps operate differentially to provide pitch

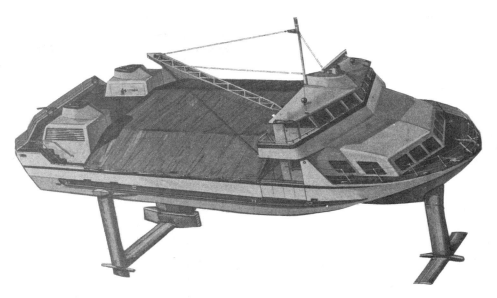

Jetfoil in utility configuration

Boeing's 106-ton Jetfoil waterjet-propelled commercial hydrofoil for service in relatively rough
waters. The craft is powered by two 3,780 hp Allison 501-K20A gas turbines and cruises at 45
knots. Five Jetfoils are on order, and the first is expected in service in the summer of 1975

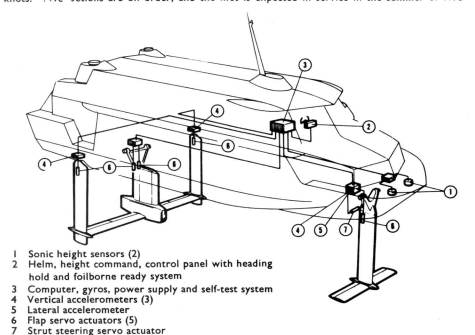

1 Sonic height sensors (2)
2 Helm, height command, control panel with heading
   hold and foilborne ready system
3 Computer, gyros, power supply and self-test system
4 Vertical accelerometers (3)
5 Lateral accelerometer
6 Flap servo actuators (5)
7 Strut steering servo actuator

variation and height control. Aft flaps operate differentially to provide roll control for changes of direction.

The vessel banks inwardly into all turns, to ensure maximum passenger comfort. The ACS introduces the correct amount of bank and steering to coordinate the turn in full. Turn rates of up to 6 degrees per second are attained within 5 seconds of providing a heading change command at the helm.

Three basic controls only are required for foilborne operation. The throttle is employed to set the speed, the height command lever to set the required foil depth, and the helm to set the required heading. If a constant course is required, a "heading hold" circuit accomplishes this automatically.

For take-off, the foil depth is set, the two throttles advanced, and the hull clears the water in about 60 seconds. Acceleration continues, until the craft automatically stabilises at the command depth and the speed dictated by the throttle setting. The throttle setting is reduced for landing, the craft settling as the speed drops. The speed normally diminishes from 45 knots (cruising speed) to 15 knots in about 30 seconds. In emergencies more rapid landings can be made by the use of the height command lever to provide hull contact within 2 seconds.

HULL: Hull and deckhouse in marine aluminium. Aircraft assembly techniques used, including high-speed mechanised welding processes.

POWERPLANT: Power for the waterjet propulsion system is supplied by two Allison 501-K20A free-power gas turbines, each rated at 3,300 shp at 80 deg F (27 deg C) at sea level. Each is connected to a Rocketdyne axial-flow pump through a gearbox drive train. The two turbine/pump systems are located in their own bays, port and starboard, separated by the slot in the hull into which the central water strut retracts for hullborne operation. The system propels the craft in both foilborne and hullborne modes. When foilborne, water enters through the inlet located at the forward lower end of the aft centre foil strut. At the top of the duct, the water is split into two paths and enters into each of the two axial flow pumps. It is then discharged at high pressure through nozzles in the hull bottom.

The water path is the same during hullborne operations with the foils extended. When the foils are retracted, the water enters through a flush inlet located in the keel. Reversing and steering for hullborne operation only are accomplished by reverse-flow buckets located immediately aft of the water exit nozzles. A bow thruster is provided for positive steering control at low forward speeds.

A 4,000 gallon (15,140 litre) integral fuel tank supplies the propulsion turbine and diesel engines. Recommended fuel is Diesel No. 2. The tank is fitted with a 2 in (5 cm) diameter fill pipe and fittings compatible with dockside refuelling equipment. Coalescent-type water separating fuel filters and remote-controlled motor-operated fuel shut-off valves are provided for fire protection.

ACCOMMODATION: Passenger accommodation is fully air-conditioned and arranged on two decks, which are connected by a wide,

Boeing Jetfoil prototype during tests on Project Sound in July 1974.

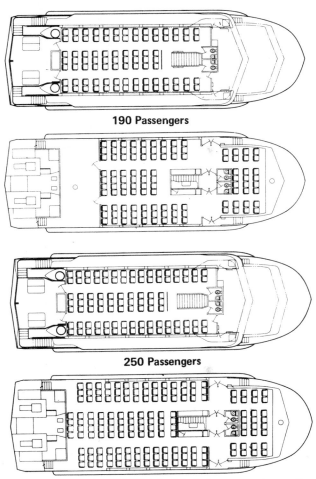

190 Passengers

250 Passengers

Typical interior arrangements on the 929-100 Jeftoil include a commuter configuration with 250 seats, a tourist layout for 190 tourists plus baggage and a mixed-traffic version for 190 passengers plus up to four compact cars. Seats are track mounted to facilitate spacing changes, removal or replacement. Food and beverage service units can be installed

enclosed stairway. The cabins have 3 ft 0 in (91.4 cm) wide aisles and 6 ft 9 in (2.06 m) headroom. In the commuter configuration 56 cu ft (1.58 cu metres) per passenger is provided and 66 cu ft (1.87 cu meters) in the tourist configuration. Floors are carpeted and 2 ft 0 in (61 cm) seats are provided. Lighting is indirect and adjustable from the

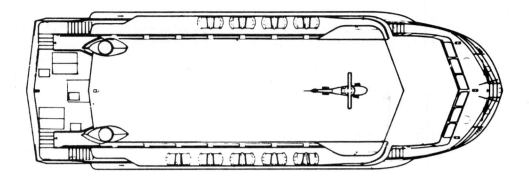

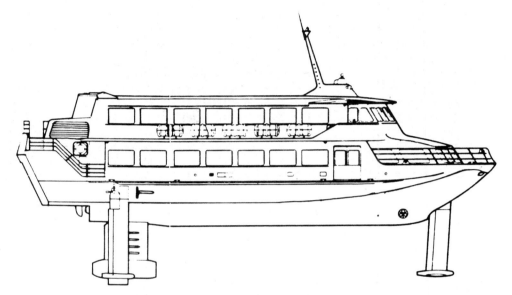

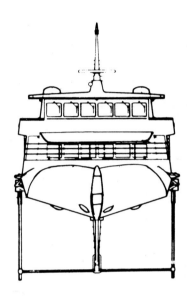

General arrangement of the Jetfoil

wheelhouse. Interior noise is near conversation level (below 68 db SIL). Passengers are entertained and informed by a public announcement system. Each deck level has two WC/washbasin units. Drinking water dispensers are located on each passenger deck.

Quality of the ride in the craft is comparable with that of a Boeing 727 airliner. The vertical acceleration at the c of g is designed to be no more than 0·04 g, with lateral acceleration less than that of the vertical. Angles of pitch and roll will be less than 1 deg RMS. Passenger discomfort in an emergency landing is prevented by a 'structural fuse', which limits deceleration to less than 0·4 g longitudinally and 0·8 g vertically so that a passenger would not be thrown from his seat in the event of the craft striking a major item of floating debris at full speed. The 'structural fuse', when actuated, causes the foil and strut to rotate backwards, protecting the system from sustaining significant damage. The fuses can be reset while

under way in some cases, depending on the degree of impact.

Crew comprises a captain and first officer plus cabin attendants.

SYSTEMS: ELECTRICAL: 60-cycle, 440 volt a.c. electrical system, supplied by two diesel-driven generators rated at 62·5 KVA each. Either is capable of supplying all vital electrical power. 90 KVA capacity shore connection facilities provided, and equipment can accept 50-cycle power. Transformer rectifier units for battery charging provide 28 volts dc from the ac system.

HYDRAULICS: 3,000 psi (210·9 kg/cm²) system to actuate control surfaces. Each pump connected to a separate system to provide split system redundancy in the event of a turbine, pump, distribution system or actuator malfunctioning.

EMERGENCY: Craft meets all applicable safety regulations of the US Coast Guard

and SOLAS. Hull provides two-compartment sub-division and a high degree of stability. Life rafts and life jackets are provided.

NAVIGATION: Equipment includes radar. A low-light-level television system covering potential collision zone is available as an optional extra.

DIMENSIONS:

Length overall	90 ft (27·4 m)
Beam overall	31 ft (9·5 m)
Draft afloat, foils retracted	4·8 ft (1·5 m)
foils extended	16 ·3 ft (5·0 m)

WEIGHTS:

Displacement	106 long tons

PERFORMANCE:

Normal service speed	45 knots
Turning radius at 45 knots	
	less than 1,000 ft (304·80 m)

DAK HYDROFOILS
HEAD OFFICE:
P.O. Box, 71 Sausalito, California 94965
TELEPHONE:
415 332-4891
PROPRIETOR AND CHIEF DESIGNER:
David A. Keiper
Dak Hydrofoils is currently developing and

marketing simple low-cost hydrofoil conversion kits for outboard powerboats. These are based on those available from the company for existing racing catamarans.

The arrangement employs identical lateral foils, positioned in a similar location, plus a fully-submerged stern foil. Lighter craft will have a simple foil beneath the outboard

engine. Heavier craft, of up to 1,500 lb (680·38 kg) loaded weight have a retractable 6 in (152 mm) chord foil, supported by twin struts.

The propeller is lowered by a combination of engine shaft extension or extensions, and/or lowering the engine by means of parallel bars.

DYNAFOIL, INC

HEAD OFFICE:
881 West 16th Street, Newport Beach, California 92660

TELEPHONE:
(714) 646-9231

DIRECTORS:
Dr Paul J. Coleman, Chairman
David J. Cliné, President
James M. Dale, Secretary/Treasurer

EXECUTIVES:
Dominic J. Bitetti, Vice President, Marketing

Dynàfoil Inc was formed in December 1971 to develop the Dynafoil sport craft. The development of this vehicle began in late 1970 with the construction of IRMA 1, and the foil configuration of this craft has been the foundation for all subsequent work. Patents for the foil configuration have been applied for in all the main consumer countries.

DYNAFOIL 1

This fibre-glass hulled sports hydrofoil is a marine counterpart to the motorcycle and snowmobile. The bow foil is mounted at the base of a handle bar equipped steering head and the handling characteristics are similar to those of a motor cycle. Production was due to start in the summer of 1974.

FOILS: Canard configuration with a fully submerged main foil located aft and bearing 60% of the load and small incidence-controlled twin-delta foil forward. The angle of incidence is controlled mechanically by a curved planing control foil to achieve a constant flying height. The aft foil has anhedral to prevent tip broaching and ventilation and is set above the propeller. The foils are in cast aluminium while the struts are of fibreglass and aluminium. Both foils retract fully, the bow foil rotating upwards and rearwards, the aft foil rearwards and upwards against the transom.

CONTROLS: Steering is accomplished by turning the front foil strut. All turns enter a fully coordinated bank.

HULL: Two-stage deep V hull, comprising two fibreglass mouldings bonded together at the beltline. After bonding, all voids not employed for functional components are filled with 2 lb density polyurethane, providing 600 lb of bouyancy.

ACCOMMODATION: Open cockpit with a motor cycle pillion style seat for two.

POWER PLANT: Mark 1 is available with a choice of two engines—either a 340 cc 40 hp or 440 cc 50 hp Xenoah 2-cylinder 2 stroke. The inboard drive train is made up from standard components—a belt-driven automatic clutch and torque converter and a secondary chain transfer case. The torque converter provides an initial 3·5 to 1 underdrive at take-off and under maximum loading, automatically shifting to ·8 to 1 overdrive at cruising speed. Final drive is through a bevel gear at the base of the rear strut. The propeller is of 3-bladed subcavitating design in cast aluminium. A single 5 gallon (US) fuel tank is located amidships, with a refuelling neck on the outside hull at the bow.

DIMENSIONS:

Length overall hull	7 ft 0 in (2·13 m)	
Length overall,		
foils retracted	8 ft 0 in (2·43 m)	
foils extended	7 ft 0 in (2·13 m)	
Hull beam	3 ft 6 in (1·06 m)	

Above and below: The Dynafoil Mark I two-seat sports hydrofoil. Note the twin delta configuration of the forward foil, the incidence of which is controlled by the curved planing foil above

Beam overall,	
foils retracted	3 ft 6 in (1·06 m)
foils extended	3 ft 6 in (1·06 m)
Draft afloat,	
foils retracted	1 ft 0 in (304 mm)
foils extended	3 in (76 mm)
Draft foilborne	1 ft 6 in (457 mm)
Freeboard	1 ft 2 in (355 mm)
Height overall, foils retracted	
	3 ft 6 in (1·06 m)

WEIGHTS:

Light displacement	350 lbs (158·75 kg)
Normal take-off displacement	
	600 lb (272·14 kg)
Max take-off displacement	
	800 lbs (362·85 kg)

PERFORMANCE:

Max speed foilborne	45 mph (72·42 km/h)
Max speed hullborne	5 mph (8·04 km/h)

Cruising speed,	
foilborne	30 mph (48·28 km/h)
hullborne	5 mph (8·04 km/h)
Designed endurance and range at cruising speed, approx	65 miles (104·60 km/h)
Turning radius at cruising speed	15 ft (4·57 m)
Fuel consumption at max speed	4 gph
at crusing speed	2 gph

SEA TEST: Craft has been tested in 3-5 ft (914 mm-1·5 m) swells and in 18·24 in (406-609 mm) chop.

DEPARTMENT OF THE NAVY, NAVAL SEA SYSTEMS COMMAND (NAVSEA)

HEADQUARTERS:

Washington DC 20360

PROGRAMME MANAGER, HOVERCRAFT AND HYDROFOILS:

James L. Schuler

OFFICE ADDRESS:

US Naval Sea Systems Command, Code 03Z, National Center 3, Room 10E54, Washington DC 20360

The Research Directorate of US Naval Sea Systems Command (NAVSEA), has been the primary technical sponsor of all US Navy hydrofoil and hovercraft programmes since 1960.

The programme manager responsible for the development of both types of vessel is Mr. James L. Schuler. Technical managers have been appointed for each of the several research and development programmes managed and directed by NAVSEA. Technical Manager of the US Navy Hydrofoil Research and Development Programme is Mr Robert Johnston, and the Technical Manager of the US Navy Amphibious Assault Landing Craft Advanced Development Programme is Mr Melvin Brown, both of the Naval Ship Research and Development Centre, Carderock, Maryland (NSRDC/C).

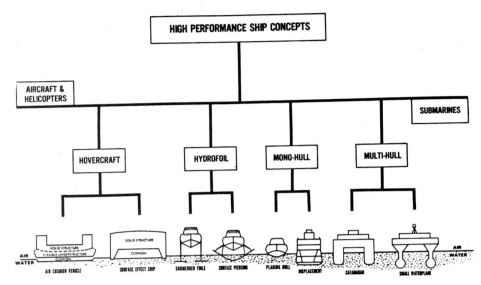

High performance ship concepts under development by US Naval Sea Systems Command

Other US Navy hydrofoils include the PGH-1 and PHM, as well as the FRESH-1 test craft. The PHM is a Patrol Hydrofoil, Guided Missile being developed by NAVSEA PMS 303 under the direction of Capt. J. R. Wilkins and Cdr K. Duff. This is a NATO project, sponsored jointly by the US Navy, the Federal Republic of Germany and the Italian Navy.

This programme includes tests and trials of the PCH-1 High Point, and the AGEH-1 Plainview, as well as the design, construction, test, trials and evaluation of larger and faster hydrofoils.

EDO CORPORATION, GOVERNMENT PRODUCTS DIVISION

HEAD OFFICE:

13-10 111th Street, College Point, New York 11356

EXECUTIVES:

L. M. Swanson, Director, Air MCM Applications

Edo Corporation has developed a foil-equipped catamaran MCM system which speeds the process of magnetic and acoustic mine clearance and reduces the hazards of mine sweeping operations. The system, the Edo Mark 105, is designed to be towed by the US Navy's RH-53D Sea Stallion and other heavy-lift helicopters of similar size and performance. The first unit formed to operate Mk 105 Airborne Minesweeping Gear was HM-12 helicopter mine countermeasures Squadron, which operated off North Vietnam to clear mines from the entrance to the port of Haiphong and undertook the aerial sweeping of the Suez Canal during the spring of 1974. The operation—code named Nimbus Star—was said to have been a complete success.

If required the equipment can be towed behind a BHC BH.7 amphibious hovercraft or other suitable ACV. Tests with this arrangement have been undertaken in the UK and USA.

Advantages claimed for the system include the following: lower acquisition and maintenance costs; fewer operating personnel required; low equipment vulnerability and bigger areas cleared within a given time.

Normally the helicopter/seasled combination is conveyed to the affected area aboard an amphibious assault craft. The helicopter

The Edo Mark 105, probably the most sophistitated of all mine countermeasures systems, has been under development for some years. It comprises a helicopter and a towed hydrofoil sea sled, on which is mounted a turbogenerator that energises magnetic sweep cables, thus simulating the magnetic field of a ship

lifts-off with the sled at the end of a line, lowers it into the water, extends its foils, and sets off to sweep the minefield.

The towline, which is 450 ft (137·16 m) long, also serves as an electric cable for carrying control signals to the sled, and as a fuel transfer line in the case of extended operations.

A portable winch in the helicopter is used to handle the craft, the sweep cables and the towing cable during launching and retrieval. The system can be operated from either ships or shore bases equipped with crane facilities and small boats for handling the sweep cables which stream out behind the seasled.

MARK 105 AIRBORNE MINESWEEPING GEAR

The Mk 105 is a helicopter-towed, magnetic minesweeping system mounted on a 27 ft 6 in (8·38 m) long catamaran seasled. Foils are fitted to permit high speed operation and provide improved seakeeping performance. Aboard the craft is a turbogenerator which provides energy for the magnetic sweep cables and powers a hydraulic pump for foil retraction.

FOILS: Surface-piercing tandem configuration with two inverted V foils forward and two aft, balancing the loading between them. High-riding pitch control subfoils of similar configuration are located ahead of the two bow foils. Bow and stern foils are rotated for retraction and extension by a self-contained hydraulic system.

HULL: Catamaran hull comprising two tubular pontoons of light metal alloy construction, connected by an aerofoil section platform on which is mounted a gas-turbine powered electric generator set and the retrieval rig structure to which handling lines are attached. The two ends of the towing bridle are attached to the inward faces of the twin pontoon hulls forward of the platform. Wheels are attached to the underside of the pontoons to facilitate deck handling. Fuel for the turbogenerator set is carried in two centrally located tanks, one in each pontoon.

TOWING: The 450 ft (137·16 m) long towing cable terminates in an electrical connector and fuel fitting. As well as providing the towing links between the platform and the helicopter, all electrical commands and supplementary fuel pass through the cable. The cable consists of an electrical core containing the individual conductors, around which is a double layer of steel wire. Surrounding this is a hose, and fuel flows through the annular space between the inner diameter of the hose and the steel wire reinforcement.

SYSTEMS: A gas turbine generator set, mounted within a nacelle on the platform provides energy for the generation of the magnetic field. The complete power pack comprises a gas turbine driven AC generator, a rectifier, a controller containing the waterborne electronics and batteries to power the electronics system.

MAGNETIC SWEEP CABLE: This is attached to the after end of the sweep boom located on the underside of the port pontoon. It comprises an upper electrode attached to the end of a trailing cable and a lower

The Edo Mark 105

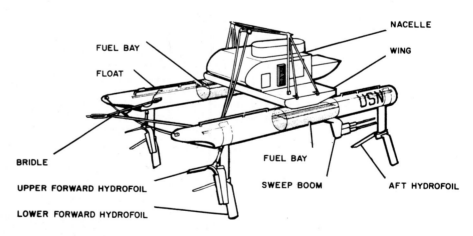

This drawing shows the surface-piercing tandem foil system of the Edo Mark 105 and the high-riding pitch-control-subfoils

electrode fitted to the boom fin. The potential between the electrodes, employing the water as a conductor, produces a magnetic field which simulates that of a ship.

CONTROL PROGRAMMER: Located in the helicopter this is the only manned station employed in the system. It contains the airborne electronics and all the controls and instrumentation necessary.

The console contains the fuel transfer control panel, turbine indicators, hydrofoil and sweep boom actuators and the generator controls and indicators.

HYDRAULICS: Gas-turbine operated pump for extending and retracting the foils and sweep boom. Manual pump for emergency operation.

DIMENSIONS:

Length overall	27 ft 6 in
Beam, catamaran structure only	11 ft 7 in
across foils	21 ft 0 in
Height, foils extended:	
to top of retrieval rig	17 ft 3 in
to top of nacelle	13 ft 6 in
foils retracted, to base of wheels	11 ft 6 in

WEIGHTS:

Empty weight	5,522 lb
Gross weight	6,432 lb

PERFORMANCE:
Towing speeds and sea state capability not available

GRUMMAN AEROSPACE CORPORATION

HEAD OFFICE:
Bethpage, Long Island, USA
CABLES:
Grumair
PRESIDENT:
J. G. Gavin Jr

Grumman entered the hydrofoil field in 1956 when it acquired Dynamic Developments Inc, producer of the experimental XCH-4, built for the Office of Naval Research in 1955. Powered by two aircraft engines with air propellers, this eight-ton vessel established a world's speed record for hydrofoil craft, by exceeding 78 knots (145 km/h). In 1958 Grumman designed and built the XCH-6 Sea Wings, also for the Office of Naval Research. Sea Wings was the first hydrofoil to employ both supercavitating foils and a supercavitating propeller and attained speeds in excess of 60 knots.

In 1960, Grumman was awarded a contract by the Maritime Administration for the design and construction of the HS Denison, an 80-ton open ocean research vessel which was launched in June 1962. This craft (described in the 1967-68 edition) was operated at speeds above 60 knots, demonstrating good foilborne manoeuvrability and seakeeping ability in rough water.

Grumman also completed the guidance design for the 328-ton, 212 ft (64·6 m) AG (EH) Plainview for the US Navy. The foils for this craft were the forerunners of those used on the Dolphin and the more recent PGH-1 Flagstaff.

The primary purpose of the Plainview is to establish the possibility of operating large submerged foil craft in high sea states, and explore many possible mission assignments including ASW, hydrographic data collection, surveillance, search and rescue and escort duties.

In December 1972 it was equipped with a single missile container and launched three NATO-configured Sea Sparrow missiles during rough water trials off the coast of Washington. The craft is currently undergoing overhaul. From early 1975 onwards it will be employed as an analysis tool in support of future large hydrofoil development for the US Navy.

Two Dolphin class hydrofoils were built for Grumman by Blohm & Voss, Hamburg but development of this class has now discontinued. The company is now concentrating on the development of military hydrofoils for use by the United States and foreign navies. Flagstaff is currently in service with the US Navy and between April and June 1971 was employed on 152 mm (6 in) gun-firing trials for the Navy Electronics Laboratory at San Diego, California.

A series of underwater explosion tests have been conducted with the Flagstaff in an experiment aimed at obtaining data on the shock responses of hydrofoil craft. The Flagstaff was the first and so far the only hydrofoil to undergo such tests.

In early 1974, the company announced that it was preparing for production an 83·5 ton derivative, the Super Flagstaff. Power is supplied by either a Rolls-Royce RM-2B or

Grumman's PGH-1 Flagstaff hydrofoil patrol gunboat equipped with a 40 mm rapid-firing cannon

Powered by a 3,550 hp Rolls-Royce Tyne gas turbine, the Flagstaff cruises at more than 40 knots

Allison 50IK20 gas turbine and the maximum foilborne speed is 50 knots.

PG(H)-1 FLAGSTAFF

The 67·5 ton PG(H)-1 Flagstaff hydrofoil gunboat was launched on January 9th, 1968. It underwent preliminary trials in July 1968, and was delivered and placed in service at West Palm Beach in September 1968.

Since then the craft has operated from the US Naval Base, Coronado, California. For five-and-a-half-months it underwent operational trials in South Vietnam. Between 1st September 1969 and 19th February 1970, Flagstaff was employed on various missions in Phase II of "Opeval" and "Market Time", operating from Da Nang.

Between November and December 1970 the craft was modified to mount a 152 mm M551 gun from a Sheridan light tank on its foredeck. The gun fires conventional 6 in shells or Shillelagh missiles and has a laser range-finder giving instant accurate ranging. It is capable of hitting a target at a range of up to 4 miles (6·43 km).

The craft is currently in use by the US Navy to evaluate fleet equipment and for the study and development of fleet hydrofoil tactics.

FOILS: Fully submerged system of con-

ventional configuration, split forward, and a single foil aft. About 70% of the weight is supported by the twin forward foils and 30% by the aft foil. Foil section is sub cavitating, 16-series. All three foils are incidence-controlled and operated by an Airesearch hydropilot. The stern foil strut rotates ±5° for steering and all three retract completely clear of the water. Foils (by Potvin Kellering) are forged 6061-T652 aluminium and struts (by Blohm & Voss) are in HYSO 4130 and HY80 steel. Foil area is 100 sq ft (9·29 m²).

HULL: The hull structure is of combined welded and riveted corrosion resistant 5456 aluminium. The pilot house roof is of fibreglass sandwich. All frames and bulkheads are welded assemblies and transverse framing is used throughout.

PROPULSION: The main engine is a 3,550 hp Rolls-Royce Tyne Mk 621/10 gas turbine, flat rated to 90°F. Power is transmitted through a mechanical right angle drive to a KaMeWa 45 in (1·14 m) diameter, 3-bladed supercavitating, controllable-pitch propeller. Nominal rpm at cruising speed 1,000. Hullborne power is supplied by two 202 hp GM 6V diesels driving twin Buehler 1 ft 4½ in (419 mm) diameter waterjets, equipped with $\pm35°$ steering and reversing nozzles.

SYSTEMS, ELECTRICAL: Ship's service generator sets: twin GM 4-53N diesels with Delco 120 volt, 50kW, 62·5 kVA, 3-phase Delta, 60-cycle at 1,800 rpm. Emergency power (generators inoperable): 2 sets batteries 200 Ah, 24 volts, for autopilot, gyroscope and navigation lights, all automatically switched.

RADIO: VHF and HF transceivers.

RADAR AND NAVIGATION: Decca TM626 at navigator's station and repeater at commander's station, Bendex ADF-162A automatic direction finder, Raytheon 726 depth sounder, Arma Mk 26 gyrocompass, Chesapeake EM-log speed log, Bendix prototype DRAI and DRT navigation system.

FIREFIGHTING AND DAMAGE CONTROL: Diesel-driven 50 gpm bilge pump, plus 50 gpm diesel-driven deck service pump, portable electric 250 gpm pumps and hand pump. Deck SW connection for fighting fires in other craft. Walter Kidd. Central CF BR fire extinguishing system in two 251 lb cylinders. Four portable $2\frac{1}{2}$ lb Ansul Foray Combo Pacs.

ARMAMENT. Main battery (until Nov 1970): single 40 mm Mk 3 Mod 0 rapid firing cannon. Machine guns: two twin mounts 50 cal Mk 56 Mod 0. Mortar: One 81 mm Mk 2 Mod 0. Small arms: M16 rifles (11), ·38 Cal pistols, 12 ga shotguns. New main gun battery as from December 1970: 152 mm M551 howitzer, firing conventional 6 in shells or Shillelagh missiles. Laser range finder.

DIMENSIONS:

Length overall hull	73 ft 0 in (22·2 m)
Length overall, foils extended	86 ft 6 in (23·36 m)
Length overall, foils retracted	89 ft 0 in (27·1 m)
Hull beam	21 ft 5 in (6·5 m)
Extreme beam, foils retracted tip-to-tip	37 ft 1 in (11·28 m)
Draft, foils extended, static	13 ft 11 in (4·26 m)
Nominal draft foilborne	5 ft 8 in (1·72 m)

WEIGHTS:

Displacement, fully loaded, as delivered	67·5 long tons
1971, with 152 mm howitzer	72 long tons

PERFORMANCE:

Cruising speed, foilborne	In excess of 40 knots
Cruising speed, hullborne	In excess of 7 knots

SUPER FLAGSTAFF

In March 1974, Grumman announced that preparations were underway for the production of a developed version of the PG(H)-1, known as the Super Flagstaff. Intended primarily for military applications, the new model is designed as a high-speed patrol gunboat or missile craft, but it can be equipped for a number of alternative roles including anti-submarine warfare, search and rescue and fast military transport.

The chief differences between this craft and its predecessor lie in the installation of a gas turbine of greater power output—either a 3,800 hp Rolls Royce Tyne RM2B or a 3,950 hp Allison 501-K20A, the introduction of an improved mechanical right-angle drive and the provision of larger foils and foil struts. The fully loaded displacement is increased from 67·5 to 83·5 long tons. Max payload, including fuel is 65,457 lbs.

Flagstaff from the forward starboard quarter showing the 152 mm M551 howitzer gun turret

The Super Flagstaff can be equipped for a variety of military roles including ASW, S & R and fast transport. Powered by either a 3,800 hp Rolls Royce Tyne RM 2B or a 3,950 hp Allison 501-K20A, it has a maximum speed of 52 knots

FOILS: Fully submerged system of conventional configuration, comprising twin inverted T foils forward and a single inverted T foil aft. Approximately 70% of the load is supported by the two forward foils and 30% by the aft foil. All three foils are incidence controlled and operated by a hydro-pilot system employing electrohydraulic actuators. The stern foil power strut, together with the propeller, rotates $\pm3°$ for steering and all three foil/strut units retract completely clear of the water for hullborne manoeuvring. The foils are in 7075-T73 aluminium and the struts are in HY-130 steel. Break joints are incorporated on the two forward struts, so that should either of them strike large items of debris each would break clean at the point of its connection to its yoke. A shear bolt releases the aft strut permitting it to rotate rearwards and upwards above the transom.

HULL: Hull is in welded 5086-H 111 and H 117 marine aluminium. The deckhouse and skin are in 1 ft 11$\frac{1}{4}$ in (587 mm) wide-ribbed and integrally stiffened extrusions, each 25 ft (7·62 m) long.

ACCOMMODATION: Crew will vary according to the nature of the missions for which the craft is employed and the type of armament carried. Minimum crew requirement is four, maximum is fourteen. The forward superstructure accommodates the bridge, which contains steering and engine control consoles and is elevated to give a 360° view. The helmsman and CO are seated on a raised deck and the chief engineer and navigator are accommodated on the main deck. All crew accommodation is air conditioned. Entry to the deckhouse is via two 2 ft 2 in × 5ft 0 in (660 mm × 1·52 m) watertight doors, one port, one starboard. An emergency exit is located aft, behind the pilothouse on the weather deck. Escape hatches are provided in the living spaces.

POWER PLANT, FOILBORNE: Foilborne propulsion is supplied by either a 3,800 hp Rolls-Royce RM 2B Tyne or a 3,950 hp Allison 501-K20A gas turbine. Power is transmitted to the propeller through a Z-drive—a horizontal shaft leading to a bevel gear over the stern in the aft foil strut, then via a vertical shaft and a second bevel gear. to a horizontal propeller shaft. A 3 ft 9 in (1·14 m) diameter KaMeWa, 3-bladed controllable-pitch, supercavitating propeller is fitted. Fuel—total capacity is 5,179 US gallons—is carried in four tanks. Oil capacity is 100 US gallons. Fuelling points are located amidships.

POWER PLANTS, HULLBORNE: Hull-borne propulsion is supplied by two 202 hp GM 6V-53N diesels, driving two 1 ft 4½ in (419 mm) diameter Buehler waterjets, equipped with steering and reversing nozzles.

SYSTEMS:

ELECTRICAL: Diesel generator set. Two GM 4-53N diesel engines driving Delco generators rated for 50 kw 440 volt 3-phase service.

HYDRAULICS: 3,000 psi for foil control and ship service systems.

ELECTRONICS: Decca Model TM 626 radar.

COMMUNICATIONS: HF system AN/ARC-94 Collins 618T-2B.

ARMAMENT:

MISSILES: Standard, Standard ARM, Harpoon, Sea Killer, Sea Sparrow, Exocet MM 38, Gabriel or Penguin surface-to-surface missiles.

GUNS: Choice of the following systems for surface engagement, shore bombardment, AA defence or missile interception: 76/62 Oto Melara, 35 mm Twin Oerlikon, 30 mm Twin Hispano Suiza, 20 mm Twin Emerson, 20 mm Vulcan, 40 mm Bofors, 30 mm Emerson GE or 20 mm Phalanx.

ASW: Variety of ASW towed or dunked sonars available for use in conjunction with appropriate weapons.

DIMENSIONS, EXTERNAL:

Length overall, hull 73 ft 0 in (22·25 m)
Length waterline, hull 66 ft 8 in (20·34 m)
Length overall, foils retracted
　89 ft 0 in (27·12 m)
Length overall, foils extended
　86 ft 10 in (26·46 m)
Hull beam 21 ft 5 in (6·62 m)
Beam overall foils retracted
　39 ft 3 in (11·963 m)
Beam overall, foils extended
　40 ft 9 in (12·420 m)
Draft afloat, foils retracted
　5 ft 1½ in (1·562 m)
Draft afloat, foils extended
　16 ft 0 in (4·87 m)
Draft foilborne 7 ft 8 in (2·33 m)
Freeboard, maximum 7 ft 1¾ in (2·18 m)
Height overall to top
　of mast 38 ft 1½ in (11·62 m)

DIMENSIONS, INTERNAL:

Cabin length 14 ft 4 in (4·36 m)
Max width 12 ft 0 in (3·65 m)
Max height 9 ft 0 in (2·74 m)
Floor area 160 sq ft (14·86 sq m)
Volume 1,280 cu ft (36·24 cu m)

WEIGHTS:

Light displacement 52·28 long tons
Normal take-off displacement 83·5 long tons

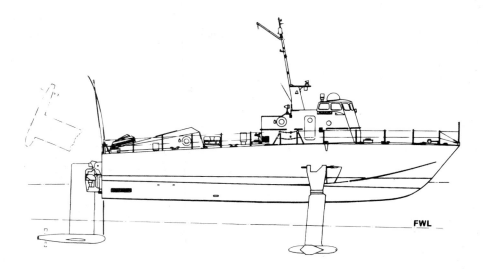

FWL

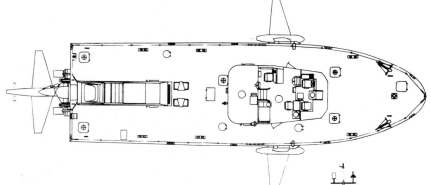

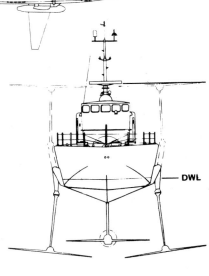

DWL

General arrangement of the Grumman Super Flagstaff, 84-ton high-speed patrol gunboat or missile craft

Normal payload 29,957 lbs (9,505·916 kg)
Max payload 65,457 lbs *including fuel* (29,690·78 kg)

PERFORMANCE:

Max speed, foilborne 52 knots
Cruising speed 47 knots
Max speed, hullborne (gas turbine power plant) 20 knots
Cruising speed, hullborne (diesl displacement engines) 9 knots
Max permissable sea state in foilborne mode 4-5
Designed endurance and range at cruising approx 840 nautical miles
Max foilborne range 1,700 nautical miles
Number of seconds to take-off 25 sec, app
Number of seconds and distance to stop craft 3 to 4 seconds, 150 ft
Fuel consumption at max speed
　2,140 lb/hour (970·643 kgs/hour)
Fuel consumption at cruising speed
　1,900 lb/hour (861·786 kg/hour)

DETAILS OF SEA TEST (based on PG(H)-1)

Location West Palm Beach, Florida
Sea states 2,3, 4 and 5
Location of accelerometer, forward and amidships
Heave 0·2± g in 8 ft (2·43 m) high waves
Average ·50± g in 4 ft 6in (1·37 m) high waves

AG(EH)-1 PLAINVIEW

The 320 ton AG (EH)—the designation means auxiliary general experimental hydrofoil—was built by the Lockheed Shipbuilding & Construction Company, Seattle, Washington. It is being used by the US Navy's

Hydrofoil Systems Testing Unit, Bremerton, Washington to investigate the performance of a large seagoing hydrofoil under operational conditions. The guidance design and preparations of contract specifications were undertaken by Grumman under the direction of the Bureau of Ships.

A contract for detailed design and construction was awarded to Lockheed Shipbuilding and Construction Company in June 1963 and the hull was launched in June 1965. The craft successfully completed her maiden flight on March 21st, 1968 at Puget Sound and was officially delivered to the US Navy on

March 1st 1969. It was given the US Navy classification "In Service, Special" in March 1969 and US Navy research and development trials are continuing.

FOILS: The foil system is fully submerged and automatically controlled by a Hamilton Standard autopilot system similar to that used in High Point. The foil arrangement is of conventional type with 90% of the weight carried on the two main foils and the remainder on the aft foil. The three foils, which have considerable sweep and taper, are geometrically similar with an aspect ratio of 3. The swept back leading edges help to delay cavitation and facilitate the shedding of seaweed and other neutrally buoyant debris. They also reduce impact loads associated with water entry after foil broaching. The main foils have some dihedral while the tail foil is flat.

Total foil area is 227·96 sq ft, and foil loading is 1,460 lb ft² max. Foils are constructed in welded HY80 steel.

The main foils are extended, retracted and locked in each terminal position by means of a hydraulically-operated activating arm, connected to the upper part of the strut. The two foils are synchronised to be raised and lowered together in the transverse plane. The aft foil operates in a similar manner, but can be raised and lowered independently.

Foil lift variation is by change in the incidence angle; each can move through +11 deg to —4 deg. The single aft foil controls pitch angle.

The aft foil strut rotates for use as a rudder. Steering can be flat (rudder only) or fully coordinated, using differential main foil angles for banked turns, with the aft strut trailing.

HULL: The hull is almost completely fabricated in 5456 aluminium alloy. All deck, side and bottom plating is made from integrally stiffened, aluminium extruded planks. The hull is predominantly welded construction with the exception of the pilot house and certain longitudinal hull seams that act as crack stoppers.

The hull shape is designed to minimise the structural loadings due to wave impact and the bow shape has been developed for this specific purpose. Bottom deadrise is carried to the transom with the same objective.

ACCOMMODATION: Crew of twenty-five, comprising four officers and twenty-one enlisted men. The pilothouse, CIC compartment, living, messing and berthing spaces are air-conditioned. Sanitary and washroom areas, galley, displacement and main engine room are all mechanically ventilated. In the wheelhouse, the pilot's position is on the left, with the principal instrumentation; the co-pilot is on the right, and the observer between and slightly aft. Entry to the deckhouse is via three standard US Navy quick-acting aluminium doors—one aft port and one forward starboard on the main deck, and one aft on the lower deck. Emergency equipment includes 7-man liferafts, seven life rings, four aircraft markers, one kapok heaving line and emergency scuttles port and starboard.

POWER PLANT: Foilborne propulsion is supplied by two General Electric LM 1500s (marine version of the J-97), each of 14,500 hp continuous rating, connected by shafting

Top: AGEH-1 Plainview, 328-ton US Navy ocean-going hydrofoil warship research vessel, moored in Puget Sound with foils retracted. Two 4-bladed propellers at the end of the pods on the main foils struts propel the vessel when foilborne

Centre: Maximum foilborne speed of the Plainview, which is powered by two 14,500 hp GE LM1500s, is 50 knots. It is designed to operate in sea state 5 conditions and has undergone trials in 8-10 ft (2·43-3·04 m) waves off Victoria BC

Bottom: In the interests of weight economy, the Plainview's hull is built largely from specially extruded aluminium planks, each 40 ft (12·19 m) in length and 2 ft 1 in (0·635 m) in width. Struts and foils are built in HY-80 and HY-100 steel alloys. The bow shape is designed to minimise structural loadings due to wave impact.

and gearing to two 4-bladed, 5 ft 0 in (1·52 m) diameter supercavitating titanium propellers at the end of the propulsion pods on the main foils. The hydrodynamic design of the propellers was undertaken by Hydronautics Inc, and they were built by Hamilton Standard. The blades are bolted to the hubs and each blade is replaceable. The air inlet for the main turbines is introduced at the top of the deckhouse. Because of the need to prevent ingestion of water or saltspray into the gas turbines, there are lowered deflectors over the inlet opening, followed by a bank of sheet metal spray separators.

There is a dam for solid water separation and four right angle turns before the air reaches the engine bellmouths.

The hullborne powerplants are two General Motors V12-71 diesels each rated at 500 hp. Each diesel drives aft through a shaft to a right angle gear drive resembling a large outboard motor, mounted on the side of the hull. Each of these right angle drives is retractable about a horizontal axis and steerable about a vertical axis through 360 deg. rotation. A 4 ft 5 in (1·34 m) diameter five-bladed subcavitating propeller is mounted at the end of each right angle drive.

Auxiliary power is supplied by two GMC V8-71 engines driving two 100 kW generators.

SYSTEMS:

AIR CONDITIONING: The pilothouse, CIC compartment, living, messing and berthing spaces are air-conditioned during the cooling season by a 15 ton capacity Trane type compressor system. Sanitary and washroom areas, galley, displacement engine room, main engine room, windlass room and the engineers control booth are all mechanically ventilated.

HYDRAULICS: 3,000 psi operates foils, steering, extension, retraction and locking of struts and anchor windlass and starts propulsion diesels.

ELECTRONICS: Raytheon Pathfinder radar with AN/SPA-25 repeater, AN/WRC-1B Bendix radio, AN/URC-58 radio RF Comm Inc, two AN/ARC-52X Collins radios.

ARMAMENT: Six Mk 32 torpedo tubes in two tri-mounts, port and starboard, aft of the deckhouse. One Mk 44 torpedo stowed in each tube. Single missile cannister fitted in late 1972 for demonstration launching of three NATO-configured Sea Sparrow missiles off the coast of Washington in December.

DIMENSIONS, EXTERNAL:

Length overall, hull   212 ft 0 in (64·61 m)

Length waterline, hull
     205 ft 1¾ in (62·48 m)
Length overall, foils retracted
     223 ft 8 in (68·17 m)
Length overall, foils extended
     219 ft ½ in (66·75 m)
Hull beam   40 ft 5 in (12·31 m)
Beam overall, foils retracted
     82 ft 8 in (25·19 m)
Beam overall, foils extended
     70 ft 0 in (21·59 m)
Draft afloat, foils retracted
     6 ft 3 in (1·90 m)
Freeboard, fwd   15 ft 6 in (4·72 m)
     aft   7 ft 6½ in (2·29 m)
Height to top of mast
     54 ft 9½ in (16·69 m)

WEIGHTS:
Light displacement   265 tons
Normal take-off   290 tons
Max take-off   328 tons

PERFORMANCE:
Max speed foilborne   50 knots
Cruising speed foilborne   35 knots
Max speed hullborne   13·4 knots
Cruising speed hullborne   12 knots
Max permissible sea state and wave height in foilborne mode
(Design sea state) Beaufort 5 Sea state 5

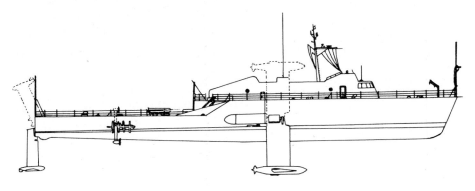
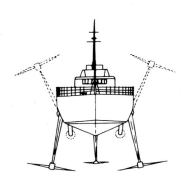

General arrangement of the AGEH-1 Plainview

INTERNATIONAL HYDROLINES INC

HEAD OFFICE:
1000 Connecticut Avenue, NW, Washington DC 20036

DIRECTORS AND EXECUTIVES:
Charles F. Willis Jr, President
Gerald O. Rennerts, Vice-President
Ira E. Dowd, Vice-President
Robert Reeves, Secretary
Milton Brucker, Director

CHIEF HYDROFOIL DESIGNER:
Helmut Kock

International Hydrolines was formed to operate hydrofoils, air cushion vehicles, surface effect ships and other marine transport vessels. Its manufacturing division is planning to build and market a 72-seat craft designed to the company's specifications by Helmut Kock.

In January 1973, it was announced that ten of these craft had been ordered from the Kettenburg Marine Division of Whittaker Corporation, Los Angeles, under a $5·5-million contract subject to loan approval by the US Maritime Administration. The craft will be employed on commuter services in the New York area. They will be operated jointly by International Hydrolines which will provide the hydrofoils, train the crews

and provide management advice and General Hydrolines.

The company has also taken over the Enterprise and Endeavour hydrofoils for operations based on Miami, Florida. The Sea Wing hydrofoil was expected to be in operation in the New York area by late June, 1974.

Since the last edition, the propulsion system on the 72-seat passenger hydrofoil has been altered from water propeller to water-jet. Photographs accompanying this entry show tank tests being undertaken with a model of the waterjet propelled version and also the aft foil arrangement, showing the water intakes.

The company's future plans include the installation of a closed cycle steam engine on an Albatross hydrofoil for test and evaluation. Total weight of the steam generator and expander is 1 lb/hp or 350 lb/350 hp. The burner accepts a number of fuels including gas, oil kerosene, gasoline and powdered coal.

Designs have been prepared for a 113 ft long, 67-ton passenger ferry with seats for 127, and a 306 seat ferry with a displacement of 138 tons.

HYDROFOIL PASSENGER FERRY

This is a 72-seat, 28-ton diesel-powered vessel designed for medium-range fast ferry services on rivers, bays, lakes and sounds. Power is supplied by twin 510 hp General Motors 12V-72 turbocharged diesels, which will provide a cruising speed of 33 knots.

Ten of these craft are to be built in San Diego by Kettenburg Marine, a division of Whittaker Corporation.

FOILS: Patented system incorporating fixed trapeze-type submerged main foils and planing sub-foils surfaces. Bow foils and struts are of hollow construction and built in stainless steel and aluminium. Rear foil is similar to the bow foil in type and construction. Bow and stern strut assemblies are attached to the hull by shear bolts.

RUDDER: Single balanced rudder of aluminium and steel construction on centre line.

HULL: V-bottom, high-speed planing hull in welded aluminium, framed on a combination of longitudinal and transverse formers.

ACCOMMODATION: The vessel has a crew of three, comprising captain, engineer or mechanic, and a deckhand. The bridge is located forward and provides a 360° view. The captain's seat together with the operating controls and instrumentation is located on the hull centreline. The single saloon aft of the bridge seats 72 passengers in commuter configuration, and 66 or less in tourist configuration. Seats are arranged in two rows of triple seats, separated by a central aisle. Two W/C washbasin units are provided aft. Access to the saloon is via two 3 ft 0 in (0·91 m) wide doors at the forward end, port and starboard, at the rear of the wheelhouse. Passenger and crew accommodation is air conditioned. An emergency exit is provided at the rear end of the saloon. A full range of safety equipment is carried including two inflatable life rafts and life jackets for each passenger and crew member. The vessel meets all the standard requirements of the US Coast Guard.

POWER PLANT: Power is supplied by two General Motors 12V-71 TI turbocharged and aftercooled diesels, each with a maximum output of 595 shp. Engine output is transferred to two waterjet pumps, from the pump outlets the water is discharged through twin fixed area nozzles beneath the transom.

Reversing is achieved by applying deflectors to reverse the waterflow.

Fuel is carried in a single integral tank located amidships beneath the saloon floor. Total capacity is 550 US gallons (2,081 l).

SYSTEMS:

Air conditioning: two units.

Electrical: 24 volts.

Auxiliary power units: 110-140 volt auxiliaty diesel.

DIMENSIONS, EXTERNAL:

Length overall, hull	65 ft 0 in (19·81 m)
Length waterline, hull	58 ft 0 in (17·67 m)
Beam overall, over foil fences	
	21 ft 6 in (6·52 m)
Draft, hullborne	7 ft 9 in (2·36 m)

DIMENSIONS, INTERNAL:

Length, saloon	37 ft 0 in (11·27 m)
Max. width	14 ft 0 in (4·26 m)
Max. height	6 ft 9 in (2·05 m)
Floor area	490 sq ft (45·52 m²)
Volume	3,600 cu ft (101·94 m³)
Baggage hold volume	150 cu ft (4·24 m³)

Above: Model of the aft foil arrangement of the IHI 72-seat ferry, showing the water intakes for the diesel-powered waterjet propulsion system. *Below:* Towed model of the waterjet propelled version of the craft undergoing tank tests

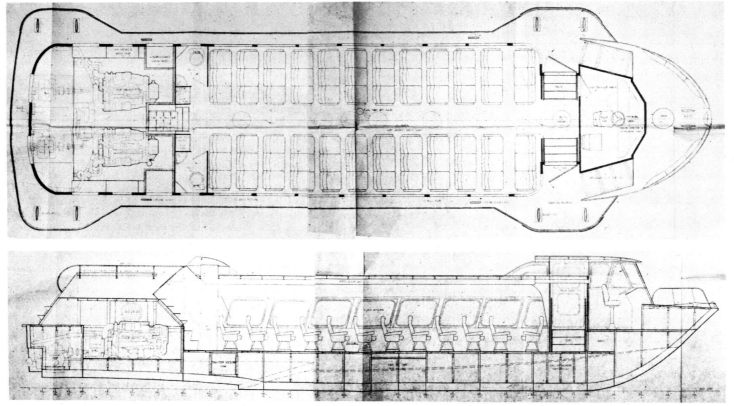

Inboard profile and passenger deck plan of General Hydrolines' 72-seat hydrofoil passenger ferry. Propulsion is by twin waterjets driven by two 595 shp General Motors 12V-71 TI marine diesels

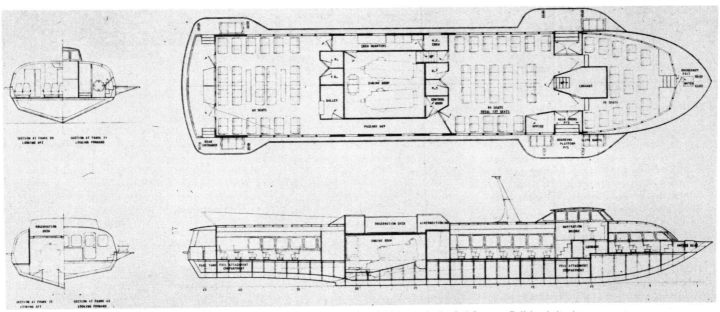

Inboard profile and deck view of IHI's proposed 127-seat hydrofoil ferry. Full load displacement
of the craft will be 67 tons and the designed cruising speed is 33 knots

WEIGHTS:

Displacement, full load	27 long tons
Light displacement	20 long tons

PERFORMANCE:

Cruising speed foilborne	33 knots

Fuel consumption:

at max speed	55 gal/hr (250·02 l/hr)
at cruising speed	52 gal/hr (236·39 l/hr)

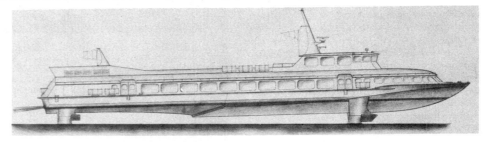

A waterjet-propelled 138-ton ferry designed for IHI by Helmut Kock. Seats would be provided
for 308 passengers. Facilities would include a small bar on the main passenger deck and a cocktail
lounge and observation deck aft of the bridge

Impression of the 72-seat, 28-ton hydrofoil ferry designed for International Hydrolines Inc by
Helmut Kock. Ten have been ordered under a $5·5-million contract subject to loan approval by
the US Maritime Administration. They will be built by Kettenburg Marine Division of Whittaker
Corporation, San Diego, for operation by Tri-State Hydrolines, who will concentrate on commuter
services on the Hudson and East River

LOCKHEED SHIPBUILDING & CONSTRUCTION COMPANY
(A subsidiary of Lockheed Aircraft Corp)

HEAD OFFICE:
2929 16th Ave SW, Seattle, Washington
98134

In June 1963 Lockheed Shipbuilding &
Construction Company was awarded the
contract for the construction of the 320 ton
AGEH-1 Plainview, the world's biggest
hydrofoil to date. The hull was launched in
June 1965 and the US Navy took delivery
of the craft in early 1969. The craft successfully completed her maiden flight in Puget
Sound on March 21st, 1968.

The AGEH-1 has been assigned to the US
Navy's Hydrofoil Systems Testing Unit and
will undergo extensive evaluation for several
years. The potential of the craft as an
ocean going vessel for the US Navy will be
fully explored. To facilitate analysis of data
obtained from the extensive instrumentation
installed aboard the craft, provision has been
made for continuous and simultaneous
recording of more than two hundred data
channels on a single magnetic tape.

The power plant at present consists of two
General Electric LM 1500 gas turbines, each
driving one propeller through a right-angle
bevel gear transmission. The design will
permit the addition of two more engines at a
later date to enable the craft to achieve
much higher speeds using a ventilated or
supercavitating foil system.

UNION OF SOVIET SOCIALIST REPUBLICS

KRASNOYE SOROMOVO SHIPYARD

HEAD OFFICE AND WORKS:
   Gorki
OFFICERS:
   M. Yuriev, Shipyard Director
   Dr Rostilav Yergenievich Alexeyev, Head
      of the Central Design Bureau for Hydro-
      foil Vessels
   Ivan Yerlykin, Chief Hydrofoil Designer
OVERSEAS REPRESENTATIVES:
   United Kingdom, British Commonwealth
      and Scandinavian countries:
   Airavia Ltd,
      20 North Road, Shanklin Isle of Wight,
      See separate entry under United Kingdom

Krasnoye Soromovo is one of the oldest established shipyards in the Soviet Union, In addition to building displacement craft of many kinds for the Soviet River Fleet, the yard constructs the world's widest range of passenger hydrofoils, the majority of which are equipped with the Alexeyev shallow draft submerged foil system. Dr Alexeyev started work at the end of 1945 on the design of his foil system which had to be suitable for operation on smooth, but open and shallow rivers and canals. He succeeded in making use of the immersion depth effect, or surface effect, for stabilising the foil immersion in calm waters by the use of small lift coefficients.

The system comprises two main horizontal lifting surfaces, one forward and one aft, with little or no dihedral, each carrying approximately half the weight of the vessel. A submerged foil loses lift gradually as it approaches the surface from a submergence of about one chord. This effect prevents the submerged foils from rising completely to the surface. Means therefore had to be provided to assist take-off and prevent the vessel from sinking back to the displacement condition. The answer lay in the provision of planing sub-foils of small aspect ratio in the vicinity of the forward struts arranged so that when they are touching the water surface the main foils are submerged approximately to a depth of one chord.

The approach embodies characteristics of the Grunberg principle of inherent angle of attack variation, with stabilizing foils and or sub-foils taking the place of the original displacement floats or partly immersed foils. As with the Grunberg approach, the system comprises a "wing", split in this case, and a stabiliser system. The lift curve of the stabiliser, plotted against its draft, is considerably steeper than the corresponding "wing" curve. Hence as the operational conditions (such as speed, weight and CG travel) change, the wing sinks or rises relative to the stabilizer, thereby adjusting to demand its angle of attack.

The foils have good riding characteristics on inland waters and in sheltered waters.

The system was first tested on a small launch powered by a 77 bhp converted car engine. Three more small craft were built to prove the idea, then work began on the Yard's first multi-seat passenger craft, the Raketa, the first of which was launched in June 1957.

Above and below: Prototype of the Voskhod II during trials at Gorky in June 1974. Intended as a replacement for the 17-year-old Raketa, its design features owe much to the more recent Kometa series. The Voskhod is due to be available in many versions to suit a variety of local naviation and traffic conditions in the USSR. Diesel and gas-turbine models are projected. The Voskhod II seats 71 passengers and cruises at 34 knots

The yard also co-operates with the Leningrad Water Transport Institute in the development of seagoing craft with fully submerged V-type and trapeze-type surface piercing foils, similar in configuration to those of the Schertel-Sachsenburg system. Craft employing V or trapeze are generally described as being of the Strela-type, Strela being the first operational Soviet design to use V foils. Seating 92-passengers, the vessel is powered by two M-50 diesels and, visually speaking, is a cross between the PT 20 and the PT 50, though smaller than the latter. A military derivative, the Pchela (Bee) is currently employed by the Soviet frontier police for coastal patrol in the Baltic, Black Sea, Caspian and other sea areas.

The first hydrofoil vessels to enter service with the Soviet Navy were the 75-ton P8-class, wooden-hulled torpedo boats which were equipped with bow foils and gas-turbine boost. These now appear to have been retired.

In the spring of 1973, a new hydrofoil fast patrol boat, based on the Osa missile-firing FPB hull, made its appearance in the Baltic. Like the earlier P8-class and the highly successful Chinese Hu Chwan-class, the new craft has a bow foil only. Powered by three 4,330 hp diesels it has a top speed of about 45 knots under calm conditions. Further military hydrofoil designs are under development.

Amongst new Soviet passenger hydrofoils being developed are the gas-turbine powered, 89-105 seat Typhoon passenger ferry, the first Soviet vessel designed for production to have a fully submerged foil system; the Voskhod, intended as a Raketa replacement, the 250-seat, 45-50 knot, Cyclone and the 350 passenger, 400-ton Luch (Ray). Included in this entry are the first photographs to be released of the Voskhod II prototype. In June 1973, it was announced that a new seagoing hydrofoil mixed-traffic ferry had been designed at Gorky. The craft will carry 200 passengers and 40 vehicles at a speed of 43 mph (70 km/h). The Typhoon, which was built in Leningrad has been undergoing operational trials carrying fare-paying passengers between Leningrad and Talinna, a journey time of 4½ hours. Further development of the seagoing Kometa-M is underway, including the fitting of a stability augmentation system which will operate flaps on the main bow foil, increased passenger accommodation and the relocation of the engine room aft to reduce noise in the passenger saloon.

Substantial numbers of Soviet hydrofoils—Kometas, Raketas and Volgas—are being exported. Countries in which they are being operated include Yugoslavia, Italy, Iran, France, Morocco, Spain, Western Germany, Poland, Rumania, the United Kingdom and the Philippines.

TYPHOON

The Typhoon, a gas-turbine powered fast ferry for 98-105 passengers, is the first production craft with automatically controlled fully-submerged foils to be built in the Soviet Union.

The prototype, constructed in Leningrad, was launched after preliminary fitting out on December 12th, 1969. It is designed to operate at a service speed of 40-42 knots under calm conditions and 38 knots in sea state 4. The craft is at present undergoing trials. Phase 1 of the test programme covered the foil system, the gas-turbine power plant, hull design and mechanical and other systems and during Phase 2, the vessel was put into passenger service to permit technical assessments to be made under commercial operating conditions.

It is stated that in waves of up to 2 m (6 ft 6 in) high, not more than 10% of the 40-42 knot service speed is lost. Under these conditions, the Typhoon can complete the journey from Leningrad to Tallina, the Estonian capital, in 4½ hours.

Ten new inventions have found application in the design and the prototype has been awarded a certificate by the State Inventions and Discoveries Committee.

FOILS: Fully submerged system of conventional configuration with 77% of the weight borne by the bow foil and 23% by the stern foil. The bow foil is supported by four vertical struts which are tapered from top to bottom. The two outboard struts are

supported by auxiliary fins which provide additional stability during the transition from displacement to foilborne mode. Twin rudders are fitted at the trailing edges of the aft foil struts. The foils are built in OCr17Ni7Al high strength stainless steel. A sonic/electronic autopilot system controls four flaps on the bow foil and two on the stern foil. The total weight of the autopilot system, including all electronic components, assemblies, drive mechanisms and cables is less than 1,320 lb (600 kg). The system stabilises the craft from take-off to touchdown in heave and all three axes—pitch, roll and yaw. It is programmed to govern the angle of trim, the c of g position in relation to speed and see that the craft makes coordinated banked turns according to speed and sea state. Overriding manual control can be introduced if necessary.

Two independent electro-hydraulic-drive systems are installed to actuate the flaps. Each has two pumps, one connected to the reduction gear of the main engine, the other to its turbo-compressor. Fluid reaches the actuating mechanisms under a pressure of 150 kg/cm². Should one of the mains leading to the actuating mechanisms become unserviceable the second is connected. The

The Typhoon, first gas-turbine powered passenger craft with fully-submerged foils to be built in the Soviet Union. Designed to operate at 36-45 knots, it seats 98-105 passengers. *Top left:* The basic similarity of the Typhoon's spoon-shaped hull to that of the Kometa -M and other Sormovo designs is apparent   *Top right:* Typhoon during take-off. Glass doors lead from the saloon into the vestibule and onto the promenade deck visible in this photo. *Bottom left:* View aft from the air-conditioned passenger saloon which can be equipped with 98-105 airliner-type seats. From the vestibule at the far end there are entrances to the baggage compartment, wheelhouse and W/C washbasin units. *Bottom right:* Captain B. V. Gromov, who has been responsible for handling the Typhoon during her trials programme, seen at the helm

failure of one bow or one stern flap in conditions up to sea state 4 does not reduce the stability of the vessel.

HULL: Similar in shape to that of the Kometa and earlier models in the Sormovo hydrofoil series, with a wedge-shaped bow, raked stem and spoon-shaped stern. There are two steps beneath the hull to facilitate take-off. The hull is of riveted construction and built in high strength aluminium magnesium alloy V-48TL. Longitudinal and transverse framing is employed with a spacing of 19·68 in (500 mm) in the hull and 39·37 in (1,000 mm) in the superstructure. By locating the wheelhouse aft of amidships, it has been possible to reduce the length of the control system cables while preserving good all-round vision.

Beneath the passenger saloon superstructure the hull is divided by transverse bulkheads into nine watertight compartments in which are accommodated the fuel tanks, diesel generators, gas turbines and diesel for hullborne propulsion. A watertight door is installed in the bulkhead separating the diesel generator and gas-turbine compartment. The craft is designed to remain afloat should any two adjacent compartments become flooded.

POWER PLANT: Foilborne power is supplied by two 1,750 hp Ivchenko AI-23C-1 marine gas-turbines, each driving a single 2·23 ft (0·68 m) diameter three-bladed propeller at 2,200 rpm cruising. The gas-turbines are started by starter generators from batteries and exhaust gases are expelled through an extension aft of the transom to prevent the craft from becoming covered with smoke or fumes.

Power from the main engines is transmitted to each propeller via a K-1700 Z-drive column, which is bolted to the transom. The drive shaft of each turbine is connected to the shaft of the upper reduction gear of the Z-drive. Power is transmitted via two sets of bevel gears and two vertical shafts to a nacelle which is divided into three compartments. The central compartment contains the lower reduction gear which transmits power from the two vertical shafts to the propeller shaft.

The stern foil is welded to the casing of the nacelle's bow compartment which contains the stern foil flap actuating mechanism.

Hullborne propulsion is supplied by a 165 hp 6ChSP13/14 low-speed diesel driving two four-bladed propellers through KP-150 right-angle drives, which rotate for steering and retract upwards when the craft is foilborne. The columns are steered either from the central control console in the wheelhouse or from a portable control panel which can be operated from any part of the vessel.

ACCOMMODATION: Passengers are accommodated in an air-conditioned saloon equipped with 98-105 airliner-type seats. Glass doors lead from the saloon into the vestibule and onto the promenade deck. From the vestibule there is an entrance to the baggage compartment, wheelhouse and WC/wash basin units. The panels along the sides of the saloon are covered in non-inflammable laminated plastic and above with Pavinol imitation leather glued onto plywood. The deckhead is covered with Pavinol on a wooden frame. A special vibration-absorbing covering has been applied to the bulkhead

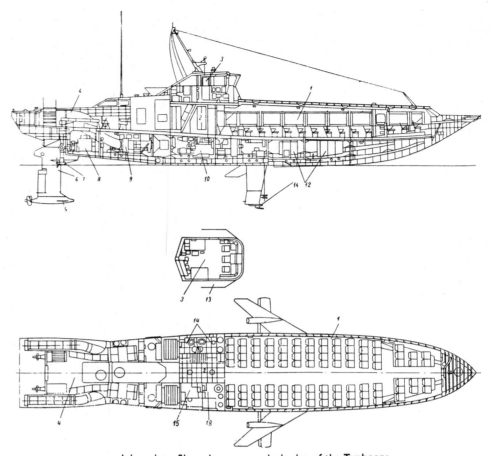

Inboard profile and passenger deck plan of the Typhoon:
I, passenger saloon; 2, vestibule; 3, wheelhouse; 4, promenade deck; 5, stern foil; 6, Z-drive foilborne transmission; 7, Z-drive hullborne transmission; 8, 165 hp diesel, 9, AI-23C-I; gas-turbines 10, diesel generators; II, bow foil; 12, fuel tanks; 13, bridge; 14, lavatories; 15, bar; 16, baggage compartment

facing the turbine compartment. The vessel carries a total of 4 crew members.

Rafts type PSN-10 are stored in containers along the sides of the vessel. These can be launched onto the water either by manual or automatic control from the wheelhouse. Lifebelts and lifejackets are carried aboard the vessel.

SYSTEMS: Electrical: Two 22 kW generators and eight batteries type 6STK-180. Main electrical equipment operates on 400H2. AC current. Shore supply is effected through a transformer.

NAVIGATION. Gyro course indicator, magnetic compass, hydraulic log and anti-collision radar.

COMMUNICATION: Ship-ship, ship-shore transceiver operating on R/T and W/T, also emergency radio.

DIMENSIONS:

Length overall	103 ft 2¼ in (31·4 m)
Width across foils	32 ft 9¾ in (10·0 m)
Hull beam	18 ft 4½ in (5·6 m)
Hull draught, displacement mode	4 ft 3⅛ in (1·3 m)
Draft, hullborne, including foils	13 ft 5⅜ in (4·1 m)
Mean draft foilborne	3 ft 7 in-4 ft 3 in (1·1-1·3 m)
Distance of bow foil below hull base line	9 ft 2 in (2·8 m)

WEIGHTS:

Normal loaded displacement	65 tons

PERFORMANCE:

Max speed	44 knots
Service speed	40-42 knots
Hullborne speed	5 knots
Max permissible sea state	
Designed to maintain a cruising speed of 36 knots in sea state 4	

SEA TESTS

In sea state 4, vertical acceleration measured in the bows has averaged approximately 0·5g. In sea state 3, maximum angle of pitch experienced has been 1·5 deg. In sea state 4, one bow flap and one stern flap out of action have not adversely affected stability.

BUREVESTNIK

First Soviet gas-turbine hydrofoil to be designed for series production, the Burevestnik has two 2,700 hp marinised aircraft gas turbines driving two two-stage waterjets The prototype was launched in April 1964 and it was intended to build two models; one for medium-range, non-stop inter-city services, seats 130 passengers, the other, for suburban services, seats 150.

There is a four-man crew, comprising captain, engineer, motorman and a seaman.

After extensive trials and modifications, the prototype Burevestnik began operating on the Gorky-Kuibyshev route (about 435 miles (700 km) on April 26, 1968. At the time of going to press with this edition, it was understood that the vessel is still under development and has not yet entered production.

FOILS: There are two main foils and a midship stabiliser foil, all built in titanium alloy. Each is square-tipped and slightly wedge-shaped in planform. The foils are secured to the hull by struts and brackets. Each foil-strut is welded to the upper surface of the foils, then bolted to the brackets. Upper and lower ends of the struts are connected by flanges. As with other craft employing the Alexeyev system, the foil incidence can be adjusted when necessary by the insertion of wedges between the flanges and the foils when the craft is in dock.

HULL: Hull and superstructure are built in aluminium-magnesium alloy. The hull is of, all-welded construction and framed on longditudinal and transverse formers.

ACCOMMODATION: The prototype has two air-conditioned saloons with airliner-style seating for a total of 150 passengers. The well glazed forward saloon seats 38, and the aft saloon 112. The saloons are decorated with pastel shade panels and sound-proofed with glass fibre insulation. The engine room is at the stern and separated from the saloon by a sound-proof double bulkhead.

POWER PLANT: Motive power is supplied by two 2,700 shp Ivchenko marinised gas turbines, adapted from those of the IL-18 airliner. These operate on either kerosene or light diesel fuel and have a consumption of 300 gallons per hour. Sufficient fuel can be carried to operate non-stop over a range of 270 nautical miles (500 Km). The shaft of each of the two double suction centrifugal pumps for the waterjets is connected with the shaft of one of the turbines by means of a flexible coupling, via a reduction gear.

Auxiliary power is supplied by two 100 hp turbo-generators, used for starting the main engines and generating the electrical supply when the craft is operating.

CONTROLS: Four rudders adjacent to the waterjet streams provide directional control. Reversing is achieved by applying deflectors to reverse the waterflow. The waterjets themselves are fixed and cannot be rotated.

Operation of the turbines, waterjets, rudders and deflectors is all effected from the wheelhouse by electro-hydraulic control.

SYSTEMS ELECTRICAL: Two 12 kw 28.5 volt generators mounted on each of the main engines supply power when the craft is operating. Two 14 kw 28.5 volt generators driven by the auxiliary turbines supply power when the craft is at rest or when the 12 kw generators are inoperative. Eight acid storage batteries are connected in series to give 24 volts supply power during short stops.

HYDRAULICS: 170 kg/cm² pressure hydraulic system for operating rudders, hydro-reversal unit and anchor.

COMMUNICATIONS: A radio transmitter/receiver with r/t and w/t facilities is installed in the wheelhouse for ship-shore and inter-ship communications on SW and MW bands. A public announcement system is fitted in the passenger saloons and a two-way crew communications system is installed in the wheelhouse, engine room, anchor, gear compartment and mooring stations.

DIMENSIONS:

Overall length	142 ft 0 in (43·3 m)
Hull beam	19 ft 8¼ in (6·0 m)
Width across foils	24 ft 3½ in (7·4 m)

Inboard profile and deck view of the waterjet-propelled Burevestnik, powered by two 2,700 hp Ivchenko AI-20 gas turbines

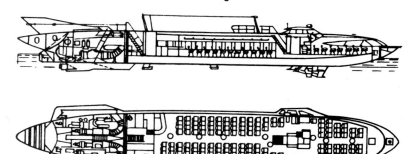

Burevestnik prototype during trials on the Volga

Draft afloat	6 ft 7 in (2·0 m)
Draft foilborne	1 ft 4 in (0·4 m)

WEIGHTS:

Light displacement	41 tons
Full load displacement (max)	67 tons

PERFORMANCE:

Max fuel load	11·5 tons
Cruising speed	50 knots (93 km/h)
Range	310 miles (500 km)
Max wave height at reduced speed	3 ft 3 in-4 ft (1 to 1·2 m)
Max wave height at full speed	2 ft (0·6 m)
Speed astern	4·6 mph (6·9 km/h)

Stop to full speed and distance 95-100 seconds, 1,203 yds (1,100 m)
Stopping time from full speed and distance 25 seconds, 394 yds (360 m)

BYELORUS

This craft was developed from the Raketa via the Chaika for fast passenger services on winding rivers less than 3 ft (1 m) deep and too shallow for vessels of the standard type.

In 1965 it was put into series production at the river shipyard at Gomel, in Byelorussia.

FOILS: The shallow draught submerged foil system consists of one bow foil and one rear foil.

HULL: Hull and superstructure are built in aluminium magnesium alloy. The hull is of all-welded construction and the superstructure is both riveted and welded.

ACCOMMODATION: The craft seats 40 passengers in aircraft-type seats, although the prototype seated only 30.

POWER PLANT: Power is supplied by an M-50 F-3 or M-400 diesel rated at 950 hp maximum and with a normal service output of 600 hp. The wheelhouse is fitted with an electro-hydraulic remote control system for the engine and fuel supply.

DIMENSIONS:

Length overall	60 ft 6 in (18·55 m)
Hull beam	15 ft 2 in (4·64 m)
Height overall	13 ft 11 in (4·23 m)
Draft foilborne	1 ft 0 in (0·3 m)
Draft hullborne	2 ft 11 in (0·9 m)

WEIGHTS:

Light displacement	9·6 tons
Take-off displacement	14·5 tons

PERFORMANCE:

Cruising speed	34 knots (60 km/h)

CHAIKA

An experimental 30-passenger craft, Chaika is used as a test bed for the development of diesel-operated waterjet systems. It was designed initially as a 30 passenger waterbus for shallow rivers but was found to be unsuitable for negotiating sharp river bends at high speed. However, craft of this type are reported as being in limited service on the Danube.

In June 1971 it was announced that the craft had been employed in the development of superventilated V and trapeze foils for a speed range exceeding 50-80 knots.

HULL: Hull and superstructure are built in aluminium magnesium alloy.

POWER PLANT: An M-50 diesel, developing 1,200 hp drives a two-stage waterjet.

CONTROLS: Rudders adjacent to the water stream govern the flow of the ejected water for directional control.

DIMENSIONS:

Length overall	86 ft 3 in (26·3 m)
Hull beam	12 ft 6 in (3·8 m)
Draught afloat	3 ft 10 in (1·2 m)
Draught foilborne	1 ft 0 in (0·3 m)

WEIGHT:

Displacement loaded	14·3 tons

PERFORMANCE:

Cruising speed, foilborne	46·5 knots (86 km/h)

CYCLONE

The Cyclone, a seagoing 250 seat hydrofoil ferry, was announced in February 1969. The prototype will be completed in 1975.

It is believed that the vessel may be powered by 5,000 hp D25B gas turbines driving water-jets, and have either fully submerged foils or surface piercing foils equipped with a stability augmentation system. In May 1972, it was announced that the vessel would have a speed of 45-50 knots and be capable of operating in heavy seas. It has also been reported that it will be the fastest of the Soviet Union's passenger hydrofoils.

NEW MIXED-TRAFFIC FERRY

In June 1973 it was announced that a new seagoing hydrofoil designed at the Sormovo shipyard will carry 200 passengers and 40 vehicles at a speed of 43·49 mph (70 km/h). It will be able to operate foilborne in waves up to 6ft 7in (2m) high. Although designed primarily for routes on the open sea, the vessel is also likely to be employed on inland waterways.

OSA HYDROFOIL CONVERSION

In the spring of 1973, the first of a new class of fast patrol boats made its appearance in the Eastern Baltic. The craft, which appears to be based on an Osa missile-equipped FPB hull, is equipped with fixed surface-piercing vee or trapeze foils at the bow only. The provision of a bow foil provides a higher speed in relatively calm conditions and improved sea-keeping ability. The reduction of the vessels wave-impact response means that its performance as a weapons platform is also greatly enhanced.

In 1974, it was reported that the class is now in series production.

Armament includes guns and torpedos, and it appears that the vessel has ASW capability.

FOILS: Fixed main foil of trapeze or vee configuration believed to be set back one-quarter of hull length from bow. At high speed in relatively calm conditions the greater part of the hull is raised clear of the water.
HULL: Standard Osa hull, steel construction.
POWER PLANT: Believed to be three 4,300 hp diesels, each driving its own inclined propeller shaft.
DIMENSIONS:

Length overall	about 130ft (39·62m)
Beam overall	about 25ft (7·62m)

WEIGHTS:

Max loaded displacement	200 tons
Normal displacement	170 tons

PERFORMANCE:

Max speed	45 knots app.

Byelorus, a 30-45 seat hydrofoil for fast ferry services on shallow waters, seen on the Irtysh river. Powered by a 735 hp M-50 diesel driving a waterjet, the craft cruises at 34 knots (60 km/h)

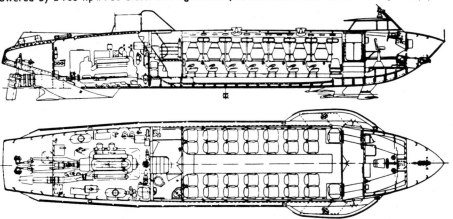

Profile and deck plan of the waterjet-propelled Byelorus, a 40-seat ferry for fast passenger services on winding rivers less than 3 ft 3 in deep

Chaika, an experimental 30-passenger craft powered by a diesel-driven waterjet, is being employed in the development of superventilated V- and trapeze-foil systems for craft with speeds in excess of 80 knots

KOMETA

Derived from the earlier Meteor, the Kometa is the first seagoing hydrofoil to be built in the Soviet Union. The prototype, seating 100 passengers, made its maiden voyage on the Black Sea in the summer of 1961, after which it was employed on various passenger routes on an experimental basis. Operating experience accumulated on these services led to the introduction of various modifications before the craft was put into series production.

Kometas are built mainly at Gorki, but in addition a number are being assembled at Poti, one of the Black Sea yards, from prefabricated sections sent from Gorki.

Kometa operators outside the Soviet Union include Inex-Nautical Touring, Split, Yugoslavia; Empresa Nacional de Cabotage, Cuba; Alilauro-Span, Naples, Italy; Vedettes Armoricaines of Brest, France, and Transports Touristiques Intercontinentaux, Morocco. Other vessels of this type have been supplied to Iran, Rumania, Poland and Bulgaria.

In the early summer of 1974, a number of Kometas were ordered by Airavia Ltd for services in the United Kingdom and elsewhere after modification to meet British Passenger Certificate Requirements.

Export orders have mainly been for the Kometa-M, which was introduced in 1968. Two distinguishing features of this model are the employment of new diesel engines, with increased operating hours between overhauls, and a completely revised piercing foil surfaces system, with a trapeze bow foil instead of the former Alexeyev shallow draft submerged type.

A fully tropicalised and air-conditioned version is now in production and this is designated Kometa MT.

The present standard production Kometa M seats 113-116. Because of the additional weight of the Kometa-MT's air-conditioning system and other refinements, the seating capacity is reduced in the interest of passenger comfort to 102.

The standard craft has proved to be exceptionally robust and has a good all-round performance. On one charter, a Kometa covered 3,300 miles (5,310 km) by sea and river in 127 hours. It can operate foilborne in waves up to 4 ft 1 in (1·25 m) high and travel hullborne in waves up to 8 ft 3 in-10 ft 0 in (2·5-3·0 m).

In June 1974 it was announced that during the forthcoming 5-year plan, starting in 1975, production of the Kometa will be significantly increased. One of the features of the latest models is the relocation of the engine room aft to reduce the noise in the passenger saloons and the employment of a vee-drive instead of the existing inclined shaft. The revised deck configuration allows more seats to be fitted.

FOILS: Bow and rear foils are welded stainless steel Cr 18Ni10Tc, while the midship foil and stabiliser are of AlMg-61 light alloy. On early production models the stern foil was supported by four struts, the two in the centre serving as end bearings for the two propeller shafts and also as rudder supports. Experience showed that the rudders, when submerged in water stirred up by the propellers, are subject to intense erosion and are additional sources of vibration. As a result, the stern foils in series production craft are supported by three struts. The strut on the centre line supports the rudder, while the end bearings of the shafts are supported by the foil. This reduces the level of vibration.

The modifications made it possible to employ 3-bladed propellers in series production craft with better propulsive characteristics than the 5-bladed propellers fitted in the early models. The bow foil struts and the outer struts of the rear foil can be unbolted from the hull for maintenance or replacement. Struts of the midship subfoil and the keel struts of the stabilizer fin and aft foil are non-detachable.

HULL: Similar in shape to that of the earlier Meteor, the hull has a wedge-shaped bow, raked stem and a spoon-shaped stern. Hull and superstructure are built in AlMg-61 and AlMg-6 alloys. The hull is of all-welded construction using contact and argon arc welding and the superstructure is mainly riveted. The hull is framed on longitudinal and transverse formers, the spacing throughout the length of the hull is 500 mm and in the superstructure 1,000 mm.

Top: One of the Kometas operated by Alilauro-Span, Italy. *Centre:* A newly built Kometa MT during trials on the Black Sea off Poti, in June 1974. Note the new high riding stability sub-foil of W configuration. The main bow foil is of surface-piercing trapeze type. *Bottom:* A Kometa MT of Empresa Nacional de Cabotage flying out of Havana harbour

Below the freeboard deck, the hull is divided by watertight bulkheads into thirteen compartments, which include the engine room, fuel compartments, and those containing the firefighting system, tiller gear and fuel transfer pump.

ACCOMMODATION: The current production model Kometa MT seats 102 passengers. It carries a four-man operating crew, comprising captain, engineer, motorman and a seaman. plus one barman. Embarkation platforms sited immediately below the

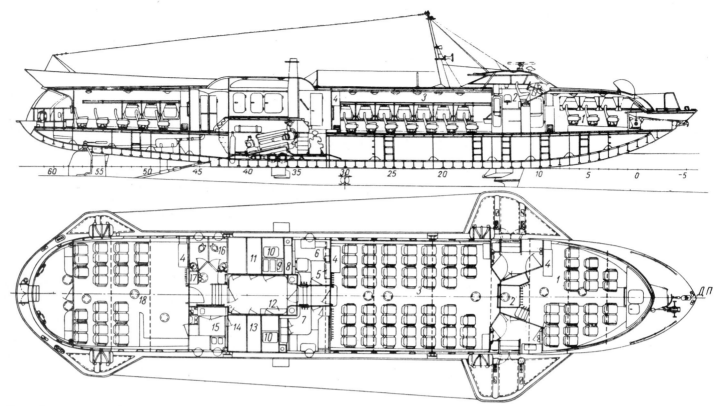

Internal arrangement of the current production Kometa-M, designed for tropical operation. 1, 22-seat forward passenger saloon; 2, wheelhouse; 3, 54-seat main passenger saloon; 6 ,control position; 7, duty cabin; 8, liquid fire extinguisher bay; 9, battery room; 10, engine room; 11, boiler room; 12, installation point for portable radio; 13, store; 14, provision store; 15, bar; 16, WC/washbasin units; 17, boatswain's store; 18, 26-seat aft passenger saloon

wheelhouse provide access for both passengers and crew.

The captain and engineer are accommodated in a raised wheelhouse located between the forward and main saloons; and equipped with two seats, a folding stool, chart table, sun shield and a locker for signal flags.

Main engine controls are installed in both the wheelhouse and engine room.

Passengers are accommodated in three compartments, a forward saloon seating 22, and central and aft saloons seating 54 and 26 respectively. The central saloon has three exits, two forward, leading to the embarkation platforms and one aft, leading to the promenade deck. This is located in the space above the engine room and is partially covered with a removable metallic awning.

To the starboard side is a crew's off-duty cabin, hydraulic system pump room, bar store and bar, and to the port are two toilets, boiler room, battery room and fire extinguishing equipment.

The aft saloon has two exits, one forward leading to the promenade deck, the other aft, leading to the weather deck, which is used for embarking and disembarking when the vessel is moored by the stern.

Floors of the passenger saloons, crew's cabins, bar and wheelhouse are covered in coloured linoleum and the deckhead in the passenger saloons, as well as bulkheads and the sides above the lower edge of the windows, are finished in light coloured pavinol. Panels of the saloons beneath the windows are covered with plastic.

Passenger saloons are fitted with upholstered chairs, racks for small hand luggage and pegs for clothing. The middle and aft saloons have niches for hand luggage and the former is fitted with cradles for babies. The bar is fully equipped with glass washers, an

Line sketch of the Luch (Ray), a projected 400-ton mixed traffic hydrofoil ferry.

ice safe, an automatic Freon compressor, electric stove, etc.

SAFETY EQUIPMENT: A full range of lifesaving equipment is carried including inflatable life rafts, each for 25 persons, 138 life jackets, and 6 circular lifebelts, two with life lines and two with luminous buoys. Life rafts are located two on the forward sponsons and two on the aft sponsons. When thrown into the water the liferafts inflate automatically. Life jackets are stowed under the seats in all saloons, and the circular life belts are stowed on the embarkation and promenade platforms. Kometas for export are provided with life jackets on the basis of 25 persons per raft.

FIRE FIGHTING EQUIPMENT: An independent fluid firefighting system is provided for the engine room and fuel bay. An automatic light and sound system signals a fire outbreak. The fire fighting system is put into operation manually from the control deck above the engine room door. Boat spaces are equipped with hand-operated foam and CO_2 fire extinguishers, felt cloths and fire axes.

POWER PLANT: Power is supplied by two M-400 watercooled, supercharged 12-cylinder V-type diesels, each with a normal service output of 900 hp at 1,650 rpm and a maximum output of 1,100 hp at 1,800 rpm. Each engine drives via a reverse gear its own inclined shaft and the twin propellers are contra-rotating. The shafts are of steel and are parallel to the craft.

The propellers are of three-bladed design and made of brass.

Main engine controls and gauges are installed in both the wheelhouse and the engine room. A diesel-generator-compressor-pump unit is provided for charging starter air bottles; supplying electric power when at rest; warming the main engines in cold weather and pumping warm air beneath the deck to dry the bilges.

Diesel oil tanks with a total capacity of 6,612 lb (3,000 kg) for the main engines and the auxiliary unit are located in the afterpeak. Two lubricating oil service tanks and one storage tank located at the fore bulkhead of the engine room have a total capacity of 551 lb (250 kg). Diesel and lubricating oil capacity is sufficient to ensure a range of 230 miles (370 km).

CONTROLS: The wheelhouse is equipped with an electro-hydraulic remote control system for the engine reverse gear and fuel supply, fuel monitoring equipment, including electric speed counters, pressure gauges, lubricating and fuel oil gauges. The boat is equipped with a single, solid aluminium magnesium alloy balanced rudder, which is controlled through an electro-hydraulic steering system or a hand operated hydraulic drive. In an emergency, the rudder may be operated by a hand tiller.

SYSTEMS:

ELECTRICAL: Power supply is 24 volts dc. A 1kW dc generator is attached to each of the two engines and these supply power while the craft is operating. A 5·6 kW generator is included in the auxiliary unit and supplies power when the craft is at rest. It can also be used when under way for supplying the heating plant or when the 1·0 kW generators are inoperative. Four 12 volt acid storage batteries, each of 180 amp/hr capacity and connected in series to provide 24 volts, supply power during short stops.

HYDRAULICS: The hydraulic system for controlling the main engines and reverse gear consists of control cylinders located in the wheelhouse, power cylinders located on the engines, a filler tank, pipe lines and fittings.

ANCHORS: The craft is equipped with two Matrosov anchors—a main anchor weighing 165 lb (75 kg) and a spare anchor weighing 110 lb (50 kg). The main anchor is raised by means of an electric winch located in the forepeak. The cable of the spare anchor can be heaved in manually and is wound over a drum fitted with a hand brake.

COMMUNICATIONS: A radio transmitter/receiver with r/t and w/t facilities is installed in the wheelhouse for ship-shore and inter-ship communications on SW and MW bands. A portable emergency radio and automatic distress signal transmitter are also installed in the wheelhouse. A broadcast system is fitted in the passenger saloons and a two-way crew communications system is installed in the wheelhouse, engine room, anchor gear compartment and mooring stations.

NAVIGATION: The following navigation aids are standard: a gyro compass, magnetic compass (reserve) and log.

DIMENSIONS:

Length	115 ft 6 in (35·2 m)
Beam	31 ft 6 in (9·6 m)
Overall height above water level when foilborne with mast raised	28 ft 7 in (8·7 m)
Draught, foilborne	4 ft 7 in (1·4 m)
Draught, hullborne	10 ft 6 in (3·2 m)

WEIGHTS:

Light displacement (max)	42 tons
Full-load displacement (max)	56 tons

PERFORMANCE:

Cruising speed (full load) Not less than 34 knots in calm water and in wind conditions up to Force 3

Sea State capability Craft is normally able to operate foilborne in waves up to 4 ft 1 in (1·25 m) high and can travel hullborne in waves up to 8 ft 4 in -10 ft0 in (2·5-3 m) high

The Moteor is powered by two 12-cylinder M-50 diesels, each with a normal service output of 908 hp. Ahead of the central fin is a removable metallic awning above the promenade deck.

Turning diameter 558-656 ft (170-200 m) when operating hullborne with the rudder shifted 35°; 1,640-1,804 ft (500-550 m) when foilborne with the rudder shifted 10-12°

KOMETA-M

The Kometa-M, featuring improved diesel engines of either the M-400 or M-401 type, a trapeze-type, surface-piercing bow foil and larger wheelhouse, was introduced in 1968. The standard model seats 116 passengers. The tropicalised version of this vessel is the Kometa MT. Because of the weight of the air-conditioning and other refinements the seating capacity in this model is reduced to 102. Brief specifications for these models are given below.

KOMETA-M

DIMENSIONS:

Length overall	115 ft 2 in (35·1 m)
Beam	31 ft 6 in (9·6 m)
Height, foilborne from waterline to tip of mast	28 ft 7 in (8·7 m)
Draft, hullborne	11 ft 9¾ in (3·6 m)
Draft, foilborne	5 ft 6⅞ in (1·7 m)

POWER PLANT:

Two 1,100 hp watercooled supercharged 12-cylinder diesels

PERFORMANCE:

Cruising speed	34-35 knots (60-63 km/h)
Fuel consumption gr/bhp/hr	180
Oil consumption gr/bhp/hr	5·0

KOMETA MT

DIMENSIONS:

Length overall	115 ft 2 in (35·1 m)
Beam	36 ft 1 in (11·0 m)
Height, foilborne, waterline to tip of mast	30 ft 2¼ in (9·2 m)
Draft, hullborne	11 ft 9¾ in (3·6 m)

Draft, foilborne	5 ft 6⅞ in (1·7 m)

POWER PLANT:

Two 900 hp watercooled, supercharged 12-cylinder diesels

PERFORMANCE:

Cruising speed	32 knots (58 km/h)
Fuel consumption, gr /bhp/hr	182
Oil consumption, gr/bhp/hr	58

Development of the Kometa is continuing. Current research is aimed at the introduction of a stability augmentation system employing control flaps on the bow foil; the reduction of labour involved in construction; the introduction of design improvements through the use of grp and sandwich construction; noise reduction in the saloons and the extension of the cruising range.

LUCH (RAY)

This is a design project for a 400-ton mixed traffic hydrofoil ferry, with seats for 350 passengers. Speed would be 47-52 mph (75/85 km/h) and the range 870 miles (1,400 km). No further details are available.

METEOR

Dr Alexeyev's Meteor made its maiden voyage from Gorki to Moscow in the summer of 1960, bringing high performance and unprecedented comfort to the river boat scene, and setting the pattern for a family of later designs.

FOILS: The foil arrangement consists of one bow and one stern set, with the stanchions of the bow system carrying two additional planing subfoils. The foils are attached to the stanchions, which are of a split type, by flanges and bolts. The foil incidence can be altered when necessary by the insertion of

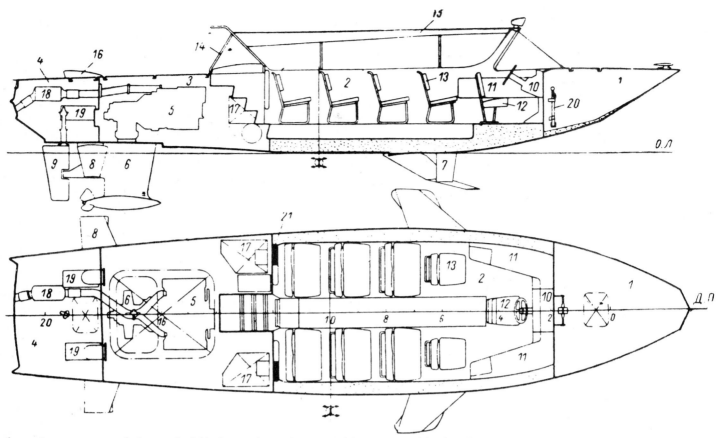

Internal arrangements of the standard Nevka, seating a driver and 14 passengers. (a) Inboard profile; (b) deck plan. 1. forepeak; 2. passenger cabin; 3, engine bay; 4, afterpeak; 5, 235 hp 3D20 four-cycle six-cylinder diesel; 6, DK-300 Z-drive; 7, bow foil; 8, rear foil; 9, rudder; 10, control panel; 11, lockers; 12, driver's seat; 13, passenger seat; 14, guard rail; 15, detachable awning; 16, engine air intakes; 17, fuel tank; 18, silencer; 19, storage batteries; 20, anchor; 21. lifebelt

wedges between the flanges and the foils when the craft is in dock.

HULL: With the exception of the small exposed areas fore and aft, the Meteor's hull and superstructure are built as an integral unit. The hull is framed on longitudinal and transverse formers and both hull and super-structures are of riveted construction with welded steel members.

POWER PLANT: The Meteor is powered by two 12-cylinder M-50 watercooled, super-charged V-type diesels, each with a normal service output of 900 hp and a maximum output of 1,200 hp. Each engine drives its own propeller shaft and the twin-screws are contra-rotating. Controls are all sited in a small wheelhouse set above and at the rear of the fore saloon. Aircraft styling is used in the wheelhouse and the throttles are of dual-lever aircraft type.

ACCOMMODATION: Up to 150 passengers are seated in a short haul version built for suburban services, while alternative models for inter-city services, seat 116-130. Meteors are fitted with full air-conditioning, a bar and an aft promenade deck.

DIMENSIONS:

Length overall	112 ft 2¼ in (34·5 m)
Hull beam	31 ft 2 in (9·5 m)
Height above waterline, foilborne to tip of mast	22 ft 3¾ in (6·8 m)
Draught afloat	7 ft 10½ in (2·4 m)
Draught foilborne	3 ft 11¼ in (1·2 m)

WEIGHTS:

Displacement loaded	52 tons

Molnia, a popular six-seat runabout powered by a 77 bhp CAZ652 Volga car engine. Maximum speed is 32 knots (60 km/h).

PERFORMANCE:

Max speed, foilborne	35 knots (65 km/h)
Maximum endurance	9 hours

MIR

First Soviet passenger craft to use a surface piercing foil system was the MIR (Peace), built in the autumn of 1961. Described as the first Soviet seagoing hydrofoil it is in many respects similar to the Supramar PT 50. The hull is of welded aluminium construction and the foils are in high tensile stainless steel. It can undertake voyages in up to State 4 seas and has a maximum speed of 47 knots (87 km/h). Power is supplied by twin M-50

diesels driving twin screws. The engines are electro-hydraulically controlled from the wheelhouse, which has an auto-pilot system for emergencies.

MOLNIA

This popular six-seat hydrofoil sports run-about was derived from Alexeyev's original test craft. Many hundreds are available for hire on Russian lakes and rivers and in slightly modified form the type is now being exported to countries including the United Kingdom and the USA. The craft is navigable in protected off-shore water up to 2 miles from the land and has particular appeal for water-taxi and joy-ride operators

FOILS: The hydrofoil assembly comprises two forward foils, one aft foil and planing sub-foils.

POWER PLANT: Powered by a 77 bhp CAZ652 Volga car engine, it has a top speed of about 32 knots (60 km/h) and a range of about 100 nautical miles (180 km).

HULL: Built in sheet and extruded light alloy, the hull is divided into three compartments by metal bulkheads. The forepeak is used for stores, the midship compartment is the open cockpit, and the compartment houses the engine, and gearbox. The cockpit is fitted with a steering wheel, throttle, reverse gear lever and an instrument panel adapted from that of the Volga car. Individual life jackets for each passenger are incorporated into the seat cushions.

DIMENSIONS:

Length overall	27 ft 11 in (8·50 m)
Hull beam	6 ft 5 in (1·95 m)
Draught afloat	2 ft 10 in (0·85 m)
Draught foilborne	1 ft 10 in (0·55 m)

WEIGHTS:

Displacement:	
loaded	1·8 tons
empty	1·25 tons

PERFORMANCE:

Max speed at 1·8 tons displacement	32 knots (60 km/h)
Fuel capacity	17 gall (80 litres)
Range	97 nautical miles (180 km)

NEVKA

This light passenger ferry and sightseeing craft is in series production at a Leningrad shipyard and the first ten have been supplied to Yalta for coastal services on the Black Sea. The standard version seats a driver and 14 passengers.

The prototype, illustrated in the accompanying photograph, has an aluminium hull, but production models are in glass fibre reinforced plastics.

The craft, which is designed to operate in waves up to 3 ft (1 m) high, is the first small hydrofoil in the Soviet Union to employ surface-piercing vee foils, and also the first to employ a diesel in conjunction with a Z-drive.

In December 1971 what is thought to be a waterjet-propelled variant was said to have made its first cruise along the Crimean coast. The 16-mile trip from Yalta to Alushta was made in half an hour.

FOILS: Bow and stern foils are of fixed V surface-piercing configuration and made of solid aluminium magnesium alloy.

HULL: Glass fibre reinforced plastic structure assembled in four basic sections. The outer hull is assembled with the transom, the deck with the rib of the windscreen, the cabin/cockpit with the engine air intakes and afterpeak, and the inner hull with the companionway at the aft of the cabin.

The hull contours are designed to facilitate easy transition from hull to foilborne mode and minimise structural loadings due to wave impact. Two transverse steps are incorporated.

ACCOMMODATION: The craft can be supplied with an open cockpit and folding canopy, as a cabin cruiser with a solid top or as a sightseeing craft with a transparent cabin roof. As a cabin cruiser, the craft is

Nevka prototype during trials. This light passenger ferry and sightseeing craft is now in series production at a Leningrad shipyard. Power is provided by a 235 hp diesel driving a 3-bladed propeller via a Z-drive

Model of a projected luxury cabin cruiser version of the Nevka

Pchela fast patrol boat. The design is derived from the Strela hydrofoil ferry

equipped with bunks, a galley and toilet. The driver's stand can be located either at the forward end of the cabin or in a raised position amidships.

POWER PLANT: Power is supplied by a single 3D20 four-cycle, six-cylinder diesel, developing 235 hp at 2,200 rpm. The engine, located aft, drives a three-bladed propeller via a DK-300 Z-drive.

CONTROLS: Craft heading is controlled by a single balanced rudder in solid aluminium alloy mounted aft of the rear foil main strut and operated by a steering wheel via a mechanical linkage. Other controls include a footpedal to control engine speed, and a reverse lever.

SYSTEMS, ELECTRICAL: Power is 24 volts d.c. A 1kW engine-mounted generator supplies power while the craft is operating. Two 12 volt acid storage batteries, each of 180 amp/hr capacity and connected in series to give 24 volts, supply power during stops.

FIRE FIGHTING: An independent fluid

firefighting system of aircraft type is installed in the engine bay and is operated remotely from the driving seat.

DIMENSIONS:

Length overall	35 ft 11 in (10·9 m)
Hull beam	8 ft 11 in (2·7 m)
Beam overall	13 ft 2 in (4·0 m)
Draft, hullborne	5 ft 3 in (1·7 m)
Draft, foilborne	2 ft 9 in (0·9 m)

WEIGHTS:

Max take-off displacement	6 tons
Displacement unloaded	4·1 tons

PERFORMANCE:

Cruising speed	30 knots
Normal cruising range	37 miles
Diameter of turn at max speed	357 ft (109 m)
Take-off time	app 30 secs
Max permissible wave height in foilborne mode	3 ft 3 in (1·0 m)

PCHELA (BEE)

This military derivative of the Strela has been in production since the mid-1960s, and is in service with the Soviet frontier police in the Baltic, Black Sea, Caspian and various other sea areas. The craft is equipped with a full range of search and navigation radar and is reported to have a speed of about 35 knots. Twenty-five are believed to have been built.

RAKETA

The prototype Raketa was launched in 1957 and was the first multi-seat passenger hydrofoil to employ the Alexeyev shallow draught submerged foil system. Several hundred are now in service on all the major rivers of the USSR.

Since 1960, an increasing number of export orders have been placed for the craft. The first, for two Raketas came from Hungary and these began operation during the summer of 1962, one serving the route Budapest-Mohacs, 118 miles (190 km) to the south, and the other between Budapest and Estergom. The following year the service was extended to Vienna. Other countries operating Raketas include Bulgaria, Finland, the German Federal Republic, the Philippines and the United Kingdom.

The vessel is now available in three basic models: the standard non-tropicalised model seating 64 passengers; the current export model, the 58-seat Raketa T, which is both tropicalised and air-conditioned, and finally the Raketa TA, modified in London by Airavia Ltd, and licensed by the UK Department of Trade to carry up to 100 passengers (58 seated) on high density commuter and tourist routes on sheltered waters. Details of this model are given in the United Kingdom section.

The description that follows applies to the Raketa T, the standard export variant, powered by an M-401A diesel and with a cruising speed of about 32 knots (58 km/h).

The vessel is designed for high-speed passenger ferry services during daylight hours on rivers, reservoirs and sheltered waters in tropical climates. It meets the requirements of the Soviet River Register Class 'O' with wave restrictions 2 ft 7 in (0·8 m) waves

Top: One of the first two Raketas imported by Airavia Ltd into the United Kingdom during unloading. *Centre:* The bow foil and planing stabilizer foils. *Bottom:* The aft foil assembly, comprising the foil, three supporting struts, and bearing for the inclined propeller shaft

when foilborne up to 4 ft 11 in (1·5 m) when hullborne

The passenger saloon is provided with natural and induced ventilation and seats 58. The crew comprises a captain, engineer, deckhand and barman.

FOILS: The foil system comprises one bow foil, one aft foil and two dart-like planing sub-foils, the tips of which are attached to the trailing edges of the outer bow foil struts. Foils, sub-foils and struts are in welded stainless steel. The bow foil, which incorporates sweepback, and the straight aft foil, are both supported by three vertical struts.

The base of the centre strut aft provides the end bearing for the propeller which is located beneath the foil.

HULL: The hull is framed on longitudinal and transverse formers and all the main elements—plating, deck, partitions, bulkheads, platforms and wheelhouse—are in riveted duralumin. The stem is fabricated in interwelded steel strips. Below the freeboard deck the hull is divided into six watertight compartments employing web framing.

ACCOMMODATION: The passenger saloon seats 58 in aircraft-type, adjustable seats.

At the aft end of the saloon is a bar. The saloon has one exit on each side leading to the promenade deck and one forward, leading to the forecastle. Aft of the saloon is the engine room, promenade deck with additional seats, two toilets, a storeroom and a companionway leading up to the wheelhouse.

The craft carries a full range of life-saving and firefighting equipment. There are 62 life jackets stowed in the passenger saloon and four for the crew in the wheelhouse and under the embarkation companionway. Two lifebelts are provided on the embarkation platform and two on the promenade deck. Firefighting equipment includes four foam and four CO_2 fire extinguishers, two fire axes, two fire buckets and two felt cloths.

POWER PLANT: Power is supplied by a single M-401A watercooled, supercharged 12-cylinder V-type diesel, with a normal service output of 900 hp. The engine drives via a reverse gear and inclined stainless steel propeller shaft a three-bladed cast bronze propeller. The fuel system comprises two fuel tanks with a total capacity of 1,400 kg, a fuel priming unit, and a hand fuel booster pump. A compressed air system, comprising a propeller shaft-driven air compressor and two 40-litre compressed air bottles is provided for main engine starting, emergency stopping, operating the foghorn and scavenging the water intake.

The diesel generator unit comprises a Perkins P3.152 diesel engine employed in conjunction with a Stamford C20 alternator.

CONTROLS: The wheelhouse is equipped with a hydraulic remote control system for the engine, reverse gear and fuel supply. The balanced rudder, made in aluminium-magnesium alloy, is controlled hydraulically by turning the wheel. A hand tiller is employed in an emergency. Employment of gas exhaust as a side-thruster to assist mooring is permitted at 850 rpm.

SYSTEMS, Electrical: A 3kW generator, rated at 27·5 V and coupled to the main engine is the main source of power while the vessel is under way. A 50 cycle, 230 V, 1,500 rpm three-phase alternator supplies ac power. Four 12 volt acid storage batteries, each with a 132 ah capacity and connected in series to give 24 volts, supply power during short stops.

HYDRAULICS: The hydraulic system for controlling the main engine, reverse gear and fuel supply, consists of control levers located in the wheelhouse and on the main engine, power cylinders located on the engine, a filler tank, pipelines and fittings.

HEATING AND VENTILATION: Passenger saloon and wheelhouse are provided with natural ventilation, using ram inflow when the boat is in motion. Norris warming air-conditioning if fitted for use in hot weather. One conditioner is installed in the wheelhouse and eight are installed in the passenger saloon and bar. The cooled air is distributed throughout the saloon by electric fans installed on the ceiling. One is provided in the wheelhouse. A radio-telephone with a range of about 19 miles (30 km) is installed for ship-to-shore and ship-to-ship communication. The vessel also has a public address system and intercom speakers linking the engine room, wheelhouse and forecastle.

A Raketa fast passenger ferry operated on the Rhine by the Koln-Dusseldorf Shipping Company

The 100 ton Sputnik, first of the Soviet Union's large hydrofoil passenger ferries

The prototype Strela during trials off the Yalta coast

DIMENSIONS:

Length overall	88 ft 5 in (26·96 m)
Beam amidships	16 ft 5 in (5·0 m)
Freeboard	2 ft 7½ in (0·8 m)
Height overall (excl mast)	
	14 ft 8 in (4·46 m)
Draft, hullborne	5 ft 11 in (1·8 m)
foilborne	3 ft 7¼ in (1·1 m)

WEIGHTS:

Displacement, fully loaded	27·09 tonnes
light	20·31 tonnes

PERFORMANCE:

Service speed, about	32 knots (58 km/h)
Max wave height, foilborne	
	2 ft 8 in (0·8 m)
Max wave height, hullborne	
	4 ft 11 in (1·5 m)
Turning diameter, hullborne	
	3-4 boat lengths
Turning diameter, foilborne	
	15-16 boat lengths

RAKETA FIRE TENDER

The Raketa fire tender has been designed to tackle fires on river ships and vessels in coastal areas.

The adaption of an existing fast craft for this purpose had the advantages of reducing development time and building costs.

FOILS: Identical arrangement to that of the standard Raketa.

HULL: Riveted D16 duralumin construction. Two monitors are mounted on the weather deck, one at the bow and one amidships. Water for the two monitors is supplied by an 8HDH rotary pump driven by a 590 hp M609 12-cylinder diesel controlled from the wheelhouse.

Outlets and valves are provided on the two monitor stands for the attachment of one 5·9 in (150 mm) fire-fighting hose to each, or two four-way forks, to which four 3·03 in (77 mm) hoses can be joined. Spray hoses are laid along the sides of the weather deck, one port and one starboard, each with four spray nozzles.

The vessel carries a 220 gal (1,000 l) foam tank and mixer for extinguishing highly inflammable and combustible liquids. Foam can be delivered either by the two monitors or fire hoses.

A special waterjet propulsion system is provided to offset the thrust of the hoses and monitors when working and keep the craft stationary. The vessel is equipped with VHF and UHF radio and a ship's broadcast system for control of the 6-man firefighting crew.

Start-up of the firefighting systems when empty takes 70 seconds and 10 seconds when full.

SPUTNIK

The 100-ton Sputnik was the first of the Soviet Union's large hydrofoils. On its maiden voyage in November 1961, the prototype carried 300 passengers between Gorki and Moscow in 14 hours. Although a heavy autumn storm was encountered en route the craft was able to continue under way at a cruising speed of 40 knots through several large reservoirs with waves running as high as 8 ft.

FOILS: The foil system comprises a bow and rear foil with the outer struts of the bow assembly carrying two additional planing subfoils.

HULL: The hull is welded in AlMg-61 aluminium-magnesium alloy. Adoption of

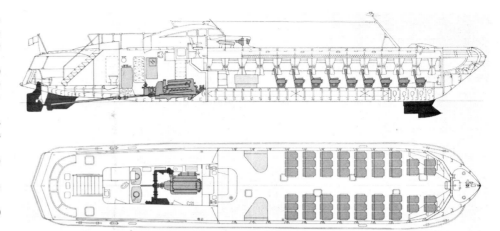

Inboard profile and plan view of the standard 50-seat Raketa. On short-range commuter services, additional passengers are seated around the promenade deck aft, and others are permitted to stand. The high density traffic version accommodates up to 100 passengers

an all-welded unit construction facilitated prefabrication of sections at the Sormovo shipyard and elsewhere, the parts being sent to other yards in the USSR for assembly. One yard used for assembling Sputniks is at Batumi, on the Caspian Sea.

POWER PLANT: Power is supplied by four 850 hp M-50 watercooled, supercharged V-type diesels, each driving its own propeller shaft and controlled electro-hydraulically from the forward wheelhouse.

ACCOMMODATION: Passengers are accommodated in three saloons, a well-glazed fore compartment seating 68, and central and aft compartments each seating 96. On short, high frequency services, the seating is increased to 108 in the latter compartments by the substitution of padded benches instead of adjustable aircraft-type seats. Two separate off-duty cabins are provided for the 5-man crew. The cabins are attractively finished in pastel shades and fully insulated against heat and sound. Full fire fighting and other emergency provisions are made and in addition to lifebelts for all passengers and members of the crew, two inflatable rubber boats are carried.

DIMENSIONS:

Length overall	157 ft 2 in (47·9 m)
Beam overall	29 ft 6 in (9·0 m)

Draught afloat	4 ft 3 in (1·3 m)
Draught foilborne	2 ft 10 in (0·9 m)

WEIGHTS:

Displacement full load	110 tons

PERFORMANCE:

Cruising speed	41 knots (75 km/h)

STRELA

Developed from the Mir and intended for services across the Black Sea, the prototype Strela (Arrow) completed its acceptance trials towards the end of 1961. The craft, which was designed and built in Leningrad, was first put into regular passenger service between Odessa and Batumi, and later between Yalta and Sebastapol. More recently a Strela 3 has been operating a service between Leningrad and Tallinn. It covers the distance in four hours, ninety minutes faster than the express train service connecting the two ports.

Two 970 hp 12-cylinder V-type M-50 F3 diesels driving twin screws give the Strela a cruising speed of 40 knots (75 km/h). The craft has a trapeze type surface piercing bow foils with a horizontal centre section between the main struts, and can operate in State 4 seas.

It carries 82-94 passengers in airliner type seats.

DIMENSIONS:

Length overall	96 ft 1 in (29·3 m)

The Vikhr employs the same hull as the Sputnik and is designed for regular year round services on the Black Sea

Beam overall   26 ft 4 in (8·3 m)
Draft afloat   7 ft 7 in (2·25 m)
Draft foilborne   3 ft 11 in (1·2 m)

WEIGHTS:
Displacement, full load   46 tons

PERFORMANCE:
Cruising speed   **40 knots**
Sea state capability   4 ft (1·22 m) waves
Range of operation   740 km
Time to reach service speed from stop
                        130 seconds
Distance from full speed to stop   **234 m**
Full speed ahead, to full speed astern 117 m

VIKHR (WHIRLWIND)

Seagoing version of the 100-ton Sputnik, Vikhr employs the same hull and is one of the most powerful passenger hydrofoils operating today. Described as a "coastal liner", it is designed to operate during hours of daylight on inshore services on the Black Sea up to 31 miles (50 km) from the coast. The craft was launched in 1962 and is currently in service on the Odessa-Herson route.

FOILS: Compared with the Sputnik, innovations include more sharply swept back foils, a form of stability augmentation, and an amidships foil, in addition to those fore and aft, to increase seaworthiness and stability. The bow and rear foils and their struts are in stainless steel, while the midship wedge-shaped bow with raised bilge line and cruiser-type stern. Two steps are aligned with the flare of the sides. Hull and superstructure are of welded ALMg-61 aluminium magnesium alloy.

ACCOMMODATION: There are three passenger saloons, seating a total of 268 passengers. The forward saloon seats 78, the central saloon seats 96, and the aft 94. At the rear of the central cabin is a large buffet and bar, beneath which is the engine room. From the bar double doors lead to the off-duty quarters for the seven-man crew.

In high seas, passengers board from the stern, across the promenade deck. In normal conditions, embarkation takes place through a wide passageway across the vessel between the fore and middle saloons. Seats are arranged in rows of four abreast across each cabin with two aisles, each 3 ft 4 in (1 m) wide, between to ease access to the seats.

POWER PLANT: Power is supplied by four 1,200 hp M50-F3 diesel engines, with DGKP (diesel generator, compressor pump) auxiliary engines. Each engine drives a 3-bladed propeller via a reverse gear and its own inclined stainless steel shaft. The central shafts are inclined at 12° 20' and the side shafts at 13° 13'.

An overriding control valve is fitted to the control systems of the main engines, so that the fuel gauges of all four can be controlled simultaneously. This makes it possible to maintain a uniform load on the engines, immediately the craft becomes foilborne, thus increasing the life of the engines. The craft can operate satisfactorily with one engine out.

CONTROLS: The wheelhouse is equipped with an electro-hydraulic remote control system for the engines, reverse gear, fuel supply etc. Twin balanced rudders are hydraulically operated by two separate systems—main and emergency.

SYSTEMS, ELECTRICAL: Power supply is 24 volts dc. A 1kw dc generator is attached to each of the engines and these supply power when operating. Two KG-5·6, 5·6kW generators are included in the auxiliary unit and supply power when at rest. They can also be used when under way for supplying the heating plant or when the 1kW generators are inoperative. Four 12 volt acid storage batteries, each of 180 amp/hr capacity and connected in series to provide 24 volts supply power during stops.

COMMUNICATIONS: A radio transmitter/receiver is installed in the wheelhouse for ship-shore and inter-ship communication on r/t, also a receiver. A ship's broadcast system is also installed with speakers in the passenger saloons.

NAVIGATION: Equipment includes radar, and a radio direction finding unit, both with displays in the wheelhouse.

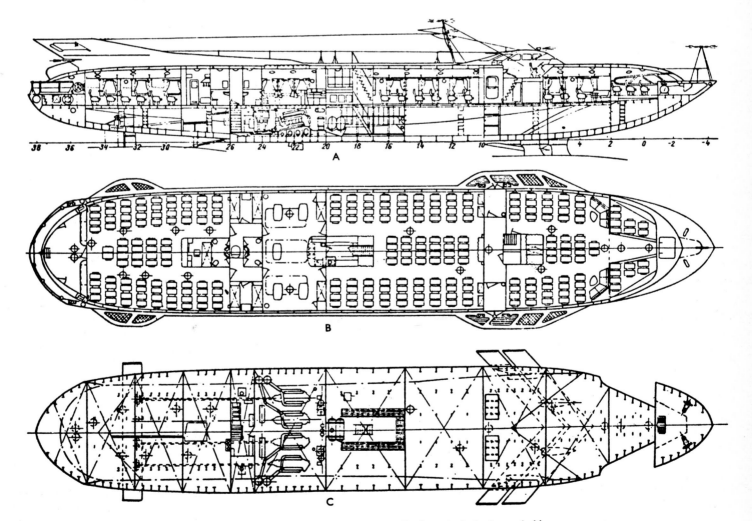

Internal arrangement of the Vikhr. a. profile; b. main deck plan; c. holds

DIMENSIONS:

Length overall	156 ft 0 in (47·54 m)
Beam	29 ft 6 in (9·0 m)
Height to hull to awning deck	
	18 ft 2 in (5·54 m)
Draft afloat	13 ft 6 in (4·1 m)
Draft foilborne	4 ft 11 in (1·5 m)

WEIGHTS:

Displacements, full load	117·5 tons

PERFORMANCE:

Max speed	43 knots (78 km/h)
Cruising speed	35·8 knots (66 km/h)
Cruising range	240 miles (386 km)
Max wave height in foilborne condition	
	4 ft 11 in (1·5 m)
Distance from full speed to full stop	
	328 yards (300 m)
Distance from full speed ahead to full speed astern	245 yards (224 m)
Time to reach service speed from stop.	
	190 seconds

Three Volga six-seat hydrofoils at speed off the coast of the Isle of Wight

VOLGA

Export version of the Molnia sports hydrofoil, the Volga incorporates various design refinements including a completely redesigned bow foil.

A new model powered by a 90 hp Volvo Penta diesel engine and designated Volga 70 was introduced at the end of 1972. The cruising speed is four km/h slower than that of the earlier model, but engine maintenance is easier and the acquisition of spares is simplified in many parts of the world. The new model has been purchased by companies and individuals in the USA, West Germany, Sweden, The Netherlands and Singapore.

FOILS: the foil system consists of a bow foil with stabilizing sub-foil and a rear foil assembly. The foils are of stainless steel.

HULL: Built in sheet and extruded light alloy, the hull is divided into three compartments by metal bulkheads. The forepeak is used for stores, the midship compartment is the open cockpit and the aft compartment houses the engine and gearbox.

ACCOMMODATION: Seats are provided for six—a driver and five passengers. The controls, instruments, magnetic compass and radio receiver are grouped on a panel ahead of the driver's seat. A full range of safety equipment is provided, including life jackets for six, life line, fire extinguisher and distress flares. A folding awning can be supplied.

POWER PLANT: Power is supplied by a 77 hp M652-Y 6-cylinder automotive engine, which drives a 3 bladed, stainless steel propeller through a V drive. The shafting comprises an intermediate shaft, propeller shaft, stern gland wirh rubber bearings, propeller shaft coupling boxes with reduction gear and propeller shaft bracket.

SYSTEMS

ELECTRICAL: 12 volt dc. Starting, instrument and navigation lights and siren, are provided by an engine-mounted generator and an acid storage battery.

DIMENSIONS:

Length overall	27 ft 11 in (8·5 m)
Beam	6 ft 11 in (2·1 m)
Draught afloat	2 ft 9½ in (0·85 m)
Draught foilborne approx.	1 ft 8 in (0·5 m)

WEIGHTS:

Total displacement	3,090 lb (1,886 kg)
Fuel	141 lb (64 kg)

Volga 70 six-seat water taxi and runabout powered by a 90 hp Volvo Penta diesel engine. Cruising speed is 32 knots.

PERFORMANCE:
  Cruising speed   32 knots (60 km/h)
  Range   112 miles (180 km)

VOLGA-70

DIMENSIONS:
Length overall	28 ft 1 in (8·55 m)
Beam	6 ft 10⅝ in (2·10 m)
Height above water when foilborne	
	3 ft 2⅝ in (0·98 m)
Draft hullborne	3 ft 0 in (0·92 m)
Draft foilborne	1 ft 8½ in (0·52 m)

PERFORMANCE:
  Cruising speed   35 mph (56 km/h)

VOSKHOD (SUNRISE)

Intended as a replacement for the Raketa, the Voskhod is now beginning to enter service. Compared with its predecessor, it has more modern lines and provides greater comfort and facilities for passengers and crew. Full air conditioning is a standard feature.

The prototype of the Voskhod II underwent trials on the Volga at Gorky in June 1974.

As with the Raketa, there is a "family" of variants to suit a wide variety of local navigation and traffic conditions throughout the Soviet Union. Models include a 65-seat craft with a cruising speed of 46 knots (85 km/h); a shallow draft version with a foilborne draft of 2·1 ft (65 cm), and a gas-turbine model to seat 85 passengers. The powerplant is located in the stern and it is reported that a vee-drive is employed. A form of modular construction has been adopted for the craft so that it can be delivered by rail to the areas in which it will be operating.

The first craft of this series are now in service. In August 1973 it was reported that two are operating on the Irtysh river.

No details of dimensions, or power had been received at the time of going to press.

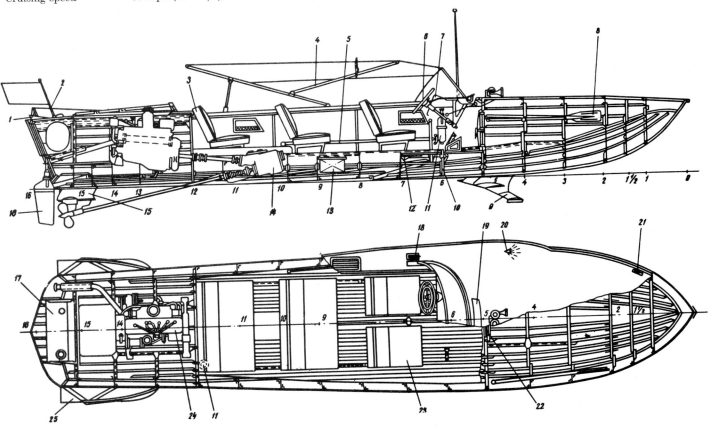

Inboard profile and plan of the Volga

1 stern light; 2 flag pole; 3 bench seat; 4 awning; 5 dog hook; 6 steering column; 7 instrument panel; 8 oar; 9 bow foil assembly; 10 anchor line; 11 fire extinguisher OY-2; 12 anchor; 13 storage battery; 14 reduction and reverse gear; 15 rear foil assembly; 16 steering and rudder gear; 17 fuel tank; 18 cleat; 19 air intake; 20 side running light; 21 fairlead; 22 cover of first bulkhead hatch; 23 seat; 24 M652-Y six-cylinder automotive engine; 25 foilguard

SAILING SKIMMERS

INSTYTUT LOTNICTWA (AVIATION INSTITUTE)

ADDRESS:
02256 Warszawa, Al Krakowska 110/114

TELEPHONE:
46-09-93

TELEX:
81-537

Dr. Jerzy Wolf is employing an ultra-light wing, constructed by the Aviation Institute while undertaking research on agricultural aircraft, as a sail for an experimental "skimmer" sailing craft.

The wing raises the hull above the water surface and also acts as a sail.

The object of Dr. Wolf's experiments is to develop a sailing vessel which offers a higher speed than that attained by current sailing hydrofoils.

The wing, which has inherent directional and lateral stability, is hinged to the mast top, slightly ahead of the centre of pressure, and pulls the craft obliquely in a similar way to a kite of high lift/drag ratio. The angles of attack and roll are controlled by lines or push-pull rods connected to a control cross-bar. Craft heading is controlled by a conventional water rudder.

ZAGLOSLIZG (Sailing Skimmer) Z-70

The Z-70, built in 1970, employs a modified Cadet class sailing dinghy hull equipped with an adapted centreboard and rudder. This particular hull design was selected because of its low weight, high rigidity and low construction cost.

The wing, built originally to aid research into an agricultural aircraft project, has been adapted by the addition of a vertical stabiliser. It is covered in Dacron material and has a sail area of 140 sq ft (13·0 m²). The all-up weight is 33 lb (15 kg) and breaking load 1,188 lb (540 kg).

The complete craft has an empty weight of app. 176 lb (80 kg). According to the designer, over-rigging the craft has proved a great help, since it facilitates the transition from hull-borne to sailborne state. Support is also provided by the centreboard and rudder plate. It is stated that very little trim is required in heel.

ZAGLOSLIZG (Sailing Skimmer) Z-71

Designed in 1971, this is equipped with a specially built lightweight strut-and-cable sail wing, differing slightly from the earlier design. It features a trimming device and simplified control.

The craft can be towed in the air behind a motor boat, like a conventional kite-glider.

Z-70 during towing trials

POLAND

Z-70 showing rigging and control systems, also the modified stretched membrane sailwing

Z-73A, based on a modified Cadet-class dinghy hull

DIMENSIONS:				
Length overall, hull	10 ft 6 in (3·20 m)	Stabiliser area	22 sq ft (2 m²)
Beam	4 ft 3 in (1·30 m)	Mast height	9 ft 6 in (2·90 m)
Draft, centreboard lowered		WEIGHTS:	
	3 ft 11 in (1·20 m)	Empty weight	154 lb (70 kg)
Sail wing span	23 ft 0 in (7·0 m)	Gross weight	330 lb (150 kg)
Max chord sail wing	11 ft 6 in (3·50 m)	Sail wing	26 lb (12 kg)
Sail wing area	150 sq ft (14 m²)	PERFORMANCE:	
Aspect ratio	3·5 : 1	Lift/drag ratio of sail wing	about 6 : 1

Max angle of wing setting	60 deg
Horizontal lift/drag ratio for 45 deg heel	4·2 : 1
Lift/drag ratio of centreboard and rudder plate	10·2 : 1
Max craft speed/wind velocity ratio	3 : 1
Optimum angle of apparent wind	19 deg
Optimum heading angle	109 deg
Wind velocity for take-off	18 fps (5·5 m/s)
Minimum speed for take-off	24 mph (40 km/h)
Optimum airborne speed	34 mph (55 km/h)

Z 73 3

Developed from the Z-70 and Z-71, the Z-73 employs a modified Cadet-class dinghy hull, equipped with a high aspect ratio centreboard and rudder.

The wing, covered in nylon, incorporates a light vertical stabilizer, and has inherent directional and lateral stability.

Altitude control is based on a combination of incidence and heel angle control. Excessive altitude results in increased drift and a loss of speed and lift. This leads to a restoration of normal trim, with the hull riding at a predetermined height above the water level. The restoring forces are described as being similar to those of a vee-foil hydrofoil.

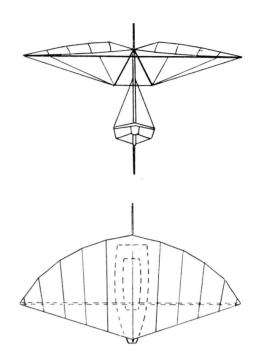

General arrangement of the Z-73A, incorporating a sketch showing the control arrangements

DIMENSIONS:

Length overall, hull	10 ft 6 in (3·20 m)
Beam	4 ft 3 in (1·30 m)
Draft, centreboard lowered	3 ft 11 in (1·20 m)
Sailwing span	21 ft 4 in (6·5 m)
Aspect ratio	4·7:1
Stabilizer area	13 sq ft (1·2 m²)

WEIGHTS:

Empty weight	150 lbs (68 kg)
Gross weight	330 lb (150 kg)
Sailwing	22 lb (10 kg)

PERFORMANCE: (Design)

Lift/drag ratio, sailwing	app 8:1	and rudder	2·1:1
Max angle of wing setting	60 deg	Wind velocity for take-off	21 fps (6·5 m/s)
Horizontal lift/drag ratio for 45 deg heel	3·5:1	Minimum speed for take-off	27 mph (45 km/h)
Lift/drag ratio of centre board		Optimum airborne speed	36 mph (60 km/h)

UNITED KINGDOM

NEW HYDROFIN LTD

HEAD OFFICE:
Burfield Flat, Bosham Lane, Bosham, Sussex.

EXECUTIVES:
Christopher Hook, Managing Director

Christopher Hook was responsible for the conception, design and development of the fully-submerged hydrofoil, which he demonstrated in the USA in 1951 with his Red Bug prototype and later with his Miami-built conversion sets. He became a partner of the late Herr G. Sachsenburg, the pioneer hydrofoil builder, and has completed hydrofoil design and consultancy contracts in the US, Israel, Holland, France, Norway and Italy, as well as with Strathclyde University.

He is currently developing a self-tending sail rig for sailing hydrofoil craft comprising sails that tilt to windward and have roller reefing.

MISS BOSHAM

Partly inspired by Walker's Planesail, the rig used on Miss Bosham—a foil-stabilized craft rather than a flying hydrofoil—eliminates the highly-stressed central mast bearing of Planesail by mounting it at the top of the short mast thus permitting it to be well stayed.

Sail tending is entirely by air vane turned

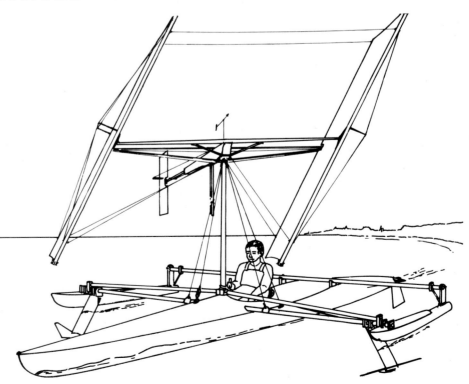

Miss Bosham, a development craft for a self-tending sail rig for sailing hydrofoils

by hand winch at the base of the central mast and in the non-flying version, lateral stability comes from two fully-submerged, differentially controlled hydrofoils on short struts connected to the pilot's control column.

Nearly square, soft sails are employed. These are roller-reefed, the lines emerging near the hinges located at the arms of the T frame, and controlled by a winch.

The leech of each sail has a stiff member and tension on the sail is maintained by a line going aft then forward along the boom to a clear rack which rotates with the T frame. In larger craft all such lines would be operated by electrical winches.

Another novel feature, of greater benefit to the flying version than the foil stabilized model, is that the sail tilts to windward, thus taking lift from the wind and almost eliminating any overturning moment.

Future models will be two-seaters and will have twin air vanes in order to shorten the boom to more reasonable proportions.

Since there are no sheets, the sailing technique requires careful study. By merely reversing the air vane one can stop dead and go astern—a useful feature when negotiating shallows.

The foil struts are easily retracted by turning about their tubes for beaching.

The basic aim of the design is to eliminate keeling by providing powerful hydrofoil stability and sail tilting, and thus enable a very small boat to carry a large sail area in complete safety. In this particular case the sail area is 70 sq ft (6·50 sq m) on a boat with a total weight of 80 lb (36·28 kg).

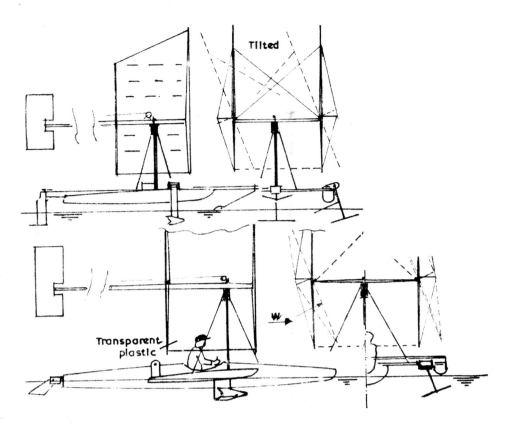

General arrangement of Miss Bosham

UNITED STATES OF AMERICA

DAK HYDROFOILS

HEAD OFFICE:
PO Box 71, Sausalito, California 94965
TELEPHONE:
415 332-4891
PROPRIETOR AND CHIEF DESIGNER:
David A. Keiper

Design of the Williwaw, the world's first seagoing sailing hydrofoil, began in 1963. Construction of the craft, which is based on a specially designed trimaran hull, began in May 1966 and tests started in November 1967.

After nearly three years of trials along the California coast, Williwaw, manned by David Keiper and one other crew member, successfully completed a 16-day passage between Sausalito, California and Kahului Harbour, Maui, Hawaii, in September 1970—the first ocean crossing by a hydrofoil sailboat.

Heavy seas and strong winds were encountered on the first two days of the voyage, during which the craft made 200 miles per day. At times the craft attained 25 knots, but light winds in mid-ocean prevented the craft from making the passage in record time.

The craft entered chartered sailing yacht service in March 1971, operating from Hanelei Hawaii and before returning to Sausalito, California, completed about 2,000 miles of inter-island sailing around Hawaii, mainly in open sea conditions.

Dak Hydrofoils is currently developing and marketing simple low-cost hydrofoil conversion kits for existing racing catamarans with lengths ranging from 12-20 ft (3·65-6·90 m). Kits are available for the Hobie-14, Hobie-16 and Venture 15 catamarans, and kits for other daysailing catamarans can be made up on request. The basic foil design is applicable to all lightweight multihulls.

The design of 16, 31 and 38 ft (4·87, 9·44 and 11·58 m) hydrofoil trimarans is continuing, and complete boats will be built to order. Price range from about US$3,000 for a complete 16 ft (4·87 m) day cruiser, to US$30,000 for a 38 ft (11·58 m) cruiser. A modified conversion kit introduced in 1974 is also suitable for outboard powerboats.

WILLIWAW

A prototype sailing hydrofoil, Williwaw has a specially designed trimaran hull attached to which are four foils—a deep V-foil at the bow, a ladder foil at the stern, and one laterally outboard of each of the port and starboard pontoons. The stern foil pivots and serves as a rudder when hullborne.

The craft accommodates 2-3 passengers, together with cruising supplies, and attains 15-17 knots in steady 11-12 knot winds. In stronger winds it has attained 25-30 knots. FOILS: The bow foil, of surface-piercing V configuration, is mounted between the pon-toon bows and that of the main hull. Foils, supporting struts and sub-foil elements, are of welded aluminium, with a protective coating of vinyl. Foil section is NACA 16-510 with 6 in (152·4 mm) chord throughout the system. The foils have fairly high aspect ratio. Foil loading during a normal take-off is: bow foil 40%, stern foil 20% and leeward lateral foil 40%, depending on sail heeling forces. Dihedral of the bow foil is 30-50 degrees.

The lateral foils, which are not as deep as the bow and stern foils, are of 4-rung ladder type, and have 35 degrees dihedral. The stern foil is of 3-rung ladder configuration with zero dihedral at rest, but craft heel gives it 10-15 degrees dihedral. Under most conditions the rungs are fully submerged. The entire stern foil pivots for steering action. Shear bolts protect bow and stern foils from damage if debris is struck.

Foil retraction arrangements are as follows:
After the removal of shear bolts the bow foil swings forward and upwards through 90 degrees; the lateral foils swing outwards and over, and are laid flat on the deck through a second pivot axis, and the stern foil swings aft and over through 180 degrees. Retraction of the bow and lateral foils is achieved through the use of a simple block and tackle. CONTROL: A tiller-operated, combined stern foil and rudder, controls direction in foilborne mode; paired struts, also tiller

operated, provide rudder control when hullborne.

HULL: Lightweight, but robust trimaran hull with small wing deck to avoid aerodynamic lift. Marine ply structure sheathed with glass fibre. Built-in attachment points for foils. Mast supported by main frame.

ACCOMMODATION: The craft is designed for 2-3 people, with cruising supplies, but has flown with nine aboard. The deep cockpit accommodates the helmsman and one crew member. The cockpit, which provides adequate shelter from the strong winds developed by high-speed sailing, forms the entrance to main and stern cabins. The main cabin seats four comfortably. There are two berths in the main cabin and one in the stern cabin. The main cabin also includes a galley, shelving and a marine head. There is generous stowage space in the pontoon hulls.

SAIL AND POWERPLANT: Sail power alone on prototype, but a small outboard auxiliary engine can be fitted if required. Total sail area is 380 ft² (35·30 m²).

SYSTEMS: Electronics: Radio direction finder normally carried.

DIMENSIONS:
Length overall hull	31 ft 4 in (9·54 m)
Length waterline hull	28 ft 0 in (8·53 m)
Length overall, foils retracted	33 ft 0 in (10·05 m)
Length overall, foils extended	32 ft 0 in (9·75 m)

Hull beam:
Main hull at WL	3 ft 0 in (0·91 m)
Hull overall, foils retracted	16 ft 4 in (4·97 m)
Beam, overall, foils extended	25 ft 0 in (7·62 m)
Draft afloat, foils retracted	1 ft 4 in (0·40 m)
Draft afloat, foils extended	4 ft 0 in (1·21 m)
Draft foilborne	1 ft 6 in-2 ft 6 in (0·45 m-0·76 m)
Freeboard	2 ft (0·61 m)
Pontoon deck	1 ft 6 in-3 ft 6 in (457-762 mm)
Main hull deck	2 ft 6 in-3 ft 6 in (762 mm-1·06 m)
Height overall to masthead	39 ft 0 in (11·88 m)

DIMENSIONS, INTERNAL:
Cabin (Wheelhouse, galley, toilet included)
Length	28 ft 0 in (8·53 m)
Max width	16 ft 0 in (4·87 m)
Max height	5 ft 4 in (1·62 m)
Volume	480 cu ft (13·78 cu m)

WEIGHTS:
Light displacement	2,200 lb (997·88 kg)
Normal take-off displacement	3,000 lb (1,360 kg)
Max take-off displacement	3,600 lb (1,632 kg)
Normal payload	800 lb (362·8 kg)
Max payload	1,400 lb (635 kg)

PERFORMANCE (in steady wind and calm water, with normal payload):
Take-off speed
Normally 12 knots. Craft is able to take-off with a 12-knot beam wind and accelerate to 18-20 knots

Above: Williwaw sailing in Hawaiin waters at a speed of 20 knots, shortly after her historic trans-ocean crossing from California. Sail twist at top is caused by the Williwaw's speed, attesting to the low drag of the foils. *Below:* Williwaw anchored in home waters at Sausalito, California, after 7,000 miles of voyaging in the Pacific

Max speed foilborne	30 knots
Cruising speed foilborne	12-25 knots

Max permissible sea state and wave height in foilborne mode:
Sea state almost unlimited at 12 knot average speed with wind aft of beam. Foils well behaved in all conditions met so far. Sails reefed down in heavy conditions to maintain comfort and ease of handling. Craft shows no tendency to pound.

Turning radius at cruising speed
150 ft (45·72 m)
Number of seconds and distance to take-off
5 secs in strong wind, two boat lengths
Number of seconds to stop craft
8 seconds, turning dead into wind

SEA TESTS: Craft tested in strong winds with steep breaking seas 15-20 ft (4·57-0·69 m) high off California coast. It has completed a return voyage from the California coast to Hawaii and sailed 2,000 miles (3,218 km) during inter-island charters in Hawaii.

Speed is significantly more than wind speed in conditions of steady wind and calm water. The craft can match wind speed in moderate seas, but not in heavy seas, In heavy seas. broad reaching or beam, it has averaged 15 knots for hours at a time, winds gusting to Force 5 and 6. Speeds may climb to 30 knots or drop to 5 knots, depending upon local wind and waves. Acceleration and decelerations are gradual and not objectionable. The ride is far smoother than that of displacement multihulls.

Total miles sailing to November 1971, 7,000 miles (11,266 km).

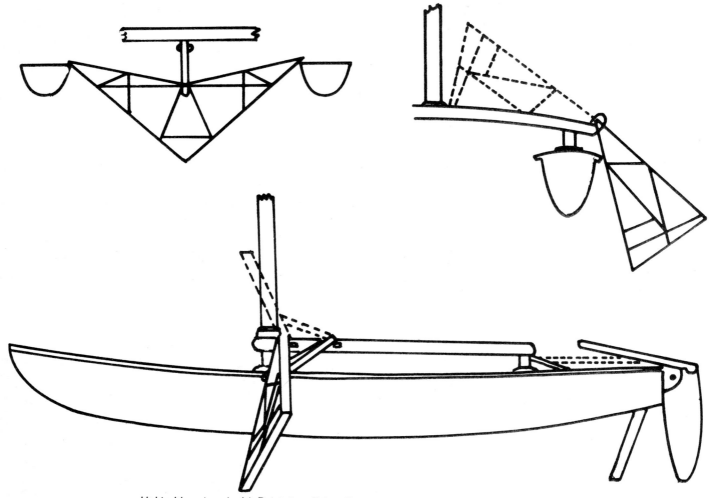

Hobie-14 equipped with Dak foils. Take-off speed is about 12 knots. The rear foil is adjusted for trim, according to the crew load and wind and wave conditions. A friction clamp allows the complete rear foil assembly to swing aft should it hit an obstruction. The lateral foils, which normally carry 60-80% of the load, are similar in design to those of the Williwaw, except for an extra lifter rung. Each unit weighs only 8 lb (3.62 kg), but either can lift the complete craft out of the water

PACIFIC EXPRESS

Successor to the Williwaw, the Pacific Express is a second generation hydrofoil cruising trimaran. It is wider than its predecessor, has fully buoyant hulls, is equipped with a more efficient hydrofoil system, and has a slightly greater load carrying capacity.

The craft is designed to operate in a wide variety of conditions, from heavy storm seas to light airs, In heavy seas. with foils set, it is exceptionally stable and capable of high speeds. The comfort level is stated to be five times that of a catamaran of similar size and the craft tends to self-steer for 90% of the time, with helm tied.

In light airs and calms, with foils retracted the craft makes the most of the available wind.

FOILS: Configuration similar to that of Williwaw. Foils have a 5 in (127 mm) chord and are fabricated in heavily anodized aluminium. Bolts, washers, etc., are in stainless steel. Bow and lateral foils are fixed while sailing. The tiller-operated combined stern foil and rudder, controls direction when foilborne. All four foils retract manually after the removal of shear bolts.

HULL: Monocoque, marine plywood hull with flush deck sheathed in epoxy-glassfibre.

SAIL: Sloop rig with working sail area of 380 sq ft (25.29 sq m).

Hobie-16 Dak-foil conversion with foils retracted

ACCOMMODATION: Four berths, settee, galley, shelves and marine head.

DIMENSIONS:

Hull length		31 ft 4 in (9.55 m)
Beam		19 ft 6 in (5.94 m)
Draft		1 ft 5 in (0.43 m)
Draft, foils extended		4 ft 0 in (1.21 m)

WEIGHTS:
Normal loaded displacement
2,400 lb (1,088.5 kg)

Light displacement   3,500 lb (1,586·5 kg)

PERFORMANCE:

Maximum speed, foilborne about 30 knots

COST:

About US $24,500, for 31 ft (9·45 m) craft, complete, FOB San Francisco. Deposit, 10% with order, balance when construction starts.

SAILING HYDROFOIL CONVERSION KITS

Dak Hydrofoils is now marketing conversion kits to fit the more popular catamarans of 12-20 ft (3·65-6·09 m) in length. First kits available fit the Hobie-14 ($180), the Venture-15 ($200) and the Hobie-16 ($220), plus shipping costs from San Francisco (shipping weight, 40 lb (18·14 kg)). Kits for other popular daysailing catamarans will be made-up on request at comparable prices.

The basic foil system is suitable for all lightweight multihulls. The kits in slightly modified form are also suitable for small trimarans.

Sail power-to-weight ratio on lightweight catamarans are approximately double that of Williwaw, described earlier. Combined with various design improvements, this provides an outstanding performance with speeds of 1·5 to 1·0 times that of true wind speed in moderate to strong winds. Speeds of up to 45 knots are anticipated.

FOILS: The kit includes aluminium foil extrusions, stainless bolts, plans and cutting patterns. Foil cutting patterns were developed mathematically to ensure perfect fitting and the pieces are joined by tapped screws and epoxy. The foils add about 30 lb (13·60 kg) weight to the basic craft. They are all fastened at deck level or higher to avoid any interference with ordinary sailing. All foils retract inboard to facilitate trailing and launching. The lateral foils have a retraction pivot axis along the spares at the sides of the trampoline deck. They clamp against a lip which comes downwards from the edge of the deck, a small eccentric disc ring rotated up under the lip, and a wing nut tightened.

The stern foil swings upwards towards the trampoline deck, retraction being controlled by a central lever which retracts, locks and holds both foils.

The change from a four foil to a three foil system was made as day sailing craft do not appear to require the same degree of longitudinal stability as that needed by a cruising craft. Crew ballast is effective on day sailing catamarans and lateral lift is of paramount importance since these craft are generally sailed at the limits of their lateral stability. The day craft also have their c.g. further aft, which leads to the bow foil being too lightly loaded. A three foil system for these craft provides greater lateral stability, better manoeuvrability, less drag in light airs, take-off at lower wind speeds and simpler construction and installation.

SPEED FREAK

This is a special racing craft which will make the maximum possible ratio of boat speed to true wind speed on one tack, although capable of sailing on both tacks.

Jake Springhorn taking-off in his Hobie-16 conversion at Port Jefferson harbour, Long Island

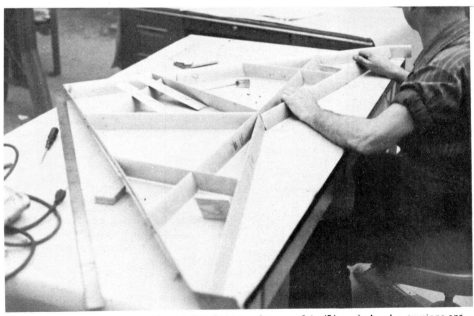

Assembling a Hobie-16 rear foil from a Dak-foil kit. Separate 2 in (51 mm) chord extrusions are used for the aerofoil shaped lifting surfaces and the symmetrical struts. Tapped screws and epoxy are used to construct the units

The design is based on a proa hull, which will incorporate special aerodynamic features. Standard 2 in (50 mm) Dak Hydro- foil foil extrusions will be used. Overall length will be 16-20 ft (4·87-6·09 m). Plans and foil materials will cost about $200·00.

NEW SAILING HYDROFOIL KIT

In 1974, the company introduced a revised sailing foil kit, details of which are shown in the accompanying drawings.

Additional reserve lifting area is provided on the lateral foil units and stabilizing fins are provided on the rudder blades. The stern V foil has been eliminated.

The employment of this arrangement enables the craft to fly with less wind, improves manoeuvrability, and facilitates conversion. Only the lateral foils need retracting. The rudder fins do not interfere with conventional sailing.

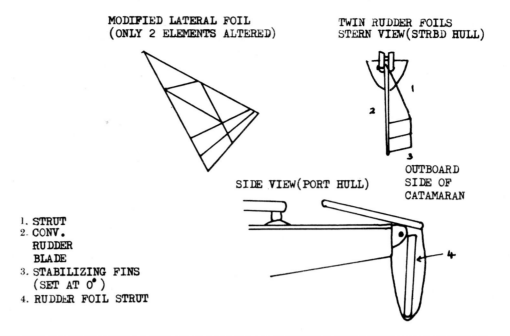

MODIFIED LATERAL FOIL
(ONLY 2 ELEMENTS ALTERED)

TWIN RUDDER FOILS
STERN VIEW(STRBD HULL)

SIDE VIEW(PORT HULL)

OUTBOARD
SIDE OF
CATAMARAN

1. STRUT
2. CONV.
   RUDDER
   BLADE
3. STABILIZING FINS
   (SET AT 0°)
4. RUDDER FOIL STRUT

DONALD J. NIGG

ADDRESS:
   7924 Fontana, Prairie Village, Kansas,
   USA 66208
TELEPHONE:
   913-642-2002

Development of the Flying Fish began in 1963 at Lake Quivira, an inland lake in Kansas. Donald Nigg believed that if the pitchpole moment and vertical stability problems could be solved, the front-steering three-point suspension system typical of the modern ice-yacht offered several advantages. Previous craft had often used three-point suspension, but all appear to have used rear steering. To develop this new approach, Exocoetus, an experimental platform was built. It was evolved through three distinct versions during 1964-67 and established the basic feasibility.

Interest in the experiments resulted in numerous requests for plans, but although the craft was ideal as a development platform, it was not a design suitable for home construction. In response to these requests the Flying Fish was developed.

To keep the costs to a minimum, the craft is designed to carry a sail area of 100-150 sq ft. It was anticipated that most of those interested in building a sailing hydrofoil would be small boat sailors, owning a boat carrying a mainsail of this size. The design thus allows the builder to share the sail and rigging with an existing dinghy.

A true development class of sailing hydrofoil has been slow to emerge, but the Flying Fish may mark the beginning of such a class. The Amateur Yacht Research Society, Hythe, Kent, United Kingdom, is promoting the design as a development class.

Sets of plans for the Flying Fish have been supplied to potential builders in many countries.

FLYING FISH

First of a development class of sailing hydrofoils, the Flying Fish has been specially developed for home builders. Built mainly in wood and with a length overall of 16 ft 6 in (5·02 m), it has a maximum foilborne speed of more than 30 knots.

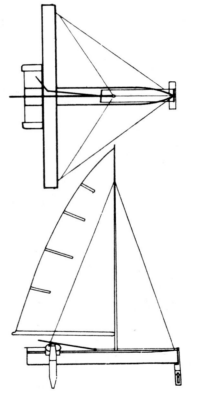

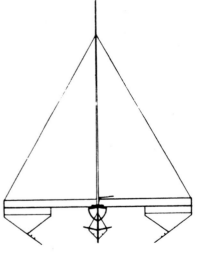

The estimated cost of constructing a craft of this type, less sail and rigging (the 125 sq ft mainsail and rigging from a Y-Flyer were used for the prototype illustrated), is US$250,00.

FOILS: The foil configuration is surface piercing and non-retractable with 16 % of the weight supported by the vee bow foil and the remaining 84 % by the outrigged main foils. The latter are also of the vee type, with cantilevered extensions at the apex. Total foil area is 1·42 m² (15·3 sq ft) and the fail loading is 300 lb sq ft max at 30 knots. The front foil and its supporting strut are built in aluminium and oak, and the main foil is in oak only.

STEERING: A basic feature of the design is the use of front rather than rear steering. Directional control is provided by the movement of the hinged bow foil.

HULL: This is an all-wooden structure built in fir plywood, ¼ in thick and sealed. Torque load is carried by the skin, and bending loads are carried by the skin and the internal beam structure.

The crossbeam provides stability when in dock and in a displacement condition at low speeds. At 2-3 knots the horizontal safety foils at the top of the vee of the rear foils provide interim foil stabilization up to the take-off speed of 5 knots and prevent dragging an end of the crossbeam in the water. At foilborne speeds the safety foils preclude the possibility of an end of the crossbeam being driven into the water by sudden heeling.

RIG: A cat rig of 9·2-13·9 m² (100-150 sq ft) area is recommended.

DIMENSIONS:

Length overall, hull (plus boom overhand at rear, dependent on sail plan)

5·02 m (16 ft 6 in)

Length waterline, hull   4·87 m (16 ft 0 in)
Beam   6·09 m (20 ft 0 in)
Draft afloat (fixed foils)   1·06 m (3 ft 6 in)
Draft foilborne

12-30 in over operating speed range
Height, approx   7·3 m (24 ft 0 in)

PERFORMANCE:

Max speed foilborne
Over 30 knots, design cruise range

optimized for 20-30 knots

Max speed hullborne   5 knots
Min wind for take-off   10 knots
Number of seconds and distance to take-off (theor. app)

3 secs with 15·2 m (50 ft) run in favourable wind

Number of seconds and distance to stop craft (theor. app)

Can land from 20 knots in 45·6 m (150 ft) in about 6 seconds

Topping 20 knots on a close reach in a light wind

SEA TEST: The craft has been tested in 10-25 knot winds, on both sheltered inland lakes and on ocean bays, with a max chop of about 18 inches. Speeds up to approx 30 knots have been attained.

HYDROFOIL OPERATORS

HYDROFOIL OPERATORS

NORTH AMERICA
USA

DEPARTMENT OF THE NAVY,
NAVAL SEA SYSTEMS COMMAND (NAVSEA)

The Boeing/NATO PHM, Patrol Hydrofoil, Guided Missile, is a NATO project, sponsored jointly by the US Navy, the Federal Republic of Germany and the Italian Navy. It is being developed by NAVSEA PMS 303. The first two vessels are due to be launched in late 1974 and delivered to the US Navy during the summer of 1975.

General Hydrolines Inc,
17th Floor, 575 Madison Avenue, New York.

See International Hydrolines, below.

International Hydrolines Inc,
HEAD OFFICE:
1000 Connecticut Ave, N.W, Washington DC 20036
DIRECTORS AND EXECUTIVES:
Charles F. Willis Jnr, President
Gerald O. Rennerts, Vice President
Ira E. Dowd, Vice President
Robert Reeves, Secretary
Milton Brucker, Director

Route(s): Company is planning to operate as a joint venture with General Hydrolines, Inc. commuter services on the Hudson and East rivers. The 72-seat, 28-ton hydrofoil ferry designed for this route is to be equipped with waterjet propulsion. IHI has recently proposed a 141 ft (42·97 m) mixed-traffic ferry to the Tri-State Regional Planning Commission.

The company's Sea Wing craft was expected to be in operation in the New York area by late June 1974. The vessel is to be employed on the route Port Washington, Nassau County, to Wall Street, Manhattan—plus a sightseeing cruise from the South Seaport Museum, East River, Manhattan. In Miami, Florida, International Hydrolines is operating two craft—Enterprise and Endeavour.

Sea World
1720 South Shores Road, Misson Bay, San Diego, California
TELEPHONE: 224-3535

This company operates three 28-seat Atlantic Hydrofoils Inc. Sea Worlds (Sprague Engineering Co) on ten minute sightseeing tours around Mission Bay. The craft were the first built on the West Coast to be licensed for commercial use by the US Coast Guard.

US Navy Pacific Fleet Amphibious Command
Type(s): Flagstaff, PGH-1
Base: San Diego

US Naval Ship Research and Development Center
Type(s): High Point, PCH-1; Plainview AGEH-1
Purpose: US Navy hydrofoil development programme.

SOUTH AMERICA
ARGENTINA

Alimar SA
Type(s): PT 50, 3 (Rodriquez)
Route: Buenos Aires-Colonia-Montevideo

BOLIVIA

Crillon Tours Ltd
ADDRESS PO Box 4785 Av Comacho 1223 Ed, Krsul, La Paz
Type(s): Albatross, 2 (Honold), modified by Helmut Kock
Route: Lake Titicaca

CUBA
Type(s): Kometa M, 1 (Sormovo)
Route(s): Batabano—Nueva Gerona

VENEZUELA

Compania Shell
Type(s): PT 20, 4 (Werf Gusto)
Route: Offshore oil drilling operations on Lake Maracaibo

Naveca SA
Type(s): PT 20, 4 (Rodriquez)
Route: Maracaibo-Cabimas

ASIA AND PACIFIC
CHINA

Navy of the Chinese People's Republic
Type(s): Hu Chwan Class, 60 plus (Shanghai)

Boeing's Jetfoil prototype was launched on March 29th, 1974. After trials on Lake Washington, it was moved to Puget Sound for high speed testing in mid July. The first scheduled Jetfoil service is due to be operated by Far East Hydrofoils Co between Hong Kong and Macao in the spring of 1975

Operational areas: Coastal waters

HAWAII
Pacific Sea Transportation Ltd.
Hawaii
Type(s): Jetfoil, 3 (Boeing).
Route(s): Daily services between a Honolulu terminal and Kauai, Maui and Hawaii island.

INDONESIA
Sundaharya Corp, Djakarta
Type(s): PT 20 (Rodriquez)
Route: Indonesia Coast

JAPAN
Boyo Kisen Co. Ltd.
Type(s): PT 50, 1 (Hitachi)
Route(s): Yanai—Matsuyama
Type(s): PT 20, 1, "Shibuki No 2" (Hitachi)
Route(s): Yanai—Matsuyama

Isizaki Kisen Co. Ltd.
Fukae, Ohaki-cho, Saeki-gun,
Hiroshima-ken, Japan
Type(s): PT 50, "Kosei" (Hitachi)
Route(s): Hiroshima-Kure-Matsuyama
Type(s): PT 50, 1 (Hitachi)
Route(s): Hiroshima-Kure-Matsuyama
Type(s): PT 20 "Kinsei", 1 (Hitachi)
Route(s): Onomichi-Matsuyama
Type(s): PT 20 "Tsobasamaru", 1 (Hitachi)
Route(s): Hiroshima-Kure-Matsuyama

Kansai Steamship Co Ltd..
Soze-che, Kita-ku, Osaka
Type(s): PT 50, 1 "Haya Kaze" (Hitachi)
Route(s): Osaka-Koke-Shodoshima-Takamatsu
Type(s): PT 20, 2, "Hayate" Nos 1 and 2 (Hitachi)
Route(s): "Hayate No 1", Himeji-Syodoshima-Takamatsu "Hayate No 2", Koke-Sumoto

Meitetsu Kaijo Kankosen Co.
99-1 Shin-miyazaka-cho, Atsuta-ku, Nagoya City
Type(s): PT 50, 1 "Osyo" (Hitachi)
Route(s): Nagoya-Toba-Gamagori-Nishiura-Irako
Type(s): PT 20, 2 "Taihomaru" and "Hayabusamaru" (Hitachi)
Route(s): Nagoya-Toba-Irako-Gamagori-Shinojima and Kowa-Shinojima-Irako-Toba-Nishiura

Nichimen Co. Ltd.
(Kinkowan Ferry Co. Ltd.)
Type(s): PT 50, 1 "Otori No 3", (Hitachi)
Route(s): Kajiki-Kagoshima-Ibusuki

Nissho-Iwai Co. Ltd.
(Hankyu Lines Co. Ltd.)
Type(s): PT 50, 2 "Zuiho" and "Houo" (Hitachi)
Route(s): Koke-Tokushima
Hankyu Lines Co. Ltd.
Type(s): PT 20, 2, "Amatsu" and "Kasugano"
Route(s): Kobe-Naruto
Setonaikai Kisen Co. Ltd.
Ujina Kaigani-chome, Hiroshima
Type(s): PT 50, 3 "Wakashio", "Otori No 1" and "Otori No 2"
(Hitachi)
Route(s): Onomichi-Setoda-Imabari and Hiroshima-Kure-Matsuyama
Type(s): PT 50, 1, "Kondoru" (Hitachi)
Route(s): Hiroshima-Kure-Matsuyama
Type(s): PT 50, 1. (Hitachi)
Route(s): Onomichi-Setoda-Imbari
Type(s): PT 50, 4 "Hibiki No 1", "No 2" and "No 3" and "Shibuki
No 1" (Hitachi)
Route(s): Onomichi-Setoda-Omishima-Imbari and ("Shibuki No 1")
Yanai-Matsuyama
HONG KONG
Shun Tak Co
Type(s): PT 20, 1 (Rodriquez)
Route: Hong-Kong Macao
Hong Kong Macao Hydrofoil Co
Type(s): PT 50, 4, RHS 140, 5, RHS 160, 2 (Rodriquez)
Far East Hydrofoils Co.
Type(s): PT 50, 4, "Guia", "Penha", "Taipa", "Balsa" (Hitachi)
PT 50, 1, RHS 110, 3, RHS 160, 1 (Rodriquez) Jetfoil 2, (Boeing)
Route: Hong Kong-Macao

CEYLON
Royal Ceylon Navy
Type(s): Waterman, 1 (International Aquavion)
Communications and patrol
KOREA
Hans Ryeo Developments Co. Ltd.
Type(s): PT 20, 1 (Rodriquez)
PHILIPPINES
Bataan Manila Ferry Services
Manila
Type(s): Raketa TA (Sormovo/Airavia)
Tourist Hotel and Travel Corporation
Type(s): PT 20, 2 (Rodriquez)
Route: Manila-Corregidor
Philippine Navy
Type(s): PT 20, 2 (Rodriquez); PT 32, 2 "Bontoc", "Baler",
(Hitachi)
Coastal Patrol

AUSTRALASIA
AUSTRALIA
Port Jackson Hydrofoils Pty.
Limited
HEAD OFFICE:
No. 2 Jetty, Circular Quay, Sydney,
N.S.W. 2000
TELEPHONE:
27.9251
CABLES:
"Manlyferries"
TERMINAL OFFICES:
No. 2 Jetty, Circular Quay   27.9251
Manly Wharf, Manly   97.3028
DIRECTORS:
J. C. Needham, Managing Director
Neil M. Barrell, Director
SENIOR EXECUTIVES:
T. S. Morrison, Secretary
G. E. Marshall, Traffic Manager
W. B. McCubbray, Superintending Engineer
OPERATIONS: Routes served and frequency. Sydney to Manly.
7 miles, every 20 minutes between 7 a.m. and 7 p.m.
Approximate number of passengers carried during year: One
million.
CRAFT IN SERVICE:
PT 20, 1 (Hitachi), 72 passengers, built 1965.

PT 50 (Rodriquez), 140 passengers, built 1966.
PT 20, 1 (Hitachi) "Manly", 72 passengers, built 1965.
PT 50 (Rodriquez), "Fairlight", 140 passengers, built 1966
PT 50 (Rodriquez), "Dee Why", 140 passengers, built 1968
RHS 140 (Rodriquez), "Curl Curl" built in 1971.

Tires Pty Ltd TD
HEAD OFFICE:
Corner Junction, Road and Gray Terrace, Rosewater, Outer
Harbour, South Australia
Type(s) Aquavion Waterman, 1.
Route: Port Adelaide to Outer Harbour.   Hourly service.   Also
educational and scenic tours of Port River, Adelaide.

NEW ZEALAND
Kerridge Odeon Corporation
Type(s): PT 20, 1 (Rodriquez)
Route: Auckland-Waiheke Island

EUROPE, MEDITERRANEAN AND NEAR EAST
ALBANIA
Albanian Navy
Type(s): Hu Chwan (White Swan) Class, 12 (Shanghai)
Operating areas: Coastal waters
BULGARIA
Bulgarian Shipping Line
Type(s): Kometa, 4
Route: Bourgas-Nesetow-Varna
Bulgarian River Fleet
Type(s): Meteor, 2; Raketa, 2
Route: Danube, between Rousse and Silistra
CHANNEL ISLANDS
Condor Ltd
Type(s): PT 50, 1, RHS 140, 2 (Rodriquez)
Route: Guernsey-Jersey-St. Malo

Above: Condor 4, one of two Rodriquez RHS 140s employed by
Condor Ltd on the route Guernsey-Jersey-St. Malo. *Below:* Lilau,
the prototype RHS 160, completed in 1974. Eight of these 160 pass
enger craft are due to be operated on services between Hong Kong and
Macao

DENMARK
Dampskipsselskapet Oresund
Type(s): PT 50, 2 (1 Rodriquez, 1 Westermoen) RHS 140, 1 (Rodriquez)
Route: Copenhagen-Malmö

EGYPT
Ministry of Commerce, Cairo
Type(s): PT 20, 3 (Rodriquez)
Route: Abu Simbel-Asswan

FINLAND
Paijanteen Kantosiipi Oy
Type(s): Raketa, 1 (Krasnoye Sormovo)
Route: Lahti-Jyvaskyla, across Lake Paijane

FRANCE
Vedettes Armoricaines
Ier Eperon,
56 rue d'Aiguillon, 29N Brest.

GERMANY
Water Police
Type(s): PT 4, 3 (German Shipyard)
Route: Patrol service on the Rhine
Koln Dusseldorf Shipping Co
Type(s): Raketa, 1 "Rhine Arrow" (Sormovo)
Routes: Cologne—Koblenz

HUNGARY
Hungarian Navigation Company
Type(s): Raketa, 2 Chaika, 2 Meteors, 2 plus (Krasnoye-Sormovo)
Route: Budapest-Vienna

IRAN
Type(s): Kometas (Sormovo)
Services(s): Persian Gulf

ITALY
Aliscafi SNAV, SpA
Type(s): PT 20, 7; PT 50, 8 and RHS 110, 1 (Rodriquez)
Route: Messina-Reggio-Isole-Lipari

Alilauro SpA
Type(s): PT 50, 2 (Westermoen) PT 20, 1 (Rodriquez)
Routes: Naples-Capri-Ischia

Alilauro Span
Naples
Type(s): Kometa and Kometa M, 8 (Sormovo)
Route(s): Naples Bay, Naples-Capri

SAS, Trapani
Type(s): PT 50, 1; PT 20, 3 (Rodriquez)
Route: Trapani-Egadi Islands

Adriatica SpA di Navigazione
Venezia
Type(s): PT 50, 1 (Rodriquez)
Route: Tremoli-Isoledi Tremiti

Ministry of Transport, Milan
Type(s): PT 20, 2, 3 RHS 70s (Rodriquez)
Route: Lake Garda

Compagnia di Navigazione
Type(s): PT 20, 2 (Rodriquez)
Route: Lake Maggiore

Compagnia di Navigazione
Type(s): PT 20, 2 (Rodriquez)
Route: Lake Como

G. & R. Salvatori, Naples
Type(s): PT 50, 2 (Westermoen)
Route: Naples-Capri

Sar Nav
(Societa Sarda per Navigazione Veloce)
HEAD OFFICE:
Via Lombardia 38, Olbia
Type(s): Seaflight L90 "Squalo Bianco", 1
Route(s): Civitavecchia-Olbia (Italian Peninsula-Sardinia)

Societa Sirena, Palermo
Type(s): PT 50, 1 (Rodriquez)
Route: Palermo-Ustica

Societa Tosco Sarda di Nav Porto Ferraio
Type(s): PT 20, 3, PT 20 Caribe, 1 (Rodriquez)
Route: Piombino-R, Matina-P. Azzutto
AGIP, Milan
Type(s): PT 20, 1, PT 50, 1 (Rodriquez)

NORWAY
De bla Omnibusser A/S
Type(s): PT 20, 2 (Westermoen)
Route: Oslofjord
Stavangerske Dampskibsselskab
Type(s): PT 50, 2; PT 20, 1; RHS 140, 1 (Rodriquez)
Route: Savanget-Haugesund-Bergen
Hardanger Sunnhordelandske Dampskibsselskap
Box 268, 5001, Bergen
Type(s): PT 20, 1 (Westermoen); RHS 140, 1 (Rodriquez)
Route: Bergen-Tittelsness
Fosen Trafikklag A/S
Skaneskaia 6, Trondheim
Type(s): PT 20 Nisen (Westermoen)
Services: Trondheim area
Haanes Rederi A/S
Kristiansand
Type(s): PT 150, 1 (Westermoen)
Route: Charter services in Scandinavian waters
Joh. Presthus Rederi
Bergen
Type(s): PT 150, 2 (Westermoen)

MOROCCO
Transports Touristiques Intercontinentaux, Tangier
Type(s): Kometa, 2 (Sormovo design)
Routes: Tangier-Algericas, Tangier-Marbella

POLAND
Central Board of Inland Navigation
Type(s): ZRYW-1
Route: Szczecin-Swinoujscie
Type(s): Kometa (Sormovo)
Route: unknown

SWEDEN
Svenska Rederiaktiebolaget Oresund
Type(s): PT 50, 2 RHS 140, 1 (Rodriquez)
Route: Copenhagen-Malmö

Nordo Rederi AB
Malmo
Type(s): PT 150 (Westermoen)
Services: Malmo-Copenhagen, in conjunction with Joh Presthus Rederi.

SWITZERLAND
Societe de Nav, sur le Lac Leman
Type(s): PT 20, 1 (Rodriquez)
Route: Lake Geneva

UNITED KINGDOM
Red Funnel Steamers Ltd
Type(s): Seaflight H 57, 1, RHS 70, 2 (Rodriquez)
Route: Southampton-Cowes

Speed Hydrofoils Ltd
World Trade Centre,
London, E1
Chairman: H. H. Snowball
Types: Raketa TA, 1 (Sormovo, modified)
Service: Tourist trips, based on St Katharine's Pier. Commuter route Gravesend-Central London, also craft offered on charter. Projected future fleet to include Raketas, Voskhods, Meteors and Kometas.

YUGOSLAVIA
INEX-Nauticki Turizam
Obala Lazareta 3, Split

PP/POB 199,

Telephone: 47-651. 45-758

Telex: 11227

Director: B. Tomic

Type(s): Replacement fleet, understood to comprise two Raketa Ts and three Kometa MTs

Route(s): Adriatic coastal services; tourist and passenger services between Italy and Yugoslavia

USSR

Ministry of the River Fleet

The Soviet Ministry of the River Fleet operates hydrofoil passenger ferries on practically all the major rivers, lakes, canals and reservoirs from Central Russia to Siberia and the Far East.

In 1958, when hydrofoils were first introduced to the rivers of the USSR, they carried ten thousand passengers. By 1968 the number of passengers carried had grown to three million. During the 1969-70 navigation season there were 80 hydrofoil services on the Volga alone, operated by vessels of the Raketa, Meteor, Sputnik and Burevestnik series. There are now more than 150 hydrofoil passenger services in the Soviet Union and it was stated that in 1972 the 200 craft operating these services carried about 20 million passengers.

In addition to craft on inland waterways employing the Alexeyev shallow draft submerged foil system, Strela-type craft, with surface-piercing foils, operate in the Gulf of Finland, and supported by Kometas and Vikhrs, provide year-round services between ports on the Black Sea.

Three new hydrofoil passenger ferry designs are under development, —the Cyclone, a gas-turbine powered craft with seats for 250 and capable of 40 knots, the Typhoon, a gas-turbine powered 90-seat vessel with fully submerged, autostabilised foils and the Voskhod (Sunrise), a Raketa replacement. The Voskhod will provide greater comfort and improved facilities for passengers and crew and air-conditioning will be installed. As with the Raketa, a family of variants will be available to suit a wide variety of operating and traffic conditions. Fastest of the series will be the Voskhod 3, powered by a gas-turbine and capable of 43 knots. In late 1972 it was reported that the Voskhod was beginning to enter service.

The Raketa has given excellent service and has extremely low operating costs. The cost of carrying passengers on the craft is stated to be lower than that of either displacement-type passenger ferries or automobiles. Similar low-cost operation is demonstrated by the 260-passenger Sputnik on the Moscow-Astrakhan route. It has been found that the cost of operating a Sputnik on this service is only 8% of that of the latest displacement-type passenger ferry of the United Volga Steamship Line. Time saving is one of the most important considerations. In many cases, hydrofoils take passengers to their destinations faster than trains. For example, a Raketa service covers the 516 miles (800 km) from Gorky to Kazan in 12 hours, while trains take 20 hours for the same journey. Price of the ticket is the same, however, whether the journey is undertaken by hydrofoil or rail.

The Meteor service from Moscow to Sormovo takes 13 hours 40 minutes to cover 559 miles (900 km). A conventional passenger ship requires about three days to cover this distance.

Soviet Frontier Police

Some twenty-five Pchela patrol hydrofoils, derived from the Strela passenger ferry, are in service with the Soviet Frontier Police in the Baltic, Caspian and the Black Sea areas.

Soviet Navy

The first sightings of a new hydrofoil fast patrol boat were made in the Baltic in the spring of 1973. It appears that this new vessel, which is thought to be equipped for ASW work, is based on the hull of the Osa missile craft. The design employs a fixed surface-piercing bow foil only. Powered by three 4,330 hp diesels it has a top speed of about 45 knots under calm conditions.

POWER PLANTS AND PROPULSION SYSTEMS

CANADA

KOHLER OF CANADA LTD

HEAD OFFICE:
6390 Northwest Drive, Malton, Ontario
TELEPHONE:
416 677-4733
TELEX: 02-29366
EXECUTIVES:

D. W. F. Seston, Director of Marketing and Sales

Several Canadian light air cushion vehicle designs are equipped with Kohler two-cycle engines.

Model:	K-295-1	K-295-2	K-340-2	K-399-2	K-440-2
		K-295-2AX	K-340-2AX	K-399-2AX	K-440-2AX
Bore:	2,953 in	2,264 in	2,441 in	2,559 in	2,667 in
	(75 mm)	(57·5 mm)	(62 mm)	(65 mm)	(68 mm)
Stroke:	2,618 in	2,205 in	2,205 in	2,362 in	2,362 in
	(66·5 mm)	(56 mm)	(56 mm)	(60 mm)	(60 mm)
Displacement:	17·93 cu in	17·69 cu in	20·62 cu in	24·28 cu in	26·60 cu in
	(294 cc)	(290 cc)	(338 cc)	(398 cc)	(436 cc)

UNITED AIRCRAFT OF CANADA LTD
(Subsidiary of United Aircraft Corporation)
HEAD OFFICE & WORKS:
P.O. Box 10, Longueuil, Quebec
EXECUTIVES:

T. E. Stephenson, President
R. H. Guthrie, Vice-President, Industrial & Marine Division
E. L. Smith, Vice-President, Operations
E. H. Schweitzer, Vice President, Product Support
K. H. Sullivan, Vice-President, Marketing
V. W. Tryon, Vice-President, Finance
E. A. Clifford, Engineering Manager, Industrial and Marine Division
L. Chisholm, PR Manager

In addition to its compact range of low-power aircraft turbines (eg the PT6A turbo-prop, PT6B, PT6T and T400 turboshafts, and JT15D turbofan), UACL also manufactures a marine derivative of the PT6, the ST6 series of turboshafts. These engines are rated at 550 shp and upwards, and are installed in a number of ACV and hydrofoil vessels. These include the FHE-400 ASW hydrofoil where ST6 engines drive the generators and hydraulic pumps for the ship's services and foil control, and also provide emergency propulsion power for hullborne operation. The US prototype Surface Effect Ship SES-100B is equipped with three ST6J-70s to power its eight lift fans: two of this same version of ST6 power Alcan's Nechako crewboat and its Hydro Drive strut units. The Britten Norman CC7 amphibious ACV is powered by an ST6B-60 which drives two centrifugal fans to provide both lift and thrust; two ST6T-75 'Twin Pac' units power the Bell Voyageur hovercraft; the US Navy has also approved the ST6-71 as marine powerplant for its Rimfakse test vehicle—there is also a USN LCM-8 test vehicle powered by the ST6 series.

UACL ST6 MARINE GAS TURBINE
UACL ST6 marine gas turbines are manufactured by United Aircraft of Canada. Details of the engine specifications are given below:
TYPE: A simple cycle free turbine engine with a single spool gas generator and a multi-stage compressor driven by a single stage turbine. Burner section has an annular combustion chamber with downstream injection. The single stage-free turbine is connected to the output shaft via a reduction gearbox.

The UACL ST6T-75 Twin Pac TM is a dual engine with the two engines mounted side-by-side and coupled to a twinning reduction gear.

United Aircraft ST6 gas turbine

AIR INTAKE: Annular air intake at rear of engine with intake screen.
COMPRESSOR: Three axial-flow stages, plus single centrifugal stage. Single-sided centrifugal compressor with 26 vanes, made from titanium forging. Axial rotor of disc-drum type with stainless steel stator and rotor blades. Stator vanes are brazed to casing. The rotor blades are dove-tailed to discs. Discs through-bolted with centrifugal compressor, to shaft. Fabricated one-piece stainless steel casing and radial diffuser.
COMBUSTION CHAMBER: Annular reverse-flow type of stainless steel construction, with 14 Simplex burners. Two glow plug igniters.
GAS GENERATOR: Single-stage axial. Rotor blades mounted by fir tree roots.
POWER TURBINE: Single-stage axial. Rotor blades mounted by fir tree roots.
BEARINGS: Gas generator and power turbine supported by one ball bearing and one roller bearing each.
SHAFT DRIVE: Single, or two stage planetary reduction gear or direct drive-depending on engine model. Torque measuring system incorporated with reduction gearing.
FUEL GRADE: Aviation turbine fuels, Diesel Nos. 1 and 2 and Navy Diesel.
JET PIPE: Single port exhaust discharging vertically upwards or at 60° port or starboard of vertical. Alternatively twin ports discharging horizontally.
ACCESSORY DRIVES: Mounting pads on accessory case including for starter or starter-generator and tacho-generator. Also tacho-generator drive on power section.

LUBRICATION SYSTEM: One pressure and four scavenge gear type pumps driven by gas generator rotor. Integral oil tank.
OIL SPECIFICATIONS: Type 2 synthetic lube oil PWA-521 MIL-L-23699.
DIMENSIONS:

Diameter		Approx 19 in
Width	ST6T-75	44·4 in
Height	ST6T-75	31·6 in
Length	ST6J-70	62 in
	ST6K-70	60 in
	ST6J-77	62 in
	ST6L-77	52·2 in
	ST6K-77	60 in
	ST6L-80	59·4 in
	ST6T-75	66·4 in

Weight (Dry):

ST6J-70	350 lb
ST6K-70	317 lb
ST6J-77	319 lb
ST6L-77	306 lb
ST6K-77	350 lb
ST6L-80	360 lb
ST6T-75	730 lb

PERFORMANCE RATINGS:
Maximum (1)

ST6J-70	620 shp at 2,200 rpm
ST6K-70	620 shp at 6,230 rpm
ST6J-77	690 shp at 2,200 rpm
ST6L-77	811 shp at 33,000 rpm
ST6K-77	690 shp at 6,230 rpm
ST6L-80	1,065 shp at 30,000 rpm
ST6T-75	1,700 shp at 6,600 rpm

Intermittent (2)

ST6J-70	580 shp
ST6K-70	580 shp
ST6J-77	620 shp
ST6L-77	—
ST6K-77	620 shp
ST6L-80	955 shp

ST6T-75	1,500 shp	ST6J-70	0·64 lb/shp/hr	ST6L-80	0·60 lb/shp/hr
Normal (2)		ST6K-70	0·64 lb/shp/hr	ST6T-75	0·63 lb/shp/hr
ST6J-70	510 shp	ST6J-77	0·62 lb/shp/hr	At normal rating:	
ST6K-70	510 shp	ST6L-77	0·589 lb/ shp/hr	ST6J-70	0·67 lb/shp/hr
ST6J-77	550 shp	ST6K-77	0·62 lb/shp/hr	ST6K-70	0·67 lb/shp/hr
ST6L-77	654 shp	ST6L-80	0·58 lb/shp/hr	ST6J-77	0·66 lb/shp/hr
ST6K-77	550 shp	ST6T-75	0·62 lb/shp/hr	ST6L-77	0·62 lb/shp/hr
ST6L-80	840 shp	At intermittent rating:		ST6K-77	0·66 lb/shp/hr
ST6T-75	1,300 shp	ST6J-70	0·65 lb/shp/hr	ST6L-80	0·62 lb/shp/hr

(1)   at 72°F and sea level
(2)   at 59°F and sea level (ISA conditions)
FUEL CONSUMPTION:
At maximum rating:

ST6K-70   0·65 lb/shp/hr
ST6J-77   0·64 lb/shp/hr
ST6L-77   —
ST6K-77   0·64 lb/shp/hr

ST6T-75   0·65 lb/shp/hr
OIL CONSUMPTION:
All models, less than 0·2 lb/hr.

FRANCE

MERLIN GERIN

OFFICES AND WORKS:

Grenoble

Merlin Gerin is a leading French constructor of heavy duty electrical switchgear and has supplied a range of large circuit breakers to the major French domestic user, Electricite de France, and to authorities overseas. The company is also engaged—through its subsidiary, Le Moteur Lineaire (LML) at Grenoble, in the development of linear induction motors and their associated electrical and mechanical hardware for the propulsion of tracked ACVs. A close association is maintained with Grenoble University.

Initial application of LML linear motors in tracked ACVs is in the Bertin Société de l'Aérotrain 44-seat, operational test vehicle, intended for short-range traffic in heavy built-up areas and for city-to-airport links.

The motor, which provides a silent and non-polluting means of traction, is rated at 400 kW and is flexibly mounted in the vehicle. Application of propulsive or braking thrust to the vehicle is through an articulated transmission system. A three-phase a.c. current is conveyed via a line set alongside the vehicle at guideway level.

During normal operation, braking is provided not only by friction pads clamping the guide rail, but also by reverse-phasing the linear motor's electrical supply.

A second projected application of LML's linear motors is in the Compagnie d'Energ-

etique Linéaire URBA 4, a prototype urban and suburban monorail transport vehicle embodying three Dynavac air bogies. Propulsion and braking is by a 25 kW LML linear motor, using a 380 volt, three-phase 50 cycle mains supply and the vehicle will operate suspended under an overhead track. Conductor rails for the current supply to the motor and lift fans are located in the base of a conductor fin which runs in the centre of the track.

Le Moteur Lineaire is now engaged in the fabrication of the linear motor power/propulsion system for the US Department of Transportation Urban TACV, under subcontract to Rohr Industries, Inc of Chula Vista, California. LML will provide a linear induction motor, the power conditioning equipment (subcontracted from English Electric Hewittic—now GEC Rectifiers—of Stafford, England) and the power collection system to propel the 60,000 lb, 60-passenger U-TACV at speeds up to 159 mph. Maximum thrust will exceed 8,000 lb.

Merlin Gerin and LML are also designing the power distribution system and linear induction motor power/propulsion system for the tracked ACV system which the French government plans to construct between Cergy and Paris (La Defense). This system will incorporate two motors per vehicle, one for starting, braking and low speed operation, and a second for high speed operation. Performance data is not available at this

LML linear motor for Bertin Aerotrain at Gometz

time.

In addition, LML has furnished a large linear motor for the Krauss-Maffei magnetically levitated test vehicle now undergoing tests near Munich.

Merlin Gerin has recently established a new subsidiary, LEM Inc., in Washington, to promote the company's linear motor activities throughout the American market.

ETS RAUZIERS

HEAD OFFICE:

11 Avenue Descartes, 92 Le Plessis Robinson

Ets Rauzieres is marketing a special propulsion unit for high performance lightwieght air cushion vehicles. The unit, given the name "Diagloo", comprises an adapted 600 cc Citroen air-cooled, automotive engine, driving a 4 ft 7¼ in (1·40 m) diameter, two-bladed Merville propeller via a reduction and reverse gearbox. Engine output is 32·5 bhp (33 cv) at 6,000 rpm.

The unit weighs 220 lb (100 kg) and is supplied complete with an aerodynamically profiled hood. Series production has begun. The price is approximately F 5,000.

The Diagloo propulsion unit for light sports ACVs

SOCIÉTÉ TURBOMÉCA

HEAD OFFICE AND WORKS:
Bordes (Pyrénées Atlantiques)

PARIS OFFICE:
1 Rue Beaujon, Paris 8c

PRESIDENT AND DIRECTOR GENERAL:
J. R. Szydlowski

The Société Turboméca was formed in 1938 by MM. Szydlowski and Planiol to develop blowers, compressors and turbines for aeronautical use.

In 1947 the company began development of gas turbines of low power for driving aircraft auxiliaries and for aircraft propulsion. Since then it has evolved over 68 different types of powerplants, of which 22 have gone into production and 10 have been manufactured under licence in five foreign countries.

Many of Turboméca's production series aircraft turbines have been adapted to industrial and marine duties including installation in French air cushion vehicles of various types. General descriptions follow of the main Turboméca turbine engines at present in production or under development. Reference is also made to air cushion vehicle and hydrofoil installations.

TURBOMÉCA ARTOUSTE

The Artouste is a single-shaft turboshaft engine which has been manufactured in quantity in two versions, the 400 shp Artouste IIC and the 563 shp Artouste IIIB. The 590 shp Artouste IIID has also been developed. More than 1,500 of the earlier Artouste II were built to power the Sud-Aviation Alouette II helicopter. The Artouste II has a single-stage centrifugal compressor, annular reverse-flow combustor and two-stage axial turbine. In the second generation Artouste III in which the pressure ratio is increased from 3·88 : 1 to 5·2 : 1, a single axial stage compressor has been added ahead of the centrifugal impeller. The turbine also has an additional stage.

A single Artouste drives the two propulsion airscrews on the Naviplane BC 8.

The following description refers to the Artouste IIIB.

TYPE: Single-shaft axial-plus-centrifugal turboshaft.

COMPRESSOR: Single-stage axial plus single-stage centrifugal compressor. Two diffusers, one radial and the other axial, aft of compressor. Pressure ratio at 33,500 rpm at S/L 5·2 : 1. Air mass flow 9·5 lb/sec (4·3 kg/sec) at 33,500 rpm at S/L.

COMBUSTION CHAMBER: Annular type, with rotary atomiser fuel injection. Torch igniters.

TURBINE: Three-stage axial type. Blades integral with discs. Row of nozzle guide vanes before each stage.

JET PIPE: Fixed type.

STARTING: Automatic with 4,000 watt starter-generator. Two Turboméca igniter plugs.

DIMENSIONS:

Length	71·46 in (1,815 mm)
Height	24·68 in (627 mm)
Width	20·47 in (520 mm)

WEIGHT (Dry):

Equipped	401 lb (182 kg)

PERFORMANCE RATING:
563 shp at 33,500 rpm

FUEL CONSUMPTION:
At T-O and max continuous rating
0·71 lb (322 gr) ehp/hr

TURBOMECA TURMO

The Turmo is a free-turbine engine available in both turboshaft and turboprop versions spanning the 1,200 to 2,000 shp power bracket. First generation Turmo IIIC and E series have a single-stage axial plus single-stage centrifugal compressor, annular reverse-flow combustor, two-stage axial compressor-turbine, and mechanically-separate single-, or two-stage power turbine. Second-generation Turmo X engines have an additional axial compressor stage and other refinements. By December 1972 more than 1,100 Turmo engines had been built.

Main versions of the Turmo at present in production or under development include: Turmo IIIC: Derived from the Turmo III B, C and C_2, this model (with two-stage power turbine) has a 1,480 shp take-off rating and powers early Sud-Aviation SA 321 Super-Frelon three-engined military helicopters. Two will power the projected Aerospatiale 46-ton patrol boat hydrofoil under development for the French navy.

The Turmo IIIF also powers the Turbotrains of SNCF.

Turmo $IIIC_4$; Based on the Turmo $IIIC_3$, this is a special version with a single-stage power turbine and powers the Sud-Aviation SA 330 Puma twin-engined military helicopter. The engine has a maximum contingency rating of 1,370 shp.

Turmo IIIC: This model (which reverts to the standard two-stage power turbine) is in the same series as the Turmo IIIC and E_3, and has a maximum emergency rating of 1,580 shp. It is installed in Sud Aviation SA 321 F and J Super-Frelon civil three engined helicopters.

Turmo $IIIC_6$: Embodies new materials

The Turbomeca Turmo III F free-turbine turboshaft

The Turbomeca Astazou II A single-shaft turboshaft of the type which provides power for lift and propulsion on the SEDAM Naviplane N 102 marine ACV

The **889 shp** Turbomeca Turmastazou XIV free-turbine turboshaft

for the gas generator turbine, and offers an emergency rating of 1,580 shp.

Turmo IIIF$_5$: With the same configuration as the Turmo IIIC$_3$ and C$_5$, this engine is rated at 1,480 shp and powers later Sud-Aviation SA 321 Super-Frelon twin-engined military helicopters. Two Turmo IIIE$_3$ each rated at 1,282 shp, also power the Bertin/Société de l'Aérotrain Orléans 250-80 tracked air-cushion vehicle. Both engines drive a ducted seven-bladed 7 ft 7 in (2·30 m) diameter Ratier-Figeac FH-201 hydraulically-operated reversible-pitch propeller for propulsion. The Turmo IIIE is rated at 1,580 shp.

Turmo IIIF: This model has been in production since 1970 to power the production version of the SNCF Turbotrain operating on the Paris-Caen-Cherbourg run.

Turmo IIIN$_3$: Rated at 1,250 shp, this version powers the twin-engined SEDAM Naviplane N300 marine air-cushion vehicle. The engines are cross-coupled to drive two three-bladed 11 ft 10 in (3·60 m) diameter Ratier-Figeac FH 195-196 hydraulically-operated variable-pitch propellers for propulsion and two eleven-bladed 6 ft 3 in (1·85 m) diameter Ratier-Figeac FD 155 hydraulically-operated variable-pitch axial fans for lift.

Turmo X: Developed from the Turmo IIIC$_2$, this second-generation model has a two-stage axial compressor ahead of the centrifugal stage. With a maximum continuous rating of 1,480 shp, the Turmo X is planned for a new SNCF Turbotrain.

Two Turmo IIIC series engines with a combined installed power of 2,564 shp, are to power the projected Sud-Aviation SA800 second-generation hydrofoil

The following details apply to the Turmo-IIIC$_3$:
TYPE: Free-turbine axial-plus-centrifugal turboshaft.
AIR MASS FLOW: 13 lb (5·85 kg)/sec.
DIMENSIONS:
Length   77·8 in (1,976 mm)
Width   27·3 in (693 mm)
Height   28·2 in (717 mm)
WEIGHT DRY:
With standard equipment   516 lb (234 kg)
PERFORMANCE RATINGS:
T-O   1,480 shp
Max continuous   1,282 shp
FUEL CONSUMPTION:
At T-O rating   0·60 lb (273 gr)/shp/hr
At max continuous rating
                 0·64 lb (291 gr)/shp/hr

TURBOMECA MARBORE

The Marbore single-shaft turbojet has been built in greater numbers than any other Turbomeca engine. By December 1972 over 9,000 880 lb (400 kg) thrust Marbore IIs and 1,058 lb (480 kg) thrust Marbore VIs had been manufactured by Turbomeca and its licensees for trainer aircraft and target drone applications. Of this total, 5,114 Marbore engines were manufactured by Turbomeca. In both these versions the engine comprises a single-stage centrifugal compressor, annular reverse-flow combustor and single-stage axial turbine.

Two Marbores will power the SA 890 hydrofoil test platform currently under development by Aérospatiale for the French Ministry of National Defence.

A Marbore II powers the lift system of the SEDAM Naviplane BC8 marine ACV. The exhaust gases are ducted along channels designed to entrain additional air to augment the efflux.

The following details relate to the Marbore VI:
DIMENSIONS:
Length with exhaust cone but without tail-
pipe   55·74 in (1,416 mm)
Width   23·35 in (593 mm)
Height   24·82 in (631 mm)
WEIGHT (Dry):
Equipped   309 lb (140 kg)
PERFORMANCE RATINGS:
T-O   1,058 lb (480 kg) st at 21,500 rpm
Cruising 925 lb (420 kg) st at 20,500 rpm
SPECIFIC FUEL CONSUMPTION:
At T-O rating   1·09
At cruising rating   1·07

TURBOMECA ASTAZOU

The Astazou is another of the later generation Turboméca engines, incorporating the experience gained with earlier series and making use of new design techniques. It has an extremely small gas-producer section and has been developed both as a turboshaft and as a turboprop driving a variable-pitch propeller.

The compressor consists of one, or two, axial stages followed by a centrifugal stage, with an annular combustion chamber and three-stage turbine. Accessories are mounted on the rear of the main intake casing. Pressure ratio is 6:1 and air mass flow 5·5 lb/sec (2·5 kg/sec) for the two-stage compressor engines, and 8 : 1 and 7·4 lb/sec (3·4 kg/sec) for the three-stage compressor engines respectively. In the turboshaft version, the rpm of the output shaft is 5,922

Well over 700 Astazou engines of various types have been built. The following are the main Astazou variants:

Astazou II. This is a 535 hp turboprop (with two-stage compressor) which powers a version of the Naviplane N 102.

Astazou IIA. A 523 shp turboshaft (two-stage compressor) version powering the Sud-Aviation SA 318C Alouette II Astazou helicopter. A 450 shp Astazou provides power for the integrated lift and propulsion system of the SEDAM Naviplane N 102 marine ACV. The engine drives a 5 ft 7 in (1·70 m) diameter axial lift fan and two three-bladed variable-pitch propellers for propulsion.

Astazou IIIN. Rated at 592 hp, is the definitive (two-stage compressor) turbo-shaft for the SA 341 Gazelle helicopter.

Astazou XII. Derived from the Astazou II, this is the first of the three-stage compressor turboprops. Rated at 741 shp, it powers the Short Skyvan Srs 2 and Potez 842. In another installation, a 720 shp Astazou provides power for the Bertin-Société de l'Aérotrain Orléans 880-seat tracked ACV. The engine drives two 2 ft 7 in (0·80 m) Ratier-Figeac FG12 24-blade axial fans supplying air to six vertical and six horizontal air cushions for lift and guidance.

Astazou XIV (alias AZ14). Current major production turboprop version (with three-stage compressor) rated at 852 shp. The engine is the standard power plant for the Naviplane N 102.

Astazou XVI (alias AZ16). First Turbomeca production engine to embody the company's new air-cooled turbine. Rated at 913 shp for Jetstream aircraft.

Astazou XVIII. An uprated version of the Astazou XVI with take-off power of 1,554 ehp and sfc of 0·512 lb (232 gr)/ehp/hr.

Astazou XX. This later version has an additional axial compressor stage, and is rated at take-off at 1,445 ehp for an sfc of 0·45 lb (204 gr)/ehp/hr.

The following details refer to the Astazou IIIN.
DIMENSIONS:
Length   40·7 in (1,433 mm)
Basic diameter   18·1 in (460 mm)
WEIGHT, DRY:
Equipped engine   325 lb (147·5 kg)
PERFORMANCE RATINGS:
T-O   592 shp at 43,500 rpm
Max continuous 523 shp at 43,500 rpm
FUEL CONSUMPTION:
At T-O rating   0·627 lb (284 gr)/shp/hr
At max continuous rating
                 0·644 lb (292 gr)/shp/hr

TURBOMECA BASTAN

A compact single-shaft turboprop in the 1,000 to 2,000 shp power bracket, the Bastan has its main application in the Nord 262. The 1,065 ehp Bastan VIC powering the original 262 series aircraft, comprises a single-stage axial compressor plus single-stage centrifugal compressor, annular reverse-flow combustor and three-stage axial turbine, and is equipped with water-methanol injection. The higher rated Bastan VII is capable of maintaining its 1,135 ehp T-O power up to an ambient temperature of 40°C. This version is entering production to power the new 262C and incorporates an additional axial compressor stage.

The following details refer to the Bastan VII:
DIMENSIONS:
Length   75·2 in (1,911 mm)
Height   31·6 in (802 mm)
Width   21·7 in (550 mm)
WEIGHT, DRY:
Basic engine   639 lb (290 kg)
PERFORMANCE RATINGS:
T-O and max continuous   1,135 ehp
FUEL CONSUMPTION:
At T-O and max continuous ratings
                 0·572 lb (259 gr)/shp/hr

TURBOMECA TURMASTAZOU

This is a new free-turbine direct-drive turboshaft comprising the Astazou XIV single-shaft gas generator section provided with a mechanically-independent power turbine. The Astazou turbine has two stages in place of its normal three, and the power turbine has two stages also. Development is underway of the 889 shp Turmastazou XIV with a view to its use in twin-engined helicopters. The engine has also been proposed for the Bertin/Société de l'Aérotrain Orléans tracked ACV.

Turmastazou XVI. This version introduces the Turbomeca air-cooled turbine, and gives a take-off rating of 1,015 shp for an sfc of 0·51 lb (231 gr)/shp/hr.

The following details refer to the Turmastazou XIV:
DIMENSIONS:
Length   54·0 in (1,371 mm)
Height   21·8 in (553 mm)
Width   17·3 in (440 mm)
WEIGHT, DRY:
Equipped engine
          approximately 341 lb (155 kg)
PERFORMANCE RATINGS:
T-O   889 shp
Max continuous   792 shp

GERMANY

MTU
Motoren-und Turbinen-Union Friedrichshafen GmbH

HEAD OFFICE:
799 Friedrichshafen, Postfach 289
TELEPHONE:
(07541) 2071
TELEX:
MTUFH 0734-360
TELEGRAMME:
MOTORUNION
DIRECTORS:
Rolf Breuning, Executive President
Hugo B. Saemann, Executive President
Dr. Hans Dinger
Dr. Karl A. Müller
Werner Niefer
Dr. Ernst Zimmermann

The MTU-group of companies, formed in 1969 by the M.A.N. AG and the Daimler-Benz AG, consists of MTU-München GmbH and MTU-Friedrichshafen GmbH.

MTU-Friedrichshafen comprises the two plants of the previous Maybach Mercedes-Benz Motorenbau GmbH at Friedrichshafen and is owned 84 p.c. by MTU-München GmbH. MTU-München, in turn is owned equally by M.A.N. and Daimler-Benz.

MTU-Friedrichshafen is today the development and production centre for high-speed diesel engines of Maybach, M.A.N. and Mercedes-Benz origin and as such embodies the experience of these companies in diesel engine technology. In addition to diesel engines, MTU-Friedrichshafen is responsible for sales and application of industrial and marine gas-turbines.

For application in hydrofoils MTU-Friedrichshafen offers the following engines:
331 engine family
12 V 493
652 engine family
538 engine family (16 + 20 V)

The areas of responsibility of the two MTU companies are as follows:
MTU-München:
Development, production and support of light-weight, advanced-technology gas turbines mainly for aircraft applications.
MTU Friedrichshafen:
Development, production and application of high-performance diesel engines.

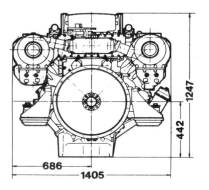
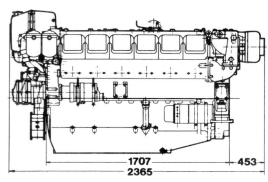

MTU 12 V 331 TC marine diesel, rated at 1,000 kW at 2,340 rpm

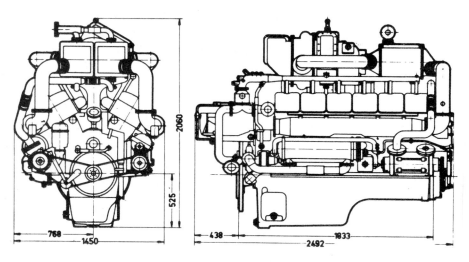

MTU 12 V 493 marine diesel rated at 1,000 kW at 1,500 rpm

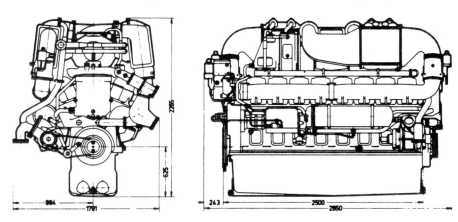

MTU 16 V 652 marine diesel rated at 1,920 kW at 1,460 rpm

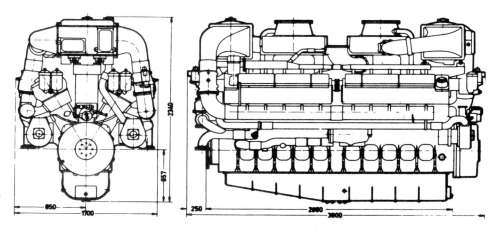

MTU 20 V 538 marine diesel rated at 2,620 kW at 1,750 rpm

The following table defines power ranges in connection with application characteristics and reference conditions.

Output characteristics of operational engin-es usually depend from special demands of the hydrofoil, from the operating profile and other application specialities and therefore will be specified individually for each system.

MTU diesel engines for main propulsion of vessels, application groups 1C and 1D:

Engine model	Continuous output			Intermittent output			Engine weight (dry)
	rpm	kW	hp	rpm	kW	hp	kg
Application group 1C	1,000 hours per year						
6 V 331 TC 70	2000	380	515	2120	450	610	1610
8 V 331 TC 70	2000	510	695	2120	610	830	1950
12 V 331 TC 71	2000	760	1035	2120	900	1225	2950
12 V 493 TY 70	1400	810	1100	1500	1000	1360	3250*
12 V 652 TB 71	1380	1220	1660	1460	1440	1960	4510*
16 V 652 TB 71	1380	1620	2205	1460	1930	2610	6240*
Application group 1D	1,000 hours per year						
6 V 331 TC 80	2260	450	610	2340	500	68ʋ	1610
8 V 331 TC 80	2260	600	815	2340	660	900	1950
12 V 331 TC 81	2260	900	1225	2340	1000	1360	2950
12 V 538 TB 81	1710	1440	1960	1760	1580	2150	5250
16 V 538 TB 81	1710	1920	2610	1760	2100	2850	6650
16 V 538 TB 81	1710	2140	2910	1760	2340	3180	6500
20 V 538 TB 82	1710	2400	3265	1760	2620	3565	8720
*Weight ot engine with light alloy housing							

—Continuous output A DIN 6270
—Intermittent output PU DIN 6270 (2 hours within 12 operating hours)
Reference conditions:
  Intake air temperature: 20°C (45°C with 331 TC, 32°C with 538 TB 81)
  Water temperature in charge air cooler: 20°C (80°C with 331 TC, 27°C with 538 TB 81)
  Barometric pressure: 1·0 bar

MTU Marine Gas Turbines built under General Electric licence

Engine Type	Max rating (hp)	Output speed (rpm)	Air mass flow (kg/sec)	Weight (kg)
LM 300	3,400	5,400	12·2	850
LM 1500	17,200	5,500	76·5	3,850
LM 2500	26,800	3,600	66·0	4,450

VOLKSWAGENWERK AG
HEAD OFFICE AND WORKS:
  Wolfsburg
UK IMPORTERS:
  Volkswagen (GB) Ltd
ADDRESS:
  Volkswagen House, Brighton Road, Purley CR2 2UQ
TELEPHONE: 01-668 4100
INDUSTRIAL ENGINES MANAGER: J. M. Savage

The air-cooled petrol engines powering over 20 million Volkswagen cars and vehicles are also produced as industrial power units in which role they have been proved reliable and economical in millions of hours running. There are three versions available, the Type 122 developed from the 1,192 cc Volkswagen car engine; the 1,584 cc Type 126A developed from the 1,500 cc van engine; and the 1,795 cc Type 127 developed from the 1,700 car engine.

TYPE 122
TYPE: Air-cooled four-cylinder, horizontally-opposed four-stroke petrol engine available with or without governor.
CYLINDERS: Four separate cylinders of special grey cast iron, with integral cooling fins. Cast alumimiun heads, one for each two cylinders, with shrunk-in sintered steel valve seats and bronze valve guides. Bore

Volkswagen Type 127 industrial engine

bhp 18D/2 engine powers the Finnish Tehi 70-passenger Raketa-type hydrofoil.

The following description relates to the mechanically supercharged CRM 18 D/2 and turbo-supercharged CRM 18 D/S.

TYPE: 18-cylinder in-line W type, four-stroke, water-cooled mechanically-supercharged (CRM 18 D/2) or turbo-supercharged (CRM 18 D/S) diesel engine.

CYLINDERS: Bore: 5·91 in (150 mm). Stroke 7·09 in (180 mm). Swept volume 194·166 cu in (3·18 litres) per cylinder. Total swept volume 3,495 cu in (57·3 litres). Compression ratio 16·25 : 1. Separate pressed-steel cylinder frame side members are surrounded by gas-welded sheet metal water cooling jacket treated and pressure-coated internally to prevent corrosion. Cylinders are closed at top by a steel plate integral with side wall to complete combustion chamber. Lower half of cylinder is ringed by a drilled flange for bolting to crankcase. Cylinder top also houses a spherical-shaped pre-combustion chamber as well as inlet and exhaust valve seats. Pre-combustion chamber is in high-strength, heat and corrosion resistant steel. A single cast light alloy head, carrying valve guides, pre-combustion chambers and camshaft bearings bridges each bank of cylinders. Head is attached to cylinder bank by multiple studs.

PISTONS: Light alloy forgings with four rings, top ring being chrome-plated and bottom ring acting as oil scarper. Piston crowns shaped to withstand high temperatures especially in vicinity of pre-combustion chamber outlet ports.

CONNECTING RODS: Comprise main and secondary articulated rods, all rods being completely machined I-section steel forgings. Big end of each main rod is bolted to ribbed cap by six studs. Big-end bearings are white metal lined steel shells. Each secondary rod anchored at its lower end to a pivot pin inserted in two lugs protruding from big-end of main connecting rod. Both ends of all secondary rods, and small ends of main rods have bronze bushes.

CRANKSHAFTS: One-piece hollow shaft in nitrided alloy steel, with six throws equi-spaced at 120°. Seven main bearings with white metal lined steel shells. Twelve balancing counterweights.

CRANKCASE: Cast light alloy crankcase bolted to bed plate by studs and tie bolts. Multiple integral reinforced ribs to provide robust structure. Both sides of each casting braced by seven cross ribs incorporating crankshaft bearing supports. Protruding sides of crankcase ribbed throughout length.

VALVE GEAR: Hollow sodium-cooled valves of each bank of cylinders actuated by twin camshafts and six cams on each shaft. Two inlet and two outlet valves per cylinder and one rocker for each pair of valves. End of stem and facing of exhaust valves fitted with Stellite inserts. Valve cooling water forced through passage formed by specially-shaped plate welded to top of cylinder.

FUEL INJECTION: Pumps fitted with variable speed control and pilot injection nozzle.

PRESSURE CHARGER: Two mechanically-driven centrifugal compressors on CRM 18 D/2, or two exhaust gas turbo-driven compressors on SCRM 18 D/.

CRM 18 D/S marine diesel rated at 1,350 bhp at 2,075 rpm

ACCESSORIES: Standard accessories include oil and fresh water heat exchangers; fresh water tank; oil and fresh water thermostats; oil filters, fresh water, salt water and fuel hand pumps; fresh water and oil temperature gauges; engine, reverse gear and reduction gear oil gauges; and engine rpm counter. Optional accessories include engine oil and water pre-heater, pre-lubrication electric pump, and other warning and pressure switches.

COOLING SYSTEM: Fresh water.

FUEL: Fuel oil having specific gravity of 0·830 to 0·840.

LUBRICATION SYSTEM: Pressure type with gear pump.

OIL: Mineral oil to SAE 40 HD.

OIL COOLING: By salt water circulating through heat exchanger.

STARTING: 24 volt 15 hp electric motor and 85 amp, 24 volt alternator for battery charge, or compressed air.

MOUNTING: At any transverse or longitudinal angle tilt to 20°.

REVERSE GEAR: Bevel crown gear wheels with hydraulically-controlled hand brake.

REDUCTION GEAR: Optional fitting with spur gears giving reduction ratios of 0·561 : 1, 0·730 : 1 and 0·846 : 1. Overdrive ratio 1·18 : 1.

PROPELLER THRUST BEARING: Incorporated in reduction gear or in overdrive. Axial thrust 6,620 lb (3,003 kg) at 1,176 rpm

DIMENSIONS:

Height	51·33 in (1,304 mm)
Width	53·15 in (1,350 mm)
Length	116·5 in (2,960 mm)

WEIGHTS, Dry:

Engine	3,690 lb (1,665 kg)
Reverse gear, generator and starter	900 lb (410 kg)
Reduction gear or overdrive, with propeller thrust bearing	330 lb (150 kg)
Total	4,920 lb (2,225 kg)

PERFORMANCE RATINGS:

CRM 18 D/S:
Maximum power   1,350 bhp at 2,075 rpm
Intermittent service
1,250 bhp at 2,020 rpm

Continuous service 1,040 bhp at 1,900 rpm

FUEL CONSUMPTION:
CRM 18 D/S at continuous service rating
0·37 lb (0·170 kg)/bhp hr

OIL CONSUMPTION:
CRM 18 D/S at continuous service rating
0·007 lb (0·003 kg)/hr

CRM 12 D/S

Second in the new CRM series of light-weight diesels is the 900 bhp 12-cylinder 12 D/S with two banks of six cylinders set at 60° to form a V assembly. The bore and stroke are the same as in the CRM 18 series, and many of the components are interchangeable, including the crankshaft, bedplate, cylinders and pistons. The crankcase and connecting rod-assemblies are necessarily of modified design; the secondary rod is anchored at its lower end to a pivot pin inserted on two lugs protruding from the big-end of the main connecting rod. The fuel injection pump is modified to single block housing all 12 pumping elements located between the cylinder banks.

A major innovation first developed on the 12 D/S (and later provided for the other engines in the series) was the introduction of an exhaust gas driven turbo-charger. This involved a complete revision of the combustion system and all components comprising the cylinder heads. Conversion to turbo-charging avoided the mechanical power loss expended in driving the blower, and enabled a greater volume of air to be forced into the cylinders. The effect on specific fuel consumption was a reduction to around 0·35 lb to 0·37 lb (160 to 170 gr)/bhp/hr in conjunction with exhaust temperatures not exceeding 530°C (986°F) at maximum rpm. Two Holset turbo-chargers are fitted.

TYPE: 12-cylinder in-line V type, four-stroke water-cooled, turbo-supercharged diesel engines.

DIMENSIONS:

Height	47·4 in (1,204 mm)

3·032 in (77 mm). Stroke 2·520 in (64 mm). Cubic capacity 72·74 cu in (1,192 cc). Compression ratio 7:1.

CRANKCASE: Two-part magnesium pressure casting with enclosed oil sump and flange for mounting the engine on machine or pedestal.

CRANKSHAFT: Forged, with hardened journals, mounted in three aluminium bearings and one three-layer, steel-backed bearing (No. 2).

CONNECTING RODS: Forged steel, I-section shank. Three-layer, steel-backed, lead-bronze big-end bearing shells with white metal running surfaces.

PISTONS: Aluminium with steel inserts, two compression rings and one scraper ring.

CAMSHAFT: Grey cast iron, with three steel-backed, shell-type bearings in crankcase, driven by helical gears.

VALVES: One inlet and one exhaust valve per cylinder. Exhaust valves have special armoured seating surfaces. 'Rotocap' valve rotating devices can be fitted on request.

COOLING: Radial fan, driven by belt from crankshaft. Protective grille on fan intake.

LUBRICATION: Forced feed gear-type pump. Full flow, flat tube oil cooler in fan airstream. Oil capacity 4·4 pints (2·5 litres).

CARBURETTOR: Downdraft Solex 26 VFIS on engine with governor. Downdraft Solex 28 PCI with accelerator pump, on engine without governor. Both have choke for cold starting.

IGNITION: With magneto; high tension, partly-supressed Scintilla-Vertex magneto with built-in automatic short-circuit switch as adjustable speed limiter. With coil ignition: 12 volt and centrifugal spark advance distributor.

PLUGS: Bosch W145 T1.

FUEL: Normal commercial petrol of 86 octane rating minimum.

STARTING: Hand cranking lever or electric starter.

GOVERNOR: Centrifugal type, operating on carburettor throttle, driven by toothed belt.

EXHAUST SYSTEM: Cylindrical muffler located transversely at bottom of engine, with exhaust pipes from cylinders and damper pipe with short tail pipe.

MOUNTING: By four bolts in the crankcase flange.

COUPLING: Engine is connected to driven shaft by a clutch or flexible fixed-coupling.

PEDESTALS AND TRANSMISSIONS: Suitable flange pedestals, with or without couplings or clutches, can be supplied as well as gearboxes with direct drives or drives of various ratios for clockwise or anti-clockwise rotation.

DIMENSIONS:

Width	29·4 in (748 mm)
Height	26·2 in (665·5 mm)
Length.	29·2 in (740·5 mm)

WEIGHT, Dry:
With standard equipment, approx 205 lb (93·5 kg)

PERFORMANCE RATINGS:
Continuous rating 34 bhp DIN at 3,600 output rpm

FUEL CONSUMPTION:
At 20 bhp at 2,000 output rpm 0·534 lb (242 gr)/bhp/hr
At 30 bhp at 3,600 output rpm 0·590 lb (268 gr)/bhp/hr

OIL CONSUMPTION:
Approx 20 to 35 cc/hr at 3,000 output rpm

TYPE 126A

TYPE: Air-cooled four-cylinder, horizontally-opposed four-stroke petrol engine available with or without governor. Construction generally similar to Type 122 with following exceptions.

CYLINDERS: Bore 3·543 in (85·5 mm). Stroke 2·717 in (69·0 mm). Cubic capacity 96·50 cu in (1,584 cc). Compression ratio 7·7 : 1.

CARBURETTOR: Downdraft Solex 26 or 28 VFIS on engine with governor. Downdraft Solex 32 PCI on engine without governor.

DIMENSIONS:

Width	29·9 in (760·0 mm)
Height	26·5 in (675·5 mm)

Length	28·5 in (723·0 mm)

WEIGHT, Dry:
With standard equipment, approx 220 lb (100 kg)

PERFORMANCE RATINGS:
Continuous rating 44 bhp DIN at 3,600 output rpm

FUEL: 90 octane minimum

FUEL CONSUMPTION:
At 28 bhp at 2,000 output rpm 0·496 lb (225 gr)/bhp/hr
At 44 bhp at 3,600 output rpm 0·562 lb (255 gr)/bhp/hr

OIL CONSUMPTION:
Approx 25 to 40 cc/hr at 3,000 output rpm

TYPE 127

TYPE: Air-cooled, four-cylinder, horizontally-opposed four-stroke petrol engine of low profile design.

CYLINDERS: Bore 3·740 in (93 mm). Stroke 2·165 in (66 mm). Cubic capacity 109·53 cu in (1,795 cc). Compression ratio 7·3 : 1.

COOLING: Radial fan on crankshaft.

CARBURETTOR: Solex 32 PCI downdraft or tewo Solex 34PDSIT downdraft.

IGNITION: 12 volt battery.

DIMENSIONS:

Width	3·780 in (960 mm)
Height (without air cleaner)	2·189 in (556 mm)
Length	3·264 in (829 mm)

WEIGHT, Dry:
With standard equipment   273 lb (124 kg)

PERFORMANCE RATINGS:
Maximum continuous ratings at 4,000 rpm
Single carburettor   62 bhp DIN
Twin carburettor   68 bhp DIN

FUEL: 90 octane minimum.

FUEL CONSUMPTION:
At 3,000 output rpm 0·506 lb (230 gr)/bhp/hr
At 4,000 output rpm 0·561 lb (255 gr)/bhp/hr

ITALY

C.R.M. FABRICA MOTORI MARINI

HEAD OFFICE:
20121 Milano, via Manzoni, 12

TELEPHONE:
708. 326/327

CABLES:
Cremme

DIRECTORS:
Ing F. Mariani
Ing. B. Piccoletti
Ing. S. Rastelli
Mr. S. Sussi
Minoja p.i. Vittorio

CRM has specialised in building lightweight diesel engines for more than twenty years. The company's engines are used in large numbers of motor torpedo boats, coastal patrol craft and privately-owned motor yachts. More recently, the engines have also been installed in hydrofoils.

During the 1960s the company undertook the development and manufacture of a family of 18, 19 and 9-cylinder diesel engines of lightweight high-speed design, providing a power coverage of 300 bhp to 1,350 bhp. These comprise the 18-cylinder CRM 18D₂ and 18 D/S of 1,050 to 1,350 bhp with mechanically-driven supercharging and turbo-driven supercharging respectively and its cylinders arranged in an unusual W arrangement of three banks of six cylinders each.

the 12-cylinder CRM 12 D/S of 900 bhp with two banks of six cylinders and first in the new series to introduce turbo-charging; and the 650 bhp CRM 9 D/S with a W arrangement of three banks of three cylinders and offering the option of turbo-charging or natural aspiration.

Details of these engines are given below.

CRM 18

First in CRM's new series of lightweight high-speed diesels, the CRM 18 is an 18-cylinder unit with its cylinders arranged in a W form comprising three banks of six cylinders. Maximum power is 1,050 bhp at 1,900 rpm with mechanically driven supercharging and 1,350 bhp, at 2,075 rpm, with exhaust gas turbo-charging. One 1,050

Width   47·64 in (1,210 mm)
Length   99·60 in (2,530 mm)
WEIGHTS, Dry:
  Engine   2,735 lb (1,240 kg)
  Reverse gear, generator and starter
                    900 lb (410 kg)
  Reduction gear or overdrive, with propeller thrust bearing   330 lb (150 kg)
  Total   3,965 lb (1,800 kg)
PERFORMANCE RATINGS:
  Max power   900 bhp at 2,035 rpm
  Continuous service   850 bhp at 2,000 rpm
  Intermittent service 750 bhp at 1,900 rpm

FUEL CONSUMPTION:
  At continuous service rating
              0·40 lb (0·18 kg)/bhp/hr

CRM 9

Third in development and smallest in the new CRM lightweight series of diesels is the nine-cylinder three-bank engine of similar configuration to the CRM 18 units. Both a naturally-aspirated version, the 415 bhp CRM 9, D/A, and a turbo-supercharged version, the 715 bhp CRM 9 D/S, are available.

TYPE: Nine-cylinder in-line W type, four-stroke, water-cooled, naturally-aspirated (CRM 9 D/A) or turbo-supercharged (CRM 9 D/S) diesel engine.

WEIGHTS, Dry:
  Engine, CRM 9 D/S   2,447 lb (1,110 kg)
Reverse and reduction gear, with prop-

CRM 9 D/S marine diesel rated at 650 bhp at 1,950 rpm

eller thrust bearing, generator and starter
              1,356 lb (615 kg)
  Total   3,803 lb (1,725 kg)
PERFORMANCE RATINGS:
  CRM 9 D/S, max power
           715 bhp at 1,950 rpm

Continuous service   550 bhp at 1,800 rpm
Intermittent service 660 bhp at 1,900 rpm

FUEL CONSUMPTION:
  CRM 9 D/S at continuous service rating
          0·385 lb (0·176 kg)/bhp/hr

FIAT/AIFO

Applicazioni Industriali Fiat OM
HEAD OFFICE: Via Carducci 29, Milan
TELEPHONE: 877-066/8

AIFO Carraro V12SS, 700 hp 12-cylinder diesel engines are installed in the H 57 60-passenger hydrofoil ferries built by Seaflight, Messina.

CARRARO V12SS

TYPE: Pre-chamber injection, vee-form 12-cylinder, turbocharged and inter-cooled four-stroke diesel engine.
OUTPUT: Basic engine, 700 bhp; maximum shaft output 650 hp at 1,500 rpm.
BORE AND STROKE: 142 × 180 mm.

FUEL INJECTION: Bosch type pumps and centrifugal governor; fuel feeding pumps; fuel cartridge filters.
ENGINE COOLING: By fresh water into closed circuit with thermostatic control valve.

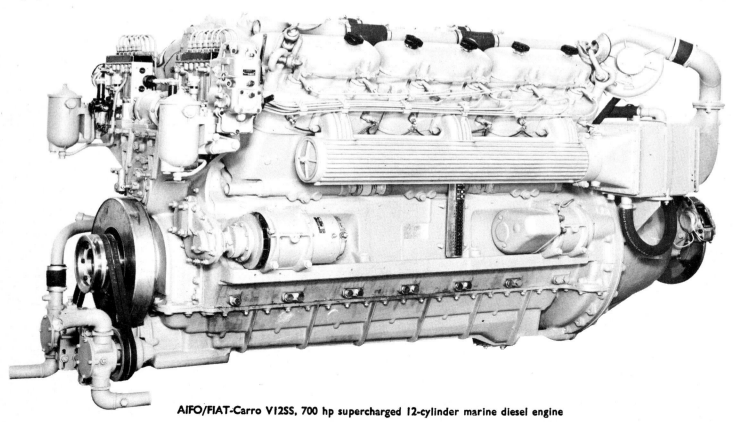

AIFO/FIAT-Carro V12SS, 700 hp supercharged 12-cylinder marine diesel engine

OIL COOLING: By salt water circulating through a heat exchanger.

STARTING: 6 hp starter motor and 600 watt generator for battery charging.

LUBRICATION: By gear pump.

REVERSE GEAR: Hydraulically operated, with brake on transmission.

REDUCTION GEAR: Standard ratios, 1·5 : 1 and 2 : 1.

DRY WEIGHT: 4,120 lb (2,200 kg).

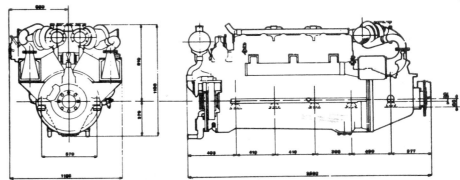

Fiat-Carraro V12SS 700 hp marine diesel. Two of these 12-cylinder water-cooled and super-charged engines power the Seaflight H57 hydrofoil passenger ferry

UNITED KINGDOM

AIR RIDER RESEARCH LTD

REGISTERED OFFICE:
  Rosehaugh Works, Newbarn Lane, Cudham Kent
SALES OFFICE:
  166 Harcourt Avenue, Sidcup, Kent
TELEPHONE:
  01-302 2133
EXECUTIVES:
  David Goodman
  Evelyn Vass

Air Rider Research is the UK distributor for German-built Fichtel & Sachs rotary engine for use in light hovercraft. The power unit for this application is the 303 cc, single-rotor, type 904 engine developing 20·19 hp (Din) at 5,000 rpm. Rotary engines have been supplied for several hovercraft and they provide the power for the 12 ft, 500 lb (unladen) light hovercraft of Air Rider Research design. Several craft of this type have been built, available in single-lift, twin-thrust (three engine) and single-lift, single-thrust (two engine) versions. The three engine version forms the basis for a Daily Express Air Rider sports hovercraft.

Relatively high power from a compact, vibration-free, lightweight engine are features of the 'Wankel-type' rotary design which fit the light hovercrafts specification in which, for the Air Rider Research design, the lift engine drives a 26·5 in (673 mm) diameter axial fan and each propulsion engine drives a 35·4 in (900 mm) H/Richmond propeller.

Specification details of the Fichtel & Sachs 904 rotary engine are as follows:

TYPE: Single rotor, four-stroke

DISPLACEMENT VOLUME: 18·5 in³ (303 cc).

COMPRESSION RATIO: 8:1

COOLING SYSTEM: Air-cooled, integral fan.

AIR INFILTRATION: Mesh type.

IGNITION: Bosch flywheel magneto, 40 watt, 12 volt.

SPARK PLUGS: Bosch or Champion.

INDUCTION SYSTEM: Tillotson carburettor

One of the two rotary propulsion engines for the Daily Express Air Rider Sports Hovercraft

with fixed or adjustable main jets, incorporating a diaphragm fuel pump.

FUEL GRADE: Gasolene.

PRE-MIX RATIO: 40:1 (fuel: oil).

WEIGHT, Dry:
  Including flywheel (approx.) 30 kg (66·1 lb)

PERFORMANCE RATING: 20·19 hp (Din) at 5,000 rpm.

AUTO DIESELS BRABY LIMITED

(Member of Economic Group Ltd)

HEAD OFFICE AND WORKS:

Cowley Mill Road, Uxbridge, Middlesex, UB8 2QG.

TELEPHONE: Uxbridge 38262

TELEX: 263835

EXECUTIVE:

R. A. Wheadon, Commercial Manager

Auto Diesels Braby are manufacturers of the A.250 and IS.250 single-shaft gas turbines. They also are distributors for the Waukesha Model T-400 fixed and free-shaft gas turbine.

A.250 and IS.250

The 250 series is available as a low-pressure compressed bleed air unit (A.250) for aircraft starting and servicing, or as a shaft output unit (IS.250) for mechanical or electrical drives. General details are as follows:

TYPE: Simple-cycle, single-shaft.

AIR INTAKE: Annular with intake screen.

COMPRESSOR: Single-shaft, centrifugal, incorporating fixed inlet guide vanes.

COMBUSTION CHAMBER: Twin, reverse-flow, positioned 180° apart and discharging tangentially into turbine casing.

TURBINE: Single-stage, centripetal, mounted back-to-back with compressor.

BEARINGS: Main rotor assembly supported in single roller and ball bearings.

SHAFT DRIVE: (IS.250): Helical reduction gears give a range of standard output speeds from 3,000 to 4,250 rpm, or speeds up to 8,000 rpm according to requirements.

AIR BLEED (A.250): Compressed air taken from main casing surrounding rotor assembly via a flow-limiting venturi and electrically-operated main air valve.

FUEL GRADE: JP1, JP3, JP4, MIL-G-5572, Kerosene, Diesel.

JET PIPE: Single, co-axial outlet.

LUBRICATION SYSTEM: Pressure fed from single gear-type pump in 'wet' sump. Integral oil tank.

OIL SPECIFICATIONS: SAE 10 or SAE 20.

IGNITION: High energy electrical unit provides current to surface discharge plugs which operate automatically during start cycle.

Twin Waukesha T.400 gas turbines, supplied through Auto Diesels Braby, power the prototype EM.2 hoverfreighter

IS.250

Width	38 in (96·5 cm)
Height	33 in (83·8 cm)
Length	48 in (121·9 cm)

DIMENSIONS:

A.250

Width	44 in (111·8 cm)
Height	40 in (102·6 cm)
Length	50 in (127·0 cm)

WEIGHT, Dry:

A.250	850 lb (385·6 kg)
IS.250	600 lb (272·2 kg)

PERFORMANCE RATINGS:

A.250 120 lb/min (54·5 kg/min) of air at 55 psia (3·85 kg/cm²) absolute at ISA conditions.

IS.250 250 hp at 25,000 turbine rpm

T.400

Providing power for electrical generation, various mechanical drives or marine duties, the T.400L powers the EM.2 hoverfreighter, under evaluation by Enfield Marine Ltd. Details of the T.400 are as follows:

TYPE: Simple, free or fixed shaft.

AIR INTAKE: Annular with intake screen.

COMPRESSOR: Single-stage, centrifugal.

COMBUSTION CHAMBER: Annular.

GAS GENERATOR TURBINE: Single-stage axial.

POWER TURBINE: Single-stage axial.

BEARINGS: Sleeve bearings on high-speed gas generator shaft.

SHAFT DRIVE: Integral gearbox provides rated power at 2,400, 3,000 or 3,600 rpm output shaft speeds.

FUEL GRADES: Multi-fuel capability diesel, kerosene, gas oil or natural gas.

JET PIPE: Single, co-axial outlet.

DIMENSIONS:

Width	28 in (71·1 cm)
Height	34 in (86·4 cm)
Length	51 in (129·5 cm)

WEIGHT, Dry: 685 lb (310·7 kg)

PERFORMANCE RATINGS:

Continuous	400 hp at 36,800 compressor rpm
Maximum (intermittent)	500 hp at 36,800 compressor rpm

BUDWORTH

David Budworth Ltd

HEAD OFFICE & WORKS:

Harwich, Essex

TELEPHONE:

Harwich 3116

EXECUTIVES:

D. D. Budworth, Managing Director

J. Blewitt, Director

J. M. Budworth, Director

David Budworth Ltd manufacture a simple and robust two-shaft gas turbine in three basic power ratings, 200 hp (Puffin), 300 hp (Blowfin) and 350 hp (Blowfly). In addition, a multi-input gearbox is available which can accommodate up to four engines coupled to a single output shaft. In this configuration, any one or more engines can be used at a time—an arrangement which gives good part-load economy, maximum flexibility in choice of power, maximum production of the basic gas generator unit, and a much simplified spares organisation. Engine diameter for each power rating is

Budworth Turbocompresser unit 6,000 cu ft/min at 1·5 atm

15 in (38·1 cm). Power turbine drive may be taken either from the exhaust end of the engine, or alternatively from the intake end, with the power turbine shaft running co-axially through the gas generator.

Budworth turbines, driving transonic axial compressors, have been delivered to the Central Electricity Generating Board for use with its air cushion equipment. Other engines have been supplied for use in a VTO research programme, together with high performance ducted fans. A complete turbofan engine is available with normal 500 lb st.

General details are as follows:
TYPE: Simple-cycle, free-turbine.

AIR INTAKE: Ram or otherwise depending on application.
COMPRESSOR: Blowfly-two-axial stages plus one centrifugal. Single-sided compressor wheel and drum-type axial rotors are precision cast in stainless steel. Axial stators manufactured in precision cast aluminium. Centrifugal diffuser is in stainless steel.

COMBUSTION CHAMBER: Annular, reverse-flow with vapourising burners.
GAS GENERATOR TURBINE: Two-stage with vacuum cast wheels and integral blading.
POWER TURBINE: Either single or two-stage with integral blading.
BEARINGS: High-speed ball and roller.
SHAFT DRIVE: Either direct or through planetary gearing at intake or exhaust end of engine.

FUEL GRADE: Kerosene or 35 sec gas oil.
STARTING SYSTEM: 24 volt electric or air start.

SPECIFIC FUEL CONSUMPTION:
For Blowfly   0·73 lb (331 gr)/bhp/hr
WEIGHT, Dry:
Gas generator   85 lb (38·6 kg)
Power turbine   Dependent on reduction gearing fitted

CATERPILLAR TRACTOR
Caterpillar Tractor Co Ltd
55 St. James's Street,
London SW1A 1LA
England
TELEPHONE:
01-493 1882

Caterpillar is the UK subsidiary of the Caterpillar Tractor Co, a leading US manufacturer of diesels who has supplied engines worldwide, equivalent to hundreds of millions of diesel horsepower. Engines are sold for marine, electrical power and industrial applications, and are supported by more than 900 Caterpillar dealer facilities for parts and service: more than 14,000 dealer servicemen provide a 24-hour service to diesel operators. The engines are designed to give a high degree of component interchangeability, equal on V-models to 90 per cent of all parts.

Major ACV outlet for Caterpillar diesels in the UK is via four financially inter-related companies using designs evolved under National Research Development Corp. grants. The companies, all based in the Southampton area, are Air Cushion Equipment Ltd, Hovertrailer International Co Ltd, Air Docks Ltd and Mackley Ace Ltd. Selection of Caterpillar diesels for their various applications has generally been because of the high power/weight ratio available. The US engines have been used from the earliest stages of the UK companies hover systems, and are now becoming regarded as the standard powerplant for this sector of the ACV market: a particular selling point for the Southampton companies' equipment when breaking into new markets such as construction, petroleum and marine, is in being able to refer to existing traditional Caterpillar-powered equipment in these industries.

Specific applications include Hovertrailer International standard, pipe, logging and high pressure trailers with lifting capacities up to 100 tons, powered by Caterpillar Model 3145, 3160, 3304, D343, D346 and D348 engines. Mackley Ace offshore hover platforms with lifting capacities of 30 tons and over, are powered by Model D334, D346 and D348 engines which are also used in Air Cushion Equipment bulk storage tank removal systems. Air Docks aircraft recovery systems in their standard form comprise twelve engine modules powered by the Model 3145.

MODEL 3304NA, 3304T AND 3306T
TYPE: Six-cylinder in-line four-stroke water-cooled, turbo-supercharged diesel engines. Counterclockwise rotation viewed from rear.

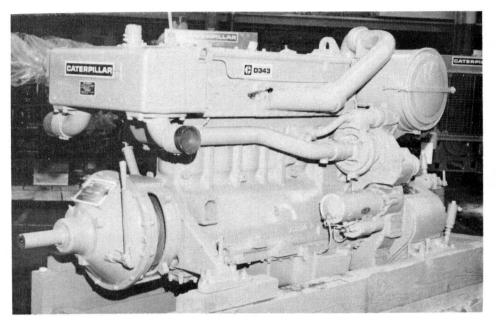
Caterpillar Model D343 marine diesel engine

CYLINDERS: Bore 4·75 in (121 mm). Stroke 6·0 in (152 mm). Total swept volume 3304NA and 3304T 425 cu in (6·9 litres), and 3306T 638 cu in (10·5 litres).
COMPRESSION RATIO: 17·5 : 1. Molybdenum alloy cast from cylinder liners water-cooled over full length, and specifically designed to give operating life equal to engine. Cylinder head assemblies cast in molybdenum and nickel alloyed grey iron, with intake manifold cast integrally with head to improve air flow and minimise maintenance. Water 'directors' located in the head force coolant against surfaces near combustion heat to eliminate hot spots.
PISTONS: Copper and nickel alloyed aluminium pistons elliptically ground and tapered from base to crown. Integrally cast iron ring band provides long-life wearing surface for top two of three piston rings. Intermediate ring is of twist design to seal efficiently and improve oil control. All rings are thick chrome plated. Gudgeon pins hardened to Rockwell 50C and ground to a 'fit' tolerance of only 0·0003 in (0·00076 cm). Retained by 'C' ring circlips.
CONNECTING RODS: Forged, hardened and shot-peened for high strength. Steel-backed aluminium bearings.
CRANKSHAFT: Steel forging, induction hardened, stress relieved and shot peened. Journals super-finished to within one micron of final smoothness.
CRANKCASE: Five or seven steel-backed aluminium bearings, with heavily ribbed bearing supports cast integrally with high tensile block.
VALVE GEAR: Valve rotators rotate 3° on each lift-off to give better valve seating and longer life. Exhaust valves faced with cobalt and tungsten alloy to retain hardness at operating temperatures. Exhaust seats have nickel based alloy replaceable inserts. Stainless steel intake valve heads and intake inserts contribute to efficient operation.
FUEL INJECTION: Precombustion chamber fuel system mixes fuel and air to atomize fuel for clean burning, and each chamber has an electric glow plug for reliable cold-weather starts. Capsule-type fuel injection valve with single large-diameter self-cleaning orifice. 'No-adjustment' fuel system with automatic fuel-air ratio control. Separate pump for each cylinder located on side of engine. Easily replaced spin-on filters with plastic-impregnated cellulose filter.
TURBO-SUPERCHARGER: Single-stage centrifugal air compressor driven by single-stage centripetal turbine energised by exhaust gases.
ACCESSORIES: Include fuel priming pump, 24-volt alternator, gear-driven jacket and auxiliary water pumps, speed governor, oil cooler, tachometer drive.
COOLING SYSTEM: Jacket water pump minimum flow 63 gal/min (3·98 litre/sec). Normal sea water pump flow 65 gal/min (4·10 litre/sec) (for six cylinders).
LUBRICATION SYSTEM: Fully-pressurised system with gear-type pump and full-flow

heavy duty filter system. Continuous oil spray lubricates piston gudgeon pins. Turbo-supercharger and engine bearings receive immediate lubrication on starts through bypass valve.

OIL COOLING: Tube-bundle type jacket water heat exchanger.

STARTING: Air motor mounted on starboard side of engine. Normal starting air pressure 90-100 lb/sq in. Or, 24-volt electric starter.

GEAR: Reverse and reduction gear hydraulically operated, full power for both clockwise and counter-clockwise propeller rotation. Gear ratio 2 : 1, 2·95 : 1, 3·83 : 1, 4·5 : 1.

DIMENSIONS with gear:
3304NA, 3304T:

Height	41·3 in (1,049 mm)
Width	36·0 in (914 mm)
Length	57·0 in (1,447 mm)

3306T:

Height	47·8 in (1,214 mm)
Width	37·2 in (945 mm)
Length	75·8 in (1,925 mm)

WEIGHTS, Dry with gear:

3304NA, 3304T	2,220 lb (1,007 kg)
3306T	2,675 lb (1,210 kg)

PERFORMANCE RATINGS:
3304NA:

Maximum (flywheel)	115 hp
Continuous (shaft)	82 hp

3304T:

Maximum (flywheel)	200 hp
Continuous (shaft)	121 hp

3306T:

Maximum (flywheel)	300 hp
Continuous (shaft)	184 hp
Normal working range	1,500-2,200 rpm

FUEL CONSUMPTIONS:
At continuous (shaft) rating:

3304NA	5·25 gal/hr (19·9 litre/hr)
3304T	7·80 gal/hr (29·5 litre/hr)
3306T	11·10 gal/hr (41·9 litre/hr)

MODELS D343T AND TA, D346, D348 AND D349

(Basic features of these models are in general similar to the D330 and D333 series, with following main differences).

TYPE: Eight, twelve and sixteen cylinder 60°V in-line (except for six-cylinder straight in-line D343), four-stroke, water-cooled, turbo-supercharger-aftercooled diesel engines. Counterclockwise rotation viewed from rear.

CYLINDERS: Bore 5·4 in (137 mm). Stroke 6·5 in (165 mm). Total swept volume D343 893 cu in (14·6 litre), D346 1,191 cu in (19·5 litre), D348 1,786 cu in (29·3 litre), and D349 2,382 cu in (39·1 litre). Compression ratio, 16·5 : 1, except for D343 16·8 : 1. One-piece nickel-chrome alloyed grey iron cast cylinder block, precision bored and milled. Conventional studs on V models are complemented by extra length studs extending into bearing saddle area.

TURBO-SUPERCHARGER AND AFTER-COOLER: Turbo-charger similar to 3304 and 3306 models with addition of water-cooled aftercooler interposed between compressor air delivery and cylinder manifold. System doubles rate of airflow to engine and lowers exhaust temperatures.

ACCESSORIES: Hydro-mechanical governor gear-driven fuel priming and transfer pumps, gear-driven jacket-water pump.

COOLING SYSTEM: Jacket water pump minimum flow 350 gal/min (22·10 litre/sec) except for D343 160 gal/min (10·10 litre/sec).

Caterpillar Model D346 marine diesel engine

GEAR: Ratio, D343 2·1 : 1, 2·5 : 1, 3 : 1, 3·5 : 1, 4·5 : 1 and 6 : 1, D346 2·19 : 1, 3·03 : 1, 4·09 : 1 and 5·17 : 1; D348 2·07 : 1, 2·92 : 1, 3·86 : 1, 5·17 : 1 and 5·88 : 1, D349 2 : 1, 2·94 : 1, 3·54 : 1, 4·67 : 1 and 5·88 : 1. All ratios at 1,800 engine continuous rpm.

DIMENSIONS with gear:
D343TA:

Height	55·65 in (1,413 mm)
Width	41·46 in (1,053 mm)
Length	84·52 in (2,147 mm)

D346:

Height	73·12 in (1,851 mm)
Width	60·12 in (1,527 mm)
Length	102·99 in (2,616 mm)

D348:

Height	77·20 in (1,960 mm)
Width	60·12 in (1,527 mm)
Length	118·73 in (3,015 mm)

D349:

Height	77·20 in (1,960 mm)
Width	60·12 in (1,527 mm)
Length	156·05 in (3,964 mm)

WEIGHTS, Dry with gear:

D343TA	6,040 lb (2,742 kg)
D346	9,320 lb (4,230 kg)
D348	11,335 lb (5,146 kg)
D349	14,855 lb (6,744 kg)

PERFORMANCE RATINGS (flywheel):
D343T:

Maximum, at 2,000 rpm	395 hp
Continuous, at 1,800 rpm	245 hp

D343TA:

Maximum, at 2,000 rpm	550 hp
Continuous, at 1,800 rpm	365 hp

D346:

Maximum, at 2,000 rpm	735 hp
Continuous, at 1,800 rpm	480 hp

D348:

Maximum, at 2,000 rpm	1,100 hp
Continuous, at 1,800 rpm	725 hp

D349:

Maximum, at 2,000 rpm	1,470 hp
Continuous, at 1,800 rpm	970 hp

FUEL CONSUMPTION:
D343T, D343TA:

	19·4 gal/hr (74 litre/hr) at 365 hp
D346:	25·8 gal/hr (95 litre/hr) at 480 hp
D348:	38 gal/hr (144 litre/hr) at 725 hp
D349:	51·6 gal/hr (190 litre/hr) at 970 hp

MODEL 3160

TYPE: Eight cylinder 90°V in-line, four-stroke, water-cooled, normally aspirated diesel engine.

CYLINDERS: Bore 4·5 in (114 mm). Stroke 5·0 in (127 mm). Total swept volume 636 cu in (10·4 litres). Compression ratio 16·5 : 1. Cast heads with integral air inlet manifold in alloyed grey iron. Intake and exhaust valve seats staggered to reduce thermal stress concentrations. Crescent-shaped bevel adjacent to each intake valve seat imparts swirl to incoming air to improve combustion. Bores honed to within 0·00005 in (0·0127 mm) tolerance between top and bottom.

PISTONS: Aluminium alloy pistons tapered and elliptically ground for correct shape under operating load and heat. One compression and one scraper ring with integrally cast nickel-iron insert for compression ring to minimise ring groove wear. Compression ring coated with molybdenum for extra life and less friction, and twisted for seal efficiency and oil control. Fully floating large 1·5 in (38 mm) diameter gudgeon pins, ground to 0·00003 in (0·00762 mm), and hardened on inner and outer surfaces.

CONNECTING RODS: Forged H-section rods, ground to precise balance. Steel-backed aluminium alloy bearings.

CRANKSHAFT: Forged, fixture-quenched, through hardened. 90°V design of engine results in balanced power strokes forces for smooth running.

CRANKCASE: Cast nickel-chrome alloyed

grey iron block featuring deep skirt design extending 4 in (101·6 mm) below centre-line of crankshaft for added strength and rigidity. Main bearing caps fit into machined recesses in block rib structure, with securing cap-screws positioned at 30° angles to obviate need for cross-bolting. Five main bearings with large wipe area, supported by ribbed block, recess-fitted bearing blocks. Steel-backed aluminium alloy bearings.

VALVE GEAR: Special heat resistant alloy steel intake and exhaust valves for corrosion resistance. Exhaust valves seat on replaceable hardened steel inserts for long life. Dual valve springs with different resonant frequencies to minimise float and prevent damage if one spring fails.

FUEL INJECTION: Fuel fed from low-pressure diaphragm transfer pump to fuel manifold. Separate pump plunger for each cylinder driven by fuel systems' own camshaft. Four orifices 0·012 in (0·305 mm) wide, spray fuel in cone-shaped pattern against shaped piston crown.

ACCESSORIES: 12-volt charging alternator, hydro-mechanical speed governor, fuel, jacket water and sea or fresh water pumps, 12-volt starter motor.

COOLING SYSTEM: Jacket water pump flow at continuous power rating 60 gal/min (3·79 litre/sec).

LUBRICATION SYSTEM: Gear-driven six-lobe pump passes oil through multi-plate oil cooler, then through two spin-on filters to oil gallery supplying all bearings surfaces with immediate lubrication.

STARTING: 12-volt electric.

GEAR: Reverse and reduction gear, with ratios 1·50 : 1, 1·97 : 1, 2·50 : 1, 2·96 : 1.

DIMENSIONS with gear:

Height	35·75 in (908 mm)
Width	34·3 in (860 mm)
Length	46·3 in (1,590 mm)

WEIGHT, Dry with gear: 1,610 lb (730 kg)

PERFORMANCE RATING (shaft):

Continuous, at 2,400 rpm   146 hp

FUEL CONSUMPTION:

At 75 per cent shaft hp

       5·9 gal/hr (22·3 litre/hr)

RUSTON PAXMAN DIESELS LIMITED (a management company of GEC Diesels Limited)

HEAD OFFICE & WORKS:
Vulcan Works, Newton-le-Willows, Lancashire, WA12 8RU

Paxman Works also at:
Hythe Hill, Colchester, CO1 2HW, Lincoln.

LONDON OFFICE (GEC Diesels Ltd):
105-109 The Strand, London WC2R 0BG

Manufactured at the Colchester Works of Ruston Paxman Diesels are three of the world's most advanced diesel designs; the vee-form 'Ventura', built in 6, 8, 12, and 16-cylinder sizes covering 450 to 2,400 bhp, the RP200 built in 8, 12 and 16-cylinder sizes covering 1,000-3,300 bhp, and the Napier 'Deltic'—an 18-cylinder engine of unique triangular configuration—in powers from 1,500 to 4,000 shaft horsepower. These engines, with their compact overall dimensions and low unit weight, are particularly suitable for the propulsion of high-speed craft including hydrofoils and hovercraft.

The 'Ventura' is being incorporated in several current designs for hydrofoils and rigid sidewall ACVs.

VENTURA (YJ) AND VALENTA (RP200) DIESELS

TYPE: YJ engines: Direct injection 60°, vee-form 6, 8, 12 and 16-cylinder, turbo-charged or turbo-charged and aftercooled four stroke diesel engine. RP200 engine: Direct injection, vee-form 8, 12 and 16-cylinder, turbocharged and water-cooled, four-stroke engine.

OUTPUT: YJ engines: 450-2,400 bhp, 1,000-1,600 rev/min. RP200 engines: 1,000-3,300 bhp, 1,000-1,600 rev/min.

BORE AND STROKE: 7·75 × 8·5 in (197 × 216 mm).

SWEPT VOLUME (per cylinder): 401 cu in (6·57 litres).

HOUSING: Fabricated high quality steel plate.

CRANKSHAFT AND MAIN BEARINGS: Fully nitrated shaft carried in aluminium tin pre-finished steel-backed main bearings. Engine fully balanced against primary and secondary forces.

CONNECTING RODS: Fork and blade type with steel-backed, aluminium tin lined large end (forked rod) and steel-backed, lead bronze lined, lead tin flashed bearings (blade rod).

PISTONS: Conventional aluminium alloy, oil cooled with Alfin bonded insert for top ring. Three compression and one oil control rings. (YJ): Three compression and one oil control ring (RP200).

CYLINDER HEAD: High grade casting carrying four valve direct injection system.

LINERS: Wet type seamless steel tube, chrome plated bore and water side surface, honeychromed for surface oil retention.

FUEL INJECTION: External Monobloc pumps located below air manifolds. (YJ): single unit pumps (RP 200). Pump plungers and camshaft lubricated from main engine pressure system. Feed and injection pump driven from engine drive end gear train; a fuel reservoir and air bleed system fitted. Injectors of the multi-hole type spray fuel into the toroidal cavity in the top of piston. Injectors retained by clamp and are external to head cover (YJ); sleeved connection inside cover (RP 200).

GOVERNOR: Standard hydraulic 'Regulateurs Europa' unit with self-contained lubricating oil system; mechanical, electrical or pneumatic controls. Alternative makes available.

PRESSURE CHARGING AND INTERCOOLING: Napier water-cooled exhaust-gas-driven turboblowers mounted above engine. Air to water intercooler of Serck manufacture for after-cooled versions (YJ and RP 200).

LUBRICATION: Pressure lubrication to all bearing surfaces; separate pressure and cooling pumps. (YJ): single pump system (RP 200). Oil coolers mounted externally and integral with engine (fresh water cooled (YJ); sea water cooled (RP 200). Full flow single or duplex oil filter can be supplied. Centrifugal filters fitted as standard (YJ).

FRESH WATER COOLING: Single pump at free end, shaft-driven from drive end gear train. Thermostatic control valve mounted above pump, giving quick warm-up and even temperature control of water and oil circuits (YJ); oil thermostat (RP 200).

Paxman 12-cylinder Valenta marine diesel developing 2,475 bhp at 1,600 rpm

EXHAUST: Single outlet from turbo-blower(s). Dry type manifolds (YJ); water-cooled manifolds (RP 200).

STARTING: Air, electric or hydraulic starting.

FUEL: Gas oil to BS.2869/1970 Class A1 and A2 or equivalent, and certain gas turbine fuels. Other classes of fuel subject to specification being made available.

LUBRICATING OIL: Oils certified to MIL-L-2104B (with a TBN of not less than 9).

OPTIONAL EXTRA EQUIPMENT: Gearboxes, starting control systems, and all associated engine ancillary equipment necessary for marine applications.

NAPIER DELTIC DIESEL

TYPE: 18-cylinder, opposed piston, liquid cooled, two stroke, compression ignition. Three banks of six cylinders in triangular configuration.

OUTPUT: Covers horsepower range of 1,500-4,000 shaft hp. Charge-cooled engine rating up to 3,000 shaft hp continuous at 1,800 rev/min. Half hour sprint rating up to 4,000 shaft hp at 2,100 rev/min. Weight/power ratio. 3·94 lb/shp.

BORE AND STROKE: Bore—5·125 in (130·17 mm). Stroke—7·25 in × 2 (opposed piston) (184·15 mm × 2).

SWEPT VOLUME (total): 5,284 in³ (88·3 litres).

COMBUSTION SYSTEM: Direct injection.

PISTONS: Two piece—body and gudgeon pin housing. Gudgeon pin housing with fully floating gudgeon pin shrunk into body and secured with taper seated circlip. Body-skirt and gudgeon pin housing in light alloy, piston crown in 'Hidurel' material. Oil cooled. Three gas, two oil control and one scraper ring.

CONNECTING RODS: Fork and blade type with steel backed, lead bronze, lead flashed, indium infused thin-wall bearings. Manufactured from drop forgings, machined and polished all over.

CRANKSHAFTS: Three crankshafts machined from forgings and fully nitrided. Each shaft fitted with viscous type torsional vibration damper. Each crankpin carries one inlet and one exhaust piston, thus, the loading on all crankpins is identical and reciprocating forces are balanced within the engine.

Deltic charge-air cooled, turbo-charged diesel engine with integral reverse reduction gear, developing 4,000 shp

CRANKCASES AND CYLINDER BLOCKS

Three crankcases and three cylinder blocks arranged in the form of an inverted equilateral triangle all of light alloy construction. Crankcases substantially webbed and carrying each crankshaft in seven, thin-wall, steelbacked, lead bronze, lead flashed indium infused main bearings. Cylinder blocks each carry six 'wet' type liners, have integrally cast air inlet manifolds and mount the injection pumps camshaft casings.

CYLINDER LINERS: 18 'wet' type liners machined from hollow steel forgings, bores chrome plated with honeychrome process applied, finished by lapping. Coolant side flash tin plated. In areas of liquid contact with exhaust coolant-area, flash chrome plated.

TURBOCHARGER: Geared-in type, single stage, axial flow turbine and single-sided centrifugal compressor mounted on common shaft. Light alloy main castings. Charge-cooled engines have charge-air coolers (one for each cylinder block) incorporated within the overall dimensions of the turbocharger unit.

PHASING GEAR: To combine the output from the three crankshafts. A light alloy gear casing containing an output gear train linked to the crankshafts by quill-shafts and passing the torque to a common output gear. All gears hardened and ground and carried in roller bearings. Gear train also provides drives for auxiliary pumps and engine governor.

FUEL SYSTEM: Pressurised system from engine driven circulating pump supplying 18 'jerk' type fuel injection pumps one per cylinder mounted in banks of six on camshaft casings secured to each cylinder block. Each pump supplies a single injector per cylinder.

LUBRICATION: Dry sump system with engine driven pressure and scavenge pumps. Twin pressure oil filters engine mounted.

COOLING: Closed circuit system with engine driven circulating pump. Engine mounted circulating pumps for sea-water system for cooling coolant heat exchanger and oil cooler, also for charge-air coolers.

STARTING: Air starting to six cylinders of one bank.

MOUNTING: Four point by resilient mounting units.

REVERSE GEAR: Marine reverse reduction gearbox incorporating a hydraulic friction clutch can be supplied as an integral unit.

ROLLS-ROYCE (1971) LIMITED (INDUSTRIAL & MARINE DIVISION)

HEAD OFFICE:
PO Box 72, Ansty, Near Coventry, Warwickshire

DIRECTORS:
R. H. Robins (Managing Director)

In April 1967 Rolls-Royce Limited formed a new division merging the former industrial and marine gas turbine activities of Rolls-Royce and Bristol Siddeley. The new division was known as the Industrial & Marine Gas Turbine Division of Rolls-Royce.

In May 1971 the present company, Rolls-Royce (1971) Limited, was formed combining all the gas turbine interests of the former Rolls-Royce company. The four divisions involved are the Industrial & Marine Division, the Derby Engine Division, the Bristol Engine Division and the Small Engine Division.

It offers a wider range of industrial and marine gas turbines based on aero-engine gas generators than any other manufacturer in the world. It has available for adaptation a large selection of the gas turbines being developed and manufactured by the Rolls-Royce Derby Engine Division, the Bristol Engine, and Small Engine Divisions. Marinised gas turbines at present being produced and developed by the Company include the Gnome, Proteus, Tyne and Olympus.

Over 1,200 of these marine and industrial engines are in service or have been ordered for operation around the world and the total value of the export orders received up to mid-1972 was approximately £63 million. 21 navies have selected the company's marine gas turbines to power naval craft, following the initial orders from the Royal Navy in the late 1950s.

HYDROFOILS: The Boeing PCH High Point is powered by two Proteus gas turbines while single Proteus turbines power the Boeing PGH-2 Tucumcari and Alinvani Swordfish. A Tyne powers the Grumman designed PG(H)-1 Flagstaff.

HOVERCRAFT: The Gnome powers the BHC SR.N3, SR.N5 and SR.N6. The Proteus powers the SR.N4 and the BH.7 and is specified for the new Vosper-Thornycroft VT2.

MARINE GNOME

TYPE: Gas turbine, free-turbine turboshaft.

AIR INTAKE: Annular. 15°C.

COMBUSTION CHAMBER: Annular.

FUEL GRADE:
D.E.R.D. 2494 Avtur/50 Kerosene.
D.E.R.D. 2482 Avtur/40 Kerosene.
Diesel fuel BSS 2869 Class A
DEF 1402 or NATO F75

TURBINE: Two-stage axial-flow generator turbine and a single-stage axial-flow free power turbine.

BEARINGS: Compressor rotor has a roller bearing at the front and a ball bearing at the rear. Gas generator turbine is supported at the front by the compressor rear bearings, and at the rear by a roller bearing.

Single stage power turbine is supported by a roller bearing behind the turbine disc and by a ball bearing towards the rear of the turbine shaft.

JET PIPE: Exhaust duct to suit installation.

ACCESSORY DRIVES: Accessory gearbox provides a drive for:—The fuel pump, the hydro-mechanical governor in the flow control unit, the centrifugal fuel filter, the dual tachometer and the engine oil pump.

LUBRICATION SYSTEM: Dry sump.

OIL SPECIFICATION: D.E.R.D. 2487.

MOUNTING: Front: three pads on the front frame casing, one on top, one on each side. Rear without reduction gearbox, mounting point is the rear flange of the exhaust duct centre-body. With reduction gearbox mounting points are provided by two machined faces on the reduction gearbox.

STARTING: Electric.

DIMENSIONS:

Length	65·6 in (1,667 mm)
Width	18·2 in (462 mm)
Height	20·75 in (527 mm)

PERFORMANCE RATINGS:

Max	1,050 bhp
Cont	900 bhp

Ratings are at maximum power-turbine speed, 19,500 rpm. A reduction gearbox is available giving an output speed of 6,650 rpm.

SPECIFIC FUEL CONSUMPTION:

Max	0·625 lb (283 gr) bhp/hr
Cont	0·650 lb (295 gr) bhp/hr

OIL CONSUMPTION:

	1·2 pints (0·67 litre)/hr
Power Turbine	1·5 pints (0·84 litres)/hr

MARINE OLYMPUS

Gas generator and single stage power turbine

TYPE: Gas turbine, two-shaft turbojet.

AIR INTAKE: Annular 15°C.

COMBUSTION CHAMBER: Eight.

FUEL GRADE: Diesel fuel B.S.S. 2869 Class A. DEF 2402 or NATO F. 75.

TURBINE (ENGINE): Two stage, each stage driving its own respective compressor—5 stage low pressure or 7 stage high pressure.

TURBINE (POWER): Single stage axial-flow.

BEARINGS: Compressor rotor forward end supported by a roller bearing and rear end by a duplex ball bearing.

The power turbine rotor assembly and mainshaft are supported as a cantilever in two white metal bearings housed in a pedestal.

JET PIPE: Exhaust duct to suit installation.

ACCESSORY DRIVES: Power turbine. Accessories are mounted on the main gearbox which is a separate unit transmitting the turbine's power output to the propeller shaft. These include pressure and scavenge oil pumps. Speed signal generator, iso-speedic switch and rev/min indicator are driven by the pedestal-mounted accessory gearbox.

Rolls-Royce Marine Tyne RM2D rated at 5,800 bhp

LUBRICATION SYSTEM: The gas generator has its own integral lubrication system which is supplied with oil from a 27 gal tank. Components in the system are:—A pressure pump, main scavenge pump, four auxiliary scavenge pumps and an oil cooler.

Power Turbine. Bearings are lubricated and cooled by a pressure oil system.

OIL SPECIFICATION: Gas generator. D. Eng R. D. 2487. Power turbine. O.E.P. 69.

MOUNTING: The mounting structure depends on the customer's requirements for a particular application.

STARTING: Air or electric.

DIMENSIONS:

Gas Generator:

Length	11 ft 9 in (3·6 m)
Width	4 ft 3 in (1·29 m)
Weight	6,500 lb (2·94 kg)

Power Turbine:

Length	12 ft 9 in (3·9 m)
Width	8 ft 0 in (2·4 m)
Height	9 ft 9 in (3 m)

Complete Unit:

Length	22 ft 3 in (6·8 m)
Width	8 ft 0 in (2·4 m)
Height	9 ft 9 in (3 m)
Weight	21 tons

PERFORMANCE RATING:

Max
28,000 bhp at max power-turbine speed of 5,660 rpm.

SPECIFIC FUEL CONSUMPTION:

Max	0·47 lb (226 gr) bhp/hr

OIL CONSUMPTION:

Gas Generator:

Max	1·5 pints (0·84 litre)/hr
Power turbine	1·5 pints (0·84 litres)/hr

MARINE PROTEUS

TYPE: Gas-turbine, free-turbine turboprop.

AIR INTAKE: Radial between the compressor and turbine sections of the engine. 15°C.

COMBUSTION CHAMBERS: Eight, positioned around the compressor casing.

FUEL GRADE: DEF 2402—Distillate diesel fuel.

TURBINE: Four stages coupled in mechanically independent pairs. The first coupled pair drive the compressor, the second pair form the free power turbine, which drives the output shaft.

BEARINGS: HP end of compressor rotor is carried by roller bearing. The rear end by a duplex ball bearing. Compressor turbine rotor shaft is located by a ball thrust bearing, as is the power turbine rotor.

JET PIPE: Exhaust duct to suit installation.

ACCESSORY DRIVES: All accessories are driven by the compressor or power turbine

systems. Compressor driven accessories are: compressor tachometer generator, fuel pump and centrifugal oil separator for the breather. The power turbine tachometer generator and governor are driven by the power turbine. The main oil pressure pump and also the main and auxiliary scavenge pumps, are driven by both the compressor and power turbines through a differential gear.

LUBRICATION SYSTEM: The engine is lubricated by a single gear type pump connected by a differential drive to both the compressor and power turbine systems.

OIL SPECIFICATION: OEP 71. D.E.R.D. 2479/1 or D.E.R.D. 2487 (OX 38).

MOUNTING: Three attachment points comprise two main trunnions one on each side of the engine close to the diffuser casing and a steady bearing located beneath the engine immediately aft of the air intake. Engines are supplied with integrally-mounted reduction gears giving maximum output shaft speeds of 5,240, 1,500 or 1,000 rpm depending on the gearbox selected.

DIMENSIONS:

Length	113 in (2,870 mm)
Diameter	42 in (1,067 mm)
Weight (dry)	3,118 lb (1,414 kg)

PERFORMANCE RATINGS:

Max	4,250 bhp
Cont	3,600 bhp
Uprated engine	
Max	4,500 bhp
95 per cent power	4,250 bhp
80 per cent power	3,600 bhp

SPECIFIC FUEL CONSUMPTION:

At max rating	0·572 lb (256 gr)/bhp/hr
Uprated engine at max rating	0·565 lb (253 gr)/bhp/hr

OIL CONSUMPTION:

Average	0·5 pints (0·28 litres)/hr

MARINE TYNE RM2D

Gas Generator and two stage power turbine.

TYPE: Gas turbine, two-shaft turboprop.

AIR INTAKE: Annular. 15°C.

COMBUSTION CHAMBER: Cannular containing ten flame tubes.

FUEL GRADE: Diesel fuel Grade A.

DEF 2402B AVCAT

TURBINE (ENGINE): Two stage, each stage driving its own respective compressor— six stage low pressure and nine stage high pressure.

TURBINE (POWER): Two-stage, axial flow free turbine.

BEARINGS: Compressor rotor forward end supported by a roller bearing and at the rear end by a thrust ball location bearing.

The power turbine front stubshaft is

supported on a roller bearing and the rear on a thrust bearing.

JET PIPE: Exhaust duct to suit installation.
ACCESSORY DRIVES: Engine and power turbines accessories are mounted on the external wheelcase of the engine and the primary gearbox accessories gearcase.
LUBRICATION SYSTEM: The gas generator lubricating oil system comprises fuel pump, scavenge pumps, filters, and magnetic plugs. The primary gearbox is also fed from the gas generator lubricating oil system.
OIL SPECIFICATION: DERD 2487.

MOUNTING: The forward engine mounting comprises two cantilever frames constructed of tubular members, one each side of the engine. The frames are joined by a diagonal strut across the uppermost members.

The reduction gearbox is supported in a similar way by three tubular steel supports, one either side and one beneath the gearbox. The ends of the engine and gearbox supports are attached to the central main engine support frame by means of spherical bearings. The centre of the unit is supported through a dogged ring into the main central frame.

STARTING: Air or electric.
DIMENSIONS:
Length	158 in (401·3 cm)
Width	50 in (127 cm)
Height	50 in (127 cm)

WEIGHT: 6,800 lb (3,084 kg)

PERFORMANCE RATINGS: RM2D.
Max 5,800 bhp (5,880 cv) at max power turbine speed of 14,500 rev/min (primary gearbox output speed as required).

SPECIFIC FUEL CONSUMPTION:
Max 0·461 lb (209 gr)/bhp hr

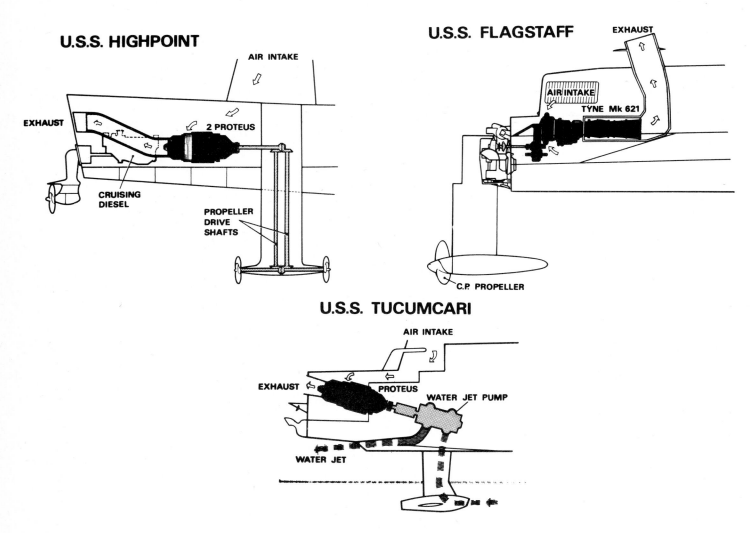

Rolls-Royce marine gas-turbines are employed on the PCH-1 High Point, the PGH-1 Flagstaff and the PGH-2 Tucumcari

---

ROWENA
ROWENA LIGHT ENGINES LTD

HEAD OFFICE & WORKS:
Bodlondeb, Llangaffo, Gaerwen, Anglesey
TELEPHONE:
0248 79 644
EXECUTIVES:
John A. Billing, Director of Engineering and Sales
Rowena Billing, Director of Administration

Rowena was formed in 1969 to manufacture specialist engines using parts in volume production for Stihl chainsaws. The lightweight, high specific output, robustness and longevity of the chainsaw engines were seen as desirable virtues in power units for the small hovercraft then projected by several manufacturers, and for the amateur field. In addition to the well-known 6507-J engine

which powers the majority of British light hovercraft and is further specified for several new models about to be produced. Two smaller engines have been prepared for use in pilotless aircraft. These are 1110 of 2·75 cu in (45 cm³) giving 4 hp, and the 1113 of 1·95 cu in (32 cm³) giving 2½ hp. Both engines operate on methanol.

ROWENA 6507-J

This is a single-cylinder two-stroke gasoline engine of 8·36 cu in (137 cm³) lubricated by oil mixed in the fuel. Power output is just over 8 bhp. The Mahle cylinder and piston are both of aluminium, with the cylinder bore direct chrome plated. This arrangement enables small running clearances to be incorporated, a feature of special value in extremes of ambient temperature. The forged crankshaft is supported in four caged

needle bearings, and the connecting rod has a split-cage big-end bearing and a caged little-end needle bearing. Rotation is clockwise on the output shaft, but counter-clockwise engines can be made available.

Ignition is by a Bosch magneto, and carburation is normally by means of a self-pumping Tillotson unit: alternatively an Amal carburettor can be fitted. Re-coil cord starting is provided, using a Siba device. The net continuous rating of over 8 bhp is available with the engine mounted close into the fan. The equivalent SAE rating is 13 hp at 6,400 rpm. The weight of the complete engine is 15 lb (6·8 kg), equipped with air filter, muffler and starter. In addition, pulleys, shafts and fan hubs can be furnished.

A governed and cowled version of the 6507-J has also been prepared.

ROWENA 6507-JL

This version is similar to the 6507-J, except that the magneto includes lighting coils, one of which is suitable for use with an ac volt-meter as a tachometer. The engine has been successfully operated in widely varying environmental conditions—ranging from Canadian winter to African jungle, and including flight at 13,000 ft (4,000 m) powering a motorised glider. While latest production engines are supplied with a diaphragm and labyrinth on the starter which renders the magneto splash proof, the ingestion of water should be avoided by careful installation design.

ROWENA 6507-K

A smaller capacity design of 5·73 cu in (95 cm³), giving a continuous rating of approximately 6 bhp. This has primarily been used in go-kart racing, but is also available with fan and cowl for stationary applications.

Rowena 6507-JL single-cylinder two-stroke engine with a net continuous rating of 8 bhp

THE UNITED STATES OF AMERICA

AIRESEARCH MANUFACTURING COM-PANY, a division of the Garrett Corporation

402 South 36th Street, Phoenix, Arizona 85034

TELEPHONE:
(602) 267-3011

EXECUTIVES:
William G. Orr, Vice President and Manager

Donald L. Cauble, Assistant Manager

Robert A. Trusela, Sales Manager

AiResearch Manufacturing Company, Phoenix, Arizona, is the world's largest manufacturer of small gas turbine engines for commercial, military, marine and industrial application, as well as a leading producer of air turbine starters, air motors, pneumatic valves and control systems for aircraft and aerospace applications. The company occupies approximately 1 million sq ft of facilities on 220 acres of land with its main facilities adjoining Phoenix Sky Harbor International Airport. Its employees number approximately 4,000.

GTP/GTPF990

Currently under development is a fully marinized 5,000 hp advanced gas turbine scheduled to be available in the mid-1970's. The engine is designed in two configurations, a free turbine (GTPF990) for propulsion, pump and compressor drive, and a coupled turbine (GTP990) for applications such as generator sets for primary and secondary power. The engine is being designed specifically for ease of maintenance and long TBO, and is expected to commence service with a TBO of 6,000 hours.

Specification details available are as follows:

TYPE: Simple-cycle, single-shaft (GTPF990) or twin-shaft (GTP990).
COMPRESSOR: Two-stage centrifugal.
COMBUSTION CHAMBER: Single, annular.
TURBINE: Two-stage axial gas generator.
FUEL GRADE: DF-2.
DIMENSIONS:
Length   108 in (274·3 cm)
WEIGHT, Dry:
    Fitted with lightweight gearbox
                          4,000 lb (1,814 kg)
    Fitted with heavy-duty gearbox
                          5,000 lb (2,449 kg)
PERFORMANCE RATING:
    Continuous S.L. 100°F: 5,000 shp at 18,000 rpm gas generator speed and 16,400 rpm power turbine speed.
    System output speed   3,600 rpm

ME 831-800

A further development by AiResearch is a fully marinized turbomarine power system, having a continuous power rating of 380 shp and an intermittant rating of 610 shp. This unit, designated ME831-800, is under development for the Boeing NATO PHM hydrofoil secondary power system, which uses two units per ship. The ME831-800 will be available in approximately 18 months.

Specification details available are as follows:

TYPE: Simple-cycle, single-shaft.
COMPRESSOR: Two-stage centrifugal.
COMBUSTION CHAMBER: Single, reverse-flow.
TURBINE: Three-stage axial.
FUEL GRADES: DF-1 and DF-2 per ASTM. D975, VV-F-800, MIL-F-16884 and MIL-R-46005, Jet A, A-1 and B per ASTM D1665. JP-4 and JP-5 per MIL-F-5624 and VV-K-211.
DIMENSIONS:
    Length   72 in (182·9 cm)
    Width   39 in (99·1 cm)
    Height   34 in (86·4 cm)
WEIGHT, Dry: 1,500 lb (680·4 kg)
POWER RATING:
    Continuous S.L. 100°F   380 shp
    Intermittent   610 shp
    Rated rotor speed   41,730 rpm (max)
    System output speed constant speed,
    two output pad speeds of 8,000 rpm
    and two at 3,600 rpm

AVCO LYCOMING
Avco Lycoming Division of Avco Corporation

HEAD OFFICE:
550 South Main Street, Stratford, Connecticut 06497

WORKS:
Stratford, Connecticut

PRESIDENT OF AVCO CORPORATION:
James R. Kerr

VICE-PRESIDENTS:
Beverly H. Warren (General Manager)

Joseph S. Bartos (Assistant General Manager)

Dr. H. K. Adenstedt (Senior Vice-President)

L. A. Shadle (Controller)

Paul A. Deegan (Administration)

Frank T. Dubuque (Factory Operations)

Michael S. Saboe (Engineering and Development)

Dr. Fritz Haber (Marketing)

DIVISIONAL DIRECTOR:
E. P. Wyman (Product Support)

R. B. LeMar (Administration)

T. B. Lauriat, Chief, Marine Industrial Applications, Avco Lycoming

K. M. Austin, Manager, Avco International Overseas Corporation

The Avco Lycoming Division is the turbine engine manufacturing division of the Avco Corporation.

Avco Lycoming is producing two families of gas turbine engines. Designated T53 and T55, these are both of the free-turbine type and are available in turboshaft and turboprop form. The T53 in particular has been built in large quantities to power US Army helicopters. Industrial and marine versions of the T53 and T55 are designated TF12A and 14B, and TF25A and 35 respectively.

TF12A and TF14B

The TF12 and TF14 engines are developments of the T53 aircraft engine. The T53 is a turboshaft with a free power turbine, which was developed under a joint, USAF/US Army contract. It has logged over 22 million hours of operation with the US armed services and operators in 28 other countries.

The TF14B is an uprated version of the TF12A. Redesigned "hot end" and initial stages of compressor section provide substantially increased power for hot day performance. Four turbine stages, compared with two in earlier models, and variable-incidence inlet guide vanes combined with redesigned first two compressor stages, permit greater airflow and lower turbine temperatures. This version has atomising combustor to facilitate operation on a wider range of fuels. Applications include US Navy ATC/CCB and ASPBs (Assault Support Patrol Boats).

TYPE: Free turbine turboshaft engine.

AIR INTAKE: Side inlet castings of aluminium alloy, supporting gearbox and front main bearings.

COMPRESSOR: Five axial stages followed by a single centrifugal stage. Four-piece aluminium alloy casing with one row of variable-incidence inlet guide vanes and five rows of steel stator blades, bolted to one-piece steel alloy diffuser casing with tangential outlet to combustion chamber. Rotor comprises one stainless steel and four aluminium alloy discs with stainless steel blades, and one titanium impeller mounted on shaft supported in forward ball thrust and rear roller bearings. Pressure ratio 6·5 : 1. Air mass flow 9·98 lb/sec (4·85 kg/sec) at 25,240 gas producer rpm.

COMBUSTION CHAMBER: Annular reverse-flow type, with one-piece sheet steel outer shell and annular liner. Twenty-two atomising fuel injectors.

FUEL CONTROL SYSTEM: Hydro-mechanical controls for gas generator and for power sections. Woodward system with one fuel pump. Pump pressure 600 lb/sq in (42 kg/cm²). Main and emergency flow controls. Separate interstage air-bleed control.

FUEL GRADE: MIL-F-16884F, JP-4, JP-5, CITE, marine diesel.

TURBINE: Four axial-flow turbine stages. Casing fabricated from sheet steel. First two stages, driving compressor, use hollow-air-cooler stator vanes and cored-out cast steel rotor blades, and are mounted on outer co-axial shaft to gas producer. Second stages, driving reduction gearing, have solid steel blades, and are spline-mounted to shaft.

EXHAUST UNIT: Fixed-area nozzle. Stainless steel outer casing and inner cone, supported by four radial struts.

ACCESSORIES: Electric starter, Bendix-Scintilla TGLN high-energy ignition unit. Four ignitor plugs.

LUBRICATION: Recirculating system with gear pump. Filter. Pump pressure 70 lb/sq in (4·9 kg/cm²).

Avco Lycoming TF12A marine gas turbine engine of 1,150 shp

Avco Lycoming TF14B Marine gas turbine engine of 1,450 shp

Avco Lycoming TF35 marine gas turbine engine of 2,800 shp

OIL GRADE: MIL-L-7808E, MIL-L 23699.

DIMENSIONS:

Length overall	51·4 in (1·30 m)
Width	30·4 in (0·72 m)
Height	42·6 in (1·08 m)

WEIGHT (Dry):

Less tailpipe	920 lb (417 kg)

POWER RATINGS:

Max intermittent (peak)*

TF12A (at 60°F)	1,275 shp
TF14C (at 60°F)	1,600 shp

Max continuous (normal)*

TF12A (at 60°F)	1,150 shp
TF14C (at 60°F)	1,400 shp

*All ratings based on no inlet pressure loss and no exhaust pressure loss.

FUEL CONSUMPTION:

At max continuous rating:

TF12A	99 US gall/hr
TF14C	118 US gall/hr

OIL CONSUMPTION:

	1·0 lb (450 gr)/hr

TF25A and TF35

These engines are developments of the T55 aircraft engine.

Current production and development versions are as follows:

TF25A. High-speed shaft-turbine engine, with output shaft speed equal to power turbine speed. Integral oil tank and cooling system. The TF25 powers the Vosper Thornycroft VT1 and the Mitsui MV-PP15 155-seat hoverferry.

TF35. Uprated and redesigned version of TF25. New turbine section with four stages and variable-incidence inlet guide vanes. First two compressor stages transonic. New atomizing fuel nozzles. Four TF 35s, maximum rated at 3,750 shp drive the Aerojet SES-100A test craft.

AIR INTAKE: Side inlet casting of aluminium alloy supporting optional reduction gearbox and front main bearings. Provision for intake screens.

COMPRESSOR: Seven axial stages followed by a single centrifugal stage. Two-piece aluminium alloy stator casing with one row of inlet guide vanes, fixed on TF25, variable on TF35, and seven rows of steel stator blades, bolted to steel alloy diffuser casing to which combustion chamber casing is attached. Rotor comprises seven stainless steel discs and one titanium impeller mounted on shaft supported in forward thrust ball bearing and rear roller bearing. TF25A pressure ratio 6 : 1, and 6·5 : 1 for TF 35.

COMBUSTION CHAMBER: Annular reverse flow type. Steel outer shell and inner liner. Twenty-eight fuel burners with downstream injection.

FUEL SYSTEM: Woodward fuel control system. Gear-type fuel pump, with gas producer and power shaft governors, flow control and shut-off valve.

FUEL GRADE: MIL J-5624 grade JP-4, JP-5, MIL-F-46005 or marine diesel, standard and wide-cut kerosene.

TURBINE: Two mechanically-independent axial-flow turbines. First turbine with single-stage on TF25A and two-stages of TF35, drives compressor. Has cored-out cast steel blades and is flange-bolted to outer co-axial drive shaft. Hollow stator vanes. Second, two-stage turbine drives output shaft. Has solid steel blades and is mounted on inner co-axial drive shaft.

Avco Lycoming TF40 marine gas turbine engine of 3,400 shp

Avco Lycoming TF25A marine gas turbine engine of 2,250 shp

EXHAUST UNIT: Fixed area nozzle, with inner cone, supported by six radial struts.

ACCESSORIES: Electric, air or hydraulic starter. Bendix-Scintilla TGLN high-energy ignition unit. Four igniter plugs.

LUBRICATION: Recirculating type. Integral oil tank and cooler.

OIL GRADE: MIL-L-17808, MIL-L-23699.

DIMENSIONS:

Length:

TF25A	49·5 in (1·26 m)
TF35	51·7 in (1·31 m)

Width:

TF25A, TF35	30·4 in (770 mm)

Height:

TF25A, TF35	42·6 in (1·08 m)

WEIGHT (Dry):

TF25A	1,100 lb (499 kg)
TF35	1,167 lb (529·4 kg)

PERFORMANCE RATINGS:

Max intermittent (peak):

TF25A	2,500 shp
TF35	3,100 shp

Max continuous (normal):

TF25A	2,250 shp
TF35	2,800 shp

FUEL CONSUMPTION:

At max continuous rating:

TF25A	198 US gall/hr
TF35	223 US gall/hr

TF40

The TF40 engine is a scaled-up TF35 with higher mass flow. It has a four stage turbine section and variable-incidence inlet guide vanes. The first two compressor stages are transonic, and new atomizing fuel nozzles are fitted.

Both the Jeff A (Aerojet General) and Jeff B (Bell Aerospace) AALCs employ TF40s. Jeff A employs six, each developing 3,350 shp continuous. Four drive individual, steerable ducted propellers, and the remaining two drive separate centrifugal lift fans. In the case of Jeff B, the six engines are arranged in two groups of three, located port and starboard. Each trio drives a single propeller and lift system through integrated gears.

Another craft due to be powered by TF 40s is the SEDAM N.500, which employs two for lift and three, mounted in separate nacelles, for propulsion.

AIR INTAKE: Side inlet casting of aluminium alloy housing internal gearing and supporting power producer section and output drive shaft. Integral or separately mounted gears are operational. Provision for intake filters and/or silencers.

COMPRESSOR: Seven axial stages followed by a single centrifugal stage. Two-piece aluminium alloy stator casing, with one row of variable inlet guide vanes, and seven rows of steel stator blades bolted to steel alloy casing diffuser, to which combustion chamber casing is attached. Rotor comprises seven stainless steel discs and one titanium impeller mounted on shaft supported in forward thrust ball bearing and rear roller bearing. TF40 pressure ratio is 7·2 : 1.

COMBUSTION CHAMBER: Annular reverse flow type. Steel outer shell and inner liner. Twenty-eight fuel burners with downstream injection.

FUEL SYSTEM: Woodward fuel control system. Gear-type fuel pump, with gas producer and power shaft governors, flow control and shut-off valve.

FUEL GRADE: MIL-T-5624, JP-4, JP-5; MIL-F-16884 diesel, standard and wide-cut kerosene.

TURBINE: Two mechanically-independent axial-flow turbines. First turbine, with two stages, drives compressor. It has cored-out cast steel blades and is flange-bolted to outer co-axial drive shaft. Hollow stator vanes. Second two-stage turbine drives output shaft. It has solid steel blades and is mounted on inner co-axial drive shaft. (Other features include: integral cast first turbine nozzle, cooled first turbine blades in both first and second stages, second turbine vane cooling, second turbine disc and blade cooling, and a modified third stage nozzle shroud).

EXHAUST UNIT: Fixed area nozzle, with inner cone, supported by six radial struts.

ACCESSORIES: Electric, air or hydraulic starter. Bendix-Scintilla TGLN high-energy ignition unit. Four igniter plugs.

LUBRICATION: Recirculating type. Integral oil tank and cooler.

OIL GRADE: Synthetic base oils.

DIMENSIONS:

Length	51·7 in (1·31 m)
Width	30·4 in (0·77 m)
Height	42·6 in (1·08 m)

PERFORMANCE RATINGS:

Max intermittent (at 60° F sea level)— 3,650 shp

Max continuous (at 60°F—sea level) 3,350 shp

FUEL CONSUMPTION:

At max continuous rating 255 US gall/hr

OIL CONSUMPTION:

1·0 lb (454 gr/hr)

BRIGGS & STRATTON CORPORATION

HEADQUARTERS AND WORKS:
Milwaukee, Wisconsin 53201

CENTRAL SERVICE DISTRIBUTORS FOR GREAT BRITAIN AND IRELAND:
Autocar Electrical Equipment Co Ltd., 16 Rippleside Commercial Estate, Ripple Road, Barking, Essex

Briggs & Stratton is a major American supplier of low-power four-stroke gasoline engines, an important application of which is in motor lawn mowers of both US and European manufacture. Several installations of Briggs & Stratton in ACVs have been made. These include the American Bartlett M-8 Flying Saucer, a small lightweight craft powered by a single 3 hp Briggs & Stratton engine mounted above a central plenum chamber driving a two-bladed Banks-Maxwell Mod 30-14 30 in diameter pusher propeller; and Coelacanth Gemco's Pluto two-seat test vehicle which has two 7 hp Briggs & Stratton engines each driving 42 in fans, one for lift and a second for propulsion.

CUMMINS ENGINE COMPANY INC

OFFICES:
Cummins Engine Company Inc, 1000 Fifth Street, Columbus, Indiana, 47201.
Cummins Engine Company Ltd, Coombe House, St Georges Square, Maldon Road, New Maldon, Surrey

DIRECTORS:
J. I. Miller
C. R. Boll
J. B. Fisk
H. H. Helm
H. L. Hillman
P. L. Miller
G. W. Newlin
H. B. Schacht
R. B. Stoner
E. D. Tull

The Cummins Engine Company was formed in 1919 in Columbus, Indiana. It produces a wide range of marine diesel engines which are now manufactured and distributed internationally. In addition to manufacturing plants in the United States, the company also produces diesel engines in Australia, India, Japan, Mexico and the United Kingdom. All these plants build engines to the same specifications thus ensuring interchangeability of parts and the same quality standards.

Cummins marine diesels power the Seaflight 46 (two VT8N-370-M) hydrofoil, and the Hovermarine HM.2 sidewall hovercraft.

On the latter, two VT8-370-Ms, each derated to 320 bhp, supply propulsive power, and a single V-504-M, derated to 185 bhp, drives the lift fans.

MODEL:	V-504-M	VT8-370-M
Rating (60°F—29·95 in Hg)		
Intermittent	210 bhp at 3,300 rpm	370 bhp at 3,000 rpm
Continuous	158 bhp at 2,500 rpm	270 bhp at 2,600 rpm
Type	*90° V Form Diesel*	*90° V Form Diesel*
No. Cylinders	8	8
Bore and stroke	$4\frac{5}{8}$ in × $3\frac{3}{4}$ in	$5\frac{1}{2}$ in × $4\frac{1}{8}$ in
Piston Displacement	504 cu in (8,460 cm³)	785 cu in (12,863 cm³)
Operating Cycle	4	4
Aspiration	Natural	Turbocharged
Fuel Consumption		
Intermittent	10·5 gph	21·5 gph
Continuous	7·5 gph	21·0 gph
Oil Consumption	0·4 pint/hr	$\frac{1}{2}$ pint/hr
Nett Weight (with std accessories)	1,700 lb (770 kg)	2,775 lb (1,259 kg)
Dimensions (with reverse gear):		
Length	5 ft $1\frac{5}{8}$ in (1·56 m)	5 ft 9 in (1·75 m)
Width	2 ft $8\frac{1}{8}$ in (0·81 m)	3 ft 3 in (0·99 m)
Height	2 ft $9\frac{3}{8}$ in (0·84 m)	2 ft $10\frac{1}{4}$ in (0·87 m)

General:

Starting	Electric
Bearings	Precision type, steel backed inserts
Accessory Drives	By 'V' belts from free end crankshaft or from PTO pulley above flywheel housing
Lubrication	Force feed to all bearings—gear type pump
Mounting	Rubber in shear type vibration isolators
Fuel Specification	Class A gas oil
Lub. Oil Specification	US Military specification MIL-L-2104A British Defence specification DEF-2101B

DOBSON PRODUCTS CO.

HEAD OFFICE:
2241 South Ritchey, Santa Ana, California
92705
TELEPHONE:
(714) 557-2987
WORKS:
Santa Ana, California
DIRECTOR:
Franklin A. Dobson

Franklin Dobson has been building and marketing light ACVs in kit and factory-built form since 1963.

His company is now specialising in the design and construction of light ACV components evolved after a more thorough engineering approach. The components will include reversible-pitch propellers and fans—the main purpose of which will be to provide light craft with adequate braking—and suitable ducts, screens, etc.

Preliminary details of the company's first 3 ft (0·91 m) diameter, variable-pitch two-bladed propeller are given below. Tests were due to start in June 1974.

DIMENSIONS:

Diameter	36 in (0·91 m)
Chord	4·25 in (104 mm)
Blades	2
Solidity (at 0·6 rad)	·125
Pitch range	60 deg (nom. +40, —20)
Max shaft dia.	1·25 in (28 mm)
Total weight	5 lb (approx) (0·45 gr)
Design rpm	3,000
Max rpm	3,250
Horsepower req.	7 to 10
Max static thrust (with shroud)	
75 lb (forward or reverse) (34·01 kg)	
Max thrust at 60 mph	50 lb (22·67 kg)

A duct with integral screen, suitable for use with this propeller, is also under development.

GENERAL ELECTRIC COMPANY AIRCRAFT ENGINE GROUP

HEADQUARTERS:
1000 Western Avenue, West Lynn, Massachusetts 01910
VICE PRESIDENT AND GROUP EXECUTIVE
Gerhard Neumann
COUNSEL:
J. W. Sack

The General Electric Company entered the gas-turbine field in about 1895. Years of pioneering effort by the late Dr Sanford A. Moss produced the aircraft turbosupercharger, successfully tested at height in 1918 and mass-produced in World War II for US fighters and bombers.

The company built its first aircraft gas-turbine in 1941, when it began development of Whittle-type turbojets, under an arrangement between the British and American Governments.

Since that time, General Electric has produced a series of successful designs, from the J47, which powered the Boeing B47 and the North American F 86 series of aircraft, to the big CF6 turbofan powering the new McDonnell Douglas DC-10 wide-body transport.

Three General Electric marinized gas-turbines are in marine service, the LM-100, the LM1500 and the new LM2500. The LM100 powers the Bell SK-5 air cushion vehicle and the Avalon high-speed ferry and the LM1500 powers the AGEH-1 Plainview and seventeen US Navy patrol gunboats.

LM100

Earliest marine application of the LM100 was in the 24-foot experimental hydrofoil vessel Sea Wings developed for the Office of Naval Research. The craft was propelled at high speeds by a single LM100 gas turbine to explore the validity of supercavitation principles. Later, it was selected as the docking and harbour manoeuvring engine for the Maritime Administration's hydrofoil ship Denison. A version of this turbine, IM100, supplied by Ishikawajima-Harima Heavy Industries, a licencee of GE in Japan, powers the Mitsui MV-PP5 hovercraft.

The LM100 is an outgrowth of the GE T58 helicopter engine, which underwent some six years of development and has amassed more than seven million hours of operation. Rolls-Royce is manufacturing the T58 under licence in the United Kingdom as the Gnome, and the T58 is also being built under licence in Italy and Japan.

TYPE: Free turbine, axial flow, simple cycle.
AIR INTAKE: Axial, inlet bellmouth on duct can be customised to installation.

GE LM100 gas-turbine

GE LM1500 gas-turbine

COMBUSTION CHAMBER: Annular.
FUEL: Kerosene, JP-4, JP-5, diesel, natural gas.
TURBINE: 2-stage gas generator, 1-stage power turbine.
JET PIPE: Customised to fit installation.
OIL SPECIFICATION: MIL-L-23699, MIL-L7808F and commercial equivalents.
MOUNTING: At power turbine and compressor front frame.
STARTING: Normally electric.
DIMENSIONS:

Length overall	6 ft 4 in (1·924 m)
Width overall	1 ft 8 in (0·508 m)
Height overall	2 ft 10 in (0·864 m)

Performance rating 1,100 shp at 80°F SLS
Specific Fuel Consumption:
0·61 lb (0·277 kg)/shp/hr
Oil Consumption   0·5 pint (0·29 litre)/hr

LM1500

The GE LM1500 turboshaft engine is the result of a company investment in a programme to adapt the J79 jet engine to a free power turbine for industrial and marine use.

On the US Navy's aluminium-hulled PG84 class gunboats an LM1500 gas turbine is used to supplement two cruise diesels whenever high speed operation is desired. By combining reduction gears, the LM1500 is used to drive two propellers.

Twin LM1500s supply foilborne propulsion power for the USS *Plainview* (AGEH).

TYPE: 2-shaft, axial flow, simple cycle.
AIR INTAKE: Axial, inlet bellmouth on duct can be customised to installation.
COMBUSTION CHAMBER: Annular.

FUEL GRADE: JP, aviation kerosene, diesel,
TURBINE: 3-stage gas generator, 1-stage power turbine.
JET PIPE: Customised to fit installation.
OIL SPECIFICATION: MIL-L-23699, MIL-L-7808F and commercial equivalent.
MOUNTING: At power turbine and compressor front frame.
STARTING: Pneumatic, hydraulic.
DIMENSIONS:

Length overall	25 ft 0 in (7·62 m)
Width overall	6 ft 6½ in (2·0 m)
Height overall	6 ft 11 in (2·11 m)

Performance rating

15,400 shp at 59°F (15°C) at sea level

Specific fuel consumption

5 lb (0·25 kg)/shp/hr

LM2500

The LM2500 marine gas turbine is a 2-shaft, simple cycle, high efficiency engine. Derived from the GE TF39 CF-6 high-bypass turbo-fan engines for the US Air Force C-5 transport and DC-10 and A300B commercial jets. The engine incorporates the latest features of compressor, combustor, and turbine design to provide maximum progression in reliability parts life, and time between overhaul. The engine has a fuel rate 25% lower than that of current production marine gas turbines in its power range. This is made possible by high compressor pressure ratio, high turbine inlet temperature and improved cycle efficiency.

The LM2500 marine gas turbine has been specified for the foilborne power of the joint U.S. Navy/NATO Patrol Hydrofoil Missile ship (PHM) being built by the Boeing Company, Seattle, Washington.

This engine is in production for the U.S. Navy's new Spruance-class destroyer fleet, the first major warships in the U.S. Navy to employ marine gas turbines for propulsion, and it will also power the U.S. Navy's new class of Patrol Frigates and the new Fast Frigates for the Italian and Peruvian navies.

Two LM2500s have completed more than 30,000 hours of operation aboard the GTS Admiral William M. Callaghan, a gas-turbine powered roll-on/roll-off cargo vessel operated for the U.S. Navy's Military Sealift Command by American Export Isbrandtsen Lines, Inc.

TYPE: 2-shaft, axial flow, simple cycle.

AIR INTAKE: Axial, inlet bellmouth on duct can be customised to installation.

COMBUSTION CHAMBER: Annular.

FUEL GRADE: Kerosene, JP4, JP5, Diesel, heavy distillate fuels and natural gas.

TURBINE: 2-stage gas generator, 6-stage power.

JET PIPE: Customised to fit installation.

OIL SPECIFICATION: Synthetic Turbine Oil (MIL-L-23699) or equal.

MOUNTING: At power turbine and compressor front frame.

STARTING: Pneumatic, hydraulic.

DIMENSIONS:

Length	20 ft 6 in (6·24 m)
Width	7 ft 7¼ in (2·3 m)
Height	7 ft 6¼ in (2·6 m)

GE LM 2500 gas turbine

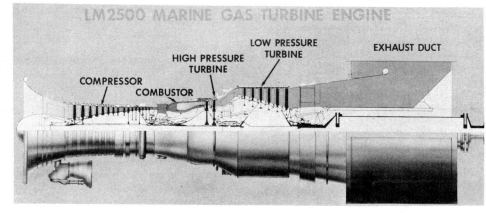

Internal arrangements of the GE LM2500 marine gas-turbine

PERFORMANCE RATINGS:

27,500 shp at 59°F (15°C) at sea level

SPECIFIC FUEL CONSUMPTION:

0·39 to 0·41 lb (0·177 to 0·186 kg)/hp/hr

McCULLOCH CORPORATION, LOS ANGELES DIVISION

HEAD OFFICE: AND MAIN PLANT

6101, West Century Blvd, Los Angeles, California 90045

PRESIDENT:

Robert P. McCulloch

CHAIRMAN:

Joseph L. Hegener

VICE-PRESIDENTS:

W. B. Burkett (Electronics)

Kenneth P. Mulkey (Marketing Services)

James L. Dooley (Engineering, World)

Stanley J. Stephenson (Marketing Services, World)

MANAGER, SPECIAL PRODUCT SALES:

Charles L. Hammond

SECRETARY AND ASSISTANT TREASURER:

J. D. Cavanaugh

McCulloch Corporation produces a variety of small gasoline engines making extensive use of aluminium and magnesium high-pressure die castings. Over the past 25 years it has supplied more than 60,000 engines to the US armed services for use in radio-controlled target aircraft and helicopters.

Amateur builders have made extensive use of McCulloch target drone engines in light aircraft and autogyros, and air cushion vehicles. Current models include improved versions of the MC49, MC91 and MC101 single-cylinder, two-stroke series and details are given hereunder. New engines planned cover 12 to 34 hp in single or twin-cylinder versions.

Although tooling for the McCulloch Model 4300 series has been acquired by Northrop Corporation (see page 307), production

continuity of the series has been maintained by McCulloch until Northrop are in full production.

McCULLOCH MODEL MC 49E

This small single-cylinder air-cooled two-stroke piston engine, together with the MC 91B/1 and MC 101A/A comprises a family of units known as McCulloch's Kart series covering a power bracket 3 hp (3·1 cv) to 14·5 hp (14·7 cv). These have applications in go-karts, sprint-karts, small speed boats, and mini-bikes and are also suited for use in light ACVs.

Improvements to this engine include a sloper manifold for cooler running, a re-designed carburettor with a pre-calibrated high-speed, fixed main jet for constant fuel flow, new power-tuned, reed valves, and adhesive bonding to insulate the coil from engine heat and protect it from vibrating loose.

TYPE: Single-cylinder air-cooled, two-stroke, loop-scavenged piston engine.

CYLINDER/CRANKCASE: Bore 2·125 in (54 mm). Stroke 1·375 in (35 mm). Displacement 4·9 cu in (80·3 cc). Compression ratio 6 : 1. Die cast aluminium alloy with precision-honed cast iron liner. Deep finned integral head.

PISTON: Heat resistant aluminium alloy. Two narrow steel racing-type piston rings with chrome-plated wear face for quick sealing and low friction. Two needle roller bearings in piston. Rings are unpinned.

CONNECTING ROD: Forged, hardened and ground alloy steel connecting rod with removable cap and integral race. No oil slot in cap. Wrist pin pressed in place. Full complement of needle bearings, hardened shaft and rod end.

CRANKSHAFT: Counter-balanced, forged steel, carburized, hardened and ground. One ball bearing and one needle roller bearing.

VALVE PORTING: Inlet valve comprises dual petal, high-flow reeds and third port.

INDUCTION: McCulloch special racing diaphragm type with low airflow restriction. Operates efficiently in any position. ¾ in (19 mm) venturi. Adjustable for idle and high-speed mixture. Butterfly throttle and choke.

FUEL/OIL SPECIFICATION: 20 : 1 fuel/oil mixture with McCulloch oil and automotive regular grade gasoline. Integral fuel pump.

IGNITION: Water-proof high tension magneto. Advanced magnetic timing system. Moisture-proof coil ensures easy starting. Champion J8J plug.

PROPELLER DRIVE: Clockwise rotation (facing power take-off shaft).

STARTING: McCulloch automatic rewind.

MOUNTING: Four bolt holes provided on bottom of crankcase. Engine operates in any position.

DIMENSIONS:

Height	8·0 in (203 mm)
Width	8·25 in (209·6 mm)
Length	9·875 in (330 mm)

WEIGHT: 12 lb (5·5 kg)

POWER RATINGS:

Open exhaust	5·5 bhp
Tuned exhaust	7·0 bhp

PRICE:
Manufacturers' suggested price.
US $102·48

McCULLOCH MODEL MC 91B/1

More powerful successor to the MC 91B, the MC 91B/1 incorporates a glass shot peened crankshaft for better heat dissipation, a permanently rivetted spark plug cover, improved matching for the thermo-couple pad, an improved coil lamination assembly to produce a hotter spark, and adhesive bonding to insulate the coil from engine heat and protect it from vibrating loose.

TYPE: Single-cylinder air-cooled, two-stroke, loop-scavenged piston engine.

CYLINDER/CRANKCASE: Bore 2·165 in (55 mm). Stroke 1·635 in (41·5 mm). Displacement 6·05 cu in (99·3 cc). Compression ratio 9·4 : 1. Die cast aluminium

alloy with precision honed cast iron liner. Deep finned detachable head.

PISTON: Free skirt on the exhaust side shields and cools the wrist pin bearings. Slipper skirt on the boost port side to give reduced drag and free airflow for increased power. Two needle roller bearings in piston. Two narrow steel racing type rings with chrome-plated wear-face for quick sealing, low friction and long life. Rings are pinned.

CONNECTING ROD: Forged hardened and ground alloy steel connecting rod with removable cap and integral race. Oil slot in cap. Wrist pin pressed in place. Full complement of needle rollers, hardened shaft and rod end.

CRANKSHAFT: Counter-balanced, forged steel, carburized, hardened and ground. One caged ball bearing and one caged needle roller bearing. Extensively glass bead shot peened.

VALVE PORTING: Inlet valve comprises dual petal, high-flow reeds on vee-block for full power at all speeds.

INDUCTION: McCulloch diaphragm pressure type carburettor with integral fuel filter and pulse fuel pump. 1⅜ in (35 mm) bore without a venturi to ensure free breathing. Adjustable for high speed and idle mixture and idle speed. Butterfly throttle.

FUEL/OIL SPECIFICATION: 20 : 1 fuel/oil mixture with McCulloch oil and automotive regular grade gasoline.

IGNITION: Water-proof high tension magneto. Advanced magnetic timing system. Moisture-proof coil ensures easy starting. Champion L-78 plug.

PROPELLER DRIVE: Clockwise rotation (facing power take-off shaft).

STARTING: McCulloch automatic rewind available.

MOUNTING: Four bolt holes provided on bottom of crankcase. Engine operates in any position.

DIMENSIONS:

Height	10·09 in (256·2 mm)
Width	6·73 in (170·9 mm)
Length	10·36 in (263·1 mm)

WEIGHT: 11 lb 9 oz (5·2 kg)

POWER RATINGS:

Open exhaust	10 bhp
Tuned exhaust	10·7 bhp

PRICE:
Manufacturer's suggested price
US $122·98

McCULLOCH MODEL MC 101A/A

Design improvements embodied in the MC 101A/A include a new carburettor with integral high-capacity fuel pump, a glass shot peened crankshaft, twin fuel/air boost ports, balanced exhaust and transfer port timing, a thicker top cylinder fin and new external spine connecting rod screws.

TYPE: Single-cylinder air-cooled two-stroke, loop-scavenged piston engine.

CYLINDER/CRANKCASE: Bore 2·280 in (58 mm). Stroke 1·835 in (46·6 mm). Displacement 7·5 cu in (123 cc). Compression ratio 9·4 : 1. Die cast aluminium alloy with precision honed cast iron liner. Deep finned detachable head.

McCulloch model Mc 101 two-stroke piston engine of 13·5 bhp

PISTON: Free skirt on the exhaust side provides shielding and cools the wrist pin bearings. Closed window skirt on boost port side forces the charge to flow through the wrist pin to lubricate and cool it. Two needle roller bearings in piston. Two narrow steel racing type rings with chrome-plated wear face for quick sealing, low friction and long life. Rings are pinned.

CONNECTING ROD: Forged, hardened and ground alloy steel connecting rod with removable cap and integral race. Oil slot in cap. Wrist pin pressed in place. Full complement of needle rollers, hardened shaft and rod end.

CRANKSHAFT: Counter-balanced forged steel, carburized, hardened and ground. Full complement of high capacity ball bearings. Extensively glass bead shot peened. Fitted with tungsten counterweights.

VALVE PORTING: Inlet valve comprises dual petal, high-flow reeds on vee-block for full power at all speeds.

INDUCTION: New type carburettor, with single throat, incorporates optimised bore and venturi dimensions with twin-stage integral high-capacity fuel pump. Also maximum volume inlet needle, seat and passages, and wide range of high and low mixture needles.

FUEL/OIL SPECIFICATION: Alcohol, nitro blended to any mixture. Also 20 : 1 fuel/oil mixture with McCulloch oil and automotive regular grade gasoline.

IGNITION: Water-proof high tension magneto. Advanced magnetic timing system. Moisture-proof coil ensures easy starting. Champion L-78 plug.

PROPELLER DRIVE: Clockwise rotation (facing power take-off shaft).

STARTING: McCulloch automatic rewind available.

MOUNTING: Four bolt holes provided on bottom of crankcase. Engine operates in any position.

DIMENSIONS:

Height	10·09 in (256·2 mm)
Width	6·70 in (170·2 mm)
Length	10·36 in (263·1 mm)

WEIGHT: 12·25 lb (5·7 kg)

POWER RATINGS:

Open exhaust	12·5 bhp
Tuned exhaust (MC 101A)	14·5 bhp

PRICE:
Manufacturer's suggested price
US $153·72

NORTHROP CORPORATION

HEAD OFFICE:

1515 Rancho Conejo Blvd, Newbury Park, California 91320.

Northrop Corp. has purchased the corporate rights of the 4300 series engines from McCulloch Corp. who will continue manufacture until Northrop commence production.

Tooling has been acquired from McCulloch for the Model 4318, which is built in various versions covering 72 to 92 hp. Details of these engines are as follows:

Model 4318

This is a series of four-cylinder, horizontally-opposed air-cooled two-stroke piston engines covering the power range 72 hp (73 cv) to 92 hp (93 cv). The Bertelsen Aeromobile 13 light amphibious air cushion vehicle is powered by two 72 hp (73 cv) 4318AX or two 90 hp (91 cv) 4318G engines providing lift and thrust through 48 in (1,219 mm) diameter 8-bladed lift fan/propellers.

Model 4318A. Basic 72 hp (73 cv) model of the series, with "free roll" silver-plated bearings on the big-end of the connecting rods.

Model 4318E. Similar to the Model 4318A except that it is intended to drive a pusher airscrew. No carburettor is supplied with the engine.

Model 4318F. This is the same as the Model 4318A except that it has a power rating of 92 hp (93 cv) at 4,100 rpm, achieved by enlarged inlet and exhaust ports in the cylinders, together with a modified piston and ring configuration.

Model 4318G. Rated at 90 hp (91 cv).

The following data relates to the Model 4318A.

TYPE: Four-cylinder horizontally-opposed air cooled two-stroke.

CYLINDERS: Bore $3\frac{3}{16}$ in (80·8 mm). Stroke $3\frac{1}{8}$ in (79·4 mm). Displacement 100 cu in (1·6 litres). Compression ratio 7·8 : 1. Heat-treated die-cast aluminium cylinders with integral heads, having hard chrome plated cylinder walls. Self-locking nuts secure cylinders to crankcase studs.

PISTONS: Heat-treated cast aluminium. Two rings above pins. Piston pins of case-hardened steel.

CONNECTING RODS: Forged steel. "Free-roll" silver-plated bearings at big end. Small

Model 4318A two-stroke piston engine of 72 bhp

end carries one needle bearing. Lateral position of rod controlled by thrust washers between piston pin bosses and end of rod.

CRANKSHAFT: Four-throw one-piece steel forging on four anti-friction bearings, two ball and two needle, one with split race for centre main bearing.

CRANKCASE: One-piece heat-treated permanent-mould aluminium casting closed at rear end with cast aluminium cover which provides mounting for magneto.

VALVE GEAR: Fuel mixture for scavenging and power stroke introduced to cylinders through crankshaft-driven rotary valves and ported cylinders.

INDUCTION: Crankcase pumping type.

McCulloch diaphragm-type carburettor with adjustable jet.

FUEL SPECIFICATION: Grade 100/130 aviation fuel.

IGNITION: McCulloch single magneto and distributor. Directly connected to crankshaft through impulse coupling for easy

starting. Radio noise-suppressor included. BG type RB 916S spark plugs. Complete radio shielding.

LUBRICATION: Oil mixed with fuel as in conventional two-stroke engines.

PROPELLER DRIVE: RH tractor. Keyed taper shaft.

STARTING: By separate portable gasoline or electric motor with suitable reduction-gear and clutch. Can be started manually by hand-cranking propeller.

MOUNTING: Three mounting lugs provided with socket for rubber mounting bushings.

DIMENSIONS:

Length	27·0 in (686 mm)
Width	28·0 in (711 mm)
Height	15·0 in (381 mm)

WEIGHT (Dry)-

Less propeller hub	77 lb (34·9 kg)

POWER RATING:

Rated output	72 hp at 4,100 rpm

CONSUMPTION:

Fuel/oil mixture	0·90 lb (0·408 kg) bhp/hr

ROCKWELL INTERNATIONAL ROCKETDYNE DIVISION

HEAD OFFICE: 6633 Canoga Avenue, Canoga Park, California 91304

TELEX: 651488

Utilizing the technology gained in the design and manufacture of high performance pumps used in the U.S. space programme Rocketdyne has designed and built the first in a new family of waterjet propulsion systems, the Powerjet 20. This has been fully tested and is currently in production for The Boeing Company's Jetfoil, a 106-ton displacement, 45 knot, passenger carrying hydrofoil. Two of the Powerjet 20 waterjet propulsion systems, driven by two Allison 501-K201 free power gas turbines are employed to power the Jetfoil.

The Powerjet 20 utilizes an advanced design, axial-flow pump which results in a compact, lightweight system. The simplicity of design minimizes the number of

components while allowing accessibility for servicing or replacing of seals and bearings without special skills or services being required. All materials have been selected for resistance to cavitation damage and galvanic corrosion.

POWERJET 20

TYPE: Single stage, Axial Flow.

ROTOR: The Rotor is a one-piece titanium casting consisting of four full and four partial blades with a second row of 16 blades. The rotor is keyed to the 17-4PH corrosion resistant steel shaft.

ACCESSORY DRIVES: The gearbox provides two drive pads for accessories. The first provides power take-off for the boat hydraulic system and the second provides power to the gearbox, pump and power turbine lubrication and scavenge pump.

LUBRICATION SYSTEM: Recirculating system utilizing gerotor type pump which contains both pressure and scavenge cavities.

Flow is 88 GPM at a pressure of 200 psig.

OIL GRADE: MIL-L-23699

MOUNTING: The pump provides three mounting points, two alignment pin types near the aft end of the pump and one fixed type near the forward end. The gearbox utilizes a similar arrangement with two pivot types near the bottom and stabilizing point at the top.

DIMENSIONS:

Propulsion Pump:

Length	80·4 in. (2·04 m)
Outside diameter	25·5 in. (0·65 m)
Inlet diameter	22·1 in. (0·56 m)

Gearbox

Height	76·4 in. (1·94 m)
Width	35·0 in. (0·89 m)
Length	16·9 in. (0·43 m)

WEIGHTS:

Propulsion pump (dry)	1,512 lb (685·8 kg)
Gearbox (includes lube pump)	1,450 lb (657·7 kg)

Miscellaneous	210 lb (95·3 kg)	Input speed	13,250 RPM	Minimum operational total inlet head	
PERFORMANCE:		Pump speed	2,080		26 ft (7·92 m)
Rated input horsepower	3,780 SHP	Pump flowrate	22,300 GPM	Thrust	18,000 lb (80,000 N)

POWER PLANTS AND PROPULSION SYSTEMS
ROCKWELL INTERNATIONAL
ROCKETDYNE DIVISION

HEAD OFFICE: 6633 Canoga Avenue, Canoga Park, California 91304

TELEX: 651488

Utilizing the technology gained in the design and manufacture of high performance pumps used in the U.S. space program, Rocketdyne has designed and built the first in a new family of waterjet propulsion systems, the Powerjet 20. This has been fully tested and is currently in production for The Boeing Company's Jetfoil a 106-ton displacement, 45 knot, passenger carrying hydrofoil. Two of the Powerjet 20 waterjet propulsion systems, driven by two Allison 501-K201 free power gas turbines are employed to power the Jetfoil.

The Powerjet 20 utilizes an advanced design, axial-flow pump which results in a compact, lightweight system. The simplicity of design minimizes the number of components while allowing accessibility for servicing or replacing of seals and bearings without special skills or services being required. All materials have been selected for resistance to cavitation damage and galvanic corrosion.

POWERJET 20

TYPE: Single stage, Axial Flow.

ROTOR: The Rotor is a one-piece titanium casting consisting of four full and four partial blades with a second row of 16 blades. The rotor is keyed to the 17-4PH corrosion resistant steel shaft.

ACCESSORY DRIVES: The gearbox provides two drive pads for accessories. The first provides power take-off for the boat hydraulic system and the second provides power to the gearbox, pump and power turbine lubrication and scavenge pump.

LUBRICATION SYSTEM: Recirculating system utilizing gerotor type pump which contains both pressure and scavenge cavities. Flow is 88 GPM at a pressure of 200 psig.

OIL GRADE: MIL-L-23699

MOUNTING: The pump provides three mounting points, two alignment pin types near the aft end of the pump and one fixed type near the forward end. The gearbox utilizes a similar arrangement with two pivot types near the bottom and stabilizing point at the top.

DIMENSIONS:

Propulsion Pump:

Length	80·4 in.	(2·04 m)
Outside diameter	25·5 in.	(0·65 m)
Inlet diameter	22·1 in.	(0·56 m)
Gearbox		
Height	76·4 in.	(1·94 m)
Width	35·0 in.	(0·89 m)
Length	16·9 in.	(0·43 m)

WEIGHTS:

Propulsion pump (dry) 1,512 lb (685·8 kg)

Above and below: The Powerjet 20 axial-flow waterjet pump employed in the Boeing Jetfoil. Lower illustration shows the complete foilborne propulsion system and rear foil assembly

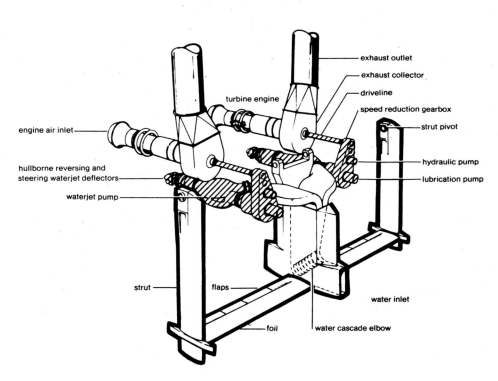

Gearbox (includes lube pump)		Pump speed	2,080
	1,450 lb (657·7 kg)	Pump flowrate	22,300 GPM
Miscellaneous	210 lb (95·3 kg)	Minimum operational total inlet head	
PERFORMANCE:			26 ft (7·92 m)
Rated input horsepower	3,780 SHP	Thrust	18,000 lb (80,000 N)
Input speed	13,250 RPM		

ROCKWELL-JLO ENGINES

HEAD OFFICE:
PO Box 268, White Plains, New York 10602

EXECUTIVES:
Harold W. Hahn, General Service Manager Rockwell Manufacturing Co, 700 Marcellus Street, Syracuse, N.Y. 13201
Rockwell is marketing a range of JLO

light ACV engines in the United States and Canada. The company's engines of 20-75 hp are employed in a number of designs, including machines built by Bertelsen and Eglen Hovercraft.

TURBO POWER AND MARINE SYSTEMS, INC.
(subsidiary of United Aircraft Corporation)

HEADQUARTERS:
1690 New Britain Avenue, Farmington, Connecticut 06032

TELEPHONE:
(area code) 203 677-4801

EXECUTIVES:
President, TPM, W. J. Closs
Vice-President, Marketing, C. W. Wincze
Marketing Manager, A. .B. Crouchley
Sales Manager, R. F. Nordin
Manager, Industrial & Marine Sales, S.D. Caplow
Manager, Engineering Programs, D. G. Assard
Manager, Systems Installation & Service, K. H. Truesdell

Turbo Power and Marine Systems, Inc., a wholly owned subsidiary of United Aircraft Corporation, designs and builds industrial and marine gas turbine power plants and power plant systems. It also provides a continuing systems support for each of its installations.

Canadian sales of TPM gas turbines are handled by United Aircraft of Canada, Limited, Post Office Box 10, Longueuil, Quebec, Canada. UACL also manufactures and handles the sales of the UACL ST6 marine gas turbine.

Over 1,000 TPM gas turbines have been delivered for electric power generation, gas transmission and industrial drives as well as for marine propulsion.

TPM MARINE GAS TURBINES

Turbo Power & Marine Systems offers the 46,000 shp FT4C-1D gas turbines for marine propulsion.

TPM is also developing a new marine gas turbine under a US Navy contract. The design of the new gas turbine is based on the extensive operating experience of the TPM FT4 marine gas turbine and the Pratt & Whitney Aircraft JT9D fan jet engine. Designated the FT9, the new gas turbine will have an initial marine rating of 33,000 shp at 100°F with inlet and exhaust duct losses of 4 and 6 inches of water. Advantages of the new FT9 gas turbine will include modular construction for maintainability and low fuel consumption. Details of the FT9 are shown in the cross section illustration.

MARINE INSTALLATIONS

TPM FT4 marine gas turbines were first used for boost power in military vessels, including two Royal Danish Navy frigates, twelve U.S. Coast Guard Hamilton Class

TPM Marine Power Pac with an FT4 gas turbine

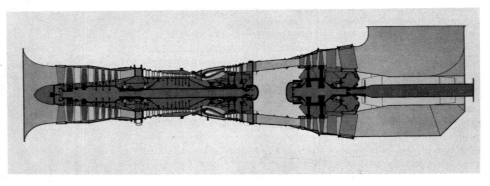

Cross-section of the TPM FT9 marine gas-turbine, rated at 33,000 shp at 100 deg F

high endurance cutters and four Canadian Armed Forces DDH-280 Iroquois Class destroyers. Another boost power application of the FT4 is in the Fast Escort and ASW vessel *Bras d'Or* also built for the Canadian Armed Forces. A later application is for two new 12,000 ton Arctic ice breakers under construction for U.S. Coast Guard. With

three TPM FT4 marine gas turbines, these vessels will be capable of maintaining a continuous speed of three knots through ice six feet thick, and will be able to ram through ice 21 feet thick.

TPM marine gas turbines are used for both the main and boost propulsion in the four new Canadian DDH-280 destroyers. These are the first military combatant vessels to be designed for complete reliance on gas turbine power. TPM marine gas turbines are also used in a military surface effect ship program.

Four 32,000 ton container ships with TPM marine gas turbines are in trans-atlantic service with Seatrain Lines. These vessels are *Euroliner*, *Eurofreighter*, *Asialiner* and *Asiafreighter*.

Another commercial vessel where TPM FT4 gas turbines will be used as the main propulsion unit is the *Finnjet*, a high speed Finnlines passenger liner being built by the Wartsila Shipyard in Helsinki for service in the Baltic Sea.

TPM MARINE POWER PAC

The photograph shows a TPM FT4 marine gas turbine completely packaged as a marine power pacs ready for installation, with the minimum of interface connections to be made. Each is built upon a rigid mounting frame and includes a housing and engine mounting system, together with controls, accessory equipment, wiring and piping. A remote control system is also provided. Installation is simple and since all the equipment is pre-tested in the factory before shipment, the time required for checkout after installation is minimized.

The gas generator portion of the gas turbine is easily removed for servicing. With a spare gas generator to replace the one removed for servicing, the ship's power plant can undergo even a major overhaul without tieing longer than necessary for a normal turn-around at dock.

TPM FT4 marine gas turbines are manufactured by the Pratt & Whitney Aircraft Division of United Aircraft Corporation. Details are given below:
TYPE: Simple cycle two spool free turbine engine. A low pressure compressor is driven by a two stage turbine and a high pressure compressor is driven by a single turbine. The burner section has eight burner cans which are equipped with duplex fuel nozzles. An independent or free power turbine drives the load through a shaft which extends through the exhaust duct elbow.
AIR INTAKE: Fabricated steel casing with 18 radial struts supporting the front compressor bearing and equipped with a hot

bleed air anti-icing system.
LP COMPRESSOR: Nine stage axial flow on inner of two concentric shafts driven by two stage turbine and supported on ball and roller bearings.
HP COMPRESSOR: Seven stage axial flow on outer hollow shaft driven by single stage turbine and running on ball and roller bearings.
COMBUSTION CHAMBER: Eight burner cans located in an annular arrangement and enclosed in a one piece steel casing. Each burner has six duplex fuel nozzles.
GAS GENERATOR: Steel casing with hollow guide vanes. Turbine wheels are bolted to the compressor shafts and are supported on ball and roller bearings. A single stage turbine drives the high compressor and a two stage turbine drives the low compressor.
POWER TURBINE: The engine is available with either clockwise or counter clockwise rotation of the power turbine. Desired direction of rotation specified by customer. Power turbine housing is bolted to gas generator turbine housing. The two stage turbine shaft assembly is straddle mounted and supported on ball and roller bearings. The output shaft is bolted to the hub of the power turbine rotor and extends through the exhaust duct.
BEARINGS: Anti-friction ball and roller bearings.

ACCESSORY DRIVE: Starter, fluid power pump, tachometer drives for low compressor, high compressor and free turbine.
LUBRICATION SYSTEM: Return system and scavange pumps with internal pressure (45 psi).
LUBRICATING OIL SPECIFICATIONS: Type 2 synthetic lube oil PWA-521 MIL-L-23699.
MOUNTING: Horizontal 5 degrees nose up or nose down. 15 degrees either side of vertical. Momentary inclination for periods of 10 seconds; pitch 10 degrees nose up or down and up to a 45 degree either side of vertical.
STARTING: Pneumatic or hydraulic.
DIMENSIONS: Length 328 in, width 76 in, height 85 ins.
FUEL SPECIFICATIONS:
Light Distillate (Naphtha)
    PWA-532(1)
Aviation Grade Kerosene
    PWA-522(1)   MIL-T-5624
Marine Diesel
    PWA-527(1)   MIL-F-16884
Heavy Distillate
    PWA-539   MIL-F-24376(2)
                or
                MIL-F-24397(3)
(1) Covered by TPM-FR-1 for series engine
(2) Navy distillate fuel, referee
(3) Navy distillate fuel

PERFORMANCE DATA: FT4C-1D MARINE GAS TURBINE

Rating	Power Output (1)	Special Fuel Consumption (2)
Max Intermittent	46,000 shp	0·46 lb (208 gr) /shp-hr
Max Continuous	42,000 shp	0·46 lb (208 gr)/shp-hr
Normal	36,900 shp	0·46 lb (208 gr)/shp-hr

(1) All ratings at 3,600 rpm shaft speed, 59°F and sea level.
(2) Based on fuel with LHV of 18,500 Btu/lb.
Oil Consumption: 0·4 gal. (1·82 litres)/hr.
                      max. as measured over a
                      10 hour period.
                      0·1 gal. (0·45 litres)/hr
                      service operation avg.

UNION OF SOVIET SOCIALIST REPUBLICS

AI

A. IVCHENKO

The design team headed by the late general designer Ivchenko is based in a factory at Zaporojie in the Ukraine, where all prototypes and pre-production engines bearing the "AI" prefix are developed and built. Chief designer is Lotarev and chief engineer Tichienko. The production director is M. Omeltchenko.

First engine with which Ivchenko was associated officially was the 55 hp AI-4G piston-engine used in the Kamov Ka-10 ultra-light helicopter. He later progressed via the widely used AI-14 and AI-26 piston-engines, to become one of the Soviet Union's leading designers of gas-turbines engines.

A 1,750 hp Ivchenko AI-23-CI marine gas-turbine

Two AI-20s in de-rated, marinised form and driving two 3-stage waterjets power the Burevestink, the first Soviet gas-turbine hydrofoil to go into series production, and a single AI-24 drives the integrated lift/propulsion system of the Sormovich 50 passenger ACV.

IVCHENKO
AI-20

Ivchenko's design bureau is responsible for the AI-20 turboprop engine which powers the Antonov An-10, An-12 and Iluyshin Il-18 airliners and the Beriev M-12 Tchaika amphibian.

Six production series of this engine had been built by the Spring of 1966. The first four series, of which manufacture started in 1957 were variants of the basic AI-20 version. They were followed by two major production versions, as follows.

AI-20K. Rated at 3,945 ehp. Used in Il-18V, An-10A and An-12.

AI-20M. Uprated version with T-O rating of 4,190 ehp (4,250 ch e). Used in Il-18D/E, An-10A and An-12.

Conversion of the turboprop as a marine power unit for hydrofoil waterjet propulsion (as on the Burevestink) involved a number of changes to the engine. In particular it was necessary to hold engine rpm at a constant level during conditions of varying load from the waterjet pump—and it was also necessary to be able to vary the thrust from the waterjet unit from zero to forward or rearwards thrust to facilitate engine starting and vessel manoeuvring.

Constant speed under variable load was achieved by replacing the engine's normal high pressure fuel pump with a special fuel regulator pump—and the waterjet pump was modified to have a variable exit area and was fitted with an air valve enabling a variable amount of air to be passed into the intake just ahead of the pump rotor. With less air passing through the waterjet, unit load on the engine increased, and vice versa if the air flow was increased by opening the air valve.

The fuel regulator pump was designed to maintain engine rpm constant and to regulate output while the AI-20 was driving the waterjet unit. Steady running conditions were shown to be satisfactorily maintained by the engine under all operating conditions— and rpm and turbine temperature were held within the limits laid down for the aircraft turboprop version: engine rpm did not fluctuate outside $\pm 2 \cdot 5$ per cent of its set speed when loading or unloading the waterjet unit.

During development of the marinised AI-20, the normal aircraft propeller and speed governor were removed and the turboprop was bench tested over the full range of its operating conditions. This demonstrated that the engine performed in a stable manner

throughout, from slow running to normal rpm. These tests were run initially using aviation kerosene Type TS-1 fuel, and then diesel fuels Types L and DS.

Following satisfactory results on the bench, the test engine was mounted on a self-propelled floating test bed equipped with a waterjet propulsion unit. Further tests with this configuration were also satisfactorily concluded, including starting checks with varying degrees of submersion of the pump section of the waterjet unit.

Electrical starting of the engine up to slow running speed (equal to approximately 25 per cent of rated rpm) was shown to take 70 to 85 seconds. For starting and ignition at ambient conditions below 10°C, fuel pre-heating is employed, and modified igniters are fitted. With this equipment, starts have been achieved down to —12°C.

Based on this experience, the marinised AI-20 for the twin-engined Burevestink was rated at 2,700 hp at 12,300 rpm. At this power output, the hydrofoil achieved speeds of up to 60 mph (97 km/hr). Specific fuel consumption was 0·71 to 0·73 lb (320-330 gr)/hp/hr.

Testing with the Burevestink exposed a number of operating characteristics of the vessel: when the two AI-20s were running while the vessel was moored or manoeuvring, residual exhaust thrust from the turbines occurred and this is required to be balanced by a negative, or reverse thrust from the waterjet by partially closing the unit's nozzle flaps. This increased the load on the engine however, and caused a rise in fuel consumption.

Also, experience showed that with a normal start following a series of wet starts, any fuel which had accumulated in the jet pipe became ignited. This resulted in a sharp rise in turbine temperature and back pressure, and flame emerged from the ejection apertures into the engine compartment and exhaust nozzle. To circumvent this, the ejection apertures were covered with a metal grid, and a spray of water is provided at the exhaust nozzle prior to starting.

Based on an overhaul life for the turboprop AI-25 of several thousand hours, special techniques have been applied to the marinised version to increase its service life. These include the use of high quality assembly procedures for the engine, efficient design of the air intake and exhaust duct, adoption of appropriate procedures for starting and on-loading of the main and auxiliary turbines at all ambient temperature conditions—and by the utilisation of highly-skilled servicing methods of the installation during operation.

The AI-20 is a single-spool turboprop, with a 10-stage axial-flow compressor, cannular combustion chamber with ten flame tubes, and a three-stage turbine, of which the first two stages are cooled. Planetary reduction gearing, with a ratio of 0·08732 : 1, is mounted forward of the annular air intake. The fixed

nozzle contains a central bullet fairing. All engine-driven accessories are mounted on the forward part of the compressor casing, which is of magnesium alloy.

The AI-20 was designed to operate reliably in all temperatures from —60°C to +55°C at heights up to 33,000 ft (10,000 m). It is a constant speed engine, the rotor speed being maintained at 21,300 rpm by automatic variation of propeller pitch. Gas temperature after turbine is 560°C in both current versions. TBO of the AI-20K was 4,000 hours in the Spring of 1966.

WEIGHT (Dry):

AI-20K		2,380 lb (1,080 kg)
AI-20M		2,290 lb (1,039 kg)

PERFORMANCE RATINGS:

Max T-O:

AI-20K	3,945 ehp (4,000 ch e)
AI-20M	4,190 ehp (4,250 ch e)

Cruise rating at 390 mph (630 kmh) at 26,000 ft (8,000 m):

AI-20K	2,220 ehp (2,250 ch e)
AI-20M	2,663 ehp (2,700 ch e)

SPECIFIC FUEL CONSUMPTION:

At cruise rating:

AI-20K	0·472 lb (215 gr) hp/hr
AI-20M	0·434 lb (197 gr) hp/hr

OIL CONSUMPTION:

Normal	1·75 Imp pints 1 litre/hr

IVCHENKO
AI-24

In general configuration, this single-spool turboprop engine, which powers the An-24 transport aircraft, is very similar to the earlier and larger AI-20. Production in 1960 and the following data refer to engines of the second series, which were in production in the Spring of 1966.

A single marinized version, developing 1,800 shp, drives the integrated lift/propulsion system of the Sormovich 50-passenger ACV.

An annular ram air intake surrounds the cast light alloy casing for the planetary reduction gear, which has a ratio of 0·08255 : 1. The cast magnesium alloy compressor casing carries a row of inlet guide vanes and the compressor stator vanes and provides mountings for the engine-driven accessories. These include fuel, hydraulic and oil pumps, tacho-generator and propeller governor.

The 10-stage avial-flow compressor is driven by a three-stage axial-flow turbine, of which the first two stages are cooled. An annular combustion chamber is used, with eight injectors and two igniters.

The engine is flat-rated to maintain its nominal output to 11,500 ft (3,500 m). TBO was 3,000 hours in the Spring of 1966.

DIMENSIONS:

Length overall	95·87 in (2,435 mm)

WEIGHT, Dry:

	1,100 lb (499 kg)

PERFORMANCE RATING:

Max T-O with water injection

2,820 ehp (2,859 ch e)

SUDOIMPORT

ADDRESS:

ul. Kaliaevskaja, 5, Moscow K-6, USSR

Russian industry has developed a variety of marine diesel engines, selected models of which have been installed in the Krasnoye Sormovo series of hydrofoil craft. Most

popular of these are the 1,100 hp M400 powering the Kometa hydrofoil, and the 1,200 hp M50 powering the Byelorus, Chaika, Meteor, Mir, Raketa, Sputnik, Strela and Vikhr hydrofoils. A third marine diesel engine is the 3D12 with a continuous rating of 300 hp. A version of this engine is

TYPE M 400

installed in the Nevka hydrofoil, now in series production in Leningrad.

These and other marine diesels are available through Sudoimport, USSR marine export, import and repair organisation.

TYPE: Water-cooled, 12-cylinder, V-type

four-stroke supercharged marine diesel engine.

CYLINDERS: Two banks of six cylinders set at 30°, each bank comprising cast aluminium alloy monobloc with integral head. Pressed-in liner with spiral cooling passages comprises inner alloy steel sleeve with nitrided working surface, and outer carbon steel sleeve. Each monobloc retained on crankcase by 14 holding-down studs. Bore 7·09 in. (180 mm). Stroke 7·87 in (200 mm). Cubic capacity 381 cu in (62·4 litres). Compression ratio 13·5 : 1.

CRANKCASE: Two-part cast aluminium alloy case with upper half carrying cylinder monoblocs, and transmitting all engine loads.

CYLINDER HEADS: Integral with cylinder monoblocs.

CRANKSHAFT: Six-crank seven-bearing crankshaft in nitrided alloy steel with split steel shells, lead bronze lined with lead-tin alloy bearing surface. Spring damper at rear end reduces torsional vibrations.

CONNECTING RODS: Master and articulated rods, with master connected to crankshaft by split big end with lead bronze lining. Articulated rods connected by pin pressed into eye of master rods.

PISTONS: Forged aluminium alloy with four rings, upper two of which are of trapeziform cross-section. Alloy steel floating gudgeon pin. Piston head specially shaped to form combustion chamber with spherical cylinder head.

CAMSHAFTS: Two camshafts acting direct on valve stems.

VALVES: Four valves in each cylinder, two inlet and two exhaust. Each valve retained on seat by three coil springs.

COOLING: Forced circulation system using fresh water with 1·0 to 1·1 per cent potassium bichromate added. Fresh water pump mounted on forward part of engine. Fresh water, and lubricating oil leaving the engine are cooled by water-to-water and water-to-oil coolers, in turn cooled by sea water circulated by engine-mounted sea water pump.

SUPERCHARGING: Single-stage centrifugal supercharger, mechanically driven and providing supercharging pressure of at least 22 lb/sq in (1·55 kg/cm^2) at rated power.

LUBRICATION: Comprises delivery pump together with full-flow centrifuge; twin-suction scavenge pump, double gauze-type strainers at inlet and outlet to oil system; and electrically-driven priming pump to prime engine with oil and fuel.

FUEL INJECTION: Closed-type fuel injection with hydraulically-operated valves, giving initial pressure of 2,845 lb/sq in (200 kg/cm^2). Each injector has eight spray orifices forming 140° conical spray. High pressure 12-plunger fuel injection pump with primary gear pump. Two filters in parallel filter oil to HP pump.

STARTING: Compressed air system with starting cylinder operating at 1,067 to 2,134 lb/sq in (75 to 150 kg/cm^2), two disc-type air distributors and 12 starting valves.

GOVERNOR: Multi-range indirect-action engine speed governor with resilient gear drive from pump camshaft. Governor designed to maintain pre-set rpm throughout full speed range from minimum to maximum.

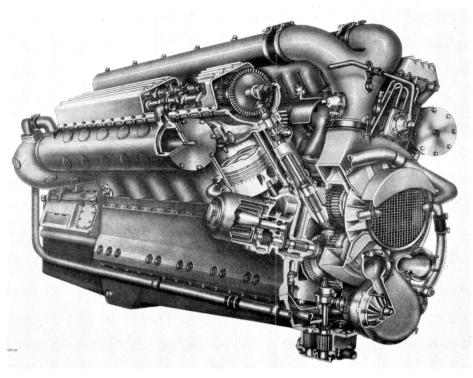

Sudoimport M400

Sudoimport 3D12

EXHAUST SYSTEM: Fresh water-cooled exhaust manifolds fastened to exterior of cylinder blocs. Provision made for fitting thermocouple or piezometer.

REVERSING: Hydraulically-operated reversing clutch fitted to enable prop shaft to run forwards, idle or reverse with constant direction of crankshaft rotation.

MOUNTING: Supports fitted to upper half of crankcase for attaching engine to bedplate.

DIMENSIONS:

Width	48·03 in (1,220 mm)
Height	49·21 in (1,250 mm)
Length	102·36 in (2,600 mm)

PERFORMANCE RATINGS:

Max	1,100 hp at 1,800 rpm
Continuous	1,000 hp at 1,700 rpm

FUEL CONSUMPTION:
At continuous rating
Not over 0·425 lb (193 gr)/hp/hr

OIL CONSUMPTION:
At continuous rating
Not over 0·013 lb (6 gr)/hp/hr

TYPE 3D12

TYPE: Water-cooled, 12-cylinder, V-type, four-stroke marine diesel engine.

CYLINDERS: Two banks of six cylinders in jacketed blocks with pressed-in steel liners. Bore 5·9 in (150 mm). Stroke 7·09 in (180 mm). Cubic capacity 237 cu in (38·8 litres). Compression ratio 14 to 15 : 1.

CRANKCASE: Two-part cast aluminium alloy case with upper half accommodating seven main bearings of steel shell, lead bronze lined type. Lower half carries oil pump, water circulating pump and fuel feed pump.

CYLINDER HEADS: Provided with six recesses to accommodate combustion chambers. Each chamber is connected via channels to inlet and outlet ports of cylinder bloc.

CRANKSHAFT: Alloy steel forging with seven journals and six crankpins. Pendulum anti-vibration dampers fitted on first two webs to reduce torsional vibration.

CONNECTING RODS: Master and articulated rods of double-T section forged in alloy steel. Master rod big-end bearings have steel shells, lead bronze lined. Small end bearings of master rods and both bearings of articulated rods have bronze bushes.

PISTONS: Aluminium alloy.

CAMSHAFTS: Carbon steel camshafts with cams and journals hardened by high frequency electrical current.

COOLING: Closed water, forced circulation type incorporating centrifugal pump, self suction sea water pump and tubular water cooler.

LUBRICATION: Forced circulation type with dry sump, incorporating three-section gear pump, oil feed pump, wire-mesh strainer with fine cardboard filtering element and tubular oil cooler.

FUEL INJECTION: Rotary fuel feed pump, twin felt filter, plunger fuel pump with device to stop engine in event of oil pressure drop in main line. Closed-type fuel injectors with slotted filters. Plunger pump carries variable-speed centrifugal governor for crankshaft rpm.

STARTING: Main electrical starting system, with compressed air reserve system.

REVERSE-REDUCTION GEAR: Non-co-axial type with twin-disc friction clutch: and gear-type reduction gear giving optional ratios, forwards, of 2·95 : 1, 2·04 : 1 or 1·33 : 1, and 2·18 : 1 astern.

DIMENSIONS:

Width	41·42 in (1,052 mm)
Height	45·63 in (1,159 mm)
Length	97·01 in (2,464 mm)

WEIGHT, Dry:

Fully equipped	4,189 lb (1,900 kg)

PERFORMANCE RATING:

Continuous	300 hp at 1,500 rpm

FUEL CONSUMPTION:

At continuous rated power

0·388 lb (176 gr)/hp/hr

OIL CONSUMPTION:

At continuous rated power

Not over 0·02 lb (9 gr)/hp/hr

A SELECTED
BIBLIOGRAPHY

A SELECTED BIBLIOGRAPHY

AIR CUSHION VEHICLES

ACVs IN NORTH AMERICA

ACV Icing Problems, J. R. Stallabras and T. R. Ringer, National Research Council, Seventh Canadian Symposium on Air Cushion Technology, June 1973.

ACV potential in New York. Leedham, C. (New York City Commissioner for Marine and Aviation) Hoverfoil News, Vol. 5, No.6 March 14th 1974.

Air Cushion Technology: the Prospects for Canadian Industry, Dr P. A. Sullivan, Institute for Aerospace Studies, University of Toronto. Sixth CASI Symposium on Air Cushion Technology, Ontario, June 1972.

Air-Cushion Vehicles, Operational use in the Arctic, Ives, G, Petroleum Eng., Vol, 46 No. 1, January 1974.

Arctic Development Using Very Large ACVs, J. L. Anderson, NASA Lewis Laboratories. Seventh Canadian Symposium on Air Cushion Technology, June 1973.

Arctic Operational Experience with SR.N6 engaged in Hydrographic Survey and Cushioncraft CC-7, L. R. Colby and G. M. Yeaton, Polar Continental Shelf Project, DEMR. Fourth Canadian Symposium on Air Cushion Technology, 1970. Canadian Aeronautics and Space Institute.

Dynamic Performance of an Air-Cushion Vehicle in a Marine Environment Fein, J. A. Magnuson, A. H. and Moran, D. D. (Naval Ship Research and Development Center, Bethesda, Md,) AIAA/SNAME Advanced Marine Vehicle Conference, San Diego, California, February 25-28 1974.

Development of the Canadian Air-Cushion Vehicle Industry, Wade, R. G. (Ministry of Transport, Ottawa). AIAA/SNAME Advanced Marine Vehicle Conference, San Diego, California, 25-28 February 1974.

Heavy Goods Transport by Air-Cushion Vehicles. Eastman, C. A. R. The Society of Engineers Journal (U.K.) Vol. LXIV Nos. 2 and 3, Apr/June and July/Sept. 1973.

Effects of Hovercraft Operation on Organic Terrain in the Arctic, Gunars Abele, US Army Cold Regions Research and Engineering Laboratory, Hovering Craft, Hydrofoil and Advanced Transit Systems Conference, Brighton May 1974.

Environmental Effects of ACV and other Off-Road Vehicle Operations on Tundra, G. Abele and W. E. Rickard, U.S. Army Cold Region Research and Engineering Laboratory. Seventh Canadian Symposium on Air Cushion Technology, June 1973.

NCTL's Voyageur Experience, B. Meade, Northern Transportation Co. Seventh Canadian Symposium on Air Cushion Technology, June 1973.

Operational Evaluation of the SK-5 in Alaska, R. A. Liston and B. Hanamoto, US Army Cold Region Research and Engineering Laboratory. Seventh Canadian Symposium on Air Cushion Technology, June 1973.

Requirements for a Canadian ACV Industry, R. G. Wade, Hovermarine (Canada) Ltd, June 1969. Third Canadian Symposium on Air Cushion Technology, Canadian Aeronautics and Space Institute, SC 2.00.

Review of Canadian Government Options for Future Action in the Development of Air Cushion Technology, I. G. Lochead, Dept of Industry, Trade and Commerce. Third Canadian Symposium on Air Cushion Technology; Canadian Aeronautics and Space Institute, June 1969. SC 2.00.

Some Air Cushion Technology Research in Canada, H. S. Fowler, National Research Council, Canada. Hovering Craft, Hydrofoil and Advanced Transit Systems Conference, Brighton, May 1974.

Small Air Cushion Vehicle Operation on Floating Ice under Winter Conditions, R. J. Weaver and R. O. Ramseier, Dept. of the Environment. Seventh Canadian Symposium on Air Cushion Technology, June 1973.

AIR CUSHION LANDING SYSTEMS
Further Developments in Surface Effect Take-Off and Landing System Concepts, A. E. Johnson, F. W. Wilson and W. B. Maguire, NSRDC. Sixth CASI Symposium on Air Cushion Technology, Ontario, June 1972.

AIR CUSHION LOAD CARRIERS

Aircraft Recovery, G. M. Parkes, Hovertrailers International Ltd., Hovering Craft, Hydrofoil and Advanced Transit Systems Conference, Brighton, May 1974.

Movement of Heavy Loads, L. A. Hopkins, Air Cushion Equipment Ltd, Seventh Canadian Symposium on Air Cushion Technology, June 1973.

On the Applications of Air Cushion Technology to Off-Road Transport, Dr J. Y. Wong, Carleton University. Sixth CASI Symposium on Air Cushion Technology, Ontario, June 1972.

River Crossing Problems Posed by the Mackenzie Highway and a Possible Solution, R. G. Wade, Canadian Ministry of Transport. Seventh Canadian Symposium on Air Cushion Technology, June 1973.

Development of a Track Laying Air Cushion Vehicle, J. R. Goulburn and R. B. Steven, University of Belfast. Hovering Craft, Hydrofoil and Advanced Transit Systems Conference, Brighton ,May 1974.

The Role of the Non-Self-Propelled Air Cushion Vehicle, L. A. Hopkins, Air Cushion Equipment Ltd. Sixth CASI Symposium on Air Cushion Technology, Ontario, June 1972.

Air Cushion Towed Raft Evaluation Project—Current Trials, J. E. Laframboise, Transportation Development Agency. Seventh Canadian Symposium on Air Cushion Technology, June 1973.

An Amphibious Hover Platform for Civil Engineering uses, D. G. W. Turner, Mackace Ltd. Hovering Craft, Hydrofoil and Advanced Transit Systems Conference, Brighton, May, 1974.

Movement of Drill Rigs Using an Air Cushion Platform, R. L. Wheeler, British Hovercraft Corporation. Fourth Canadian Symposium on Air Cushion Technology, June 1970. Canadian Aeronautics and Space Institute.

A 1,000-ton River Hovercraft, R. A. Shaw, V. E. Barker and D. M. Waters, Hoverprojects Ltd., Hovering Craft, Hydrofoil and Advanced Transit Systems Conference, May, 1974.

AIR LUBRICATED HULLS
The Application of the Air Cushion Principle to Very Large Vessels—A Case for Further Research, J. W. Grundy, Naval Architect. Hovering Craft, Hydrofoil and Advanced Transit Systems Conference, Brighton, May 1974.

COMMERCIAL OPERATION
Air-Cushion Vehicles in the Gulf Offshore Oil Industry: A Feasibility Study, Pruett, J. M. (Louisiana State University, Baton Rouge). Final Report on Sea Grant Project (NOAA Contract 04-3-158-19), December 1973.

Air Cushion Vehicles in the Search and Rescue Role, Commander B. W. Mead, Canadian Coast Guard, June 1969. Third Canadian Symposium on Air Cushion Technology, Canadian Aeronautics and Space Institute, SC 2.00.

Air Cushion Vehicles in Support of the Petroleum Industry, Wilfrid J. Eggington, Donald J. Iddins, Aerojet-General Corporation. American Petroleum Institute Meeting; Shreveport, Louisiana, March 1969.

Domain of the Air Cushion Craft, Peter J. Mantle and David R. Lavis, Bell Aerosystems Corporation, Society of Automative Engineers, Air Transportation Meeting, New York, May 1968.

Experience of Design and Operating the Naviplane, A. Thomas, SEDAM and J. Bertin, Bertin et Cie Institution of Production Engineers, Second International Hovercraft Conference, April 1971.

Current User Experience, E. W. H. Gifford, Hovertravel Ltd,

Institution of Production Engineers, Second International Hover-craft Conference, April 1971.

The Contribution of Sidewall Hovercraft to the Evolution of the Marine Ferry, E. G. Tattersall, Hovermarine Ltd. International Hovercraft Conference (Southampton Section), April 1968.

Cross-Channel Hovercraft Operations. L. R. Colquhoun, Hoverlloyd Ltd. Fourth Canadian Symposium on Air Cushion Technology. June 1970. Canadian Aeronautics and Space Institute.

Operational and Technical Problems of Commercial Hovercraft L. R. Colquhoun, (Leslie Colquhoun & Associates, Ramsgate, England.) AIAA/SNAME Advanced Marine Vehicle Conference, San Diego, California, 25-28 February 1974.

Operational Engineering Reliability in Commercial Hovercraft, Cdr. J. M. Lefeaux, British Rail Hovercraft, Institution of Production Engineers, Second International Hovercraft Conference, April 1971.

ACV PROJECTS
ACV Technology Programs at Aerojet-General, R. W. Muir, Aerojet-General Corporation, June 1969. Third Canadian Symposium on Air Cushion Technology, Canadian Aeronautics and Space Institute, $C 2.00.

Development of Surface Effect Technology in the US Industry, John B. Chaplin, Bell Aerospace Company. AIAA/SNAME/USN Advanced Marine Vehicles Meeting, Annapolis, Maryland, July 17-19, 1972.

Control of a Single Propeller Hovercraft, with Particular Reference to BH7, R. L. Wheeler, British Hovercraft Corporation Ltd. Fourth Canadian Symposium on Air Cushion Technology, June 1970. Canadian Aeronautics and Space Institute.

New Advanced Design ACVs, Jean Bertin, Bertin et Cie. Third Canadian Symposium on Air Cushion Technology, June 1969. Canadian Aeronautics and Space Institute, $C 2.00.

Voyageur Trials and Operating Experience, T. F. Melhuish, Bell Aerospace, Canada. Seventh Canadian Symposium on Air Cushion Technology, June 1973.

Operational Experience on VT1s, R. D. Hunt, Hovercraft Division, Vosper Thornycroft Ltd. Institute of Production Engineers, Second International Hovercraft Conference, April 1971.

DESIGN
A Theoretical Note on the Lift Distribution of a Non-Planar Ground Effect Wing, Kida, T. and Miyai, Y. (University of Osaka Prefecture, Japan). The Aeronautical Quarterly, Vol. 24. August 1973. Part 3.

A Linearized Potential Flow Theory for the Motions of Air-Cushion Vehicles in a Seaway, T. K. S. Murthy, Portsmouth Polytechnic. Ninth Symposium on Naval Hydrodynamics, Paris, August 1972.

A Comparison of Some Features of High-Speed Marine Craft, A. Silverleaf and F. G. R. Cook, National Physical Laboratory. Royal Institution of Naval Architects, March 1969.

Development of the Axial-flow Surface Effect Vehicle, A. M. Jackes, AirSeamobile Co, Santa Ana, Calif. Advanced Marine Vehicle meeting AIAA/SNAME/USN, Annapolis, July 1972.

Some Design Aspects of Air Cushion Craft, Peter J. Mantle, International Congress of Subsonic Aeronautics, New York Academy of Sciences, April 1967.

On the Determination of the Hydrodynamic Performance of Air-Cushion Vehicles, S. D. Prokhorov, V. N. Treshchevski, L. D. Volkov, Kryloff Research Institute, Leningrad. Ninth Symposium on Naval Hydrodynamics, Paris, August 1972.

On the Prediction of Acceleration Response of Air-Cushion Vehicles to Random Seaways and the Distortion Effects of Cushion Inherent in Scale Models, D. R. Lavis and R. V. Bartholemew, Aerojet-General

Corporation Advanced Marine Vehicle meeting, AIAA/SNAME/USN, Annapolis, July 1972.

Ram-Wing Surface Effect Boat, Capt R. W. Gallington, USAF, US Air Force Academy, Colorado, Advanced Marine Vehicle Meeting AIAA/SNAME/USN Annapolis, July 1972.

Resultats d'Exploitation des Aeroglisseurs Marins "Naviplane", M. P. Guienne, Bertin et Cie. Seventh Canadian Symposium on Air Cushion Technology, June 1973.

The Design, Fabrication and Initial Trials of a Light Amphibious Arctic Transporter, J. H. Kennedy and A. M. Garner, Jr, Transportation Technology Inc. Fourth Canadian Symposium on Air Cushion Technology, 1970. Canadian Aeronautics and Space Institute.

Some Design Aspects of an Integrated Lift/Propulsion System, D. Jones, Jones, Kirwan and Associates. Sixth CASI Symposium on Air Cushion Technology, Ontario, June 1972.

Some Aspects of Optimum Design of Lift Fans, T. G. Csaky, NSRDC. Sixth CASI Symposium on Air Cushion Technology, Ontario, June 1972.

Trade-Off Methodology for Evaluation of Design Alternatives of Air Cushion Vehicles, O. Gokcek and J. H. Madden, Aerojet General Corporation. Sixth CASI Symposium on Air Cushion Technology, Ontario, June 1972.

Aerodynamic Challenges for the Faster Interface Vehicles, P. R. Shipps, Rohr Corporation. Sixth CASI Symposium on Air Cushion Technology, Ontario, June 1972.

A Method for Generating Aerodynamic Sideforces on ACV Hulls, Dr R. J. Kind, Carleton University. Sixth CASI Symposium on Air Cushion Technology, Ontario, June 1972.

Vortex Shedding from the Ram Wing Vehicle, Technical Progress Report, Gallington, R. (Air Force Acadamy, Colorado) Jan-July 1973. AD-767234. August 1973. Available N. T. I. S.

EXTERNAL AERODYNAMICS
The External Aerodynamics of Hovercraft, Professor E. J. Andrews College of Aeronautics, Cranfield. Royal Aeronautical Society Rotorcraft Section, April 1969.

INDUSTRIAL APPLICATIONS
Hoverpallets for Material Handling, A. J. I. Poynder, British Hovercraft Corporation. Institution of Production Engineers, International Hovercraft Conference, April 1968.

Industrial Applications of Air Cushion Technology, P. H. Winter, Air Vehicle Developments Ltd, June 1969. Third Canadian Symposium on Air Cushion Technology, Canadian Aeronautics and Space Institute, $C 2.00.

LIGHTWEIGHT ACVs
Control and Guidance of Light Amphibious Hovercraft up to a Gross Weight of 5,000 lbs, R. L. Trillo, Robert Trillo Ltd. Seventh Canadian Symposium on Air Cushion Technology, June 1973.

Small Hovercraft Design, P. H. Winter, Air Vehicle Developments. International Hovercraft Conference, 1968, the Institution of Production Engineers (Southampton Section).

Small Hovercraft Structure, A. J. English, Sealand Hovercraft Ltd, Hovering Craft, Hydrofoil and Advanced Transit Systems Conference, Brighton, May 1974.

MILITARY APPLICATIONS and OPERATING EXPERIENCE
A Review of British Army Hovercraft Activity—1967-72, Major G. G. Blakey, Royal Corps of Transport. Sixth CASI Symposium on Air Cushion Technology, Ontario, 1972.

Development of the SR.N6 Mk 5 Vehicle-carrying Hovercraft, Major M. H. Burton, Dept of Trade and Industry, UK. Seventh Canadian Symposium on Air Cushion Technology, June 1973.

ACV Military Applications—Experience and Potential, J. B. Chaplin. Bell Aerosystems Company, June 1969. Third Canadian Symposium on Air Cushion Technology, Canadian Aeronautics and Space Institute, $C 2.00.

Air Cushion Vehicles in a Logistical Role, Col H. N. Wood (Ret), US Army Combat Development Command Transportation Agency. Fourth Canadian Symposium on Air Cushion Technology, 1970. Canadian Aeronautics and Space Institute.

BH.7 Mk 2—Experience during the first 2,000 hours of Operation, Cdr L. G. Scovell, Dept of Trade and Industry, UK. Seventh Canadian Symposium on Air Cushion Technology, June 1973.

Military Experience, Commander D. F. Robbins, RN, Interservice Hovercraft Unit. International Hovercraft Conference, April 1968. The Institution of Production Engineers (Southampton Section).

US Army ACV Operations, Major D. G. Moore, US Army Air Cushion Vehicle Unit, June 1969. Third Canadian Symposium on Air Cushion Technology, Canadian Aeronautics and Space Institute, $C 2.00.

UK Military Hovercraft, Commander N. T. Bennett, AFC, RN, Interservice Hovercraft Unit. Second International Hovercraft Conference, Institute of Production Engineers, April 1971.

LEGISLATION and REGULATIONS
Lloyd's Register's Requirements for ACVs, A. K. Buckle, Lloyd's Register of Shipping. Second Canadian Symposium on Air Cushion Technology, June 1968. Canadian Aeronautics and Space Institute, $C 2.00.

Operating Legislation for ACVs, Captain J. Doherty, Department of Transport, June 1968. Second Canadian Symposium on Air Cushion Technology. Canadian Aeronautics and Space Institute, $C 2.00.

The Air Registration Board and Hovercraft, S. Gardner, Air Registration Board, June 1968, Second Canadian Symposium on Air Cushion Technology, Canadian Aeronautics and Space Institute, $C 2.00.

United States Requirements for Commercial Surface Effect Ships, W. A. Cleary Jr and Lt D. H. Whitten, US Coast Guard. Second Canadian Symposium on Air Cushion Technology, June 1968. Canadian Aeronautics and Space Institute, $C 2.00.

POWERPLANTS
Some Aspects of Free Turbine Engine Hovercraft Control, W. Bloomfield, T. B. Lauriat, AVCO Corporation Lycoming Division. Institute of Production Engineers, Second International Hovercraft Conference, April 1971.

The Selection of the Optimum Powerplant for the Air Cushion Vehicle, R. Messet, United Aircraft of Canada Ltd. Fourth Canadian Symposium on Air Cushion Technology, June 1970. Canadian Aeronautics and Space Institute.

PRODUCTION
The Production of Air Cushion Vehicles, E. F. Gilberthorpe, British Hovercraft Corporation. Institution of Production Engineers (Southampton Section), International Hovercraft Conference, April 1968.

Hovercraft from a Shipbuilder, A. E. Bingham, Vosper Thornycroft Ltd., Hovering Craft, Hydrofoil and Advanced Transit Systems Conference, Brighton, May 1974.

RESEARCH and DEVELOPMENT
A Decade of Development—The SR.N6 Family of Hovercraft, R. L. Wheeler, British Hovercraft Corporation, Hovering Craft, Hydrofoil & Advanced Transit Systems Conference, Brighton, May 1974.

Development of Hovermarine Transport Vehicles, E. G. Tattersall, Hovermarine Transport Ltd. Institute of Production Engineers, Second International Hovercraft Conference, April 1971.

Minimum Induced Drag of a Semi-Circular Ground Effect Wing, Mamada, H. (Aichi University of Education) and Ando, S. (Nagoya University) (Japan). Journal of Aircraft, Vol. 10 No. 11, November 1973.

Research Requirements for the Development of Air Cushion Vehicles, Dr. P. A. Sullivan, Institute of Aerospace Studies, University of

Toronto. Fourth Canadian Symposium on Air Cushion Technology. Canadian Aeronautics and Space Institute.

The Amphibious Hovercraft, R. L. Wheeler, British Hovercraft Corporation. Second Canadian Symposium on Air Cushion Technology, 1968, Canadian Aeronautics and Space Institute, $C 2.00.

The BHC Contribution to Hovercraft Development, P. R. Crewe, British Hovercraft Corporation. Hovercraft Conference, Adelaide, November 1968.

The Development Phase of the Mountbatten Class (SR.N4) Hovercraft, D. J. Hardy, British Hovercraft Corporation Ltd., June 1969. Third Canadian Symposium on Air Cushion Technology. Canadian Aeronautics and Space Institute, $C 2.00.

Hovercraft Research and Development, R. L. Wheeler, British Hovercraft Corporation Ltd. Institute of Production Engineers, Second International Hovercraft Conference, April 1971.

Development of the Hovergem Range of Commercial Air Cushion Vehicles, G. L. Green, Hovergem Australasia Pty Ltd, Institute of Production Engineers, Second International Hovercraft Conference, April 1971.

The MV-PP5, Dr T. Tomita, Mitsui Shipbuilding and Engineering Co Ltd, Second Canadian Symposium on Air Cushion Technology, June 1968. Canadian Aeronautics and Space Institute, $C 2.00.

Some Aspects of Hovercraft Dynamics, J. R. Richardson, NPL Hovercraft Unit, Institution of Production Engineers, Second International Hovercraft Conference, April 1971.

Recent Developments in Hovercraft Performance Testing, B. J. Russell, Interservice Hovercraft Unit, HMS Daedalus. Hovering Craft, Hydrofoil & Advanced Transit Systems Conference, Brighton, May 1974.

Research and Development Work Associated with the Lift and Propulsion of Air Cushion Vehicles, J. G. Russell, Dowty Rotol Ltd, Hovering Craft, Hydrofoil & Advanced Transit Systems Conference, Brighton, May 1974.

STRUCTURAL DESIGN
Some Aspects of Reinforced Plastics applied to the Structure of Marine Hovercraft, P. J. Hill, Hovermarine Ltd. Institution of Production Engineers (Southampton Section), International Hovercraft Conference, April 1968.

The Use of Glass Reinforced Plastics for Hovercraft Structures, A. Marchant, Hovermarine Ltd, June 1969. Third Canadian Symposium on Air Cushion Technology. Canadian Aeronautics and Space Institute, $C 2.00.

A Method of Testing Models of Hovercraft in Open Waters, Prof. L. Koblinski and Dr. M. Krezelewski, Ship Research Institute, Technical University of Gdansk. Institution of Production Engineres, Second International Hovercraft Conference, April 1971.

SYSTEMS
Airscrews for Hovercraft, G. K. Ketley, Hawker Siddeley Dynamics Ltd. Second Canadian Symposium on Air Cushion Technology, 1968. Canadian Aeronautics and Space Institute, $C 2.00.

Ducted Propeller Installation for An Amphibious Hovercraft, R. Trillo & P. H. Winter, Hovering Craft, Hydrofoil and Advanced Transit Systems Conference, May 1974.

ACV Design Technology, J. B. Chaplin. Bell Aerosystems Co. Second Canadian Symposium on Air Cushion Technology, 1968 Canadian Aeronautics and Space Institute, $C 2,00.

An Accumulator Control System for Alleviating SES Craft Heave motions in waves, P. Kaplan and T. P. Sargent, Oceanics Inc, and James L. Decker, US Navy Surface Effect Ships Project Office, Washington DC. Advanced Marine Vehicle meeting AIAA/SNAME/USN. Annapolis, July 1972.

Aspects of Performance Evaluation of Waterjet Propulsion Systems and a Critical Review of the State of the Art, J. H. Brandan. AIAA/SNAME Paper No 67-360, May 1967.

Deterioration of Hovercraft Skirt Components on Craft Operating over Water, M. D. Kelly, J. Morris & E. R. Gardner, Avon Rubber

Co. Ltd., Hovering Craft, Hydrofoil and Advanced Transit Systems Conference, Brighton, May 1974.

Evolution of Integrated Lift, Propulsion and Control in the Aeromobile ACV, Dr W. R. Bertelsen, Bertelsen Manufacturing Co, June 1969. Third Canadian Symposium on Air Cushion Technology. Canadian Aeronautics and Space Institute, $C 2.00.

Experience of Using the Gas Turbine Engine for the Propulsion of the Fully Amphibious Air Cushion Vehicle, M. L. Woodward, Rolls-Royce (1971) Ltd. Sixth Canadian Symposium on Air Cushion Technology, Ontario, June 1972.

Hovercraft Skirts, R. L. Wheeler, British Hovercraft Corporation, Hovering Craft, Hydrofoil and Advanced Transit Systems Conference, Brighton, May 1974.

Jets, Props and Air Cushions, Propulsion Technology and Surface Effect Ships, Alfred Skolnick. Z. G. Wachnik, Joint Surface Effect Ships Program Office. Gas Turbine Conference and Products Show. The American Society of Mechanical Engineers, March 1968.

Pneumatic Power Transmission Applied to Hovercraft, J. F. Sladey Jnr. and R. K. Muench, United States Naval Academy and Naval Ship Research and Development Centre. Sixth CASI Symposium on Air Cushion Technology, Ontario, June 1972.

Skirt Design for Small Hovercraft, J. A. Eglen, National Association of ACV Enthusiasts, June 1969. Third Canadian Symposium on Air Cushion Technology. Canadian Aeronautics and Space Institute, $C 2.00.

Characterisation and Testing of Skirt Materials, Dr R. C. Tennyson and J. R. McCullough, University of Toronto, Institute for Aerospace Studies. Seventh Canadian Symposium on Air Cushion Technology, June 1973.

Study of the Performance of a Partially Submerged Propeller, W. T. Lindemuth and R. A. Barr, Hydronautics Inc. Technical Report 760-1, July 1967.

Surface Effect Vehicle Propulsion: A Review of the State of the Art, J. B. Chaplin, R. G. Moore and J. L. Allison, Bell Aerospace. Sixth Canadian Symposium on Air Cushion Technology, Ontario, June 1972.

The French Technique of Aeroglisseurs Marins, C. Marchetti, SEDAM. Second Canadian Symposium on Air Cushion Technology, June 1968, Canadian Aeronautics and Space Institute, $C 2.00.

The Influence of Plenum Chamber Obstructions on the Performance of a Hovercraft Lift Fan, G. Wilson, Dr D. J. Myles and G. Gallacher, National Engineering Laboratory, June 1969. Third Canadian Symposium on Air Cushion Technology. Canadian Aeronautics and Space Institute, $C 2.00.

The Potential of an Air Cushion Landing Gear in Civil Air Transport, T. D. Earl, Bell Aer systems Co. Second Canadian Symposium on Air Cushion Technology, 1968. Canadian Aeronautics and Space Institute, SC 2.00.

Water-Jet Propulsion, S. Kuether and F. X. Stora, Tamco Ltd US Army Mobility Equipment, R & D Center. Second Canadian Symposium on Air Cushion Technology, 1968. Canadian Aeronautics and Space Institute, SC 2.00.

Waterjet Propulsion for High Speed Surface Ships, P. Duport M. Visconte, J. Merle, SOGREAH. Ninth Symposium on Naval Hydrodynamics, Paris, August 1972.

SURFACE EFFECT SHIPS
An Analysis of Desired Manoeuvring Characteristics of Large SEVs, W. Zeitfuss Jr and E. N. Brooks Jr, Naval Ship Research and Development Centre, Washington DC. Advanced Marine vehicle meeting, AIAA/SNAME/USN. Annapolis, July 1972.

American Surface Effect Ship Activities, E. K. Liberatore, Aeromar Corporation. Jane's Surface Skimmer Systems, Second Edition 1968-69. Pages 210-212.

Some Special Problems in Surface Effect Ships, Robert D. Waldo, Aerojet-General Corporation. Journal of Hydronautics. July 1968. American Institute of Aeronautics and Astronautics.

Surface Effect Ships for Ocean Commerce (SESOC), Final Report, February 1966. The SESOC Advisory Committee, Commerce

Technical Advisory Board, US Department of Commerce, Washington D.C.

Large High Speed Surface Effect Ship Technology. P. J. Mantle Aerojet-General Corporation, Hovering Craft, Hydrofoil & Advanced Transit Systems Conference, Brighton, May 1974.

The Surface Effect Ship in the American Merchant Marine, Final Report for the US Department of Commerce, Maritime Administration, Booz-Allen Applied Research Inc.

The Nuclear Powered Ocean-Going SES. E. K. Liberatore, Aeromar Corporation, Jane's Surface Skimmers, 1971-72.

Transocean Surface Effect Ships, Dr A. Skolnik, Director of Technology, Surface Effect Ships Program Office. Proceedings of the IEEE Vol 56, No 4, 1968. Institute of Electrical and Electronics Engineers Inc.

TRACKED AIR CUSHION VEHICLES
Aerotrain Tridim for Urban Transportation, Jean Bertin and Jean Berthelot (Bertin & Cie and Soc. Aerotrain), Hovering Craft, Hydrofoil & Advanced Transit Systems Conference, Brighton, May 1974.

A New Linear Air Turbine Vehicle—TACV, Dr Yau Wu, Virginia Polytechnic Institute and State University. Sixth CASI Symposium on Air Cushion Technology, Ontario, June 1972.

Applications du Coussin d'Air Aux Transports en Zones Urbaines, André Garnault, Société d l'Aérotrain, June 1973.

The Operational Performance and Economics of URBA, M. E. Barthalon and L. Pascual, Seturba, Hovering Craft, Hydrofoil and Advanced Transit Systems Conference, Brighton, May 1974.

Canadian Research Activities Applicable to Tracked Levitated Vehicle Systems, P. L. Eggleton, Transportation Development Agency. Seventh Canadian Symposium on Air Cushion Technology, June 1973.

High Speed Ground Transportation, Documentation of Preliminary Engineering, Los Angeles International Airport and the San Fernando Valley, Kaiser Engineers, Los Angeles, California, April 1972.

Metrotran - 2,000, a study of future concepts in Metropolitan Transportation for the year 2,000, by Robert A. Wolf. Final Report CAL Internally Supported Project, October 1967. Cornell Aeronautical Laboratory Inc, Cornell University, Buffalo, NY 14221.

Problems Posés à Propos des Technologies non Conventionnelles de Transports Rapide au Sol, Jean Bertin, President Directeur Général de la Société de l'Aérotrain, June 1973.

Linear Propulsion by Electromagnetic River, Prof. E. R. Laithwaite, Imperial College of Science and Technology, Hovering Craft, Hydrofoil & Advanced Transit Systems Conference, Brighton, May 1974.

The Invention and Development of a Suspended Air Cushion Passenger Transport System in France, Maurice Barthalon, ScM, MIT. The Inventor, Journal of the Institute of Patentees and Inventors, Vol 9, No 1, March 1969.

The Pendair Suspension System, D. S. Bliss, Pendair Ltd, Hovering Craft, Hydrofoil and Advanced Transit Systems Conference, Brighton, May 1974.

Tracked Air-Cushion Research Vehicle Dynamics Simulation Program User's Manual Final Report, Magnani, E., Lee, R. and Coppolino, R. (Grumman Aerospace Corp., Bethpage, N. Y.) PB-219 984/2. October 1972.

Tracked Air-Cushion Vehicle Suspension Models: Analysis and Comparison, Garg, D. P. (Duke University, North Carolina) and Platin, B. E. (M.I.T., Cambridge.) Vehicle System Dynamics (Holland) Vol. 2 No. 3, November 1973.

Tracked ACVs for Urban Applications, N. McQueen and H. R. Ross, Sverdrup & Parcel & Associates Inc, June 1969. Third Canadian Symposium on Air Cushion Technology. Canadian Aeronautics and Space Institute, $C 2.00.

Tracked Air Cushion Vehicle Research and Development by the US Department of Transportation, A. F. Lampros and C. G. Swanson, Mitre Corporation. Hovering Craft, Hydrofoil and Advanced Transit Systems Conference, Brighton, May 1974.

Status of "Transrapid" Development Programme. G. Winkel (Krauss-Maffei, Augsburg), Second Intercity Conference on Transportation, Denver, Colorado, September, 1973.

LIM—Suspension Interaction, Parker, J. H. and Charles R. J. (Ministry of Transportation & Communications, Ontario), Second Intersociety Conference on Transportation, Denver, Colorado, September 23-27, 1973. ASME Paper No. 73-ICT-116.

ACV PUBLICATIONS, BOOKS and GENERAL LITERATURE
Air Cushion Vehicles: Their Potential for Canada. National Research Council of Canada, December 1969. Catalogue No. NRCC 10820 518 pages.

Air Cushion Technology in Canada, 1972. Associate Committee on Air Cushion Technology, National Research Council of Canada. June 1972. 115 pages. Price $C 2.00.

Air Cushion Vehicle Evaluation, Cdr Thomas C. Lutton, Commanding Officer ACV Evaluation Unit, San Francisco, California 94129.

Homebuilt Hovercraft, G. H. Williams. Reprinted from Air-Cushion Vehicles, Iliffe Transport Publications Ltd, London £2.25.

Hovercraft Design and Construction, G. H. Elsley and A. J. Devereux, David & Charles, Newton Abbot.

Hovercraft (General) Order 1972, HMSO, London, June 1972

Hovercraft (Application of Enactments) Order 1972, HMSO, London June 1972.

Skirt Design for Homebuilt Hovercraft by J. A. Eglen, an NAACVE publication, 2912 Andros, Costa Mesa, California $1.00.

Marine Hovercraft Technology, Robert Trillo. Leonard Hill. £8.50.

Hoveringcraft and Hydrofoil, Kalerghi Publications, 51 Welbeck Street, London, WIM 7HE. Telephone: 01-935 8678. Monthly. Annual Subscription UK £15.00. USA $40.

Hoverfoil News, Horizon Publications Ltd, Shoemaker's House, Montacute, Somerset, TA15 6XQ £20 (US $63) for 24 issues. Direct subscription only.

Hoversport, Horizon Publications Ltd, Shoemaker's House, Montacute, Somerset TA15 6XQ, UK. £4.00 for yearly subscription, 8 issues. US $10.00. For subscribers wishing to start with Issue 1 and requiring copies up to the end of 1974, the ten issues are available at a cost of £5.00 (US $12), plus airmail postage rates.

HYDROFOILS
BOOKS
Hydrofoils, Christopher Hook and A. C. Kermode. Sir Isaac Pitman & Sons Ltd, London, £ 1 12 6.
Hydrofoil Sailing, A. J. Alexander, J. L. Grogono, Donald J. Nigg. 96 pages. Price £3·00. Kalerghi Publications, 51 Welbeck Street, London WIM 7HE.

PAPERS, ETC.
COMMERCIAL OPERATION
Future of the Commercial Hydrofoil, Baron H. von Schertel, Supramar. Meeting, Business Aspects of Hovercraft and Hydrofoils, London. May 1968.
Running and Maintenance of Supramar Hydrofoils in Hong Kong, D. Hay and N. J. Matthew, Institute of Marine Engineers, April 1970.
The U.S. Gets Serious about Hydrofoils, Aronson, R. B., Machine Design, Vol 45 No. 25, 18th October 1973.

Safety, Reliability and Maintainability of Supramar Commercial Hydrofoils, Baron H. von Schertel, Supramar, 7th Reliability and Maintainability Conference, San Francisco, July 1968.

Die Antriebsanlagen von Schnellen Marinefahrzeugen und die Muglichkeit iher Verwendung auf Passágier-Tragflugelbooten,

E. Faber, Supramar, Sonderdruck MTZ Motor-technische Zietschrift, published June 1968.

DESIGN
A High-Speed Hydrofoil Strut and Foil Study, Wermter, R. and Shen, Y. T. (Naval Ship Research & Development Center, Bethesda, Md.). AIAA/SNAME Advanced Marine Vehicle Conference, San Diego, California, 25-28 February 1974. Paper 74-310.
A Universal Digital Autopilot for a Hydrofoil Craft, Pierre Dogan and Frederick Gamber, M.I.T. Advanced Marine Vehicle meeting, AIAA/SNAME/USN, Annapolis, July 1972.
Hydrofoil Craft Designers Guide, R. Altmann, Hydronautics Inc, Technical Report 744-1, March 1968.
Bending Flutter and Torsional Flutter of Flexible Hydrofoil Struts, P. K. Beach, Y. N. Liu (U.S. Naval Ship Research and Development Centre). Ninth Symposium on Naval Hydrodynamics, Paris, August 1972.
Canadian Advances in Surface Piercing Hydrofoils, N. E. Jeffrey and M. C. Eames, Defence Research Establishment, Atlantic, Dartmouth, Nova Scotia. Advanced Marine Vehicle Meeting. AIAA/SNAME/USN, Annapolis, July 1972.
Hydrodynamics and Simulation in the Canadian Hydrofoil Program, R. T. Schmitke and E. A. Jones Defence Research Establishment Atlantic, (Canada). Ninth Symposium on Naval Hydrodynamics, Paris, August 1972.
Large Hydrofoil Ships Feasability Level Characteristics, James R. Greco, Naval Ship Engineering Center, Hyattsville, Md. Advanced marine Vehicle meeting, AIAA/SNAME/USN, Annapolis, July 1972.

Special Problems in the Design of Supercavitating Hydrofoils, Dobay, G. F. and Baker, E. S. (Naval Ship Research & Development Center, Bethesda, Md). AIAA/SNAME Advanced Marine Vehicle Conference, San Diego, California, 25-28 February 1974. Paper 74-309.

Tragflugelschiff Supramar PT 150 DC, V. Jost (Schiff); E. Faber (Maschine); D. Cebulla (Tragflugel), Supramar. Sonderdruck aus Fachzeitschrift, "Schiff und Hafen", published May 1968.

Typhoon—A Seagoing Vessel on Automatically Controlled Submerged Foils, I. I. Baskalov and V. M. Burlakov, Sudostroyeniye. Hovering Craft & Hydrofoil. October 1972.
100 Passagier-Tragflugelboote mit schnellaufenden Dieselmotoren im Verkehr, E. Faber, Supramar, Sonderdruck MTZ Motortechnische Zeitschrift, published November 1967.

Bau und Erprobung von Tragflugelbooten, A. Mattl, Supramar, Schweizerischer Technischer Verband, Uzwil, Aarau, 1968.
A Comparison of Some Features of High-Speed Marine Craft, A. Silverleaf and F. G. R. Cook, National Physical Laboratory Royal Institute of Naval Architects, March 1969.

NAVAL CRAFT
The NATO PHM Programme, Cdr Karl M. Duff, USN, Naval Ship Systems Command, Washington D.C. Advanced Marine Vehicle Meeting, AIAA/SNAME/USN, Annapolis, July 1972.

High Speed and U.S. Navy Hydrofoil Development, Jewell, D. A. (Naval Ship Research & Development Center, Bethesda, Md). AIAA/SNAME Advanced Marine Vehicle Conference, San Diego, California, 25-28 February 1974. Paper 74-307.

HMCS Bras d'Or—Sea Trials and Future Prospects, M. C. Eames and T. G. Drummond, Defence Research Establishment Atlantic, Canada. Royal Institution of Naval Architects, April 1972

Operational and Developmental Experience on the US Navy Hydrofoil High Point, D. M. Petrie, The Boeing Company. AIAA/USN Marine Systems and ASW Conference. March 1965.

Military Hydrofoils, Baron H. Von Schertel, Dipl. Ing. Egon Faber, Dipl. Ing. Eugen Schatte, Supramar AG. Jane's Surface Skimmers, 1972-73.

Research on Hydrofoil Craft, Prof. Dr. Siegfried Schuster, Director Berlin Towing Tank. International Hydrofoil Society Winter Meeting, 1971. Hovering Craft and Hydrofoil, December ,1971.

SEAKEEPING CHARACTERISTICS
Prediction of the Seakeeping Characteristics of Hydrofoil Ships, Irving A. Hirsch, The Boeing Company. Paper 67-352 at the AIAA/SNAME Advanced Marine Vehicles Meeting, Norfolk Va, May 1967.

SYSTEMS
Heaving Motions of Ventilated Trapezoidal Hydrofoils, Tsen, L. F. and Guilbaud, M. (University of Poitiers, France). 4th Canadian Congress of Applied Mechanics, CANCAM '73, 28 May—1 June 1973. Ecole Polytechnique, Montreal.

The Longitudinal Behaviour of a Hydrofoil Craft in Rough Seas, M. Krezelewski, Institute of Ship Research, Gdank University, Hovering Craft, Hydrofoil and Advanced Transit Systems Conference, Brighton, May 1974.

On the Design of Propulsion Systems with Z-Drives for Hydrofoils Ships, A. A. Rousetsky, Kryloff Research Institute, Leningrad. Ninth Symposium on Naval Hydrodynamics, Paris, August 1972.

RESEARCH AND DEVELOPMENT
Key Problems Associated with Developing the Boeing Model 929-100 Commercial Passenger Hydrofoil, William Shultz, Boeing International Corporation. Hovering Craft, Hydrofoil and Advanced Transit Systems Conference, Brighton, May 1974.

Waterjet Propulsion for Marine Vehicles, V. E. Johnson, Jr. AIAA Paper 64-306, 1964. American Institute of Aeronautics and Astronautics.

Waterjet Propulsion for Marine Vehicles, J. Traksel and W. E. Beck. AIAA Paper 65-245, 1965. American Institute of Aeronautics and Astronautics.

The Design of Waterjet Propulsion Systems for Hydrofoil Craft, J. Levy, Soc Naval Architects and Marine Engineers, Marine Technology, 2, 15-25 41, January 1965.

Selection of Hydrofoil Waterjet Propulsion Systems, Ross Hatte and Hugh J. Davis, The Boeing Company. Journal of Hydronautics, Vol 1, No. 1, 1967. American Institute of Aeronautics and Astronautics.

The Development of Automatic Control Systems for Hydrofoil Craft, R. L. Johnston & W. C. O'Neill, Naval Ship Research & Development Centre, Bethesda, Maryland. Hovering Craft, Hydrofoil and Advanced Transit Systems Conference, Brighton, May 1974.

Hydrodynamic Study on Fully Submerged Foils of Hydrofoil Ships in a Sea Way up to 140 kt at Constant Froude Number. Dr de Witt. Supramar. Hovering Craft and Hydrofoil, Vol 8, No. 5, February 1969.

Machinery of the PT 150 DC Hydrofoil, E. Faber, Supramar, Marine Engineer and Naval Architect, January 1968.

Control of the Hydrofoil Ship, Dr P. Magini and Dr J. Burroughs, Advanced Marine Systems—Alinavi SpA. Journal of the Institute of Navigation, July 1967.

Controls Technology in Hydrofoil Ship Design, J. J. Jamieson, The Boeing Company. Ship Control Systems Symposium, November 1966.

Nine Year's History of the Hitachi-Supramar Hydrofoil Boat, Hovering Craft & Hydrofoil, November 1970.

The Economics of an Advanced Hydrofoil System, A. M. Gonnella, W. M. Schultz, Hydrofoil Systems Organisation, The Boeing Company, Hovering Craft & Hydrofoil, November 1970.

Air-Feed Stabilisation of Hydrofoil Craft, Baron H. von Schertel. Supramar. NATO, Brussels, September 1968.

Stabilisierung von Tragflugelbooten durch Luftspeisung der Flugel, Baron H. von Schertel, Supramar. Tagung der Schiff bautechnischen Gesellschaft, Lucerne, June 5, 1968.

Betriebserfahrungen mit der Antriebsanlage des Tragflugalschiffes PT 150, E. Faber, Supramar. Sonderdruck aus MTZ Motortechnische Zeitschrift, published October 1968.

An Examination of the Hazards to Hydrofoil Craft from Floating Objects, Christopher Hook. Society of Environmental Engineers Symposium, The Transport Environment, April 1969.

PGH Tucumcari: Successful Application of Performance Specification, Gene R. Myers, The Boeing Company, Naval Engineers Journal, June 1970.

50-knot Hydrofoils We Could Start Building Today, Gene R. Myers The Boeing Company, Aeronautics & Astronautics, June 1970.

SAILING SKIMMERS
The Basic Mechanics of Sailing Surface Skimmers and their Future Prospects, Dr Jerzy Wolf, Aviation Institute, Warsaw. Hovering Craft & Hydrofoil, March 1972.

Hydrofoil Ocean Voyager "Williwaw", David A. Keiper, PhD, Hydrofoil Sailing Craft. Third AIAA Symposium on the Aero/Hydronautics of Sailing, November, 1971.

Why Sailing Hydrofoils?—Christopher Hook, "Ancient Interface IV" Symposium, American Institute of Aeronautics and Astronautics, January 1973.

Hydrofoil Sailing, James Grogono, Hovering Craft, Hydrofoil and Advanced Transit Systems Conference, Brighton, May 1974.

ACV AND HYDROFOIL
LICENSING AUTHORITIES

ACV and HYDROFOIL LICENSING AUTHORITIES

ARGENTINA
ACVs and Hydrofoils
Prefectura Nacional Maritima
Paseo Colón 533
Buenos Aires.

AUSTRALIA
ACVs and Hydrofoils
Department of Transport
Childers Street,
Turner,
Australian Capital Territory,
Australia

AUSTRIA
ACVs and Hydrofoils
Bundesministerium für Handel,
Gewerbe und Industrie,
Stubenring 1,
Vienna 1.
Telephone 575655

BELGIUM
ACVs and Hydrofoils
Administration de la Marine et de la
Navigation Interieure,
30, Rue Belliard,
B-1040 Bruxelles.

CANADA
ACVs and Hydrofoils
Air Cushion Vehicle Division, Marine Safety
Branch,
Canadian Marine Transportation Admin-
istration,
Minister of Transport,
Tower "C",
Place de Ville,
Ottawa, Ontario, K1A 0N5

DENMARK
ACVs
Handelsministeriet,
3 Atdeling,
Slotsholmsgade 12,
1216 Copenhagen K.
Hydrofoils
Generaldirektoratet for Statsbanerne,
Solvgade 40
1307 Copenhagen K.

EIRE
ACVs and Hydrofoils
Department of Transport and Power,
Kildare Street,
Dublin 2.

FIJI
ACVs and Hydrofoils
Director of Marine,
Marine Department,
Suva,
Fiji.

FINLAND
Board of Navigation,
Vuorimiehenkatu 1,
POB 158,
SF-00141 Helsinki 14

FRANCE
ACVs and Hydrofoils
Marine Marchande
3 Place de Fontenoy,
75007 Paris

GAMBIA
ACVs and Hydrofoils
Ministry of Works and Communications.
Bathurst,
Gambia

GERMANY
Hydrofoils (safety authority)
See-Berufsgenossenschaft,
D-2000 Hamburg 11,
Reimertswiete 2.

GREECE
ACVs and Hydrofoils
Ministry of Merchant Marine,
Piraeus,
Greece.

HUNGARY
ACVs only
Ministry of Foreign Trade,
1880 Budapest,
Honvéd u. 13-15

ICELAND
Directorate of Shipping,
PO Box 484,
Reykjavik,
Iceland

INDIA
ACVs and Hydrofoils
Directorate-General of Shipping,
Bombay,
India

INDONESIA
ACVs and Hydrofoils
Departemen Perhubungan
Medan Merdeka, Barat 8,
Jakarta,
Indonesia

ISRAEL
ACVs and Hydrofoils
Ministry of Transport,
Division of Shipping and Parts,
102, Ha'atzmauth Road,
Haifa,
Israel

IVORY COAST
ACVs and Hydrofoils
Ministère des Travaux Publics et des Trans-
ports,
B.P. V6,
Abidjan,
Republic of the Ivory Coast

ITALY
ACVs and Hydrofoils
Ministero Della Marina Mercantile,
Ispettorato Tecnico,
Viale Asia,
00100 Roma.

JAMAICA
The Collector General's Department,
146 Harbour Street,
Kingston,
Jamaica

JAPAN
ACVs and Hydrofoils
Japanese Ministry of Transportation,
Tokyo.

KHMER REPUBLIC
(Formerly Cambodia)
ACVs and Hydrofoils
Ministère des Travaux Publics,
Phnom-Penh,
Khmer Republic

KUWAIT
ACVs and Hydrofoils
Department of Customs and Ports,
Kuwait,
Arabian Gulf.

LEBANON
ACVs and Hydrofoils
Ministère des Travaux Publics,
Direction des Transports,
Beiruit, Lebanon.

LUXEMBOURG
ACVs
Ministère des Transports,
4 Boulevard Roosevelt,
Luxembourg.

MALAGASY REPUBLIC
ACVs and Hydrofoils
Ministère de l'Amina,
Jement du Territoire,
Anosy,
Tananarive,
Madagascar

MALAYSIA
The Ministry of Communications,
Bangunan Kerajaan,
Jalan Gurney,
Kuala Lumpur,
Malaysia

MEXICO
ACVs
Secretaria De Marina,
Jose Azueta 9,
Mexico D.F.

MOROCCO
Ministère des Travaux Publics
Rabat,
Morocco

NETHERLANDS
ACVs and Hydrofoils
Directoraar-General van Scheepvaart,
Afdeling Scheepvaartinspectie,
Plesmanweg 1,
's-Gravenhage (The Hague)

NEW ZEALAND
*ACVs and Hydrofoils (Certificates of Construc-
tion and Performance)*
Operating approval and licences:
Ministry of Transport,
Marine Division,
Private Bag,
Wellington,
New Zealand

NORWAY
ACVs and Hydrofoils
The Maritime Directorate,
Thv. Meyersgt 7,
Oslo-Dep,
Norway

SOUTH AFRICA
Department of Transport,
Private Bag X193,
Pretoria 0001,
South Africa

SOUTH KOREA
Ministry of Transportation,
Seoul,
Republic of Korea,

SPAIN

ACVs and Hydrofoils

The Subsecretaria de la Marina Mercante,
Ruiz de Alarcon No. 1,
Madrid 14.

SWEDEN

ACVs and Hydrofoils

The National Board of Shipping and Navigation,
Fack S-102 50,
Stockholm 27
Sweden

SWITZERLAND

Contanal licensing authorities for ACVs and Hydrofoils

Lake Zurich

Kantonale Seepolizei,
Werkhof Wädenswil.
Städtische Seepolizei,
Dienstgebäude,,
Bellerivestrasse 260,
8008 Zürich.

Lake Constance

Polizeidepartement des Kantons Thurgau,
Regierungsgebaude,
8500 Frauenfeld.
Polizeidepartement des Kantons St Gallen
Schiffahrts- und Hafenverwaltung,
9400 Rorschach

Lake Lucerne

Polizeidepartement des Kantons, Luzern,
Bahnhofstrasse 17,
6000 Luzern.

Lake Geneva

Departement de Justice et Police Service de
la Navigation
Place Bourg-de-Four 1,
1200 Geneva

Departement de la Justice,
de la Police et des affaires militaire,
Service de la police administrative,
Place Chateau 6,
1000 Lausanne

Lake Lugano

Ufficio contonale de polizia,
VC Ghiringhelli 27b
6500 Bellinzona

Lake Thoune and Lake Brienz

Polizeidirektion des Kantons Bern,
Kramgasse 20,
3000 Bern

Lake Neuchatel

Departement de Police,
2000 Neuchatel

TURKEY

ACVs and Hydrofoils

T.C. Ulastirma Bakanligi,
Liman ve Denis Isleri Dairesi Baskanligi,
Ankara,
Turkey

UNITED ARAB REPUBLIC

ACVs

The Arab General Organisation for Air
Transport,
11 Emad El Din Street,
Cairo.

UNITED STATES OF AMERICA

ACVs and Hydrofoils

Department of Transportation,
Commandant (G-MMT-4),
U.S. Coast Guard,
Washington, DC 20590

UNITED KINGDOM

Hovercraft

Safety and Experimental Certificates; Certificates of Construction and Performance:

Civil Aviation Authority,
Hovercraft Department,
Airworthiness Division,
Brabazon House,
Redhill, Surrey RH1 1SQ

Hovercraft and Hydrofoils

Hovercraft Operating Permits and Hydrofoil Passenger Certificates,

Department of Trade,
Marine Division,
Sunley House,
90-93 High Holborn,
London WC1V 6LP

ACVs and Hydrofoils

Operating approval and licences:
Board of Trade,
Marine Branch,
Sunley House,
90-93 High Holborn,
London, W.C.1.

VENEZUELA

Ministerio de Comunicaciones,
Direccion de Marina Mercante,
Esquina Carmelitas, Edificio Ramia,
Caracas, Venezuela

YUGOSLAVIA

Yugoslav Federal Economic Secretariat,
Transport Department,
Bulevar AVNOJ-a 104,
Belgrade,
Yugoslavia

UK CIVIL ACV
REGISTRATIONS

U.K. HOVERCRAFT REGISTRATIONS – 1974

Registration Mark	Craft Type and No.	Constructor	Operator, Owner or Charterer
GH-2002	VT1-002	Vosper Thornycroft Ltd.	Lombard North Central Ltd.
GH-2003	VT1-003	Vosper Thornycroft Ltd.	Lombard North Central Ltd.
GH-2004	SR.N4-002	British Hovercraft Corporation Ltd.	Hoverlloyd Ltd.
GH-2005	SR.N4-003	British Hovercraft Corporation Ltd.	Hoverlloyd Ltd.
GH-2006	SR.N4-001	British Hovercraft Corporation Ltd.	British Rail Hovercraft Ltd.
GH-2007	SR.N4-004	British Hovercraft Corporation Ltd.	British Rail Hovercraft Ltd.
GH-2008	SR.N4-005	British Hovercraft Corporation Ltd.	Hoverlloyd Ltd.
GH-2009	SR.N5/A-001	British Hovercraft Corporation Ltd.	Air Vehicles Ltd.
GH-2010	SR.N6-022	British Hovercraft Corporation Ltd.	Hovertravel Ltd.
GH-2011	SR.N6-024	British Hovercraft Corporation Ltd.	Hovertravel Ltd.
GH-2012	SR.N6-026	British Hovercraft Corporation Ltd.	Hovertravel Ltd.
GH-2013	SR.N6-130	British Hovercraft Corporation Ltd.	Hovertravel Ltd.
GH-2014	SR.N6-009	British Hovercraft Corporation Ltd.	British Rail Hovercraft Ltd.
GH-2015	SR.N6-011	British Hovercraft Corporation Ltd.	British Rail Hovercraft Ltd.
GH-2016 (lapsed)	HM2-004	Hovermarine Transport Ltd.	
GH-2017 (lapsed)	HM2-007	Hovermarine Transport Ltd.	
GH-2018	HM2-005	Hovermarine Transport Ltd.	International Hoverservices Ltd.
GH-2019	HM2-012	Hovermarine Transport Ltd.	London Hoverservices Ltd.
GH-2020	HA5 Mk IIIW-101	Hover Air Ltd.	Lord Hotham (Contract Hover Ltd.)
GH-2021	SR.N6-016	British Hovercraft Corporation Ltd.	British Hovercraft Corporation Ltd.
GH-2022	SR.N6-028	British Hovercraft Corporation Ltd.	British Hovercraft Corporation Ltd.
GH-2023	HM2-002	Hovermarine Transport Ltd.	Hovermarine Transport Ltd.
GH-2024	HM2-303	Hovermarine Transport Ltd.	London Hoverservices Ltd.
GH-2025	HQ-007	Mr. R. Parkhouse	Messrs. R. D. Warman & R. B. Pott
GH-2026	SH2-004	Sealand Hovercraft Ltd.	Sealand Hovercraft Ltd.
GH-2027 (lapsed)	SH2-005	Sealand Hovercraft Ltd.	Noosa Heads Hovercraft Co., Australia
GH-2028 (lapsed)	HM2-304	Hovermarine Transport Ltd.	Hellenic Hovercraft Lines, Greece
GH-2029	SH2-008	Sealand Hovercraft Ltd.	Sealand Hovercraft Ltd.
GH-2030 (lapsed)	HM2-319	Hovermarine Transport Ltd.	Dolphin Ferries Ltd, Australia
GH-2031	SR.N6-025*	British Hovercraft Corporation Ltd.	British Hovercraft Corporation Ltd.
GH-2032	SH2-006	Sealand Hovercraft Ltd.	Sealand Hovercraft Ltd.
GH-2033	HM2-320	Hovermarine Transport Ltd.	London Hoverservices Ltd.
GH-3034	SH2-013	Sealand Hovercraft Ltd.	Airgo Ltd., Scotland
GH-2035	SR.N6-055**	British Hovercraft Corporation Ltd.	
GH-2036	SH2-014	Sealand Hovercraft Ltd.	Sealand Hovercraft Ltd.
GH-2037	SH2-001	Sealand Hovercraft Ltd.	Sealand Hovercraft Ltd.

Notes

A   Although originally built by BHC this craft (GH-2009) was re-built by Air Vehicles Ltd.

*   This craft has been modified and is now in an SR.N6 Mk 6 configuration with twin-props.

**   This craft has been constructed from components from other SR.N6 hovercraft by Hovertravel, Hoverwork and Air Vehicles Ltd.

Block of numbers issued to manufacturers for use with hovercraft subject to Test and Experimental Certificates. Each number is used only once.

British Hovercraft Corporation Ltd. East Cowes Isle of Wight	GH-9001 to GH-9050 inclusive
Hovermarine Transport Ltd Hazel Wharf Hazel Road Woolston Southampton SO2 7GB	GH-9051 to GH-9100 inclusive
Vosper Thornycroft Ltd Paulsgrove Portsmouth PO6 4QA	GH-9101 to GH-9150 inclusive
Cushioncraft Ltd The Duver St. Helens Isle of Wight	GH-9151 to GH-9200 inclusive
Sealand Hovercraft Ltd Millom Cumberland	GH-9251 to GH-9300 inclusive

SELECTED AMATEUR
BUILT HOVERCRAFT

SELECTED AMATEUR BUILT HOVERCRAFT

D. R. BARNES

Address:
20 Salhouse Road, Rackheath, Norwich,
NOR 01Z

AIR-LUBRI-CAT 4 ("STREAKER")

The fourth craft built by this enthusiastic and enterprising amateur constructor, "Streaker" was completed during the summer of 1974 and is currently undergoing further trials. The cost of construction was about £130. Non-rigid sidewalls are fitted to the craft.

LIFT AND PROPULSION: An integrated lift/thrust system is employed on Streaker with a VW 1500cc engine rated at 54 bhp at 4000 rpm driving through vee-belts a pair of 24 in (0·60 m) diameter ducted fans each fitted with five, 35° pitch blades. The fans are situated at the front of the superstructure and air from each is forced into the cushion and allowed to leak out through vents at the rear of the craft.

HULL: Construction is from 3 mm thick plywood with grp joints and grp super-structure. Three sealed compartments filled with air are located at the bow and three more at the stern. A further two are located along the sides of the craft. A bag skirt is fitted at the bow and along the sides in the form of a flexible sidewall.

Air-Lubri-Cat 4 ("Streaker") built by Derek Barnes of Norwich. This photo shows the craft operating below "hump" during trials in June 1974 (*photo: Neil MacDonald*)

ACCOMODATION: The craft is designed as a two or three-seater.

CONTROLS: A foot accelerator controls the engine and the air rudder and flexible sidewalls provide directional control.

DIMENSIONS:

Length overall	14 ft 6 in (4·41 m)
Width overall	7 ft 3 in (2·20 m)

Height overall   4 ft 0 in approx (1·21 m)

WEIGHTS:

Empty weight	500 lb estimated (226·78 kg)
Normal payload	160 lb (72·57 kg)
All-up weight	660 lb (299·35 kg)

PERFORMANCE:
Not yet fully tested

B. WILKINSON

Address:
90 Barfield, Ship Lane, Sutton-at-Hone,
Dartford, Kent DA4 9EL

SNOOPY TOO

The successor to this builder's earlier craft "Snoopy" (JSS 73-74), this new craft was completed in May 1974 at a cost of £140. During recent hovercraft events the craft has shown itself to be a reliable and fast machine and took part in speed trials in Scotland where it achieved speeds over a measured mile of about 29 mph. (40·67 km/h).

LIFT AND PROPULSION: For lift a single JLO 250cc engine rated at 15 bhp at 3500 rpm is fitted and this drives a 22 in-diameter axial fan fitted with five 30° pitch blades. For thrust a JLO 340 cc engine rated at 26 bhp at 6,500 rpm is installed and this drives by vee-belt a single 30 in (·76 m) -diameter ducted fan fitted with ten, 45° pitch blades. Fuel capacity of the craft is 8 gallons (30·28 l).

HULL: Built almost entirely from glass reinforced plastic with wooden bulkheads of 6 mm thick marine plywood, Snoopy Too has twelve sealed air tanks contained in the craft structure to provide buoyancy. An extended segment skirt system is used made from 4 oz/sq yd polyurethane coated nylon material.

Barry Wilkinson of Dartford, Kent, driving "Snoopy Too" during speed trials in Scotland in May 1974. (*Photo: Neil MacDonald*)

ACCOMMODATION: Seating is for two persons sitting astride the central structure of the craft.

CONTROLS: For control of the lift engine a quadrant lever is fitted and a twist grip fitted to a pair of handlebars controls the thrust engine throttle. The handlebars also activate via morse cable a single rudder in the craft slipstream to give directional control.

DIMENSIONS:

Length overall	12 ft 0 in (3·65 m)
Width overall	6 ft 10 in (2·08 m)
Height overall	4 ft 2 in (hovering) (1·27 m)

WEIGHTS:

Empty weight	380 lb (172·35 kg)
Normal payload	380 lb (172·35 kg)
All-up weight	760 lb (344·71 kg)

PERFORMANCE:

Maximum speed estimates:

land	35 mph (56·32 km/h)
water	30 mph (48·28 km/h)

OBSTACLE CLEARANCE:

8 in	(203 mm)

MESSRS. T. & T. WILCOX

ADDRESS:

15 Verney Close, East Howe, Bournemouth, Hants, BH11 8DD

AGGRO

Aggro was completed in June 1973 but since that date had been modified and re-engined. Although the craft has competed in a number of events organised by the Hoverclub it has not achieved any major placings.

LIFT AND PROPULSION: A single Briggs & Stratton engine rated at 5 bhp at 3,600 rpm, driving a 21 in (0·53 m) dia, 30° pitch, ten-bladed, axial fan supplies lift. Propulsion is provided by a Triumph Tiger T100 500 cc engine producing 32 bhp at 6,000 rpm, and driving via vee-belts a pair of 24 in (0·60 m) dia, 45° pitch, five-bladed ducted fans. The craft has a cushion pressure of about 8 lb/sq ft.

HULL: Construction is from a variety of materials including 4 mm and 6 mm thick exterior grade ply and 1·5 in square box tube. Also provided for in the hull is 150% buoyancy. Aggro is fitted with a bag skirt of PVC/coated nylon material weighing 5 oz/sq yd.

ACCOMMODATION: The craft has an open cockpit with seating for one person.

CONTROLS: Control for the lift engine is by a lever throttle and for the thrust engine there is a throttle fitted to the craft control column. Directional control is supplied by twin rudders operating in the craft slip stream.

"Aggro" takes to the water for the first time with its new thrust unit

DIMENSIONS:

Length overall	13 ft 4 in (4·06 m)
Width overall	6 ft 7 in (2·00 m)
Height overall	4 ft 6 in (1·37 m)

WEIGHTS:

Empty weight	400 lb approx (181·42 kg)
Normal payload	150 lb (68·03 kg)
All-up weight	570 lb (258·53 kg)

PERFORMANCE:

Maximum speed:

water	30 mph recorded (48·28 km/h)
land	unknown

Obstacle clearance: 7 in (177 mm)

REV. W. G. SPEDDING & J. GREEN

ADDRESSES:

14 Avondale Road, Farnworth, Bolton, Lancs. BL4 0PA and

469 Plodder Lane, Farnworth, Bolton, Lancs. BL4

JR5

This craft was completed in May 1974 and is a two seater design. Cost of building was about £150 and the craft took part in trials on Loch Lubnaig in Scotland shortly after being completed.

LIFT AND PROPULSION: A single Villiers 9E 250 cc engine rated at 6 bhp at 2,800 rpm drives a 22 in (·55 mm) dia, 30° pitch, ten-bladed, axial lift-fan. A Hillman Imp 875 cc engine producing 39 bhp at 5,000 rpm drives via vee-belts a pair of 22 in (·55 mm) dia, 45° pitch, ten-bladed, ducted fans for propulsion. Approximately 160 lb (72 kg) of static thrust is produced by this thrust arrangement. Craft cushion pressure is 9 lb/sq ft. Fuel tank capacity is 5 gallons (22 l).

JR5 in the paddock at a race meeting, showing the cockpit and the twin ducted fans (*Neil MacDonald*)

HULL: JR5 is built from wood with a frame of ½ in square spruce stringers overlaid with 4 mm thick marine ply and 1·5 mm thick birch exterior grade ply. Foam in the forward sections of the hull and sealed compartments in the stern provide craft buoyancy. A bag skirt system is fitted to the hull and is made from a light neoprene coated material

ACCOMMODATION: Seats two in an open cabin.

CONTROLS: Craft heading is controlled by twin rudders each in the slipstream of the ducted thrust fan.

DIMENSIONS:

Length overall	11 ft 9 in (3·58 m)
Width overall	6 ft 6 in (1·98 m)
Height overall 3 ft 6 in (hovering) (1·06 m)	

WEIGHTS:

Empty weight	450 lb approx (204·10 kg)
Normal payload	300 lb (136·07 kg)
All-up weight	750 lb approx (340·17 kg)

PERFORMANCE:

Maximum speed, estimates:

land	40 mph (64·37 km/h)
water	20 knots
Obstacle clearance:	9 in (228 mm)

G. PORTER

ADDRESS:

15 Watling Street, Dartford, Kent
DA1 1RP

NIMBUS

Nimbus was completed in May 1974 at a cost of £350 and is the owner's follow up to his last craft, Avenger (see JSS 1973-74). The craft has attended a number of organised hovercraft race meetings since completion but has not achieved any major placings.

LIFT AND PROPULSION: A single JLO 250 cc engine rated at 15 bhp at 3,500 rpm supplies power to a 22 in (0·55 m) dia, 30° pitch, five-bladed, axial fan for lift. Thrust is supplied by a JLO 440 cc engine rated at 34 bhp at 6,500 rpm which drives, via toothed belts a pair of 27 in (0·68 m) dia, two-bladed, Horden Richmond ducted propellers. Cushion pressure is 12 lb/sq ft and the craft has capacity for 7 gallons of fuel.

HULL: The craft is built from glass reinforced plastic with 6 mm thick plywood bulkheads. An extended segment skirt, made from polyurethane coated nylon material weighing about 4 oz/sq yd, is fitted.

ACCOMMODATION: Seating is astride a central bench set longitudinally and is sufficient for two persons.

CONTROLS: A lever throttle is fitted for the lift engine and a twist grip is used to control the thrust engine. A single rudder in each thrust duct provides directional control which is achieved by moving a pair of motorcycle handlebars.

"Nimbus", with Graham Porter at the controls, taking part in one of the Hover Club race events. In the background is a Scarab craft. (Photo : Neil MacDonald)

DIMENSIONS:

Length overall	12 ft 0 in (3·05 m)
Width overall	6 ft 10 in (2·08 m)
Height overall 4 ft 1 in (hovering) (1·24 m)	

WEIGHTS:

Empty weight	420 lb approx (190·50 kg)
Normal payload	400 lb (181·42 kg)
All-up weight	820 lb (371·92 kg)

PERFORMANCE:

Maximum speed:

land	45 mph estimated (72·42 km/h)
water	40 mph estimated (64·37 km/h)
Obstacle clearance:	9 in (228 mm)

G. NUTT, G. BRAN & J. LYNE

ADDRESS:

7 St Nicholas Road, Wallingford, Berks.

SCARAB TWO

This craft, a two seater version of an earlier design was completed in August 1973. Cost of construction was about £190 and the craft was displayed at the London Boat Show in January 1974.

LIFT AND PROPULSION: A Rowena Stihl 137 cc engine rated at 6 bhp at 3,800 rpm drives direct a single 19 in (0·48 m) dia, 30° pitch, five-bladed axial lift fan.

Propulsion is provided by a Canadian Curtiss Wright (CCW) 339 cc engine rated at 21 bhp at 5,500 rpm. This drives a single 24 in (0·60 m) dia, 45° pitch, five-bladed ducted fan, producing a static thrust of 96 lb (46·54 kg). Cushion pressure is 9·5 lb/sq ft. Fuel capacity is 4 gallons.

HULL: Construction of Scarab Two is from wood with a pinewood framework skinned with plywood. Built into the hull are five separate buoyancy compartments each filled

"Scarab Two" on the River Balvag, Scotland, where it was used for hover cruising (photo: Neil MacDonald)

with closed cell polyurethane foam. This provides 150% buoyancy. Scarab Two is fitted with a full flow bag skirt.

ACCOMMODATION: Seating is provided for two persons sitting side by side in an open cockpit.

CONTROLS: Directional control is provided by a single air rudder situated at the rear of the propulsion duct and activated by a joystick lever. Also on the joystick is the thrust engine throttle. A separate lever operates the lift engine throttle.

DIMENSIONS:

Length overall	11 ft 6 in (3·50 m)
Width overall	6 ft 0 in (1·82 m)
Height overall (hovering)	4 ft 0 in (1·21 m)

WEIGHTS:

Empty weight	220 lb (99·78 kg)
Normal payload	400 lb (181·97 kg)
All-up weight	620 lb (281·21 kg)

PERFORMANCE:
Maximum speed estimates:

land	35 mph (56·32 km/h)
water	35 knots
Obstacle clearance:	9 in (228 mm)

JOB'S DAIRY

ADDRESS:
Raleigh Way, Hanworth, Feltham, Middlesex, TW13 7NN

DAIR-E-GOES Mk II

Based upon their experience in building and operating the first Dair-E-Goes (see JSS 1973-74) in 1972 and 1973, the staff of this company completed an improved version of a similar design in April of this year. Building the craft, which is slightly shorter than its predecessor, cost about £400. During speed trials on a Scottish loch in June 1974 the craft achieved a speed of 37 mph (59·54 km/h) over the measured mile.

LIFT AND PROPULSION: Lift is supplied by a single Rowena Stihl 137 cc engine rated at 8 bhp at 7,000 rpm, which drives direct a 24 in (0·60 m) dia, 25° pitch, five-bladed, axial fan. For propulsion two further Rowena Stihl engines, identical to the one used for lift, are installed and these each drive via vee-belts a 24 in (0·60 m) dia, 45° pitch, five-bladed, ducted fan. This arrangement is believed to produce 115 lb of static thrust. The craft has a 5·5 gallon fuel tank.

HULL: The craft is made from glass reinforced plastic and has polystyrene fitted to the base of the hull to provide buoyancy. Also fitted to the hull is a deep bag skirt made from a nylon material coated with rubber.

ACCOMMODATION: The craft is a two seater with driver and passenger sitting in the open astride the main craft longitudinal structure.

CONTROLS: Engine controls are by a lever throttle for lift and two separate foot pedals. operate the twin thrust engines. The separate foot operated thrust throttles can be used to achieve differential thrust for directional control in addition to an air rudder located in each thrust duct.

DIMENSIONS:

Length overall	11 ft 6 in (3·50 m)
Width overall	6 ft 6 in (1·98 m)
Height overall (hovering)	4 ft 3 in (1·29m)

WEIGHTS:

Empty weight	350 lb
Normal payload	150 lb (one person)
All-up weight	600 lb

"Dair-E-Goes" Mk II during speed trials in Scotland during May 1974 (photo: Neil MacDonald

"Dair-E-Goes" Mk II slides onto the water during the start of a hovercraft race organised by the Hover Club

PERFORMANCE:
Maximum speed:

land	40 mph approx (64·37 km/h)	
water	37 mph recorded (59·54 km/h)	
Obstacle clearance:	11 in (279 mm)	

R. HALL

ADDRESS:

Church Farm, Bramley, Nr Basingstoke, Hants.

SKYBOY

Although based upon a standard design this craft contains a number of modifications and cost in the region of £250 to construct. It was completed in May of this year and has since been entered in a number of race meetings.

LIFT AND PROPULSION: A single JLO 250 cc engine rated at 15 bhp and driving direct to a 21 in (·53 m) diameter axial fan fitted with five 30° pitch blades provides lift. Thrust for forward movement is supplied by a JLO 440 cc engine rated at ·34 bhp at 6,500 rpm which drives a single 27 in (·68 m) diameter Horden Richmond ducted propeller. Drive is by vee-belt.

HULL: The craft is built from wood with a frame of 2 in by 1 in stringers to form the basic hull shape and these are covered with ⅛ in and ¼ in thick sheets of marine plywood. Craft buoyancy is supplied by large polythene cannisters fitted into the bow and stern sections of the craft and filled with air and sealed. The skirt system employed is of the deep bag, full flow type made from polyurethane coated nylon material weighing 4 oz/sq yd.

ACCOMMODATION: At present the cockpit can only seat one person comfortably but it is intended to increase the seating to two in the near future.

"Skyboy" built and driven by Robert Hall of Basingstoke (*photo: Neil MacDonald*)

CONTROLS: For lift engine control a quadrant lever is fitted in the cockpit and a twist grip operates the throttle of the thrust engine. Directional control is achieved by a single air rudder in the ducted propeller's slipstream, activated by a central control column.

DIMENSIONS:

Length overall	13 ft 4 in (4·06 m)
Width overall	6 ft 6 in (198 m)
Height overall (hovering)	4 ft 2 in (1·27 m)

WEIGHTS:
Unknown

PERFORMANCE:
Maximum speed estimates

land	35 mph (56·32 km/h)
water	35 mph (56·32 km/h)
Obstacle clearance:	8 in (203 mm)

ACV CLUBS AND ASSOCIATIONS

ACV CLUBS AND ASSOCIATIONS

THE HOVER CLUB OF GREAT BRITAIN LTD.

The Hover Club is the national organisation for amateur hovercraft and exists to encourage the participation by individuals, schools and colleges throughout the British Isles, in the construction and safe operation of light hovercraft. It is able to provide some technical advice to constructors and each year organises several race meetings and other events in which up to thirty craft take part. Events take place over land and water and the new sport of hovercraft racing is proving exciting and popular. Although catering mainly for light hovercraft enthusiasts in the United Kingdom, the Hover Club also has members overseas and keeps them all regularly informed with a monthly magazine.

COUNCIL:

Michael Bentine, President
G. G. Harding, Chairman
K. Oakley, Vice Chairman
G. K. Porter, Hon. Treasurer
J. E. C. Bliault, Hon. Secretary
N. Beale
C. Fox-Robinson
G. Kent
P. Mayer
N. Smith
D. M. Waters
G. Wickington

Correspondence regarding membership and other matters should be addressed to The Hover Club of Great Britain Ltd, 128 Queens Road, Portsmouth, Hants. PO2 7NE or telephone Portsmouth (STD 0705) 61211.

BRANCHES OF THE HOVER CLUB

BIRMINGHAM AND DISTRICT
Mrs. I. Mantell,
24 Bourne Avenue, Fazely, Nr Tamworth, Staffs.

CHILTERN
Mrs. E. Naylor
18 Langton Road, Harrow Weald, Harrow, Middlesex. Tel: 01-428 5030

EAST ANGLIAN
Mr. C. Seago
33 Acacia Road, Thorpe St Andrew, Norwich. NOR 71T

ESSEX
Mr. E. W. Sangster,
53 Elm View Road, Benfleet, Essex. SS7 5AR

ISLE OF WIGHT
Mr. M. G. Weller
34 Birmingham Road, Cowes, Isle of Wight PO31 7BH Tel: Cowes 2882

LONDON
Mr. K. Oakley
7 Charles Close, Snodland, Kent.

MIDLAND
Mr. D. Waters
30 Shepherds Close, Loughborough, Leics.

NORTH WESTERN
Rev. W. G. Spedding
14 Avondale Road, Farnworth, Nr Bolton, Lancs. BL4 0PA Tel: Bolton 73307

SOUTHERN
Mr. P. Hampson
1 Rednel House, Greetham Street, Southsea

The Paddock, filled with light hovercraft at a race meeting in Poole Harbour, Hampshire, in June 1974 (*photo: Neil MacDonald*)

Hants. Tel: Portsmouth 29677

SOUTH WESTERN
Mr. C. Fox-Robinson
695 Dorchester Road, Broadway, Weymouth, Dorset. Tel: Upwey 2398

THE UNITED KINGDOM HOVERCRAFT SOCIETY

The society was formed in 1971 as the United Kingdom constituent member of the 'International Air Cushion Engineering Society' and its membership is drawn mainly from manufacturing industry, design groups, universities, government departments and agencies, financial and insurance interests and the Armed Forces. The Society is also open to members outside of the U.K.

Principal objectives of the Society are:

The encouragement of education, research and invention related to the hovercraft and the air-cushion principle.

Research, education and discussion on the operating, design and trading aspects of hovercraft.

To hold meetings for the presentation of papers and exchange of information.

Circulation of a regular newsletter.

Establishment of a library of books, films and papers on the history and development of the hovercraft.

1973-74 COUNCIL
Sir Christopher Cockerell, President
L. A. Hopkins, Chairman
W. F. S. Woodford, OBE; Hon Secretary
J. Bentley, Hon Treasurer
A. E. Bingham
D. S. Bliss
A. Brindle
M. Charity
L. R. Colquhoun
A. G. Course
C. M. G. Fox
E. F. Davison
Miss. J. Kalerghi
F. Lane
A. Latham
Dr T. K. S. Murthy
J. E. Rapson
D. R. Robertson
R. A. Shaw, OBE
R. L. Trillo
R. L. Wheeler
P. H. Winter
P. A. Yerbury

Correspondence should be addressed to the

UK Hovercraft Society, 146 Cromwell Road, London SW7 4EF   Tel: 01-370 6981

HOVERMAIL COLLECTORS CLUB
Honorary Secretary: C. J. Richards
93 Aldershot Road, Fleet, Hants
GU13 9NW, United Kingdom

INTERNATIONAL FEDERATION OF HOVER CLUBS
Honorary Secretary: J. E. C. Bliault

128 Queens Road, Portsmouth, Hants PO2 7NE
Telephone: 0705-61211

AUSTRALIA
Hover Club of Australia, 34 Gaven Avenue, Mermaid Beach 4218, Australia

FRANCE
Club Francais des Aergolisseurs, 85, Rue de la Republique, Suresnes 92, France

UNITED STATES
National Association of Air Cushion Vehicles, 801 Poplar Street, Terre Haute, Indiana 47807, USA

TRINIDAD AND TOBAGO
Hover Club of Trinidad and Tobago, 1 Richardson Street, Point Fortin, Trinidad, West Indies

ACV CONSULTANTS

CONSULTANTS IN AIR-CUSHION VEHICLE TECHNOLOGY AND OPERATION

ISRAEL

HYDRONAUTICS-ISRAEL, LTD

HEAD OFFICE:

10 Heassor Street,
Ness Ziona, Israel

This company is a wholly-owned subsidiary of Hydronautics, Inc, Laurel, Maryland, q.v.

UNITED KINGDOM

AIR CUSHION EQUIPMENT LTD

HEAD OFFICE:

360 Shirley Road Southampton
TELEPHONE: Southampton 776468
TELEX: 477258
CABLES: Hoverace Southampton
DIRECTORS:

L. A. Hopkins, Chairman and Technical Director
T. C. A. Horn, Managing
W. A. Melhuish, Finance
O. J. Colman
J. M. Horn
P. B. A. Hopkins
B. H. Wright

The company, besides developing products and systems for its own benefit and the benefit of its associate companies, also offers a comprehensive design and technical consulting service to any organisation with a load-moving problem. Many such problems have been considered and air cushion systems designed and built to cope with them. New products are under development for the mechanical handling industry and also for the civil engineering and construction industries specialising in very heavy and awkward steel and concrete erection projects. The largest load considered so far is a steel jacket structure for North Sea Oil drilling, and ACE has proved satisfactorily that this load could be moved on a 3-part system of air platforms operating at no more than 7 psi.

AIR VEHICLES LTD.

HEAD OFFICE.

1, Sun Hill, Cowes, Isle of Wight
TELEPHONE: Cowes 3194 & 4439
OFFICERS AND DIRECTORS:

P. H. Winter, Msc., Director
C. D. J. Bland, Director
C. B. Eden, Director

Formed in 1968, Air Vehicles Ltd has specialised in the design and manufacture of small hovercraft, mainly in the 5-6 seater range, and also in the development of ducted propellers for hovercraft. The largest installation is a quiet ducted propeller for the N6 craft designed and built by Air Vehicles in early 1974. The company acts as consultants and designers for a wide range of hovercraft applications, from fan testing to large 350 ton hoverbarges. The company has also developed over several years, large soft wheels especially designed for swampy or rugged ground and proposals are available for a range of towing vehicles, trailers and lifting devices, all based on these wheels. The design and fitting out of hovercraft for special duties such as cargo carrying and survey work is also undertaken. With unrivalled experience in the operation of 5-6 seater hovercraft under working charter conditions Air Vehicles is able to advise on and evaluate a wide range of applications and routes. It can also call on the world-wide experience of its associated companies, Hoverwork Ltd and Hovertravel Ltd. Air Vehicles Ltd offer its N5 Hoverfreighter for charter.

C. A. BRINDLE & ASSOCIATES

ADDRESS:

10 Cliff Road, Cowes, Isle of Wight, PO31 8BN, England
TELEPHONE: (098 382)2218

C. A. Brindle & Associates provides a consultancy service specialising in maritime rapid transit systems, transportation economics

hydrofoil and hovercraft operation in all parts of the world. Contractors to British and other Governments.

Work undertaken has included world-wide surveys for potential hovercraft and hydrofoil operation and the technical assessment of specific craft.

Detailed application studies have been carried out in the United Kingdom, United States of America, Canada, Mediterranean, Africa, France, Holland, Scandinavia and the Caribbean.

Practical experience with scheduled commercial services and specialised operations and maintenance in domestic and international fields. Adviser to United Nations Organisation and OECD on maritime operations in developing countries.

BRITISH RAIL HOVERCRAFT LIMITED

HEAD OFFICE

Royal London House, 22/25 Finsbury Square, London EC2P 2BQ
TELEPHONE: (01) 628 3050
Managing Director: J. M. Lefeaux
Commercial and Planning Manager: A. J. Tame
Chief Engineer: P. A. Yerbury

British Rail Hovercraft Limited is the most experienced commercial hovercraft in operation the world. It is the only company to have operated commercially both amphibious and non-amphibious craft on estuarial and open water services.

Studies have been conducted on behalf of clients in many parts of the world and the Company is able to provide a route costing and viability appraisal service based on "real time" operating experience.

LESLIE COLQUHOUN ASSOCIATES LTD.

HEAD OFFICE:

The Oast House, Way Hill, Minster, Ramsgate, Kent CT12 4HS
Telephone: Minster Thanet 357 STD 0843-88-357
LONDON OFFICE: 119 New Bond Street, London, W. 1.

Leslie Colquhoun Associates was formed in 1973 to provide a hovercraft transport consultancy service using the unique experience of L. R. Colquhoun who has been closely associated with the hovercraft industry since 1959. This experience involved the testing, development and marketing of Vickers Ltd. hovercraft projects from 1959-1965, and from 1966-1973 the setting up and running of Hoverlloyd's Ramsgate to Calais hovercraft service with the SR.N6 and SR.N4. Mr Colquhoun was Managing Director of the Company when he resigned in December 1972 to set up the Consultancy.

The Consultancy is contracted to Hoverlloyd and has completed on their behalf a report on the Company's SR.N4 cross channel operations for the S.E.S.P.O. P.M.17 office of the Department of the US Navy.

Further work has been contracted in U.K., France, Hungary, America, Iran and Malaysia.

The Consultancy also provides assistance to International Hoverservices Ltd. and London Hoverservices Ltd. with regard to sidewall hovercraft operations on the River Thames.

Through a close association with Comasco International Ltd. the Consultancy is involved in pollution and waste disposal schemes using both chemical and incineration processes.

PETER G. FIELDING, CEng, FRAeS

OFFICES:

UNITED KINGDOM:

Dock House, Niton Undercliff, Ventnor, Isle of Wight.
PO38 2NE
Telephone: Niton 730 252

USA:

1701 North Fort Myer Drive, Suite 908 Arlington, Virginia 22209
Telephone: (703) 528-1092
7910 Woodmont Avenue, Suite 1103, Bethesda, Maryland 20014

Telephone: (301) 656-5991

Consultant in air cushion systems, air cushion operations, and air cushion technology since 1959 to the US Army, the US Navy, US Department of Defense, the Advanced Research Projects Agency-DOD, US Department of Commerce-Maritime Administration, the Office of Naval Research, the US Naval Ships Research and Development Center, the US Army TRECOM, the Executive Office of the President USA, the US Navy-Chief of Naval Operations, the US Marine Corp, the Institute for Defense Analysis, the Center for Naval Analysis, the Bell Aerosystems Corporation, the Aerojet Corporation, the Research Analysis Corporation, Science Applications Incorporated, Hoverlift Applications Incorporated, Booz-Allen Applied Research Incorporated, Associated Consultants International Inc, and SeaSpan Inc. Services for the above organizations have included state of the art reports, technical and economic analysis, route surveys, environmental impact studies, sub-system analysis, operational plans, test plans, mission studies, advanced technology estimates, test site selection, cost analysis, structural and materials analysis and market research.

RECENTLY COMPLETED ASSIGNMENTS INCLUDE:

1. Review and assessment of the Arctic SEV advanced technology programme for the Advanced Research Projects Agency US Dept of Defence.
2. Analysis of "paddle wheel" propulsion and sealing systems for SES, for S.A. Inc. McLean, Va, U.S.A.
3. "The Surface Effect Vehicle (SEV) in Search and Rescue Missions in Alaska"—for the Research Analysis Corporation, McLean, Va.
4. "An Assessment of the Technological Risk and Uncertainty of Advanced Surface Effect Vehicles (SEV) for the Arctic"—for the US Naval Ships Research and Development Center, Carderock, Md.
5. "An Evaluation of Advanced Surface Effect Vehicle Platforms Performing Military Missions in the Arctic"—for Science Applications Inc, La Jolla, California, and Arlington, Virginia.
6. "An Exhaustive Bibliography of Air Cushion Subjects" for the Research Analysis Corporation, McLean, Virginia.
7. "Preliminary Findings of the Economic Suitabilities of the Surface Effect Ship to Various Routes in the US"—for SEASPAN Inc, Washington, D.C.
8. "Appraisal of Heavy Lift Systems for Commercial Applications"—for Hoverlift Applications Inc, Arlington, Virginia.

S. GARDNER

HEAD OFFICE:

Hurlands, The Haven, Billingshurst, Sussex

Telephone: Rudgwick 646

ASSOCIATES:

S. Gardner, CEng, AFRAeS, Project Engineer (ACV)

A. Marchant, CEng, MICE, MIMechE, AFRAeS, Project Engineer (Structural).

Consultants in Air Cushion Vehicle and related Civil and Structural Engineering.

S. Gardner:

1969 Project design mechanical, structural and systems engineering of Enfield Marine Freight Hovercraft.

1964-69 Senior Hovercraft Surveyor to UK Air Registration Board.

1959-64. Project Engineer, Hovercraft Development Ltd. Supervision of Design and Construction of H.D.1 experimental ACV.

A. Marchant:

1966-69. Design specialist in ACV structures including HM.2 Hovercat, F.M.1 and E.M.2

HOVERCRAFT DEVELOPMENT LTD

HEAD OFFICE:

Kingsgate House, 66-74 Victoria Street, London, SW1E 6SL

TELEPHONE: 01-828-3400

TECHNICAL OFFICE:

Forest Lodge West, Fawley Road, Hythe, Hants SO4 6ZZ

TELEPHONE: Hythe (Hants) 3178 STD Code 042 14

DIRECTORS:

T. G. Fellows (Chairman)

M. W. Innes

Prof. W. A. Mair

J. E. Rapson

T. A. Coombs

SECRETARY:

P. N. Randell

Hovercraft Development Ltd, was established by the National Research Development Corporation in 1959 to develop and exploit the hovercraft patents of Christopher Cockerell. The Technical Group of the Company was set up in 1960. It provided technical services for the Company's hovercraft manufacturing licensees until that part of HDL was taken over by Mintech (now the Department of Trade and Industry) to become a unit of the National Physical Laboratory. The office at Hythe continues to provide technical information for interested parties and particularly for the Company's licensees and for hovercraft operators. It also advises HDL on technical matters associated with development projects and the craft designs of prospective licensees.

HOVERWORK LIMITED

HEAD OFFICE:

12 Lind Street, Ryde, Isle of Wight, PO33 2NR

TELEPHONE: Ryde 5181

CABLES: Hoverwork Ryde

TELEX: 86513 (A/B Hoverwork Ryde)

DIRECTORS:

C. D. J. Bland (Managing)

D. R. Robertson

E. W. H. Gifford

A. C. Smith

Hoverwork Limited is a subsidiary of Hovertravel Limited and was formed in 1966. The company provides crew training and charter facilities for all available types of ACVs, thus bridging the gap between the operators and manufacturers.

Hoverwork and its parent, Hovertravel, own the largest fleet of hovercraft available for charter in the world. Types include the SR.N6, the SR.6N freighter, SR.N5 passenger/freighter and AV.2. In recent years the company has concentrated on providing craft for seismic, gravity and hydrographic survey work in shallow water areas and terrain impossible to other forms of transport.

The company, jointly with Hovertravel Limited, offers a route feasibility investigation service.

R. A. SHAW

(Managing Director Hoverprojects Limited)

ADDRESS:

21 Standring Rise, Boxmoor, Hertfordshire

Telephone: 0442 59623

Consultancy services to governments, local authorities and private enterprise on all aspects of fast transport with special emphasis on hovercraft and hydrofoils. Services include financial, economic and operational assessments in all conditions and new designs to meet particular requirements.

Contracts have included:

1. A study for the State of Washington to assess the feasibility of introducing hovercraft and hydrofoils into the Puget Sound ferry system.
2. A feasibility appraisal of proposed hovercraft operations in British Columbia.
3. Reporting to a local authority on prospects of establishing a hoverport within their borough.
4. A study for the greater London Council on fast passenger services on the Thames.
5. Three independent studies on the potential for hovercraft in the venetian lagoon.
6. Examination of world potential market for hovercraft.
7. Design and Economics of 1000 ton River Hovercraft.
8. Planning and operating consultancy for Airavia Ltd. and Speed Hydrofoil Ltd. for hydrofoils on the River Thames.

ROBERT TRILLO LIMITED

HEAD OFFICE:

Broadlands, Brockenhurst, Hampshire. SO4 7SX.

Telephone: Brockenhurst (05902) 2220

Managing Director:

R. L. Trillo, CEng., FIMechE, FRAeS, AFAIAA, AFCASI

Author "Marine Hovercraft Technology" (ISBN 0 249 44036 9) Operating since 1969 as a consultancy engaging principally in air-cushion vehicle technology and economics, the firm has worked for industry and government departments in a number of countries and has undertaken transport feasibility studies, preliminary design investigations and experimental investigations. Studies have also been undertaken on applications of amphibious wheeled vehicles, suitable as air-cushion platform support and tug vehicles. Other work in the last year has been concerned with the design of three ducted propeller installations and two inflatable hovercraft, one of which is the largest built to date. Recent commissions have included work in Canada for the National Research Council, Ottawa, and in Australia for the Department of Aboriginal Affairs. The firm publishes bi-monthly bibliography services on air-cushion and hydrofoil systems and on high-speed ground transportation and urban rapid transit systems.

REPRESENTATIVES:
CANADA:
Vice Admiral K. L. Dyer, RCN Rtd.,
Dodwell, Dyer & Associates,
    1177 St. Laurent Boulevard,
    Ottawa,
    Ontario KIK 3B7.

DENMARK:
Mr Leif Hansen,
A. B. C. Hansen Comp. A/S,
Hauchsvej 14,
DK-1825 Copenhagen V.

Affiliate member of Northern Associates Reg'd, Canada, Canadian Arctic consulting group.

JOHN VASS
ADDRESS:
Beaverbrook Newspapers, Fleet Street, London E.C.4
Telephone: 353-8000
Home: Rosehaugh Farm, Newbarn Lane, Cudham, Kent
Telephone: Biggin Hill 2718
Received first official light hovercraft licence issued by Air Registration Board 1968. Elected first Life Member of Hoverclub of Gt. Britain, 1974. Author "Hovercraft" and "Express Air Rider Handbook" Hovercraft Correspondent, Daily Express. Light Hovercraft consultant, British Petroleum, Air Rider Research Ltd, and McCulloch & Associates, Ontario, Originator of National Schools Hovercraft Contest, (first held 1968).

UNITED STATES
AEROPHYSICS COMPANY
ADDRESS:
3500 Connecticut Avenue, N.W., Washington D.C. 20008
TELEPHONE: (202) 244-1926
OFFICERS:
Dr. Gabriel D. Boehler, President
Mr. William F. Foshag, Chief Engineer
Aerophysics Company was formed in 1957 to conduct fundamental research of the ground effect principle. Dr. Boehler had previously performed private feasibility work with Mr. M. Beardsley. Since then, Aerophysics has undertaken work in various areas of ACV design, including, skirt design, control techniques, parametric analysis, conceptual and design studies, studies of ACV lift air systems including various types of blowers and propulsion systems.

BOOZ-ALLEN & HAMILTON INC.
135 South La Salle Street, Chicago, Illinois 60603
ACTIVITIES:
General Management Consulting,
Computer Systems and Software
Market and Social Science Research
Industrial Engineering Systems
Pollution and Environmental Resources Management
Defence and Space Research
Product, Process and Equipment Development
Transportation and Airport Planning and Engineering

DAVIDSON LABORATORY
STEVENS INSTITUTE OF TECHNOLOGY
HEAD OFFICE:
Castle Point Station Hoboken, New Jersey 07030
Telephone: 201-792-2700
OFFICERS:
Dr. J. P. Breslin, Director
Daniel Savitsky, Assistant Director
Organised in 1935 as the Experimental Towing Tank, the Laboratory is active in basic and applied hydrodynamic research, including smooth water performance and manouvrability; seakeeping, propulsion and control of marine vehicles including ACV and hydrofoil craft. Special model test facilities are available to investigate the dynamic behaviour of ACV and hydrofoil craft in smooth water and waves.

FORRESTAL LABORATORY
ADDRESS:
Princeton University, Princeton, N.J.
OFFICERS:
T. E. Sweeney
ACTIVITIES:
Research prototypes (ACVs)

GIBBS & COX
ADDRESS:
40 Rector Street, New York, N. Y. 10006 Ph: (212) 487-2800
ACTIVITIES:
Project coordination, consultation, conceptual and preliminary designs and "working" drawing efforts for commercial or Naval vessels of the SES/ACV, semi-planing or of the submerged hydrofoil type.

GLOBAL MARINE INC
HEAD OFFICE:
811 West 7th Street, Los Angeles, California 90017
Telephone: 213-680-9550
OFFICERS:
A. J. Field, President
R. B. Thornburg, Group Vice-President
O. D. Blankenship, Vice-President, General Manager
Arctic Engineers & Constructors
1770 St James Place, Suite 504, Houston, Texas 77027
Telephone: 713-626-9773
Global Marine Inc was incorporated in 1959, and is engaged primarily in offshore drilling and engineering. However, in 1968 the company undertook an engineering feasibility study directed towards developing equipment and techniques for drilling in Arctic areas. This engineering study led to the selection of ACT (Air Cushion Transport) units as the most feasible for operating in the area, and it has a continuing design programme directed towards various size ACT (Air Cushion Transport) drilling rigs with various drilling capabilities. This design work is handled by Global Marine Inc (Los Angeles), and the sales and operational aspects, with respect to the Arctic, are handled by Arctic Engineers & Constructors (see above). Arctic Engineers & Constructors is a joint venture between Global Marine and Raymond International, Houston, Texas.

AEC constructed the ACT-100 in Canada in 1971. This unit was test operated in the Arctic during 1971, and at the time of going to press was being test operated by the Canadian government in connection with the Mackenzie River Highway. Design work on larger ACV drilling rigs continues.

Affiliations with other organizations:
The company is currently retaining Air Cushion Equipment Ltd, Southampton as skirt designers and general ACV consultants.

HYDRONAUTICS, INCORPORATED
HEAD OFFICE:
Pindell School Road, Howard County, Laurel, Maryland 20810

Telephone: 301-776-7454
OFFICERS:

Marshall P. Tulin, Chief Executive Officer
Phillip Eisenberg, President
Phillip A. Weiner, Vice President
Alex Goodman, Vice President
Virgil E. Johnson, Jr, Vice President
Bennett L. Silverstein, Vice President and Secretary
Harvey Post, Treasurer

The company was founded in July of 1959, and has undertaken research, development and design of air cushion vehicles, hydrofoil craft and other high speed marine vehicles under United States Government and industrial contracts. Hydronautics has its own ship model basin suitable for the evaluation of air cushion vehicles and hydrofoils.

INSTITUTE FOR DEFENSE ANALYSES (IDA)

HEAD OFFICE:

400 Army-Navy Drive, Arlington, Virginia 22202
Telephone: (703) 558-1000
ACTIVITIES:

Systems analysis, policy analysis, economics, military operational studies. Study of technology and applications.

E. K. LIBERATORE COMPANY

ADDRESS:

567 Fairway Road, Ridgewood, N.J. 07450
PERSONNEL:

E. K. Liberatore, Head
James V. Liberatore, Staff Engineer
John Curry, Design Draftsman

Formed in 1964, the company specialises in systems engineering, vehicle design and in operations in the fields of ACVs, SESs, and VTOL aircraft. Work includes requirements, integration, analysis, design, costing, FAA and other certification, route and market surveys and methodology.

LIPPISCH RESEARCH CORPORATION
Consultants Ram-Wing Vehicles

HEAD OFFICE:

3450 Cottage Grove Avenue, S. E
Cedar Rapids, Iowa 52403
Telephone: 319, 365-0175

DESIGN FACILITIES:

Cedar Rapids, Iowa: Friedrichshafen, West Germany (In cooperation with Dornier GmbH), and Mönchengladbach (in co-operation with VFW-Rhein-Flugzeugbau GmbH)

SALES OFFICE:

Ten Old Post Office Road, Silver Spring, MD 20910
Telephone: 301, 588-3311

STAFF PERSONNEL:

Dr Alexander M. Lippisch, President
George G. Lippisch, Vice-President
Bryce M. Fisher, Treasurer
Dr. Herschel Shosteck, Director of Marketing

Lippisch Research Corporation was organised by Dr. Alexander M. Lippisch in 1966 to continue developmental work on high lift-drag ratio free-flying ram-wing and STOL vehicles. Building on the research concepts originated by Dr. Lippisch, the company, singly and in co-operation with airframe manufacturers, has designed, constructed and successfully test-flown several advanced design ram-wing craft as well as the "aerodyne" wingless STOL.

The major research work on ram-wing craft has been executed under contracts with VFW-Rhein-Flugzeugbau GmbH.

As a result of this work, Lippisch Research Corporation has successfully overcome the fundamental problems of pitch instability which had previously precluded development of successful ram-wing vehicles. The "aerofoil boat" class of vehicles operates from surface effect to free-flight and back again without difficulty.

Their free-flight capabilities permit successful operation in high to precipitous sea states.

Current experimental prototypes achieve lift-drag ratios of approximately 25:1. Larger vehicles in the concept stage are designed for over double these efficiencies.

The "aero-skimmer" is an over-water class vehicle designed to operate in the immediate proximity of the surface. Vessels of this type are powered by standard outboard motors, with only the propeller in contact with the water. This design eliminates all supercavitation-induced drag on the hull of the craft. Test vehicles readily exceed 100 knots maintaining high stability and manoeuvrability. To-date, craft performance has been limited only by the capacity of the power plant.

Lippisch concepts include ram-wing vehicles designed as ASW craft, military assault craft, ocean transports, inland river boats, and arctic transportation vehicles.

Lippisch Research Corporation supplies engineering design and consulting services to other design organizations and airframe manufacturers.

GEORGE E. MEESE

ADDRESS:

194 Acton Road, Annapolis, Md USA 21403
Telephone: 301 263-4054
Cable: Meesmarine Annapolis
ACTIVITIES:

SES structures.

M. ROSENBLATT & SON, INC

HEAD OFFICE:

350 Broadway, New York, 10013 New York

Telephone: (212) 431-6900
OFFICERS

Lester Rosenblatt, President
E. F. Kaufman, Vice President and Manager, Western Division
L. M. Schlosberg, Vice President and Design Manager
R. E. Stark, Vice President

BRIEF HISTORY:

The firm was founded in 1947 and has since grown to be one of the largest engineering design firms of its type, specialising in naval architecture and marine engineering. An organization of experienced engineers, designers and draftsmen has been assembled which is fully capable of providing the engineering, design and research and development services associated with ship and marine vehicle design.

Since its establishment, the company has successfully completed approximately eighteen hundred ship design and related assignments for government and private customers. These assignments embrace work on commercial and naval ships and on almost every type of floating vessel. Merchant vessels include: passenger ships, containerships, oceanographic ships, general cargo ships, bulk carriers, tankers, surface effect ships, drilling platforms, survey vessels, tugs, etc. Naval vessels include: carriers, cruisers, destroyers, frigates, destroyer-escorts, tenders and auxiliaries of all kinds, submarines, LPDs, LPHs, LSTs, LSDs, hydrofoils and patrol craft.

Typical ACV assignments include:

1. ARPA Advanced Surface Effect Vehicles

Conceptual studies, parametric studies and propulsion machinery analysis for phase "O" studies of Advanced Surface Effect Vehicles for Advanced Research Project Agency. Work performed for American Machine and Foundry Company.

2. JSESPO Surface Effect Ship Testcraft

Conceptual and feasibility design studies of candidate SES vehicles for the JSESPO sizing study for second generation SES testcraft in the 1,000 to 3,000-ton range. The work included studies of various candidate versions of SES to identify and evaluate their unique operational and design capabilities; technological assessment of various structural materials and systems; preparation of a proposed development programme with required supporting R&D. Work performed for Joint Surface Effect Ship Program Office.

3. Amphibious Fleet Conceptual Studies

Conceptual design studies of various types of ships for future amphibious fleets, including submarine, displacement, planing, hydrofoil and ACV type ships. Studies included technological assessment of performance of the concepts, taking into account various operational capabilities, including speed, propulsion systems, manning, weapons, materials, payloads and costs. Work performed for Stanford Research Institute under basic contract with ONR.

STANFORD RESEARCH INSTITUTE
ADDRESS:
  Menlo Park, California 94025
  Telephone: (415) 326-6200

EXECUTIVES:
  Clark Henderson, Staff Scientist, Transportation

ACTIVITIES:
  Operational tradeoff studies; optimising vehicles with missions; demand studies; economic evaluations; hydrofoils; ACVs.

SYSTEMS EXPLORATION INC.
HEAD OFFICE:
  3687 Voltaire Street, San Diego, California
Telephone: (714) 223 8141
REPRESENTATIVES:
  Richard E. Stedd
  Sam W. Braly
  Dale K. Beresford
  Erwin J. Hauber

ACTIVITIES:
  Consultants to the US Navy on ACV and hydrofoil development programmes. Developed high-speed aspect ratio displacement (HARD) hydrofoil concept.

MARTIN STEVENS
ADDRESS:
  Woodhull Cove, Oldfield Village, Setauket, Long Island, N.Y.
ACTIVITIES:
  Mechanical design, drive systems.

WATER RESEARCH COMPANY
HEAD OFFICE:
  3003 North Central Avenue, Suite 600, Phoenix, Arizona 85012
  Telephone: (602) 265-7722
EXECUTIVES:
  Richard R. Greer, President
  John H. McMasters, Chief Engineer
  The Water Research Company was formed in 1972 to consolidate activities surrounding the patents held or applied for by Mr. Richard R. Greer relating to various aspects of water-borne vehicles. The company has subsequently prepared conceptual studies on a class of winged surface effect vessels (WSEV) intended to fill a variety of missions for the US Navy. These vehicles are intended for use in conjunction with the patented Water Research Company hydrofoil/SES docking system. The company presently has the capability of performing analylical studies on hydrofoil, SES and WIG systems, and can provide contract coordinating services for such systems. The company has no immediate plans for acquiring hardware development facilities.

HYDROFOIL CONSULTANTS

CONSULTANTS IN HYDROFOIL TECHNOLOGY AND OPERATION

ISRAEL

Hydronautics-Israel Ltd

HEAD OFFICE:

10 Heassor Street, Ness Ziona, Israel

SWITZERLAND

Supramar AG

HEAD OFFICE:

Denkmalstrasse 2

6006 Lucerne, Switzerland

Telephone: (041) 36 96 36

Telex: 78228

MARKETING DEPARTMENT:

Supramar Trade Ltd.,

Address as above

MANAGEMENT:

Hussain Najadi, Chairman and Managing Director

Volker Jost, Ing., Technical Director and Assistant Managing Director

Baron Hans von Schertel, Technical Director

DESIGN:

Dipl Ing Ernst Jaksch, Chief

SECTION HEADS:

Dipl-Ing Georg Chojka, Marine Engineering

Dipl-Ing Ernst Jaksch, Foil Design

Ing Volker Jost, Hull Design

RESEARCH AND DEVELOPMENT:

Baron Hanns von Schertel, Head of Development

SECTION HEADS:

Dipl Ing Eugen Schatté, Propulsion and Tests

Dr Ing Hermann de Witt, Hydrodynamics

Supramar was founded in Switzerland in 1952 to develop on a commercial basis the hydrofoil system introduced by the Schertel-Sachsenberg Hydrofoil Syndicate and its licensee, the Gebrüder Sachsenberg Shipyard.

From this early date Supramar have provided a consultancy service on a world-wide basis covering not only their hydrofoil vessels but also other aspects of fast marine transportation. Their scientists have delivered papers to most of the world's leading professional bodies.

The company has been under contract to many Governments and military services.

UNITED KINGDOM

AIRAVIA

ADDRESS:

20 North Road, Shanklin, Isle of Wight

Telephone:

Shanklin 3643 and 2580

H. H. Snowball

K. M. Wainwright

R. Snowball

Count A. de Lasta

General H. Alexander

Formed in January 1968, Airavia is the representative for Sudo import hydrofoils in the United Kingdom, British Commonwealth countries, and Scandinavia.

The company provides training facilities and technical staff to undertrke feasibility studies of proposed hydrofoil routes.

C. A. BRINDLE & PARTNERS

See main entry under ACV consultants.

CHRISTOPHER HOOK

ADDRESS:

Burfield Flat, Bosham Lane, Bosham, Sussex

Christopher Hook was responsible for the conception, design and development of the fully submerged hydrofoil which he demon-strated in the USA in 1951 with his Red Bug, and later with Miami-built conversion sets. He became a partner of the late Herr G. Sachsenberg, the pioneer hydrofoil builder and has completed hydrofoil design and consultancy contracts in the USA, Israel, Holland, France, Norway, Italy as well as with Strathclyde University. He is currently developing a self-tending sail rig for sailing hydrofoil craft, comprising sails that tilt to windward and have roller reefing. He is the holder of two gold and one silver medal for invention, President of the Repubic Prize, France.

UNITED STATES

ATLANTIC HYDROFOILS INC

HEAD OFFICE:

Hancock, New Hampshire 03449

Telephone: 605 525-4403

DIRECTORS:

John K. Roper

Atlantic Hydrofoils' mechanically-controlled submerged foil system was the first to be approved for use on hydrofoil passenger ferries. The company has completed a number of Technical Reports for the United States Government on hydrofoil design and testing.

DAVIDSON LABORATORY

STEVENS INSTITUTE OF TECHNOLOGY

HEAD OFFICE:

Castle Point Station Hoboken, New Jersey 07030

Telephone: 201-792-2700

OFFICERS:

J. P. Breslin, Director

Daniel Savitsky, Assistant Director

Organised in 1935 as the Experimental Towing Tank, the Laboratory is active in basic and applied hydrodynamic research, including smooth water performance and manouverability; sea-keeping, propulsion and control of marine vehicles including ACV and hydrofoil craft. Special model test facilities are available to investigate the dynamic behaviour of ACV and hydrofoil craft in smooth water and waves.

GIBBS & COX

ADDRESS:

40 Rector Street, New York, N.Y. 10006 Ph: (212) 487-2800

6525 Belcrest Road, Hyattsville, Md. 20782 Ph: (301) 277-1919

ACTIVITIES:

Project coordination, consultation, conceptual and preliminary designs and "working" drawing efforts for commercial or Naval vessels of the SES/ACV, semi-planing or of the submerged hydrofoil type.

W. A. GRAIG

ADDRESS:

307 Troy Towers, Union City, N. J. 07087, USA

Telephone: (201) 864-3993

W. A. Graig (formerly Grunberg) is the inventor of the Grunberg foil system, first patented in 1936. His approach provided the basis for the Aquavion series and many other designs, and his influence is still to be found in vessels in production today.

The Grunberg principle of inherent angle of attack variation is fully compatible with Forlaninis' concept of area variation. Both can be incorporated in the same structure and in number of modern hydrofoils the two principles work in association.

Among Mr Graig's recent developments are several foil systems which provide lateral stability without impinging on the original Grunberg concept. One of these takes over directional control and ensures co-ordinated turns.

HOERNER

ADDRESS: Hoerner Fluid Dynamics

2 King Lane,

Brick Town, New Jersey 08723, USA

S. F. Hoerner, Dr-Ing habilitatus

Hydrodynamicist of hydrofoils "Sea Legs" and "Victoria", since 1951.

Author of **"Fluid-Dynamic Drag"** (1965) and **"Fluid-Dynamic Lift"** (to be published 1974).

HELMUT KOCK

ADDRESS:

3132 Carleton Street, San Diego, California 92106

Helmut Kock designed the Albatross, first hydrofoil in the United States to be certificated by the US Coast Guard for passenger services in lakes, bays and sounds. Twenty of these craft were built. A 72 passenger hydrofoil ferry designed by Helmut Kock is to be built for International Hydrolines Inc.

HYDRONAUTICS INCORPORATED

ADDRESS, TELEPHONE AND COMPANY OFFICERS:

See main entry under ACVs in this section.

M. ROSENBLATT & SON. INC

HEAD OFFICE:

350 Broadway, New York, 10013 New York

Telephone; (212) 431-6900

OFFICERS:

Lester Rosenblatt, President

E. F. Kaufman, Vice President and Manager, Western Division

L. M. Schlosberg, Vice President and Design Manager

F. K. Serim, Vice President and Manager, Basic Ship Design

R. E. Stark, Vice President

BRIEF HISTORY:

The firm was founded in 1947 and has since grown to be one of the largest engineering design firms of its type, specialising in naval architecture and marine engineering. An organization of experienced engineers, designers and draftsmen has been assembled which is fully capable of providing the engineering, design and research and development services associated with ship and marine vehicle design.

Since its establishment, the company has successfully completed approximately eighteen hundred ship design and related assignments for government and private customers. These assignments embrace work on commercial and naval ships and on almost every type of floating vessel. Merchant vessels include; passenger ships, containerships, oceanographic ships, general cargo ships, bulk carriers, tankers, surface effect ships, drilling platforms, survey vessels, tugs, etc. Naval vessels include: carriers, cruisers, destroyers, frigates, destroyer-escorts, tenders and auxiliaries of all kinds, submarines, LPD s, LPH s, LST s, LSD s, hydrofoils and patrol craft.

Typical hydrofoil assignments include:

AGEH

Preliminary design and naval architectural services for preparation of proposal for design and construction of 300-ton AG(EH) Hydrofoil Research Vessel—for Lockheed Aircraft Corp.

HYDROFOIL (LVH)

Provided naval architectural services, including development of lines, powering predictions, stability curves and loading criteria for design and development of a 37-foot Landing Force Amphibious Support Vehicle Hydrofoil (LVH)—for Lycoming Division, Avco Corporation.

SYSTEMS EXPLORATION INC.

HEAD OFFICE:

3687 Voltaire Street, San Diego, California

Telephone: (714) 223 8141

REPRESENTATIVES:

Richard E. Stedd

Sam W. Braly

Dale K. Beresford

Erwin J. Hauber

ACTIVITIES:

Consultants to the US Navy on ACV and hydrofoil development programmes. Developed high-speed aspect ratio displacement (HARD) hydrofoil concept.

WATER RESEARCH COMPANY

HEAD OFFICE:

3003 North Central Avenue, Suite 600, Phoenix, Arizona 85012

Telephone: (602) 265-7722

EXECUTIVES:

Richard R. Greer, President

John H. McMasters, Chief Engineer

The Water Research Company was formed in 1972 to consolidate activities surrounding the patents held or applied for by Mr. Richard R. Greer relating to various aspects of water-borne vehicles. The company has subsequently prepared conceptual studies on a class of winged surface effect vessels (WSEV) intended to fill a variety of missions for the US Navy. These vehicles are intended for use in conjunction with the patented Water Research Company hydrofoil/SES docking system. The company presently has the capability of performing analytical studies on hydrofoil, SES and WIG systems, and can provide contract coordinating services for such systems. The company has no immediate plans for acquiring hardware development facilities.

THE AEROFOIL BOAT
A FREE-FLYING RAM-WING/SURFACE EFFECT VEHICLE

DR ALEXANDER M.LIPPISCH, F.R.A e.S

Lippisch Research Corp

368

THE AEROFOIL BOAT
A FREE FLYING RAM WING/SURFACE EFFECT VEHICLE

by Dr. Alexander M. Lippisch, F.R.Ae.S.

LIPPISCH RESEARCH CORPORATION

X-113 Am Flying in Ground Effect

Introduction

I would like to describe our research and development work on the phenomenon of aerodynamic surface effect and its application to the design of an Air Cushion Vehicle. I am grateful to have this opportunity to explain the different stages of this work and to tell you about some of the results we have obtained so far.

In the earliest years of commercial aviation and through the 1930's, reliance on surface effect was often made by pilots on transoceanic flights. Lufthansa pilots, particularly over the South Atlantic, would cruise in surface effect only feet above the water. This not only extended their range by 50%, but provided a remarkably smooth flight. Some pilots even released their controls entirely, permitting their plane to "fly itself" in the stability of the surface effect cushion. Even today, in naval flying schools, surface effect is frequently noted as a last resource for bringing home a crippled plane on the verge of "ditching".

However, despite the widespread recognition of this phenomenon and early experimental investigations on surface effect by A. Betz,[1] it has not yet been applied in the systematic design of a transportation vehicle.

Our early research on the design of planing boats showed a natural speed barrier for waterborne craft which is caused by the physical properties of the fluid water. Wave resistence and cavitation restrict the cruising speed of the ship to velocities in the lower speed ranges. On the basis of this experience we arrived at a conclusion also reached by other researchers.

To develop an efficient vehicle for higher speed waterway transportation *one must design a craft which flies over the water surface. That means the ship must rise above the water, being supported in the surface effect region by the higher pressure layer of air between the vehicle and the water surface.*

Abstracting a step further, one can see that this mode of transportation is equally applicable to travel over relatively flat and open land areas.

On this basis we have concluded that the concept of an aerodynamic surface effect—or "ram wing"—vehicle is the best possible solution for general purpose medium speed transport over waterways and over those land areas where low population density precludes investment in capital intensive highway or rail systems.

Since our determination that a highly efficient planing boat is impossible to build, I have turned my attention to the research and development of a craft utilizing the aerodynamic surface effect principle. On the basis of our theoretical investigations, I have designed and supervised the construction of several manned test vehicles.

Two of these have been designed for full free flight as well as operation in surface effect. The successful flights of these craft—in surface effect and full free flight—have proven conclusively the practicality of the ram wing principle for the design of a new generation transportation system.

▶ ▶

Dr. Alexander M. Lippisch

Born in Munich, Germany, in 1894, Alexander M. Lippisch began his career in Aeronautics in February, 1918, when he joined the aircraft manufacturing plant of Zeppelin-Dornier in Lindau, Germany as an aerodynamicist.

He developed methods of aerodynamic performance and stability calculations for aircraft and designed the first systematic series of wing sections tested in Göttingen in August 1918.

After the first World War he joined a small group of engineers and surveyors to develop practical methods of aerophotogrammetry for mapping. This project was stopped by the Entente (Versailles Treaty.)

In 1921, Dr. Lippisch began his work on the development of sailplanes and gliders. He designed several successful sailplanes, among them R. Kronfeld's WIEN, G. Groenhoff's FAFNIR and H. Dittmar's SAO PAULO. At the same time he worked on the development of tailless and Delta-wing aircraft (1925-1939).

In 1939, he joined the Messerschmitt A. G. Augsburg with a group of his assistants for the development of a high speed rocket-propelled experimental aircraft, the Me 163A. The considerable success of this airplane led to the development of the rocket-propelled interceptor fighter Me 163B, which was the fastest military aircraft during World War II. (This aircraft has been described in several publications). In 1943, Dr Lippisch took over the Aeronautical Research Institute (LFW) in Vienna, Austria, where he remained until the end of the war. There he developed the shape of the supersonic Delta wing and tested several ramjet configurations.,

After the war, Dr. Lippisch was in custody of the Air Technical Intelligence of the U. S. Army Air Force in Paris and London. He was transferred to the USA in 1946 and worked for the U.S. Air Force and Navy Liaison Office in Wright Field, Ohio. In 1947, he joined the Navy as an aeronautical scientist at the Naval Air Material Command (NAMC) in Philadelphia. He left this position in 1950 to join the Collins Radio Company in Cedar Rapids, Iowa, as a consultant on aeronautical problems. At Collins Radio he set up the Collins Aeronautical Laboratory which developed the two and three dimensional smoke tunnels for visual flow observations and the Aerodyne—the wingless VTOL aircraft configuration.

In 1959, Dr Lippisch became head of the Collins Hydrodynamic Laboratory, where a tow-tank was built and a large number of tests with different planing surfaces were carried out. Later tests concerned models of the aerodynamic surface effect—or "ram wing"—vehicle which he named the Aerofoil Boat X-112. The test flights of this craft were very successful.

Dr. Lippisch resigned from his position at Collins Radio Company in 1964 to form Lippisch Research Corporation.

In 1967, the West German Defense Department awarded contracts for the research and development of an Aerofoil Boat and an Aerodyne test bed under the scientific and technical supervision of Dr. Lippisch. Both projects are still in progress. Initial tests with a single place test vehicle of the Aerofoil Boat X 113 Am were highly satisfactory. Further development work is currently underway.

Dr. Lippisch lives in Cedar Rapids, Iowa. He is married and has five children.

He is a member of the following professional societies:

AIAA (American Institute of Aeronautics and Astronautics)
AAAS (American Association for the Advancement of Science)
ASNE (American Society of Naval Engineers)
SNAME (Society of Naval Architects and Marine Engineers)
DGLR (Deutsche Gesellschaft für Luft-und Raumfahrt)
EAA (Experimental Aircraft Association)
Club der Luftfahrt, Bonn, Germany
Fellow of the Royal Aeronautical Society, London

▶ ▶

The Efficiency Basis for Technical Evaluation

Before going into some of the details of our work, I would like to review the formulation of Giuseppe Gabrielli and Theodore von Kármàn, the generally accepted basis of appraising the efficiency of any means of transportation. On the basis of their statistical investigations, Gabrielli and von Kármàn concluded that for an optimally efficient transportation system, the product of the speed of the vehicle (in knots) times its lift/drag performance will lie in the range of $5\text{-}10 \times 10^3$.

To represent the comparative efficiency of transportation modes graphically, these men designed the Gabrielli-von Kármàn diagram. As shown in Figure 1, this diagram positions the efficiency of different means of transportation on the lift/drag-speed axes.

Examination of the Gabrielli-von Kármàn diagram shows a void in the speed range of around 50-200 knots. In other words, at our current stage of technology, man has yet to develop a means of transportation in the middle speed ranges which reaches the limiting line of efficiency attained by low speed cargo ships (represented by the upper portion of the diagram) or the high speed jet planes (represented on the lower portion).

It is most instructive to observe the position on the Gabrielli-von Karman diagram of some of the more recent innovations in methods of transportation. Let us consider, in particular, hydrofoil boats and ground effect machines of the "hovercraft" variety.

Without question, in certain cases, these craft offer substantial advantages over other forms of transportation. Hydrofoils, especially when equipped with supercavitating foils, are much faster than commercial ships; hovercraft-type ground effect machines offer almost the same speed, and when properly designed remarkable amphibious capabilities.

However, in terms of transportation efficiency, both of these vehicles provide less than desirable performance. At their highest speeds (60-90 knots) both generate lift/drag ratios of well under 10:1. In contrast, a properly designed ram wing operated in aerodynamic surface effect will travel at higher speeds and still generate lift/drag ratios in excess of 40:1 *. This fact has been the prime stimulus to our work.

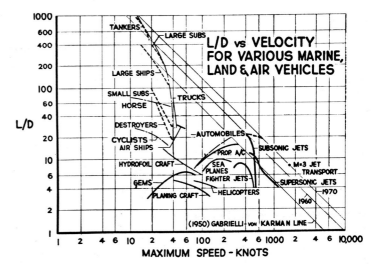

1. Gabrielli-von Kármàn Diagram

*In a remarkable paper, Captain Robert J. Trauger, USN, concludes that the desirable region for the development of such a surface effect vehicle would be in the speed range of 100-200 mph and in a L/D range of 50-30:1. "The second Generation of Ground Effect Machines," (Naval Research Reviews 62-2).

The Theoretical Basis for Aerodynamic Surface Effect

The theory of wings in ground effect was published by Wieselberger, who based his derivation on the biplane theory by Prandtl[2].

A wing and its image with equal but opposite lift and angles of attack form a symmetrical biplane. Applying Pohlhausen's influence factors, the reduction of induced drag on a wing flying near the ground can be calculated. The improvement in closer vicinity to the ground is considerable. For instance, at a distance of 10% of the span, the L/D improvement amounts to 40% (Figures 2, 3, and 4).

Since this theory replaces the wing by a single vortex line—as used in the induced drag derivation—the statements of this theory should be valid only at larger distances from the ground. Nonetheless, the theory has proven to give fairly accurate values even at smaller distances from the ground (Figure 5 and 6). This has been validated by several measurements.

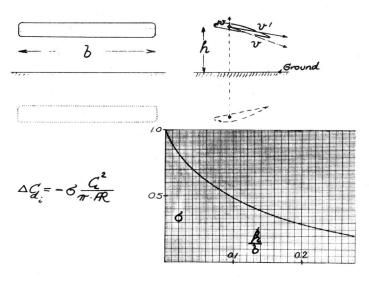

$$\Delta C_{d_i}' = -\delta \frac{C_i^2}{\pi \cdot AR}$$

2. Ground Effect Theory (Wieselsberger)

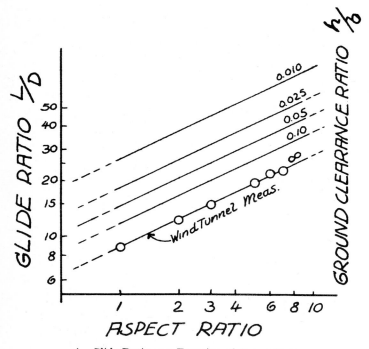

4. Glide Ratio as a Function of Aspect Ratio

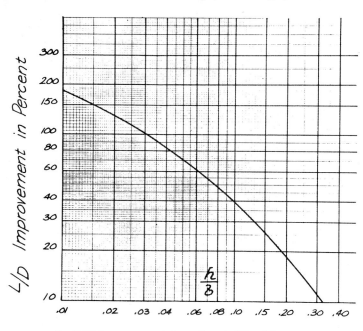

3. L/D Improvement According to Wieselsberger

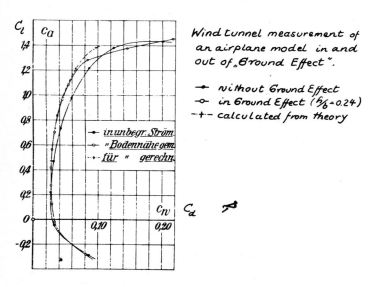

Wind tunnel measurement of an airplane model in and out of "Ground Effect".

- —•— without Ground Effect
- —○— in Ground Effect ($h/b = 0.24$)
- —+— calculated from theory

— in unbegr. Ström.
"Bodennähe gem.
für " gerechn.

5. Wind Tunnel Measurement of an Airplane Model (Göttingen)

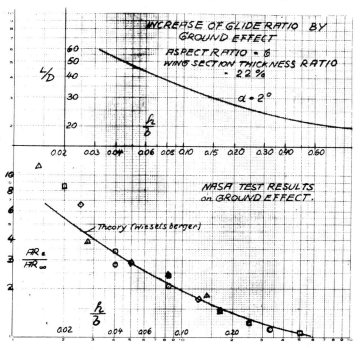

6. NASA Measurements of Ground Effect (TN D-926, D-960)

The ground effect makes it possible to obtain high L/D values with wings of extremely low aspect ratio. This matter of·fact is most advantageous regarding the design of ram-wing vehicles which will be equipped with low aspect ratio wings of limited span.

The question of the aerodynamic characteristics of wings in close vicinity of the ground was first investigated by G. Dätwyler.[3] Here Dätwyler shows that as the wing approaches zero distance from the ground, its lift increases considerably. This can be theoretically calculated from the potential flow on an inclined flat plate touching the ground. Dätwyler found that the measured lift increase even exceeds the theoretical expectations.

We can approach the problem of the flow around the body near a straight wall in a different way. Imagine a symmetrical body— for instance, a streamline body—and place half of the body on the plane of symmetry. If this "half-body" now moves forward along its axis on the plane of symmetry, we will have the same flow conditions on the body as in the case of the flow around the streamline body in open air. If we now hollow out the "half-body" and make an opening on the front, the air will enter the inner space of the body and stagnate there (Figure 7).

It is not difficult to estimate the lift (CL) which this ram body will produce as it moves over the ground. With low leakage around the edges, the stagnation pressure of the inner space will produce a lift coefficient close to 1 relative to the area of the ground plane, which is equivalent to a wing area. The outer flow over the curved surface also produces lift. This can be calculated from the potential flow condition around such streamline bodies. Both lift components together will result in a lift coefficient larger than 1. For usual shapes this will approximate $C_L = 1.5$.

We can also estimate the drag (CD) of the half-body. The C_D of streamline bodies related to their cross-section is in the range of 0·04-0·06. The base area of the streamline body is about 4 to 6 times as large as 1/2 of the cross section. The drag-coefficient related to the base area is, therefore, in the range of $C_D - 0·010 - 0·015$. This means that the lift/drag ratio without leakage losses would approximate $L/D = 100$. We can certainly state that with proper shape and flying over even moderately smooth water or land, the L/D of larger vehicles of such shape would be in the range of $L/D = 50-80$.

Let us now think of a somewhat wider streamline body more of the low aspect ratio wing type. In this case, we can make a similar performance estimate from the measurements of symmetrical wing sections. Such calculations result in higher L/D values, even when we allow for a considerable loss due to leakage.

The important knowledge we learn from this consideration is that the flow over a half-body moving close to a plane is the *only case* of a three-dimensional flow condition which under ideal conditions produces lift without drag. The actual drag will consist only of friction drag and certain pressure losses due to the leakage between the rim of the body and the flat ground.

At the beginning of my work in this field, we made some measure-

ments of an elliptical wing-body of low aspect ratio. Even within small Re-numbers ranges, we measured L/D values reaching 40. It would certainly be very helpful if this entire region of lift producing potential flow could be investigated systematically.

The problem here is the proper arrangement of such tests. Measurements of a wind tunnel model above a fixed straight surface are only valid at larger distances from the surface. Dätwyler already pointed out that such measurements were of limited value, and he could prove this experimentally. Using an equal model as mirror image opposite to the model which is being measured produces more satisfactory results. This method was used by Dätwyler and also by the NASA.

However, in wind tunnel test situations, a complete similarity to the flow on the body moving over the ground is difficult to achieve. In actual flight, the air inside the cavity of the body comes into contact with the solid ground and a circulation of the air in this cavity takes place due to friction on the ground surface. Replicating this condition in wind tunnel is extremely difficult.

These and other important problems can only be investigated under true flight conditions. It will be neccessary to develop a proper test procedure for such phenomena and to observe the flow conditions inside and around the body in surface effect.

I might mention here that some recent research about the calculation of the pressure distribution on different wing sections in ground effect was accomplished by W. Melzer and other members of the Aeronautical Institute at the Technical University Darmstadt. This theoretical work agreed closely with wind tunnel tests.

The Experimental Work

The most important question concerning the aerodynamic—ram wing—surface effect vehicle is the problem of longitudinal stability at different distances from the ground. It was stated that the shift in the center of pressure position from 45% chord length in surface effect to 25% at larger distances from the ground prohibits the practical application of the ram-wing principle to surface effect vehicles. The tow tank measurements which we conducted showed that the stability characteristics depend upon the shape and aspect ratio of the ram wing, and the shift of the CP could be avoided.

From the previous tests of a planing boat with swept-forward planing surfaces and the ground effect test of a half elliptical wing with low aspect ratio, we developed a triangular shape wing with negative dihedral.

With the addition of a fin, rudder and elevator, we evolved an aircraft configuration suitable *for both surface effect and free flight operation*. The evolution of this configuration is shown in Figure 8.

From the beginning of our work on aerodynamic surface effect vehicles, I attached considerable importance to the free flight capability. The application of these craft as universal means of transportation would require the ability to pass over natural obstacles along the waterways and to fly over terrains which are not suitable for surface effect flying. On the basis of this work, we

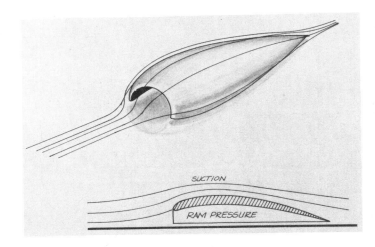

7. Lift of a Half-Body in Ground Effect

8. Evolution of the Aerofoil Boat X-112

designed and built our first manned ram wing surface effect vehicle or as we call it, the X-112 Aerofoil Boat (Figure 9).

The first flights of this craft were made in tow of a fast motor boat. On the basis of these tests, we enlarged the rudder and made the winglets on top of the floats larger with small flaps for aileron control. Power was provided with a 25 hp Richter drone engine. We added small counter vanes behind the engine to eliminate the rotation of the propeller slipstream. Figure 11 is the overall drawing of this Aerofoil Boat. The empty weight of this craft was 400 pounds. The Aerofoil Boat was test flown during the autumn of 1963 by Mr. Clayton Lander of the Collins Radio Company (Figure 10).

Extensive test flights in and out of surface effect conclusively proved full stability and control under all flight conditions. These included manoeuvres in surface effect and free flight over water and over land (Figure 12).

Our first measurements of the aerodynamic characteristics of the X-112 were made while towing the motorless craft and measuring the drag on the tow line. These measurements are presented in Figure 13.

Most of the measured points show the drag of the boat on the water as a planing craft. The maximum resistance is around 14% of the weight which is better than that of most planing boats. The aerodynamic lift begins at 30 mph. The drag diminishes rapidly to 4-5% in the 50 mph range. This corresponds to an L/D = 20-25. Since we did not pay much attention to streamlining—with the open pilot cockpit and without fairing the steps—a larger scale Aerofoil Boat of the same general proportions will have L/D values between

9. X-112 motorless at Initial Tests

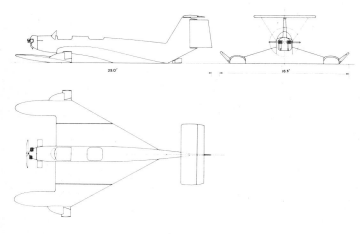

10. General view of the Aerofoil Boat X-112

11. X-112 with 25 HP Richter Engine—Pilot Clayton Lander

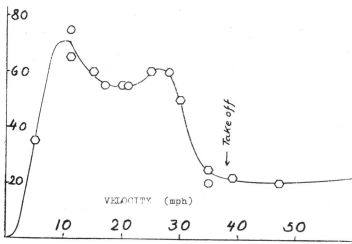

13. X-112 Drag Measurements in Tow

12. Flight Testing of X-112

30 and 40. This will provide transport economy in the range of 50 ton miles per gallon of fuel. That means that a larger Aerofoil Boat will be more economical than most other means of transportation in this speed range. Equally as satisfactory experimental results were obtained with different configuration as shown in Figures 14 and 15, where we used water propulsion.

We were unable to obtain additional support for the Aerofoil Boat development in this country. Presentations in Germany of our results with the X-112 initiated the research project X-113 supported by the West German Ministry of Defense.

Figures 16, 17 and 18 show the original design of the X-113. Its close resemblance to the X-112 test vehicle is clear.

We intended to test these configurations more thoroughly at different surface conditions of the water. Extensive model tests

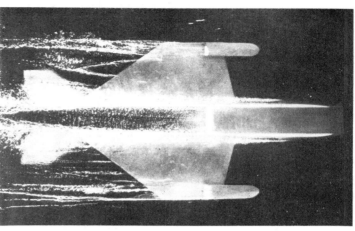

15. Aero-Skimmer X-114 Test Run

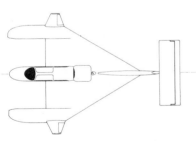

16. Design of Aerofoil Boat X-113

14. Tow Tank of Collins Hydrodynamic Laboratory Testing X-114

17. X-113 Model

18. R/C Model (Scale 1:8) of Aerofoil Boat X-113

with the low-wing as well as the high-wing configuration led to the design of a smaller one-man test vehicle, since there were indications from wind-tunnel tests that the longitudinal stability between flying in surface effect and in free flight would undergo considerable changes.

We chose the high-wing configuration with the fuselage as major displacement body so that the loads on the outer floats would be considerably reduced. The size of this craft—the X-113 Am—can be seen from Figure 19.

As a separate structural test, this Aerofoil Boat was built entirely of fibreglass on a special sandwich construction developed by the Rhein-Flugzeugbau GmbH. The first test flights were carried out in October 1970 on the Lake of Constance on the German-Swiss border. The vehicle was piloted by Herr W. Späte, who also piloted the Me 163 Komet rocket fighter during World War II.

We found that our suspicions regarding the longitudinal instability in and out of surface effect were *not* confirmed. No change in trim was necessary at different distances from the ground. The X-113 was completely stable both in surface effect and in free flight. Figures 20, 21 and 22 show the craft during these tests.

In order to obtain some flight characteristics under higher sea state conditions flight tests on the estuary of the Weser River near the North Sea shore line were accomplished in November-December 1972 with very satisfactory results. The small X-113 Am Aerofoil Boat negotiated wave heights of 2½ feet at wind speeds of 25 knots successfully.

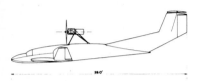

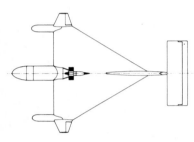

19. One Man Model of the Aerofoil Boat X-113 A (High Wing Version)

20. Aerofoil Boat X-113 Am ready for testing

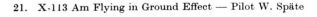

21. X-113 Am Flying in Ground Effect — Pilot W. Späte

22. X-113 Am in Free Flight Outside Ground Effect

A Concluding Note

Further development of this concept will lead to larger Aerofoil Boats as means of transportation along waterways, coastal areas and arctic regions.

We could distinguish three different classes of Aerofoil Boats:

(a) The smaller vehicles for sport, recreation and inland transport missions on rivers and lakes. These boats will be in the range of ½ to 3 tons at velocities of 60-100 mph.

b) The medium size Aerofoil Boats up to 50 tons and cruising speeds in the range of 200 mph.

c) The large ocean going surface effect ships of the ram-wing type up to 1000 tons and more. Very low aspect ratios of less than AR = 1. These vessels do not have the capability of free flight, but can rise to distances of ½ span to overfly high wave regions and smaller obstacles. Their cruising speed ranges up to 350 mph.

Some of the designs which we have investigated are shown in Figures 23, 24 and 25.

The military applications of these configuration range from fast patrol boats and ASW vehicles to troop carriers and landing craft.

From the research work that we have accomplished, we conclude that the application of the aerodynamic ground effect principle is only a question of applying existing technology. The basic problems of stability and control have been resolved satisfactorily.

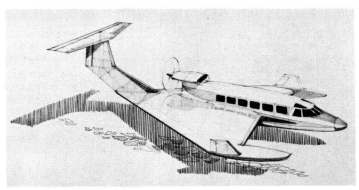

24. Artist Sketch of a 6 ton Aerofoil Boat "River Bus"

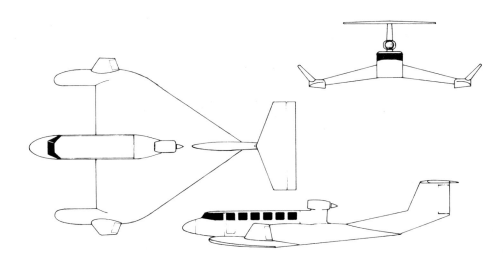

23. A 24 Passenger 6 ton Aerofoil Boat

25. Design of a 500 Ton Aerofoil Boat Transport

References in Text

1. Betz, A. Auftrieb und Widerstand einer Tragfläche in der Nähe einer horizontalen Ebene (Erdboden). Zeitschrift für Flugtechnik und Motorluftschiffahrt, 1912, No. 17.

3. Wieselsberger, C. Uber den Flugwiderstand in der Nähe des Bodens. Zeitschrift für Flugtechnik ünd Motorluftschiffahrt, 1921, No. 10.

3. Dätwyler, G. Untersuchungen über das Verhalten von Tragflügeln sehr nahe am Boden. Diss. Zürich, 1934.

SUPPLEMENTARY REFERENCES

4. Fink, M. P. and Lastinger, J. L. Aerodynamic Characteristics of Low Aspect Ratio Wings in Close Proximity to the Ground. NASA TN D-926 (1961)

5. Carter, A. W. Effect of Ground Proximity on the Aerodynamic Characteristics of Aspect Ratio 1 Airfoils with and without End Plates, NASA TN D-970 (1961)

6. Lippisch, A. M. and Colton, R. F. Tow Tank Tests of a Low Aspect Ratio Ground Effect Surface. Collins Radio Engineering Report (CER) 1117-8 (1963)

7. Lippisch, A. M. Der "Aerodynamische Bodeneffekt" und die Entwicklung des Flugflächen-(Aerofoil Bootes)

8. Wagner, W. Comeback der Grossflugbotte/Interview mit Aerofoil Pilot Wolfgang Späte. Deutscher Aerokurier No. 3, 1971

DEH, A HIGH ENDURANCE ESCORT HYDROFOIL FOR THE FLEET

RICHARD ARONER & ROBERT M. HUBBARD

Naval Systems Division, Boeing Aerospace Co.

Abstract

Eventually, an "advanced marine vehicle", having arrived at a point of technical maturity, must relinquish its special classification in order to gain eligibility to assume a major fleet role. In support of the proposition that the 50 knot submerged foil hydrofoil has arrived at that position, this paper describes the results of preliminary design studies which make use of the available technology base to produce a conceptual design for a Destroyer Escort Hydrofoil (DEH).

Starting with a set of mission requirements and choices of weapons suites, the effort proceeds to a definition of vehicle physical and performance parameters, while invoking an absolute minimum of technology advances not now in hand. Full recognition is given to the need for providing routine on-board services, self-maintenance features and internal systems that will generate few demands for new or unusual logistic support.

Of several iterations, the principal results reported are for a 200 foot LBP ship with a vehicle gross weight of 1,363 tons. Foilborne endurances typically range from 3,700 to 2,800 nautical miles dependent on payload selection, with hullborne speeds into the 20 knot range and hullborne endurance of 4,000 miles. A range of payloads from 100 to 177 tons is investigated to make visible the arrangement and performance variations that result. Accommodations for crews ranging from 63 to 91 officers and men on a standard habitability basis are incorporated into the alternate mission variants.

It is concluded that a mission-capable, high-endurance, open-ocean hydrofoil escort ship is feasible within the existing framework of developed technology.

Introduction

For more than a decade, developmental hydrofoils have explored many technical alternatives in way of establishing a firm foundation to capture the recognized military advantages offered by the hydrofoil concept. The ongoing PHM program, as the first full "class acquisition" is a direct result of this past development.

However, we can not afford to dwell on accomplishments of the past but must proceed immediately to attack the questions of the future. Specifically, we have not yet publicised a valid basis for a true appreciation of the full potential that has accrued from this excellent buildup of available, demonstrated technology. For this reason, there still exists an all too general opinion that the hydrofoil does not lend itself to extrapolation into the domain of a full-blown open ocean escort ship with all the attendant implications of long endurance, self-maintenance and integration into the existing fleet logistics situation. In addition, the often discussed "size barrier" ascribed to hydrofoils has not been adequately challenged in the context of a real design based on contemporary data.

For over one year, specific preliminary design studies have been underway to define and quantify the properties of a large hydrofoil ship suitable for task force escort deployment, which makes use of the existing technology base and requires only engineering design (6·4 level of RDT & E) to support a fleet prototype procurement.

In this paper, we not only present the principal results of this work, but also elaborate on our conclusion that a 50 knot Escort Hydrofoil (DEH) can be designed and constructed which offers:

(a) A quantum improvement in speed and seaway performance.
(b) Foilborne and hullborne endurance suitable for open ocean escort service.
(c) Size to support an effective payload suite with adequate crew and conventional facilities for high endurance missions.

The Operational Perspective

The incentive for advanced marine platforms stems from a desire for more speed, better seakeeping or a combination of both. Displacement ships with destroyer type hull forms succeeded in making speeds in the 35-40 knot range some 60 years ago but over the years the usual problems of deck wetness, structural limitations and habitability factors have prevented the utilization of this speed regime under adverse sea conditions. Captain J. R. Keyhoe in a recent article (Ref. 1) graphically summarized the existing situation for U.S. and U.S.S.R. destroyers as regards seaway speeds.

Figures 1 and 2 contain data taken from his treatise. We have superimposed a point on Fig. 1 and a curve on Fig. 2 which compares the hydrofoil (DEH) to his conventional escort data as regards the seaway effect for a typical voyage.

The speed capabilities of several vehicle types as a function of sea state are plotted in Fig. 3. It will be noted that the very large

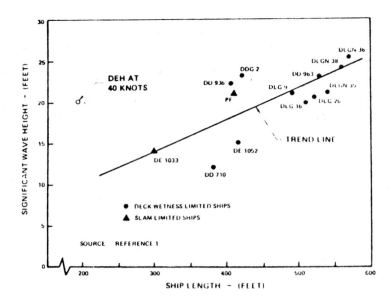

Fig. 1 Maximum Wave Height Capability in Head Seas at 20 knots

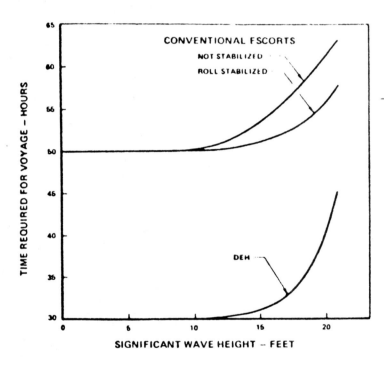

Fig. 2 1,500 Mile Voyage Time Comparison

conventional ship (CVAN) suffers only slight degradation in usable speed until significant wave heights of 20-25 feet are reached. The performance of the conventional destroyer escort begins to degrade at seas of about 10 feet and for significant wave heights of 20 feet can be optimistically credited with an average speed of about 15 knots. The large SES with calm water capabilities of 80 knots must give up much of this performance in the higher sea conditions for many of the same reasons that apply to the displacement hull. The 50 knot hydrofoil, although not completely immune to sea effects retains its speed properties because the main hull is decoupled from the sea surface and its seaway response is largely governed by the design length of the struts and the specific type of dynamic control system employed. It is the only escort vehicle which can match or exceed the seaway performance of the task force nucleus.

The many tactical benefits of hydrofoil high speed capabilities are summarized in Fig. 4. Notably, as speed increases, the number of ships required for most tasks, decreases the investment in force size tends to go down, and the number of escort ships per task force group or element is smaller.

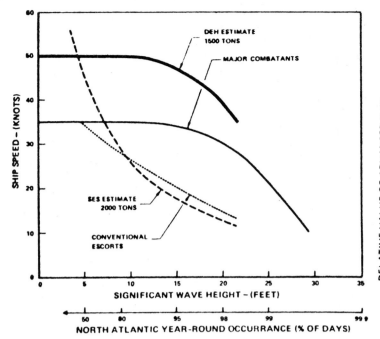

Fig. 3 Ocean Escort Operational Envelopes

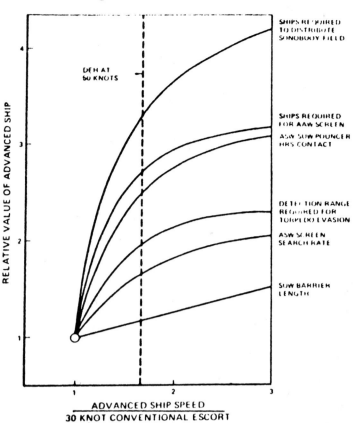

Fig. 4 Comparison of Effectiveness of High Speed Advanced
Ships to 30 Knot Conventional Escorts

The hydrofoil payoff can be realized merely by exploiting the body of design practice and operating experience that constitutes the technological base produced by a 15 year investment in the subcavitating submerged-foil hydrofoil. Accordingly, this paper describes an escort ship sized to meet specific performance and mission goals, but predicted on meeting the given requirements while invoking an absolute minimum of technology not on hand.

CHARACTERISTICS FORMULATION

Operational experience is the only sure route to provide the guidance needed to derive a firm "best set" of military vehicle design characteristics. Presently, we must make the best visualization or forecast to produce the most flexible set of properties to design into DEH. Certain areas are worthy of explanation insofar as they represent a break in the pattern of development of previous military hydrofoils.

It is postulated that DEH should offer a dual capability. It will provide the high speed, high sea state characteristics of the hydrofoil but also be required to operate for long periods in a hullborne mode at speeds into the 20 knot range, with hullborne endurance comparable to existing escorts (5,000 N.M.). Continuous foilborne endurance should be much greater than that of previous

hydrofoils and provide an "ocean-crossing" capability (at least 2,600 N.M.) so that no new or unusual logistic demands will be placed on existing fleet operations.

It will be necessary to make available an adequate complement along with stores, maintenance facilities and range of crew skills so that the level of self maintenance will be comparable to that of conventional escorts. There is no inherent basis to persist in the notion that a hydrofoil can only support a minimum operating crew with a high degree of logistic dependence on base facilities. On the other hand, we endeavor to take advantage of the manning economies inherent in the gas turbine propulsion system and the general degree of automation otherwise characteristic of the newest ships, coupled with the smaller overall size of the platform.

For seakeeping criteria, it is proper that we fully utilize one of

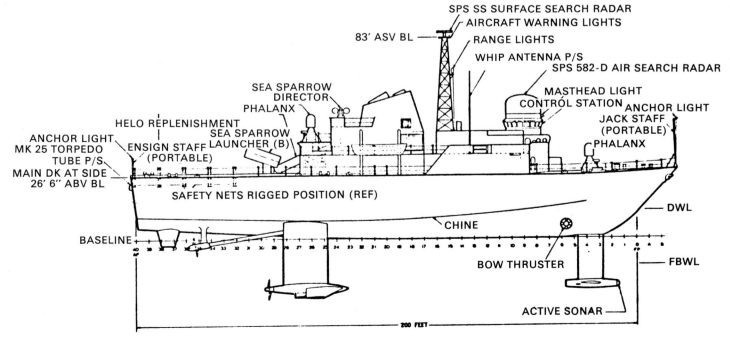

Model 002B (Baseline ASW) Profile

the prime features of the craft. This is a design goal for DEH to operate foilborne 98% of the time in seas representative of the North Atlantic on a year round basis. This quantifies to a design significant wave height of 20′ (upper sea state 6). This is not a "wish" goal and selection of this criterion is based on extensive seakeeping studies utilizing known hydrofoil response characteristics.

As for allocation of missions, roles and weapons systems, an authoritative determination must be left to the formal military planning procedure. It is our objective to select representative suites that will display the feasible range of possibilities. Consequently, configurations have been developed which include a basic ASW ship utilizing available weapons systems, a variant housing one SH2-D helicopter and a third arrangement cast as a multi-mission platform employing weapons concepts still in the planning stage.

For propulsion, past hydrofoils have employed either waterjet or angle drive propeller systems. The attractive feature of the waterjet system is its mechanical simplicity combined with a high

set up, each to produce the best overall ship design solution for a waterjet thruster and an angle-drive propeller system respectively. Table 1 summarizes the characterizing data of the several DEH versions as derived by our studies and selection processes. Configurations are set forth in Figures 5 through 8. It should be noted that some additional operational considerations, including at least maintenance and mission equipment compatability, need to be further studied before a definitive decision can be made.

PERFORMANCE

Thrust-drag relationships and smooth water foilborne endurance vs. speed are plotted in Figure 9. Take-off conditions are adjusted to provide a minimum thrust margin of 25% assuming an outside air temperature of 100°F. The apparent "excess" foilborne range indicated for the propeller ship over a nominal goal of 2600 miles is subject to some degradation when service factors and rough water cruise power increments are applied. Beyond this, the difference may be considered as a performance margin convert-

TABLE 1: SHIP CHARACTERISTIC SUMMARY

MODEL	WATERJET SHIP	PROPELLER SHIP VERSIONS		
	001E BASELINE ASW	002B BASELINE ASW	102B HELICOPTER ASW	202A MULTI-MISSION
PHYSICAL PARAMETERS				
LENGTH BP, FT.	200	200	200	200
MAX. HULL BEAM, FT.	48.4	48.4	48.4	48.4
MAX. WL BEAM, FT.	40.5	40.5	40.5	40.5
AFT FOIL SPAN, FT.	120	108	108	108
GROSS WEIGHT, TONS	1625	1363	1363	1363
FOIL DRAFT, FT.	39.5	36.7	36.7	36.7
PERFORMANCE				
MAXIMUM SPEED, KTS.	49	50.7	50.7	50.7
F/B ENDURANCE, N.M.	2300 AT 42 KNOTS	3670 AT 42 KNOTS	3530 AT 42 KNOTS	2900 AT 42 KNOTS
H/B ENDURANCE, N.M.	4000 AT 19 KNOTS	4000 AT 19 KNOTS	3850 AT 19 KNOTS	3060 AT 19 KNOTS
ACCOMMODATIONS				
OFFICERS	10	12	14	14
CPO	2	2	2	5
ENLISTED	51	56	60	72
TOTAL	63	70	76	91
STORES	45 DAYS	45 DAYS	45 DAYS	45 DAYS
ARMAMENT	COMMON TO BOTH MODELS (2) PHALANX (1) SEA SPARROW BOX LAUNCHER (8 RELOADS) (2) MK 25 TORPEDO TUBES (8) MK 48 TORPEDOES (2) HARPOON MISSILES		(1) PHALANX (1) OTO MELARA 76MM (240 RDS) (2) MK 32 TORPEDO TUBES (16) MK 46 TORPEDOES (2) HARPOON MISSILES	(2) PHALANX (16) SM-2 VERTICAL LAUNCHERS (16) HARPOON/TARPON MISSILES (1) OTO MELARA 76MM (240 RDS) (2) MK 25 TORPEDO TUBES (8) MK 48 TORPEDOES
SONAR	COMMON TO ALL MODELS (1) PASSIVE TOWED ARRAY, (1) VDS, (1) FOIL MOUNTED CTFM			
ELECTRONICS	COMMON TO BOTH MODELS SPS-55 SURFACE SEARCH RADAR SPS-58-2D AIR SEARCH RADAR SEA SPARROW FC NAV & COMM. SUITE STANDARD FOR TYPE ESM SUITE		SPS-55 SURFACE SEARCH RADAR MK 92 FC RADAR NAV & COMM. SUITE STD. FOR TYPE ESM SUITE	SPS-55 SURFACE SEARCH RADAR MK 49 AIR SEARCH RADAR MK 74 TRACKER ILLUMINATOR NAV & COMM. SUITE STD FOR TYPE ESM SUITE
AVIATION FEATURES	HELO REPLENISHMENT		(1) LAMPS (SH2-D HANGERED)	HELO REPLENISHMENT
TOTAL PAYLOAD, TONS*	100	100	94	177

*INCLUDES: PARTIAL GRP. 4, GRP. 7, AMMUNITION, CREW & EFFECTS, PROVISIONS AND POTABLE WATER WEIGHTS.

degree of accessibility of the mechanical components resulting in reliable trouble-free performance as demonstrated fully on TUCUMCARI. Although many factors are involved, it is noted that the one hydrofoil with waterjet propulsion, of the four major developmental ships, has accumulated 43% of the total foilborne time.

Appreciating that the demands for very long foilborne range represent one of the more significant departures as compared to previous hydrofoil characteristics, competing design teams were

ible to payload optimization, and growth margins. The waterjet ship is initially more limited and does not offer this flexibility.

Hullborne performance is summarized in Figure 10. In the higher hullborne speed range overall craft L/D is improved by utilizing foil lift, assuming the constant hydrofoil lift coefficient that would be appropriate for a 32 knot takeoff. This helps to overcome the relatively high hull resistivity as indicated by the comparative drag curves applicable to the propeller ship.

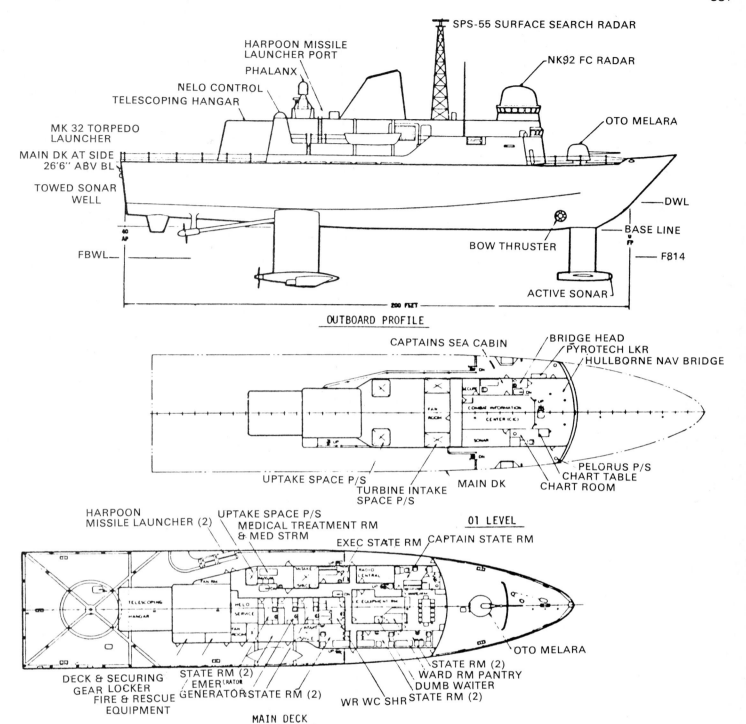

Fig. 6 Model 102B (Helicopter ASW) Profile and Arrangement

TABLE 2: PROPULSION SYSTEMS COMPARISON

PROPULSION SYSTEM	FOILBORNE WATERJET SYSTEM	FOILBORNE PROPELLER SYSTEM	HULLBORNE SYSTEM
ENGINE TYPE 2-REQUIRED FOR EACH SYSTEM	TURBO-POWER AND MARINE SYSTEMS FT9-D (MARINE VERSION, NOT IN PROD.)	GENERAL ELECTRIC LM-2500 (IN PRODUCTION TO BE USED ON PF, DD963 AND PHM)	AIRESEARCH GTPF 990 (G) (UNDER USN DEVELOPMENT NOT IN PRODUCTION)
TAKEOFF POWER INTERMITTENT RATING AT 100°F, PER ENGINE	45,000 SHP WITH WATER INJECTION	25,000 SHP	--
CRUISE POWER CONTINUOUS RATING AT 80°F, PER ENGINE	39,200 SHP	23,400 SHP	7,560 SHP
CRUISE PROPULSIVE EFFICIENCY, PERCENT**	43.9 AT 49 KNOTS	61.8 AT 50 KNOTS	57.8 AT 19 KNOTS
SHIP GROSS WEIGHT, TONS	1625	1363	--
NOMINAL ENDURANCE, N.M.	2,300 AT 42 KNOTS	3,670 AT 42 KNOTS	4,000 AT 19 KNOTS
CRUISE SHP/TON	48.2	34.3	--
SPECIFIC PROPULSION SYSTEM WEIGHT LBS/SHP	5.34*	2.74*	4.90
AVAILABLE FUEL, TONS	587	546	587/546

**PROPULSIVE EFFICIENCY = NET THRUST HP/ENGINE SHP.   *INCLUDES ALL PROPULSION SYSTEM FLUIDS EXCEPT USABLE FUEL

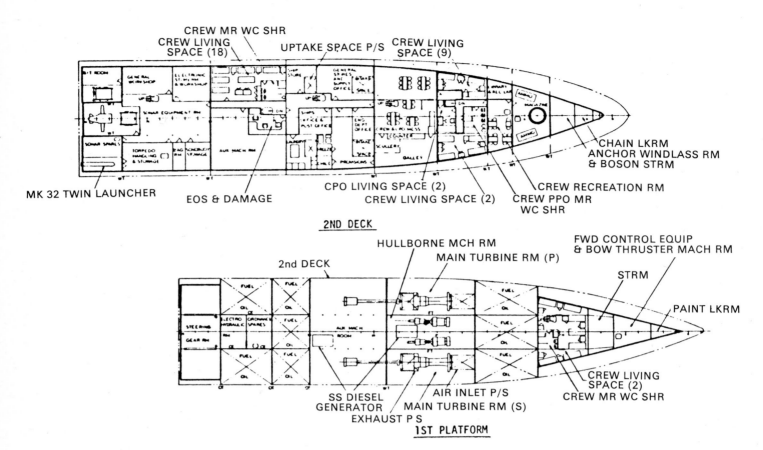

2ND DECK

1ST PLATFORM

Fig. 7 Model 102B (Helicopter ASW) Arrangement

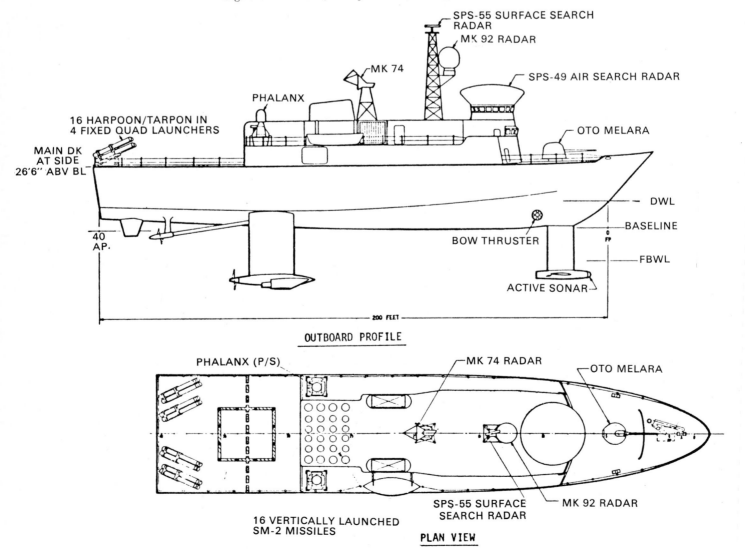

OUTBOARD PROFILE

PLAN VIEW

Fig. 8 Model 202A (Multi-Mission) Profile and Plan

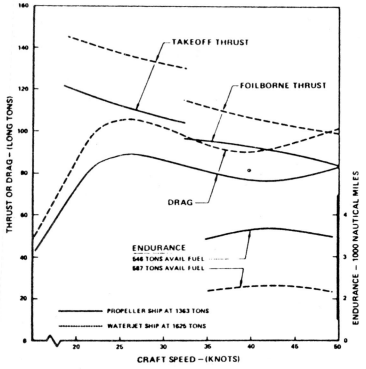

Fig. 9 Craft Performance and Foilborne Endurance

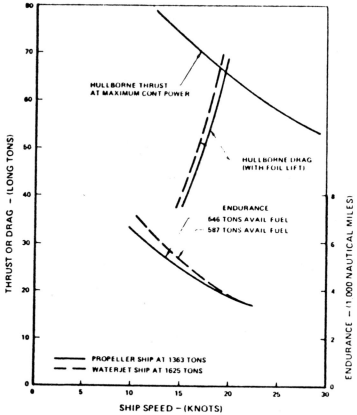

Fig. 10 Hullborne Performance and Endurance

PROPULSION

As noted previously, our work has encompassed waterjet and propeller foilborne propulsion systems on the basis of common hulls and payloads. The selection of gas turbines was unrestricted and performance was optimized where possible by designing up to the full capability of available engines. A common hullborne propeller system was used in all cases. Overall comparative data of these systems is summarized in Table 2.

There are a number of contingent effects inherent in the above tabulation. The lower efficiency and higher weight of the waterjet system drives one towards higher fuel loads and heavier takeoff weights which in turn provides incentive to go to higher rating prime movers. The increased weight drives the foil area up resulting in both larger main foil and forward steerable T-foil. The process of optimization of the waterjet plant itself brings in variations in inlet duct influencing strut size and drag. The large pumps make greater demands on available space so that total volume allocated to machinery is increased. In this ship, we must weigh the above effects against the waterjet system's demonstrated mechanical simplicity and high reliability that has resulted in the choice of waterjets on TUCUMCARI, PHM and the Boeing JETFOIL.

Earlier experience with high power-density angle drive propeller systems on hydrofoils resulted in significant hardware problems and lack of operational reliability. Today we can take advantage of much of this experience and of improved manufacturing technology to design reliable drive trains for the hydrofoil environment. In this regard, the Navy developed AGEH gear system is the highest rated train to date and has turned in a generally excellent performance in approximately 200 hours of sea trials. Originally designed to handle the output of two LM 1500 engines/shaft (30,000 H.P.) it has been deployed with half the designed input power. Table

3 sets forth the key angle drive train parameters needed for DEH and their relationship to acceptable gear design factors. Our assessment indicates that bearing life would be the limiting factor. With available bearing technology it is confidently anticipated that a system exhibiting a MTBO in excess of 40,000 hours can be produced. Figure 11 is a schematic of the foilborne and hullborne propulsion trains.

Employment of a pod mounted 4:1 ratio planetary reducer is a key factor in keeping system weights down, and operating the right angle train at low torques. A fortuitous investment by the Navy Department in the early period of the hydrofoil technology buildup has resulted in the development, construction and shop testing of a very lightweight high performance planetary gear box. This unit produced by Curtiss-Wright was designed as a 40,000 SHP reducer and has been shop tested up to 50,000 SHP. Its physical dimensions, light weight, and overall ratio precisely fit the needs of our proposed ship and it provides necessary visibility to one of the key components of the concept.

Supercavitating propeller estimates are derived from an existing successful supercavitating blade series. The selected characteristics are shown in Table 4. Figure 12 offers comparative data which indicate that although the diameter is somewhat larger than previous propellers, disc loading as an overall comparator falls well within the body of previous practice. Figure 13 illustrates a rationale for characteristics selection. Some compromise in peak efficiency has been taken to improve take-off thrust performance and to ensure suitable transmission system reduction ratios.

TABLE 3: RIGHT ANGLE BEVEL GEAR PARAMETERS APPLICABLE TO DEH FOILBORNE DRIVE PINION

PARAMETER	VALUE	COMMENT
NO. OF TEETH	50	SAME AS AGEH
DIAMETRAL PITCH	2.228	SMALLER THAN AGEH
PITCH DIAMETER	22.442 IN.	26 IN. MANUFACTURING LIMIT
PRESSURE ANGLE	20 DEGREES	SAME AS AGEH
SPIRAL ANGLE	30 DEGREES	SAME AS AGEH
TORQUE	241,000 LB-IN.	300,000 LB-IN (AGEH DESIGN)
RPM	3,600	3,130 (AGEH DESIGN)
BENDING STRESS	24,400 PSI	30,000 PSI IS GLEASON STANDARD
CONTACT STRESS	141,500 PSI	LOWER THAN GLEASON FOR 10^9 CYCLES
PITCH LINE VELOCITY	21,600 RPM	30,000 FPM SHOULD BE POSSIBLE

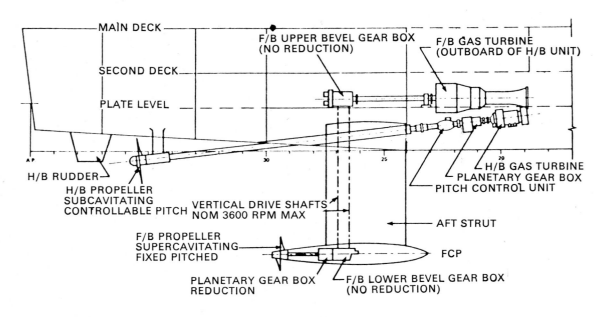

Fig. 11 Propulsion Systems Schematic

TABLE 4: FOILBORNE PROPELLERS

TYPE	SUPERCAVITATING-FIXED-PITCH
DIAMETER, FEET	7.0
PITCH-DIAMETER RATIO	1.10
BLADE AREA RATIO	0.60
NUMBER OF BLADES	3
PERFORMANCE:	
DESIGN CONDITION	
SPEED, KNOTS	50
POWER, PROPELLER HP	22,230
RPM, MAXIMUM	850
NET THRUST, LBS PER PROPELLER	96,300
TAKEOFF OPERATION	
SPEED, KNOTS	25
POWER, PROPELLER HP	23,180
RPM,	750
NET THRUST, LBS PER PROPELLER	125,600

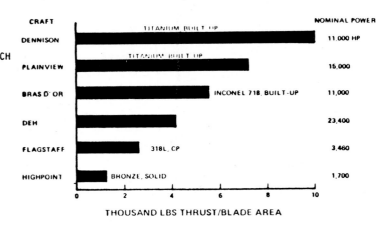

Fig. 12 Comparison of Propeller Thrust Loading

Hullborne driving equipment is identified in Table 2 and utilizes 10ft diameter controllable pitch subcavitating propellers. Because of the conventional drive arrangement, specific weights are high and it would appear desirable to delete the entire hullborne system in favour of exclusive utilization of the foilborne thruster. Figure 14 gives estimated hullborne endurance/speed comparisons assuming all hullborne operation on a foilborne controllable pitch supercavitating propeller. Further development of this idea is reserved for downstream consideration which must take into account the viability of supercavitating blade operation in this speed regime, the possible implementation of forced ventilation, the physical aspects of pitch control and a more astute definition of desired underwater acoustic properties for the ship.

Overviewing the entire propulsion situation, the utilization of an angle drive propeller system emerges as substantially superior from the performance and weight point of view. The basic power system elements are either developed components or have undergone engineering development and shop level testing. What is needed for a propeller drive DEH is a detailed design, development and qualification program of all the components of the propulsion system. This requires careful consideration to avoid past problems as regards preventing lube system contamination, subsequent bearing deterioration, over-emphasis on weight economy, seal integrity and reliability of attached auxiliaries, all factors that have contributed to "downtime" on the existing developmental propeller ships.

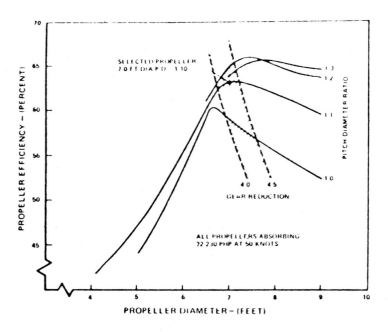

Fig. 13 Pitch-Diameter Effects on Propeller Efficiency

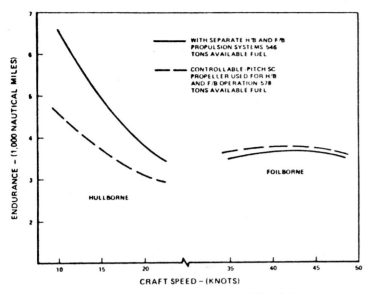

Fig. 14 Endurance with Alternate Propulsion Scheme

STRUCTURE

Generation of loads data for structural design purposes is an area where the hydrofoil designer, motivated by the necessity to fully appreciate the dynamic loads imposed on the vehicle, has built up a body of practice that departs from the conventional approach to ship hull design. The loads criteria directly relate significant wave height for the design sea state to a "limit load" represented as the highest single load that can be imposed by the environment for the condition investigated. The governing limit load is compared to material yield properties, or when increased by an arbitrary factor of 1.5 is designated as an "ultimate load" which may be compared to the ultimate properties of the material. Stresses must be adjusted so that neither criterion exceeds the nominal material properties. Dependent on the condition under investigation, additional dynamic factors are inserted to account for "springing" effects or freebody vehicle response dynamics. Figure 15 graphically summarizes the various loads conditions investigated. Dynamic sea loading on decks and superstructure is related via the significant wave heights to dynamic pressures encountered in breaking waves.

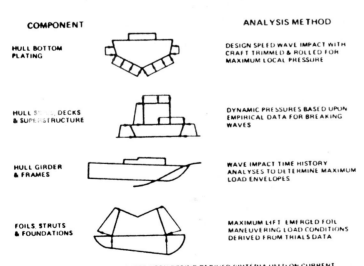

THE DESIGN LOADS ARE BASED UPON BOEING DERIVED CRITERIA USED ON CURRENT HYDROFOIL CRAFT ANALYSIS METHODS HAVE INCORPORATED EMPIRICAL DATA FROM TECHNICAL TRIALS

Fig. 15 Hull Design Loads

At-sea experience has demonstrated the serviceability of hydrofoil hulls and it can be noted that no primary structural failures have occurred, even during operations in sea states substantially higher than design conditions.

Figure 16 is a typical structural section of the DEH hull. Despite the 200' length, main hull scantings are controlled by bottom impact

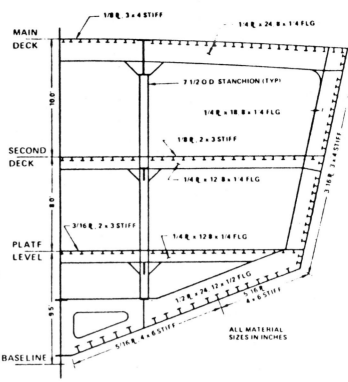

Fig. 16 Typical Structural Section

and local loads on sides and decks, except for distributing strut/hull intersection loads into the main girder. Based on a web spacing of five feet. the structure is conventional except that efforts to minimize weight lead to a rather dense spacing of longitudinals. Further optimization studies will be conducted involving hull weight —manufacturing cost trades. The use of ordinary T-stiffener to shell assembly techniques are assumed. Extruded plate-stiffener sections have been used in the past for additional weight economy. Because of the narrow extrusion panels and the attendant increase in welded plate seams required, it was judged that our larger ship would be better served with conventional assembly practices.

Hull materials are the conventional 5456 aluminium. The use of HY-80 as an alternate has and is being considered but with the probable need for a corrosion allowance and a redistribution of elements to avoid impracticably thin materials, it is not likely that the latter material will be weight competitive.

Structural design criteria for struts and foils take a more conservative approach in deference to the influence of corrosion fatigue. In this case the governing ultimate load conditions which include appropriate dynamic magnification factors are compared to yield stresses. This reduces the design working stress by a factor of one third. In addition, in the detail design stage, statistical load profiles resulting from computer foilborne simulations for a given environmental situation can be applied to specific joint designs for analysis of fatigue life including crack propagation propensity.

17-4PH stainless steel of 120,000 psi yield or HY-130 are candidate materials for struts and foils. The former has excellent corrosion and cavitation erosion resistant properties but requires a high temperature post-fabrication heat treatment although recent technology investigations indicate a high probability of eliminating heat treatment above aging temperatures. HY-130 requires reliable coatings for corrosion/erosion protection. This matter is being actively pursued and it is anticipated that the present Navy program of HY-130 development will include designing and building an alternate set of strut-foils for PHM, which now utilizes a 17-4PH stainless alloy. The 6Al-4V type of titanium would have excellent general properties and save considerable weight. However relative costs, mill availability and fabrication variables have not been adequately investigated to elevate this material to an equal level of interest.

HULL FORM SELECTION

Selection of the hydrofoil hull encompasses some of the usual considerations encountered in conventional hull design, introduces a few interesting novelties, and also "liberates" the designer in other

TABLE 5: HULL CHARACTERISTICS

DISPLACEMENT, L. TONS	1363
TAKEOFF DYNAMIC LIFT, L. TONS	1255
DESIGN LCG, AFT OF MIDSHIP, FT.	15.37
DESIGN DRAFT, FT.	11.61
LENGTH OVERALL, FT.	216.66
LENGTH BETWEEN PERPENDICULARS, FT.	200
MAXIMUM BEAM, FT.	48
MAXIMUM BEAM AT CHINE, FT.	38.5
WATERLINE MIDSHIP BEAM, FT.	40.5
DEADRISE ANGLE, MIDSHIP, DEG.	22.5
WETTED SURFACE, SQ. FT.	8350
WATERPLANE AREA, SQ. FT.	6696
BLOCK COEFFICIENT (C_B)	0.494
MIDSHIP COEFFICIENT (C_M)	0.65
WATERPLANE COEFFICIENT (C_{NP})	0.81

respects. The novelty occurs in the need to have hull resistence data for many waterlines in order to suitably evaluate overall vehicle drag during the take-off phase. In the interests of reducing foil-borne bottom impact and minimizing wetted surface at take-off, deadrise angles of about 22° are employed. A relatively fine fore-foot and bow flare are needed to reduce spray when cresting at high speed. Freed from the customary speed/length limitations, the hull is characterized by a high displacement length ratio as compared to destroyer forms. This allows for generous internal deck area, volume for arrangement purposes and freedom from stability limitations often encountered in destroyer forms. An additional important factor in beam selection is the arrangement of main struts to provide effective foil span equalization without excessive strut splay angle. The hull lines utilized are fully supported by an extensive series of towing basin tests. Table 5 lists the characterizing hull data. Analysis of resistance indicated that performance of this hull would be quite satisfactory under takeoff conditions. (75% of total drag at the takeoff hump is vested in the strut/foil.) system Hull resistance is rather high at the 20 knot hullborne cruise condition. However, investigation indicated that the investment in hullborne propulsion equipment was reasonable and acceptable.

STRUT/FOIL CONFIGURATION

Selection of Strut/Foil Configuration is influenced not only by operational criteria, but by external physical limitations which become operative in this large vehicle. Specifically these are:

Foil span (Drydocking and canal limitations)

Navigational draft hullborne
Nominal foilborne keel height (sea state related)
Design sea state
Foil loading and foil distribution
Control dynamics and ride quality
Structural feasibility
Ship arrangement
Fabrication and material considerations
Contiguous use of strut (i.e., waterjet ducts or angle drive transmission components)

Obviously these are interrelated factors and command much attention in prosecuting our design.

The selected foil arrangement is a fully submerged canard, with a relatively high ratio of main to forward foil area distribution. Experience has shown that, holding the proportion of total lift supported by the forward foil to a low value gives the best overall ride and minimizes perturbations caused by forward foil broaching and "flyout". Also, in the large hydrofoil the smallest possible forward steerable "T"-foil is of benefit from the point of mechanical actuation and hydraulic power demands. The high distribution ratio also brings the main foil forward for better interfacing with the main machinery in a fore and aft location which facilitates locating inlet ducts and stacks free of interference with afterdeck ordnance or helicopter installations. Rapid automatic course corrections are available from the faster responding small "T"-foil. The balancing effect of this general approach is that the larger resulting main foil reaches an imposed span limit sooner, or that compromises in foil aspect ratio are required, impacting take-off L/D. To allow maximum design latitude, a main foil span limit of 120ft (dry docking limit) was established along with a limiting hullborne draft of 40ft with expectation of reducing these dimensions as the ship definition developed.

Figure 17 shows the key planform and sectional dimensional properties of the foils selected for the propeller ship. The use of taper and variable t/c promotes optimum structural utilization of material and is a very important consideration in holding foil weights down.

The two conventional control systems in use are (a) incidence control and (b) trailing edge (plain flap) control. The former is not structurally feasible for a ship of DEH size and general arrangement. The latter is feasible but because of inherent hinge point unbalance entails very large hydraulic power commitments. The detached control foil concept indicated in Figure 18 has been adopted for use on DEH. This permits placing the flap hinge point nearer the quarter chord reducing hinge moments by at least a factor of four

TABLE 6: PROPELLER SHIP WEIGHT COMPARISONS

	002B BASELINE ASW	102B HELICOPTER ASW	202B MULTI-MISSION
FULL LOAD WEIGHT	1363 TONS	1363 TONS	1363 TONS
USABLE FUEL	546 (40.1)*	526 (38.6)*	433 (31.7)*
			86 (6.3)
	USEFUL LOAD 649 (47.6)	USEFUL LOAD 624 (45.8)	USEFUL LOAD 614 (45.0)
OTHER LOADS	55 (4.0)	58 (4.3)	95 (7.0)
ARMAMENT + MIL. P/L OF C&S	48 (3.5)	40 (2.9)	84 (6.2)
MARGINS	75 (5.5)	77 (5.7)	84 (6.2)
ELECTRICAL + BASIC C&S	55 (4.0)	57 (4.2)	60 (4.4)
OUTFIT & FURNISHINGS	63 (4.6)	63 (4.6)	69 (5.1)
AUX. SYSTEMS LESS FOIL AND STRUT SYSTEMS	80 (5.9)	89 (6.5)	80 (5.9)
FOIL AND STRUT SYSTEMS	134 (9.8)	134 (9.8)	134 (9.8)
	LIGHT SHIP 762 (55.9)	LIGHT SHIP 779 (57.1)	LIGHT SHIP 844 (61.9)
PROPULSION PLANTS	90 (6.6)	90 (6.6)	90 (6.6)
HULL AND SUPERSTRUCTURE	217 (15.9)	229 (16.8)	232 (17.0)

*WEIGHT, TONS (PERCENT OF FULL LOAD WEIGHT)

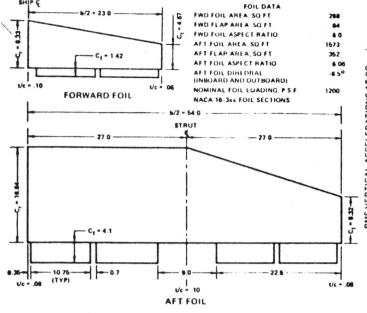

FOIL DATA

FWD FOIL AREA. SQ FT — 288
FWD FLAP AREA. SQ FT — 64
FWD FOIL ASPECT RATIO — 80
AFT FOIL AREA. SQ FT — 1673
AFT FLAP AREA. SQ FT — 362
AFT FOIL ASPECT RATIO — 6 06
AFT FOIL DIHEDRAL — -6 5°
(INBOARD AND OUTBOARD)
NOMINAL FOIL LOADING, P S F — 1200
NACA 16-3xx FOIL SECTIONS

Fig. 17 Foil Geometry

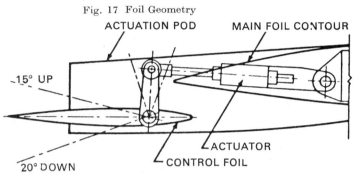

Fig. 18 Control Foil Arrangement

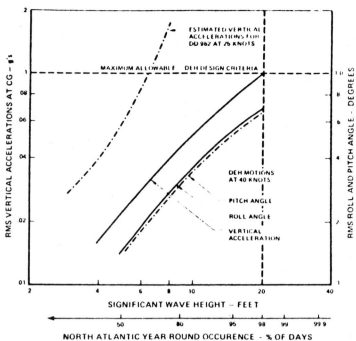

Fig. 19 Foilborne Motions

as compared to the trailing edge flap. This promises to offer an excellent solution to the "hydraulic power limit" conventionally associated with large hydrofoils. The Boeing Company is presently conducting wind tunnel and flow channel tests of this concept to provide engineering design data.

Placing very strong emphasis on reliability and effectiveness of the entire flap control system, our design provides sufficient flap area and enough redundant flap segments to provide adequate, albeit somewhat degraded, control if one half of the flap elements on either or both sides of the foil system become inoperative. Two feasible concepts for flap actuation power trains are under study, one involving a dual redundant mechanical system from the main hull, through the struts and into the foils. The other employs redundant, independent flap segment power/servo loops which have the advantage of much reduced weight and mechanical complexity.

WEIGHTS

Table 6 summarizes weight statements for the various versions of the propeller driven ship. At the present state of development 68% are calculated weights and the remainder estimated or ratiocinations. The Group 1 (hull) includes 40 tons for foundations and strut/hull interfacing allowances. Group 2 (propulsion) are discrete components weights and system estimates. Group (3) (electrical) is based on employment of an optimized 60 cycle system using diesel prime movers. Although 400 cycle power has been utilized on previous hydrofoils, it was felt that cost, logistic and acoustic problems would outweigh the possible lower weight of the 400 cycle electric plant. Group 4 (communications and control) combines both component and system estimates. The sonar equipment weights which form a large part of this system are estimated from developmental models and would require verification. Group 5 (auxiliary systems) is generally the most difficult group to support with estimates in the preliminary design phase, particularly when there is no parent form precedent. Each three digit group was addressed and direct system estimates were made in the light of the most probable available system development. Heating, ventilating and air conditioning weights in example were based on utilization of standard

Navy type system arrangements and components with a view towards logistic continuity and available standard maintenance skills. On the other hand, the anchoring system reflect weights appropriate to a lightweight anchor and nylon-line mooring system as a means of reducing weight over the conventional chain/wildcat arrangement.

FOILBORNE CONTROL AND MOTION DYNAMICS

Of the several sectors of developed hydrofoil technology, the present state of the art as regards the foilborne control system emerges as one of the more noteable achievements, with significant contributions creditable to Navy planners, technical personnel and their supporting contractors.

Introduction of the acoustic height sensor, reliable accelerometers, Boeing manufactured solid state analog electronics, and selective system redundancy have combined to produce very reliable highly effective controls. Tucumcari, representative of 1967 control system technology, has never experienced an operational foilborne incident attributed to the control loop. Automation features relieve the helmsman of all coordination activity except for ordered course, turn rate and set foil depth. Ref. 2 offers a comprehensive description of the modern foilborne control systems.

Utilizing stability and control derivatives for our propeller DEH, a linear behaviour analysis based on typical controller parameters is set forth in Figure 19 with a superimposed comparison of vertical accelerations typical of destroyers.

CONCLUSIONS

A 15 year investment in technological development of the 50 knot hydrofoil has reached maturity. Without the inauguration of any new significant research and developemnt effort, a mission effective high endurance hydrofoil escort ship in the 1200-1600 ton size range is feasible, viable and available to the fleet. Of the several "advanced marine vehicle" concepts of the 1960's, the 50 knot hydrofoil can become the advanced performance escort ship of the 1980 s.

ACKNOWLEDGEMENTS

The authors are indebted to the members of the Boeing DEH preliminary design team who have largely produced the material for this paper.

REFERENCES

(1) Captain James W. Kehoe, Jr., USN, "Destroyer Seakeeping: Ours and theirs," U.S. Naval Institute Proceedings, November 1973.
(2) James E. Vogt, "Automatic Control of the Hydrofoil Gunboat, Tucumcari," Proceedings—AIAA 2nd Advanced Marine Vehicles and propulsion Meeting.

GLOSSARY

GLOSSARY OF ACV AND HYDROFOIL TERMS

ACV. Air cushion vehicle.

AMPS. Abbrev. Arctic Marine Pipelaying System. Method of laying pipelines in ice-covered Arctic waters employing a skirted air-cushion barge as an icebreaker. System was devised after Arctic Engineers successfully and continuously broke ice up to 27 in (0·68 m) thick using the 250-ton ACT-100 platform. On contact with the ice sheet, the skirt rises above it, maintaining its seal. As the ice sheet enters the cushion zone, the water level beneath it is depressed by the air pressure. Having lost flotation support, the ice becomes a cantilevered ledge and when it reaches its critical length, it breaks off into the water below. The broken ice is then thrust aside by a plough-like deflector.

APU. Auxiliary power unit.

abeam. Another craft or object seen at the side or beam.

actuator. Unit designed to translate sensor information and/or computer instructions into mechanical action. Energy is transferred to control surfaces hydraulically, pneumatically or electrically.

A to N. Abbrev. Aids to navigation.

aeration. See **air entry.**

Aerofoil boat. Name given by Dr Alexander M. Lippisch, the inventor and aircraft designer, to his range of aerodynamic ram-wing machines.

aeroglisseur, (French, air-glider). Name given to range of passenger-carrying amphibious ACVs designed in France by Société Bertin & Cie in conjunction with Société D'Études et de Développement des Aéroglisseurs Marins (SEDAM). The name **Aerobac** is given to mixed passenger/car ferries and freighters designed by Bertin and SEDAM.

aeroplane foil system. Arrangement in which the main foil is located forward of the centre of gravity to support 75% to 85% of the load, and the auxiliary foil, supporting the remainder, is located aft as a tail assembly.

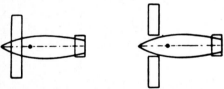

Aeroplane or conventional foil systems. The main foil may be divided into two to facilitate retraction

aerosuspendu (French, air-suspended). Form of suction-suspended monorail designed in France by Maurice Barthalon for mass public transportation on urban and suburban routes. The vehicle is suspended from its track by an air lift system in which the pressure is sub-atmospheric. Propulsion is by linear induction motor, q.v.

Aerotrain. Generic name for a range of tracked air cushion vehicles under development in France by Société de l'Aerotrain.

aft. At, near or towards the stern of the craft.

air bleed (hyd). See **air stabilisation.** Occasionally used instead of earation or air entry.

air bleed (ACV). One method of preventing "plough in" on a skirted ACV is to bleed air from the cushion through vent holes on the outer front of the skirt to reduce its water drag by air lubrication.

air cushion vehicle. A vehicle capable of being operated so that its weight, including its payload, is wholly or significantly supported on a continuously generated cushion or 'bubble' of air at higher than ambient pressure. The air bubble or cushion is put under pressure by a fan or fans and generally contained beneath the vehicle's structure by flexible skirts or sidewalls. In the United States large or ship size air-cushion vehicles are called **surface effect ships** or **surface**

Three aerostatic-type air cushion vehicles. Each is supported by air put under pressure by a fan or fans and contained beneath the vehicle by flexible skirts or sidewalls. *Left to right:* The projected 2,000-ton Bell 2KSES; the Mitsui MV-PP5 50-seat hoverferry and the BHC BH.7 Mk. 4 of the British Interservice Hovercraft Unit

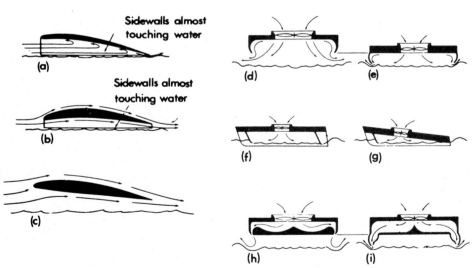

(a) ram wing; (b) channel-flow wing; (c) wing-in-ground effect; (d) plenum chamber; (e) plenum chamber with skirt; (f) captured air bubble; (g) hydrokeel; (h) annular jet; (i) trunked annular jet

effect vessels.

Broadly speaking, there are two main types of air-cushion vehicles, those supported by a self-generated cushion of air and those dependent upon forward speed to develop lift. The former are designated *aerostatic*, and the latter, *aerodynamic*.

Aerodynamic craft include the *ram-wing*, the *channel-flow wing* and the *wing-in-ground-effect*. The *ram-wing* (a) can be likened to a short-span wing with sidewalls attached to

its tip. The wing trailing edge and the sidewalls almost touch the water surface. At speed, lifting forces are generated by both the wing and the ram pressure built up beneath. One of the first concepts utilising a *channel-flow* wing (b) was the Columbia, designed in the USA by Vehicle Research Corporation in 1961 (JSSS 1967-8 edition). The design featured a peripheral jet sidewall system for use at low speeds and an aerofoil shaped hull to provide lift at high speeds during forward flight. The side curtains of the peripheral jet were to be retained to seal the high pressure "channel" of air developed beneath it from the low pressure airflow above and along the sides of the craft, down to the water surface. A 30 ft long manned model of the Columbia was successfully tested in 1964.

The *wing-in-ground-effect* (c) is essentially an aircraft designed to fly at all times in close proximity to the earth's surface, in order to take advantage of the so-called "image" flow that reduces induced drag by about 70%. In the Soviet Union this type of machine is known as an **Ekronoplan.**

Aerostatic-type air cushion vehicles can be divided into two categories—plenum chamber craft and peripheral or annular jet craft. *Plenum chamber craft* (d) employ the most simple of surface effect concepts. Air is forced from the lift fan directly into a recessed base where it forms a cushion which raises the craft. The volume of air pumped into the base is just sufficient to replace the air leaking out beneath the edges.

Variants of this category include the *skirted plenum craft* (e), in which a flexible fabric extension is hung between the metal structure and the surface to give increased obstacle and overwave clearance capability. The Naviplanes and Terraplanes designed by Bertin and SEDAM employ separately fed multiple plenum chambers, each surrounded by lightweight flexible skirts. Skirted plenum chamber types are also favoured by builders of light air cushion vehicles because of their relatively simple design and construction.

Another variant is the *sidewall ACV* (f), in which the cushion air is contained between solid sidewalls or skegs and deflectable seals, either solid or flexible, fore and aft. Stability is provided by the buoyancy of the sidewalls and their planing forces. Sidewall craft are also known as captured air bubble vessels (*CABs*) a term used widely in the United States. One of the derivatives of the sidewall type is the *hydrokeel* (g) which is designed to plane on the after section of its hull and benefit to some degree from air lubrication.

In *peripheral* or *annular jet craft* (h) the ground cushion is generated by a continuous jet of air channelled through ducts or nozzles around the outer periphery of the base. The flexible skirts fitted to this type can take the form either of an extension to the outer wall of the duct or nozzle only, or an extension to both outer and inner walls. In the latter form it is known as a *trunked annular jet* (i).

air entrainment. See **air entry.**

air entry. Entry of air from the atmosphere that raises the low pressures created by the flow due to a foil's cambered surface.

air gap; also daylight gap, daylight clearance and **hover gap.** Distance between the lowest component of the vehicle's understructure, e.g. skirt hem, and the surface when riding on its cushion. **air gap area:** area through which air is able to leak from a cushion.

air pad. Part of an air pallet assembly into which compressed air is introduced and allowed to escape in a continuous flow through communicating holes in the diaphragm.

air pallet, also **hoverpallet.** Air cushion supported, load-carrying structure, which bleeds a continuous low pressure volume of air between the structure and the reaction surface, creating an air film.

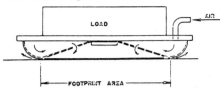

An air pad with a flexible plastic diaphragm

air-port system, also **thrust port.** See **puffport.**

air-rider. Alternative generic name for air cushion vehicles or weight carrying structures lifted off the surface by a cushion or film of air.

air stabilised foils. See **foil systems.**

amidships. (1) Midway between the stem and stern of a hull. (2) abbreviated to **midships** and meaning the rudder or helm is in a mid-position.

angle of attack. The angle made by the mean chord line of an aero- or hydrofoil with the flow.

angle of incidence. The angle made by the mean chord line of a hydrofoil in relation to the fixed struts or hull.

Aquavion type foil. Adapted from the Grunberg system. About 85% of the load is carried by a mainfoil located slightly aft of the centre of gravity, 10% by a submerged aft stabiliser foil, and the remainder on a pair of planing sub-foils at the bow. The planing subfoils give variable lift in response to wave shapes, whether skimming over them or through them, and so trim the angle of the hull in order to correct the angle of attack of the main foil.

articulated air-cushion vehicle. A modular type load-carrying platform designed by Charles Burr of Bell Aerospace. A number of skirted platforms can be joined to form a variety of ACVs of different load carrying capacities. An application envisaged for craft of this type is the movement of containers and other heavy machinery in the American arctic and middle north.

aspect ratio. (1) the measure of the ratio of a foil's span to its chord. It is defined as

$$\frac{span^2}{total\ foil\ area}$$

(2) for ACVs it is defined as

$$\frac{cushion\ beam}{cushion\ length}$$

athwart, athwartship. Across the hull in a transverse direction from one side of the craft to the other.

axial-flow lift fan. A fan generating an airflow for lift that is parallel to the axis of rotation.

b.h.p. Brake horse power.

backstrap. A fabric strap used to secure a lift jet exit nozzle in a flexible skirt at the correct angle.

baffle plates. See **fences.**

ballast. Fuel, water or solids used to adjust the centre of gravity or trim of a craft.

ballast system. A method of transferring water or fuel between tanks to adjust fore and aft trim. In Mountbatten class ACVs, four groups of tanks, one at each corner of the craft, are located in the buoyancy tanks. A ring main facilitates the rapid transfer of fuel between the tanks as ballast and also serves as a refuelling line.

ballast tank or box. Box or tank containing the liquids or solids used to trim a craft.

base ventilated foil. A system of forced ventilation designed to overcome the reduction in lift/drag ratio of a foil at supercavitating speeds. Air is fed continuously to the upper surface of the foil un-wetting the surface and preventing the formation of critical areas of decreased pressure. Alternatively the air may be fed into the cavity formed behind a square trailing edge.

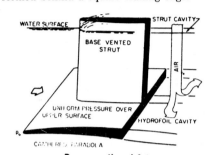

Base ventilated foil

beam. Measurement across a hull at a given point.

Beaufort Scale. A scale of wind forces described by name and range of velocity and classified as from force 0 to force 12, or in the case of strong hurricanes to force 17. Named after Admiral Sir Frances Beaufort, 1774-1857, who was responsible for preparing the scale.

Beaufort Force Number	State of Air	Description	Wind Velocity in Knots
0	calm	Smoke ascends vertically. Sea mirror-like	Less than 1
1	light air	Wind direction shown by smoke. Scale-like ripples on surface but no crests	1-3

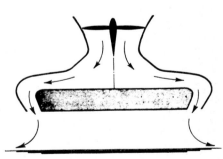

Axial flow lift fan

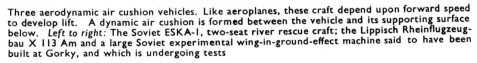

Three aerodynamic air cushion vehicles. Like aeroplanes, these craft depend upon forward speed to develop lift. A dynamic air cushion is formed between the vehicle and its supporting surface below. *Left to right:* The Soviet ESKA-1, two-seat river rescue craft; the Lippisch Rheinflugzeugbau X 113 Am and a large Soviet experimental wing-in-ground-effect machine said to have been built at Gorky, and which is undergoing tests

2	slight breeze	As force 1, but wavelets more pronounced	4-6
3	gentle breeze	Flags extended. Short pronounced wavelets; crests start to break, scattered white horses	7-10
4	moderate breeze	Small waves, lengthening. Frequent white horses	11-16
5	fresh breeze	Waves more pronounced and longer form. More white horses some spray	17-21
6	strong breeze	Larger waves and extensive white foam crests. Sea breaks with dull rolling noise. Spray	22-27
7	moderate gale	White foam blown in streaks in direction of wind Spindrift appears Noise increases	28-33
8	fresh gale	Moderately high waves breaking into spindrift: well marked foam	34-40
9	strong gale	High waves and dense streaks of foam along direction of wind. Sea begins to roll	41-47
10	whole gale	Sea surface becomes white. Very high waves with over-hanging crests. Rolling of sea heavy. Visibility affected	48-55
11	storm	Waves exceptionally high, visibility affected	56-65
12	hurricane	Air full of foam and spray. Visibility seriously affected	above 65

bilge. Point of the hull where the side and the bottom meet. Also water or fuel accumulated in the bilges.

bilge system. A pumping system devised to dispose of water and other fluids which have accumulated in the bilges. In air-cushion vehicles bilge systems are installed to clear the buoyancy tanks. Small craft generally have a hand operated pump which connects directly to pipes in the tanks. In larger craft, like the 190-ton BHC Mountbatten, because of the large number of buoyancy compartments, four electrically driven pumps are provided, each of which can drain one compartment at a time.

block speed. Route distance divided by block time.

block time, also **trip time.** Journey time between lift off and touchdown.

boating. Expression used to describe an air cushion vehicle when operating in displacement condition. The boating or **semi-hover** mode is used in congested terminal areas, when lift power and spray generation is kept to a minimum. Some craft have water surface contact even at full hover for stability requirements.

bow. Forward part of a craft. The stem.

bow-up. Trim position or attitude when a craft is high at the bow. Can be measured by eye or attitude gyro.

breast, to. To take waves at 90° to their crests.

bridge. Elevated part of the superstructure, providing a clear all round view, from which a craft is navigated and steered.

broach, to. Sudden breaking of the water surface by a foil, or part of a foil, resulting in a loss of lift due to air flowing over the foil's upper surface.

to broach to. Nautical expression meaning to swing sideways in following seas under wave action.

bulkheads. Vertical partitions, either transverse or longitudinal, which divide or subdivide a hull. May be used to seperate accommodation areas, strengthen the structure, form tanks or localise fires or flooding.

buoyancy. The reduction in weight of a floating object. If the object floats its weight is equal to (or less than) the weight of fluid displaced.

buoyancy chamber. A structure designed in such a way that the total of its own weight and all loads which it supports is equal to (or less than) the weight of the water it displaces.

buoyancy, reserve. Buoyancy in excess of that required to keep an undamaged craft afloat. See **buoyancy.**

buoyancy tubes. Inflatable tubular members providing reserve buoyancy. May be used as fenders if fitted to the outer periphery of a craft.

CAA (Abbrev.) Civil Aviation Authority.

CAB. Captured Air Bubble. See **air cushion vehicle.**

c.p. Centre of pressure.

CP shifter. A control system which moves the centre of pressure of an air cushion to augment a craft's natural stability in pitch and roll.

CWL. Calm water line.

camber. (1) A convexity on the upper surface of a deck to give it increased strength and/or facilitate draining. (2) The convex form on the upper surface of a foil. The high speed flow over the top surface causes a decrease in pressure and about two-thirds of the lift is provided by this surface.

canard foil system. A foil arrangement in which the main foil of wide span is located near the stern, aft of the centre of gravity, and bears about 65% of the weight, while a small central foil is placed at the bow.

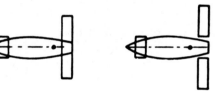

Canard foil configuration. The main foil area may be divided into two to facilitate retraction

captain. Senior crew member aboard a hovercraft. Defined as the person designated by the operator to be in charge of a hovercraft during any journey, under the UK government's "The Hovercraft (Application of Enactments) Order 1972". Equivalent in rank to airliner or ship's captain. Alternative terms: pilot, driver, helmsman, coxswain and ACV operator.

captured air bubble craft (see also **sidewall craft** and **surface effect ship**). Vessel in which the cushion (or air bubble) is contained by rigid sidewalls and flexible bow and stern skirts. Occasionally used for any air cushion craft in which the air cushion (or air bubble) is contained within the cushion periphery with minimal air leakage.

cavitation. Cavitation is the formation of vapour bubbles due to pressure decrease on the upper surface of a foil or the back of a propeller's blades at high speeds, and falls into two categories, unstable and stable. Non-stable cavities or cavitation bubbles of aqueous vapour form near the foil's leading edge and extend down stream expanding and collapsing. At the points of collapse positive pressure peaks may rise to as high as 20,000 psi These cause erosion and pitting of the metal. Cavitation causes an unstable water flow over the foils which results in abrupt changes in lift and therefore discomfort for those aboard the craft.

Foil sections are now being developed which either delay the onset of cavitation by reduced camber, thinner sections, or sweepback, or if the craft is required to operate at supercavitating speeds, stabilise cavitation to provide a smooth transition between sub-cavitating and super-cavitating speeds.

centrifugal flow lift fan. A cushion lift fan which generates an airflow at right angles to the axis of rotation.

chain ties. Chains used to maintain the correct shape of an air jet exit nozzle on a flexible skirt.

chord. The distance between the leading and trailing edges of a foil section measured along the chord line.

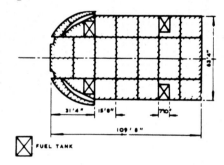

31'4"   15'8"   70'   109'8"

⊠ FUEL TANK

WATERTIGHT COMPARTMENT

Typical buoyancy tank unit on the SR.N4. The basic structure of the SR.N4 is the buoyancy chamber, built around a grid of logitudinal and transversal frames, which form twenty-four watertight sub-divisions for safety. Below, the SR.N4 buoyancy tank layout.

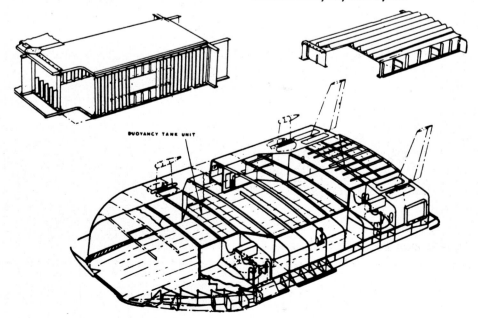

BUOYANCY TANK UNIT

chord-line. A straight line joining the leading and trailing edges of a foil or propeller blade section.

classification, also certification. Seagoing and amphibious craft for commercial appli-

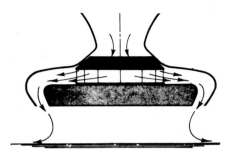

Centrifugal flow lift fan

cation are classified by mode and place of construction, in the manner of the registration system started in the City of London by Edward Lloyd, and continued since 1760 by Lloyd's Register of Shipping. Outside the British Isles classification socities now include Registro Italiano Navale, Germanischer Lloyd, Det Norske Veritas, American Bureau of Shipping and the Japanese Ministry of Transport.

A classification society's surveyors make a detailed examination of craft certificated by them at regular intervals to ensure their condition complies with the particular society's requirements.

continuous nozzle skirt. See **skirt**.

contour, to. The motion of an air cushion vehicle or hydrofoil when more or less following a wave profile.

craft. Boats, ships, air cushion vehicles and hydrofoils of all types, regardless of size.

crew. Those responsible for manning a craft of either boat or ship size, including the officers. The company of an ACV or hydrofoil.

cross-flow. The flow of air, transversally or longidutinally within an air cushion.

cryogenics. Science of refrigeration, associated in particular with temperatures of —260 deg C and lower.

cushion. A volume of higher than ambient pressure air trapped beneath the structure of a vehicle and its supporting surface causing the vehicle to be supported at some distance from the ground.

cushion area. Area of a cushion contained within a skirt or sidewall.

cushion beam. Measurement across an air cushion at a given point.

cushion borne. A craft borne above the sea or land surface by its air cushion.

cushion length. Longitudinal cushion measurement.

cushion length, mean. Defined as:

$$\frac{\text{cushion area}}{\text{cushion beam}}$$

cushion seal. Air curtains, sidewalls, skirts, water-jets or other means employed to contain or seal an air cushion to reduce to a minimum the leakage of trapped air.

cushion thrust. Thrust obtained by the deflection of cushion air.

DWL. Displacement water line.

daylight clearance. See **air gap**.

daylight gap. See **air gap**.

deadrise. The angle with the horizontal made at the keel by the outboard rise of a vessel's hull form at each frame.

diffuser-recirculation. See **recirculation system.**

direct operating cost. Cost of operating a craft, excluding company overheads and indirect costs.

displacement. The weight in tons of water displaced by a floating vessel. Light displacement is the craft weight exclusive of ballast.

ditch, to. An emergency landing on water while under way due to a local navigation hazard, loss of cushion air or failure of a powerplant.

Doppler, navigator An automatic dead

reckoning device which gives a continuous indication of position by integrating the speed derived from measuring the Doppler effect of echoes from directed beams of radiant energy transmitted from the vessel.

down-by-the-head. Trim or sit of a craft with its bow more deeply immersed than the stern. The opposite expression is 'down by the stern'.

drag. (1) ACVs—aerodynamic and hydrodynamic resistances encountered by an air cushion vehicle resulting from aerodynamic profile, gain of momentum of air needed for cushion generation, wave making, wetting or skirt contact.

(2) hydrofoils—hydrodynamic resistances encountered by hydrofoils result from wave making, which is dependent on the craft shape and displacement, frictional drag due to the viscosity of the water, the total wetted surface and induced drag from the foils and transmission shafts and their supporting struts and structure, due to their motion through the water.

draught. Depth between the water surface and the bottom of a craft. Under the Ministry of Transport Merchant Shipping (Construction) rules, 1952, draught is defined as the vertical distance from the moulded base line amidships to the sub-division load waterline.

draught marks. (1) marks on the side of a craft showing the depth to which it can be loaded. (2) figures cut at the stern and stem to indicate draught and trim.

drift angle. Difference between the actual course made and the course steered.

ESKA (Russian). Abbrev. Name given to series of small wing-in-ground-effect machines developed by the Central Laboratory of Lifesaving Technology, Moscow. Shortened form of Ekranolytny Spasatyelny Kater Amphibiya (screen-effect amphibious lifeboat). Also known as **Ekranolyet** or **Nizkolet** (skimmer).

Ekranoplan. (USSR). Composite word based on *ekran*, a screen or curtain, and *plan*, the principal supporting surface of an aeroplane. Employed almost exclusively to describe types of ACVs in the Soviet Union raised above their supporting surfaces by dynamic lift. Western equivalent, wing-in-ground-effect machines (WIG) and aerodynamic ram-wing.

elevator. Moveable aerodynamic control surface used on small hovercraft to provide a degree of fore and aft trim control. Elevator surfaces are normally located in the slipstream of the propulsive units in order to provide some control at low speed.

FWL. Foilborne water line.

fathom. A depth of 6 ft.

fences. Small partitions placed at short intervals down the upper and lower surfaces of a hydrofoil tending to prevent air ventilation passing down to destroy the lift. They are attached in the direction of the flow.

ferry. A craft designed to carry passengers across a channel, estuary, lake, river or strait.

fetch. The number of miles a given wind has been blowing over open water or the distance upwind to the nearest land.

finger skirt. See **skirts**.

fire zone. A compartment containing a full supply and ignition source which is walled with fire resisting material and fitted with an independent fire warning and extinguishing system.

fixed annual cost. Major component of a vehicle's direct operating cost. This com-

prises depreciation, craft insurance and operating and maintenance crew salaries, all of which are incurred regardless of whether the craft is operated or not.

flare. Upward and outward curvature of the freeboard at the bow, presenting additional, rising surface to oncoming waves.

flexible skirt. See **skirt**.

flying bridge. A navigating position atop the wheel or chart house.

foilborne. A hydrofoil is said to be foilborne when the hull is raised completely out of the water and wholly supported by lift from its foil system.

foil flaps. Foils are frequently fitted with (a) trailing edge flaps for lift augmentation during take-off and to provide control forces, (b) upper and lower flaps to raise the cavitation boundary.

foil systems. Foil systems in current use are generally either **surface piercing**, **submerged** or **semi-submerged**. There are a number of craft with hybrid systems with a combination of submerged and surface piercing foils, recent examples being the Supramar PT.150 and the De Havilland FHE-400.

surface piercing foils are more often than not vee-shaped, the upper parts of the foil forming the tips of the Vee and piercing the surface on either side of the craft. The

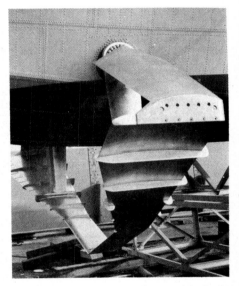

Fences on the bow foil of a Supramar hydrofoil

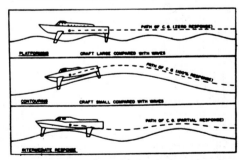

Comparison of platforming and contouring modes, and the intermediate response of a craft equipped with fully submerged, automatically controlled foil system

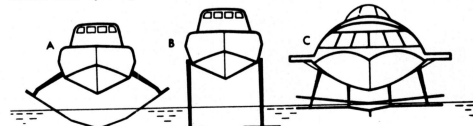

Foil systems in current use. A surface piercing: B submerged and C shallow draught submerged

vee foil, with its marked dihedral is area stabilised and craft employing this configuration can be designed to be inherently stable, and, for stability, geometry dependent.

The forces restoring normal trim are provided by the area of the foil that is submerged. A roll to one side means the immersion of increased foil area, which results in the generation of extra lift to counter the roll and restore the craft to an even keel.

Equally, a downward pitching movement at the bow means an increase in the submerged area of the forward foil, and the generation of extra lift on this foil, which raises the bow once more. Should the bow foil rise above its normal water level the lift decreases in a similar way to restore normal trim. This type of foil is also known as an **emerging foil system.**

As the vee-foil craft increases its speed, so it generates greater lift and is raised further out of the water—at the same time reducing the wetted area and the lift. The lift must be equal to the weight of the craft, and as the lift depends on the speed and wetted foil area, the hull rides at a pre-determined height above the water level.

ladder foils. Also come under the heading surface piercing, but are rarely used at the present time. This is one of the earliest foil arrangements and was used by Forlanini in his 1905 hydro-aeroplane, which was probably the first really successful hydrofoil. In 1911 Alexander Graham Bell purchased Forlanini's patent specifications and used his ladder system on his Hydrodromes, one of which, the HD-4, set up a world speed record of 61·5 knots in 1919. Early ladder foils, with single sets of foils beneath the hull, fore and aft, lacked lateral stability, but this disadvantage was rectified later by the use of two sets of forward foils, one on each side of the hull. The foils were generally straight and set at right angles to their supporting struts, but were occasionally of vee configuration, the provision of dihedral preventing a sudden change of lift as the foils broke the surface. Both the vee foil and the ladder systems are self stabilising to a degree. The vee foil has the advantage of being a more rigid, lighter structure and is less expensive.

Primary disadvantages of the conventional surface-piercing systems in comparison with the submerged foil system are: (a) the inability of vee-foil craft without control surfaces to cope with downward orbital velocities at wave crests when overtaking waves in a following sea, a condition which can decrease the foil's angle of attack, reducing lift and cause either wave contact or a stall; (b) on large craft the weight and size of the surface piercing system is considerably greater than that of a corresponding submerged foil system; (c) restoring forces to correct a roll have to pass above the centre of gravity of the craft, which necessitates the placing of the foils only a short distance beneath the hull. This means a relatively low wave clearance and therefore the vee foil is not suited to routes where really rough weather is encountered.

shallow-draught submerged foil system. This system which incorporates the Grunberg angle of attack variation approach, is employed almost exclusively on hydrofoils de-

signed and built in the Soviet Union and is intended primarily for passenger carrying craft used on long, calm water rivers, canals and inland seas. The system, also known as the immersion depth effect system, was evolved by Dr. Rostislav Alexeyev. It generally comprises two main horizontal foils, one forward, one aft, each carrying approximately half the weight of the vessel. A submerged foil loses lift gradually as it approaches the surface from a depth of about one chord, which prevents it from rising completely to the surface. Means therefore have to be provided to assist take-off and prevent the vessel from sinking back into the displacement mode. Planing subfoils, port and starboard, are therefore provided in the vicinity of the forward struts, and are so located that when they are touching the water surface, the main foils are submerged at a depth of approximately one chord.

submerged foils have a greater potential for seakeeping than any other, but are not inherently stable to any degree. The foils are totally immersed and a sonic, mechanical or air stabilisation system has to be installed to maintain the foils at the required depth. The system has to stabilise the craft from take-off to touchdown in heave and all three axes—pitch, roll and yaw. It must also see that the craft makes co-ordinated banked turns in heavy seas to reduce the side loads on the foil struts; ensure that vertical and lateral accelerations are kept within limits in order to prevent excessive loads on the structure and finally, ensure a smooth ride for the passengers and crew.

The control forces are generated either by deflecting flaps at the trailing edge of the foil or varying the incidence angle of the entire foil surface. Incidence control provides better performance in a high sea state.

A typical sonic electronic autopilot control system is that devised for the Boeing PCH-1 High Point. The key element is an acoustic height sensor located at the bow. The time lag of the return signal is a measure of the distance of the sensor from the water.

Craft motion input is received from dual sonic ranging devices which sense the height above the water of the bow in relation to a fixed reference; from three rate gyros which measure yaw, pitch and roll; from forward and aft accelerometers which sense vertical acceleration fore and aft and from a vertical gyro which senses the angular position of the craft in both pitch and roll. This information is processed by an electronic computer and fed continuously to hydraulic actuators of the foil control surfaces, which develop the necessary hydrodynamic forces for stability producing forces imposed by wave action manoeuvring and correct flight.

mechanical incidence control. The most successful purely mechanically operated incidence control system is the Hydrofin autopilot principle, designed by Christopher Hook, who pioneered the development of the submerged foil. A fixed, high-riding crash preventer plane is mounted ahead of and beneath the bow.

The fixed plane, which is only immersed when the craft is in a displacement mode, is also used as a platform for mounting a lightweight pitch control sensor which is hinged to the rear.

The sensor rides on the waves and continuously transmits their shape through a connecting linkage to vary the angle of incidence of the main foils as necessary to maintain them at the required depth. A filter system ensures that the craft ignores small waves and that the hull is flown over the crests of waves exceeding the height of the keel over the water.

Two additional sensors, trailing from port and starboard immediately aft of the main struts, provide roll control. The pilot has overriding control through a control column, operated in the same manner as that in an aircraft.

air stabilisation system. A system designed and developed by Baron Hanns von Schertel of Supramar AG, Lucerne. Air from the free atmosphere is fed through air exits to the foil upper surface and under certain conditions the lower surface also (i.e. into the low pressure regions). The airflow decreases the lift and the flow is deflected away from the foil section with an effect similar to that of a deflected flap, the air cavities extending out behind producing a virtual lengthening of the foil profile. Lift is reduced and varied by the quantity of air admitted, this being controlled by a valve actuated by signals, from a damped pendulum and a rate gyro.

The pendulum causes righting moments at static heeling angles. If exposed to a centrifugal force in turning, it causes a moment, which is directed towards the centre of the turning circle, thereby avoiding outside banking (coordinated banking). The rate gyro responds to angular velocity and acts dynamically to dampen rolling motions.

following sea. A sea following the same or similar course to that of the craft.

force time effectiveness. Time to land an effective landing force ashore.

fore peak. The space forward of the fore collision bulkhead, frequently used as storage space.

forward. Position towards the fore end of a craft.

frames. The structure of vertical ribs or girders to which a vessel's outside plates are attached. For identification purposes the frames are numbered consecutively, starting aft.

freeboard. Depth of the exposed or free side of a hull between the water level and the freeboard deck. The degree of freeboard permitted is marked by load lines.

freeboard deck. Deck used to measure or determine loadlines.

free power turbine. A gas turbine on which the power turbine has a separate shaft from the compressor and its turbine.

full hover. Expression used to describe the condition of an ACV when it is at its design hoverheight.

g. Gravitational acceleration.

g.r.p. Glass-reinforced plastics.

GEM. Ground effect machine.

gross tonnage. Total tonnage of a vessel, including all enclosed spaces, estimated on the basis of 100 ft^2 = 1 ton.

ground effect machine. Early generic term for air cushion vehicles of all types.

ground crew and **ground staff.** Those responsible for craft servicing and maintenance. Also those responsible for operational

These military hydrofoil designs illustrate three different foil systems. *Left to right:* The De Havilland Canada MP-100, a 100-ton missile craft with its inherently stable 'canard' surface-piercing system, incorporating a trapeze configuration main foil aft; the 83·5 ton Super Flagstaff with incidence-controlled fully submerged foils in "aeroplane" configuration and the Boeing NATO/PHM. The latter has a fully submerged canard system with 32% of the dynamic lift provided by the bow foil and 68% by the aft foil. Lift control is provided by trailing edge flaps on each foil

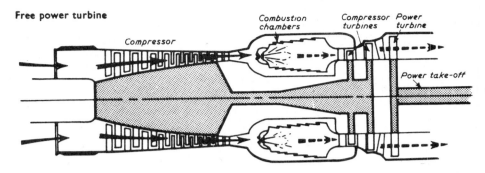

Free power turbine

administration.

Grunberg Foil System. First patented in 1936, the Grunberg principle of inherent angle of attack variations comprises a "stabilizer" attached to the bow or a forward projection from the latter, and behind this a 'foil'. Both foil and stabilizer can be "split" into several units. The lift curve of the stabilizer, plotted against its draft, is considerably steeper than its corresponding foil lift curve. Hence as the operational conditions (speed, weight, CG travel) change, the foil sinks or rises relative to the stabilizer, automatically adjusting its angle of attack. The "foil" is set at an appropriate angle of incidence in order to prevent it from approaching the interface. The system is fully compatible with Forlanini's concept of area variation and both can be incorporated in the same structure.

HDL. Hovercraft Development Ltd.

hp. Horsepower.

Hz (abbrev). Unit of wave frequency employed especially in acoustics and electronics. 1 hertz = 1 cycle per second. Named after Heinrich Hertz (1857-1894), German physicist.

hard chine. Hull design with the topsides and bottom meeting at an angle, rather than curving to a round bilge.

head sea. A sea approaching from the direction steered.

heave. Vertical motion of a craft in response to waves.

heel. (a) To incline or list in a transverse direction while under way. (b) Lower end of a mast or derrick. (c) Point where keel and stern post meet.

Helibarge. System devised by A Walter. Crowley (USA) combining a helicopter with an air-cushion barge. The downwash of the helicopter rotor pressurizes the air-cushion.

hourly running cost. That part of the direct operating cost incurred when the craft is operated, i.e., fuel, maintenance and overhauls.

hoverbarge. Fully buoyant, shallow-draught hovercraft built for freight carrying. Either self-propelled or towed.

hovercraft. (a) Originally a name for craft using the patented peripheral jet principle invented by Sir Christopher Cockerell, in which the air cushion is generated and contained by a jet of air exhausted downward and inward from a nozzle at the periphery at the base of the vehicle. (b) Classification in the USA for skirted plenum chamber and annular jet-designs. (c) In the British Hovercraft Act 1968, a hovercraft is defined as a vehicle which is designed to be supported when in motion wholly or partly by air expelled from the vehicle to form a cushion of which the boundaries include the ground, water or other surface beneath the vehicle.

hoverplatform. Non self-propelled hovercraft designed primarily to convey heavy loads across terrain impassable to wheeled and tracked vehicles under load.

hoverport. Defined by the British Hovercraft Act, 1968 as any area, whether land or elsewhere, which is designed, equipped, set apart or commonly used for affording facilities for the arrival and departure of hovercraft.

hover gap. See **air gap.**

hover height. Vertical height between the hard structure of an ACV and the supporting surface when a vehicle is cushion-borne.

hover-listen. Expression covering ACVs employed for anti-submarine warfare while operating at low speeds to detect a target.

hover-pallet. See **air pallet.**

hover-time. Time logged by an air cushion vehicle when cushion borne. Often called **power hours.**

hovertrailer. A steel structure platform around which is fitted a flexible segmented skirt, cushion lift being provided by fans driven by petrol or diesel engines on the platform. The system devised by Air Cushion Equipment Ltd and Hovertrailers International Ltd is designed to increase the load capacity of tracked and wheeled vehicles many times. In cases where it is impossible for a tow vehicle to operate, the trailer can be winched.

A hovertrailer.   Payload at 100 psf is 6.7 tons

hull cresting. Contact of a hydrofoil's hull with the waves in high seas. The term

hull slamming q.v., or slamming, is used if the hull contact is preceeded by foil broaching.

hull slamming. Contact of a hydrofoil's hull with the water following a foil broach. See **broach, to.**

hump. The "hump" formed on the graph of resistance against the speed of a displacement vessel or ACV. The maximum of the "hump" corresponds to the speed of the wave generated by the hull or air depression.

hump speed. Critical speed at which the curve on a graph of wave making drag of an ACV tends to hump or peak. As speed is increased, the craft over-rides its bow wave; the wave making drag diminishes and the

rate of acceleration rapidly increases.

hydrofoils. Small wings, almost identical in section to those of an aircraft, and designed to generate lift. Since water has a density some 815 times that of air, the same lift as an aeroplane wing is obtained for only $\frac{1}{815}$ of the area (at equal speeds).

hydroskimmer. Name given originally to experimental air cushion vehicles built under contract to the US Navy Bureau of Ships. Preference was given to this name since it gave the craft a sea-service identity.

inclined shaft. A marine drive shaft used in small vee foil and shallow-draught submerged foil craft, with keels only a limited height above the mean water level. The shaft is generally short and inclined at about 12°-14° to the horizontal. On larger craft, designed for operation in higher waves, the need to fly higher necessitates alternative drive arrangements such as the vee drive and Z-drive, the water jet system or even air propulsion.

Indirect operating cost. Costs incurred apart from running a craft. Includes advertising, buildings, rents, rates and salaries for terminal staff other than those employed for craft maintenance.

induced wave drag. Drag caused by the hollow depressed in the water by an ACV's air cushion. As the craft moves forward the depression follows along beneath it, building up a bow wave and causing wave drag as in a displacement craft until the hump speed has been passed.

integrated lift-propulsion system. An ACV lift and propulsion system operated by a common power source, the transmission and power-sharing system allowing variation in the division of power.

JP-4. Liquid fuel, based on kerosene, used widely in gas turbines.

keel. (a) The "backbone" of a hull.
(b) An extension of an ACV's fore-and-aft stability air jet, similar in construction and shape to a skirt, and taking the form of an inflated bag.

knitmesh pads. Thick, loosely woven pads, in either metal or plastic wire fitted in the engine air intake to filter out water and solid particles from the engine air.

knot. A nautical mile per hour.

land to. At the end of a run hydrofoils and ACVs are said to settle "down" or "land".

LIMRV. Abbrev. Linear Induction Motor Research Vehicle.

landing pads, also **hard points.** Strengthened areas of the hull on which an ACV is supported when at rest on land. These may also provide attachment points for towing equipment, lifts and jacks.

leading frequency of sea waves. See **significant wave height.** Sea waves are com-

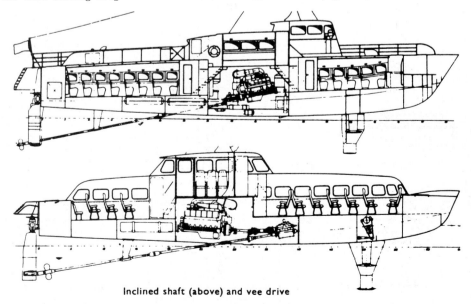

Inclined shaft (above) and vee drive

posed of different frequencies. The sea wave of greatest energy content is called the sea wave of leading frequency.

lift fan. See also **axial flow lift fan** and **centrifugal flow lift fan.** A fan used to supply air under pressure to an air cushion, and/or to form curtains.

lift off. An ACV is said to lift off when it rises from the ground on its air cushion.

linear induction motor. Linear induction motors show considerable promise as a means of propulsion for tracked skimmers, and are now under development in France, the United Kingdom, West Germany, Italy, Japan, the United States and USSR. An attractive feature of this method of electric traction is that it does not depend upon the vehicle having contact with the track or guideway. The motor can be likened to a normal

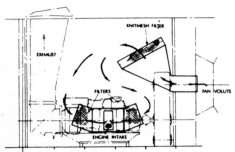

Gas turbine air filtration path on the Vosper Thornycroft VT 1, showing the knitmesh filter pad

induction motor opened out flat. The "stator" coils are attached to the vehicle, while the "rotor" consists of a flat rail of conductive material which is straddled by the stator poles. The variable frequency multiphase AC current required for the linear motor can either be generated aboard the vehicle or collected from an electrified track.

Although the mounting of the stators on the vehicle appears to be preferred in Europe at present they can also be built into the guideway. In this case the rotor, in the form of a reaction rail, would be suspended from the vehicle. It would be of sufficient length to span several of the fixed stators simultaneously to avoid jerking.

load factor. Relationship between the payload capacity available, and the capacity filled.

logistics. Science of transporting, accommodating and supplying troops.

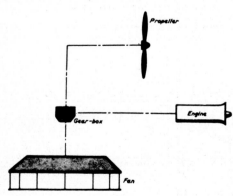

Integrated lift-propulsion system

longitudinal framing. Method of hull construction employing frames set in a fore and aft direction or parallel to the keel.

maglev (abbrev). magnetic levitation.

multiple skirt. System devised by M. Jean Bertin, employing a number of separate flexible skirts for his system of individually fed, multiple air cushions.

nautical mile. A distance of 6,080 ft or one minute of latitude at the equator.

Naviplane. Name for the overwater or amphibious air cushion vehicles developed in France by SEDAM.

net tonnage. Total tonnage of a craft based on cubic capacity of all space available for carrying revenue-producing cargo less allowance for the engine room, crew quarters, water ballast, stores and other areas needed to operate the craft.

orbital motion. Orbital or circular motion of the water particles forming waves. The circular motion decreases in radius with increasing depth. It is the peculiar sequence of the motion that causes the illusion of wave translation. In reality the water moves very little in translation. The circular directions are: up at the wave front, forward at the crest, down at the wave back and back at the trough.

payload weight. Weight of revenue earning load, excluding crew and fuel.

PTO. See **power take-off unit.**

peripheral jet. See **air curtain** and **hovercraft.**

peripheral jet cushion system. A ground cushion generated by a continuous jet of air issued through ducts or nozzles around the outer periphery of the base of a craft. The cushion is maintained at above ambient pressure by the horizontal change of momentum of the curtain.

peripheral trunk. See **skirt.**

pitch. Rotation or oscillation of the hull about a transverse axis in a seaway. Also angle of air or water propeller blades.

pitch angle. Pitch angle a craft adopts relative to a horizontal datum.

platform, to. Approximately level flight of a hydrofoil over waves of a height less than the calm water hull clearance.

plenum. Space or air chamber beneath or surrounding a lift fan or fans through which air under pressure is distributed to a skirt system.

plenum chamber cushion system. The most simple of air cushion concepts. Cushion pressure is maintained by pumping air continuously into a recessed base without the use of a peripheral air curtain.

"plough in". A bow down attitude resulting from the bow part of the skirt contacting the surface and progressively building up a drag. Unless controlled this can lead to a serious loss of stability and possibly an overturning moment.

With the skirts' front outer edge dragging on the water towards the centre of the craft (known as 'tuck under') there is a marked reduction in righting moment of the cushion pressure. As the downward pitch angle increases, the stern of the craft tends to rise from the surface and excessive yaw angles develop. Considerable deceleration takes place down to hump speed and the danger of a roll over in a small craft is accentuated by following waves which further increase the pitch angle.

Solutions include the provision of vent holes on a skirt's outer front to reduce its drag through air lubrication, and the development of a bag skirt which automatically

bulges outwards on contact with the water, thereby delaying tuck under and providing a righting moment.

power take off unit. Unit for transmitting power from the main engine or engines, generally for auxiliary services required while a craft is under way, such as hydraulics, alternators and bilge pumps.

pvc. Polyvinylchloride.

puff ports. Controlled apertures in a skirt system or cushion supply ducting through which air can be expelled to assist control at low speeds.

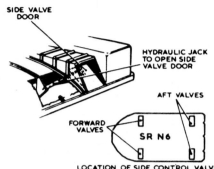

Puff port arrangement on the BHC SR.N6

ram wing. See **air cushion vehicles.**

recirculation system. An air curtain employing a recirculating air flow, which is maintained within and under the craft.

reliability factor. Percentage relationship between the number of trips scheduled and those achieved.

Ro-Ro. (abbrev USA). Roll-on roll-off. Applied to ships and air cushion vehicles with decks providing straight through loading facilities, i.e. with cargo ramps or loading doors fore and aft.

roll. Oscillation or rotation of a hull about a longitudinal axis.

roll attitude. Angle of roll craft adopts relative to a longitudinal datum.

running time. Time during which all machinery has been in operation, including idling time.

SAR. Abbrev. Search and rescue.

SES. See **surface effect ship.**

SEV. Surface effect vehicle. Currently used in the USA to describe air cushion vehicles of all types. In the Soviet Union, the term is employed to describe large sea- or ocean-going wing-in-ground effect machines.

Savitsky Flap. Hinged vertical control flaps employed for foil lift variation, attached to the trailing edge of the foil struts, and canted out at an angle. The flaps are attached mechanically to the trailing edge flaps on the foil. At the normal flying height only the lower part of the Savitsky flap is submerged.

As more of the flap becomes submerged due to increased wave height, the moment of the flap increases causing it to raise the the foil flap, thus increasing lift and restoring normal inflight attitude and flying height. The system can be adjusted to react only to lower-frequency layer waves. The system is employed on the Atlantic Hydrofoils Flying Cloud and Sea World. It was invented by Dr Daniel Savitsky of the Davidson laboratory.

seal. See cushion seal.

sea state. A scale of sea conditions classified from state 1, smooth, to state 8, precipitous, according to the wind duration, fetch and velocity, also wave length, period and velocity.

semi-submerged propeller. A concept for the installation of a partially submerged, supercavitating propeller on ship-size air cushion vehicles, driven through the sidewall transom. The advantages of this type of installation include considerable drag reduction due to the absence of inclined shafts and their supporting structures, and possibly the elimination of propeller erosion as a result of appendage cavity impingement.

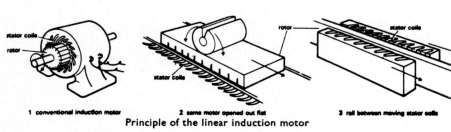

Principle of the linear induction motor

service speed. Cruising speed obtained by an average crew in an average craft on a given route.

set down. To lower an air cushion vehicle onto its landing pads.

skirt. Flexible fabric extension hung between an ACV's metal structure and the surface to give increased obstacle and overwave clearance capability for a small air gap clearance and therefore reduced power requirement. The skirt deflects when encountering waves or solid obstacles, then returns to its normal position, the air gap being increased only momentarily. On peripheral jet ACV's the skirt is a flexible extension of the peripheral jet nozzle with inner and outer skins hung from the inner and outer edges of the air duct and linked together by chain ties or diaphragms so that they form the correct nozzle profile at the hemline.

skirt, bag. Simple skirt design consisting of an inflated bag. Sometimes used as transverse and longitudinal stability skirts.

skirt, finger. Skirt system designed by British Hovercraft Corporation, consisting of a fringe of conically shaped nozzles attached to the base of a bag or loop skirt. Each nozzle or finger fits around an air exit hole and channels cushion air inwards towards the bottom centre of the craft.

skirt, segmented. Conceived by Hovercraft Development Ltd's Technical Group, this skirt system is employed on the HD.2, Vosper Thornycroft VT1, VT2 and many new craft either under design or construction. It is also being employed for industrial applications, including hoverpallets and hovertrailers.

The flexible segments are located around the craft periphery, each being attached to the lower edge of a sheet of light flexible material, which inflates to an arc shape, and also to the craft hard structure.

The system enables the craft to clear high waves and obstacles as the segments occupy a substantial part of the full cushion depth. No stability skirts or other forms of compartmentation are necessary. A smooth ride is provided as the skirt has good response due to low inertia.

The cushion area can be the same as the craft hard structure plan area. The skirt inner attachment points can be reached without jacking the craft up from its off-cushion position, simplifying maintenance.

skirt shifting. A control system in which movement of the centre of area of the cushion is achieved by shifting the skirt along one side, which has the effect of tilting the craft. Pitch and roll trim can be adjusted by this method.

sidewall vessel. An ACV with its cushion air contained between immersed sidewalls or skegs and transverse air curtains or skirts fore and aft. Stability is provided by the buoyancy of the sidewalls and their planing forces.

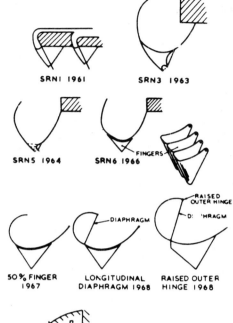

SRN1 1961   SRN3 1963

SRN5 1964   SRN6 1966   FINGERS

RAISED OUTER HINGE

DIAPHRAGM   DIAPHRAGM

50% FINGER 1967   LONGITUDINAL DIAPHRAGM 1968   RAISED OUTER HINGE 1968

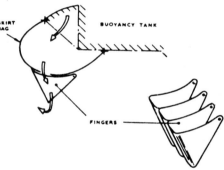

SKIRT BAG   BUOYANCY TANK

FINGERS

Types of finger skirts developed by British Hovercraft Corporation

single shaft gas turbine. A gas turbine with a compressor and power turbine on a common shaft.

significant wave height. Sea waves are composed of different frequencies and have different wave heights (energy spectrum). A wave with the leading frequency of this spectrum and energy content is called the significant wave. It is from this wave that the significant wave height is measured.

split foil. A main foil system with the foil area divided into two, either to facilitate retraction, or to permit the location of the control surfaces well outboard, where foil control and large roll correcting moments can be applied for small changes in lift.

stability curtain. Transverse or longitudinal air curtains dividing an air cushion in order to restrict the cross flow of air within the cushion and increase pitch and roll stability.

stability skirt. A transverse or longitudinal skirt dividing an air cushion so as to restrict cross flow within the cushion and increase pitch or roll stability.

strake. (a) a permanent band of rubber or other hard wearing material along the sides of a craft to protect the structure from chafing against quays, piers and craft alongside. (b) lengths of material fitted externally to a flexible skirt and used to channel air downwards to reduce water drag.

submerged foil system. A foil system employing totally submerged lifting surfaces. The depth of submergence is controlled by mechanical, electronic or pneumatic systems which alter the angle of incidence of the foils or flaps attached to them to provide stability and control. See **foil systems.**

supercavitating foil. A general classification given to foils designed to operate efficiently at high speeds while fully cavitated. Since at very high speeds foils cannot avoid cavitation, sections are being designed which induce the onset of cavitation from the leading edge and cause the cavities to proceed downstream and beyond the trailing edge before collapsing. Lift and drag of these foils is determined by the shape of the leading edge and undersurface.

surf. The crests of waves that break in shallow water on a foreshore.

surface effect ship. Term implying a large ship-size ACV, regardless of specific type.

The various surface effect ship concepts are illustrated. For further definitions see **air cushion vehicles.**

surface piercing-a.c.v. A craft with rigid sidewalls that penetrate the water surface. The air cushion is contained laterally by the sidewalls and at the bow and stern by flexible seals. (see sidewall air cushion vehicles or surface effect ships).

surf zone. Area from the outer waves breaking on the shore to the limit of their uprush on a beach.

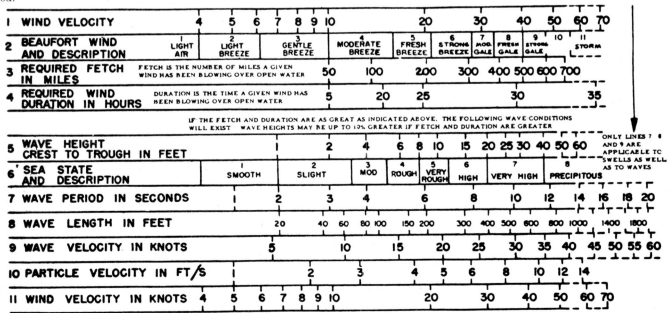

	4	5	6	7	8	9	10		20	30	40	50	60	70
1 WIND VELOCITY	4	5	6	7	8	9	10		20	30	40	50	60	70
2 BEAUFORT WIND AND DESCRIPTION	1 LIGHT AIR	2 LIGHT BREEZE		3 GENTLE BREEZE			4 MODERATE BREEZE		5 FRESH BREEZE	6 STRONG BREEZE	7 MOD. GALE	8 FRESH GALE	9 STRONG GALE	10 · 11 STORM
3 REQUIRED FETCH IN MILES	FETCH IS THE NUMBER OF MILES A GIVEN WIND HAS BEEN BLOWING OVER OPEN WATER					50	100		200	300	400 500 600 700			
4 REQUIRED WIND DURATION IN HOURS	DURATION IS THE TIME A GIVEN WIND HAS BEEN BLOWING OVER OPEN WATER					5	20	25		30			35	

IF THE FETCH AND DURATION ARE AS GREAT AS INDICATED ABOVE, THE FOLLOWING WAVE CONDITIONS WILL EXIST. WAVE HEIGHTS MAY BE UP TO 10% GREATER IF FETCH AND DURATION ARE GREATER

5 WAVE HEIGHT CREST TO TROUGH IN FEET	1		2	4	6	8	10	15	20 25 30	40	50 60			ONLY LINES 7 & 9 ARE APPLICABLE TO SWELLS AS WELL AS TO WAVES
6 SEA STATE AND DESCRIPTION	1 SMOOTH		2 SLIGHT		3 MOD	4 ROUGH	5 VERY ROUGH	6 HIGH		7 VERY HIGH		8 PRECIPITOUS		
7 WAVE PERIOD IN SECONDS	1	2	3	4		6		8	10	12	14	16	18 20	
8 WAVE LENGTH IN FEET		20	40	60	80 100	150 200		300	400	500	600	800 1000	1400	1800
9 WAVE VELOCITY IN KNOTS		5		10		15		20	25	30	35	40	45 50 55 60	
10 PARTICLE VELOCITY IN FT/S	1		2		3		4	5	6	8	10	12 14		
11 WIND VELOCITY IN KNOTS	4	5	6	7	8	9 10		20		30	40	50	60 70	

Chart of sea state conditions. Corresponding values lie on a vertical line

TLACV. Abbrev. Track-laying air cushion vehicle. Air cushion vehicle employing looped caterpillar-like tracks for propulsion. The air cushion and its seals may be located between the flexible tracks, as in the case of the Soviet MVP-3 series, or it can take the form of a broad belt or track that loops round the complete air cushion. The latter approach is being developed by the Ashby Institute, Belfast.

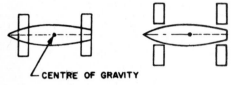

Track laying air cushion vehicle operating on a broad track that loops around the air cushion. This approach is being developed at the Ashby Institute, Belfast

TLRV. Abbrev. Tracked Levitated Research Vehicle.

take-off speed. Speed at which the hull of a hydrofoil craft is raised clear of the water, dynamic foil lift taking over from static displacement or planing of the hull proper.

tandem foils. Foil system in which the area of the forward foils is approximately equal to that of the aft foils, balancing the loading between them.

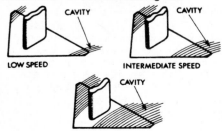

Tandem foil system. The foil areas can be "split" into two to facilitate retraction

terramechanics. Study of the general relationship between the performance of an off-road vehicle and its physical environment.

thickness-chord ratio. Maximum thickness of a foil section in relation to its chord.

thruster. Controlled aperture through which air can be expelled to assist control at low speeds.

Tietjens-type foil. Named after Professor Tietjens, this system was based on a forward swept (surface piercing) main foil located almost amidships and slightly ahead of the centre of gravity. It was intended that the pronounced sweep of the vee foils would result in an increasing area of the foil further forward coming into use to increase the bow up trim of the craft when lift was lost. The considerable length of unsupported hull ahead of the centre of gravity meant the craft was constantly in danger of "digging in" in bad seas and it was highly sensitive to loading arrangements.

transcavitating foil. Thin section foil designed for smooth transition from fully wetted to supercavitating flow. By loading the tip more highly than the root, cavitation is first induced at the foil's tip, then extends spanwise over the foil to the roots as speed increases.

transisting foil. See **transcavitating foil.**
transit foil. See **transcavitating foil.**

Transit foil operation

Single shaft gas turbine

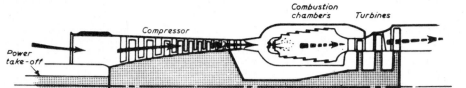

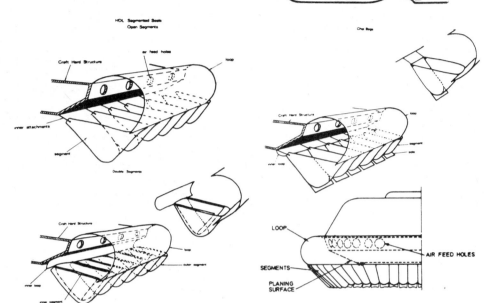

Segmented skirt developed by Hovercraft Development Ltd and employed on the HD.2. The separate segments occupy the full depth of the cushion between the hard structure and the supporting surface

Underside of the SR.N4 showing stability skirts

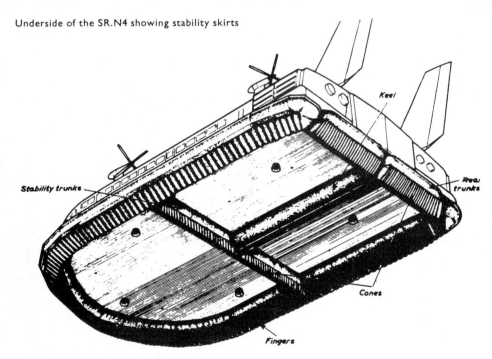

transom. The last transverse frame of a ship's structure forming the stern board.
transverse framing. Steel frames running athwartships, from side to side, instead of in a fore and aft direction.
trapped air cushion vehicle. A concept for a skirt-type surface effect ship with 20 ft skirts separated from the water surface by a thin film of air lubrication.
trim. Difference between drafts forward and aft in a displacement vessel and by extension of the general idea. ACV and hydrofoil hull attitude relative to the line of flight.
turnround time. Time from doors open to doors closed between trips.
utilisation. Operating hours timed from doors closed to doors open, including manoeuvring time.
utilisation, annual. Annual total of utilisation time.

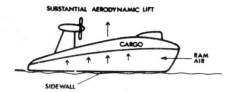

Ram wing SES

Wing-in-ground-effect SES

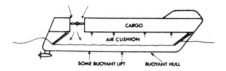

Aircat SES with wide buoyant hulls

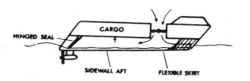

Hybrid SES with rigid sidewalls and bow skirt

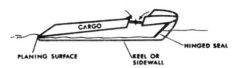

Air lubricated hull or hydrokeel SES

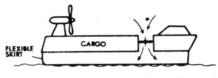

Air-propelled amphibious SES

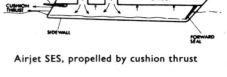

Airjet SES, propelled by cushion thrust

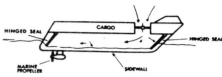

Sidewall SES. Also known as a captured air bubble or CAB type

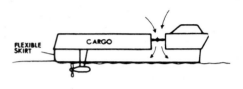

Water propelled, semi-amphibious SES

SURFACE EFFECT SHIP CONFIGURATIONS

variable-pitch propeller. A propeller with blades which can be rotated about their longitudinal axes to provide forward or reverse thrust.

ventilation. See **air entry.**

water wall ACV. A craft employing a curtain of water to retain its air cushion instead of an air curtain.

waterjet propulsion. A term now applied to a propulsion system devised as an alternative to supercavitating propellers for propelling high speed ship systems. Turbines drive pumps located in the hull, and water is pumped through high velocity jets above the water line and directed astern. The system weighs less than a comparable supercavitating propeller system and for craft with normal operating speeds above 45 knots it is thought to be competitive on an annual cost basis. First high speed applications include the Soviet Burevestnik and Chaika hydrofoils the Aerojet-General SES-100A testcraft and two products of the Boeing Company—the PGH-2 hydrofoil gunboat and the NATO PHM Fast Patrol Ship Guided Missile.

Waterjets are also being employed for propulsion at relatively low speeds. In the Soviet Union the Zarya shallow-draught waterbus (24 knots) and the Gorkovchanin sidewall ACV are propelled by waterjets. In the USA the PGH-1 and PGH-2 hydrofoils use waterjets for hullborne propulsion The jet can be turned easily to give side propulsion to facilitate docking which is not so easy for a normal propeller.

wave height. The vertical distance from wave trough to crest or twice the wave amplitude.

wave length. The horizontal distance between adjacent wave crests.

wave velocity. Speed at which a wave form travels along the sea surface. (The water itself remaining without forward movement).

weights. The subject of weights involves definition of format, nomenclature, and units. There are no generally accepted standards with respect to ACV and SES weights, except that small ACVs tend to follow aircraft practice and large types follow ship practice. The hydrofoil concepts are ship orientated. A consistently used format aids in evaluating the concept and permits usage on, or direct comparison with other designs. Format 1, below is according to US Naval practice and is suitable for all sizes of ACVs, SES, and hydrofoils. The actual terminology used for the totals is optional, so that the nomencla-

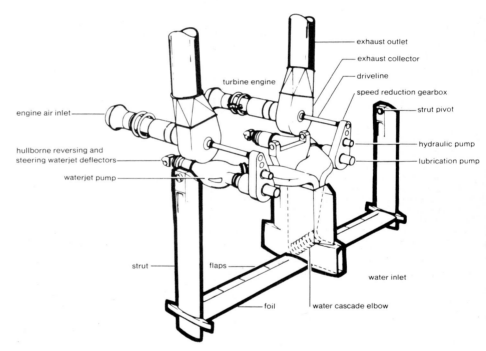

Waterjet propulsion system employed on the Boeing 929-100 Jetfoil, 106-ton, 190-250 passenger hydrofoil fast ferry

ture can be consistent with the size of the vessel. In presenting results, the units (short tons, long tons, metric tons, pounds, etc) should be clearly indicated.

Format 2 is used by the Hovercraft industry in the United Kingdom. This emphasises equipment options, and by breaking down the expendable or useful load, the payload/range performance can be readily determined. It is also useful in defining first costs and operating costs.

winged hull. Alternative name given by Dr Alexander M. Lippisch to his range of aerodynamic ram-wing machines. See also **Aerofoil boat.**

wing-in-ground-effect. See **air cushion vehicle.** An aerodynamic-type air cushion vehicle which depends upon forward speed in order to develop lift. At speed lifting forces are generated both by the wing and a dynamic cushion of air built up beneath the vehicle

and its supporting surface.

yaw angle. Rotation or oscillation of a craft about a vertical axis.

yaw-port. See **puff port.**

Z-drive. A drive system normally employed on hydrofoils to transmit power from the engine in the hull to the screw. Power is transmitted through a horizontal shaft leading to a bevel gear over the stern, then via a vertical shaft and a second bevel gear to a horizontal propeller shaft, thus forming a propeller "Z" shape.

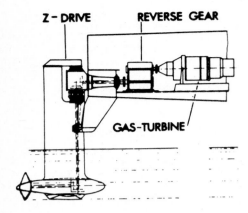

Z-Drive

HOVERCRAFT WEIGHT TERMS

Format 1

	Group	Typical Items
1	Hull (or structure)	Basic structure, planting, frames, stringers, scantlings, decks, foundations, fittings, super-structure, doors and closures.
2	Propulsion	Engines, turbines, propellers, fans, gearboxes, shafting, drive systems, associated controls, nuclear plant, associated fluids.
3	Electrical	Power generation, switching. lighting, load canters, panels, cable
4	Communication and Control	Communications (internal, external) and navigation equipment, military electronics, computers, displays (note ship controls are in Group 5)
5	Auxiliary Systems	Fuel, heating, ventilation, fresh water, ship controls, rudder, cushion seal (flexible or articulated), plumbing, oil, fire extinguishing, drainage, ballast, mooring, anchoring, hydrofoils distilling plant.
6	Outfit and Furnishings	Hull fittings, marine hardware, ladders, furnishings, boats, rafts, preservers, stowages, lockers, painting, deck covering, hull insulation, commissary equipment, radiation shielding (other than at reactor area)
7	Armament	Weapons, mounts, ammunition stowage, handling systems, special plating
Total: Light Ship or Light Displacement or Empty Weight		(sum of the above items)
Variable Load or Useful Load		Operating personnel and effects, cargo, freight fuel, passengers, baggage, water, ammunition, aircraft, stores, troops, provisions.
Full Load Displacement or Load Displacement or Gross Weight or All Up Weight		(sum of empty weight and useful load)

Format 2

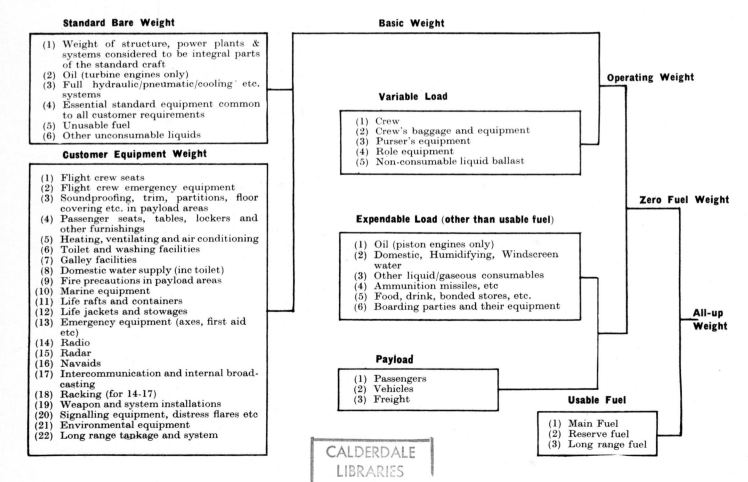

ADDENDA

Left and right: Two military variants of the Russian Skate, 50-seat amphibious ACV ferry. A limited number of these craft, NATO code name "Gus", are in service with the Soviet navy and marine infantry. Note the raised commander's or observer's position above the wheelhouse on the craft on the right.   (MRA copyright photo)

ACV'S
JAPAN
MITSUI SHIPBUILDING & ENGINEERING Co. Ltd.

Mitsui has placed an order with Air Bearings Ltd, Gosport, Hants, for an AB II Crossbow general-purpose amphibious ACV. The craft, a 2-3 seater, was due to be shipped to Tokyo in October 1974. It has been reported that Mitsui is interested in negotiating a licence agreement to build the craft in Japan.

UNITED KINGDOM
AIRAVIA LTD

Two Zarya waterjet-propelled, air-lubricated hull ACVs have been ordered by Airavia Ltd. The vessel seats 65, and an additional 20 standing passengers are accommodated on short routes.

AIR VEHICLES
UNITED KINGDOM

A massive, 350-ton hoverbarge is being developed by Air Vehicles Ltd in conjunction with Transarctic Inc of Houston, Texas. The barge is employed as a chain ferry across the Yukon river, and carries trucks, trailers and equipment for Alyeska Pipeline Services Inc which is setting up a major

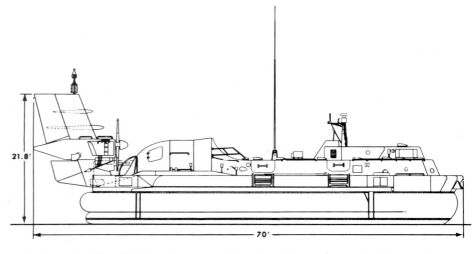

Outboard profile of the Soviet navy version of the 27-ton Gus-class multiduty ACV

oil pipeline.

Between October and April each year the Yukon is completely frozen. In order to continue the operation during the winter months, the barge is being converted into a hoverbarge. Air Vehicles, in conjunction with Avon Rubber Co, is building a skirt

system which will be flown to Alaska, assembled onto modular frames, and clipped into place on the barge.

Lift will be supplied by two 800 hp General Motors diesel engines, each driving 4 ft 2 in diameter centrifugal fans. The barge has roll-on, roll-off facilities.

USA
BELL AEROSPACE

Division of Textron Inc.
HEAD OFFICE:
Buffalo, New York 14240

TELEPHONE:
Area Code 716 297-1000
Bell New Orleans Operation
PO Box 29307, New Orleans,

Louisiana 70189

On July 2nd, 1974, the US Naval Material Command's Surface Effect Ship Project Office (PM17) announced that Textron's Bell Aerospace Division and Rohr Industries had won contracts to develop a 2,000-ton Surface Effect Ship. Bell was awarded a cost plus fixed fee contract of $36,232,080. Work will be performed at the Bell Aerospace facility at Michoud, New Orleans, and at selected sub-contractor facilities.

The company states that the 18-month contract calls for the design, development and testing of full-scale subsystems and components.

Plans call for the development of the SES propulsion system, including the transmission and waterjet inlet and pump, the air-cushion and containment system, and a system to control the vessel's ride characteristics in a variety of sea states.

The new award has led to 150 engineering and professional personnel being added to

Rohr's preliminary design for a waterjet-propelled 2,000-ton surface effect ship for the US Navy

Bell's New Orleans work force, which now totals about 750.

Bell's initial study resulted in preliminary plans for an all-aluminium vessel, designed for speeds in excess of 80 knots.

It would be approximately 242 ft long and have a beam of 106 ft. Power would be supplied by six 20,000 shp General Electric LM-2500 marinized gas-turbines, two for lift and four driving the vessel's waterjet propulsion system.

ROHR INDUSTRIES INC

HEAD OFFICE:
Foot of H. Street,
P. O. Box 878,
Chula Vista,
California 92012
Telephone: 714 426 711

EXECUTIVES:
(See company entry in ACV section).

The Aerospace and Marine Systems group of Rohr Industries has received a $35,213,993 award from Naval Material Command's Surface Effect Ship Project Office (PM17) to develop a 2,000-ton surface effect ship.

The 18-month contract calls for the design, development and testing of full-scale sub-system and components.

Rohr is planning a vessel with a length of about 254 ft, a beam of more than 100 ft and powered by LM-2500 gas-turbines.

Most of the work will be undertaken by the company in Chula Vista, which is adjacent to San Diego Bay.

ITALY

Alilauro and Alispan, the two Neopolitan hydrofoil operators, have merged to form a new company Aliscafi del Tirreno. Both companies have been operating a number of Kometa hydrofoils between Naples and nearby islands in the Tyrrhenian Sea. The vessels, which seat 116 passengers, were built at Sochi during 1971-72.

SOVIET UNION

A Kometa-M arrived in Japan on September 12th after a 2,000 mile voyage from Singapore, which included a visit to the Philippines.

The vessel made several publicity trips calling at points on the Japanese inland sea. About 20 ferry operators expressed interest in purchasing Kometa-Ms.

A contract for the delivery of eleven Volga-70s was signed by Mackawa, a Japanese import company and Sudoimport, the Soviet foreign trade organisation.

UNITED KINGDOM

Airavia Ltd, the UK hydrofoil company, is to take delivery of the first Cyclone 250-300 seat hydrofoil ferry.

The prototype is due to be completed in 1975. On completion of tests it will be delivered to the United Kingdom for its British Passenger Certificate. The vessel is designed to operate in heavy seas and will have a top speed of 45-50 knots.

UNITED STATES OF AMERICA
MARTIN MARIETTA

The possibility of using small hydrofoil craft, armed with a specially modified version of the US Army's SAM-D missile, as picket ships is being studied by Martin Marietta. The system, named Sea Fence, would be employed to protect large surface craft from air attack. The hydrofoils would be equipped with Hughes Aircraft AWG-9 fire control units.

BOOKS AND PUBLICATIONS

Light Hovercraft Handbook
Comprehensive guide to the construction and maintenance of small hovercraft.
Available from:
Hoverclub of Great Britain Ltd,
128 Queens Road,
Portsmouth,
PO2 7NE
Price 50p
Robert Trillo Ltd.
Broadlands,
Brockenhurst,
Hampshire SO4 7SX
Telephone: Brockenhurst 2220

Air-Cushion and Hydrofoil Systems
Bibliography Service also *High Speed Ground Transportation and Urban Rapid Transit Systems*
Bibliography Service.

High-speed Ground Transportation Service
Annual subscription including Air Mail:
£5 UK and Europe; £6 the Americas, Middle East and India; and £6.50 Australasia and Far East.

Air-Cushion and Hydrofoil Bibliography Service
£5 UK and Europe; £5.50 the Americas, Middle East, Africa and India; and £6 Australasia and Far East.

A Bell Voyageur during a logistics-over-the-shore (LOTS) exercise. Reports indicate that an advanced version of the Voyageur is to be ordered by the US Army for fast lighterage work and utility applications in Alaska

Zaryas in production at the Moscow Shipbuilding and Ship Repair Yard. Two of these waterjet-propelled, 65-seat water buses are due to be delivered to Airavia Ltd for service in the United Kingdom   (MRA copyright)

INDEX

20121 milano via manzoni 12 tel. 708326/708327 telegr.cremme

DIESEL ENGINES LIGHT AND POWERFUL

FINNISH HYDROFOIL TEHI

Displacement : tons. 25,2 (fully loaded)
Dimensions : mts. 26,9 × 5,0
Engine : 18 cylinder, CRM. 18 D/2 —Diesel engine, 1050 HP. 2100 rpm. —73 Km/h.

PRODUCTION RANGE:
DIESEL ENGINES FROM 100 TO 1350 HP
GASOLINE ENGINES FROM 1000 TO 2000 HP INVERSION, REDUCTION GEARS - V. DRIVES

VT2
60 knots and fully amphibious